Standard Catalog of

CHEVROLET TRUCKS

Pickups & Other Light-Duty Trucks, 1918-1995

By John Gunnell

Published by

**krause
publications**

700 E. State Street • Iola, WI 54990-0001

Please call or write for our free catalog of automotive publications. Our toll-free number to place an order
or obtain a free catalog is 800-258-0929 or please use our regular business telephone 715-445-2214
for editorial comment and further information.

Library of Congress Catalog Number: 95-60365
ISBN: 0-87341-364-4

Printed in the United States of America

CONTENTS

FOREWORD

The concept behind Krause Publication's "Standard Catalogs" is to compile massive amounts of information about motor vehicles and present it in a standard format which the hobbyist, collector or professional dealer can use to answer some commonly asked questions.

These questions include: What year, make and model is the vehicle? What did it sell for when new? Is it original or modified? How rare is it? What's special about it? How much is it worth today as a collector vehicle?

Some answers are provided by illustrations in the catalogs; others by information found in the charts or text.

Each catalog represents the efforts of both professional research-historians and enthusiasts who collect facts and factory literature on one make or model.

The standardized format presents the following data: (1) a contributor's personal description of the vehicle's appearance; (2) where available, a list of standard factory equipment; (3) vehicle and/or engine identification codes and advice on how to interpret these; (4) a chart giving model codes, type descriptions, original retail price, original shipping weight and available production totals; (5) engine specifications; (6) a description of chassis features in a concise, generalized manner; (7) some technical information about the drive train and running gear; (8) specific option lists or a description of accessories seen in original period photos of such vehicles; (9) a "thumbnail" history of the vehicle and/or manufacturer and, in many instances, (10) a "ballpark" estimate of current prices being paid for such (pre-1980) models in today's collector vehicle market (located in rear of the catalog).

No claims are made as to the catalogs being history textbooks or encyclopedias. They are not repair manuals or "bibles" for motor vehicle enthusiasts. They are intended as collectors' guides, much like the popular spotter's books, buyers' digests and pricing guides. However, they are much larger in size, broader in scope and more deluxe in format. In addition, they represent the combined efforts of a large research team, rather than one individual's work.

All of the catalogs published to date reflect, to some degree, a balance between generalized research carried on by professional authors, and material prepared by individuals who know many facts about a single model or make through their personal hobby interests.

Part of the catalog concept is to coordinate future assignments in such a manner that each section in the book will ultimately feel both the skilled touch of the professional writer and the in-depth enthusiasm of the hobby expert. All contributors are requested to maintain an ongoing file of new research, corrections and additional photos which can be used to refine and expand future editions.

The long-range goal of Krause Publication's is to have a series of catalogs that are as near-perfect as possible. We're told that these books provide many hobbyists with hours of enjoyable reading. Some also consider them essential guides to carry along when they travel to car shows, wrecking yards and swap meets. And, of course, they can be particularly useful to the hobbyist/collector when cruising the highways or back roads in search of new vehicle acquisitions. You will know, immediately, what type of vehicle you've found, how rare it is and how much it's worth when restored.

Other catalogs currently available include *The Standard Catalog of American Cars 1805-1942 (Second Edition); The Standard Catalog of American Cars 1946-1972 (Third Edition); The Standard Catalog of American Cars 1976-1986 (Second Edition); The Standard Catalog of Imported Cars 1946-1990; The Standard Catalog of American Light-Duty Trucks 1896-1986; The Standard Catalog of AMC 1902-1987; The Standard Catalog of Buick 1903-1990; The Standard Catalog of Cadillac 1903-1990; The Standard Catalog of Chevrolet 1912-1990; The Standard Catalog of Chrysler 1924-1990; The Standard Catalog of Ford 1903-1990; The Standard Catalog of 4x4s 1946-1990; The Standard Catalog of Military Vehicles 1940-1965;* and *The Standard Catalog of Automotive Restoration.* For a complete hobby books catalog write: Krause Publications/Old Cars Weekly, 700 E. State St., Iola, WI 54990.

INTRODUCTION

You'll like the *Standard Catalog of Chevrolet Pickups & Light-Duty Trucks 1918-1995* because it is a useful guide for Chevrolet truck collectors. It has many new features. It is even more Chevrolet fact-filled than the Chevrolet section of Krause Publication's highly acclaimed *Standard Catalog of American Light-Duty Trucks 1896-1986.* There is a greater emphasis on the mainstream of Chevrolet truck collecting. And, of course, all of the Chevrolet collector-truck pricing data, located near the rear of the book, has been brought completely up to date.

Revisions to our Chevrolet database reflect improvements throughout. Many new facts and photos related to early Chevrolet trucks built from 1918 through the end of World War II have been added to our system. Our researchers have placed a special concentration on the popular Advance-Design and Task-Force models of the 1940s and 1950s. They have added complete paint code charts for these years and expanded their photographic coverage of both common and rare Chevrolet trucks.

A number of technical advisors from the Vintage Chevrolet Club of America (VCCA) helped out with this massive project. There's special advice on how to identify Chevrolet trucks by their appearance, as well as through vehicle identification numbers. The lists of factory options and accessories have been improved by adding the RPO code numbers for many extra-cost equipment items. The '50s and '60s interior trim lists have also been upgraded.

Chevrolet model-years included in the *Standard Catalog of American Light-Duty Trucks* (last published in 1994) were limited to 1918-1986. This new "Chevy-trucks-only" catalog expands the descriptive and specifications coverage through 1995 models. Even though these trucks do not yet have "collector" prices, the rarer and more exotic models are sure to be come collectible and valuable in the future. Information included in this book will give you the "jump" on identifying and buying future collectibles.

Over 300 new Chevrolet truck photos appear in the *Standard Catalog of Chevrolet Pickups & Light-Duty Trucks 1918-1995.* They include original photos of restored collectible models, and authentic "factory photos" of trucks of all vintages, particularly 1987-1995 models. In addition to enhanced photo layouts, the book also features better organization of footnotes to charts and text and greater editorial consistency throughout. In short, it is the biggest, best, and most accurate book about Chevrolet light-duty trucks that has ever been produced.
John "Gunner" Gunnell
January 1, 1995

CATALOG STAFF
Publisher: Greg Smith
Manager of Books: Pat Klug
Editorial Director: John A. Gunnell
Editors: Brad Bowling, Chad Elmore, Ron Kowalke, James T. Lenzke
Pricing: Ken Buttolph
Production: Barb Lefeber, Tom Payette, Tom Nelson, Kathy Hines, Ethel Thulien

Photo Graphics: Ross Hubbard, Wayne Conner
Camera Room: Julie Mattson, Gerald Smith
OCR Scanning: Marge Larson
Cover Design: Greg Krueger, Phil LaFranka, Kevin Ulrich
Marque Researchers: Robert C. Ackerson; Bob Adler; Steve Hanson; Robert Hensel; Fred K. Fox; John Gunnell; Frank Senkbeil; Bill Siuru; Forest "Chip" Sweet; Charles Webb; Donald F. Wood.

ABBREVIATIONS

AC AC....................Electric Division of General Motors
AC/DC..................... Alternating current/direct current
AIR................................ Air Injection Reactor
ALAM ....Association of Licensed
Automobile Manufacturers
AMC.....................American Motors Corp.
AMP.................................. . Amperes
APPROX...............................Approximate
ATA ....American Trucking Association
BBL................................. Barrel
BC.............................. Business Car
BHP............................Brake horsepower
BL............................Bonus Load (pickup)
Bros... Brothers
BSW.............................. Black sidewall
BUS.................................. Business
CC..............................Commercial Car
CC.............................Cubic Centimeters
CAFE.....................Corporate Average Fuel Economy
CALIF...................................California
CARB..................................Carburetor
CB............................ Citizen's Band (radio)
CIBA...............................Cast iron block
CID........................Cubic-inch diameter
CJ................................ Civilian Jeep
CO. .... Company
COBRA...................Copper Brazed Engine
COE............................Cab-Over-Engine
COMM. ....Commercial
COPO ....Central Office Production Option
C.R.............................Compression ratio
CS................................Custom (Chevrolet)
CST.............Custom Sport Truck (Chevrolet)
CU. FT.............................. Cubic Feet
CUST.................................. Custom
CYL..................................Cylinder
DEL...................................Deluxe
DELY...................................Delivery
DIA...................................Diameter
DIV. .... Division
DJ ....Jeep 4x2 Dispatcher
DR.............................(2-dr.) Door (two-door)
DRW ....Dual rear wheels
EFI ....Electronic fuel injection
EIGHT...........................Eight-cylinder engine
EPA.......................Enviornmental Protection Agency
ESC ....Electronic spark control
EXC. ....Except
EXP. ....Express
EXT. ....Extended
E-Z-Eye..............................Tinted glass
F (3F)...................... Forward (three forward speeds)
FC ....Forward control
F.F. ....Cowl Flat-face cowl
F-HEAD ....Vales in head and block
FLARE ....Flareside pickup (Ford)
FLEET...................Fleetside pickup (Chevy)
FM.......................Frequency modulation (radio)
FOB .... Free on board
FOUR..................................Four-cylinder
4x2 .... Two-Wheel-Drive
4x4 .... Four-Wheel-Drive
4-DR. .... Four-door
4-SPD. ....Four-speed (transmission)
4V ....Four-barrel carburetor
FRT. .... Front
FS ....Fender-side pickup
FT.................................... Foot/Feet
GAL.................................... Gallon
GATE .... Tailgate

GBR .... Glass-belted radial (tire)
GM ....General Motors
GMAD ....General Motors Assembly Division
GMC ....General Motors Corp.,
GM Truck & Bus, GM Truck & Coach
GMR .... GM Research
GT.................................Gran Turismo
GVW ....Gross Vehicle Weight
GVWR....................Gross Vehicle Weight Rating
H-D .... Heavy-duty
HEI .... High-Energy Ignition
HP.................................Horsepower
HR.......................................Hour
HWY. ....Highway
I ....Inline
ICC...................... Interstate Commerce Commission
I.D. ....Identification
IHC.....................International Harvester Co.
IN(S). ....Inch(es)
INC. .... Incorporated
INCL. ....Included
I.P. .... Instrument Panel
JR. ....Junior
KM ....Kilometers
L..................... (L-head) Side-valve engine
L.....................(5.0L) Engine Displacement in liters
LB(s). ....Pound(s)
LBS.-FT. ....Pounds-feet
LCF ....Low-Cab-Forward
L-D ....Light-Duty
LE ....Luxury Edition
LPG .... Liquified Petroleum Gas
LH .... Left-hand
LHD .... Left-hand Drive
LTD .... Limited
LUV ....Light Utility Vehicle
LWB ....Long Wheelbase
MAX. .... Maximum
MFG. ....Manufacturing
MM. .... Milimeters
MPG .... Miles Per Gallon
MPH .... Miles Per Hour
MX ....Multi-plex
N/A .... Not Available
NACC ....National Automobile
Chamber of Commerce
NC ....No charge
NADA ....National Automobile Dealers Assoc.
NHP ....Net Horsepower
NO. ....Number
NP .... New Process (Dodge/Plymouth)
NPA ....National Production Authority
O.F. ....Open front
OHC ....Overhead camshaft
OHV ....Overhead valves
OPEC ....Organization of Petroleum
Exporting Countries
OPS ....Office of Price Stability
OPT. .... Optional
OSRV .... Outside rearview mirror
OZ.......................................Ounce
P ....Passenger
PCV .... Positive Crankcase Ventilation
PDV ....Parcel Delivery Van
P. FRT. ....Power front
PMD ....Pontiac Motor Division
PR ....Ply-rated (tires)
PROD. .... Production

PTO.................................Power Take-Off
RBL.........................Raised black letter (tires)
RDS. ....Roadster
REG. ....Regular
REMOTE .... Remote Control
REQ. ....Requires
RH. ....Right-hand
RHD................................Right-hand drive
RPM.........................Revolutions per minute
RPO .... Regular Production Option
RV..............................Recreational Vehicle
RWL................................Raised white-letter
SAE...................Society of Automotive Engineers
SBR .... Steel-belted radial (tires)
SC ....Super Cab
SCREEN..........................Screenside Delivery
SDL .... Sedan Delivery
SE ....Special Edition
SED. .... Sedan
SIG...Signal
SIX ....Six-cylinder
SPD. .... Speed
SPD. REG. ....Speed regulator
SPL. ....Special
SPT. .... Sport
SQ. IN. ....Square inch(es)
SR. .... Senior
SRW.............................Single Rear Wheel
SS .... Super Sport
STA. WAG. .... Station Wagon
STD. ....Standard
STEP........................Stepside pickup (Chevy)
STYLE. ....Styleside pickup (Ford)
SUB. ....Suburban
SWB............................Short wheelbase
TACH. ....Tachometer
TAX. ....Taxable (horsepower)
TBI ....Throttle-Body Injection
TEMP. .... Temperature
T-HEAD...................Type of engine valve layout
THM........................Turbo-Hydramatic transmission
3F/1R .... 3 speeds forward/1 reverse
3S ....Three-seat
3x2V .... Three two-barrel carburetors
TRANS.............................. Transmission
TU-TONE .... Two-Tone (Ford and Jeep)
TV .... Television
2-dr. ....Two-door
2V .... Two-barrel (carburetor)
U.S. .... United States
U.S.A. ....United States of America
UTIL. ....Utility
V ....Venturi (carburetor)
V ....Vee-block engine
VIN...................Vehicle identification number
VP ....Vice-president
VV ....Vision & ventilating windshield
W/ .... With
WAG. .... Wagon
WB ....Wheelbase
W/O. ....Without
WPB........................War Production Authority
WS ....Wide-Side Pickup (GMC)
W/S ....Windshield (Chassis & W/S)
WSW................................ White sidewall (tires)

Many different abbreviations are used in sales literature printed by truck manufacturers over the years. We have tried to standardize the use of abbreviations. However, original sales literature is used as a reference source by many editorial contributors and some rely on the abbreviations as printed in the factory materials. Thus, there may be slight variations in the use of terms used in this catalog. (For example, 4x4 and four-wheel drive both appear). The above list shows most abbreviations used, except for those so common (months, states, etc.) that no special explanation is required.

HOW TO USE THIS CATALOG

APPEARANCE AND EQUIPMENT: Word descriptions help identify trucks down to details such as styling features, trim and interior appointments. Standard equipment lists usually begin with low-priced base models. Then, subsequent data blocks cover higher-priced lines of the same year.

VEHICLE I.D. NUMBERS: This edition features expanded data explaining the basic serial numbering system used by each postwar vehicle manufacturer. This data reveals where, when and in what order your vehicle was built. There is much more information on assembly plant, body style and original engine codes.

SPECIFICATIONS CHART: The first chart column gives series or model numbers for trucks. The second column gives body type. The third column tells factory price. The fourth column gives GVW. The fifth column gives the vehicle's original shipping weight. The sixth column provides model year production totals (if available) or makes reference to additional notes found below the specifications chart. When the same vehicle came with different engines or trim levels at different prices and weights, slashes (/) are used to separate the low price or weight from the high one. In some cases, model numbers are also presented this way. In rare cases where data is non-applicable or not available the abbreviation "N.A." appears.

BASE ENGINE DATA: According to make of vehicle, engine data will be found either below the data block for each series or immediately following the specifications chart for the last vehicle-line. Displacement, bore and stroke and horsepower ratings are listed, plus a lot more data where available. This edition has more complete engine listings for many models. In other cases, extra-cost engines are listed in the "options" section.

VEHICLE DIMENSIONS: The main data compiled here consists of wheelbase, overall length and tire size. Front and rear tread widths are given for most trucks through the early 1960s and some later models. Overall width and height appears in some cases, too.

OPTIONAL EQUIPMENT LISTS: This section includes data blocks listing all types of options and accessories. A great deal of attention has been focused on cataloging both the availability and the original factory retail prices of optional equipment. Because of size and space limitations, a degree of selectivity has been applied by concentrating on those optional features of greatest interest to collectors. Important option packages have been covered and detailed as accurately as possible in the given amount of space. When available, options prices are listed.

HISTORICAL FOOTNOTES: Trucks are already recognized as an important part of America's automotive heritage. Revealing statistics; important dates and places; personality profiles; performance milestones; and other historical facts are highlighted in this "automotive trivia" section.

SEE PRICING SECTION IN BACK OF BOOK.

1/2-TON; 3/4-TON; 1-TON CONVENTIONAL — MODEL C; K/SERIES 10; 20; 30 — SIX/V-8: Styling changes for light-duty conventional trucks were headed by revamped grille with a larger gridwork, clear-lensed parking lights, and new front fender model identification combining model nameplates and series identification plaques. A restyled tailgate with a quick-release control was used. The C10/K10 Pickups with a 6-1/2 ft. box came on the standard 117-1/2 in. wheelbase, which was used only for these models and small chassis models. The C10/K10 Pickups with an 8 ft. box featured a 131-1/2 in. wheelbase. This wheelbase was also used for 1/2-ton chassis models and all basic C30 models. The C20/K20 trucks, except Suburbans, were on a 127 in. wheelbase. All Suburbans, both 1/2-ton and 3/4-ton, were on a 129.5 in. wheelbase. Longer wheelbases were provided for Chassis & Cab and the new Crew Cab trucks. Crew cab bodies that seated six could be had as an option on all 3/4-ton and 1-ton pickups. The Crew Cab was actually an option costing about $1,000. The box used for factory-made Crew Cab Pickups was the 8 ft. Fleetside box. Custom Deluxe was the base interior. It included a foam-padded bench seat with blue, green, red or saddle plaid upholstery; a body color steel roof panel; black rubber floor mat; padded armrests; courtesy lamps; prismatic rearview mirror; foam padded dash; bright upper and lower grille outline moldings; bright headlamps bezels; silver plastic grille insert; bright outside rearview mirror; bright door handles; bright Custom Deluxe nameplates and white-painted bumper, hubcaps and wheels. The next-step-up was Scottsdale trim ($137-$199 extra), full-depth foam padded seat; which included woodgrain door trim inserts; an ashtray cigarette lighter; door or manually-operated courtesy lamps; bright door sill plates; color-keyed rubber floor mats; a high-note horn; patterned nylon cloth upholstery with vinyl trim; and all Custom Deluxe exterior features, plus a chrome bumper; chrome hubcaps; chrome bodyside moldings on Fleetsides; bright windshield and window trim..

I.D. DATA: Serial number located. Combination VIN and rating plate located on: [El Camino] Top left side of dash; [Conventionals] left door pillar. Serial number systems: [El Camino] First symbol indicates manufacturer, 1=Chevrolet. Second symbol indicates car-line/series: C=El Camino; D=El Camino Custom. Third and fourth symbols indicate body type: 80=Sedan-Pickup. Fifth symbol indicates engine: [El Camino] H=350 cid/145 nhp two-barrel V-8; L=350 cid/160 nhp four-barrel V-8; U=402 cid/175 nhp four-barrel V-8; Y=454 cid/235 nhp four-barrel V-8. Sixth symbol indicates model year: 5=1975. Seventh symbol indicates assembly plant. Symbols 8-13 indicate the production sequence number starting at 100,001. Ending numbers not available. [All Light-Duty] The first symbol indicates manufacturer: 1=Chevrolet Motor Div. The second symbol indicates chassis type: C=96 in. or 106 in. Conventional Cab including Blazer; G=Chevy Van or Sportvan; K=106 in. wheelbase Conventional cab 4x4; P= Forward-Control.

Model	Body Type	Price	Weight	Prod. Total
1/2-Ton LUV — Model L/Series 82 — 102.4 in. w.b.				
CL10503	Mini-Pickup	2976	2380	Note 1

NOTE 1: Calendar year sales: [974] 30,328.

Model	Body Type	Price	Weight	Prod. Total
1/2-Ton Vega — Model HV/Series 14000 — 97 in. w.b. — Four				
1HV05	Panel Express	2822	2401	—

Model	Body Type	Price	Weight	Prod. Total
El Camino — Model C/Series 13000 — 116 in. w.b. — Six				
1AC80	Sedan-Pickup	3828	3706	Note 2

Model	Body Type	Price	Weight	Prod. Total
El Camino Classic — Model D/Series 13000 — 116 in. w.b.				
1AD80	Classic Sedan-Pickup	3966	3748	Note 2

NOTE 2: Total El Camino production was 33,620.

ENGINE [Optional K10/K20/El Camino — $113]: V-block. OHV. Eight-cylinder. Cast iron block. Bore & stroke: 4-1/8 in. x 4 in. Displacement: 400 cid. Compression ratio: 8.5:1. Net horsepower: 175 at 3600 rpm. Five main bearings. Hydraulic valve lifters. Carburetor: four-barrel.

ENGINE [Optional C10/C20/C30]: V-block. OHV. Eight-cylinder. Cast iron block. Bore & stroke: 4-1/8 in. x 4 in. Displacement: 454 cid. Compression ratio: 8.25:1. Net horsepower: 230 at 3800 rpm. Five main bearings. Hydraulic valve lifters. Carburetor: Rochester four-barrel Quadra-Jet.

ENGINE [El Camino]: V-block. OHV. Eight-cylinder. Cast iron block. Bore & stroke: 4-1/8 in. x 4 in. Displacement: 454 cid. Compression ratio: 8.25:1. Net horsepower: 235 at 3800 rpm. Five main bearings. Hydraulic valve lifters. Carburetor: Rochester four-barrel Quadra-Jet.

CHASSIS [P10]: Wheelbase: 102 in. Height: 75 in. Tires: G78-15B.

CHASSIS [C20]: Wheelbase: 117.5 in./131.5 in./164.5 in. Overall length: [Fleetside] 191-1/4 in./211-1/4 in./244-1/4 in.; [Step-Side] 210-1/4 in./244-1/4 in. Height: 69.8 in. Front tread: 65.8 in. Rear tread: 62.7 in. Tires: [Standard] 8.75 x 16.5C; [Crew Cab] 9.50 x 16.5D

CHASSIS [K20]: Wheelbase: 131.5 in. Overall length: [Fleetside] 211-1/4 in.; [Step-Side] 210-1/4 in. Height: 73.9 in. Front tread: 65.8 in. Rear tread: 62.7 in. Tires: 8.75 x 16.5C.

CHASSIS [P20]: Wheelbase: 125 in./133 in. Overall length: 220.75 in./244.75 in. Tires: 8.75 x 16.5C.

CHASSIS [P30]: Wheelbase: 125 in./133 in./157 in. Overall length: 220.75 in./268.75 in. Tires: 8.75 x 16.5C.

OPTIONS: Radio: AM or AM/FM. Windshield embedded antenna. Gauge package (ammeter, oil pressure, temperature) available with either tachometer or clock or with exomomindor gauge only. Tachometer. Drip molding. Exterior tool and storage compartment. Air-conditioning. Stainless steel Wheelcovers. White sidewall tires (Series 10 only). Below-Eyeline mirrors. Comfortilt steering wheel. Rear step bumper. Special trim molding (Fleetside only). Chrome bumpers. Chrome front bumper with rubber impact strips. Woodgrain exterior trim (Fleetside only). Sliding rear window. Cargo area lamp. Box-mounted spare tire. Glide-out spare tire carrier.

HISTORICAL: Introduced Sept. 2, 1973. Calendar year registrations: 803,864. Calendar year registrations by weight class: [6,000 lbs. and less] 575,348; [6,000-10,000 lbs.] 228,516. Calendar year production: 838,959 units (not including Vega/El Camino/LUV). Chevrolet held 29.44 percent of the U.S. truck market. On a calendar year basis, this was Chevrolet's second best year in truck sales in history with sales of 885,362 units and production of 896,130. The model year figures were, however, even more impressive with 975,257 sales and 925,696 trucks built to 1974 specifications. This production total includes trucks built in Canada for sale here, but does not include LUVs (which are included in the sales total). An all-time production record, for the Flint, Mich. factory (339,678 trucks) was set. On a calendar year basis, 85.5 percent of Chevrolet's output was V-8 powered; 15.1 percent had six-cylinder engines and a mere 0.4 percent was diesel engined.

CHEVROLET BODY STYLES

Body style designations describe the shape and character of a truck. Over the years, truck-makers have exhibited great imagination in coining words to name their products. Here we have broken various types of trucks into five major groups: 1) Chassis; 2) Pickup; 3) Utility; 4) Delivery and 5) Station Wagon. A little background on each category is provided, along with illustrations showing representative examples. Of course, these descriptions and plates don't cover every possible variation. They are meant chiefly as a guide to the basic product lines offered by most light-duty truck manufacturers over the years.

CHASSIS MODELS: A glance at the available production break-outs in this catalog will prove that many 3/4-ton or 1-ton trucks (as well as a few lighter-duty models) left the factory as a bare or partially built-up chassis. These are supplied to one of the hundreds of vendors who supply purpose-built bodies to the light-duty truck industry. They may be sold as a chassis-only; chassis-and-flat-face cowl; chassis-and-cowl and chassis-and-windshield with all front end sheet metal except the cab.

CHASSIS-ONLY: The term chassis-only is self-explanatory. This configuration dates back to the early days of the truck-building industry, when few manufacturers built their own commercial vehicle bodies. The chassis only is used for a wide variety of purpose-built trucks, as well as motorhomes, buses and an assortment of other vehicles. Most manufacturers worked in conjunction with "approved" equipment suppliers in merchandising their bare chassis. Chevrolet, for example, annually prints the Silver Book, an interesting piece of factory literature that describes the kinds of specialty bodies recommended for Chevrolet chassis-trucks.

CHASSIS-AND-CAB: The chassis-and-cab is the starting point for conventional pickups and many other light-duty trucks. At the start of pickup truck history, most manufacturers sold the various vehicle components as options for a buyer to add to his chassis-and-cab.

PICKUP: Dictionaries define this type of vehicle as a small, open-body delivery truck built on a chassis comparable to a passenger car. This seems slightly outdated when you think of a modern 1-ton Crew-Cab Pickup with flared rear fenders, dual rear wheels and a fiberglass camper shell. Common among all pickups, however, is a box-like cargo container called an express box, pickup box, cargo box, grain box or any of several other names. Early pickups were known as ``express'' models. The term "pick-up" was adopted and later became "pickup."

FARM WAGON: Farmers used horsedrawn buckboards with cargo boxes before cars were even invented. Early motorized versions became known as farm wagons. Among the companies producing such a model in the Teens and 1920s was Chevrolet. By 1918, most car-makers could supply delivery boxes — often with flared-out sideboards — for installation on the chassis of a touring car with the rear tonneau removed. These were called delivery wagons at first and later became known as express trucks. Different names were also used by other companies.

COUPE-EXPRESS: The coupe-express was more of a business car than a truck, although it fits the dictionary definition of a pickup perfectly. In many cases, this type of vehicle was originated in the late 1920s, when slip-in cargo boxes were released as optional equipment for business coupes. By the mid-1930s, the coupe-express (or coupe-pickup) was a regular model in numerous companies' commercial car-lines. The cargo box designs varied: some were bolted-on, some slipped into the trunk and others telescoped in-and-out like a dresser drawer. A few manufacturers preferred a fixed-position box, sometimes having a tailgate.

SEDAN PICKUP: In simple terms, this type of vehicle combines the front sheet metal of a two-door sedan with the cargo box of a pickup. But, describing trucks isn't simple. For one thing, some coupe-express trucks are actually similar to sedan pickups. For another thing, a few of the best known sedan pickups have actually evolved from station wagons. Many compare these trucks to the "utes" offered, for years, in Australia. However, American predecessors can also be found. Some historians prefer calling these vehicles "pickup-cars" or "sport-pickups" since they heavily resemble automobiles and come with numerous sporty options.

STEP-SIDE PICKUP: Chevrolet uses this trade name to describe the type of pickup on which the cargo box walls are flush with the inside of the rear wheels, with their fenders entirely outside the box. This permits the use of small running boards — or "steps" — between the lower rear corner of the cab and the back fenders. From the 1920s to the mid-1950s, virtually all pickup trucks were made this way. In recent years, there has been a revival in the popularity of Chevrolet Step-Side Pickup trucks.

FLEETSIDE PICKUP: Chevrolet's Fleetside Pickup features double-wall box construction, making the exterior walls of the box flush with the sides of the cab. This permits a wider box, except where the inner wheel wells protrude. A 25 percent increase in cargo capacity over the Step-Side model is typical. The Fleetside Pickup was popularized in the mid-1950s and has been the industry sales leader ever since. Some models come only in this form.

"BIG DOOLEY": This is the term Chevrolet uses to describe a big pickup truck with many heavy-duty options including an extra-long cargo box, flared rear fenders and dual rear wheels. In many cases, these will also be ordered with extended cabs providing either extra stowage or auxiliary seating. Often, these trucks come with slightly larger tires at the rear. Most also include optional interior and exterior trim packages, roof clearance marker lamps and West Coast type outside rear view mirrors.

EXTENDED-CAB PICKUP: Extra-long wheelbase pickups can be ordered with "stretched" cargo boxes and cabs. Shown here is an Extended-Cab model which has two doors with a cab extension behind the seat. Also available are Crew-Cab versions with four doors and a full back seat. On Extended-Cab models the added room may be utilized for a secured storage area. Folding auxiliary seats can also be ordered for dual purpose use. In most cases, large "or can be ordered with fixed or folding auxiliary seats for dual purpose use. In most cases, large "opera" windows will be added to the extended section of the cab.

MINI-PICKUP: The "energy crunch" of the early 1970s popularized the mini-pickup, a down-sized version of the regular model. Today's minis have all of the big truck features including stretched cabs and extended wheelbases, although all are trimmer and lighter than comparable full-size models. This makes the use of smaller engines with fewer cylinders possible. In most cases, numerous sporty options are offered and look great on these pint-size pickups.

EXTENDED-CAB MINI-PICKUP: Extended cab versions of the latest generation mini-pickups began to come on the market around 1982 and have been growing in popularity ever since. These trucks carry a 1/2-ton rating, just like their bigger brothers. They are roughly 10 in. shorter in wheelbase and some 2,000 pounds lighter than a full-size extended-cab model. The size and weight advantage adds up to improved efficiency, although the cargo carrying ability of these big "little" trucks is not that much less than a conventional light-duty pickup.

FORWARD-CONTROL PICKUP: These are pickups in which the operator sits ahead of, or above, the front wheels. In the early days of the trucking industry, this configuration was seen in open-cab express form. By the early 1960s, Chevrolet's Corvair spawned a truck-line that used the forward-control layout. It had a unique Rampside model with box sides that lowered to form a ramp. When the first compact vans appeared, in the mid-1960s, some manufacturers created forward-control pickups based on them, but Chevrolet did not.

Standard Catalog of Chevrolet Trucks

SPORTS UTILITY VEHICLE: There is no dictionary definition of a sports utility vehicle. The term utility is defined as the "state or character of being useful." Thus, in truck industry terms, one must think of a vehicle that is useful in many different ways. This surely describes a dual-purpose model like the Chevrolet Blazer, which can be used as a car, pickup, or station wagon; for civilian or military purposes and for highway transportation or off-road use.

UTILITY PICKUP: Descriptions of this body style should start with a reading of the US Army's specifications for a 1/4-ton military reconnaissance car it wished to have built prior to World War II. This became the Jeep. After World War II, the Universal Jeep became the basis for a whole line of 4x4 and 4x2 utility models in all light-duty tonnage classes. In the 1960s, the sports utility vehicle was born. Chevrolet developed the first Blazer in 1969.

SPORT UTILITY WAGON: Hardtops' turned the utility pickup into a utility wagon. With the introduction of the Chevrolet Blazer, the popularity of this body type increased by leaps and bounds. Variations include fixed and removable tops and either tailgate/liftgate or tailgate-and-window rear end treatments.

MINI-SPORT UTILITY: Like the mini-pickup, the down-sized sports utility wagon was a reaction to the energy crisis of the early 1970s. Some models, like the Scout II, were available in topless configuration, but most are fixed-top wagons featuring crisply tailored styling. Inline four-cylinder engines or V-6s are the power plants of choice in these scaled-down utility models. Both 4x2 and 4x4 drive trains are available in this type of vehicle. Large expanses of glass are characteristic of the latest versions.

VAN/PANELS: Van is a British word that was used to describe both a railroad baggage car and a kind of vehicle, open or covered, used by tradesmen for carrying light goods. The primary dictionary definition is a "covered vehicle (usually of considerable size) for moving furniture or household effects." The term panel mainly describes a type of construction with a flat piece of material supported between girders. This is much more applicable to early auto (and truck)building methods, but has come to mean any vehicle with panel sides.

DELIVERY CAR: This style appeared very early in the history of light-duty trucking. The delivery car or van was actually the first type of panel truck, although it was usually on a car chassis. These vehicles are characteristically narrow and high. On some larger versions, the sides are bowed (or flared) outward to provide extra load space. Cabs on these trucks may be fully open or open-sided, as well as partly or fully enclosed. Early enclosed versions were called "vestibuled" delivery vans. On some closed-cab' trucks, the roof curved upward for higher headroom. The open-cab models sometimes had a "C"-shape. Windows were often provided in the cab in various configurations.

Standard Catalog of Chevrolet Trucks

SEDAN DELIVERY: This type of vehicle is built on either a standard or beefed-up passenger car (sometimes station wagon) chassis. Passenger car front end sheet metal is used in conjunction with a low, car-like roof line. Most sedan deliveries have panel sides, usually in place of station wagon windows. However, this name has also been used to identify commercial or business cars with two-door sedan bodies on which the rear seats are foldable, or removable, to provide a cargo stowage area. Most, if not all, sedan deliveries are two-door models.

WALK-IN DELIVERY VAN: High, forward-control delivery vans are known by numerous names such as walk-in, door-to-door, All-Purpose, parcel delivery, or Step-Van trucks. Early milk and bakery vans of this type (usually electrics) were geared so that drivers could make door-to-door deliveries as the truck rolled slowly down the street. Bodies for such trucks are usually an aftermarket addition with many custom touches. They are of steel- or aluminum-panel construction. Dual rear wheels are a very common option. Small bus - and more recently camper - bodies are frequently seen on this type of chassis. Typical rear door configurations include double-panel and roll-up types.

PANEL DELIVERY: The panel delivery or panel truck characterizes the evolution of the delivery car type on a truck chassis. Most are lower and wider than their automobile-based ancestors. They utilize a conventional drive train layout with the engine in front, transmission amidships and drive axle (typically) at the rear. During and after World War II, some 4x4 versions were offered, usually as an option. These are fairly rare. Panels have the front end sheet metal of trucks. Their cabs are nearly always fully enclosed.

PANEL DELIVERY VAN: These are known by a number of generic names such as Cargo Van or Commercial Van. They also go by manufacturer's trade names such as Chevy Van or Sportvan. Basically, these trucks are forward-control (driver-up-front) models intended for use by tradesmen. They can have hinged or sliding cargo doors on one or both sides and usually have double panel doors at the rear. Since the late 1970s, it has been common to see long wheelbases, extended-bodies, optional windows and protruding hoods (for better engine service access) on such models.

CUT-AWAY DELIVERY VAN: This somewhat self-explanatory term is a good one to describe what's actually a van-based cab-and-chassis truck. Various types of bodies are essentially substituted for the "cutaway" rear portion of a standard van. Some have very large, high and wide cube-like cargo holds. Others are fitted with camper or mini-motorhome units. Ambulances, too, are built off the cutaway van type chassis. Steel bodies are predominant, but aluminum models are optional for their weight-saving advantages. In some cases, smaller models are marketed as semi-factory vehicles, while larger configurations have to be specially-ordered and purpose-built.

CANOPY DELIVERY: This style dates back to the early days of light-duty trucking when express models were available with four- or eight-post tops and roll-down curtains for use in cold or stormy weather. These became popularly known as curtain-side or canopied deliveries. This was a standard model, from nearly all manufacturers, for many years. In the 1930s, the same concept was used to create a version of the panel truck which had open sides to allow the display of items such as produce.

SCREENSIDE DELIVERY: Like the canopy delivery, the screenside delivery truck allowed the businessman-owner to transport his goods to a location and display them to people when he got where he was going. However, in this case there were screens over the open sides. These were used either to keep merchandise from falling out or to foil would be thieves. This type of truck was also well-suited for police paddy wagon work and some services, like the Milwaukee Police Department, have restored such trucks to use in their safety and public affairs programs.

STATION WAGON/CARRYALL: The original dictionary definition of a station wagon is "an automobile having an enclosed wooden body of paneled design with removable seats behind the driver." The term "Carryall" was originally applied to a light, covered, one-horse family carriage, with two seats - later came to mean a closed motorcar having two passenger benches extending the length of the station wagons were usually considered to be commercial vehicles until the late 1930s. Thereafter, two types were often seen. One was built off of the passenger car chassis, while the other type was truck-chassis-based. Steel-bodied station wagons were known as carryall suburbans for a while. Passenger vans are sometimes called wagons, too. Whatever their idiosyncrasies, the "wagons" included in this book are basically passenger-carrying light-duty trucks.

CARRYALL SUBURBAN: The station wagon grew popular in the 1930s as Americans moved from urban areas into smaller communities adjacent to cities. These were called "suburbs." station wagons were seen as the perfect dual-purpose vehicle for suburbanites. In 1935, Chevy introduced an all-steel station wagon on its light-duty truck chassis. It was called the Carryall Suburban.

COMMERCIAL STATION WAGON: This term describes station wagons built on a truck chassis. As early as 1920, Chevrolet's 490 Light Delivery catalog showed a truck identified as a "station wagon." It was a canopied express with three bench seats for nine passengers. In the postwar era Chevrolet sold a limited number of wood-bodied wagons on their truck chassis. These rare vehicles are highly sought after by collectors.

MINIVAN: The minivan is a small van. Chevrolet's entry in this market segment is the Astro. Unlike other minivans, which are vans riding on front-wheel-drive passenger car platforms, the Astro is a front-engine, rear-wheel-drive vehicle similar to a S-10 mini-pickup. This makes it more of a true "truck" or "van" in terms of its construction, handling, and utility.

STANDARD PASSENGER VAN: The forward-control Volkswagen van was first seen in the early 1950s and grew increasingly popular, in the United States, as its society became more mobile. By the early 1960s, Chevrolet had developed the "Corvan" as a domestic counterpart. This truck-line included the Greenbrier passenger wagon.

EXTENDED-BODY PASSENGER VAN: After the popularity of vans exploded in the 1960s, there came a time for refinements upon the theme. Hoods were extended for better engine accessibility and bodies were stretched to provide even more room for people and their luggage. These "king-size" passenger vans had all of the features — windows, fancy trim, extra seats — of the standard passenger van on a larger scale. Some could accommodate up to 15 passengers when equipped with special option packages.

APV (ALL-PURPOSE VEHICLE): The Lumina APV also looks like a small van. However, it is built on a front-wheel-drive passenger car chassis. Because of this, Chevrolet uses the term APV (all-purpose vehicle) to describe the Lumina. However, a Cargo Van version has been offered.

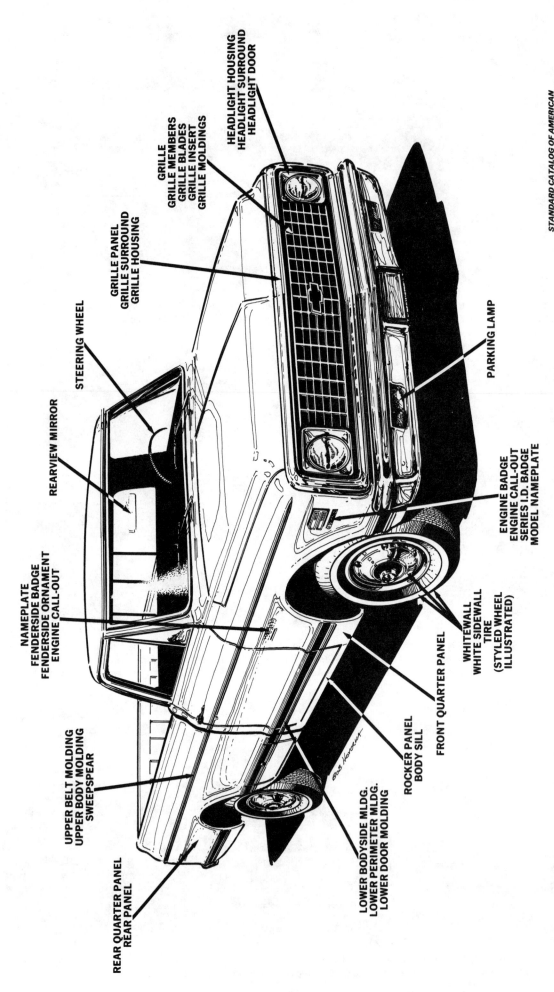

HEADLIGHT HOUSING
HEADLIGHT SURROUND
HEADLIGHT DOOR

GRILLE
GRILLE MEMBERS
GRILLE BLADES
GRILLE INSERT
GRILLE MOLDINGS

GRILLE PANEL
GRILLE SURROUND
GRILLE HOUSING

STEERING WHEEL

REARVIEW MIRROR

PARKING LAMP

NAMEPLATE
FENDERSIDE BADGE
FENDERSIDE ORNAMENT
ENGINE CALL-OUT

ENGINE BADGE
ENGINE CALL-OUT
SERIES I.D. BADGE
MODEL NAMEPLATE

UPPER BELT MOLDING
UPPER BODY MOLDING
SWEEPSPEAR

REAR QUARTER PANEL
REAR PANEL

WHITEWALL
WHITE SIDEWALL
TIRE
(STYLED WHEEL
ILLUSTRATED)

ROCKER PANEL
BODY SILL

FRONT QUARTER PANEL

LOWER BODYSIDE MLDG.
LOWER PERIMETER MLDG.
LOWER DOOR MOLDING

Bob Honour

BODY I.D. GUIDE

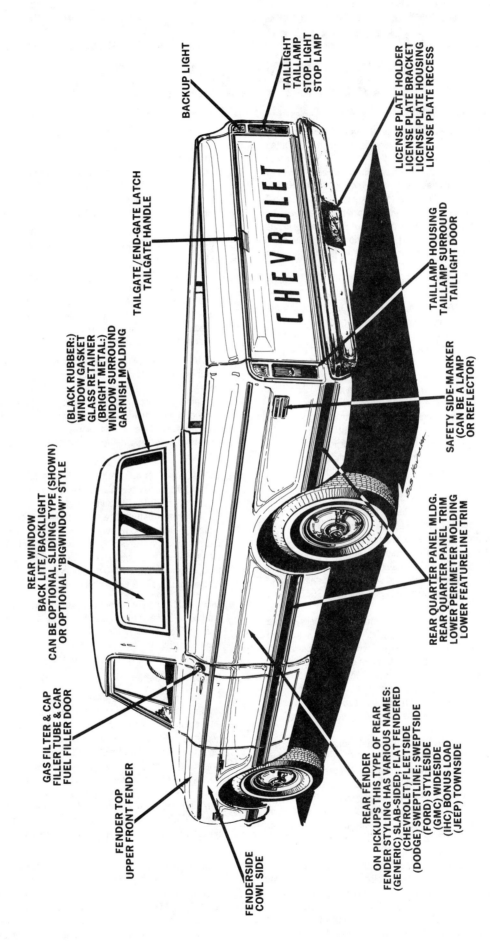

BODY I.D. GUIDE

BACKUP LIGHT

TAILLIGHT
TAILLAMP
STOP LIGHT
STOP LAMP

LICENSE PLATE HOLDER
LICENSE PLATE BRACKET
LICENSE PLATE HOUSING
LICENSE PLATE RECESS

TAILGATE/END-GATE LATCH
TAILGATE HANDLE

TAILLAMP HOUSING
TAILLAMP SURROUND
TAILLIGHT DOOR

(BLACK RUBBER:)
WINDOW GASKET
GLASS RETAINER
(BRIGHT METAL:)
WINDOW SURROUND
GARNISH MOLDING

SAFETY SIDE-MARKER
(CAN BE A LAMP
OR REFLECTOR)

REAR WINDOW
BACK LITE/BACKLIGHT
CAN BE OPTIONAL SLIDING TYPE (SHOWN)
OR OPTIONAL "BIGWINDOW" STYLE

REAR QUARTER PANEL MLDG.
REAR QUARTER PANEL TRIM
LOWER PERIMETER MOLDING
LOWER FEATURELINE TRIM

GAS FILTER & CAP
FILLER TUBE & CAR
FUEL FILLER DOOR

FENDER TOP
UPPER FRONT FENDER

REAR FENDER
ON PICKUPS THIS TYPE OF REAR
FENDER STYLING HAS VARIOUS NAMES:
(GENERIC) SLAB-SIDED; FLAT FENDERED
(CHEVROLET) FLEETSIDE
(DODGE) SWEPTLINE; SWEPTSIDE
(FORD) STYLESIDE
(GMC) WIDESIDE
(IHC) BONUS LOAD
(JEEP) TOWNSIDE

FENDERSIDE
COWL SIDE

STANDARD CATALOG OF AMERICAN
Light Duty TRUCKS

STANDARD CATALOG CONTRIBUTORS

ROBERT C. ACKERSON is a writer and historian from Schenevus, N.Y. He authored the *Standard Catalog of 4x4's 1945-1993* and contributed to the *Standard Catalog of American Cars 1805-1942*. He has also written the *Encyclopedia of the American Supercar* and the *Ford Ranchero Source Book*. His latest book, also available from Krause Publications, is *Chevrolet High Performance*. Ackerson received special recognition from the Society of Automotive Historians for material he contributed to *The Lincoln Motor Car, Sixty Years of Excellence*. He has done numerous articles for *Old Cars* and other periodicals. His work on this catalog includes factual research on Chevrolet 4x4s and Chevrolet photo contributions.

BOB ADLER is a former research biochemist who opened his restoration business in 1978. Chevrolet Advance-Design trucks filled the need for business transportation for Adler's Antique Autos, Inc. This led to the shop's specialty of restoring these models. Bob Adler has accumulated over 70 Advance-Design trucks. He is a technical advisor on these models for both the Vintage Chevrolet Club of America and the National Chevrolet-GMC Truck Association. Adler has authored numerous articles on their restoration and preservation.

GREG CARSON of Penhold, Alberta, Canada, is a 1954-1955 First Series Chevrolet truck owner and enthusiast. His special interests are in the fine points of the history of these models and the four-wheel drive conversions offered for them by NAPCO Products, Division, a Minneapolis, Minn. company that built the Powr-Pak four-wheel drive system that Chevrolet dealers merchandised. Greg did a fine job rewriting the 1954-1955 First Series Chevrolet section of this catalog and improving the accuracy of the information that it includes.

JOHN A. GUNNELL was born in Staten Island, N.Y. and attended Brooklyn Technical High School to study industrial design. He later studied English, history and fine art and earned a Bachelor of Arts degree in art. Writing about antique cars as a creative outlet, Gunnell began working as editor of several club publications. In 1978, he took an editorial position with *Old Cars* and relocated to Iola, Wis. Since 1975 he has written articles and books and edited six standard catalogs. John owns 1936 and 1953 Pontiacs and someday wants a 1958 Chevy Apache pickup.

STEVE HANSON and partner Tim Huehn operate H & H Trucks, a Rice Lake, Wis. restoration company that specializes in the sales and restoration of 1960-1972 Chevrolet trucks. Steve also specializes in locating parts for such vehicles. Steve Hanson has owned dozens of the light-duty Chevrolet trucks and is well-versed in their history and technology. A large collection of original literature for these vehicles has enabled Steve to research their original features and authenticity. He has written articles about 1960-1972 Chevrolet trucks for *Old Cars* and other hobby publications.

ROBERT HENSEL of Brillion, Wis., is internationally known as an expert on vintage Chevrolet cars and trucks, including a 1926 Chevrolet fire truck that he brings to many antique auto meets. Hensel's company, Chevy Acres, specializes in publications, parts and restoration services for older Chevrolets of all types. A longtime member of the Vintage Chevrolet Club of America (VCCA), Hensel serves as the group's National Coordinator of Technical Advisor Services. He is also the club's technical advisor for 1919-1920; 1923-1924; 1926-1928; 1934-1936; 1938; and 1960-1974 commercial vehicles.

TOM MELEO of Lindsay, Calif., serves as a vice-president for the Vintage Chevrolet Club of America (VCCA). He is also the VCCA Technical Advisor for 1921-1922 Series D, Series G and Series H Chevrolet trucks. In this volunteer role, Mr. Meleo provides technical services and advice to VCCA members nationwide who are restoring Chevrolet trucks made in those years. Tom reviewed the 1921-1922 Chevrolet section of *The Standard Catalog of Light-Duty Chevrolet Trucks*.

FRANK SENKBEIL serves as director of the Vintage Chevrolet Club of America's Chattahoochee Region, based in Jonesboro, Ga. In the area of Chevrolet trucks, his specialty is the 1954 commercial models and Senkbeil is the VCCA Commercial Technical Advisor for that model year. His research for the *Standard Catalog of Light-Duty Chevrolet Trucks* revealed some interesting information, such as the fact that Hydra-Matic transmission was used in 13,000 Chevrolet trucks built during 1954.

FOREST "CHIP" SWEET serves as 1931-1933 Commercial Vehicle Technical Advisor for the Vintage Chevrolet Club of America. A native of Lake Jackson, Texas, Sweet is well-versed in the historical background and the mechanical make-up of the Chevrolet trucks built during the lean years of the Great Depression. He has collected a great deal of factory literature and specialized information these models. His goal is to disseminate accurate information to those involved in the vehicle collecting hobby. "No one wants collectors to waste time and money as a result of improper information," he says.

DONALD F. WOOD is a professor of transportation in the School of Business at San Francisco State University. He co-authored of several college textbooks and served as a consultant to numerous government and private agencies. Don writes about old trucks as a hobby. He has done over 50 articles and several books on the development of trucks and trucking. One of his works is *Chevy El Camino 1959-1982 Photofacts*. Professor Wood's contributions to this catalog include Chevrolet truck photos.

LESLIE WALL is a light-duty truck collector with a specialized interest in the 1958 Chevrolet Cameo Carrier. Produced in four model years, beginning in 1955, the Cameo Carrier was a limited-production model combining the features of a sporty passenger car with the functionality of a pickup. During model year 1958, the Cameo was produced for only a few months, then replaced with a new Fleetside model featuring double-wall steel box construction with Cameo-like styling. Leslie is a native of Independence, La. who has gathered numerous factory references to document the 1958 Cameo's history.

BOB LICHTY began his automotive art career at B.F. Goodrich. He has worked for collector publications, Kruse auctions, Carlisle Productions, and the Blackhawk Automobile Collection. He also operated a collector car dealership in California. Lichty has written numerous articles and compiled the first-ever directory to hobby events.

SPECIAL THANKS

In addition to the Marque Researchers listed above, Krause Publications would like to give special thanks to the following people who went above and beyond the call of duty to help make this catalog possible: Terry V. Boyce, Detroit, Mich. (1960-1970s Chevrolet data); George H. Dammann, Crestline Publishing, Sarasota, Fla. (1973-1986 Chevrolet Photos); Seth Doulton, Golden State Pickup Parts, Santa Barbara, Calif. (proofreading Chevrolet section); Edward S. Lechtzin, public relations, Chevrolet Motor Division (Chevrolet truck photos); Jack L. Martin, Society of Automotive Historians, Indianapolis, Ind. (photos of Indy 500 Official Trucks); The Spokesman, Inc., Tulsa, Okla. (general photos); James A. Wren, Automotive Research, Detroit, Mich. (Chevrolet truck photos).

As with any work of this scope, scores of other researchers, hobbyists, collectors, dealers, historians, writers and experts provided much information without which this catalog would never have become a reality. We'd like to thank everyone who took the time to send letters, notes, memos, clippings and advice. It was impossible to personally answer all of the mail that arrived at the Iola office, but it has all been carefully read and considered in the creation of this second edition.

PHOTO CREDITS

Whenever possible in this catalog we have tried to picture light-duty Chevrolet trucks with photographs that show them in original form. Non-original features are usually noted. Some photo captions show the full name (or first initial and last name) of hobbyists and collectors who are owners of light-duty Chevrolet trucks and sent photos of their own vehicles. Photos contributed by other sources are identified with alphabetical codes corresponding to those in the list below. Double codes separated by a slash mark indicate the photo came from a collector who obtained it from another source. The double codes identify both sources. Photos without codes are from the *Old Cars* photo archives.

(A&A) Applegate & Applegate
(ABA) Anheuser-Busch Archives
(ATA) American Trucking Association
(ATC) Antique Truck Club of America
(ATHS) American Truck Historical Society
(BH) Bob Hensel/Chevy Acres
(BLHU) Baker Library Harvard University
(BMM) Bill & Mary Mason
(BOR) U.S. Bureau of Reclamation
(BWA) Burkhart Wilson Associates
(CHP) California Highway Patrol
(CMD) Chevrolet Motor Division
(CP) Crestline Publishing Company
(CPC) Calendar Promotions Company
(CW) Charles Webb
(DFW) Donald F. Wood (SFU)
(DPL) Detroit Public Library (NAHC)
(FLP) Free Library of Philadelphia
(FLW) Franklin L. Walls
(GHD) George H. Dammann
(HACJ) Henry Austin Clark Jr.
(HTM) Hays Truck Museum
(ICS) Iola Car Show

(IMSC) Indianapolis Motor Speedway Corp.
(JAG) John A. Gunnell Collection
(JAW) James A. Wren Automotive Research
(JB2) Jerry Beno (1928 Chevrolet)
(JLB) James L. Bell
(JLC) Jefferson/Little Carlisle Auto Show
(JLM) Jack L. Martin
(LC) Linda Clark
(LOC) Library of Congress
(MC) Michael Carbonella
(MS) Mitch Stenzler
(MTFCA) Model T Ford Club of America
(MVMA) Motor Vehicle Manufacturer's Association
(OCW) Old Cars Weekly
(OHS) Oregon Historical Society
(RCA) Robert C. Ackerson
(RT) Robert Trueax
(RVM) Rearview Mirror Museum
(SAB) Saskatchewan Archives Board
(TSC) The Stockland Company
(VCCA) Vintage Chevrolet Club of America
(VHTM) Van Horn's Truck Museum
(WPL) Wisconsin Power & Light Company
(WS) Wayne Sorenson

CHEVROLET
1918-1995

1958 Chevrolet Apache 10 Fleetside Pickup

Chevy light-duty trucks are "rock" solid hobby vehicles
By Robert C. Ackerson

Chevrolet's first trucks, a 1/2-ton and a 1-ton, were made in 1918. From a start of 879 production units, the total number of Chevrolet trucks on the road grew to 8,179 by the end of 1919. By 1921, the company began installing outside-sourced bodies on its truck chassis at Chevrolet factories. An all-steel, enclosed cab model and a Panel truck were introduced in 1925.

Truck number 500,000 was made in 1929, when six-cylinder engines were adopted. By the end of the year, all-time sales hit 641,482 units. In 1930, hydraulic shocks, electric fuel gauges, vacuum wipers, and outside mirrors became standard. Late that season, Martin-Parry Corp., one of the world's largest truck body makers, was acquired. This led to the offering of complete 1/2-ton Pickups, Panels, and Canopy Express trucks as factory models.

Passenger car-like styling graced the trucks of 1937. Three-quarter and 1-ton models joined the line. Race driver Harry Hartz traveled the country's perimeter in a Chevrolet truck. His gas bill was under one-cent-per-mile, and he had no breakdowns. By 1939, Chevrolet offered 45 models on eight wheelbases. Cumulative output was up to two million units. World War II halted production briefly, but it resumed in 1944.

Strong fleet sales, expanded color choices, and a new synchromesh transmission helped the sales of trucks in the 1930s. Chevrolet's market share was 32.7 percent in 1930, and 50 percent in 1933 when the one-millionth unit was assembled. The Carryall Suburban appeared in 1935 as an all-steel station wagon on the 1/2-ton truck chassis. The next year, one-piece all-steel cab roofs, and hydraulic brakes were used on the trucks.

A war-weary public gobbled up nearly 260,000 Chevrolet trucks in 1947. They had 30 advanced features including an alligator-jaw hood and a "breathing" cab. A new body and steering column gear shifting bowed in 1947. The new Advance-Design models would last eight years with only modest changes like vent windows (1951), push-button door latches (1952), cross-bar grilles (1954) and Hydra-Matic shifting (1954).

In mid-1955, the truck-line was revolutionized with wraparound windshields, a 12-volt electric system, optional V-8 engines, and a limited-edition "dream truck" called the Cameo. Its load box had slab-side fiberglass outer skins for an all-new fender-less look. Chevrolet's six millionth truck was built. During 1958, Chevrolet introduced dual headlamps and began a long-term association with Union Body Co. to produce Step-Van door-to-door delivery trucks.

The El Camino, a cross between a car and truck, was a 1959 highlight. Positraction axles were introduced that year, too. Fleetside pickups took the Cameo's place in line. In 1960, Chevrolet introduced a light-duty truck first with torsion bar front suspension. A total body redesign was done, and the 3100/3600/3800 series designations were switched to the C10/C20/C30 identifiers still in use today.

Full-size El Caminos disappeared by 1961, the same year an all-new line of forward-control trucks was introduced. These used the Corvair platform, and its air-cooled "pancake" six-cylinder engine/transaxle setup. Panels, passenger "Corvans," and Pickups were available in this Corvair 95 series. One "Rampside Pickup" had a drop-down box wall that doubled as a cargo loading ramp.

Chevrolet's eight millionth truck sale came in 1962. Two years later, the El Camino, now based on the mid-sized Chevelle, reappeared. Full-size trucks featured self-adjusting brakes, and 6,000 mile chassis lubrication intervals. In mid-

1964, a compact Chevy Van was phased-in as the Corvair truck's replacement. The nine millionth Chevrolet truck was retailed, too.

A growing recreational vehicle market brought changes in 1965. They included more powerful 325-cid V-8 engines. Long Box models with 8-1/2- or 9-ft. cargo beds grew popular with buyers wishing to install camper-backs in Chevy C/K Pickups. A Camper Special option package was also introduced. It had beefed-up power train and chassis components. Safety equipment was emphasized after 1966, becoming standard on all light-duty trucks. Chevrolet truck number 10 million left the factory during the year.

A three-door Suburban bowed in 1967, when Pickups got a redesign, and new CS and CST trim packages. A 108-in. wheelbase Chevy Van was offered, along with new, more rounded van bodies having a larger windshield. Safety side markers were added to trucks in 1968, when the El Camino became a 116-in. wheelbase model with flying buttress roof line. The following season, Chevrolet went one up on Ford with a full-size 4x4 utility truck named Blazer. Bucket seats and a center console became available as CST-level options in Pickups. In 1970, Step-Vans adopted an "Easy Access" front end design.

Front disc brakes were standardized in 1971, when vans grew larger and gained coil spring front suspensions and sliding side doors. They also had new extended hoods for easier servicing. A new P-30 Class A motorhome chassis was available, as well as a Panel Delivery version of Chevrolet's subcompact Vega Station Wagon. Mini-Pickups sourced from Isuzu, of Japan, bowed under the Chevy LUV name in 1972, the initials standing for "Light Utility Vehicle."

Half-ton and 3/4-ton light-duty trucks adopted optional full-time 4x4 systems in 1973, a year that saw the sale of Chevrolet's 15 millionth truck. Gas tanks were moved from in the cab, and all-leaf spring rear suspensions were used. Trim levels were now called Custom, Custom Deluxe, Cheyenne, and Cheyenne Super (the last with woodgrained exterior body panels). Sales zoomed to 923,189 units.

Light truck sales tapered off in 1973, due to the Arab oil embargo. Nevertheless, the a new 454-cid engine was released. Hi-Cube Vans were a 1974 innovation. Silverado and Scottsdale trim packages bowed in 1975. By 1977, Chevrolet had gained domination of the 4x4 market as light-duty truck sales zoomed above the one-million-per-year level. A 5.7-liter diesel V-8 was 1978's big news. A 4x4 version of the LUV pickup was added in 1979, when Chevrolet announced a figure of 21,850,083 total sales of trucks since 1918.

In mid-1980, Chevrolet abandoned the heavy-duty truck field to concentrate on light- and medium-duty sales. 1982 brought the compact S10 pickup (replacing the LUV) and a new 6.2-liter diesel V-8. Maxi-Cab and 4x4 versions of the S10 models were a headline happening for 1983. The 5.7-liter diesel was made available in El Caminos, while the full-size 4x2 Blazer was discontinued. Production of the down-sized Astro Van started in the summer of 1984, for 1985 release.

Chevrolet turned its light-duty truck strengths into industry sales leadership in 1985. The midyear introduction of the Astro put it ahead of Ford in the minivan market, while the Blazer S10 (particularly the 4x2 model) dominated the compact Sport Utility Vehicle category. Total sales for the year were 1,300,130, good for a 2.2 percent margin of market share over Ford. All-new big Pickups, the first in more than a decade, were scheduled for 1986, but didn't make it. Chevy truck sales dropped four percent below the all-time record set in 1985. Bright spots in the marketing picture included the hot-selling Astro and a four percent increase in deliveries of the highly profitable Suburban.

Debuting in the spring of 1987 as 1988 models, the all-new Pickups based on the GMT400 platform featured aero styling, fancier interiors, and rear antilock brakes. A GM-Gertag five-speed transmission was optional and independent front suspension was featured on 4x4s for the first time. The new trucks were tagged C/K models and the old-style C/Ks were renamed R/V models. The 3/4-ton and 1-ton Pickups (including chassis models and Crew-Cabs) did not get the new aero body immediately., and retained the R/V image until the end of the 1987 run. Suburbans and K-series Blazers made in the Flint, Michigan factory retained the "old" sheet metal even longer.

The "real" 1988 was a winning Chevrolet year with sales of 1,336,407 units and booming business in the new-styled C/K1500 big trucks. Ford retained its 1987 lead in the truck segment of the market, but only by 106,000 units. The S10 Pickup truck and S-Blazer also saw rising popularity.

Another contributor for 1989 was the Tracker, a captive-import mini-SUV sourced from Suzuki Motor Co. Ltd. It entered

production, at midyear, in a Canadian factory. Also initiated during 1989 was production of the all-new GMT200 APV (All-Purpose-Vehicle), better known to consumers as the Lumina. This front-wheel-drive minivan was aimed more directly at the front-wheel-drive Dodge Caravan /Plymouth Voyager/Chrysler Town & Country trio, since the rear-wheel-drive Astro did not have the same appeal to family-van buyers. However, an all-wheel-drive Astro was introduced, along with an Extended-Body model. Chevy held onto second place in trucks in 1989.

The first year of the 1990s brought two new full-size Pickups. The limited-edition 454 SS was an exciting, high-performance spin-off of the full-size Pickup. The new WT 1500 (or "Work Truck") package was an option for big Pickup fans who needed a get-down-to-business hauler. The S10/S-Blazer models added a Gertag designed, Hydramatic-built five-speed manual gear box, while the K-Blazer and Suburban got rear antilock brakes. Retail sales for calendar-year 1990 included 1,241,452 domestic-made trucks, and 1,450 imports. A new four-door version of the S-Blazer was introduced in the spring of 1990 as a 1991 model.

Standard engine in the 1991 Chevy SS454 Pickup was a new 7.4-liter V-8 with an electronically-controlled heavy-duty four-speed automatic overdrive transmission. The base S10 engine offered 11 added horsepower, and the K-Blazer was improved with the addition of Throttle-Body-Injection to the standard 5.7-liter V-8. At midyear, the Astro got a 165 hp Vortec high-output V-6. For the calendar-year, light-duty truck sales slipped to 1,066,541 units. That was second to Ford's 1,211,654. However, if you added the 285,424 GMC light-duty trucks sold that year, General Motors was on top of the industry.

Restyled full-size Blazers and Suburbans headlined the product revisions for 1992. They now had the more aerodynamic front end of the C/K Pickups, plus new wagon styling. Chevrolet's calendar-year sales total went up to 1,152,346, while GMC tabulated 339,107 light-duty truck sales. Ford had 1,397,073 that year. In August of that year, a controversy erupted after the Center for Auto Safety charged that 1973-1987 C/K Pickups with side-saddle fuel tanks were unsafe because the tanks were vulnerable to punctures in side impact collisions. GM defended the trucks as safe, noting that they met 1977 federal standards limiting fuel leaks in crashes. In February, a jury in Atlanta, Ga. ordered GM to pay a $105 million settlement in a case involving the older C/K trucks. Ten days later, at a Detroit press conference, GM revealed that a crash test of the trucks aired on the television news program "NBC Dateline" had shown a truck that was rigged to explode. NBC then apologized and several of its employees resigned or were fired. GM stressed the episode as an example of improper representation of auto safety issues.

Product alterations for 1993 Chevrolet light-duty trucks were mainly technical in nature. S10 Pickups got a new ECT transmission, while big trucks could now get an optional Hydramatic 4L60-E four-speed automatic gear box. The 4.3-liter CPI V-6 was made optional for S10 Pickups, while the Chevy Van and Sportvan got the Vortec V-6 with 155 hp. A power sliding door was a new extra for Lumina APVs. A healthy retail sales increase was registered for calendar-year 1993, with 1,309,879 units leaving Chevy showrooms.

For 1994, Chevy put the spotlight on the compact Blazer. Formerly promoted as the S-Blazer, it was now simply called the Blazer. A total redesign left the compact Sport Utility Vehicle with an all-new body and a standard 4.3-liter/200-hp V-6. Though launched in August 1994, it was considered a 1995 model. It came in two- and four-door versions with 4x2 or 4x4 running gears. Also totally restyled was the S10 Pickup. It had an aerodynamic exterior, a new interior, a sporty SS option package, and a ZR2 option for off-road enthusiasts. Astros got safety improvements including side door beams, and a standard driver's side air bag. A new 6.5-liter/180-hp turbo-diesel was made available for the big Blazer. It could also be added to C/K Pickups, and Suburbans. Full-size vans got a normally-aspirated version of the "6.5." In the Lumina APV, Chevrolet added a driver's air bag and integral child seat as standard equipment.

Chevy's "all-new" truck for 1995 was the Tahoe, a total re-work of the full-size K-Blazer no longer called "K" or "Blazer." It first came in a two-door version, with a longer four-door coming out later in the model run. Standard features included a 200-hp 5.7-liter V-8, an ECT four-seed automatic transmission, and GM's Insta-Trac system. Geo Trackers had no major changes. S-Series Pickups were modestly updated.

1919 Chevrolet Platform Stake (DFW/FLP)

1923 Chevrolet Superior Light Delivery (BH)

1931 Chevrolet-Hercules Commercial Station Wagon (DFW/BC)

1937 Chevrolet Coupe-Delivery (DFW/MVMA)

1949 Chevrolet 1-Ton Series 3800 Pickup (OCW)

1952 Chevrolet 1/2-Ton Series 3100 Pickup (OCW)

1966 Chevrolet 1/2-Ton C10 Fleetside Pickup (DFW)

1974 Chevrolet 1/2-Ton K5 Blazer Utility Wagon (JAG)

1978 Chevrolet 1/2-Ton LUV Mini-Pickup (DFW/TSC)

1979 Chevrolet 1/2-Ton C10 Fleetside Pickup (CP)

Chevrolet Model Names

Various terms are used in Chevrolet factory documents and sales literature to describe light-duty commercial vehicles. Sometimes different terms are used to describe the same trucks. The following chart sorts out some of the confusion:

Model Name	Type of Truck	Other Names or Nicknames
[1918-1932]		
Light Delivery	Passenger w/heavy springs	Commercial Car
Light Truck	3/4-ton truck	Commercial Car; 3/4-ton truck
Medium-Heavy	1-ton truck	Commercial Car; 1-ton Worm-Drive truck

NOTE 1: All three types formed Chevrolet's Commercial Car series.
NOTE 2: Some literature groups Sedan Delivery with passenger cars.

[1933-1934]		
Light-Delivery	Passenger car-based delivery	1/2-ton Sedan Delivery, Commercial Car; Light-Delivery

NOTE 3: Some factory model listings indicate 1/2-ton Sedan Delivery for 1933 models and 1/2-ton for 1934 models. There were Pickups and Panels available in the same series, so it seems most correct to call this a 1/2-ton or 1/2-ton Light-Delivery series.

[1935-1946]		
Commercial Car	Sedan Delivery; Coupe-Delivery Coupe-Express	1/2-ton Commercial SDL;
Light-Delivery	1/2-ton to 1-ton truck	Light-Duty for 1/2-ton; Medium-Duty for 3/4- to 1-ton
Dubl-Duti	Forward-Control Chassis	Commercial Dubl-Duti 3/4-ton Heavy-Duty; Parcel Delivery; Driver-Forward; Walk-in Panel

NOTE 4: Chevrolet military vehicle model names not included.
NOTE 5: Technically, Forward-Control described the chassis and Dubl-Duti described the truck body category.
NOTE 6: Trucks heavier than 1-ton were described as Heavy-Duty, Utility, Heavy-Duty COE and Utility COE models.

[1946-1957]		
Sedan Delivery	Passenger car based delivery	Commercial Car
El Camino	Coupe-Pickup (1959-'60 only)	1/2-ton Pickup; Pickup-Car
Commercial	1/2-ton to 1-ton conventional	
Dubl-Duti	Forward-Control chassis	Commercial (Dubl-Duti); Step-Van; Parcel Delivery; Walk-in; Stand-up Delivery

[1958-1963]		
Sedan Delivery	Station Wagon based delivery	Commercial Car
El Camino	Passenger car based delivery	Commercial Car; 1/2-ton Pickup; Pickup-Car
Commercial	1/2-ton to 1-ton conventional	Light-duty (1/2-ton); Medium-duty (3/4-ton to 1-ton); Conventional
Dubl-Duti	Forward-Control chassis	Commercial (Dubl-Duti); Step-Van; Parcel Delivery; Walk-in; Stand-up Delivery

[1964-1969]		
El Camino	Passenger car based Pickup	Sedan-Pickup two-door; Coupe-Pickup
Chevy Van	Compact driver-forward van	Van; Panel Van; Bus (windows)
Commercial	1/2-ton to 1-ton conventional	Light-Duty (1/2-ton); Medium-duty
Step-Van	Forward-Control chassis	Dubl-Duti; Walk-in; Parcel Delivery; Stand-up Delivery
Blazer	4x4 Open Utility Pickup	Sports Utility; 4x4 Utility
[1970-up]		
El Camino	Passenger-based Pickup	Sedan-Pickup two-door
Chevy Van	Commercial Panel Van	Van; Panel Van; Compact Van
Sportvan	Passenger Window Van	Bus; Window Van; Beauville; Bonaventure
Hi-Cube Van	Van Chassis With Cargo Box	Cutaway Van
Conventional	1/2-ton to 1-ton conventional	Commercial; Light-duty (1/2-ton); Medium-duty (3/4-ton to 1-ton)
Big-Dooley	1-ton Crew Cab Fleetside Long	"Country Cadillac" Box Pickup w/dual rear wheels
Step-Van	Parcel Delivery Truck	Forward-Control
Step-Van King	High, wide, Aluminum Step-Van (10 ft. to 14.5 ft.)	Forward Control
Vega	Subcompact wagon-based Panel	Panel Express; Panel
LUV	Imported Mini-Pickup	Mini-Pickup; Fleetside Mini
S10	Mini-Truck	Mimi-Pickup; Maxi-Cab Mini-Pickup; Mini Fleetside, Sport Pickup
S10 Blazer	Mini-Sport Utility Wagon	Sport Utility; Sport Utility Wagon

Other descriptive terms: 1100= Sedan Delivery; 1500 or 1508=Sedan Delivery; 3100=1/2-ton; 3124=Cameo Carrier (1955-1958); 3200=Long Wheelbase 1/2-ton; 3600=3/4-ton; 3800=1-ton; 3700=3/4-ton Dubl-Duti; 3900=1-ton Dubl-Duti; C10 = 1/2 ton; K10 = 1/2-ton 4x4; C14=1/2-ton Long Wheelbase; K14=1/2-ton Long Wheelbase 4x4; C20=3/4-ton; K20=3/4-ton 4x4; C30=1-ton; K30=1-ton 4x4; C25=Heavy-Duty 3/4-ton; Carryall=Suburban; Canopy=Canopy Delivery; Panel=Panel Delivery; Step-Side=Pickup with "pontoon" rear fenders; Fleetside=Pickup with slab-side rear quarters.
Common Chevrolet trim and equipment names: Custom Cab; Apache; Long Horn; Custom/10; Custom Deluxe; Custom Sport Truck (CST); Camper-Special; Cheyenne; Cheyenne Super; Scottsdale; Silverado; Chevy Sport; Beauville; Bonaventure; El Camino Custom; El Camino SS or SS-396 (Super Sport and Super Sport with 396-cid V-8); El Camino Conquista; El Camino Royal Knight; Big Dooley; S10 Tahoe; S10 Durango; S10 High-Sierra; LUV Mikado.

1918 CHEVROLET

1918 Chevrolet 1-Ton Series T Panel (DFW/OHS)

LIGHT DELIVERY — MODEL 490 — FOUR-CYLINDER: Chevrolet began production of a Light Delivery in January 1918. It was a 490 passenger car chassis beefed-up with heavier springs. The truck used the cowl and 15-degree, backwards-slanting windshield of open-body Chevrolet automobiles. Standard equipment included a speedometer, ammeter, tire pump, electric horn and demountable rims. Chevrolet manufactured only the chassis, fenders and cowl and included accessories such as headlamps. Dealers or customers then had bodies built and installed by aftermarket firms. Martin-Parry Co., of Indianapolis, Ind., was one major supplier of commercial bodies for the Chevrolet chassis. The Light Delivery had a 1,000 lb. or 1/2-ton "load for trucks" (payload). Styling was simple and straightforward. Appearance features included semi-circular fenders and wood spoke wheels.

1918 Chevrolet Series T 1-Ton Eight-Post Curtain Top Express (BH)

MEDIUM/HEAVY TRUCK — SERIES T — FOUR-CYLINDER: Also new for 1918 was the Series T. This was Chevrolet's 1-ton medium-duty worm-drive truck. "Chevrolet one-ton trucks are sanely designed, properly constructed, and built of known material," said an announcement printed in *Chevrolet Review*, Volume 1, Number 10 (January 1918). "They are the direct result of long and careful study of motor truck transportation problems. Deeply appreciating the responsibility attached to the manufacture of a commercial unit, we have subjected these trucks to the most grueling tests! They have been driven the distance across the continent and back again. They have been put to the road tests and load tests. And from these tests we know just what the trucks will do under the most trying conditions." The Series T was characterized by a honeycomb radiator with rounded Chevrolet bow tie badge, sloping seven-louver hood and cowl-mounted headlights. These lights had hand grips on the back of them to aid the driver's entry into the cab. Three models were available: The chassis for $1,325, the Flare Board Express for $1,460 and Eight Post Curtain Top Express for $1,545. The curtain top was supported, on each side, by four posts with a 1-1/2 x 2 inch cross section. It was removable by releasing the posts at the sill cross members. Mounted on the sides of the Series T were flare boards having a width of eight-in. on the slope and overhanging the vertical sides of the body by approximately six in.. The flares were braced from the sill cross members to the undersides of the boards. "Sturdiness of each vital unit making up the running gear is a striking feature of the truck," said *Chevrolet Review*. "Each one is meant for plain, hard work. Axles, front and rear, motor, clutch, transmission, frame, springs — all have been designed with the idea of giving steady, uninterrupted service. Each stands for maximum strength. In material, each part represents the best for the purpose." Two compartments were provided under the three-man seat. One held the gas tank and one was intended for carrying purposes. Standard equipment included electric lights and starter (highest two-unit system), complete lamp equipment (including headlamp dimmers), electric horn, odometer, side curtains for driver's seat, windshield, and complete tool equipment. The 1918 Series T used the passenger car engine and transmission. The transmission was a selective type with three speeds forward and one reverse. Chevrolet's FA engine was used in this model only in 1918. "In the true Chevrolet way, the 'beaten path' of design and construction has been followed only so far as dependable, economical operation demanded," added *Chevrolet Review*. "A number of innovations and exclusive features have been incorporated that make the Chevrolet truck a noteworthy product — one that represents most thoroughly and completely the high merchandising ideals of this company."

1918 Chevrolet 1-Ton Series T Flare Board Express (BH)

I.D. DATA: [Series T]: Serial number stamped on cross member at left front of engine. Serial numbers were: 1-1020-1-1081, 2-1000 to 2-1269 9-01 to 9-028. [Series 490]: Serial number located on dash nameplate. Engine numbers stamped on flywheel.

Model	Body Type	Price	Weight	Prod. Total
Light Delivery — Model 490 — 1/2-Ton — 102 in. w.b.				
490	Chassis	595	1785	Note 1
Medium-Heavy Truck — Series T — 1-Ton — 125 in. w.b.				
T	Worm Drive Chassis	1325	2840	Note 2
T	Flare Board Express	1460	3300	Note 2
T	Curtain Top Express	1545	3420	Note 2

NOTE 1: Light Delivery production included with 490 passenger car total. **NOTE 2:** Series T production through Sept. 23, 1919 was 359 units. Of these, 61 were built in Flint, Mich. (factory no. 1), 270 were built in Tarrytown, N.Y. (factory no. 2) and 28 were built in Canada (factory no. 9). **ENGINE:** [490] OHV. Inline. Four-cylinder. Cast-iron block. Cast-in-block cylinders. Bore & stroke: 3-11/16 x 4 in. Displacement: 170.9 cid. Compression ratio: 4.25:1. Brake horsepower: 26 at 1800 rpm. Net horsepower: 21.70. Three main bearings. Solid valve lifters. Carburetor: Zenith model V one-barrel. **ENGINE:** [Series T] OHV. Inline. Four-cylinder. Cast iron block. Cast-in-block cylinders. Bore & stroke: 3-11/16 x 5-1/4 in. Displacement: 224 cid. Compression ratio: 4.25:1. Brake horsepower: 37 at 2000 rpm. Net horsepower: 21.75. Three main bearings. Solid valve lifters. Carburetor: Zenith improved double-jet. **CHASSIS:** [Series 490] Wheelbase: 102 in. Tires: 30 x 3-1/2. **CHASSIS:** [Series T] Wheelbase: 125 in. Length of body from inside tailboard to inside of headboard was 114-1/2 in. Width inside boards was 45-3/4 in. Height of top from frame to highest point of top was 63-1/4 in. Overall length of top: 156-1/4 in. Tread: 56 in. Tires: [Front] 31 x 4 in. pneumatic, clincher type, non-skid with wrapped tread. [Rear] 32 x 4 in., solid. **TECHNICAL:** [Series 490] Selective sliding gear transmission. Speeds: 3F/1R. Center-control floor shift. Cone clutch with adjustable compensating springs. Three-quarter floating rear axle with wheel bearing carried on wheel hub and in axle housing (not shaft). Hyatt roller bearings. Brakes: [Emergency] Internal-expanding type. [Service] External-contracting type. 10 in. brake drums. Foot control. Wood artillery type wheels with demountable rims and large hub flanges. **TECHNICAL:** Selective sliding gear transmission. Speeds: 3F/1R. Center floor-mounted gear-shift. Cone clutch with adjustable compensating springs. Semi-floating rear axle. Brakes: Two sets internal-expanding type acting on rear wheel brake drums. Artillery type wheels of standard dimensions with 12 hickory spokes and front equipped with Timken tapered roller bearings of extra-large size. **OPTIONS:** Front bumper. Rear bumper. Single sidemount. Heater. Spotlight. Cowl lamps. Rear view mirror.

1918 Chevrolet 1/2-Ton Model 490 Light Delivery Wagon

HISTORICAL: Introduced in late 1917. World War I drove prices upward, yet Chevrolet continued in good economic health, selling all the cars it could make. It was during this war that Chevrolet was purchased by General Motors, bringing it into what would be the world automotive power of the future. The year 1917 saw the first truck (a 1918 model) roll off a Chevrolet assembly line in St. Louis, Missouri. It was a Light Delivery vehicle based on the "beefed-up" 490 platform. Truck bodies were supplied to owners by body builders, or were handmade to individual needs. Calendar-year sales: Chevrolet reported 879 truck sales. Calendar-year production: [Series T] 61 at Flint, Mich., 270 at Tarrytown, N.Y., 28 in Canada. Innovations: First Chevrolet commercial vehicles. Chevrolet's four-cylinder engine had first been used in 1914 on its Baby Grand and Royal Mail passenger cars. It had a four-inch stroke. The 5-1/4 in. stroke FA engine was introduced in 1918 for passenger cars and Series T trucks. The smaller 490 engine was used in Light Delivery models. Other than the engine, few changes were made in the Series T truck during the five years that it was available.

1919 CHEVROLET

LIGHT DELIVERY — MODEL 490 — FOUR-CYLINDER: Chevrolet's 1919 truck line was largely unchanged. Several improvements were made to all Chevrolet 490 models including the Light Delivery Wagon. The new spare tire carrier was of the 3/4-circle type with a lever. Standard equipment included windshield, speedometer, ammeter, tire pump, electric horn and demountable rims.

1919 Chevrolet 1-Ton Series T Eight-Post Curtain Top Express (BH)

MEDIUM/HEAVY TRUCK — SERIES T — FOUR-CYLINDER: The Series T 1-ton worm-drive truck was also much the same as in 1918. Chevrolet claimed its design combined graceful good looks with maximum utility. The cab was clean and simple. Features included a gear-shift lever and emergency brake lever positioned right at hand for the operator. Dash equipment consisted of a conveniently arranged speedometer, carburetor choke, ammeter, oil pressure gauge, lighting switch and ignition switch. Chevrolet's FB engine was used this season. It had the same basic specifications as the 1918 FA truck power plant. Its cylinders were cast in the block and integral with the upper half of the crankcase. Poured rod bearings were featured. The three exhaust port cylinder head was detachable. Other mechanical features included a gear-driven oil pump, Remy ignition system, water pump, worm-and-gear type steering, I-beam front axle, semi-floating rear axle, semi-elliptic front and rear springs, and 13-gallon gas tank. Standard equipment included electric lights and starter (highest two-unit system), complete lamp equipment (including headlamp dimmers), electric horn, odometer, side curtains for driver's seat, windshield and complete tool equipment. The transmission was a selective type with three speeds forward and one reverse.
I.D. DATA: [Series T]: Serial number stamped on frame cross member at left front of engine. Also on nameplate on dash. [Series 490]: Serial number located on dash nameplate. Serial numbers: [Series T] 1-1082 to 1-2284 2-1270 to 2-2201 3-1000 to 3-1300 6-1047 to 6-1644 and 9-029 to 9-355. Explanation of assembly plant code: The numerical prefix identifies manufacturing plant as follows, 1=Flint, Mich. 2=Tarrytown N.Y. 3=St. Louis, Mo. 6=Oakland Calif. and 9=Oshawa Ontario, Canada. Engine numbers: located on flywheel.

Model	Body Type	Price	Weight	Prod. Total
Light Delivery — Model 490 — 1/2-Ton — 102 in. w.b.				
490	Chassis	735	1865	Note 1
Medium-Heavy Truck — Series T — 1-Ton — 125 in. w.b.				
T	Worm Drive Chassis	1325	2840	-
T	Flare Board Express	1460	3300	-
T	Curtain Top Express	1545	3420	-

NOTE 1: Light Delivery production included with 490 passenger car total.
ENGINE: [490] OHV. Inline. Four-cylinder. Cast iron block. Cast-in-block cylinders. Bore & stroke: 3-11/16 x 4 in. Displacement: 170.9 cid. Compression ratio: 4.25:1. Brake horsepower: 26 at 1800 rpm. Net horsepower: 21.70. Three main bearings. Solid valve lifters. Carburetor: Zenith model V one-barrel.
ENGINE: [Series T] OHV. Inline. Four-cylinder. Cast iron block. Cylinder cast en-bloc. Bore & stroke: 3-11/16 x 5-1/4 in. Displacement: 224 cid. Compression ratio: 4.25:1. Brake horsepower: 37 at 2000 rpm. Net H.P.: 21.75. Three main bearings. Solid valve lifters. Carburetor: Zenith improved double-jet.
CHASSIS: [Series 490] Wheelbase: 102 in. Frame thickness: 4 in. Front frame width: 30-1/2 in. Rear frame width: 35-1/8 in. Length behind seat: 109 in. Loaded frame height: 25 in. Springs: Semi-elliptic, [front] 2-1/4 x 37-1/2 in. [rear] 2-1/2- x 53 in. Tires: 30 x 3-1/2.
CHASSIS: [Series T] Wheelbase: 125 in. Length of body from inside tailboard to inside of headboard was 114-1/2 in. Width inside boards was 45-3/4 in. Height of top from frame to highest point: 63-1/4 in. Overall length of top: 156-1/4 in. Tread: 56 in. Tires: (Front) 31 x 4 in., pneumatic, non-skid with wrapped tread, [rear] 32 x 4 in.

TECHNICAL: [Both models] Selective sliding gear transmission. Speeds: 3F/1R. Floor-mounted gear-shift. Cone type clutches, same as 1918. [Model 490] Three-quarter floating rear axle. [Series T] Semi-floating rear axle. External-contracting mechanical rear wheel brakes. Wooden spoke wheels of same type as 1918. Series T drive shaft was of high-carbon seamless steel tubing 1-3/8 in. in diameter. Center of drive shaft supported on double row of self-aligning ball bearings close to middle U-Joint. Bearing housing filled with lubricant and fitted with compression grease cup for refilling. Worm gear drive: The steel worm was cut, hardened and finish-ground by special machine. The bronze gear was of special alloy, accurately cut, with teeth burnished to reduce friction. The gear ran in oil and acted as a pump that picked up and circulated oil over the worm and through the bearings. A governor was fitted on the Series T and set for 25 mph maximum speed, with a lock to prevent operator tampering.
OPTIONS: Front bumper. Rear bumper. Heater. Cowl lamps. Rear view mirror.
HISTORICAL: Introduced: Late 1918. Calendar-year sales: 8,179 trucks. Calendar-year production: [Series T] 1,203 at Flint, Mich., 932 at Tarrytown, N.Y., 301 at St. Louis, Mo., 597 at Oakland, Calif., 326 in Oshawa, Canada. Innovations: The popularity of Chevrolet trucks was starting to rise. Sales of Samson trucks and tractors (aother GM brand) were assigned to the Chevrolet dealer organization. Martin-Parry Co. continued as the major supplier of bodies for Chevrolet chassis. William C. Durant was in control of Chevrolet this year. The company was a branch of General Motors.

1920 CHEVROLET

LIGHT DELIVERY — MODEL 490 — FOUR-CYLINDER: "The Chevrolet Light Delivery Wagon is designed to meet the requirements of those who have need of a commercial car with slightly less capacity and of considerably lighter weight then is afforded by a 1-ton truck," said Chevrolet's *1920 Commercial Cars* sales catalog. "It is sturdily constructed and amply powered for all transportation needs. It is light enough to be speedy, easy riding and economical with fuel and tires." Appearance improvements for the 490 included use of a reverse-curve fender line and full-crown fenders. Headlamps were mounted to the fenders, eliminating the tie-bar previously used. A couple of technical changes were made. Chevrolet still refrained from truck body building. However, the company put out a contract to source delivery wagon bodies from outside and install them at the factory level. Besides the Chassis-and-Cowl truck, two models were cataloged with express bodies. Both had four-post curtain tops. The first included driver's seat and side curtains for use in cold or stormy weather. Two extra seats were provided in the second series to make it useful as a station wagon or for other passenger transportation requirements. One seat was at the extreme rear and one was at the center of the express box. Standard equipment included: Electric lights, self-starter, complete lamps (including adjustable headlamps), top and curtains, adjustable windshield, speedometer, electric horn, extra rim, tire carrier, and complete tools including tire pump and jack.

1920 Chevrolet 1/2-Ton Model 490 Light Delivery Wagon (BH)

1920 Chevrolet 1/2-Ton Model 490 Light Delivery Station Wagon (BH)

MEDIUM/HEAVY TRUCK — SERIES T — FOUR-CYLINDER: Chevrolet's 1-ton Series T truck was also back in 1920. Its worm drive system was de-emphasized in sales literature. Instead, the *1920 Commercial Car* sales catalog stressed the abilities of the FB power plant and sturdy construction that insured maximum service and minimum wear. Included with the basic chassis model were radiator, hood, cowl, front fenders, and running boards. The single driver's seat was mounted on top of a tall platform housing the gas tank and a storage compartment. Also available was a Flare Board Express body measuring 114-1/2 in. long from the inside of the tailboard to inside of headboard, with a 44-in. width inside the boards. A third model added an eight-post curtain top. The standard equipment list included electric lights and starter (highest two-unit system), complete lamp equipment (including headlamp dimmer), electric horn, odometer, side curtain for driver's seat, windshield, and complete tool equipment.

1920 Chevrolet 1-Ton Series T Eight-Post Curtain Top Express (BH)

I.D. DATA: Serial number stamped on frame cross member at left front of engine. Also on nameplate on dash. Serial numbers: [490] 2-1000 to 2A-24086 and 9-115 and up. [Series T]: 1-2285 to 4199 2-2202 to 3616 3-1301 to 1953 6-1645 to 2362 and 9-356 to 9-847. The numerical prefix (such as 2-) identifies manufacturing plant as follows: 1=Flint, Mich. 2=Tarrytown, N.Y. 3=St. Louis, Mo. 6=Oakland Calif. and 9=Oshawa Ontario, Canada. Engine numbers located on flywheel.

1920 Chevrolet 1/2-Ton Model 490 Light Delivery Farm Wagon (BH)

1920 Chevrolet 1-Ton Series T Worm-Drive Chassis-and-Cowl With Windshield (BH)

ENGINE: [490] Inline. Cast en-bloc. OHV. Four-cylinder. Cast-iron block. Bore & stroke: 3-11/16 x 4 in. Displacement: 170.9 cid. Compression ratio: 4.25:1. Brake horsepower: 26 at 1800 rpm. Net horsepower: 21.70. Three main bearings. Solid valve lifters. Carburetor: Zenith model V.
ENGINE: [T] Inline. OHV. Cast en-bloc. Four-cylinder. Cast iron block. Bore & stroke: 3-11/16 x 5-1/4 in. Displacement: 224 cid. C.R.: 4.25:1. Brake horsepower: 37 at 2000 rpm. Net horsepower: 21.75. Three main bearings. Solid valve lifters. Carburetor: Zenith improved double-jet.
CHASSIS: [Series 490] Wheelbase: 102 in. Tires: 30 x 3-1/2 in. Steering: Spur-and-gear type (adjustable for wear) with 15 in. steering wheel.

1920 Chevrolet 1-Ton Series T Flare Board Express (BH)

CHASSIS: [Series T] Wheelbase: 125 in. Tires: [Front] Pneumatic 33 x 4 in. demountable type, non-skid with wrapped tread. [Rear] Pneumatic 35 x 5 in. cord type. Steering: Worm-and-gear type with 16-in. steering wheel. Steering arm of drop-forged steel, heat treated.
TECHNICAL: [490] Selective sliding gear transmission. Speeds: 3F/1R. Floor-mounted center gear-shift. Cone clutch with adjustable compensating springs. Three-quarter floating rear axle. Wheel bearing carried on wheel hub in axle housing (not shaft). Hyatt roller bearings. Brakes: [Emergency] Internal expanding type, [Service] External contracting type with 10-in. brake drums and foot control. Wheels: Wood artillery type, demountable rim, large hub flanges.

Model	Body Type	Price	Weight	Prod. Total
Light Delivery — Series 490 — 1/2-Ton — 102 in. w.b.				
490	Light Delivery Chassis	685	1865	Note 1
490	Delivery Wagon 1-seat	735	-	Note 1
490	Delivery Wagon 3-seat	770	-	Note 1
Medium-Heavy Truck — Series T — 1-Ton — 125 in. w.b.				
T	Chassis & Cowl	1325	3300	Note 2
T	Flare Board Express	1460	-	Note 2
T	Covered Flare	1545	-	Note 2

NOTE 1: Light Delivery production included with 490 passenger car total.
NOTE 2: Series production was 5,288 units at all factories.

1920 Chevrolet 1-Ton Series T Eight-Post Curtain Top Express (BH)

TECHNICAL: [T] Selective type transmission. Speeds: 3F/1R. Center floor shift control. Leather-faced cone clutch with adjustable compensating springs. Governor provided and set and locked at 25 mph maximum speed. Semi-floating rear axle made of heat treated steel. Worm gear drive has cut and hardened, finish-ground steel worm requiring no adjustment at any time. Brakes: Same as 1918-1919. Wheels: Artillery spoke, standard dimensions, 12 hickory spokes, front brakes equipped with Timken tapered roller bearings of extra large size.

OPTIONS: Front bumper. Rear bumper. Heater. Cowl lamps. Driver's seat ($50). Pair of auxiliary seats ($85). Rear view mirror.

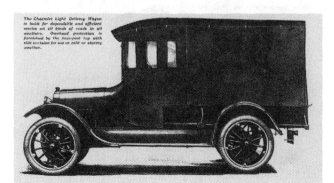

1920 Chevrolet 1/2-Ton Light Delivery Four-Post Top & Curtains (BH)

1920 Chevrolet 1-Ton Series T Eight-Post Curtain Top Express (BH)

HISTORICAL: Introduced: January, 1920. Calendar-year production: [Series T] 1,914 at Flint, Mich, 1,414 at Tarrytown, N.Y., 652 at St. Louis, Mo., 717 at Oakland, Calif., 591 in Oshawa, Canada. Innovations: New fender treatment for 490 Series commercial cars. Factory-installed aftermarket bodies. Headlamp tie-bar eliminated on 490 models. W.C. Durant was forced out of General Motors by angry stock holders. Pierre S. Durant became president of the corporation. Karl W. Zimmerschied took over as president of Chevrolet.

1921 CHEVROLET

1921 Chevrolet 1/2-Ton Model 490 Light Delivery Station Wagon (BH)

LIGHT DELIVERY — MODEL 490 — FOUR-CYLINDER: The 490 was basically unchanged. Chevrolet's copywriters described it as a profitable investment for all light handling and delivery purposes. Standard equipment listed in the COMMERCIAL CARS catalog included: Electric lights, self-starter, complete lamps (including adjustable headlamps), top and curtains, adjustable windshield, speedometer, electric horn, extra rim, tire carrier, and complete tools including tire pump and jack. The catalog also promoted several of the more popular bodies including a Station Wagon, Delivery Wagon, Express Wagon, and Farm Wagon. All Chevrolet truck bodies continued to be sourced from outside firms. However, some truck bodies (as shown in the sales catalog) were mass-produced for delivery to and installation at Chevrolet factories. Other bodies were purchased by dealers or buyers for aftermarket attachment to the Chevrolet chassis.

1921 Chevrolet 3/4-Ton Model G Light Truck chassis (BH)

LIGHT TRUCK — MODEL G — FOUR-CYLINDER: An all-new commercial vehicle was the Model G Light Truck. It was essentially the front end of the 490 mated with the longer and heavier frame and rear axle of a truck. Chevrolet described it as, "the product of years of experience" and said it was "built to supply

the demand for a 3/4-ton truck whose strength and performance equal(s) cars of greater capacity." This model used the larger engine. Base model offerings included the Chassis, Chassis-and-Cab, Open Express, and Curtain Top Express. Larger than the 490, the Model G had slanting hood louvers, reverse curve fenders, and torpedo type front-fender-mounted headlamps. Body length was 97-7/8 in. from tailboard to headboard, with a width of 46 in. between flareboards. Drive was from the left-hand side with center control. Spark and throttle were located under the steering wheel. There was a foot accelerator. Standard equipment included: Electric lights and starter, highest two-unit system, complete lamp equipment, side curtains, adjustable windshield, speedometer, demountable rims, electric horn, and complete tool equipment including pump and jack.

MEDIUM-HEAVY TRUCK — MODEL T — FOUR-CYLINDER: Cowl-mounted headlamps remained a distinctive styling characteristic of the Model T 1-ton in 1921. It had overall larger dimensions and a narrower cowl with "scooped-out" sides. Aftermarket bodies depicted in the sales catalog included a Passenger Bus, Fire Engine, Wholesale Hauler, Farm Wagon, and Panel Delivery. Standard equipment was the same as in 1920.

1921 Chevrolet 1-Ton Model T Medium-Heavy Chassis & Seat (BH)

I.D. DATA Serial number located on nameplate on dash. Serial numbers: [490 series] 1-A20821 to 57835, 2-A24086 to 54564, or 2-3020 and up. [Model G] 1-13 to 1-384, 2-77 to 2-303, 3-58 to 3-122, 6-59 to 6-182, 9-115 to 9-194. [Model T] 1-4200 to 4454, 2-3617 to 2-3631, 3-1954 to 3-2081, 6-2363 to 6-2446 and 9-356 up. The numerical prefixes indicated the factory, as follows: 1=Flint, Mich., 2=Tarrytown, N.Y., 3=St. Louis, Mo., 6=Oakland, Calif., 9=Oshawa, Canada. Engine numbers located on flywheel and left side of front motor support.

Model	Body Type	Price	Weight	Prod. Total
Light Delivery — Model 490 — 1/2-Ton — 102 in. w.b.				
490	Chassis & Cowl	625	-	-
490	Open Express	620	1865	Note 1
490	Covered Express 3-seat	855	-	Note 1
Light Truck — Model G — 3/4-Ton — 120 in. w.b.				
G	Chassis	920	2450	Note 2
G	Chassis & Cowl	995	-	Note 2
G	Open Express	1030	-	Note 2
G	Canopy Express	1095	-	Note 2
Medium-Heavy Truck — Model T — 1-Ton — 125 in. w.b.				
T	Chassis	1325	3300	Note 3
T	Open Express	1460	-	Note 3
T	Canopy Express	1545	-	Note 3
T	Canopy Express 3 seat	1595	-	Note 3

NOTE 1: Light Delivery production included with 490 passenger car total.
NOTE 2: G production was 855 units.
NOTE 3: T production was 478 units.
NOTE 4: Prices for the Model Gs decreased during the year to: (Chassis) $745, (Chassis-and-Cowl) $820, (Open Express) $855, and (Canopy Express) $920.

1921 Chevrolet 1/2-Ton Model 490 Light Delivery Wagon (BH)

ENGINE: [490 series] Inline. Cylinder cast-in-block. Overhead valves. Four-cylinder. Cast iron block. Bore & stroke: 3-11/16 x 4 in. Displacement: 170.9 cid. Compression ratio: 4.25:1. Brake horsepower: 26 at 2800 rpm. SAE net horsepower: 21.70. Three main bearings. Solid valve lifters. Carburetor: Zenith model one-barrel.
ENGINE: [G and T series] Inline. Cylinders cast-in-block. Overhead valves. Four-cylinder. Cast iron block. Bore & Stroke: 3-11/16 x 5-1/4 in. Displacement: 224 cid. C.R.: 4.25:1. Brake horsepower: 37 at 2000 rpm. SAE net H.P.: 21.75. Three main bearings. Solid valve lifters. Carburetor: Zenith improved double-jet.
CHASSIS: [490 series] Wheelbase: 102 in. Front axle: Drop-forged I-beam. Springs: Cantilever type front and rear. Spur-and-gear steering, adjustable for wear. 15 in. steering wheel. Tires: 30 x 3-1/2 non-skid front and rear.
CHASSIS: [G series] Wheelbase: 120 in. Front axle: Drop-forged I-beam. Ample-sized steering knuckles and steering arms (drop-forged and heat treated). Springs: [Front] Cantilever type, 21-7/8 in. long x 1-3/4 in. wide, [Rear] One-half elliptic type, 43-1/4 in. long x 2-1/2 in. wide. Five-in. deep frame. Front frame width: 28 in. Rear frame width: 37 in. Length in back of driver's seat: 76 in. Frame height: 23-1/2 in. loaded. Tires: All-pneumatic, demountable type with wrapped tread, [Front] 31 x 4 in., [Rear] 34 x 4-1/2 in. All-weather tread. Gas tank: 10 gallons.

1921 Chevrolet 1-Ton Model T Passenger Bus (BH)

CHASSIS: [T series] Wheelbase: 125 in. Front axle: Drop-forged I-beam. Springs: Semi-elliptic front and rear, [Front] 38 x 2-1/4 in., [Rear] 54 x 2-1/2 in. Worm-and-gear steering. Steering arm of drop-forged, heat-treated steel, 16 in. wheel. Tires: [Front] pneumatic, 33 x 4 in., demountable type, non-skid with wrapped tread, [Rear] 35 x 5 in. pneumatic, cord type. Gas tank capacity: 13 gallons.

TECHNICAL: [490 series] Selective sliding gear transmission. Speeds: 3F/1R. Floor-mounted gear-shift. Cone type clutch with adjustable compensating springs. Three-quarter floating rear axle with Hyatt roller bearings. Brakes: [Emergency] internal-expanding type, [Service] external-contracting type with 10-in. brake drums and foot control. Wood artillery wheels with demountable rims and large hub flanges.

TECHNICAL: [G series] Selective sliding gear transmission. Speeds: 3F/1R. Cone clutch with adjustable compensating springs. Semi-floating rear axle made of heat-treated nickel steel. Brakes: [Emergency] Internal-expanding type, [Service] External-contracting type with 12-in. brake drums and foot control. Artillery type wheels of standard dimension with 12 hickory spokes (front wheels have Timken tapered roller bearings).

TECHNICAL: [T series] Selective sliding transmission. Speeds: 3F/1R. Governor, lockable, with 25-mph maximum speed. Leather-faced cone clutch with adjustable compensating springs. Semi-floating rear axle made of heat-treated steel. Worm drive. Artillery wheels of standard dimension with 12 hickory spokes (front wheels have Timken tapered roller bearings).

OPTIONS: Front bumper. Rear bumper. Single sidemount. Heater. Cowl lamps.

1921 Chevrolet 1-Ton Model T Fire Truck (BH)

HISTORICAL: Introduced: January 1921. Calendar-year production: [Model G] 371 at Flint, Mich., 226 at Tarrytown, N.Y., 64 at St. Louis, Mo., 123 at Oakland, Calif., and 71 in Oshawa, Canada. (Model T) 255 at Flint, Mich., 14 at Tarrytown, N.Y., 127 at St. Louis, Mo., and 83 at Oakland, Calif. Innovations: New 3/4-ton Model G. Colors for new Model G varied according to body style. It was painted black when sold without cowl and Chevrolet green when sold with cowl. Standard aftermarket bodies were again listed in the Chevrolet catalog.

1922 CHEVROLET

$650
F.O.B. Flint Mich.
For specifications see page 18

1922 Chevrolet 3/4-Ton Model G Light Truck Chassis-and-Cowl (BH)

LIGHT DELIVERY — MODEL 490 — FOUR-CYLINDER: The 490 was basically unchanged. A number of technical changes were made. Valve adjustment was moved to the rocker arms. Larger 9/16-in. king bolts replaced the previous 1/2-in. type. An emergency brake lever was introduced to replace the old ratchet on the right-hand foot pedal. The service brakes were now operated by the right-hand pedal and the left-hand pedal was for the clutch. A spiral type of ring gear and pinion replaced the old straight-cut type. Also, a new type of differential bearing was used. Standard equipment included: Electric lights and starter (highest type two-unit system), complete lamp equipment, including adjustable headlamps, four-post top, side curtains, adjustable windshield, speedometer, electric horn, extra rim, tire carrier, and complete tool equipment including pump and jack. There were no major exterior design changes. Mifflinburg Body Co. of Pennsylvania supplied some models for the factory catalogs, including: Station Wagon, Delivery Wagon, Express Wagon, and Farm Wagon.

LIGHT DELIVERY — NEW SUPERIOR — FOUR-CYLINDER: Copies of a late 1922 Chevrolet sales catalog entitled Chevrolet For Economical Transportation Commercial Cars do not include the 490 Light Delivery Wagon. They show the "New Superior" Light Delivery truck, plus the Model G and Model T. This indicates that the New Superior series was available in calendar-year 1922. It may have been a midyear model. However, most references treat the New Superior Series as a 1923 line. Refer to 1923 for details about it.

1922 Chevrolet 1/2-Ton Model 490 Light Delivery Panel Body (OCW)

LIGHT TRUCK — MODEL G — FOUR-CYLINDER: For 1922, the Model G adopted a centrally-mounted emergency brake lever and conventional clutch and brake pedals. Chevrolet literature noted that the "chassis and body are balanced so as to make the utmost power available for the load itself and to reduce gasoline consumption to a minimum." The Model G again measured 97-7/8 in. from tailboard to headboard, with 46 in. of width inside the boards. Standard equipment included: Electric lights and starter, highest type two-unit system, complete lamp equipment, side curtains, adjustable windshield, speedometer, demountable rims, electric horn, and complete tool equipment including pump and jack. This model now used Chevrolet's smaller engine. Basic model offerings included the Chassis, Chassis-and-Cab, Open Express, and Curtain Top Express. The Model G was larger than the 490. It had slanting hood louvers, reverse curve fenders and torpedo type front-fender-mounted headlamps. Body length was 97-7/8 in. from tailboard to headboard, with a width of 46 in. between flareboards. Drive was from the left-hand side with center control. Spark and throttle were located under the steering wheel. There was a foot accelerator.

MEDIUM-HEAVY TRUCK — MODEL T — FOUR-CYLINDER: Cowl-mounted headlamps remained a distinctive styling characteristic of the Model T 1-ton truck in 1921. It had overall larger dimensions and a narrower cowl with "scooped-out" sides. Aftermarket bodies depicted in the sales catalog included a Passenger Bus, Fire Engine, Wholesale Hauler, Farm Wagon, and Panel Delivery. New for the 1922 Model T was the provision of poured rod bearings in the FB engine. A new three-exhaust-port cylinder head, also used in Chevrolet's Model FB cars, was adapted to the trucks. As had been the case since 1920, pneumatic tires were used front and rear. A cab was not provided by the factory. Standard chassis features included a platform-mounted seat and a windshield. Bodies sourced from outside suppliers often had tops designed to extend out to the windshield. The frame was four-inch channel iron. It was 30-1/2 in. wide in the front and 35-1/2 in. wide at the rear. The front axle was of the drop-forged I-beam type. The rear axle was semi-floating with worm drive. The equipment consisted of a starter, generator, horn, headlamps (with dimmers), speedometer, ammeter, side curtains for driver's seat, complete tool equipment, and a governor locked at 25 mph.

1922 Chevrolet 1/2-Ton Model 490 Vestibuled Curtain Express (L. Kuntz owner)

I.D. DATA: Serial numbers stamped on frame cross member at left front of engine. Serial number on the 490 found on a dash-mounted nameplate. Serial numbers: [490 series] 1-A59934 to 928881, 2-A55239 to 88858, 3-A53242 to 87572, 6-A54959 to 76001. [Model T] 1-4455 to 4792, 2-3632 to 4359, 3-2082 to 2107 and 6-2447 to 2631. [Model G] 1-385 to 683, 2-304 to 623, 3-123 to 229, 6-183 to 6-386 and 9-195 to 202. The numerical prefixes indicated the factory, as follows: 1=Flint, Mich., 2=Tarrytown, N.Y., 3=St. Louis, Mo., 6=Oakland, Calif., 9=Oshawa, Canada. Engine number is stamped on the flywheel.

Model	Body Type	Price	Weight	Prod. Total
Light Delivery — Model 490 — 1/2-Ton — 102 in. w.b.				
490	Wagon	510	1860	Note 1
490	Panel Delivery (*)	-	2010	Note 1
490	Station Wagon (*)	-	-	Note 1
(*) Mifflinburg body.				
Light Truck — Model G — 3/4-Ton — 120 in. w.b.				
G	Chassis & Cowl	745	2450	Note 2
G	Chassis & Cab	820	-	Note 2
G	Express	855	2600	Note 2
G	Canopy Express	920	-	Note 2
Medium-Heavy Truck — Model T — 1-Ton — 125 in. w.b.				
T	Chassis	1125	3300	Note 3
T	Open Express	1246	3450	Note 3
T	Canopy Express	1325	-	Note 3
T	Canopy/Curtain Express	1545	-	Note 3

NOTE 1: Included with 490 passenger cars.
NOTE 2: Series production was 273 units.
NOTE 3: Series production was 1,093 units.
ENGINE: [490/G series] Inline. Cylinders cast-in-block. Overhead valves. Four-cylinder. Cast iron block. Bore & stroke: 3-11/16 x 4 in. Displacement: 170.9 cid. Compression ratio: 4.3:1. Brake horsepower: 26 at 2000 rpm. Three main bearings. Mechanical valve lifters. Carburetor: Zenith one-barrel model.
ENGINE: [T series] Inline. Cylinders cast-in-block. Overhead valves. Four-cylinder. Cast iron block. Bore & stroke: 3-11/16 x 5-1/4 in. Displacement: 224 cid. Compression: 4.25:1. Brake horsepower: 37 at 2000 rpm. SAE net horsepower: 21.75. Three main bearings. Solid valve lifters. Carburetor: Zenith improved double-jet.
CHASSIS: [490 series] Wheelbase: 102 in. Tires: 30 x 3-1/2.
CHASSIS: [G series] Wheelbase: 120 in. Tires: All-pneumatic, demountable type, with wrapped tread: [Front] 31 x 4 in., [Rear] 34 x 4-1/2 in.
CHASSIS: [T series] Wheelbase: 125 in. Tires: [Front] pneumatic 33 x 4 in. demountable type, non-skid, wrapped tread, [Rear] 35 x 5 in. all-weather tread.

1922 Chevrolet 1-Ton Model T Medium-Heavy Chassis-and-Cowl (BH)

TECHNICAL: [All series] Selective sliding transmission. Speeds: 3F/1R. Floor-mounted gear-shift. Cone type clutch. Rear axle: [490 series] Three-quarter floating, [G/T series] Semi-floating. Artillery type wood spoke wheels.
OPTIONS: Front bumper. Rear bumper. Single sidemount. Heater. Cowl lamps. Motormeter. Rear view mirror.
HISTORICAL: Introduced January 1922. Calendar-year production: [Model G series] Flint, Mich.=298, Tarrytown, N.Y.=319, St. Louis, Mo.=106, Oakland, Calif.=203, and Canada=7. [Model T] Flint, Mich.=337, Tarrytown, N.Y.=727, St., Louis, Mo.=25, and Oakland, Calif.=184. Innovations: New clutch/brake pedal system. Lever action parking brake. W.S. Knudsen became the new general manager of Chevrolet. The Janesville, Wis., factory where Samsons were built, became a Chevrolet assembly plant.

1923 CHEVROLET

1923 Chevrolet 1/2-Ton Light Delivery With Hercules Panel Body (DFW/BC)

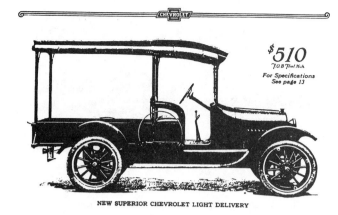

1923 Chevrolet 1/2-Ton New Superior F Light Delivery Wagon (BH)

LIGHT DELIVERY — SUPERIOR SERIES A/SERIES B — FOUR-CYLINDER: The Superior A and B trucks were Light Delivery models with a 1/2-ton load capacity. They could be identified by their raised hood lines, higher radiators with a flatter top surface, crown paneled fenders, and a narrower cowl section. Bodies were still sourced from outside firms, although some styles were included in Chevrolet truck catalogs as factory-installed models. Prices are listed for chassis and factory-installed-body models only. The Utility Delivery had a large open flareboard express box and closed cab. Standard features included a speedometer, ammeter, generator, starter, battery, drum type integral headlamps, dimmers, taillight, complete wiring system, oil pressure gauge, choke control, license brackets, motor hood, special combination dash and instrument board, front and rear fenders, running boards with shields, demountable rims with extra front and rear rims, tire carrier, jack, and complete tool equipment. The Series B replaced the Series A as a running production change at each factory. It had several distinctions, including a curved front axle and cable-operated brakes.
UTILITY EXPRESS — SUPERIOR SERIES D — FOUR-CYLINDER: The Superior Ds had the same general design characteristics as 1/2-ton models, but they were 1-ton Utility Express trucks. The same four-cylinder engine used in the 1/2-ton trucks was employed, but the wheelbase was 17 in. longer and larger tires were mounted.
I.D. DATA: Serial numbers located on a plate found on the left side of the front seat frame. Serial numbers were: [Superior Series A/Series B] 1A-92882 to 1B-72773, 2A-88766 to 2B-92891, 3A-86295 to 3B-98370, 6A-72320 to 6B-41755, and 21B-1000 to 21B-22373. [Series D] 1-D-1000 to 1-D-1654, 2-D-1000 to 2-D-2236, 3-D-1000 to 3-D-2155, 6-D-1000 to 6-D-1817, and 21-D-1000 to 21-D-1515. The number(s) in the prefix indicated the factory and the letter indicated the series. Factory codes were: 1=Flint, Mich., 2=Tarrytown, N.Y., 3=St. Louis, Mo., 6=Oakland, Calif., 21=Janesville, Wis. Example: 1A-92882 indicates a Flint, Mich. (1) built Superior model (A Series) with sequential production number 92882. Motor numbers were located on the flywheel.

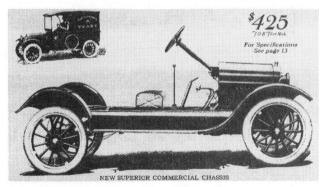

1923 Chevrolet 1/2-Ton Superior A/B Light Delivery Chassis-and-Cowl (BH)

Model	Body Type	Price	Weight	Prod. Total
Light Delivery — Series A/Series B — 1/2-Ton — 103 in. w.b.				
A/B	Chassis	395	1830	-
A/B	Canopy Express	510	1965	-
A/B	Panel	-	-	-
A/B	Station Wagon	-	-	-
Utility Express — Series D — 1-Ton — 120-125 in. w.b.				
D	Chassis	375	1860	-
D	Utility Express	-	2780	-
D	Cattle Body	-	-	-
D	Delivery	-	-	-

ENGINE: [All series] Inline. Overhead valves. Four-cylinder. Cast iron block. Bore & stroke: 3-11/16 x 4 in. Displacement: 170.9 cid. Compression ratio: 4.3:1. Brake horsepower: 35 at 1900 rpm. SAE net horsepower: 21.7. Three main bearings. Mechanical valve lifters. Carburetor: Zenith one-barrel.
CHASSIS: [Series A/Series B] Wheelbase: 103 in. Length: 142 in. Height: 74.25 in. Front tread: 58 in. Rear tread: 58 in. Tires: 30 x 3.5 in.
CHASSIS: [Series D] Wheelbase: 120-125 in. Tires: 31 x 4 in.
TECHNICAL: Manual, sliding gear transmission. Speeds: 3F/1R. Column-mounted gear-shift. Cone type clutch. Semi-floating rear axle. Overall ratio: [Superior Series A/Series B] 3.6:1, [Series D] 3.77:1. External-contracting rear wheel brakes. Wood spoke wheels.
OPTIONS: Front bumper. Rear bumper. Single sidemount. Heater. Cowl lamps. Motor Meter. Rear view mirror. Cattle body with chute type side ramps.

Price, Chassis only
$650
FOB Flint Mich

For specifications see page 18

MODEL G CHEVROLET CHASSIS

1923 Chevrolet 3/4-Ton Model G Truck Chassis-and-Cowl (BH)

HISTORICAL: Introduced: Aug. 1, 1922. Innovations: [Superior Series A/Series B] First year with crown paneled fenders, [Series D] New 120-in. wheelbase. Alfred P. Sloan, Jr. took over as president of General Motors.

1924 CHEVROLET

1924 Chevrolet 1/2-Ton Superior F Light Delivery Panel Body (WPL)

LIGHT DELIVERY — SUPERIOR SERIES B/SERIES F — FOUR-CYLINDER: This year, the 1/2-ton Superior four started as a continuation of the 1923 series and evolved into the Series F. Both were actually commercial cars, riding a beefed-up version of the Chevrolet passenger-car chassis. Curved front axles and cable-operated brakes characterized the B models again. The F models had a straight front axle and rod-operated brakes.

UTILITY TRUCK — SUPERIOR SERIES D/SERIES H — FOUR-CYLINDER: Available again was the Superior Utility Express line of 1-ton trucks. These were now simply called Utility Trucks. The D models continued into the early part of the model-year before being superseded by the H models. Body making was still an all-aftermarket operation, with some of the more popular styles available on factory-installed basis. As a running change, the H may have been replaced by a J model late in the series.

I.D. DATA: Serial numbers located on either side of dash under cowl and seat frame. Numbers were: [Series B/Series F] 1B-72774 to 1F-36881, 2B-92892 to 2F-511400, 3B-98371 to 3F-56585, 6B-41756 to 6F-29296, 9B-1166 to 9F-27125, 12B-1064 to 12F-35270, and 21B-22374 to 21F-33581. [Series D/Series H] 1D-1655 to 1H-1307, 2D-2237 to 2H-2383, 3D-2156 to 3H-4177, 6D-1818 to 6H-1813, 9D-1000 to 9H-1372, 12D-1000 to 12H-1732 and 21D-1516 to 21H-2106. The number(s) in the prefix indicated the factory and the letter indicated the series. Factory codes were: 1=Flint, Mich., 2=Tarrytown, N.Y., 3=St. Louis, Mo., 6=Oakland, Calif., 9=Norwood, Ohio, 12=Buffalo, N.Y. 21=Janesville, Wis. Example: 1B-72774 indicates a Flint, Mich. (1) built Superior model (B Series) with sequential production number 72774. Motor numbers were located on the flywheel.

Model	Body Type	Price	Weight	Prod. Total
Light Delivery — Superior Series B/Series F — 1/2-Ton — 103 in. w.b.				
B/F	Chassis	395	1790	-
Utility Truck — Superior Series D/Series H — 1-Ton — 120 in. w.b.				
D/H	Chassis	550	1850	-

ENGINE: [All series] Inline. Overhead valves. Four-cylinder. Cast iron block. Bore & stroke: 3-11/16 x 4 in. Displacement: 170.9 cid. Compression ratio: 4.3:1. SAE net horsepower: 21.70. Brake horsepower: 35 at 1900 rpm. Three main bearings. Solid valve lifters. Carburetor: Zenith one-barrel model.

CHASSIS: [Series B/F] Wheelbase: 103 in. Length: 142 in. Front tread: 58 in. Rear tread: 58 in. Tires: 30 x 3.5 in.

CHASSIS: [Series D/H] Wheelbase: 120 in. Front tread: 56 in. Rear tread: 56 in. Tires: [Front] 30 x 3.5 in., [Rear] 30 x 5 in.

TECHNICAL: Manual transmission. Speeds: 3F/1R. Floor-mounted gear-shift. Cone type clutch. Semi-floating rear axle. Overall ratio: 3.82:1. External-contracting mechanical rear brakes. Wooden spoke wheels.

1924 Chevrolet 1/2-Ton Superior A/B Light Delivery Fire Truck Body (DFW/WS)

OPTIONS: Front bumper. Rear bumper. Single sidemount. Heater. Rear view mirror. Spare tires. Bodies: [1/2-ton] Panel truck. [1-ton series] Open Cab Grain truck, Open Cab Stock truck, Flare Board Express, Fully-enclosed Cab Grain truck, Fully-enclosed Cab Stock truck, Panel truck, Coal truck, three-compartment Tanker truck.

HISTORICAL: Introduced: Aug. 1, 1923. Under W.S. Knudsen's direction, Chevrolet sales began to increase at an unprecedented pace.

1925 CHEVROLET

LIGHT DELIVERY — SUPERIOR SERIES F/SERIES K — FOUR-CYLINDER: The Series F Superior models were sold as 1925 trucks from Aug. 1, 1924 to Jan. 1, 1925. At that point, a new line of 1/2-ton Light Delivery trucks was introduced as the Superior Series K. The K Series offered a new Fisher bodies with vertical ventilating (VV) windshields. The 1925 models could be distinguished from 1926 Superior Ks by their fender-mounted headlamps. The VV windshield, along with a slightly angled windshield position, contributed to a more modern appearance. The K also had a one-piece rear axle with semi-elliptic springs. Other major technical changes were announced.

UTILITY TRUCK — SUPERIOR SERIES H/SERIES M — FOUR-CYLINDER: For 1-ton truck buyers, the Series H Utility Truck was still being sold when the 1925 model-year started on Aug. 1, 1924. The Series M was a running change introduced Jan. 1, 1925 as part of a second 1925 series. One way to spot an M is to look in a new location for the engine number.

1925 Chevrolet 1-Ton Superior H Vestibuled Express (Lee Hoovler photo)

I.D. DATA: Serial number located: [Series F] Nameplate on dash, [Series K] Nameplate on seat frame, [Series H/Series M] Nameplate on dash. Serial numbers: [Model F] 1F-36882 to 1K-1 up, 2F-51141 to 2K-1, 3F-56586 to 3K-1, 6F-29297 to 6K-1 up, 9F-27126 to 9K-1 up, 12F-33271 to 12K-1 up, and 21F-33582 to 21K-1 up. [Series K] 1K-1000 to 1K33751, 2K-1000 to 2K-45726, 3K-1000 to 3K-48220, 6K-1000 to 6K-27866, 9K-1000 to 9K-27519, 12K-1000 to 12K-36081, 21K-1000 to 21K-32544. [Model H] were 1H-1308 to 1M-1812, 2H-2384 to 2M-4188, 3H-4178 to 3M-2496, 6H-1814 to 6M-1371, 9H-1373 to 9M-1719, 12H-1733 to 12M-2185 and 21H-2107 to 21M-1721. [Model M] 1M-1000 to 1M-1812, 2M-1000 to 2M-4188, 3M-1000 to 3M-2496, 6M-1000 to 6M-1371, 9M-1000 to 9M-1719, 12M-1000 to 12M-2185, 21M-1000 to 21M-2185. The number(s) in the prefix indicated the factory and the letter indicated the series. Factory codes were: 1=Flint, Mich., 2=Tarrytown, N.Y., 3=St. Louis, Mo., 6=Oakland, Calif., 9=Norwood, Ohio, 12=Buffalo, N.Y. 21=Janesville, Wis. Engine number location: [Series F] On flywheel and left engine support, [Series K] Right side of block on boss just forward of oil filler tube, [Series H] On flywheel, [Series M] Right side of block on boss just forward of oil filler tube.

34

Model	Body Type	Price	Weight	Prod. Total
[Early 1925: See I.D. Data]				
Light Delivery — Superior Series F — 1/2-Ton — 103 in. w.b.				
F	Chassis	410	1430	-
Utility Truck — Superior Series H — 1-Ton — 120 in. w.b.				
H	Chassis	550	1850	-
[Late 1925: See I.D. Data]				
Light Delivery — Superior Series K — 1/2-Ton — 103 in. w.b.				
K	Chassis	425	1500	-
Utility Truck — Superior Series M — 1-Ton — 120 in. w.b.				
M	Chassis	550	1850	-

ENGINE: [All series] Inline. Overhead valves. Four-cylinder. Cast iron block. Bore & stroke: 3-11/16 x 4 in. Displacement: 170.9 cid. Compression ratio: 4.3:1. Brake horsepower: 35 at 1900 rpm. SAE net horsepower: 21.70. Three main bearings. Mechanical valve lifters. Carburetor: Zenith or Carter RXO one-barrel. Lubrication: Force feed and splash. Radiator: Cellular. Cooling: Water pump and fan. Ignition: Storage battery. Starting System: Two-unit. Lighting System: Electric. Gasoline System: Vacuum.

CHASSIS: [Series F/Series K] Wheelbase: 103 in. Length: 142 in. Front tread: 58 in. Rear tread: 58 in. Tires: 30 x 3.5 in.

CHASSIS: [Series H/Series M] Wheelbase: 120 in. Front tread: 56 in. Rear tread: 56 in. Tires: [Front] 30 x 3.5 in., [Rear] 30 x 5 in.

1925 Chevrolet 1-Ton Superior H Utility Truck Flat Bed Body (OCW)

TECHNICAL: [All series] Manual sliding gear transmission. Speeds: 3F/1R. Floor-mounted gear-shift. Single-plate dry-disc clutch introduced on Series K, cone type clutch on other models. Semi-floating rear axle. External-contracting mechanical rear only brakes. Wooden spoke wheels.

OPTIONS: Front bumper. Rear bumper. Single sidemount. Heater. Rear view mirror. Spare tire. Two spares were required for 1-ton trucks, due to different sizes being used front and rear. Bodies: Martin-Parry Co. Panel truck. Springfield Body Mfg. Panel truck. Mifflinburg Body Co. Station Wagon.

HISTORICAL: Introduced: Jan. 1, 1925. Innovations: Redesigned engine. Disc clutch. All-steel closed truck cabs introduced in late 1925 for 1926 model-year. A Chevrolet based U.S. Army Scout Car was supplied to the government this year. On June 3, 1925, the 100,000th Chevrolet built in Janesville, Wis. was assembled. It was a Series M 1-ton Utility Express chassis. Series M trucks were the last Chevrolets to use quarter-elliptic front springs.

1926 CHEVROLET

1926 Chevrolet 1/2-Ton Superior K Light Delivery Express (Lee Hoovler photo)

LIGHT DELIVERY — SUPERIOR SERIES K/SERIES V — FOUR-CYLINDER: Chevrolet's 1/2-ton Superior Series K was carried over as the early 1926 Light Delivery model from Aug. 1, 1925 to Jan. 1, 1926. A change from the 1925 Series K was that the headlights, formerly fastened to the fenders, were now mounted on a tie-rod between the fenders. On Jan. 1, 1926, a new Series V was introduced as the K's replacement. This series introduced the use of a belt-driven electric generator instead of a gear-driven type. The oil pump was driven by the camshaft, instead of a gear on the front end of the engine. One-half inch wider brakes with a 2-1/2 in. surfaces were another improvement. The Series V included a chassis on which aftermarket light-duty truck bodies could be installed. Most commonly seen in old photographs are depot hack type Station Wagons and vestibule type Panels. The term vestibule referred to a fully-enclosed cab. Express Wagons and other truck body styles were also built on this chassis. Two new models were a Roadster Pickup with cargo bed instead of rumbleseat, and a Commercial Roadster with enclosed cargo box in the rear.

1926 Chevrolet 1-Ton Superior Model R Utility Truck Stake (V. Kovlak)

1926 Chevrolet 1-Ton Superior X Utility Truck Chassis-and-Cowl (OCW)

TILITY TRUCK — SUPERIOR SERIES R/SERIES X — FOUR-CYLINDER: The Utility Truck was rated for 1-ton loads. The R Series trucks had a new, four-inch longer wheelbase. They used the Series K passenger car's engine, transmission, clutch, hood, fenders, lights, and radiator. However, the truck radiator was made of pressed steel, instead of the cast aluminum used for the car radiators. From serial numbers, it appears that many Series R trucks were built in 1926. This line was then replaced by the new Series X, which was technically similar. The Series X used the hood, fenders, lights and running gear of the late 1926 passenger cars. However, an innovation was the availability of a production-type truck body, which was factory-built with an all-steel enclosed cab. This new series spanned two model-years, with many X models sold in model-year 1927.

1926 Chevrolet 1-Ton Superior X Utility Truck Canopy Express Body (OCW)

1926 Chevrolet Superior 1/2-Ton Superior V Springfield Suburban (OCW)

I.D. DATA: Serial number located: [Series K/Series V] Nameplate on seat frame, [Series R/Series X] Nameplate on dash. Serial numbers: [1926 Series K] 1K-33911 to 1V-1 up, 2K-45727 to 2V-1 up, 3K-48221 to 3V-1 up, 6K-27867 to 6V-1 up, 9K-27520 to 9V-1 up, 12K-36082 to 12V-1 up, 21K-32545 to 21V-1 up. [Series V] 1V-1000 to 1V-48370, 2V-1000 to 2V-49190, 3V-1000 to 3V-83241, 6V-1000 to 6V-27138, 9V-1000 to 9V-52906, 12V-1000 to 12V-38609, 21V-1000 to 21V-54157. [Series R] 1R-1000 to 1X-10000, 2R-1000 to 2X-1000, 3R-1000 to 3X-10000, 6R-1000 to 6X-1000, 9R-1000 to 9X-1000, 12R-1000 to 12X-1000, 21R-1000 to 21X-10000. [Series X] 1X-1000 to 1X-4050, 2X-1000 to 2X-9072, 3X-1000 to 3X-11503, 6X-1000 to 6X-2940, 9X-1000 to 9X-5724, 12X-1000 to 12X-4001, 21X-1000 to 21X-6582. The number(s) in the prefix indicated the factory and the letter indicated the series. Factory codes were: 1=Flint, Mich., 2=Tarrytown, N.Y., 3=St. Louis, Mo., 6=Oakland, Calif., 9=Norwood, Ohio, 12=Buffalo, N.Y. 21=Janesville, Wis. Engine numbers location: Engine number location: [All series] right side of block on boss just forward of oil filler tube.

Model	Body Type	Price	Weight	Prod. Total
[Early 1926: See I.D. Data]				
Light Delivery — Superior K Series K — 1/2-Ton — 103 in. w.b.				
K	Chassis	425	1500	-
Utility Truck — Superior V Series R — 1-Ton — 124 in. w.b.				
R	Chassis	550	1955	-
[Late 1926: See I.D. Data]				
Light Delivery — Superior V Series V — 1/2-Ton — 103 in. w.b.				
V	Chassis	375	1490	-
Utility Truck — Superior V Series X — 1-Ton — 124 in. w.b.				
X	Chassis	495	1985	-
X	Springfield Suburban	-	-	-
X	Screenside Express	-	-	-

ENGINE: [All series] Inline. Overhead valves. Four-cylinder. Cast iron block. Bore & stroke: 3-11/16 x 4 in. Displacement: 170.9 cid. Compression ratio: 4.3:1. Brake horsepower: 35 at 1900 rpm. SAE net horsepower: 21.7. Three main bearings. Mechanical valve lifters. Carburetor: Carter one-barrel model.
CHASSIS: [Series K/Series V] Wheelbase: 103 in. Length: 142 in. Front tread: 58 in. Rear tread: 58 in. Tires: 29 x 4.40 in.
CHASSIS: [Series R] Wheelbase: 124 in. Front tread: 56 in. Rear tread: 56 in. Tires: [Front] 30 x 3.5 in., [Rear] 30 x 5 in.
CHASSIS: [Series X] Wheelbase: 124 in. Tires: [Front] 30 x 5 in., [Rear] 30 x 3.5 in.

1926 Chevrolet 1-ton Superior K Fire Truck (owner Bob Hensel)

TECHNICAL: Manual, sliding gear transmission. Speeds: 3F/1R. Floor-mounted gear-shift. Single-plate, dry-disc type clutch. Semi-floating rear axle. Overall ratio: 3.8:1 [V-series]. Mechanical, external-contracting rear brakes. Wood spoke wheels.
OPTIONS: Front bumper. Rear bumper. Single sidemount. Heater. Side curtains. Spare tires. Rear view mirror. Optional bodies for Series X, as seen in old photos, include: (1) Springfield Panel with vestibule cab, (2) Suburban (Woodie), by Springfield Body Co., (3) Gravity Dump body for coal delivery, by Proctor-Keefe Co., (4) Mifflinburg combination Jitney/Express, (5) Rack Body by Springfield Body Co., (6) Hercules Body Co. Vestibuled Panel.

HISTORICAL: Introduced: [Superior K/Superior R] Aug. 1, 1925, [Superior V/Superior X] Jan. 1, 1926. Calendar-year registrations: [All series] 113,682. Innovations: New all-steel factory bodies on the 1-ton Series X chassis. Bus-like depot wagons built for 1-ton chassis. All-new series designations. Late in the year, a new Peddler's Wagon was introduced. It proved very popular. A rail coach was built for a Louisiana Railroad using a Chevrolet Series X truck chassis. A panel version of the X was used by a Michigan college professor to search for rare fish in the Northwestern U.S. (Chevrolet donated the truck to him). Three times a day an Australian-bodied Series X bus made a 15 mile trip between Barwon Heads and Geelong in Australia. It carried up to 14 passengers.

1927 CHEVROLET

LIGHT DELIVERY — SUPERIOR V SERIES V — FOUR-CYLINDER: Chevrolet's 1/2-ton Superior Series V was carried over as the early 1927 Light Delivery model from Aug. 1, 1926 to Jan. 1, 1927. A change from the 1926 Series K was a new cross member supporting the transmission. The headlamps remained mounted on a tie-rod between the fenders, but the rod was heavier and channeled. Gas and spark controls were relocated above the steering wheel.

1927 Chevrolet 1/2-Ton Capitol AA Light Delivery Screenside (OCW)

LIGHT DELIVERY — CAPITOL AA SERIES AA — FOUR-CYLINDER: Chevrolet's newest light-duty trucks were identified by a new radiator shell with a dipped center, bullet-shaped headlights with black enamel finish and bright trim rings, and fuller one-piece crowned fenders. Other new features included a coincidental lock, air cleaner and oil filter. The 1/2-ton Series AA was marketed as a commercial car chassis for use with aftermarket bodies.
UTILITY TRUCK — SUPERIOR V SERIES X — FOUR-CYLINDER: After Aug. 1, the Superior V Series X 1-ton Utility Truck was sold as an early 1927 model. Specifications were the same as the late 1926 Superior V.

1927 Chevrolet 1-Ton Capitol AA Express (L. Kemp owner/CPC photo)

UTILITY TRUCK — CAPITOL AA SERIES LM — FOUR-CYLINDER: This was marketed as a 1927 1-ton series between Jan. 1, 1927 and Aug. 1, 1927. The same trucks were also sold as early 1928 models, until the real 1928 models arrived. General Motors bodies, designed for installation at Chevrolet factories, were used on the LM truck chassis. Of course, this big truck could also be purchased as a Chassis-only, if the customer wished to add his or her own truck body.
I.D. DATA: Serial number located on right or left side of dash under the cowl and seat frame. Serial numbers: [1927 Series V] 1V-48371 to 1AA-1, 2V-49191 to 2AA-1, 3V-83242 to 3AA-1, 6V-27139 to 6AA-1, 9V-52907 to 9AA-1, 12V-38607 to 12AA-1, 21V-54158 to 21AA-1. [Series AA] 1AA-1000 to 1AA-81763, 2AA-1000 to 2AA-79094, 3AA-1000 to 3AA-128735, 6AA-1000 to 6AA-44695, 9AA-1000 to 9AA-44695, 12AA-1000 to 12AA-68390, 21AA-1000 to 21AA-71646. [1927 Series X] 1X-4060 to 1LM-1000, 2X-9073 to 2LM-1000, 3X-11501 to 3LM-1000, 6X-2941 to 6LM-1000, 9X-4002 to 9LM-1000, 12X-4002 to 12LM-1000, 21X-6583 to 21LM-1000. [Series LM] 1LM-1000 to 1LM-9002, 2LM-1000 to 2LM-18539, 3LM-1000 to 3LM-19889,

6LM-1000 to 6LM-5251, 9LM-1000 to 9LM-9842, 12LM-1001 to 12LM-8644, 21LM-1000 to 21LM-10911. The number(s) in the prefix indicated the factory and the letter(s) indicated the series. Factory codes were: 1=Flint, Mich., 2=Tarrytown, N.Y., 3=St. Louis, Mo., 6=Oakland, Calif., 9=Norwood, Ohio, 12=Buffalo, N.Y. 21=Janesville, Wis. Engine numbers located on block ahead of fuel filter.

1927 Chevrolet 1/2-ton Capitol AA Light Delivery Panel Body (DFW/LOC)

Model	Body Type	Price	Weight	Prod. Total
[Early 1927: See I.D. Data]				
Light Delivery — Superior V Series V — 1/2-Ton — 103 in. w.b.				
V	Chassis	410	1520	-
Utility Truck — Superior V Series X — 1-Ton — 124 in. w.b.				
X	Chassis	495	1985	-
X	Springfield Suburban	-	-	-
X	Screenside Express	-	-	-
[Late 1927: See I.D. Data]				
Light Delivery — Capitol AA Series AA — 1/2-Ton — 103 in. w.b.				
AA	Chassis	395	1550	-
Utility Truck — Capitol AA Series LM — 1-Ton — 124 in. w.b.				
LM	Factory Panel Delivery	755	2850	-
LM	Factory Stake Bed	680	3045	-
LM	Chassis	495	2030	-

ENGINE: [All series] Inline. Overhead valves. Four-cylinder. Cast iron block. Bore & stroke: 3-11/16 x 4 in. Displacement: 170.9 cid. Compression ratio: 4.3:1. Brake horsepower: 35 at 1900 rpm. SAE net horsepower: 21.8. Three main bearings. Mechanical valve lifters. Carburetor: Carter one-barrel model.
CHASSIS: [Series V/Series AA] Wheelbase: 103 in. Usable load space length: [Panel] 64 in. Width: [Panel] 42 in. Tires: 29 x 4.40 in.

1927 Chevrolet 1/2-Ton Capitol AA Light Delivery Express (DFW/SAB)

1927 Chevrolet 1-Ton Capitol AA Utility Truck Dump Body (OCW)

CHASSIS: [Series X/Series LM] Wheelbase: 124 in. Width: [Panel] 44 in. (*).
* Hercules Standard Panel width. Hercules Body Co. also produced a Flareside Panel Truck that had a 51-in. width and appropriate wheel cutouts. This larger Panel Truck was 94.5 in. long, compared to the Standard Panel's 93-in. length. The factory type LM Panel body was 42 in. wide by 45 in. high and had a usable load length of 102 in..

1927 Chevrolet 1/2-Ton Capitol AA Light Delivery Panel Body
(Jack Lukeman photo)

TECHNICAL: Manual transmission. Speeds: 3F/1R. Floor-mounted gear-shift. Single-plate, dry-disc type clutch. Semi-floating rear axle. Overall ratio: 3.82:1. External-contracting, two-wheel rear brakes. Wood spoke wheels.
OPTIONS: Front bumper. Rear bumper. Single sidemount. Spare tire(s). Side curtains. Motormeter. Dual taillamps. Heater. Disc wheels (on commercials). Cowl lamps. Outside rear view mirror. Optional bodies from old photos: (1) Martin-Parry Dump, (2) Hercules dump, (3) Kentucky Wagon Works Jitney Bus/School Bus, (4) Hercules Vestibule Panel (Standard or Flareside), (5) Hercules Cattle Body.
HISTORICAL: Introduced: [1927 Superior V] Aug. 1, 1926, [Capitol AA] Jan. 1, 1927, [Capitol LM] January 1927. Calendar-year registrations: [All series] 104,832. Innovations: New Capitol AA Light Delivery series. New 1-ton Capitol LM series. New bullet headlights. Dipped style radiator shell adopted. Rectangular brake and clutch pedals. New coincidental lock. A South African built series LM Series truck carried supplies and communications equipment on a Cape Town-to-Stockholm (by way of Cairo and London) Chevrolet promotional tour in 1927.

1928 CHEVROLET

LIGHT DELIVERY — CAPITOL AA SERIES AA — FOUR-CYLINDER: As usual, a carryover line of Capitol Series trucks was marketed as 1928 models from August to January. Capitol models could again be identified by a radiator shell with a dipped center, bullet-shaped headlights with shiny black enamel finish, and one-piece crowned fenders. Other features included a coincidental lock, air cleaner, and oil filter. The 1/2-ton chassis was marketed as a commercial car for use with aftermarket bodies.

1928 Chevrolet 1/2-Ton Capitol AB Light Delivery Express (JB)

LIGHT DELIVERY — NATIONAL AB SERIES AB — FOUR-CYLINDER: The new series introduced Jan. 1, 1928 was designated National AB. These trucks were very similar to the models of the previous year, but had some distinctions. Four-wheel brakes were installed on light-duty models. The wheelbase was now 107 in., up from 103 in. for 1927. Telltale engine features included thermostatic control and a crankcase breather. With a higher compression ratio, larger valves, increased valve lift, and a two-piece exhaust manifold, the Chevrolet engine developed 35 hp at a higher 2200 rpm.

UTILITY TRUCK — CAPITOL AA SERIES LM — FOUR-CYLINDER: The 1-ton Utility LM Series was introduced as a 1927 model. Beginning Aug. 1, 1927, it was marketed as a 1928 truck. The styling, motor and use of a 120-in. wheelbase were unchanged. LMs sold between the above date and Jan. 1, 1928 were titled as 1928 models.

1928 Chevrolet 1/2-Ton Capitol AB Light Delivery Express Body (OCW)

UTILITY TRUCK — CAPITOL AB SERIES LO/SERIES LP — FOUR-CYLINDER: On Jan. 1, 1928 a new 1-ton line began. These LO Series trucks had the same engine as previous models, but a 124-in. wheelbase. The LP Series was a running change as the range of serial numbers for late 1928 models started with LO-1000 at each factory and ended with numbers having LP prefixes.

1928 Chevrolet 1-Ton Capitol LP Utility Truck Depot Body (FLW)

I.D. DATA: Serial number located on right or left side of dash under the cowl and seat frame, also placed on front door heel board, on either the left or right side. Serial numbers: [1928 Series AA] 1AA-81764 to 1AB-1, 2AA-79088 to 2AB-1, 3AA-128736 to 3AB-1, 6AA-44706 to 6AB-1, 9AA-66289 to 9AB-1, 12AA-68391 to 12AB-1, 21AA-71647 to 21AB-1. [1928 Series LM] 1LM-9003 to 1LO-1000, 2LM-18540 to 2LO-1000, 3LM-19800 to 3LO-1000, 6LM-5252 to 6LO-1000, 9LM-9843 to 9LO-1000, 12LM-8645 to 12LO-1000, 21LM-10912 to 21LO-1000. [1928 Series AB] 1AB-1000 up, 2AB-1000 up, 3AB-1000 up, 6AB-1000 up, 9AA-1000 up, 12AB-1000 up, 21AB-1000 up. [1928 Series LO/Series LP]: 1LO-1000 to 1LP-7248, 2LO-1000 to 2LP-12986, 3LO-1000 to 3LP-18133, 6LO-1000 to 6LP-4355, 9LO-1000 to 9LP-7007, 12LO-1000 to 12LP-6535, 21LO-1000 to 21LO-8841. The number(s) in the prefix indicated the factory and the letter(s) indicated the series. Factory codes were: 1=Flint, Mich., 2=Tarrytown, N.Y., 3=St. Louis, Mo., 6=Oakland, Calif., 9=Norwood, Ohio, 12=Buffalo, N.Y. 21=Janesville, Wis. Engine numbers located on engine block ahead of oil filter, near fuel pump.

1928 Chevrolet 1-Ton Capitol LP Utility Truck Panel Body (DFW/MS)

Model	Body Type	Price	Weight	Prod. Total
[Early 1928: See I.D. Data]				
Light Delivery — Capitol AA — 1/2-Ton — 103 in. w.b.				
AA	Chassis	495	1550	-
Utility Truck — Capitol LM/LO/LP — 1-Ton — 124 in. w.b.				
LO	Factory Panel Delivery	755	2850	-
LO	Factory Stake Bed	680	3045	-
LO	Chassis	520	2170	-
[Late 1928: See I.D. Data]				
Light Delivery — National AB — 1/2-Ton — 107 in. w.b.				
AB	Chassis	495	2130	-
AB	Pickup	-	-	-
AB	Canopy	-	-	-
AB	Screenside	-	-	-
AB	Panel	-	-	-
AB	Sedan Delivery	690	2450	1004
AB	Roadster Pickup	545	2130	-
AB	Commercial Roadster	575	2190	-
AB	Henney Hearse	1500	2800	-
AB	Henney Ambulance	1600	2800	-
Utility Truck — National LP — 1-Ton — 124 in. w.b.				
LP	Chassis	520		

ENGINE: [All series] Inline. Overhead valves. Four-cylinder. Cast iron block. Bore & stroke: 3-11/16 x 4 in. Displacement: 170.9 cid. Compression ratio: 4.5:1. Brake horsepower: 35 at 2200 rpm. SAE net horsepower: 21.7. Three main bearings. Mechanical valve lifters. Carburetor: Carter one-barrel model.

1928 Chevrolet 1-Ton Capitol LP Light Delivery Suburban (ATC)

CHASSIS: [Series AA] Wheelbase: 103 in. Usable load space length: [Panel] 64 in., Width: [Panel] 42 in. Tires: 29 x 4.40 in.
CHASSIS: [Series AB] Wheelbase: 107 in. Length: 156 in. Load Space: 72 in. Front tread: 56 in. Rear tread: 56 in. Tires: 30 x 4.50 in.
CHASSIS: [Series LO] Wheelbase: 124 in.
CHASSIS: [Series LP] Wheelbase: 124 in.
TECHNICAL: Manual transmission. Speeds: 3F/1R. Floor-mounted gear-shift. Single-plate, dry-disc type clutch. Semi-floating rear axle. Overall ratio: 3.82:1. Mechanical brakes. Wood spoke or steel disc wheels.
OPTIONS: Front bumper. Rear bumper. Heater. Wood spoke wheels. Exterior rear view mirror. Slip-in pickup box for AB roadster. Commercial cargo box for AB roadster (called Panel Carrier).
HISTORICAL: Introduced: January 1928. Calendar-year registrations: [All series] 133,682. Innovations: Four-wheel brakes. New four-speed transmission standard on Series LP. Refinements to engine. Last year for 170.9 cid four-cylinder. All-new Sedan Delivery. Chevrolet was becoming a serious threat to Ford's sales leadership in both the car and truck markets.

1929 CHEVROLET

LIGHT DELIVERY — INTERNATIONAL AC SERIES AC — SIX-CYLINDER: The 1929 Chevrolet Light Delivery models again represented a 1/2-ton Commercial Car series. They had more rectangular radiators, fewer louvers (at the rear side of the hood only), bullet-shaped headlights, and full-crowned fenders. Of great importance was the introduction of the "Cast iron Wonder," Chevrolet's long-lived and extremely successful overhead valve six-cylinder engine. Also new was a headlight foot control switch and electrolock feature. Features of specific 1929 models included a standard sidemount spare tire on the driver's side of the Sedan Delivery. A new Deluxe Panel Delivery (built by the Geneva Body Co.) was called the Ambassador. It had wood framing with steel outer paneling, imitation Spanish black leather upholstery, and multi-tone finish. The body was medium-light blue on upper portions and dark blue on the lower portion. The hood, fenders and disc wheels were black. An orange belt line panel set off the attractive color scheme. There was only one 1929 series, since the depressed U.S. economy began changing the manner in which cars and trucks were marketed.

1929 Chevrolet 1/2-Ton International AC Light Delivery Pickup Body (OCW)

CONVENTIONAL — INTERNATIONAL AC SERIES LQ — SIX-CYLINDER: Models in both lines used passenger car sheet metal and the same black radiator shell as cars. LQ was the year's bigger truck line. It was a 1-1/2-ton series, which does not fit into the scope of this study. However, it was essentially very similar to the late 1928 Series LO/LP Utility trucks and had the same 124 in. wheelbase. It could probably be ordered with a 1-ton chassis option.

1929 Chevrolet 1/2-Ton International AC Roadster Delivery Body (OCW)

I.D. DATA Location of serial number: nameplate on dash. Starting number: [AC Series] 1AC-1001 to 1AC-111583, 2AC-1001 to 2AC-104076, 3AC-1001 to 3AC-199422, 5AC-1001 to 5AC-62550, 6AC-1001 to 6AC-67343, 8AC-1001 to 8AC-48890, 9AC-1001 to 9AC-93867, 12AC-1001 to 12AC-99298, 21AC-1001 to 21AC-106392. [LQ Series] 1LQ-1001 to 1LQ-14282, 2LQ-1001 to 2LQ-20188, 3LQ-1001 to 3LQ-42724, 5LQ-1001 to 5LQ-15512, 6LQ-1001 to 6LQ-11162, 8LQ-1001 to 8LQ-13324, 12LQ-1001 to 12LQ-16356, 21LQ-1001 to 21LQ-18045. The number(s) in the prefix indicated the factory and the letter (s) indicated the series. Factory codes were: 1=Flint, Mich., 2=Tarrytown, N.Y., 3=St. Louis, Mo., 5=Kansas City, Mo., 6=Oakland, Calif., 8=Atlanta, Ga., 9=Norwood, Ohio, 12=Buffalo, N.Y. 21=Janesville, Wis. Engine number location: right side of cylinder block behind fuel pumps.

1929 Chevrolet 1/2-Ton International AC Roadster Delivery Body (MC)

ENGINE: Inline. Overhead valves. Six-cylinder. Cast iron block. Bore & stroke: 3-5/16 x 3-3/4 in. Displacement: 194 cid. Compression ratio: 5.02:1. Brake horsepower: 46 at 2600 rpm. SAE net horsepower: 26.3. Three main bearings. Solid valve lifters. Carburetor: Carter one-barrel model 150S.
CHASSIS: [Series AC] Wheelbase: 107 in. Length: 156 in. Front tread: 56 in. Rear tread: 56 in. Tires: 20 x 4.50 in.
CHASSIS: [Series LQ] Wheelbase: 124 in.
TECHNICAL: Manual transmission. Speeds: 3F/1R. Floor-mounted gear-shift. Single-plate, dry-disc type clutch. Semi-floating rear axle. Overall ratio: 3.82:1. Mechanical four-wheel brakes. Disc wheels.
OPTIONS: Front bumper. Rear bumper. Single sidemount. Heater. Cigar lighter. Wire wheels. Exterior mirror. Slip-in pickup box for Roadster. Cargo carrier for Roadster.

HISTORICAL: Introduced: Nov. 24, 1928. Calendar-year registrations: [All series] 160,959. Innovations: New six-cylinder engine. One-piece full-crowned fenders. New bullet type lamps. Electrolock. Banjo type rear axle. Chrome-plated radiator shell. New multi-color finish with contrasting double belt panel. Longer 107-in. wheelbase and 17 in. rubber-covered steering wheel. New line of panel bodies by Geneva Body Co., of Geneva, N.Y. The new six-cylinder engine was a strong selling point that carried Chevrolet's car and truck sales to record levels. During 1929, the company produced its 500,000th commercial vehicle and reported accumulated retail sales of 641,482 trucks since 1918. The majority of these were light-duty models of 1-ton or less capacity. In 1930, a military gun wagon was constructed as a U.S. Army munitions experiment. Forest "Chip" Sweet, 1931-1933 Commercial Technical Advisor for the Vintage Chevrolet Club of America, believes it was probably built on a 1929 Series AC 1/2-ton chassis. It had an armored gun turret and 50-caliber machine gun.

1929 Chevrolet 1-1-1/2-Ton International AC Paddy Wagon (Art Whalers)

Model	Body Type	Price	Weight	Prod. Total
Light Delivery — International AC Series AC — 107 in. w.b.				
AC	Chassis	400	1815	-
AC	Sedan Delivery	595	2450	-
AC	Pickup	-	-	-
AC	Canopy or Screen	-	-	-
AC	Panel	-	-	9640
Utility Truck — International AC Series LQ — 124 in. w.b.				
AC/LQ	Chassis	545	2340	-

1930 CHEVROLET

1930 Chevrolet 1/2-Ton Universal AD Light Delivery (DFW/ABA)

LIGHT DELIVERY — UNIVERSAL SERIES AD — SIX-CYLINDER: Chevrolet trucks for light-duty use had a new instrument panel like Chevrolet passenger cars. An electric gasoline gauge was included in its array of circular gauges. The rear brakes were fully enclosed and a stronger rear axle was used. The Chevrolet commercial engine developed 46 hp. Chevrolet factories initially assembled only the Commercial Chassis, the Chassis-and-Cab (including the Roadster Delivery) and the Sedan Delivery. Before Chevrolet's purchase of Martin Parry Body Co. in November 1930, all other commercial bodies were sourced from manufacturers such as Hercules, which made most Panel Delivery bodies. The Sedan Delivery used cowl and body panels similar to a coach in the passenger car line, which meant it had a new sloping windshield. The Roadster Delivery (Open Cab Pickup) used the same cowl as the Roadster and Phaeton passenger cars. It had the Roadster's doors. A different cowl was used for other 1/2-ton Light Delivery models. It was called the commercial cowl. Beginning in 1929 and continuing through 1933, Chevrolet supplied the commercial cowl. The door and windshield frames bolted to it. In most models, the windshield was a fold-out type that pivoted at the top on a piano hinge. The Open Cab windshield pivoted approximately three-quarters of its height.
UTILITY TRUCK — UNIVERSAL AD SERIES LR — SIX-CYLINDER: The Utility truck may have come in 1-ton chassis options for 1930. Wheelbases up to 124 in. were available. Bodies were still supplied by independent body makers.

1930 Chevrolet 1/2-Ton Universal AD Light Delivery Canopy (MC)

I.D. DATA: Location of serial number: On plate nailed to side of passenger seat bottom cushion support. Starting number: [AD series] 1AD-1001 up, 2AD-1001 up, etc., [LR series] 1LR-1001 up, 2LR-1001 up, etc. The number(s) in the prefix indicated the factory and the letter(s) indicated the series. Factory codes were: 1=Flint, Mich., 2=Tarrytown, N.Y., 3=St. Louis, Mo., 5=Kansas City, Mo., 6=Oakland, Calif., 8=Atlanta, Ga., 9=Norwood, Ohio, 12=Buffalo, N.Y. 21=Janesville, Wis. There was also a model identification plate screwed to the firewall above the starter motor on the passenger side. Engine number location: on right side of motor block behind fuel pump. Engine numbers not given.

1930 Chevrolet 1-Ton Universal LR Utility Truck Vending Body (R. Barbour/CPC)

Model	Body Type	Price	Weight	Prod. Total
Light Delivery — 1/2-Ton — Universal AD — 107 in. w.b.				
[Factory assembled]				
AD	Chassis	365	1815	-
AD	Sedan Delivery	595	2450	6522
[Aftermarket bodies]				
AD	Roadster Delivery	-	-	-
AD	Panel Delivery	-	-	-
AD	Deluxe Delivery	-	-	-
AD	Canopy Delivery	-	-	-
AD	Screenside Delivery	-	-	-
Utility Truck — 1-1/2-Ton- Universal LR — 124 in. w.b.				
LR	Chassis	520	2375	

NOTE 1: Aftermarket bodies or pickup box not manufactured or serviced by Chevrolet. Other suppliers such as Martin-Parry Co., etc., supplied bodies through the Chevrolet factory and dealer network. The chassis included rear fenders and spare tire rim supplied by Chevrolet.

1930 Chevrolet 1-Ton Universal LR Utility Truck Tank (Kyle Moore)

ENGINE: [All series] Inline. Overhead valves. Six-cylinder. Cast iron block. Bore & stroke: 3-5/16 x 3-3/4 in. Displacement: 194 cid. Compression ratio: 5.0:1. Brake horsepower: 46 at 2600 rpm. SAE net horsepower: 26.3. Three main bearings. Mechanical valve lifters. Carburetor: Carter one-barrel model RJH08-150S, casting no. RJH08.
CHASSIS: [Series AD] Wheelbase: 107 in. Tires: 4.75 x 19 in.
CHASSIS: [Series LR] Wheelbase: 124 in.

TECHNICAL: [Typical] Manual transmission. Speeds: 3F/1R. Floor-mounted gear-shift. Single-plate type clutch. Shaft drive. Semi-floating rear axle. Overall ratio: 4.1:1. Internal-expanding four-wheel mechanical brakes. The brakes changed to fully-enclosed design. Wire or disc wheels.

OPTIONS: Front bumper. Wire wheels. Hinged radiator cap. Thermostat. Tire cover. Fender well tire lock. Dash lamp. Single sidemount. Side curtains. Special paint. Cargo box tarpaulin. Heater. Spare tire(s). Cigar lighter. Lettering stencils. External sun shade. Spotlight. Rear view mirror. [Sedan Delivery] Rear bumper. Right-hand taillamp. Cowl lamps.

HISTORICAL: Introduced: Dec. 4, 1930. Calendar-year registrations: [All series] 118,253. Innovations: More powerful six-cylinder engine. New Deluxe Sedan Delivery. New Roadster Delivery (open cab pickup) becomes a separate model, rather than Roadster with slip-in cargo box. The U.S. Department of Agriculture maintained a large fleet of Chevrolet Sedan Deliveries for use in Midwestern states during a corn blight.

1931 CHEVROLET

1931 Chevrolet 1/2-Ton Model AE Canopy Express (OCW)

1/2-TON LIGHT DELIVERY — INDEPENDENCE SERIES AE — SIX-CYLINDER: A new Independence series of Chevrolet trucks featured a 1/2-ton Light Delivery line and a 1-1/2-ton Conventional Truck line. The 1/2-ton models of the Independence series of Chevrolet trucks featured a longer set of hood louvers than the 1930 models. Early versions of the optional front bumpers were of a two-piece design, but this was changed during the model run to a single-piece design. Bumpers were not available for the rear of commercial models, except for the Sedan Delivery. Some collectors believe that special bumper or "fender guard" brackets were available for other 1/2-ton models, but Chip Sweet, who is 1931-1933 Commercial Technical Adviser for the Vintage Chevrolet Club of America, has been unable to confirm this. The size of the 1931 radiator was unchanged from 1930. It was not higher or larger. However, the lower portion of the radiator shell was open and not covered with a guard. This can make the 1931 radiator look larger than the 1930 style in photographs. A black radiator shell and headlamp buckets were standard. A DeLuxe Sedan Delivery was available. The DeLuxe Sedan Delivery had a bright radiator shell, bright headlight buckets, wire wheels and a sidemount on the driver's side. It was shown in advertising literature with whitewall tires. Also available was a Panel with insulated side panels, a coupe-like driver's compartment and disc wheels. It had a load space 72 in. long by 45 in. wide and 48 in. high. Another 1/2-ton was the Canopy Express. It had similar body dimensions, but open body sides with curtain or screen options. Its standard equipment included waterproof curtains for the sides and rear (screens were optional), a sedan-type roof, a coupe-type cab and disc wheels. There was also an Open Cab Pickup with a cargo box 66 in. long, 45 in. wide and 13 in. deep. Its body sides were designed to meet the floor at right angles. Equipment included a roadster-type cab and disc wheels. Chevrolet changed from the worm-and-gear steering used through 1930 to worm-and-sector steering. A new three-spoke steering wheel also replaced last year's four-spoke design.

1931 Chevrolet 1/2-Ton Model AE Canopied Express (OCW)

1931 Chevrolet 1/2-Ton Model AE Huckster (owner: Jerry Cross)

I.D. DATA: Serial number located on dash-mounted nameplate. Starting numbers: 1AE-1001 and up, 2AE-1001 and up, 3AE-1001 and up, 5AE-1001 and up, 6AE-1001 and up, 8AE-1001 and up, 9AE-1001 and up, 12AE-1001 and up, 21AE-1001 and up. Engine number on right side of motor block behind fuel pump.

Model	Body Type	Price	Weight	Prod. Total
AE	Chassis	355	1880	-
AE	Sedan Delivery	575	2585	-
AE	Chassis & Cab	460	2215	-
AE	Chassis & Open Cab	-	2100	-
AE	Closed Cab Pickup	488	2425	-
AE	Canopy	550	-	-
AE	Canopy (Screenside)	569	-	-
AE	Panel	555	2710	-
AE	Open Cab Pickup	440	2310	-

ENGINE: Inline. OHV. Six-cylinder. Cast-iron block. Bore & stroke: 3-5/16 x 3-3/4 in. Displacement: 194 cid. Compression ratio: 5.0:1. Brake horsepower: 50 at 2600 rpm. Net horsepower: 26.3. Three main bearings. Mechanical valve lifters. Carburetor: Carter one-barrel model RJHO8-150S. Casting number RJHO8.

1931 Chevrolet 1/2-Ton Model AE Pennsylvania Quality Mower Truck (B. Beard)

CHASSIS: [Series AE] Wheelbase: 109 in. Tires: 4.75 x 19 in.
TECHNICAL: Manual transmission. Speeds: 3F/1R. Floor-mounted gear-shift. Single disc type clutch. Semi-floating rear axle. Overall ratio: 4.1:1. Four-wheel, internal-expanding mechanical brakes. Steel disc or wire wheels. Changed to worm-and-sector steering gear with new three-spoke steering wheel.
OPTIONS: [All models] Hinged radiator cap. Thermostat. Tire cover. Fender well tire lock. Dash lamp. Front bumper. Single sidemount. White sidewall tires. Sidemount cover(s). Wire wheels. DeLuxe hood ornament. OSRV mirror. Heater. Cigar lighter. Screen-sides for Canopy. Special paint colors. Stencils for company name application. Spotlight. Wheel trim rings. DeLuxe equipment. [Sedan Delivery only] Rear bumper. Right-hand taillamp. Dual sidemounts. Lovejoy shock absorbers.
HISTORICAL: Introduced: November 1930. Calendar-year registrations: [All series] 99,600. Innovations: New vibrator horn below left headlight. Revised hood louver design. Two-inch longer wheelbase. New crankshaft vibration dampener. Late in 1930, Chevrolet purchased the Martin-Parry Co. of Indianapolis, Ind., which allowed the company to finally offer factory truck bodies. A new DeLuxe 1/2-ton chassis was introduced using passenger car front end sheet metal. It became the basis of many station wagons, hearses, ambulances and other special bodies where a non-truck appearance was preferable. This was the first year that a variety of finish colors were available. Before 1929, trucks were painted black. From 1929 to this year, Blue Bell Blue was the standard color. Chevrolet had about 32.7 percent sales penetration in the light-truck market this year. The acquisition of Martin-Parry Co. would send this figure skyrocketing upwards. The model referred to as a Roadster Pickup or Open Cab Pickup is called a Roadster Delivery in Chevrolet factory literature.

1932 CHEVROLET

1/2-TON LIGHT DELIVERY — CONFEDERATE SERIES BB — SIX-CYLINDER: The 1932 Chevrolet Sedan Deliveries had the 1932 Chevrolet passenger car front end appearance, including a new hood with louver doors. DeLuxe 1/2-ton models used the 1931 passenger series fenders, splash aprons, running boards, radiator shell, chrome headlamps and horn. They had the louvered 1931 style hood, too. Light Deliveries were now equipped with a silent synchromesh transmission. Trucks did not get the same engine improvements as cars. They had a 53 hp six, while the passenger cars' carburetor combination produced 60 hp. The trucks also retained the 1929-1931 style solid rear engine mounting, instead of the new rubber insulated mounts attached to the clutch housing that passenger cars adopted. Also, a spring mount was used at the front of the engine, in place of the rubber mount used on passenger cars. Standard trucks had flat-side bodies and black-finished radiators and headlamp buckets. Equipment varied by model. The standard 1/2-ton Panel included an insulated interior, flush floor straps, locks on all doors, and hinged seats. The Special 1/2-ton Panel featured an insulated body, chrome-plated headlamps, chrome-plated radiator tie-bar, and five wire wheels. The DeLuxe 1/2-ton Panel included fully lined interior with dome light, hinged seats, chrome moldings, embossed panels, French-style roof, plate glass windows, five wire wheels, front fender well, automatic windshield wiper, and rear vision mirror. The Sedan Delivery included a chrome-plated front end and adjustable hood ports. Rear bumper brackets were listed for the Panel, Canopy Express and DeLuxe Panel.

1932 Chevrolet Model BB Sedan Delivery (DFW/ABA)

I.D. DATA: Serial number located on dash-mounted nameplate. Starting number: BB-1001 and up. Engine number on right side of motor block behind fuel pump.

Model	Body Type	Price	Weight	Prod. Total
Confederate Series — 1/2-Ton				
BB	Chassis	355/345	1935	-
BB	Chassis & Cab	460/440	2270	-
BB	Special Chassis	365	1970	-
BB	Chassis & Open Cab	-	2155	-
BB	Open Cab & Box	440/430	Note 2	-
BB	Closed Cab Pickup	470/440	2465	-
BB	Canopy	560	2735	-
BB	Open Cab Canopy	500/470	-	-
BB	Sedan Delivery	575	2630	-
BB	DeLuxe Delivery	-	-	-

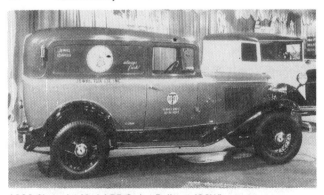

1932 Chevrolet Model BB Sedan Delivery (OCW)

NOTE 1: Slash indicates midyear price changes due to depression. Others may have also changed.
NOTE 2: Factory literature shows 2,045/2,370/2,350 lb. weights for Open Cab.
ENGINE: Inline. OHV. Six-cylinder. Cast-iron block. Bore & stroke: 3-5/16 x 3-3/4 in. Displacement: 194 cid. Compression ratio: 5.2:1. Brake horsepower: 53 at 2800 rpm. Net horsepower: 26.3. Three main bearings. Mechanical valve lifters. Carburetor: Carter one-barrel downdraft type W-1, model 222S or 222SA.
CHASSIS: [Series BB] Wheelbase: 109 in. Tires: 5.25 x 18 in.

1932 Chevrolet 1/2-Ton Model BB Panel (DFW)

TECHNICAL: Manual, synchromesh (without freewheeling on Light Delivery models). Speeds: 3F/1R. Floor-mounted gear-shift. Improved single-plate dry-disc clutch (pressure plate operated by three throw out levers, clutch plate resilient-mounted and driven through eight springs). Dash-operated manifold heat control valve. Torque tube drive (longer torque tube than passenger cars in 1933 Light Delivery models). Semi-floating rear axle. Axle shafts of finest alloy and increased in size, axle bearings larger and stronger. Overall drive ratio: 4.1:1. Four-wheel internal-expanding mechanical brakes with 12 in. drums and linings increased from 1.5 to 1.75 in. wide. Wire wheels. New counter-balanced crankshaft. New harmonic balancer. Built-in air cleaner with flame arrester, accelerating pump and carburetor heat control.

1932 Chevrolet 1/2-Ton Model BB Chassis With Walk-in Delivery Body (DFW/SI)

OPTIONS: Tire. Mirror. Electric clock. Gear-shift ball. Tire chains. Tire locks. Hub protectors. Snap spokes. Hot water heater. Spotlight. Radiator cap. Dash lamp. Front bumper. Single sidemount. Heater. Cowl lamps. Dual wipers. Fender well tire lock. Metal tire cover. Standard tire cover. DeLuxe models were offered with a chrome-plated radiator shell, chrome-plated headlamps, chrome-plated headlamp tie-bar, and four hydraulic shock absorbers. A rear bumper was now available on three different 1/2-ton models: Panel, Canopy Express and DeLuxe Panel. A wide assortment of Chevrolet built bodies was available in attractive colors.
HISTORICAL: Introduced: December 1931. Calendar-year registrations: [All series] 60,784. Innovations: Higher horsepower engine. First year for different styling appearance on cars and trucks. New 18-in. wire wheels standard for all models. Greater emphasis on marketing DeLuxe equipment for trucks. Chevrolet began placing great emphasis on improvements of its fleet sales program during this model-year. William S. Knudsen was general manager of Chevrolet from 1922-1932.

1933 CHEVROLET

1933 Chevrolet 1/2-Ton Model CB Sedan Delivery (OCW)

1/2-TON SEDAN DELIVERY — EAGLE/MASTER EAGLE SERIES CB — SIX-CYLINDER: In 1933, the Chevrolet Sedan Delivery continued to be related more to passenger vehicles than other commercial vehicles. It was actually what was called a "Commercial Car." However, it wasn't until 1934 that Chevrolet officially

recognized the difference by giving the Sedan Delivery different coding than Light Delivery models. This year, the Sedan Delivery (which is often coded SDL in factory literature) was still part of the Series CB 1/2-ton line. There was also a DeLuxe Sedan Delivery with coach lamps on the body rear quarters, a sidemount cover, bright metal trim parts and, in some cases, the ventilator door style hood. A single sidemount spare tire was now standard equipment on 1/2-tons, since the gas tank was relocated to the location where the spare tire had been carried. Dual side mounts were optionally available on most models. Safety plate glass was used in the 1933 windshield.
1/2-TON LIGHT DELIVERY — EAGLE/MASTER EAGLE SERIES CB — SIX-CYLINDER: This was the last year Chevrolet used names such as Eagle and Master, as well as letters, to identify its truck models. On some models, Chevrolet continued its inconsistent policy of fitting some light-duty trucks with a grille virtually identical to that introduced one year earlier on passenger cars. The hood louver design, however, was still of the 1931 style. Providing 56 hp at 2750 rpm was the commercial version of the Chevrolet "Stovebolt Six." A four-speed transmission was now optional in light-duty models. Standard equipment varied by model. The pickup truck came with a 66 x 45 x 13-in. cargo box, all-steel box construction, double security chains, and a left-hand sidemount spare. The standard Sedan Delivery had a load space 57 x 50 x 44.5 in. and 36 in. wide curb side opening rear door. Its sheet metal was truck-like, but bright metal headlamp shells, radiator shell and cowl molding were standard, as well as a left-hand sidemount (a single sidemount spare tire was now standard equipment on 1/2-tons, since the gas tank was relocated to the location where the spare tire had been carried). A safety plate glass windshield was adopted for 1933. The 1/2-ton Special Panel came with a recessed-panel body, chrome headlamps, a chrome radiator shell, a bright metal headlight tie-bar, chrome bumpers, and a bright Outside rear view mirror. Its load space was 72 x 45 x 48 in. Insulation and a dome lamp were found inside. The Canopy Express was similar-sized, with 18-in. deep steel sides, chrome trim parts and a slanted windshield. (* Measurements given above are length by width by height).
I.D. DATA: Serial number located on dash-mounted nameplate. The serial number consists of a group of numerals and letters which indicate the assembly plant, the model-year, the series, the month of assembly, and the number of units (plus 1,000) assembled at that plant. The first symbol indicates assembly plant: 1=Flint, Mich., 2=Tarrytown, N.Y., 3=St. Louis, Mo., 5=Kansas City, Kan., 6=Oakland, Calif., 8=Atlanta, Ga., 9=Norwood, Ohio, 14=Baltimore, Md., 20=Los Angeles, Calif., 21=Janesville, Wis. The second and third symbols indicate the model/series symbols. The fourth symbol indicates month of assembly: 01=Jan., 02=Feb., etc. Remaining numbers are the sequential unit production number. Each series is separately numbered in sequence beginning with 1001 at each plant. Starting number: CB-1001 and up. Engine number on right side of motor block behind fuel pump.

Model	Body Type	Price	Weight	Prod. Total
CB	Chassis	330	1995	-
CB	Chassis & Cab	420	2345	-
CB	Special Chassis	345	2025	-
CB	Sedan Delivery	545	2750	3628
CB	Special Sedan Delivery	560	-	Note 1
CB	Standard Panel	530	2750	-
CB	Closed Cab Pickup	440	2565	-
CB	Special Panel	545	2775	-
CB	Open Cab Canopy	-	-	-
CB	Closed Cab Canopy	-	-	-

NOTE 1: Special Sedan Delivery price estimated, production for Special Delivery model included with Sedan Delivery.

1933 Chevrolet 1/2-Ton Model CB Canopy Express (R. Streval)

ENGINE: Inline. OHV. Six-cylinder. Cast-iron block. Bore & stroke: 3-5/16 x 4 in. Displacement: 206.8 cid. Compression ratio: 5.2:1. Brake horsepower: 56 at 2750 rpm. Net horsepower: 26.33. Three main bearings. Mechanical valve lifters. Carburetor: Carter one-barrel model W1.
CHASSIS: [Series CB] Wheelbase: 109 in. Tires: 5.25 x 18 in.
TECHNICAL: Manual, synchromesh (without freewheeling on Light Delivery models). Speeds: 3F/1R. Floor-mounted gear-shift. Improved single-plate dry-disc clutch (pressure plate operated by three throw out levers, clutch plate resilient-mounted and driven through eight springs). Dash-operated manifold heat control valve. Torque tube drive (longer torque tube than passenger cars in 1933 Light Delivery models). Semi-floating rear axle. Axle shafts of finest alloy and increased in size, axle bearings larger and stronger. Overall drive ratio: 4.1:1. Four-wheel internal-expanding mechanical brakes with 12 in. drums and linings increased from 1.5 to 1.75 in. wide. Wire wheels. Counter-balanced crankshaft. Harmonic balancer. Dual spark control and octane selector. Built-in air cleaner with flame arrester, accelerating pump and carburetor heat control. New center camshaft bearing.
OPTIONS: [All models] Front bumper. Outside rear view mirror. Special paint. Bumper guards. Right-hand taillight. Heater. Dual windshield wipers. Special paint. Seat covers. White sidewall tires. Lettering stencils. Spotlight. Dual sidemounts (most models). Pedestal mirrors for sidemounts. Leatherette sidemount cover. [DeLuxe Equipment] Chrome radiator shell. Chrome headlamp buckets. Chrome headlamp tie-bar. Four hydraulic shock absorbers. [Sedan Delivery models] Rear bumper. Coach lights. [DeLuxe Panel models] Spare tire. Highly-polished Duco finish. [Special Chassis Equipment] Chrome radiator shell. Chrome headlamp buckets. Chrome headlamp tie-bar. Four hydraulic shock absorbers.

HISTORICAL: Introduced: December 1932. Calendar-year registrations: [All series] 99,880. Innovations: New larger, more powerful Blue Flame six-cylinder engine. Completely new appearance with 1932 car-type radiator grille, fenders and headlights and 1931 car type hoods (except vent-door hoods optional on DeLuxe Sedan Delivery). Factory-built body availability and the strong sales to fleet operators and government agencies increased Chevrolet's penetration of the light-truck market to nearly 50 percent in 1933. The company produced its one-millionth commercial vehicle during the model-year. Chevrolet was now selling as many trucks in the 1/2-ton and 1-1/2-ton weight classes as all other makers put together. M.E. Coyle took over as general manager of Chevrolet when William S. Knudsen was promoted to a General Motors executive vice presidency.

1934 CHEVROLET

SEDAN DELIVERY — MODEL DA — SIX-CYLINDER: During the early part of the 1934 model-year, the Sedan Delivery (Chevrolet Job Number 34570) was offered. This was no longer considered a part of the 1/2-ton Light Delivery series. It was moved to the Series DA passenger car line. The passenger style hood with three horizontal louvers that descended in length was used. Standard models had painted trim, DeLuxe models had chrome trim. The early 1934 Sedan Delivery had a 112-in. wheelbase, which was the same as 1934 Series DB 1/2-ton trucks, but it was a DA Master Series model. The DA Master Series passenger car line also had a 112-in. wheelbase. Interestingly, this was the last Sedan Delivery that factory literature specified as a 1/2-ton. Later Sedan Deliveries were never (or rarely) referred to, by Chevrolet, in terms of tonnage class.

1934 Chevrolet 1/2-Ton Model EA/EC Canopy Top Pickup (DFW/SI)

SEDAN DELIVERY — MODEL EA/EC — SIX-CYLINDER: Thanks to Chip Sweet, Commercial Technical Adviser for the Vintage Chevrolet Club of America, we have discovered that some truck collectors have 1935 Chevrolet Sedan Deliveries that are titled/registered as 1934 models. This indicates that the new EC line was brought out in the middle or late part of the 1934 model-year. Chevrolet coded these as 1935 models. The Model EC standard Sedan Delivery (with straight axle suspension) was coded with Fisher Body Style Number 35-1271A (35=1935, 12=1200 Series, 71=Sedan Delivery, A=straight axle). There was also a Model EA DeLuxe-chassis Sedan Delivery (also with straight axle) coded with Fisher Body Style Number 35-1271 (35=1935, 12=1200 Series, 71=Sedan Delivery). The DeLuxe description identified that DeLuxe trim or equipment features were used. Although these were manufactured as 1935 vehicles, states with title/registration laws based on the calendar-year date of the actual registration, would have registered the trucks as 1934 models. Also, Chip Sweet reports that some Chevrolet factory literature describes the Model EA chassis as a "1934 DC" chassis (which it was identical to) and the Model EC chassis as a "1935 EC" chassis (which was new). These trucks are considered 1935 models in this book and details about them are in the next section.

1934 Chevrolet 1/2-Ton Model DB Pickup With Utility Body (DFW)

1/2-TON LIGHT DELIVERY — SERIES DB — SIX-CYLINDER: Dramatic new styling was a highlight of the latest Chevrolet trucks. Accentuating the smoother body contours and more fully-crowned fenders were two-tone color combinations available on most body styles. The elimination of the front tie-bar support for the headlights gave the Chevrolets a fresh contemporary look. Standard models had a hood with four vertical louvers that slanted slightly backwards. DeLuxe models used the same front end trim parts, but they were painted on lower-priced trucks and plated on the fancier ones. Dimensions for specific models, following the previous format, were: Pickup: 72 x 45 x 54 in., Panel: 72 x 52 x 51 in., Canopy: 72 x 52 x 54 in.

1934 Chevrolet 1/2-Ton Model DB Closed Cab Pickup (DFW/SI)

I.D. DATA: Serial number located on dash-mounted nameplate. The serial number consists of a group of numerals and letters which indicate the assembly plant, the model-year, the series, the month of assembly, and the number of units (plus 1,000) assembled at that plant. The first symbol indicates assembly plant: 1=Flint, Mich., 2=Tarrytown, N.Y., 3=St. Louis, Mo., 5=Kansas City, Kan., 6=Oakland, Calif., 8=Atlanta, Ga., 9=Norwood, Ohio, 14=Baltimore, Md., 20=Los Angeles, Calif., 21=Janesville, Wis. The second and third symbols indicate the model/series symbols. The fourth symbol indicates month of assembly: 01=Jan., 02=Feb., etc. Remaining numbers are the sequential unit production number. Each series is separately numbered in sequence beginning with 1001 at each plant. Starting number: [DA Series] DA-1001 up, [EA/EC Series] EA-1001, EC-1001, [DB Series] DB-1001 and up. Engine number on right side of motor block behind fuel pump.

Model	Body Type	Price	Weight	Prod. Total
Sedan Delivery — Series DA — 112 in. w.b.				
DA	Sedan Delivery	600	-	-
Light Delivery — Series DB — 112 in. w.b.				
DB	Chassis	355	2120	-
DB	Chassis & Closed Cab	445	2465	-
DB	Closed Cab Pickup	465	2695	-
DB	Canopy Top Pickup	495	2850	-
DB	Special Chassis	375	2150	-
DB	Special Chassis & Cab	465	2485	-
DB	Special Pickup	485	2720	-
DB	Panel	575	2935	-
DB	Special Panel	615	2960	-

NOTE 1: See 1935 section for EA/EC Sedan Delivery data.
ENGINE: Inline. OHV. Six-cylinder. Cast-iron block. Bore & stroke: 3-5/16 x 4 in. Displacement: 206.8 cid. Compression ratio: 5.2:1. Brake horsepower: 56 at 2750 rpm. Net horsepower: 26.33. Three main bearings. Mechanical valve lifters. Carburetor: Carter one-barrel model W1 model 285S.
CHASSIS: [Series DA] Wheelbase: 112 in. Tires: 5.50 x 17 in.
CHASSIS: [Series DB] Wheelbase: 112 in. Tires: 5.50 x 17 in.
CHASSIS: [Series EA/EC] See 1935 section.

1934 Chevrolet 1/2-Ton Model DB Closed Cab Pickup (OCW)

TECHNICAL: Manual, synchromesh transmission. Speeds: 3F/1R. Floor-mounted gear-shift. Semi-floating rear axle. Overall ratio: 4.11:1. Mechanical four wheel brakes. Wire spoke wheels.
OPTIONS: [All models] Front bumper. Outside rear view mirror. Special paint. Bumper guards. Right-hand taillight. Heater. Dual windshield wipers. Special paint. Seat covers. White sidewall tires. Lettering stencils. Spotlight. Dual sidemounts (most models). Pedestal mirrors for sidemounts. Leatherette sidemount cover. [DeLuxe Equipment] Chrome radiator shell. Chrome headlamp buckets. Chrome headlamp tie-bar. Four hydraulic shock absorbers. Sidemount cover(s). Heater. Seat covers. [Sedan Delivery/Panel models] Rear bumper.

1934 Chevrolet-Holden 1/2-Ton "Ute" Roadster Utility (Lee Hoover photo)

1934 Chevrolet-Holden 1/2-Ton "Ute" Roadster Utility
(Lowell E. Eisenhour photo)

1934 Chevrolet-Holden 1/2-Ton "Ute" Roadster Utility
(owner Gary R. Halford)

HISTORICAL: Introduced: December 1933. Calendar-year registrations: [All series] 157,507. Innovations: All-new styling. Sedan Delivery adopts shorter wheelbase. Engine moved further forward in chassis. For the first time since 1918, Chevrolet trucks (except the Sedan Delivery) had their own exclusive front sheet metal, which was non-interchangeable with passenger car components.
1934 Chevrolet-Holden "Ute" Research by Gary R. Halford
According to Sir Laurence Harnett, head of the General Motors-Holden branch in the 1930s, the "Ute" was created because Australian farmers wanted a vehicle that would combine the comfort of a passenger car with the work horse utility of a pickup truck. Ute stood for "Utility," and the Utility model came two ways. The open-body version was called a Roadster Utility (or Commercial Roadster) and the closed-body version was known as a Coupe-Utility. GM-Holden began to offer this model, for the Australian market, in 1934. Ford had lead the way by introducing its own Ute in 1933.
The chassis and front of the 1934 Chevrolet-Holden Roadster Utility were of Canadian origin. All of the electrical equipment carried the Delco-Remy trade name and was made by McKinnenn Industries, of St. Catharines, Ontario, Canada. The Utes were shipped to Australia in CKD (completely knocked-down) form. They were then assembled at a Holden plant, using local labor to do the assembly work. From the firewall back, the body was designed, fabricated, and finished by the Australian automaker
I own a 1934 Chevrolet Standard (DC Series) Roadster Utility. Unfortunately, the aluminum Chevrolet cowl tag is missing, but a small body tag is still attached to the left-hand wood floor framing, between the seat and the door. It reads "7242/32." There is no other identification. My interpretation is that it has body number 32 on a Holden series 7242 type vehicle. The engine block has a January 23, 1934 casting date. The cylinder head was cast on December 14, 1933
In his book *The History of Holden Since 1917*, Norman A. Darwin says 259 Chevrolet Commercial Roadsters were built in 1934. I believe this figure includes both Standard DC and Master DA models. The highly knowledgeable Australian Chevrolet enthusiasts who helped me purchase my vehicle and container ship it to the United States said they have never seen another of this particular model.
In 1934, Holden built Ute bodies for both Chevrolet and Bedford vehicles. A new Chevrolet Coupe Utility body was introduced for 1936, while the Bedford model was carried over, unchanged, through 1938. The Bedford versions came in three Coupe Utility models spanning small and medium payload ranges. This changed in 1936, when the Bedford models were cut back to smaller payload ranges only and the Chevrolet Ute became the large models. This program was continued in 1937.
Minor changes graced the 1938 Chevrolet Ute body to complement changes in fender lines. In 1940, Holden Utes were not Chevrolet products. They had a 113-1/2-in. wheelbase and wore GMC grilles and nameplates. A number of Chevrolet Coupe Utilities were built in 1942 and 1943. In 1944, a 115-in. wheelbase was adopted and Holden returned to the use of Chevrolet grilles and badges. The same basic body on the Chevrolet chassis was employed through 1952, although minor revisions were made in 1949.

Holden brought out a redesigned Coupe Utility body in January 1951 and the Chevrolet-based Holden Coupe Utility vanished at that point. Thereafter, the GM-Holden Coupe Utility was a distinct product not related to American Chevrolets. In the late 1970s, the Isuzu-built KB Pickup replaced the Holden WB Ute and ended (most likely forever) the career of this uniquely Australian model.

1935 CHEVROLET

1935 Chevrolet 1/2-Ton Model EB Suburban (John Lee photo)

SEDAN DELIVERY — MODEL EC/EA — SIX-CYLINDER: The Sedan Delivery was again part of the passenger car line. Frontal styling of the Model EC was virtually identical to that of standard 1935 passenger cars, which had a hood with three horizontal louvers that grew smaller from top-to-bottom. The Model EA front was styled similar to Master Series cars, which had only two horizontal hood louvers (the top one slightly longer). The EC Sedan Delivery was smaller, with a 107-in. wheelbase. It had a straight, I-beam front axle. The Model EA Sedan Delivery had a 113-in. wheelbase. It also had the straight front axle. Trucks in both lines were brought out in the middle or late part of the 1934 model-year and are sometimes registered as 1934 models, but Chevrolet manufactured and coded them as 1935 vehicles. The Model EC standard Sedan Delivery was coded with Fisher Body Style Number 35-1271A (35=1935, 12=1200 Series, 71=Sedan Delivery, A=straight axle). The Model EC DeLuxe Sedan Delivery was coded with Fisher Body Style Number 35-1271 (35=1935, 12=1200 Series, 71=Sedan Delivery). Although these were manufactured as 1935 vehicles, states with title/registration laws based on the calendar-year date of the actual registration, would have registered the trucks as 1934 models. A passenger side sidemount spare tire was standard equipment.

1935 Chevrolet 1/2-Ton Model EB Suburban (OCW)

1935 Chevrolet 1/2-Ton Model EB Suburban (owner Edward Brouillet)

1/2-TON LIGHT DELIVERY — MODEL EB — SIX-CYLINDER: Changes for 1935 were very minor, except for the introduction of a new model that would have great significance upon the light-duty truck field. This was the Carryall Suburban. An all-steel eight-passenger station wagon, it was part of the upper-level Master series. An unusual thing about this truck was that it would eventually be sold with several entry-door configurations including two-, three- and four-doors. The original had two, plus a tailgate type rear load entrance. There were also some braking improvements in 1935. The 1/2-ton trucks had four curved vertical louvers on the rearmost surface of the hood sides. Wire wheels, chrome hubcaps and a right-hand sidemount were standard. Chrome headlights, a chrome grille screen, radiator shell band, headlamp supports, spare tire hold down and shock absorbers were part of the year's special equipment package. Rear bumpers were optional.

1935 Chevrolet 1/2-Ton Model EB Suburban (owner Edward Brouillet)

I.D. DATA: Serial number located on nameplate and dash. The serial number consists of a group of numerals and letters which indicate the assembly plant, the model-year, the series, the month of assembly, and the number of units (plus 1,000) assembled at that plant. The first symbol indicates assembly plant: 1=Flint, Mich., 2=Tarrytown, N.Y., 3=St. Louis, Mo., 5=Kansas City, Kan., 6=Oakland, Calif., 8=Atlanta, Ga., 9=Norwood, Ohio, 14=Baltimore, Md., 20=Los Angeles, Calif., 21=Janesville, Wis. The second and third symbols indicate the model/series symbols. The fourth symbol indicates month of assembly: 01=Jan., 02=Feb., etc. Remaining numbers are the sequential unit production number. Each series is separately numbered in sequence beginning with 1001 at each plant. Starting numbers: [EC Sedan Delivery] EC-1001 and up, [EA Sedan Delivery] EA-1001 up, [EB models] EB-1001 and up. Engine number on right side of motor block behind fuel pump. Engine numbers: 4708995 and up.

1935 Chevrolet Model EA Sedan Delivery (OCW)

Model	Body Type	Price	Weight	Prod. Total
Sedan Delivery — Series EC — 107 in. w.b.				
EC	Sedan Delivery	515	2675	538
Sedan Delivery — Series EA — 113 in. w.b.				
EA	Sedan Delivery	625	2920	4688
1/2-Ton Light Delivery — Series EB — 112 in. w.b.				
EB	Chassis	355	2135	-
EB	Special Chassis	375	2235	-
EB	Panel Delivery	500	2920	-
EB	Special Panel	580	3035	-
EB	Chassis & Cab	445	2480	-
EB	Pickup	465	2700	-
EB	Special Pickup	485	2810	-
EB	Canopy	495	2795	-
EC	Sedan Delivery	515	2675	6192

ENGINE: Inline. OHV. Six-cylinder. Cast-iron block. Bore & stroke: 3-5/16 x 4 in. Displacement: 206.8 cid. Compression ratio: 5.45:1. Brake horsepower: 60 at 3000 rpm. Net horsepower: 26.33. Three main bearings. Mechanical valve lifters. Carburetor: Carter one-barrel model W1 model 284S.
CHASSIS: [Series EC] Wheelbase: 107 in. Tires: 5.25 x 17 in.
CHASSIS: [Series EA] Wheelbase: 113 in. Tires: 5.50 x 17 in.
CHASSIS: [Series EB] Wheelbase: 112 in. Tires: 5.50 x 17 in.
TECHNICAL: Manual, synchromesh transmission. Speeds: 3F/1R. Floor-mounted gear-shift. Semi-floating rear axle. Overall ratio: 4.11:1. Mechanical four wheel brakes. Wire spoke wheels.
OPTIONS: DeLuxe equipment. Rear bumper. Metal sidemount covers. Fabric sidemount covers. Fender skirts. Bumper guards. Radio. Heater. Clock. Cigar lighter. Radio antenna. Seat covers. Fog lights. Spotlight. Special paint. Wheel trim rings. Canopy top for pickup. License plate frames. Two-tone paint. Lettering stencils. Screen-sides for Canopy Express. Pickup box tarpaulin. Outside rear view mirror. Pedestal mirrors for sidemounts.

1935 Chevrolet 1-Ton-Rated Parcel Delivery Van (JAW)

HISTORICAL: Introduced: December 15, 1934. Calendar-year registrations: [All series] 167,129 (all series). Innovations: All-new Carryall Suburban. Improved brakes. Carryall Suburban was first all-steel station wagon, although Checker produced a somewhat similar model in 1930-1931 period, as did Chrysler in its Fargo truck line. However, both of these were more sedan-like than the new "Suburban" (as it came to be called later on.)

1936 CHEVROLET

1936 Chevrolet Model FC Coupe-Delivery (DFW/DPL)

STANDARD SERIES COMMERCIAL CAR — MODEL FC — SIX-CYLINDER: This year a Coupe Delivery joined the Sedan Delivery in the small Commercial Car series. Both were based on the standard I-beam front axle) Chevrolet Model FC passenger cars, which grew two inches in wheelbase. Front end appearance was similar to FC cars with an oval-shaped grille with vertical moldings, grille shell-mounted headlamps, and a hood with two horizontal louvers (the shorter louver was on the bottom). The Sedan Delivery had panel body sides and a curbside opening rear door.
MASTER SERIES COMMERCIAL CAR — MODEL FD — SIX-CYLINDER: Also available was a line of Commercial Cars on the longer 113-in. wheelbase Master Series chassis. These had larger tires. There's no indication these body styles were built on the Model FA chassis with Knee-Action, but it is possible.

1936 Chevrolet 1/2-Ton Model FB Pickup (Lee Hoovler)

1936 Chevrolet 1/2-Ton Model FB Pickup (Calendar Promotions)

1936 Chevrolet 1/2-Ton Model FB Pickup (DFW)

1/2-TON LIGHT DELIVERY — MODEL FB — SIX-CYLINDER: The Light Delivery line included the 1/2-ton conventional trucks. All 1936 Chevrolet trucks had horizontal hood louvers in place of the vertical openings found on the 1935 models. Above the louvers, in the center, was a large Chevrolet bow tie emblem. The radiator grille resembled that of 1935 passenger cars, as did the new valanced (deep-skirted) front fenders.

1936 Chevrolet 1/2-Ton Model FB Pickup (Owner: Gus Chompf)

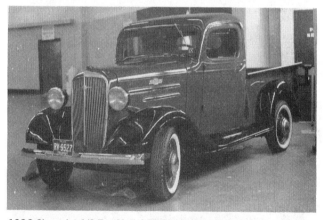

1936 Chevrolet 1/2-Ton Model FB Pickup (John Lee photo)

1936 Chevrolet 1/2-Ton Model FB Pickup (OCW)

I.D. DATA: Serial number located on nameplate on dash. The serial number consists of a group of numerals and letters which indicate the assembly plant, the model-year, the series, the month of assembly, and the number of units (plus 1,000) assembled at that plant. The first symbol indicates assembly plant: 1=Flint, Mich., 2=Tarrytown, N.Y., 3=St. Louis, Mo., 5=Kansas City, Kan., 6=Oakland, Calif., 8=Atlanta, Ga., 9=Norwood, Ohio, 14=Baltimore, Md., 20=Los Angeles, Calif., 21=Janesville, Wis. The second and third symbols indicate the model/series symbols. The fourth symbol indicates month of assembly: 01=Jan., 02=Feb., etc. Remaining numbers are the sequential unit production number. Each series is separately numbered in sequence beginning with 1001 at each plant. Starting numbers: [FC Sedan Delivery] FC-1001 and up, [FD Sedan Delivery] FD-1001 up, [FB models] EB-1001 and up. Engine number on right side of motor block behind fuel pump. Engine numbers: K-5500179 and up.

1936 Chevrolet 1/2-Ton Model FB Pickup (Lowell E. Eisenhour)

Model	Body Type	Price	Weight	Prod. Total
Commercial Cars — Series FC — 109 in. w.b. — Six				
FC	Sedan Delivery	535	2705	9404
FC	Coupe Pickup	535	2760	3183
Commercial Cars — Series FD — 113 in. w.b. — Six				
FD	Sedan Delivery	-	-	Note 1
FD	Coupe Pickup	-	-	Note 1
1/2-Ton Light Delivery — Series FB — 112 in. w.b. — Six				
FB	Chassis	360	2095	-
FB	Chassis & Cab	450	2450	-
FB	Pickup	475	2075	-
FB	Panel	565	2895	-
FB	Special Panel	577	3000	-
FB	Carryall Suburban	685	3255	-

NOTE 1: Commercial car production believed to be FC/FD combined total.
ENGINE: Inline. OHV. Six-cylinder. Cast-iron block. Bore & stroke: 3-5/16 x 4 in. Displacement: 206.8 cid. Compression ratio: 6.0:1. Brake horsepower: 79 at 3200 rpm. Net horsepower: 26.3. Three main bearings. Mechanical valve lifters. Carburetor: Carter one-barrel model 319S.
CHASSIS: [Series FC] Wheelbase: 109 in. Tires: 17 x 5.25 in.
CHASSIS: [Series FD] Wheelbase: 113 in. Tires: 5.50 x 17 in.
CHASSIS: [Series FB] Wheelbase: 112 in. Tires: 5.50 x 17 in.

1936 Chevrolet 1/2-Ton Model FB Pickup (OCW)

TECHNICAL: Manual, synchromesh transmission. Speeds: 3F/1R. Floor-mounted gear-shift. Diaphragm type clutch. Semi-floating rear axle. Overall ratio: [FC models] 4.11:1, [Other models] Not available. Four-wheel hydraulic brakes. Short-spoke wheels.
OPTIONS: DeLuxe equipment package. Rear bumper. Single sidemount. Pedestal mirrors for sidemounts. Sidemount cover(s). Fender skirts. Bumper guards. Radio. Heater. Clock. Cigar lighter. Radio antenna. Seat covers. Fog lamps. Spotlight. Screen-sides for canopy express. White sidewall tires. Wheel trim rings. Outside rear view mirror. Special paint. Stencils for lettering. Pickup box tarpaulin. Pressed steel wheels. DeLuxe radiator ornament. License plate frames. Dual windshield wipers. Side curtains. Right-hand taillight.
HISTORICAL: Introduced: November 2, 1935. Calendar-year registrations: [All series] 204,344. Innovations: Introduction of hydraulic brakes. New Carter carburetor. Coupe-Pickup model bows. All new truck cabs with one-piece, all-steel construction brought out at midyear. Dupont paint company sales representatives drove a fleet of standard Chevrolet Sedan Deliveries.

1937 CHEVROLET

COMMERCIAL CAR — MODEL GB — SIX-CYLINDER: This year the Sedan Delivery and Coupe Delivery were based on the Model GB line of Master Series passenger car without Knee-Action front suspension. The year's new "waterfall" style passenger car grille was seen on all small trucks. However, the Commercial Cars also used the car-type front sheet metal with spear-shaped embossments on the hood sides and a streamlined groove running from the fender onto the door, where it faded into the sheet metal. There were three small slashes at the front upper corner, ahead of the hood feature line, and multiple chrome slashes along the hood side embossments. The Sedan Delivery had a 68 x 54 x 41-in. load space. The Coupe Delivery was again a standard Business Coupe with a right-hand sidemount, a cargo box inside the luggage compartment, and step pads on the rear bumper. A trunk lid was supplied and could be swapped for the cargo box by loosening four bolts and substituting one accessory for the other. A change was the spare tire carried under the floor of the Sedan Delivery.

1937 Model GB Sedan Delivery (JAW)

1/2-TON LIGHT DELIVERY — MODEL GC — SIX-CYLINDER: The Light Delivery trucks had a grille design similar to the Commercial Cars, but the rest of their styling was different. There were again twin horizontal hood louvers. Both were now of the same length. A large Chevrolet bow tie emblem was placed above the center of the top louver. Double-bead belt moldings, with scallops at the side of the cowl, were seen. Chevrolet offered many important new features for 1937. They began with an all-steel cab and streamlined styling. The result was a modern looking truck with rounded, fuller fenders. It had smoother lines. The 1/2-ton Pickup box was 77 in. long by 45 in. wide. It had 16-in. high sidewalls. Dimensions for the GC 1/2-ton Panel were 86 x 54 x 51 in.. Headlights on all models were torpedo-shaped and mounted on the side of the hood.
3/4-TON LIGHT TRUCK — MODELS GD — SIX-CYLINDER: Important to Chevrolet's marketing strategy was the return of 3/4-ton models midway through the year. These had the same general design as the smaller trucks. The 3/4-tons had a longer wheelbase than the 1/2-tons, and longer bodies and boxes. A larger, more powerful engine than used in 1936 models was standard. It was the same engine used in all 1937 Chevrolet trucks.
1-TON LIGHT-MEDIUM TRUCK — MODEL GE — SIX-CYLINDER: A new 1-ton series with a 122-1/4-in. wheelbase was also added late in 1937. Styling was again basically of similar design in larger proportions. The wheelbase was the same as the 3/4-tons. The 3/4-ton and 1-ton frames were identical, both having section modulus of 3.18 cu. in. The bodies were longer than 1/2-ton bodies. Larger brakes and larger 17-in. tires were fitted.

1937 Chevrolet 1/2-Ton Model GC Pickup (Lowell E. Eisenhour)

I.D. DATA: Serial number located on right side of cowl under the hood. The serial number consists of a group of numerals and letters which indicate the assembly plant, the model-year, the series, the month of assembly, and the number of units (plus 1,000) assembled at that plant. The first symbol indicates assembly plant: 1=Flint, Mich., 2=Tarrytown, N.Y., 3=St. Louis, Mo., 5=Kansas City, Kan.,

6=Oakland, Calif., 8=Atlanta, Ga., 9=Norwood, Ohio, 14=Baltimore, Md., 20=Los Angeles, Calif., 21=Janesville, Wis. The second and third symbols indicate the model/series symbols. The fourth symbol indicates month of assembly: 01=Jan., 02=Feb., etc. Remaining numbers are the sequential unit production number. Each series is separately numbered in sequence beginning with 1001 at each plant. Starting numbers: [GB Commercial Cars] GB-1001 and up, [GC Light Delivery] GC-1001 up, [GD Light Truck] GD-1001 and up, [GE Light-Medium Truck] GE-1001 and up. Engine number on right side of motor block behind fuel pump. Engine numbers: [GB/GC models] K-1 and up, [Other models] T-1 and up.

Model	Body Type	Price	Weight	Prod. Total
Commercial Cars — Series GB — 112.25 in. w.b.				
GB	Sedan Delivery	595	2810	9404
GB	Coupe Delivery	-		
1/2-Ton Light Delivery — Series GC — 112 in. w.b.				
GC	Chassis	390	2190	-
GC	Chassis & Cab	485	2575	-
GC	Pickup	515	2805	-
GC	Panel	605	3030	-
GC	Canopy	600	3050	-
GC	Suburban	725	3330	-
3/4-Ton Light Truck — Series GD — 122.25 in. w.b.				
GD	Chassis	460	2410	-
GD	Chassis & Cab	555	2780	-
GD	Pickup	595	3020	-
GD	Stake	630	3290	-
1-Ton Light-Medium Truck — Series GE — 122.25 in. w.b.				
GE	Chassis	495	2585	-
GE	Chassis & Cab	590	2955	-
GE	Pickup	630	3195	-
GE	Stake	665	3465	-

ENGINE: [Sedan Delivery] Inline. OHV. Six-cylinder. Cast-iron block. Bore & stroke: 3.5 x 3.75 in. Displacement: 216.5 cid. Compression ratio: 6.25:1. Brake horsepower: 85 at 3200 rpm. Net horsepower: 29.4. Torque: 170 lb.-ft. Four main bearings. Mechanical valve lifters. Carburetor: Carter one-barrel type W1 model 346-S. Same engine used in passenger cars. (Code T)
ENGINE: [All Trucks] Inline. OHV. Six-cylinder. Cast-iron block. Bore & stroke: 3.5 x 3.75 in. Displacement: 216.5 cid. Compression ratio: 6.25:1. Brake horsepower: 78 at 3200 rpm. Net horsepower: 29.4. Torque: 170 lb.-ft. Four main bearings. Mechanical valve lifters. Carburetor: Carter one-barrel type W1 model 346-S. (The truck engine used heavier 27-oz. pistons with part no. 602806, and the extra reciprocating inertia caused the horsepower curve to peak at a lower point, although both engines developed the same torque rating.)

1937 Chevrolet 1/2-Ton Model GC Pickup (WPL)

CHASSIS: [Model GB] Wheelbase: 112-1/4 in. Tires: 6.00 x 16 in. (7.50 x 15 in. and 5.50 x 18 in. optionally available).
CHASSIS: [Model GC] Wheelbase: 112 in. Tires: 6.00 x 16, 6.50 x 17, 7.50 x 15.
CHASSIS: [Model GD] Wheelbase: 122.25 in. Tires: 7.00 x 17, 7.50 x 17.
CHASSIS: [Model GE] Wheelbase: 122.25 in. Tires: 7.00 x 17, 7.50 x 17.
TECHNICAL: Manual, synchromesh transmission. Speeds: [GB/GC/GD models] 3F/1R, [GE models] 4F/1R. Floor-mounted gear-shift. Coil spring type clutch. Sedan Delivery and 1/2-ton had a nine-inch disc clutch. Larger trucks had a 10-in. clutch. [Sedan Delivery] Semi-floating rear axle with hypoid gears, [all other models] semi-floating rear axle with spiral-bevel gears. Overall ratio: [Sedan Delivery] 3.73, [GC models] 4.11:1 (or 3.82), [Other models] 4.11. Hydraulic, four-wheel brakes. Pressed steel wheels.
OPTIONS: DeLuxe equipment package. Rear bumper. Single sidemount. Pedestal mirrors for sidemounts. Sidemount cover(s). Fender skirts. Bumper guards. Radio. Heater. Clock. Cigar lighter. Radio antenna. Seat covers. Fog lamps. Spotlight. Screen sides for canopy express. White sidewall tires. Wheel trim rings. Outside rear view mirror. Special paint. Stencils for lettering. Pickup box tarpaulin. Pressed steel wheels. DeLuxe radiator ornament. License plate frames. Dual windshield wipers. Side curtains. Right-hand taillight.
HISTORICAL: Introduced: November 1936. Calendar-year registrations: [All series] 183,674. Innovations: New 3/4-ton and 1-ton series. New "Diamond Crown" styling. Safety glass introduced. Trucks again share appearance features with current Chevrolet cars. Larger and more powerful "Blue Flame" six used. Chevrolet produced some unusual 1/2-ton walk-in delivery trucks on the 1/2-ton chassis. One used a body by Metro Body Company, which later become a part of International-Harvester Corp. Race driver Harry Hartz drove a 1/2-ton Pickup on a "Round the Nation Economy Run" sponsored by Chevrolet under American Automobile Association (AAA) sanctioning. Hartz was at the wheel of the truck as it rolled off the assembly line in Flint, Mich. The 72-day excursion covered 10,244.8 miles around the rim of America and did it, without mechanical failure, for less than a penny a mile. A new 1-1/2-ton COE truck was introduced this season.

1938 CHEVROLET

1938 Chevrolet Model HB Coupe-Delivery (DFW/BLHU)

COMMERCIAL CAR — MODEL HB — SIX-CYLINDER: The 1938 Chevrolet grille was made up of horizontal bars on either side of a vertical center divider. More massive horizontal bars were used to divide the thinner ones into six segments on each side. The top bar of the grille was lower and straighter than the 1937 style, on the same level as the horizontal feature line of the hood. The Coupe-Pickup and Sedan Delivery had long, horizontal louver vents similar to those of cars. These had sort of an ice cube tray look. The Coupe-Delivery had a cargo box measuring 66 x 38 x 12 in.

1938 Chevrolet 1/2-Ton Model HC Pickup (DFW/C. Chasteen)

1/2-TON LIGHT DELIVERY — MODEL HC — SIX-CYLINDER: Conventional trucks had a different hood side treatment with four, somewhat shorter horizontal louvers. They were angled at the front. All trucks up to 1-1/2-ton had the same cab, except for fenders. A Chevrolet bow-tie emblem was seen above them. Unlike the year's passenger cars, trucks had a flat, one-piece windshield. A double-bead belt molding with scalloped front was used. The 1/2-ton Pickup's load area was 77 x 45 x 16 in. Measurements for the 1/2-ton Model HC Panel body were 86 x 56 x 51 in. The Panel's rear door opening was 47 in. wide by 43 in. high.

3/4-TON LIGHT TRUCK — MODEL HD — SIX-CYLINDER: The 3/4-ton conventional trucks also had the new hood with horizontal louvers angled at the front and a flat, one-piece windshield. All trucks up to 1-1/2-ton had the same cab, except for fenders. A double-bead belt molding with scalloped front was used. The wheelbase was 10-1/4 in. longer than that of the 1/2-ton. The 3/4-ton Express (Pickup) had a long, sturdier cargo box larger than that of the 1/2-ton. A stake truck was in this series.

1938 Chevrolet 3/4-Ton Model HD Panel (OCW)

1-TON MEDIUM-LIGHT TRUCK — MODEL HE — SIX-CYLINDER: The 1-ton conventional trucks also had the new hood with horizontal louvers that were angled at the front, and a flat one-piece windshield. All trucks up to 1-1/2-ton had the same cab, except for fenders. A double-bead belt molding with scalloped front was used. The wheelbase was 10-1/4 in. longer than that of the 1/2-ton, and the same as that of the 3/4-ton. The 1-ton Express (Pickup) had a long, sturdier express type cargo box larger than that of the 1/2-ton, and identical to that of the 3/4-ton. A stake truck was in this series, too. A four-speed transmission, heftier springs and larger tires were standard.

1938 Chevrolet 1-Ton Model HE Platform Body (OCW)

I.D. DATA: Serial number located on nameplate positioned on firewall on all models. The serial number consists of a group of numerals and letters which indicate the assembly plant, the model-year, the series, the month of assembly, and the number of units (plus 1,000) assembled at that plant. The first symbol indicates assembly plant: 1=Flint, Mich., 2=Tarrytown, N.Y., 3=St. Louis, Mo., 5=Kansas City, Kan., 6=Oakland, Calif., 8=Atlanta, Ga., 9=Norwood, Ohio, 14=Baltimore, Md., 20=Los Angeles, Calif., 21=Janesville, Wis. The second and third symbols indicate the model/series symbols. The fourth symbol indicates month of assembly: 01=Jan., 02=Feb., etc. Remaining numbers are the sequential unit production number. Each series is separately numbered in sequence beginning with 1001 at each plant. Starting: [HB models] HB-1001 and up, [HC models] HC-1001 and up, [HD models] HD-1001 and up, [HE models] HE-1001 and up. The engine numbers of all 1938 Chevrolet cars and trucks was relocated to a boss on the right side of the engine to the rear of the ignition distributor. Starting: [HB models] 1187822 and up, [HC models] K-1187822 and up, [HD models] AT-1187822 and up, [HE models] AT-1187822 and up.

Model	Body Type	Price	Weight	Prod. Total
Commercial Car — Model HB — 112.25 in. w.b				
HB	Coupe-Delivery	689	2945	-
HB	Sedan Delivery	694	2835	5742
1/2-Ton Light-Delivery — Model HC — 112 in. w.b.				
HC	Chassis	465	2200	-
HC	Chassis & Cab	562	2580	-
HC	Pickup	592	2805	-
HC	Panel	684	3015	-
HC	Canopy	678	3030	-
HC	Suburban	834	3295	-
3/4-Ton Light Truck — Model HD — 122,25 in. w.b.				
HD	Chassis	543	2420	-
HD	Chassis & Cab	639	2785	-
HD	Pickup	680	3035	-
HD	Stake	716	3300	-
HD	Panel	792	3280	-
1-Ton Light-Medium Truck — Model HE — 122.25 in. w.b.				
HE	Chassis	585	2575	-
HE	Chassis & Cab	681	2950	-
HE	Pickup	722	3200	-
HE	Stake	757	3440	-
HE	Panel	833	3445	-

1938 Chevrolet 1/2-Ton Model HC Flatbed Truck (OCW)

ENGINE: [Sedan Delivery] Inline. OHV. Six-cylinder. Cast-iron block. Bore & stroke: 3.5 x 3.75 in. Displacement: 216.5 cid. Compression ratio: 6.25:1. Brake horsepower: 85 at 3200 rpm. Net horsepower: 29.4. Torque: 170 lb.-ft. Four main bearings. Mechanical valve lifters. Carburetor: Carter one-barrel type W1. Same engine used in passenger cars. (Code T)

ENGINE: [All Other Trucks] Inline. OHV. Six-cylinder. Cast-iron block. Bore & stroke: 3.5 x 3.75 in. Displacement: 216.5 cid. Compression ratio: 6.25:1. Brake horsepower: 78 at 3200 rpm. Net horsepower: 29.4. Torque: 170 lb.-ft. Four main bearings. Mechanical valve lifters. Carburetor: Carter one-barrel type W1. (The truck engine used heavier 27-oz. pistons with part no. 602806, and the extra reciprocating inertia caused the horsepower curve to peak at a lower point, although both engines developed the same torque rating.)

CHASSIS: [Model HB] Wheelbase: 112-1/4 in. Tires: 6.00 x 16 in. (7.50 x 15 in. and 5.50 x 18 in. optionally available).

CHASSIS: [Model HC] Wheelbase: 112 in. Tires: 6.00 x 16, 6.50 x 17, 7.50 x 15.

CHASSIS: [Model HD] Wheelbase: 122.25 in. Tires: 7.50 x 15.

CHASSIS: [Model HE] Wheelbase: 122.25 in. Tires: 7.00 x 17, 7.50 x 17.

TECHNICAL: Manual, synchromesh transmission. Speeds: [HB/HC/HD models] 3F/1R. [HE models] 4F/1R. Floor-mounted gear-shift. New diaphragm-spring type clutch. Sedan Delivery and 1/2-ton had a nine-inch disc clutch. Larger trucks had an 11-in. clutch. [Sedan Delivery] Semi-floating rear axle with hypoid gears, [all other models] semi-floating rear axle with spiral-bevel gears. Overall ratio: [Sedan Delivery] 3.73, [GC models] 4.11:1 (or 3.82), [Other models] 4.11. Hydraulic, four-wheel brakes. Steel short-spoke wheels.

OPTIONS: DeLuxe equipment. Rear bumper. Outside rear view mirror. Spotlight. Fog lights. Cargo bed tarpaulin. Bumper guards. Radio. Heater. Clock. Cigar lighter. Radio antenna. Seat covers. External sun shade. Dual windshield wipers. Right-hand taillight. White sidewall tires. Wheel trim rings. License plate frames. Sidemount spare tires (special order). Two-tone paint. Special paint colors. [Canopy Delivery] Side curtains. Screen sides.

HISTORICAL: Introduced: Oct. 23, 1937. Calendar-year registrations: [All Series] 119,479. Innovations: Heavier valve springs. Larger water pump. New ball bearing water pump introduced at midyear. New diaphragm spring type clutch. New voltage regulator and generator. New starter with overrunning clutch replaced Bendix drive starter. Ball bearing water pump was lubricated for life, so the grease fitting on the hub was deleted. M.E. Coyle was general manager of Chevrolet.

1939 CHEVROLET

1939 Chevrolet Model JB Sedan Delivery (MVMA)

COMMERCIAL CARS — MODEL JB — SIX-CYLINDER: The JB models had the passenger car's more rounded horizontal bar grille and "ice cube tray" hood side vents. Both models, the Coupe-Delivery and Sedan Delivery, also had larger, more streamlined headlamp buckets. A new body with a straighter back was used for the Sedan Delivery, which had a 66 x 54 x 4-in. load space.

1939 Chevrolet 1/2-Ton Model JC Pickup (owner Gary Wendt)

1/2-TON LIGHT DELIVERY — MODEL JC — SIX-CYLINDER: Chevrolet used a new front end design with heavier horizontal members and straighter vertical edges. A Chevrolet script was found on the top grille bar. Chevrolet also adopted a two-piece, V-shaped windshield that replaced the old one-piece flat windshield. The hood now had a single louver and a single side trim strip was used. The same image characterized all light-duty trucks. Popular models included the Pickup with steel cargo box and wooden load floor (the box being the same size as 1938), the Panel with a one-inch wider load space, and the Suburban. This was again a two-door station wagon type vehicle having a front seat on which the right third of the back rest folded forward for passenger ingress/egress. Also somewhat changed was the Canopy Express, which gained a partition behind the driver's seat. This reduced the load space to a length of 80 in., from last season's 86 in.

1939 Chevrolet 3/4-Ton Model JD Chassis Cab Utility Body (Joe Egle)

3/4-TON LIGHT TRUCK — MODEL JD — SIX-CYLINDER: The 3/4-ton commercial trucks had the same general front end and cab styling updates as the 1/2-ton Light Delivery line with a wheelbase nearly 10 in. longer. The Pickup had a larger, express type cargo box and longer running boards. The Panel had larger dimensions. There was a Stake truck in this series, but no Suburban. These trucks had 11-in. diameter brakes.

3/4-TON SPECIAL TRUCK — MODEL JE — SIX-CYLINDER: The JE models were a heavy-duty version of the JD 3/4-ton commercial models. These trucks had 14-in. diameter brakes and 17-in. diameter wheels. These trucks succeeded the previous 1-ton (GE/HE) models. Chevrolet called the heavy-duty 3/4-ton the "3/4-ton Special" through 1942. The frames and axles are the same capacity as the standard 3/4-ton. There was no separate 1-ton nominally rated series, as the old 1-ton became the 3/4-ton Special.

1939 Chevrolet 1-Ton Model VA Canopy Express (owner Richard Salem)

1-TON MEDIUM-LIGHT TRUCK — MODEL VA-S — SIX-CYLINDER: The VA Chevrolet trucks had a 133-in. wheelbase. This line is listed as a 1-1/2-ton series in some Chevrolet literature. The VAs came in two chassis configurations, plus a Panel. A 1-ton chassis option was available for the Panel. These were considered VA-S models. The VAs were available with single or dual rear wheels. The single rear wheel jobs could be confused with a 1-ton, but had a true 1-1/2-ton truck chassis. In Kentucky, Pennsylvania, and North Carolina, they came with light eight-leaf rear springs and were designated VA-S models. These springs had a deflection rate of 490 lb. per square inch. Chevrolet Service News (Feb. 1937) lists 6.00 x 20 6-ply tires front and back with Chevrolet's narrowest five-inch rims part number 602540 available for "Panel Job only, with light rear springs, 1-ton load."

1939 Chevrolet 1/2-Ton Model JC Pickup (J. Prodoehl)

I.D. DATA: Serial number located on a plate on the right front cowl side under hood [JB/JD/JE models]. The serial number consists of a group of numerals and letters which indicate the assembly plant, the model-year, the series, the month of assembly, and the number of units (plus 1,000) assembled at that plant. The first symbol indicates assembly plant: 1=Flint, Mich., 2=Tarrytown, N.Y., 3=St. Louis, Mo., 5=Kansas City, Kan., 6=Oakland, Calif., 8=Atlanta, Ga., 9=Norwood, Ohio, 14=Baltimore, Md., 20=Los Angeles, Calif., 21=Janesville, Wis. The second and third symbols indicate the model/series symbols. The fourth symbol indicates month of assembly: 01=Jan., 02=Feb., etc. Remaining numbers are the sequential unit production number. Each series is separately numbered in sequence beginning with 1001 at each plant. Serial numbers: [JB models] JB-1001 to 33221, [JC models] JC-1001 to 12094, [JD models] JD -1001 to 12094, [VA models] VA-1001 to 12094. Engine number located on boss on right side of engine block to the rear of the ignition distributor. Engine numbers: [JB-Coupe-Delivery] 1915447 to 2697267, [JB-Sedan Delivery] B-10503 to 105461, [JC-Chassis/Chassis-and-Cab/Pickup] K-1915447 to 2697267, [JC-all other models] B-10503 to 105461, [JD-Chassis/Chassis-and-Cab/Pickup] AT-1915447 to 2697267, [JD-all others] B-10503 to 105461, [VA models] T-1915447 to 2697267. The B prefix indicates motor built in Chevrolet's new plant in Buffalo, N.Y.

1939 Chevrolet 1/2-Ton Model JC Pickup (OCW)

Model	Body Type	Price	Weight	Prod. Total
Commercial Car — Model JB — 112.25 in. w.b.				
JB	Coupe Delivery	669	3095	-
JB	Sedan Delivery	673	3005	8090
1/2-Ton Light Delivery — Model JC — 113.5 in. w.b.				
JC	Chassis	450	2185	-
JC	Chassis & Cab	542	2580	-
JC	Pickup	572	2785	-
JC	Panel	658	3030	-
JC	Canopy	714	3025	-
JC	Suburban	808	3210	-
3/4-Ton Light Truck — Model JD — 123.75 in. w.b.				
JD	Chassis	528	2570	-
JD	Chassis & Cab	619	2945	-
JD	Pickup	660	3200	-
JD	Stake	690	3465	-
JD	Panel	767	3460	-
3/4-Ton Light Truck — Model JE — 123.75 in. w.b.				
JE	Chassis	-	2715	-
JE	Chassis & Cab	-	3110	-
JE	Panel	-	3625	-
JE	Pickup	-	3365	-
JE	Stake	-	3605	-
1- to 1-1/2-Ton Medium Light Truck — Model VA/VA-S — 133 in. w.b.				
VA	Panel	821	3975	-

1939 Chevrolet 1/2-Ton Model JC Pickup (owner Gary Wendt)

ENGINE: [Sedan Delivery] Inline. OHV. Six-cylinder. Cast-iron block. Bore & stroke: 3.5 x 3.75 in. Displacement: 216.5 cid. Compression ratio: 6.25:1. Brake horsepower: 85 at 3200 rpm. Net horsepower: 29.4. Torque: 170 lb.-ft. Four main bearings. Mechanical valve lifters. Carburetor: Carter one-barrel type W1. Same engine used in passenger cars. (Code T)
ENGINE: [All Other Trucks] Inline. OHV. Six-cylinder. Cast-iron block. Bore & stroke: 3.5 x 3.75 in. Displacement: 216.5 cid. Compression ratio: 6.25:1. Brake horsepower: 78 at 3200 rpm. Net horsepower: 29.4. Torque: 170 lb.-ft. Four main bearings. Mechanical valve lifters. Carburetor: Carter one-barrel type W1.
CHASSIS: [Model JB models] Wheelbase: 112-1/4 in. Tires: 6.00 x 16 four-ply.
CHASSIS: [Model JC models] Wheelbase: 113-1/2 in. Tires: 6.00 x 16 four-ply.
CHASSIS: [Model JD models] Wheelbase: 123-3/4 in. Tires: 7.50 x 15 six-ply.

1939 Chevrolet 1-Ton Model JD Stake Truck (A. Lovick/CPC)

CHASSIS: [Model JE models] Wheelbase: 123-3/4 in. Tires: 6.50 x 15 six-ply (chassis models 7.00 x 17 6-ply standard or 7.50 x 17 8-ply for rear only).
CHASSIS: [Model VA-S models] Wheelbase: 133 in. Tires: 6.00 x 20 six-ply, single rear.
TECHNICAL: Manual transmission. Speeds: [JB] 3F/1R vacuum-assisted with steering column gear shift. [JC/JD] 3F/1R synchromesh with floor-mounted gear shift. [JE/VA-S models] 4F/1R non-synchromesh with floor-mounted gear shift. Diaphragm-spring type clutch. JBs and 1/2-ton had a nine-inch disc clutch. Larger trucks had an 11-in. clutch. [JB] Semi-floating rear axle with hypoid gears, [all other models except VA] semi-floating rear axle with spiral-bevel gears, [VA-S] Full-floating. Overall ratio: [JB] 3.73, [JC models] 4.11:1 (or 3.82), [Other models] 4.11. Hydraulic, four-wheel brakes. Steel short-spoke wheels.
OPTIONS: [All Trucks and Commercial Cars] Wheel trim rings. License plate frames. Outside rear view mirror. Spotlight. Fog lights. Radio and antenna. Bumper guards. Radio. Heater. Clock. Cigar lighter. Seat covers. External sun shade. Dual windshield wipers. Two-tone paint. Special paint colors. [All Trucks] DeLuxe equipment. Rear bumper. Cargo bed tarpaulin. Right-hand taillight. [All Trucks, Special order option] Sidemount spare tire. [Canopy Delivery] Side curtains. Screenside equipment.

1939 Chevrolet 1/2-Ton Model JC Canopy Express (OCW)

HISTORICAL: Introduced: October 1938. Calendar-year registrations: [All Series] 169,457. Innovations: New carburetor. New Sedan Delivery. Partition added to Canopy Express models. *Chevrolet Service News* (Nov. 1938) introduced steering column gear shift for all passenger cars, including Sedan Delivery and Coupe-Pickup, as standard equipment. Chevrolet built and sold its two millionth truck in the 1939 model-year, which (including larger capacities) featured 45 models on eight wheelbases.

1940 CHEVROLET

1940 Chevrolet Model KH Sedan Delivery (OCW)

COMMERCIAL CARS — MODEL KB/KH — SIX-CYLINDER: This year's Sedan Delivery looked particularly handsome with its 1940 passenger car styling. It had a 65 x 55 x 41-in. cargo area and 34 x 34-in. rear door opening. It could be had with Knee-Action suspension for the first time. Its counterpart, the Coupe-Delivery, was available with Master DeLuxe trim on special order. A special left-hand taillight was required to show up when the removable box was carried. In its place, the conventional trunk lid could be substituted. The KB model "Master 85" commercial cars had Chevrolet's Special DeLuxe trim. The KH models had fancier Master DeLuxe trim.

1940 Chevrolet 1/2-Ton Model KC Pickup (DFW/R. McFarland)

1/2-TON LIGHT DELIVERY — MODEL KC — SIX-CYLINDER: Sealed beam headlights became a feature of 1940 Chevrolet trucks. Parking lights were now positioned on the fender. The top grille bar was wider than in 1939. A new dash panel, similar to that used on Chevrolet automobiles, was introduced for the trucks. The Pickup had a slightly longer, 78-in.-long load floor. Standard equipment on the Panel included insulated roof and side panels, an adjustable seat, a wood floor with steel skid rails, and latex-impregnated horsehair seat padding. Either a tailgate or double rear load doors could be had on the Suburban. The Canopy Express came with a tailgate that latched automatically when raised. Side curtains were standard on this model, but screen side equipment was optional.

1/2-TON DUBL-Duti — MODEL KP — SIX-CYLINDER: The Dubl-Duti Panel truck was introduced in *Chevrolet Service News* (April 1940). "With the addition of the new Dubl-Duti panel truck to the Chevrolet truck line, truck buyers will find many new and interesting features incorporated in its design. The chassis of the Dubl-Duti panel truck is the 1/2-ton truck chassis with a specially-reinforced frame, using the 3/4-ton truck rear axle ratio of 4.44:1 and the same carburetor and manifolds as used on the Cab-Over-Engine truck." This new line offered a forward-control chassis for a walk-in delivery truck. Bodies were supplied by various independent contractors. Some were factory-recommended. The term "Dubl-Duti" was used for many years to describe these. They were what we call Step-Vans today. They were similar to the trucks that UPS drivers use. The COE carburetor was used on the engine in these trucks since it was an updraft carburetor, which created a more compact engine "package" to build the "doghouse" around.

1940 Chevrolet 3/4-Ton Model KD Open Express (DFW/ASL)

3/4-TON LIGHT TRUCK — MODEL KD — SIX-CYLINDER: The 3/4-ton commercial trucks had the same general front end and cab styling updates as the 1/2-ton Light Delivery line with a wheelbase nearly 10 in. longer. The Pickup had a larger, express type cargo box and longer running boards. The Panel had larger dimensions. There was a Stake truck in this series, but no Suburban. Technical improvements included a 4.55:1 hypoid, semi-floating rear axle.

3/4-TON SPECIAL TRUCK — MODEL KE — SIX-CYLINDER: The KE models were a heavy-duty version of the JD 3/4-ton commercial models. They had larger wheels and brakes. Technical improvements included a 4.55:1 rear axle. These are called Special Commercial models.

1-TON MEDIUM-LIGHT TRUCK — MODEL KF — SIX-CYLINDER: This series consisted of a long wheelbase (133 in.) Panel using the 1-1/2-ton body with special lighter-duty tire equipment. It is mentioned in *Chevrolet Service News* (Oct. 1940) where the new 1941 models were described and compared to 1940 models. It said, "All 1941 Commercial, Heavy-Duty (1-1/2-ton) and Cab-Over-

Engine truck frames are 1-1/2 in. longer in keeping with a 1-1/2 in. increase in wheelbase to provide a longer and more comfortable driver's compartment. To maintain the same front axle position on the 3/4-ton long wheelbase Panel, Heavy-Duty, and Cab-Over-Engine models, the front spring hangers have been increased in length to compensate for the longer front springs." Basically, these trucks were described in a number of different ways. They were sometimes referred to as 3/4-ton models. Basically, they took the 1-1/2-ton frame off the shelf and hung lighter springs on it. So these look like 1-1/2-ton trucks, but have lighter springs and single 6.00 x 20-in. tires. The *1940 Truck Data Book for Chevrolet Salesmen* lists "1-ton Special tire equipment" on page 229 in the heavy-duty section.

1-TON MEDIUM-LIGHT TRUCK — MODEL WA-S (SPECIAL) — SIX-CYLINDER: According to the *1950 Chevrolet Master Parts Catalog* series WA trucks had a 133-in. wheelbase 1-1/2-ton chassis. The Chassis-with-Flat-Face Cowl, Chassis-and-Cab, and Panel models had two options of interest to light-duty truck collectors. Optional dual wheels were available at extra cost. Also optional was a 1-ton-rated version with eight-leaf rear springs, single rear wheels and 6.00 x 20 six-ply tires. These were technically WA-S models (the "S" most likely standing for "special"). There is no documentation that Series WA Canopy Express, Pickup, and Stake models offered the lighter-sprung WA-S option.

I.D. DATA: Serial number located on plate on right side of cowl under hood on trucks. The serial number consists of a group of numerals and letters which indicate the assembly plant, the model-year, the series, the month of assembly, and the number of units (plus 1,000) assembled at that plant. The first symbol indicates assembly plant: 1=Flint, Mich., 2=Tarrytown, N.Y., 3=St. Louis, Mo., 5=Kansas City, Kan., 6=Oakland, Calif., 8=Atlanta, Ga., 9=Norwood, Ohio, 14=Baltimore, Md., 20=Los Angeles, Calif., 21=Janesville, Wis. The second and third symbols indicate the model/series symbols. The fourth symbol indicates month of assembly: 01=Jan., 02=Feb., etc. Remaining numbers are the sequential unit production number. Each series is separately numbered in sequence beginning with 1001 at each plant. Last indicates month of manufacture. Serial numbers: [KB models]: KB-1001 to 20946, [KH models] KH-1001 to 37644, [KC models]: KC-1001 to 17658, [KP models] KP-1001 to 17658, [KD models] KD-1001 to 17658, [KF models] KF-1001 to 17658, [WA models] WA-1001 to 18041*. (*) was designation for Kentucky, Pennsylvania, North Carolina. Plate with letter S added. Engine number location same as 1939. Starting engine number: [KB, KH models] 2697268 to 3665902, [KC models] K-2697268 to 3665902, [KD models] AT-2697268 to 3665902, [ATB models] 105462 to 221935, [WA models] T-2697268 to 3665902, [TB models] 105462 to 221935.

1940 Chevrolet 1/2-Ton Model KC Pickup (E.F. Higgins)

Model	Body Type	Price	Weight	Prod. Total
Commercial Cars (Master 85/I-beam front axle) — Model KB — 113 in. w.b.				
KB	Sedan Delivery	694	2915	2590
KB	Coupe-Delivery	699	3025	538
Commercial Cars (Master DeLuxe/Knee-Action front axle) — Model KH — 113 in. w.b.				
KH	Sedan Delivery	719	2970	-
KH	Coupe-Delivery	725	3090	-
1/2-Ton Light Delivery — Model KC — 113.5 in. w.b.				
KC	Chassis	450	2195	-
KC	Chassis & Cab	541	2595	-
KC	Pickup	572	2840	-
KC	Panel	658	3050	-
KC	Canopy	694	3050	-
KC	Suburban	808	3300	-
1/2-Ton Dubl-Duti — Model KP — 113.5 in. w.b.				
KP	Walk-in	1028	3650	
3/4-Ton Light Truck — Model KD — 123.75 in. w.b.				
KD	Chassis	528	2355	-
KD	Chassis & Cab	619	2755	-
KD	Pickup	660	3110	-
KD	Platform	670	3150	-
KD	Stake	691	3330	-
KD	Panel	766	3325	-
1-Ton Commercial — Model KF — 133 in. w.b.				
KF	Panel	813	3700	-
1- to 1-1/2-Ton Light-Medium Truck — Model WA-S — 133 in. w.b.				
WA	Chassis	558	2940	-
WA	Chassis & Cab	649	3335	-
WA	Panel	826	3985	-

ENGINE: [Sedan Delivery] Inline. OHV. Six-cylinder. Cast-iron block. Bore & stroke: 3.5 x 3.75 in. Displacement: 216.5 cid. Compression ratio: 6.25:1. Brake horsepower: 85 at 3200 rpm. Net horsepower: 29.4. Torque: 170 lb.-ft. Four main bearings. Mechanical valve lifters. Carburetor: Carter one-barrel type W1. Same engine used in passenger cars. (Code T)
ENGINE: [All Other Trucks] Inline. OHV. Six-cylinder. Cast-iron block. Bore & stroke: 3.5 x 3.75 in. Displacement: 216.5 cid. Compression ratio: 6.25:1. Brake horsepower: 78 at 3200 rpm. Net horsepower: 29.4. Torque: 170 lb.-ft. Four main bearings. Mechanical valve lifters. Carburetor: Carter one-barrel type W1.
CHASSIS: [KB models] Wheelbase: 113 in. Tires: 6.00 x 16 four-ply.
CHASSIS: [KH models] Wheelbase: 113 in. Tires: 6.00 x 16 four-ply.
CHASSIS: [KC models] Wheelbase: 113-1/2 in. Overall length: 193 in. Tires: 6.00 x 16 four-ply.

CHASSIS: [KP models] Wheelbase: 113-1/2 in. Tires: 6.00 x 16 six-ply.
CHASSIS: [KD models] Wheelbase: 123-3/4 in. Tires: 7.50 x 15 six-ply.
CHASSIS: [KF models] Wheelbase: 133 in. Overall length: 208 in. Tires: 7.00 x 17 six-ply.
CHASSIS: [WA-S models] Wheelbase: 133 in. Tires: [front] 6.00 x 20 in. six-ply.
TECHNICAL: Manual transmission. Speeds: [KB] 3F/1R vacuum-assisted with steering column gear shift. [KC/KD] 3F/1R synchromesh with floor-mounted gear shift. [KE/WA-S models] 4F/1R non-synchromesh with floor-mounted gear shift. Diaphragm-spring type clutch. KBs and 1/2-ton had a nine-inch disc clutch. Larger trucks had an 10-3/4-in. clutch. [KB] Semi-floating rear axle with hypoid gears, [all other models except WA-S] semi-floating rear axle with spiral-bevel gears, [WA-S] Full-floating. Overall ratio: [KB] 3.73, [KC models] 4.11:1 (or 3.82), [Other models] 4.11. Hydraulic, four-wheel brakes. Steel short-spoke wheels.
OPTIONS: DeLuxe equipment. Rear bumper. Chrome trim rings. White sidewall tires. Outside rear view mirror(s). Bumper guards. Radio. Heater. Clock. Cigar lighter. Radio antenna. Seat covers. External sun shade. Spotlight. Two-tone paint. Special paint. Bumper step-pads. License plate frames. Fog lights. [Commercial Cars] Oversize tires on Master DeLuxe Coupe-Delivery. Knee-Action. Vacuum gear shift. Column-mounted gear control. [Suburban] Panel doors in lieu of tailgate. [Canopy Express] Screenside equipment.

1940 Chevrolet 1/2-Ton Model KC Pickup (DFW)

HISTORICAL: Introduced: October 1939. Calendar-year registrations: [All series] 185,636. Innovations: New Dubl-Duti package delivery truck added to 1/2-ton KP line. Knee-Action available on Sedan Delivery. Coupe-Pickup and Sedan Delivery have all-new styled body. The Foster Parents Plan for War Children purchased a number of Series KF 1-ton Panels fitted with dual rear wheels and special interiors for ambulance service and other wartime use in France and other parts of Europe.XXX (CR25 SCLT) 1934 Chevrolet 1/2-Ton Model EA/EC Canopy Top Pickup (DFW/SI)

1941 CHEVROLET

1941 Chevrolet Model AG Sedan Delivery (DFW/HTM)

SEDAN DELIVERY — MODEL AG — SIX-CYLINDER: A new front end treatment was found on the 1941 Coupe-Pickup and Sedan Delivery, both of which used current passenger car sheet metal and trim. Both were now on a three-inch. longer wheelbase. The Sedan Delivery had a usable load space measuring 66 in. long, 56 in. wide, and 41 in. high. Its rear door opening was 34 x 34 in. The same rear door panel was used on all 1941-1948 Sedan Deliveries. Standard features included Knee-Action front suspension, hydraulic shock absorbers front and rear, and vacuum-assisted gear shift. Interestingly, the Sedan Delivery used the same windshield as the four-door Sport Sedan, rather than the Station Wagon.
1/2-TON LIGHT DELIVERY — MODEL AK — SIX-CYLINDER: The 1941 models were easily identified by their new front end with fender-mounted headlight pods which were crowned by swept-back parking lights. The grille had two distinct sections. The upper unit was similar to the 1940 version . It had two thick horizontal bars capped by a top bar with a thin divider and a bottom bar with Chevrolet lettering. The remaining grille elements consisted of broad vertical bars sweeping outward from a center post carrying a Chevrolet logo. No hood ornament was fitted. Hood side trim consisted of a single horizontal chrome stripe extending backward from the upper grille region and three shorter horizontal stripes dividing the side hood louvers into three sections. A 115-in.-wheelbase made the new trucks larger. The base GVW rating for 1/2-ton models with 6.00 x 16 four-ply tires was 4,400 lb. It rose to 4,600 lb. with 6.00 x 16 six-ply tires.

1941 Chevrolet 1/2-Ton Model AK Pickup (R. Troutman)

1/2-TON DUBL-DUTI — MODEL AJ — SIX-CYLINDER: The Dubl-Duti package delivery truck chassis was moved to the new 115-in.-wheelbase. This forward-control truck chassis had a base 5,000 *-lb.* -lb. GVW. This model does not show up in all factory literature, but is clearly listed in the *NADA Truck Reference Book* (1950 edition). Standard bodies were sourced from factory-approved manufacturers or the buyer could add his own body.
3/4-TON LIGHT TRUCK — MODEL AL — SIX-CYLINDER: The 3/4-ton truck shared the year's new styling. The Pickup had an larger load box and longer running boards. Platform Stake and Panel models were also offered, along with a bare chassis and the Chassis-and-Cab. The standard GVW rating for trucks in this series was 5,200 lb.
3/4-TON HEAVY-DUTY — MODEL AM — SIX-CYLINDER: The 3/4-ton heavy-duty truck also shared the year's new styling. The Pickup had a larger load box and longer running boards. Platform Stake and Panel body models were also offered, along with a bare chassis and the Chassis-and-Cab. All had larger brakes, wheels and tires than AM models. The standard GVW rating for trucks in this series was 5,800 lb.
1-TON MEDIUM-LIGHT — MODEL AN — SIX-CYLINDER: The 1-ton series consisted of only a very large and long panel body truck called the Special Panel. It had a 134-1/2-in. wheelbase. The standard GVW rating for this model with 6.00 x 20 six-ply tires was 6,700 lb. The load is higher with optional tires or in an optional 1-1/2-ton configuration.
I.D. DATA: Serial number located: [Sedan Delivery] on right side of floor pan ahead of seat. [Cab models/Panels/Suburbans] on plate on right side of cowl under hood. [Chassis models] on plate temporarily attached near steering column, with final location per body maker. The first symbol indicated the assembly plant. 1=Flint, Mich., 2=Tarrytown, N.Y., 3=St. Louis, Mo., 5=Kansas City, Kan., 6=Oakland, Calif., 8=Atlanta, Ga., 9=Norwood, Ohio, 14=Baltimore, Md., 20=Los Angeles, Calif., and 21=Janesville, Wis. The second and third symbols indicate model/series as follows: AG=2100, AK=3100, AL=3600, AM=3600 (This model was called a 3/4-ton Special in sales department terminology), AN=3800 (This model was called a 3/4-ton Long Wheelbase Panel in sales department terminology). The fourth symbol indicates month of assembly. 01=Jan., 02=Feb., 03=March, 04=April, 05=May, 06=June, 07=July [end of 1941 model production, system changes]. The following symbols indicated the sequential production number. Each series was separately numbered in sequence, starting with 1001 at each assembly plant. Starting number: [AG] AG-1001 & up, [AK] AK-1001 & up, [AL] AL-1001 & up, [AN] AN-1001 & up, [AAN] AAN-1001 & up*, [AN] AN-1001 & up*. Engine number location: On right side of engine on boss just to rear of ignition distributor. Starting engine number: [AG] AA-1001 & up, [AJ] AM-1001 & up, [AK] AD-1001 & up, [AL/AN] AAF-1001 & up, [YR] AF-1001 & up. * For trucks built at Tonawanda.

1941 Chevrolet 1/2-Ton Model AK Pickup (Owner: Donald Laraway)

Model	Body Type	Price	Weight	Prod. Total
Commercial Car — Series AG — 116 in. w.b.				
AG	Sedan Delivery	748	3045	9918
AG	Coupe-Pickup	754	3195	1135
1/2-Ton Dubl-Duti — Model AJ — 115 in. w.b.				
AJ	Chassis	1058	3665	

Model	Body Type	Price	Weight	Prod. Total
1/2-Ton Light Delivery — Model AK — 115 in. w.b.				
AK	Chassis	478	2235	-
AK	Chassis & Cab	569	2630	-
AK	Pickup	600	2870	-
AK	Panel	686	3090	-
AK	Canopy	722	3090	-
AK	Suburban	837	3320	-
3/4-Ton Light Truck — Model AL — 125.25 in. w.b.				
AL	Chassis	556	2400	-
AL	Chassis & Cab	648	2795	-
AL	Pickup	689	3120	-
AL	Platform	699	3205	-
AL	Stake	719	3355	-
AL	Panel	795	3355	-

NOTE 1: Model designation AM used on 3/4-tons with heavy-duty chassis equipment.

1-Ton Medium-Light Truck — Model AN — 134.5 in. w.b.

AN	Special Panel	848	3770	-

1941 Chevrolet 1/2-Ton Model AK Pickup (Lowell E. Eisenhour photo)

ENGINE: Inline. OHV. Six-cylinder. Cast-iron block. Bore & stroke: 3-1/2 x 33/4 in. Displacement: 216.5 cid. Compression ratio: 6.5:1. Brake horsepower: 90 at 3300 rpm. Net horsepower: 29.4. Torque: 174 lb.-ft. at 1200-2000 rpm. Four main bearings. Mechanical valve lifters. Carburetor: Carter model W1-483S.
CHASSIS: [Model AG] Wheelbase: 116 in. Overall length: 195-3/4 in. Height: 65-7/8 in. Front tread: 57-5/8 in. Rear tread: 60.0 in. Tires: 6.00 x 16 four-ply.
CHASSIS: [Model AK] Wheelbase: 115 in. Overall length: 195-198 in. Tires: 6.00 x 16 four-ply.
CHASSIS: [Model AJ] Wheelbase: 115 in. Overall length: 195 in. Tires: 6.00 x 16 four-ply.
CHASSIS: [Model AL] Wheelbase: 125-1/4 in. Tires: 15 six-ply.
CHASSIS: [Model AM] Wheelbase: 125-1/4 in. Tires: 7.00 x 17 six-ply.
CHASSIS: [Model AN] Wheelbase: 134-1/2 in. Tires: 7.00 x 17 six-ply.

1941 Chevrolet 1/2-Ton Model AK Pickup (OCW)

TECHNICAL: Transmission type: [1-Ton] Four-speed manual with floor shift, [Others] three-speed synchromesh with vacuum-assisted column gear shift on Commercial Cars, floor-shift on trucks. Clutch: [3600-up] 10-3/4-in. diameter, [Others] 9-1/8-in. diameter. Shaft drive. Rear axle: [AG/AK/AL/AM] Semi-floating rear axle, [All others] full-floating rear axle. New for 1941 was an open Hotchkiss drive for 3/4-ton and 3/4-ton Special series. It incorporated the open propeller shaft and universal joints, and the rear spring seats were welded to the rear axle housing. There was still a short torque tube extending from the transmission to a hanger with the universal joint halfway back enclosing the front propeller shaft. Hydraulic, four-wheel brakes. Wheels: [AG/AJ/AK/AL] One-piece drop-center, [Others] Multi-piece split rims.
OPTIONS: [General, all] Chrome trim rings. White sidewall tires. Outside rear view mirror(s). Bumper guards. Radio. Heater. Clock. Cigar lighter. Radio antenna. Seat covers. External sun shade. Spotlight. Two-tone paint. Special paint. Oversize tires (standard on Suburban). License plate frames. Fog lights. [Light Deliveries/Trucks] Deluxe cab equipment. Rear bumper. [Canopy Express] Screenside equipment. [Coupe-Pickup] Bumper step-pads. [Coupe-Pickup/Sedan Delivery]. Master Deluxe trim. Vacuum gear shift. Column-mounted gear control.

1941 Chevrolet Model AG Master DeLuxe Coupe-Pickup (BMM)

HISTORICAL: Introduced: Sept. 1940. Calendar-year registrations: [All series] 212,797. Innovations: Knee-Action becomes standard on Sedan Delivery. Double doors not listed as regular equipment for Suburban. All-new grille design for trucks. Longer wheelbases for small trucks. It appears that 1941 was a unique year in that the 134-1/2-in. wheelbase Panel came in both a long 3/4-ton chassis with 17-in. tires (called the 3/4-ton Special Long or AN model) or a light 1-1/2-ton chassis with 20-in. tires (part of series YR). According to Bob Adler, both of these trucks shared the same body. Adler notes that the 1941 *Chevrolet Truck Shop Manual* (page 52) says, "The 3/4-ton long wheelbase Panel and 134-1/2-in. wheelbase 1-1/2-ton truck frames are identical, with the exception to a slight difference in the brake cross shaft bracket. Each frame has five cross members." In addition, the section modulus for both long 3/4-ton frames and short 1-1/2-ton frames are 5.41-in. cubed. This reinforces Adler's opinion that the 1-1/2-ton frame was used for the long wheelbase 1-ton Panel. "Throughout the 1941 shop manual, there is no mention of a 1-ton truck," says Adler. "It discusses the 3/4- and 3/4-ton Special, then jumps up to the 1-1/2-ton. The 1942 shop manual does likewise. Also, the 3/4-ton long wheelbase Panel takes the 4.55:1 ratio semi-floating rear axle, indicating this is a 3/4-ton rear end. I find it interesting that there is no reference or illustration of eight-lug wheels in 1941. All wheels used on trucks below 1-1/2 ton are six-lug types and all 1-1/2-ton wheels have 10 lugs."

1942 CHEVROLET
(Early Series)

COMMERCIAL CAR — MODEL BG/SERIES 1500 — SIX-CYLINDER: The Commercial Car series included a Sedan Delivery. The Stylemaster Business Coupe was also considered part of this series when equipped with an optional, slide-in-the-trunk cargo box. Both models had the new "American Eagle" grille used on 1942 passenger cars. It was a heavier-looking design with lower and wider horizontal chrome bars. There was also a lower, longer and more massive body appearance, longer and deeper front fenders and a longer, larger hood. A splash shield was added between the bumper and grille. Parking lights were built into the grille, instead of mounted on the fenders. A stronger, deeper-crowned bumper was fitted. Technical changes included heavier front coil springs, improved front wheel bearings, larger flywheel bolts, an improved accelerator, and a redesigned headlamp switch. Both models remained on a 116-in. wheelbase. The Sedan Delivery had a usable load space measuring 66 in. long, 56 in. wide, and 41 in. high. Its rear door opening was 34 x 34 in. The same rear door panel was used on all 1941-1948 Sedan Deliveries. The windshield was the same one specified for the four-door Sport Sedan. Standard features included Knee-Action front suspension, hydraulic shock absorbers front and rear. Even though Chevrolet did not promote a truck tonnage rating for the Sedan Delivery, this year the company made a heavy-duty truck clutch optional. Its use was indicated with a BY engine prefix. In addition, a deep oil pan, better suited for climbing 45 percent grades, became a Central Office Production Option (COPO).

1942 Chevrolet Model BK Pickup (OCW)

1/2-TON LIGHT DELIVERY — MODEL BK/SERIES 3100 — SIX-CYLINDER: The 1942 Chevrolet trucks had the 1941-style front end. The grille had two distinct sections. The upper grille had two horizontal bars curving around the nose. The bottom grille elements consisted of broad vertical bars sweeping outward from a center post carrying a Chevrolet logo. Grilles and trim moldings were painted from the start of 1942 production. Side hood trim consisted of a single horizontal stripe extending backward from the upper grille region and three shorter horizontal stripes dividing the side hood louvers into three sections. The headlamps were fender-mounted with parking lights on top of them. No hood ornament was fitted. A 115-in. wheelbase was used again. The base GVW rating for 1/2-ton models climbed back up to 4,400 lb. with standard four-ply tires.

1/2-TON DUBL-DUTI — MODEL BJ/SERIES 3100 — SIX-CYLINDER: The forward-control Dubl-Duti package delivery truck chassis remained on the 115-in. wheelbase. It had a base 5,000-lb. GVW. Standard bodies were sourced from factory-approved manufacturers, or the buyer could add his own.

1942 Chevrolet 3/4-Ton Model BL Pickup (OCW)

3/4-TON LIGHT TRUCK — MODEL BL/SERIES 3600 — SIX-CYLINDER: The 3/4-ton truck shared the year's new styling. The Pickup had an larger load box and longer running boards. Platform Stake and Panel body models were also offered, along with a bare chassis and the Chassis-and-Cab. The standard GVW rating for trucks in this series was 5,200 lb.

3/4-TON HEAVY-DUTY — MODEL BM/SERIES 3600 — SIX-CYLINDER: Series BM coding was used for 3/4-tons with heavy-duty equipment. They had larger brakes, wheels, and tires.

1-TON MEDIUM-LIGHT — MODEL BN/SERIES 3800 — SIX-CYLINDER: The 1-ton series consisted of only a very large panel body truck called the Special Panel. The standard GVW rating for trucks in this series was 5,800 lb.

I.D. DATA: Serial number located: [Sedan Delivery] on right side of floor pan ahead of seat. [Cab models/Panels/Suburbans] on plate on right side of cowl under hood. [Chassis models] on plate temporarily attached near steering column, with final location per body maker. The first symbol indicated the assembly plant: 1=Flint, Mich., 2=Tarrytown, N.Y., 3=St. Louis, Mo., 5=Kansas City, Kan., 6=Oakland, Calif. 8=Atlanta, Ga., 9=Norwood, Ohio, 14=Baltimore, Md., 20=Los Angeles, Calif., and 21=Janesville, Wis. The second and third symbols indicate model/series as follows: BG=1500, BK=3100, BL=3600, BM=3600 (This model was called a 3/4-ton Special in sales department terminology), BN=3800 (This model was called a 3/4-ton Long Wheelbase Panel in sales department terminology). The fourth and fifth symbols indicate month of assembly. Due to unusual circumstances during World War II, Chevrolet had to modify its date code system to identify "1942 models" built in 1941-1943 (civilian and military) and 1944-1945 (civilian). The 1942 trucks assembled late in 1941 had the month codes: 08=August, 09=September, 10=October, 11=November, 12=December. Codes for units built early in 1942 were 01=Jan., 02=Feb., 03=March, 04=April, 05=May, 06=June, 07=July. For trucks made in late 1942, the month codes were determined by adding 12 months to the codes used on late 1941 models and were: 20=August, 21=September, 22=October, 23=November, 24=December. For trucks made in early 1943, the month codes were determined by adding 12 months to the codes used on early 1942 models and were: 13=Jan., 14=Feb., 15=March, 16=April, 17=May, 18=June, 19=July. For trucks made in late 1943, the month codes were determined by adding 12 months to the codes used on late 1942 models and were: 32=August, 33=September, 34=October, 35=November, 36=December. (Chevrolet engineering bulletins do not specifically indicate any light-duty truck production during 1943, but we assume the same coding was used on big trucks built for the military). This modified system was used through 1945. The symbols following the date code were the sequential production number. Each series was separately numbered in sequence, starting with 1001 at each assembly plant. Starting number: Serial numbers starting: [BG] 2AA-1001 and up, [BJ] 2AM-1001 and up, [BK] 2AD-1001 and up, [BL] 2AAF-1001 and up, [BN] 2AAF-1001 and up. Engine number location: On right side of engine on a boss just to the rear of the ignition distributor. Starting engine number: [BG] BA-1001 and up, [BJ] BM-1001 and up, [BK] BD-1001 and up, [BL] ABF-1001 and up, [BN] ABF-1001 and up. Note: Some engines with 1941 engine numbers were used in 1942 trucks. These have a 2 stamped ahead of the regular engine prefix.

1942 Chevrolet 1/2-Ton Model DP Panel (OCW)

Model	Body Type	Price	Weight	Prod. Total
Commercial Car — Model BG — 116 in. w.b.				
BG	Sedan Delivery	853	3080	2996
BG	Coupe-Pickup	865	3230	206
1/2-Ton Light Delivery — Model BK — 115 in. w.b.				
BK	Chassis	536	2235	-
BK	Chassis & Cab	629	2630	-
BK	Pickup	660	2870	-
BK	Panel	748	3090	-
BK	Canopy	785	3085	-
BK	Suburban	905	3320	-
1/2-Ton Dubl-Duti — Model BJ — 115 in. w.b.				
BJ	Chassis	1127	3665	-
3/4-Ton Light Truck — Model BL — 125.25 in. w.b.				
BL	Chassis	617	2400	-
BL	Chassis & Cab	710	2795	-
BL	Pickup	752	3120	-
BL	Platform	763	3205	-
BL	Stake	783	3355	-
BL	Panel	860	3355	-

NOTE 1: BM designation was used for 3/4-ton trucks with heavy-duty equipment.

1-Ton Light-Medium Truck — Model BN — 134.5 in. w.b.				
BN	Panel	915	3770	-

ENGINE: Inline. OHV. Six-cylinder. Cast-iron block. Bore & stroke: 3-1/2 x 3-3/4 in. Displacement: 216.5 cid. Compression ratio: 6.50:1. Brake horsepower: 90 at 3300 rpm. Net horsepower: 29.4. Four main bearings. Mechanical valve lifters. Carburetor: Carter type W-1, downdraft, one-barrel Model 839534.

CHASSIS: [Model BG] Wheelbase: 116 in. Tires: 6.00 x 16 four-ply.
CHASSIS: [Model BJ] Wheelbase: 115 in. Tires: 6.00 x 16 six-ply.
CHASSIS: [Model BK] Wheelbase: 115 in. Tires: 6.00 x 16 four-ply.
CHASSIS: [Model BL] Wheelbase: 125.25 in. Tires: 15-in. six-ply.
CHASSIS: [Model BM] Wheelbase: 125.25 in. Tires: 6.00 x 15 six-ply.
CHASSIS: [Model BN] Wheelbase: 134.5 in. Tires: 7.00 x 17 six-ply. (7.50x17 eight-ply optional).

TECHNICAL: Transmission type: [1-Ton] Four-speed manual with floor shift, [Others] three-speed synchromesh with vacuum-assisted column gear shift on Commercial Cars, floor-shift on trucks. Clutch: [3600-up] 10-3/4-in. diameter, [Others] 9-1/8-in. diameter. Shaft drive. Rear axle: Semi-floating. Hydraulic, four-wheel brakes. Wheels: [15-in. and 16-in.] One-piece drop center, [17-in. and 20-in.] Multi-piece split rims.

OPTIONS: [General, all] Chrome trim rings. White sidewall tires. Outside rear view mirror(s). Bumper guards. Radio. Heater. Clock. Cigar lighter. Radio antenna. Seat covers. External sun shade. Spotlight. Two-tone paint. Special paint. Over-size tires (standard on Suburban). License plate frames. Fog lights. [Light Deliveries/Trucks] Deluxe cab equipment. Rear bumper. [Canopy Express] Screenside equipment. [Suburban] Double rear doors in place of tailgate. [Coupe-Pickup] Bumper step-pads. [Coupe-Pickup/Sedan Delivery] Master Deluxe trim.

HISTORICAL: Introduced: October, 1941. Calendar-year production [Trucks up to 1-ton] 119,077 (This does not include Sedan Deliveries). Innovations: New styling and trim for passenger car based commercial vehicles. Regular panel door option for Suburban reinstated. Black-out trim used on late-production models. Civilian truck production ended in January 1942, with America's entry into World War II. Chevrolet was later given permission to produce trucks for high-priority civilian use. This allowed more BK/BL/BN trucks to be built on a limited basis between Jan. 1, 1944 and Aug. 31, 1945. Factory literature indicates that Chevrolet's engineering department called these "1942" models. However, it's likely that they were sold/titled as new models in the calendar-year they were purchased, either 1944 or 1945. All Chevrolet plants participated in the war effort, except the Saginaw service and manufacturing facility, which was used to supply replacement parts for trucks on the road at that time. Chevrolet changed the date coding system used in the truck serial numbers so that military trucks built in 1942-1943 and civilian trucks built in 1944-1945 could be dated to the month of manufacture. This was the last year that the Coupe-Pickup model was offered.

1944-1945 CHEVROLET
(1942-Late)

1/2-TON LIGHT DELIVERY — MODEL BK/SERIES 3100 — SIX-CYLINDER: Production of a limited line of Chevrolet trucks for the civilian market started up again Jan. 1, 1944. It represented a continuation of the 1942 series. Chevrolet engineering department bulletins refer to these as 1942 models. However, the trucks were titled in the calendar-years that they were built and sold (1944-1945). Date codes in the serial number can be used to determine which year and month a truck was built. In the under 1-ton category, this was a continuation of the 1942 conventional trucks Models BK, BL and BN. Larger conventionals, buses and COE trucks were also put back into production. Styling and features were unchanged from 1942, except that all (or nearly all) of the 1944-1945 (and early 1946) trucks came with painted grilles, bumpers, hubcaps and hood trim. Most were painted Turret Gray. White, Cream, Yellow, and Orange finishes were also available.

3/4-TON LIGHT TRUCK — MODEL BL/SERIES 3600 — SIX-CYLINDER: The 3/4-ton truck returned to production. The Pickup had an larger load box and longer running boards. Platform Stake and Panel body models were also offered, along with a bare Chassis model and the Chassis-and-Cab. The standard GVW rating for trucks in this series was 5,200 lb.

3/4-TON HEAVY-DUTY — MODEL BM/SERIES 3600 — SIX-CYLINDER: Series BM coding was used for 3/4-tons with heavy-duty equipment.

1-TON MEDIUM-LIGHT — MODEL BN/SERIES 3800 — SIX-CYLINDER: The 1-ton series consisted of only a very large panel body truck called the Special Panel. The standard GVW rating for trucks in this series was 5,800 lb.

I.D. DATA: Serial number located: [Cab models/Panels/Suburbans] on plate on right side of cowl under hood. [Chassis models] on plate temporarily attached near steering column, with final location per body maker. The first symbol indicated the assembly plant: 1=Flint, Mich., 2=Tarrytown, N.Y., 3=St. Louis, Mo., 5=Kansas City, Kan., 6=Oakland, Calif., 8=Atlanta, Ga., 9=Norwood, Ohio, 14=Baltimore, Md., 20=Los Angeles, Calif., and 21=Janesville, Wis. The second and third symbols indicate model/series as follows: BK=3100, BL=3600, BN=3800 (This model was called a 3/4-ton Long Wheelbase Panel in sales department terminology). The fourth and fifth symbols indicate month of assembly. Due to unusual circumstances during World War II, Chevrolet had to modify its date code system to identify "1942 models" built in 1944-1945 (civilian). For trucks made in early 1944, the month codes were determined by adding 12 months to the codes used on early 1943 models and were: 25=Jan., 26=Feb., 27=March, 28=April, 29=May, 30=June, 31=July. For trucks made in late 1944, the month codes were determined by adding 12 months to the codes used on late 1943 models and were: 44=August, 45=September, 46=October, 47=November, 48=December. For trucks made in early 1945, the month codes were determined by adding 12 months to the codes used on early 1944 models and were: 37=Jan., 38=Feb., 39=March, 40=April, 41=May, 42=June, 43=July. (A new series went into production in August, 1945 and the month codes changed to the regular Chevrolet system.) The numbers following the date codes indicated the sequential production number. Each series was separately numbered in sequence, starting with 1001 at each assembly plant. Starting number: Serial numbers starting: [BK] BK-2127 up, [Others] not available. Engine number location: On right side of engine on boss just to rear of ignition distributor. Starting engine numbers BG-580921 up.

Model	Body Type	Price	Weight	Prod. Total
1/2-Ton Light Delivery — Series 3100/Model BK — 115 in. w.b.				
BK	Pickup	757	2870	-
3/4-Ton Light Truck — Series 3600/Model BL — 125.25 in. w.b.				
BL	Chassis	617	2400	-
BL	Chassis & Cab	710	2795	-
BL	Pickup	752	3120	-
BL	Platform	763	3205	-
BL	Stake	783	3355	-
BL	Panel	860	3355	-

NOTE 1: BM designation was used for 3/4-ton trucks with heavy-duty equipment.

1-Ton — Light-Medium Truck — Series 3800/Model BN — 134.5 in. w.b.

BN	Special Panel			

NOTE 2: List prices authorized by Office of Price Administration (OPA).
NOTE 3: Higher prices allowed for synthetic tires after April 18, 1944.
NOTE 4: Most sources list only 3100 Pickup.
NOTE 5: Chevrolet references indicate 3600/3800 trucks also built.
ENGINE: Inline. OHV. Six-cylinder. Cast-iron block. Bore & stroke: 3-1/2 x 33/4 in. Displacement: 216.5 cid. Compression ratio: 6.50:1. Brake horsepower: 90 at 3300 rpm. Net horsepower: 29.4. Four main bearings. Mechanical valve lifters. Carburetor: Carter type W-1, downdraft, one-barrel model 839534.
CHASSIS: [Model BK] Wheelbase: 115 in. Tires: 6.50 x 16 four-ply.
CHASSIS: [Model BL] Wheelbase: 125.25 in. Tires: 15-in. six-ply.
CHASSIS: [Model BM] Wheelbase: 125.25 in. Tires: 7.00 x 17 six-ply.
CHASSIS: [Model BN] Wheelbase: 134.5 in. Tires: 7.00 x 17 six-ply. (7.50x17 eight-ply optional.)
TECHNICAL: Transmission type: [1-Ton] Four-speed manual with floor shift, [Others] three-speed synchromesh with vacuum-assisted column gear shift on Commercial Cars, floor-shift on trucks. Clutch: [3600-up] 10-3/4-in. diameter, [Others] 9-1/8-in. diameter. Shaft drive. Rear axle: [BK] Semi-floating. [All others] full-floating rear axle. Overall drive ratio: 3.73:1. Hydraulic, four-wheel brakes. Wheels: [BK] Single-piece drop center rims, [Others] Multi-piece split rims.
OPTIONS: Outside rear view mirror(s). Bumper guards. Heater. Seat covers. Special paint. Fog lights. Rear bumper.
HISTORICAL: After a massive national mobilization, production of nearly all military vehicles for World War II was completed in 1943. Chevrolet then got permission to put the 1942 models back into limited production to turn out trucks for essential users on the homefront. Chevrolet factory records show that BK (1/2-ton), BL (3/4-ton) and BN (1-ton) trucks were built between Jan. 1, 1944 and Aug. 31, 1945. The Coupe-Pickup and Sedan Delivery were discontinued. The Sedan Delivery would be reintroduced as a May, 1946 addition to the new line of Chevrolet passenger cars that debuted on Oct. 30, 1945. Chevrolet factory literature indicates that the Dubl-Duti models did not go back into production until after May 31, 1947.

1946 CHEVROLET
(Interim Series)

1946 Chevrolet 1/2-Ton Model CK Pickup (OCW)

1/2-TON COMMERCIAL — MODEL CK/SERIES 3100 — SIX-CYLINDER: Between Sept. 1, 1945 and May 1, 1946 Chevrolet built a line of trucks that were called "Interim" models. Factory service bulletins said, "These are not to be considered postwar models, but they do represent a continuation of the regular 1942 lines, which are being produced under War Production Board (WPB) authorization from Sept. 1, 1942 to the release of the postwar models." These trucks had no significant changes from the 1942 BK/BL/BM light-duty trucks. In fact, they continued to come with painted grilles, bumpers, hubcaps and hood trim. Paint color choices were unchanged. Turret Gray was the color most often seen. Factory nomenclature was slightly modified to favor use of the term Commercial over Light Delivery, although the latter was still seen in technical service bulletins.
I.D. DATA: Serial number located: [Cab models/Panels/Suburbans] on plate on right side of cowl under hood. [Chassis models] on plate temporarily attached near steering column, with final location per body maker. The first symbol indicated the assembly plant: 1=Flint, Mich., 2=Tarrytown, N.Y., 3=St. Louis, Mo., 5=Kansas City, Kan., 6=Oakland, Calif., 8=Atlanta, Ga., 9=Norwood, Ohio, 14=Baltimore, Md., 20=Los Angeles, Calif., and 21=Janesville, Wis. The second and third symbols indicate model/series as follows: CK=3100. (This model was called a 3/4-ton Long Wheelbase Panel in sales department terminology. The fourth and fifth symbols indicate month of

assembly: 09=September, 10=October, 11=November, 12=December, 1=January (1946), 2=February (1946), 3=March (1946), 4=April (1946). The numbers following the date codes indicated the sequential production number. Each series was separately numbered in sequence, starting with 1001 at each assembly plant. Starting number: [CK] 1001 up. Engine number on right side of engine block behind fuel pump.

Model	Body Type	Price	Weight	Prod. Total
1/2-Ton Commercial — Model CK/Series 3100 — 115 in. w.b.				
CK	Chassis	637	2235	-
CK	Chassis & Cab	727	2630	-
CK	Pickup	757	2870	-
CK	Panel	842	3090	-
CK	Suburban (door)	987	3320	-
CK	Suburban (gate)	987	3330	-
CK	Canopy	877	3085	-

ENGINE: Inline. OHV. Six-cylinder. Cast-iron block. Bore & stroke: 3-1/2 x 33/4 in. Displacement: 216.5 cid. Compression ratio: 6.5:1. Brake horsepower: 90 at 3300 rpm. Net horsepower: 29.4. Four main bearings. Mechanical valve lifters. Carburetor: Downdraft one-barrel model W1-574S.
CHASSIS: [Model CK] Wheelbase: 115 in. Overall length: 198 in. (Suburban). Tires: 6.00 x 16.
TECHNICAL: Manual transmission. Speeds: 3F/1R. Floor-mounted gearshift. [Model CK] Semi-floating rear axle, [all others] full-floating rear axle. Single disc clutch, 9-1/8 in. Four-wheel hydraulic brakes. Wheels: [CK] One-piece drop center rims.
OPTIONS: Double-acting shock absorbers (No. 200). Economy rear axle (No. 201). Low rear axle ratio (No. 205). Long running boards and rear fenders (No. 207). Rear view mirrors and brackets (No. 210). Panel type rear bumper (No. 213). Spare wheel and tire carrier (No. 215). Oil bath air cleaner (No. 216). Heavy-duty clutch (No. 227). Screenside equipment for Canopy Express (No. 228). Frame extensions (No. 232). Paint Options (No. 234 for Commercial Trucks only):

RPO	Basic Color	Body/Hood/Radiator Shell Molding Color	Body/Hood/Rad. Shell Molding Stripe Color
Standard	Brewster Green	Kildare Green	Emerald Green
234-A	Swift's Red	Mayland Black	Gold Bronze
234-B	Armour Yellow	Omaha Orange	Mayland Black
234-C	Apple Green	Cream Medium	Emerald Green
234-D	Cream Medium	Export Blue	Argent Silver
234-E	Export Blue	Argent Silver	Totem Scarlet
234-F	Omaha Orange	Chess Blue	White
234-G	Hollywood Tan (1)	Mayland Black	White
234-H	Airdale Brown (2) Circassian Brown	Kildare Green	White
234-J	Bordeaux Maroon	Mayland Black	Gold Bronze
234-K	Black (3)	Emerald Green	Cream Medium
234-L	White	Kildare Green	White
234-M	Boatswain Blue	Argent Silver	Totem Scarlet

NOTE 1: Hollywood Tan finish only on trucks assembled at the Oakland, Calif. factory.
NOTE 2: This two-tone combination used on Suburbans only. The Airdale Brown color was used only on the side and rear window panels.
NOTE 3: Black was the regular color on all fenders, but fenders were done in basic body color upon request.
NOTE 4: 1/2-Ton Light-Duty Commercial Specifications for 1946 indicates the body belt line, hood, and radiator shell moldings are painted a contrasting color to the body and then, within the belt line, a pinstripe is then applied. The Truck Data Book has a similar chart on page 311. Chevy truck expert Bob Adler is unsure if this was done in earlier years, but it was not used on Advance-Design trucks.

Oil filter (No. 237). Governor (No. 241). Bumper guards (No. 245). Master grille guard for radiator (No. 247). Dual tail and stop lamp equipment (No. 249). Rear fender irons (No. 250). Heavy-duty cooling system (No. 256). Sun shade interior visors (No. 261). Right-hand front seat (No. 263). Double-acting rear springs (No. 268). Radiator overflow return tank (No. 271). Heavy-duty three-speed transmission (316). Heavy-duty four-speed transmission (No. 317). Sign panel (No. 351). Right-hand windshield wiper (No. 320). Tru-stop brake equipment (348). DeLuxe platform body skirt (No. 353). Rear bumper (No. 357).

HISTORICAL: Production began Sept. 1, 1945 and ended May 1, 1946. Calendar-year production: [All, except Sedan Delivery] 270,140 (not limited to CK models). Market share: 28.567 percent. Innovations: M.E. Coyle was elevated to a new position as executive vice-president of General Motors Corporation. Cadillac general manager Nicholas Dreystadt was appointed to Coyle's former position as president of Chevrolet.

1946 CHEVROLET
(Late Series)

SEDAN DELIVERY — MODEL DJ/SERIES 1500 — SIX-CYLINDER: Production of 1946 Chevrolet passenger cars started very soon after World War II ended. A Chevrolet Technical Service Bulletin of Oct. 30, 1945 announced the new Stylemaster 1500s (serial prefix DJ) and Fleetmaster 2000 (serial prefix DK) models. However, it was not until May, 1946 that the Sedan Delivery was brought back as a running addition in the Stylemaster DJ line. The Coupe-Pickup did not return, although this model is listed in some early postwar used car guides. Perhaps Chevrolet considered bringing it back, then decided not to. Essentially, the Stylemaster models were updated 1942 Master Deluxe models. The grille was modified, the parking lamps were relocated and chrome-plated trim returned. The Sedan Delivery continued to share the windshield of the four-door Sport Sedan. Its rear panel door was the same part used on 1942 Sedan Deliveries.

1946 Chevrolet 1/2-Ton Model DP Pickup (OCW)

1/2-TON LIGHT-DUTY COMMERCIAL — MODEL DP/SERIES 3100 — SIX-CYLINDER: A new series of light-duty trucks started production May 1, 1946. These were officially considered the first postwar models. However, they still had the prewar appearance. Chevrolet promoted many refinements, saying, "To help refill the war-depleted highways of America as soon as possible, Chevrolet presents, with no engineering delay, new lines of time-tested trucks for 1946. Based on the 1941 model vehicles, our last truly prewar trucks and the best-designed trucks Chevrolet has ever manufactured heretofore, the new trucks are improved by the experience gained in five years of developing military trucks, five years of intense research in materials, five years of study of the operation of Chevrolet trucks on the largest proving ground in the world...the highways of America...in the particularly tough job of war transportation." There was said to be a general refinement of design to make all trucks more efficient, stronger and more durable. These trucks (unlike the 1946 Interim models) had the 1941 style polished chrome grille with curved horizontal front hood louvers and vertical bars in the lower radiator grille. The bottom of the front hood louver had molding stripes accented with Swift's Red. It also had Chevrolet lettering painted in red enamel. At the top of the center bar in the radiator grille was a chrome badge with red and blue baking Dulux enamel finish. A polished chrome plate regular front bumper (curved-type) was standard. The similar polished chrome plate rear bumper was standard on all 3100s as well. Other bright-finished parts included outside door handles, a windshield division molding, cab assist handles, headlamp rims, and taillamp rims. Front and rear hubcaps with chrome plating were standard. The 3100 hubcaps had small blue Chevrolet letters surrounded by blue speed lines and red-painted "hood ornament" decorations. Standard features for all 3100s marked a return to 1941 equipment levels and included Synco-perlite beige-finished metal panels in driver's compartment, hair and cotton seat cushion pads, rubber floor mats, rubber anti-squeak and sealing parts, improved windshield and window glass sealing, all-rubber windshield wiper hoses, more secure rear door weather-strips, more durable side door locks, check links and window sash channels, more comfortable, reshaped and reconstructed cab seat and back cushions with more attractive and durable plastic (vinyl resin) upholstery, and double-laced seat cushion springs with filled-in tops. Paint colors included Brewster Green, Apple Green, White, Omaha Orange, Hollywood Tan (Oakland factory only), Bordeaux Maroon (Tarrytown and Baltimore only), Swift's Red, Medium Cream, Armour Yellow, Export Blue, and Boatswain Blue. An Airdale Brown and Circassian Brown combination was available for the Suburban. Black was the regular color for all fenders, which could be painted body color when requested. The 1/2-ton Dubl-Duti truck was discontinued. All 1/2-ton 3100s had a 4,600 -lb. -lb. GVW rating.

1946 Chevrolet 1/2-Ton Model DP Pickup (OCW)

3/4-TON LIGHT-DUTY COMMERCIAL — MODEL DR/SERIES 3600 — SIX-CYLINDER: The 3/4-ton trucks had a longer wheelbase. The Pickup load box was longer and had more stake pockets. Long running boards were used. No Suburban was offered in this line. There were Platform and Stake models. Hubcaps were larger and had only red Chevrolet lettering. The regular curved-type chrome bumper was standard on all models. The regular chrome rear bumper was standard on all except the Platform and Stake models. Base tires on 3600s were 15 in. six-ply-rated on 15 x 5.50 semi-drop center rims. There were numerous tire options. The 3/4-ton heavy-duty model was discontinued. Standard GVWs for these trucks were 5,200 to 5,800 lb.

1-TON COMMERCIAL — MODEL DS/SERIES 3800 — SIX-CYLINDER: The Special Panel (Model 3805) was continued and more 1-ton models were added. This line now had a full range of models including an Express (large Pickup), Panel, Canopy, Platform and Stake. The Platform and Stake were also available with dual rear wheels. General styling and features were the same as on 3100/3600 models. The Express had a longer wheelbase than the 3600 Pickup, plus longer running boards, and a longer load box with extra stake pockets. A chrome-plated hood louver and radiator grille were standard. A regular curved-type chrome front bumper was standard on Pickup, Panel and Canopy models. A heavy-duty, channel section front bumper was standard for chassis models and Platform and Stake trucks. A regular chrome rear bumper was standard on Panels and Canopy models only. The standard tires were 7.00 x 17 six-ply rated for trucks with single rear wheels or 7.00 x 18 eight-ply rated for trucks with dual rear wheels. They were mounted on new wider five-inch rims of advanced design. There were many tire and wheel options. Hubcaps were shared with 3600s and had only red Chevrolet lettering. No hubcaps were fitted on the 18 x 5 in. wheels used for the Chassis-and-Cab, Platform and Stake models, which had eight bolts and eight circular openings. The standard GVWs for these trucks was 6,000-6,700 lb. (depending on tire options) with single rear wheels, or 8,800 lb. with a new dual rear wheels option. A four-speed manual transmission was standard.

1946 Chevrolet 1/2-Ton Model DP Pickup (P. George)

I.D. DATA: Serial number located: [Sedan Delivery] On right hinge pillar about nine inches above the rocker panel. [Cab models/Panels/Suburbans] on plate on right side of cowl under hood. [Chassis models] on plate temporarily attached near steering column, with final location per body maker. The first symbol indicated the assembly plant: 1=Flint, Mich., 2=Tarrytown, N.Y., 3=St. Louis, Mo., 5=Kansas City, Kan., 6=Oakland, Calif., 8=Atlanta, Ga., 9=Norwood, Ohio, 14=Baltimore, Md., 20=Los Angeles, Calif., and 21=Janesville, Wis. The second and third symbols indicate model prefix/series as follows: DJ=Series 1500, DP=3100, DR=3600, DS=3800. The fourth symbol indicates month of assembly: A=Jan., B=Feb., etc. The following symbols indicated the sequential production number. Each series was separately numbered in sequence, starting with 1001 at each assembly plant: [DJ] DJ-1001 and up, [DP] DP-1001 and up, [DR] DR-1001 and up, [DS] DS-1001 and up. Engine number location: Engine number on right side of engine block to the rear of the distributor.

1946 Chevrolet 1/2-Ton Model DP Suburban (OCW)

1946 Chevrolet 1/2-Ton Model DP Pickup (OCW)

1946 Chevrolet 1/2-Ton Model DP Pickup (A. Kaylor)

Model	Body Type	Price	Weight	Prod. Total
Sedan Delivery — Model DJ/Series 1500 — 116 in. w.b.				
1508	Sedan Delivery	1173	3135	-
1/2-Ton Commercial — Model DP/Series 3100 — 115 in. w.b.				
3102	Chassis	796	2300	-
3103	Chassis & Cab	922	2680	-
3104	Pickup	963	2925	-
3105	Panel	1077	3145	-
3107	Canopy	1126	3135	-
3106	Suburban (door)	1283	3370	-
3116	Suburban (gate)	1281	3385	-
3112	Chassis & W/S	817	2350	-
3/4-Ton Commercial — Model DR/Series 3600 — 125.25 in. w.b.				
3602	Chassis	891	2495	-
3603	Chassis & Cab	1016	2890	-
3604	Pickup	1069	3215	-
3605	Panel	1212	3450	-
3608	Platform	1101	3300	-
3609	Stake	1127	3450	-
3612	Chassis & W/S	911	2545	-
1-Ton Commercial — Model DS/Series 3800 — 134.5 in. w.b.				
[Single Rear Wheels]				
3802	Chassis	892	2835	-
3803	Chassis & Cab	-	3560	-
3812	Chassis & W/S	914	2885	-
3804	Express	1139	4095	-
3805	Panel	1264	4080	-
3807	Canopy	1318	4095	-
3808	Platform	-	4065	-
3809	Stake	-	4315	-
[Dual Rear Wheels]				
3803	Chassis & Cab	1106	3560	-
3808	Platform	1200	4065	-
3809	Stake	1235	4315	-

ENGINE: Inline. OHV. Six-cylinder. Cast-iron block. Bore & stroke: 3-1/2 x 3-3/4 in. Displacement: 216.5 cid. Compression ratio: 6.5:1. Brake horsepower: 90 at 3300 rpm. NACC horsepower: 29.4. Four main bearings. Mechanical valve lifters. Carburetor: Carter downdraft one-barrel model W1-616S.
CHASSIS: [Model DJ] Wheelbase: 116 in. Tires: 6.00 x 16 four-ply.
CHASSIS: [Model DP] Wheelbase: 115 in. Tires: 6.00 x 16 six-ply.
CHASSIS: [Model DR] Wheelbase: 125.25 in. Tires: 15 in. six-ply.
NOTE 1: What is a 15-in. six-ply tire? This obsolete size is comparable to size 7.50 x 15 according to Chevrolet truck expert Bob Adler, who adds, "The 15-in. tires are 'beefier' than the 16-in. tires and the 15-in. wheels weigh considerably more than the 16-in. wheels."
CHASSIS: [Model DS] Wheelbase: 134.50 in. Tires: [Single rear wheels] 7.00 x 17 six-ply. [Dual rear wheels] 7.00 x 18 eight-ply.
TECHNICAL: Manual transmission. Speeds: [1500/3100/3600] 3F/1R, [3800] 4F/1R. Floor-mounted gear shift. Single-disc dry-plate clutch. [1500/3100] Semi-floating rear axle. [3600/3800] Full-floating rear axle. The 3600/3800 series full-floating rear axle was all-new for 1946. (This was the introduction of the 8-lug axles and wheels, which were popular and were used until 1988 with only minor modifications.) Hydraulic brakes. Wheels: [1500/3100] One-piece drop center 16-in. wheels. [3600/3800] Multi-piece split rims.

1946 Chevrolet 1/2-Ton Model DP Panel (OCW)

OPTIONS: [RPO] Hydraulic shock absorbers (No. 200). Economy rear axle, Sedan Delivery only (No. 201). Long running boards and rear fenders (No. 207). Rear view mirrors and brackets (No. 210). Panel type rear bumper bar (No. 213). Wheel and tire carrier (No. 215). Oil-bath air cleaner (No. 216). 1-ton eight-leaf rear springs for 3600. Heavy-duty clutch (No. 227). Screen shield for Canopy Express model (No. 228) Frame extensions (No. 232). Paint options (No. 234 for Commercial Trucks only):

RPO	Basic Color	Body/Hood/Radiator Shell Molding Color	Body/Hood/Rad. Shell Molding Stripe Color
Standard	Brewster Green	Kildare Green	Emerald Green
234-A	Swift's Red	Mayland Black	Gold Bronze
234-B	Armour Yellow	Omaha Orange	Mayland Black
234-C	Apple Green	Cream Medium	Emerald Green
234-D	Cream Medium	Export Blue	Argent Silver
234-E	Export Blue	Argent Silver	Totem Scarlet
234-F	Omaha Orange	Chess Blue	White
234-G	Hollywood Tan (2)	Mayland Black	White
234-H	Airdale Brown (3) Circassian Brown	Kildare Green	White
234-J	Bordeaux Maroon	Mayland Black	Gold Bronze
234-K	Black (4)	Emerald Green	Cream Medium
234-L	White	Kildare Green	White
234-M	Boatswain Blue	Argent Silver	Totem Scarlet

NOTE 2: Hollywood Tan finish only on trucks assembled at the Oakland, Calif. factory.
NOTE 3: This two-tone combination used on Suburbans only. The Airdale Brown color was used only on the side and rear window panels.
NOTE 4: Black was the regular color on all fenders, but fenders were done in basic body color upon request.
NOTE 5: 1/2-Ton Light-Duty Commercial Specifications for 1946 indicates the body belt line, hood, and radiator shell moldings are painted a contrasting color to the body and then, within the belt line, a pinstripe is then applied. The Truck Data Book has a similar chart on page 311. Chevy truck expert Bob Adler is unsure if this was done in earlier years, but it was not used on Advance-Design trucks.
Oil filter (No. 237). Governor for standard 216 cid engine (No. 241). Propeller shaft guard (No. 244). Chrome-plated bumper guards, except on rear of 3600 Platform/Stake (No. 245). Radiator master grille guard (No. 247). Dual tail and stop lamp equipment for Sedan Delivery, Suburban, Panel, and Canopy Express (No. 249). Fender irons (No. 250) 16-quart heavy-duty cooling system (No. 256). Sun shades/sun visors (No. 261). Auxiliary seat for Canopy and Panel (No. 263). Double-acting (two-stage) rear springs (No. 268). Radiator overflow return tank (No. 271). Heavy-duty three-speed transmission for Sedan Delivery only (No. 316). Heavy-duty four-speed transmission (No. 318). Right-hand windshield wiper (No. 320). Tru-Stop brake equipment (No. 348). Deluxe platform body skirt (No. 353). Rear bumper (No. 357). Various tire options, as follows:

1946 Chevrolet 1/2-Ton Model DP Pickup (EK)

Light Duty Truck Tire Options

Tires Size	Ply Rating	Capacity (lb.)	PSI	Section (in.)
15 in.	Six-ply	1500	40	7.74
15 in.	Eight-ply	1700	48	7.74
6.00 x 16	Four-ply	990	32	6.25
6.00 x 16	Six-ply	1065	36	6.21
6.50 x 16	Six-ply	1290	40	6.65
7.00 x 17	Six-ply	1550	45	7.30
7.00 x 17	Eight-ply	1725	45	7.30
7.50 x 17	Eight-ply	2000 (each)	55	7.36
7.00 x 18	Eight-ply	1800	55	7.24

OPTIONS: [Dealer Accessories] Adjustable fabrikoid radiator cover. Left- and right-hand door arm rests for cab, Panel, Pickup, and Canopy Express models. Defroster fan with two-speed electric motor. Dual horns. Gasoline filter. 20-in. high by 64-in. wide chrome-plated steel radiator grille guard for chrome bumpers. 20-in. high by 68-in. wide chrome-plated steel grille guard for channel-type bumpers. Heater shut-off valve. Fog lamps. DeLuxe heater and defroster. Load compartment light for Panel trucks. Under hood light. Back-up lamp for Sedan Delivery. Safety spot light. Outside rear view mirror, long or short arm types. red Reflex reflector. Cigarette lighter. DeLuxe radio and whip antenna. Sun shades (visors). Tire traction mat assembly. Windshield washer.
HISTORICAL: Manufactured May, 1 1946 to May 31, 1947. Calendar-year registrations: [All Chevrolet trucks] 171,618 (This does not include the Sedan Deliver total). Calendar-year production: [All Chevrolet trucks, except Sedan Delivery] 335,343. Note: The registration/production totals are not limited to 1-ton and under models, production of Sedan Deliveries was included with passenger car production. Innovations: Full 1-ton series reintroduced for first time since 1941. Suburban with panel doors and Suburban with tailgate now merchandised as separate models. Dual rear wheel models in 1-ton line. Chevrolet promoted these as postwar models, although they were based on the prewar appearance. They had some technical refinements and returned to offering the bright metal trim and leather interiors last featured for 1942 models. These trucks were titled as both 1946 and 1947 models, depending upon which calendar-year they were sold in. Certainly, after the fall of 1946, dealers and salesmen sold them with 1947 titles to compete with new models from other manufacturers like Dodge and Ford.

1947 CHEVROLET

1947 Chevrolet Model EJ Sedan Delivery (OCW)

SEDAN DELIVERY — MODEL EJ — SIX-CYLINDER: The 1947 Sedan Delivery entered production on May 1, 1947, along with the all-new Advance-Design trucks. There were few differences from 1946. It had a new grille with a softer, more horizontal appearance and blades contoured into three distinct sections. Chevrolet lettering appeared on the top grille bar. There was a more horizontally-designed hood emblem with Chevrolet bow tie. No body side moldings appeared. Short, spear-shaped hood side nameplates said Stylemaster. The windshield was the same part used for four-door Sport Sedans. The curb side-opening rear panel door had the same part numbers as used from 1941 to 1946. The 1947 interior was trimmed in blue-gray imitation leather, code 137. Chevrolet did not emphasize a tonnage class for the Sedan Delivery. A three-speed manual transmission was standard. A heavy-duty three-speed was optional. The Sedan Delivery had a 4,100--lb. GVW rating.

1947 Chevrolet 1/2-Ton Model EP Pickup (OCW)

1/2-TON LIGHT-DUTY COMMERCIAL — MODEL EP/SERIES 3100 — SIX-CYLINDER: On May 1, 1947, the all-new Advance-Design truck series entered production. It featured new "Unisteel" cab styling and revised interiors. Chevrolet advertised "stronger frames," but marque expert Bob Adler says this cannot be borne out by study of the section modules of 1/2-ton frame rails. "For 1947, the section modulus is 2.46-in. cubed," notes Adler. "From 1938 to 1946, it was 2.40-in. cubed, derived from the exact same cross sectional dimensions. This was more advertising than engineering, but they did not say *significantly* stronger." Rear corner windows for cab models were optional. Trucks with this option had a different rear roof panel section. The new look was neat and uncluttered. The grille had five broad horizontal bars topped by a broad hood ornament containing a blue bow tie and vermilion Chevrolet lettering. Rectangular parking lights were placed in chrome housings at the ends of the uppermost pair of grille bars. A painted grille was standard equipment. On all commercial trucks except Suburbans, the outer and inner grille bar assemblies were both done in the body color (Forester Green was standard). The grilles had specific color striping (Cream Medium striping was standard) with one stripe on each bar. There was no contrasting color on the backsplash. On Suburbans, the outer bars were chrome-plated and the inner bar assemblies were finished in a grayish-green called Channel Green Baking Dulux. The chrome radiator grille package was a regular production option (RPO) on models other than the Suburban. A polished chrome Chevrolet Thriftmaster nameplate was installed near the rear edge of the "alligator" hood. Underscore lines and the word Thriftmaster were painted Vermilion Baking Dulux, while the background of the nameplate was set off with Black Baking Dulux finish. Chrome-plated curved-type front bumpers were standard on all 3100s. Similar rear bumpers were standard on most models. Chrome hubcaps with vermilion Chevrolet lettering were standard. A two-piece, flat windshield was used. It had a black rubber seal and polished stainless steel divider bar. Polished stainless steel windshield reveal moldings were standard on Suburbans and optional on other models. Front and rear fenders retained their individual forms. Their rounded shape, in conjunction with the rounded corners of the body, gave the Chevrolet trucks a more up-to-date appearance. The filler tube for the under-frame-mounted gas tank came out the right-hand side of the body, ahead of the rear wheels. Cab models and single-unit body models had one belt molding stripe, which was Cream Medium with standard finishes. Forester Green was the standard truck color, but was not used on Suburbans. The Suburbans were finished with a Fathom Green upper body and Channel Green lower body. The following no-cost color options (pinstripe colors in parentheses) were offered on all models except the Suburban: Swift's Red (Argent Silver), Armour Yellow (Black), White, (Emerald Green), Jet Black (Argent Silver), Omaha Orange (Black), Cape Maroon (Gold),

Mariner Blue (Cream Medium), Windsor Blue (Cream Medium), Seacrest Green (Cream Medium), Sun Beige (Totem Scarlet), and Cream Medium (Black). The interior was highlighted by wider seats, improved vision through the larger windshield and side and rear windows, plus a redesigned instrument panel. The instrument panel featured electric type fuel and battery charge indicators and pressure-type heat indicator and oil pressure gauge. The speedometer was driven by a flexible shaft. Interior panels were finished in slate gray or brown metallic enamel. The 3100 (EP model prefix) trucks had a base 4,600-lb. GVW rating.

1947 Chevrolet 3/4-Ton Model ER Pickup (OCW)

3/4-TON LIGHT-DUTY COMMERCIAL — MODEL ER/SERIES 3600 — SIX-CYLINDER: The 3/4-ton trucks had the same new Advance-Design styling, features and finish as other conventional trucks. They rode a longer wheelbase. The Pickup load box was longer and had six stake pockets. Long running boards were used. No Suburban was offered in this line. There were Platform and Stake models. Hubcaps looked like the ones on 3100s with vermilion Chevrolet lettering. The eight-lug wheel that was used had a big bolt pattern that required a larger hubcap to cover it. Features and finish were similar to those for 3100 models. The hubcaps were of a similar design, but larger. They interchanged with the hubcaps used on 3800 models. Curved-type chrome front bumpers were standard on all models. Base tires on 3600s were 15 in. six-ply rated on 15 x 5.50 semi-drop-center rims. Standard GVW rating for these trucks was 5,200-5,800 lb. depending upon tire options.

1-TON MEDIUM-DUTY COMMERCIAL — MODEL ES/SERIES 3800 — SIX-CYLINDER: The 1-ton had the same new Advance-Design styling, features and finish as other conventional trucks. The basic model lineup was unchanged. It included single and dual rear wheel options for all except the Express, Canopy and Panel. The Express had a longer wheelbase than the 3600 Pickup, longer running boards, and a longer load box with eight stake pockets. A curved-type chrome front bumper was standard on all models. Regular equipment tires were 7.00 x 17 six-ply rated for trucks with single rear wheels or 7.00 x 18 eight-ply rated for trucks with dual rear wheel options. The basic hubcap design was shared with 3100s. However, 3600s and 3800s used larger, interchangeable hubcaps. The eight-lug wheel that they took had a big bolt pattern that required a larger hubcap to cover it. The hubcaps had vermilion Chevrolet lettering. No hubcaps were used on the 18 x 5 in. wheels of the Chassis-and-Cab, Platform and Stake models, which had eight bolts and eight circular openings. The standard GVWs for trucks with single rear wheels were 5,700, 6,100, and 6,700 lb. depending on tire options. A base GVW of 8,800 lb. was listed for trucks with optional dual rear wheels. A four-speed manual transmission was standard.

1947 Chevrolet 1-Ton Model ES Panel (OCW)

I.D. DATA: Serial number located: [Sedan Delivery] On right hinge pillar about nine in. above rocker panel. [Cab models/Panels/Suburbans] On plate attached to rear face of left-hand door hinge pillar. [Chassis models] on plate temporarily attached near steering column, with final location per body maker. The first symbol indicated the assembly plant: 1=Flint, Mich., 2=Tarrytown, N.Y., 3=St. Louis, Mo., 5=Kansas City, Kan., 6=Oakland, Calif., 8=Atlanta, Ga., 9=Norwood, Ohio, 14=Baltimore, Md., 20=Los Angeles, Calif., and 21=Janesville, Wis. The second and third symbols indicate model prefix/series as follows: EJ=Series 1500, EP=3100, ER=3600, ES=3800. The fourth symbol indicates month of assembly, A=Jan., B=Feb., etc. The following symbols indicated the sequential production number. Each series was separately numbered in sequence, starting with 1001 at each assembly plant: Serial numbers: [Series 1500] EJ-1001 to EJ-33745, [Series 3100] EP-1001 and up, [Series 3600] ER-1001 and up, [Series 3800] ES-1001 and up. Engine numbers: Stamped on boss on right side of cylinder block, to the rear of the distributor.

Model	Body Type	Price	Weight	Prod. Total
Sedan Delivery — Model EJ/Series 1500 — 116 in. w.b.				
1508	Sedan Delivery	1233		20,303
1/2-Ton Commercial — Model EP/Series 3100 — 116 in. w.b.				
3102	Chassis & Cowl	843	2420	-
3103	Chassis & Cab	1030	2915	-
3104	Pickup	1087	3345	-
3105	Panel	1238	3555	-
3107	Canopy	1289	3545	-
3116	Suburban	1474	3745	-
3/4-Ton Commercial — Model ER/Series 3600 — 125.25 in. w.b.				
3602	Chassis & Cowl	941	2660	-
3603	Chassis & Cab	1128	3180	-
3604	Pickup	1201	3440	-
3608	Platform	1211	3560	-
3609	Stake	1258	3720	-
1-Ton Commercial — Model ES/Series 3800 — 137 in. w.b.				
3802	Chassis & Cowl	988	2910	-
3803	Chassis & Cab	1176	3440	-
3804	Pickup	1279	3845	-
3805	Panel	1445	4220	-
3807	Canopy	1523	4210	-
3808	Platform	1295	3965	-
3809	Stake	1362	4195	-

1947 Chevrolet 3/4-Ton Model ER Pickup (K. Kutz)

ENGINE: Inline. OHV. Thriftmaster Six. Six-cylinder. Cast-iron block. Bore & stroke: 3-1/2 x 3-3/4 in. Displacement: 216.5 cid. Compression ratio: 6.5:1. Gross horsepower: 90 at 3300 rpm. Gross torque: 174 lb.-ft. at 1200-2000 rpm. NACC horsepower: 29.4. Four main bearings. Mechanical valve lifters. Carburetor: Carter downdraft one-barrel model WI-574S.
CHASSIS: [Model 1500] Wheelbase: 116 in. Overall length: 197.5 in. Front tread: 57.6 in. Rear tread: 60 in. Tires: 6.00 x 16 in.
CHASSIS: [Model 3100] Wheelbase: 116 in. Overall length: 196.6 in. Tires: 6.00 x 16 in.
CHASSIS: [Model 3600] Wheelbase: 125.25 in. Overall length: 206 in. Tires: 6.00 x 15 in.
NOTE: What is a 15 in. six-ply tire? This obsolete size is comparable to size 7.50 x 15 according to Chevrolet truck expert Bob Adler, who adds, "The 15 in. tires are `beefier' than the 16 in. tires and the 15 in. wheels weigh considerably more than the 16 in. wheels."
CHASSIS: [Model 3800] Wheelbase: 137 in. Overall length: 223.88 in. Tires: 7.00 x 17 in.
TECHNICAL: Manual transmission. Speeds: [1500/3100/3600] 3F/1R, [3800] [4F/1R] Floor-mounted gearshift. Single-disc, diaphragm spring clutch. [1500/3100] Semi-floating hypoid rear axle, [3600/3800] full-floating rear axle. Hydraulic, four-wheel brakes. Wheels: [1500/3100] One-piece drop center 16 in. wheels, [3600/3800] Multi-piece split rims. Standard rear axles: [1500] 4.11:1, 3.73:1, [3100] 4.11:1, [3600] 4.57:1, [3800] 5.14:1.
OPTIONS: [RPO] 1-1/2-in. hydraulic shock absorbers for series 300 trucks (No. 200). Economy rear axle for Sedan Delivery only (No. 201). Low-ratio rear axle (No. 204-A). Outside rear view mirror and bracket (No. 210). Oil-bath air cleaner. (No. 216) Two-stage rear springs. Heavy-duty clutch for house-to-house delivery units (No. 227). Paint Options (No. 234 for Commercial Trucks/No. 235 for Sedan Delivery).

Option No.	Body Color	DuPont No. (Air-Drying)	Wheel Stripe Color	DuPont No. (Duco)
STD Suburban				
	Fathom Green (upper)	99-20953	Cream Medium	289-6595
	Channel Green (lower)	99-20952		
STD Other 3000				
	Forester Green	93-62006	Cream Medium	289-6595
234-A	Swift's Red	93-1863R	Argent Silver	289-4202
234-B	Armour Yellow	93-3421	Mayland Black	253-2122
234-C	White	93-508	Emerald Green	289-3133
234-D	Jet Black	93-005	Argent Silver	289-4202
234-E	Omaha Orange	93-082	Mayland Black	253-2122
234-F	Cape Maroon	93-64539	Gold Bronze	SM-681-A
234-G	Mariner Blue	93-63203	Cream Medium	289-6595
234-H	Windsor Blue	93-63205	Cream Medium	289-6595
234-J	Seacrest Green	93-62201	Cream Medium	289-6595
234-K	Sun Beige	93-61083	Totem Scarlet	289-50165
234-L	Cream Medium	93-530	Mayland Black	253-2122
STD Sed. Dly.				
	Mayland Black	246-2048	Argent Silver	289-4202
235-A	Oxford Maroon	202-39638M	Argent Silver	289-4202
235-B	Lullwater Green	202-39406	Argent Silver	289-4202
235-C	Battleship Gray	202-54791	Argent Silver	289-4202
235-D	Sport Beige	246-51737	Scout Brown	289-50964
235-E	Freedom Blue	246-50633	Argent Silver	289-4202
Sedan Delivery Two-Tones				
235-G	Lullwater Green	202-39406	Argent Silver	289-4202
	Lakeside Green	202-36865		
235-H	Freedom Blue	246-50633	Argent Silver	289-4202
	Ozone Blue	202-52418		
235-J	Scout Brown	246-50964	Argent Silver	289-4202
	Sport Beige	246-51737		

2-1/2-quart dry capacity oil filter (No. 237). Chrome-plated 13-gauge steel heavy-duty bumper guards for all models equipped with chrome bumpers (No. 245). Tail and stop lamp equipment for installation on Sedan Delivery, Carryall Suburban, Panel, and Canopy Express. 17-1/2-quart heavy-duty cooling system, including heavy-duty radiator core and shroud for fan (No. 256). Right-hand auxiliary fold-forward front bucket seat for Panel and Canopy models. Double-acting, "progressive" two-stage rear springs recommended for fragile loads (No. 268). Radiator overflow return tank (No. 271). Heavy-duty three-speed transmission for Sedan Delivery only (No. 316). Heavy-duty four-speed transmission (No. 318). Tru-Stop brake equipment (No. 348). Sign panel for advertising on Stake and Stake Express models. The panel is 36 x 28 in. for model 3809 and 35 x 38 in. for others (No. 351). 18-gallon inside-the-frame (not cab) fuel tank for models 3802/3803/3812/3822/and 3832 (No. 379). Wide running boards for model 3104 Pickup only (No. 389). Fresh-Air heater/defroster system (No. 385). Chrome radiator grille for all series 3000 (No. 386). Cab rear corner windows for all cab models (No. 387). DeLuxe Cab equipment consisting of bare corner windows, bright metal windshield and door window reveals, door window garnish molding, seat back trim panel, arm rest on driver's side door, and right-hand sun shade and chrome-plated radiator grille on 3000 series models (No. 390) DeLuxe Panel equipment, including bright metal reveals for side door windows, bright metal reveals for rear door windows, bright metal windshield reveals, garnish moldings for side door windows, arm rest for driver's side door, bright metal moldings for front and rear fenders, right-hand sun shade, and chrome-plated radiator grille (No. 390; not available on Canopy Express or Carryall Suburban). Various tire options, as follows:

Light Duty Truck Tire Options

Size	Ply Rating	Capacity (lb.)	PSI	Section (in.)
15 in.	Six-ply	1500	40	7.74
15 in.	Eight-ply	1700	48	7.74
6.00 x 16	Four-ply	990	32	6.25
6.00 x 16	Six-ply	1065	36	6.21
6.50 x 16	Six-ply	1290	40	6.65
7.00 x 17	Six-ply	1550	45	7.30
7.00 x 17	Eight-ply	1775	55	7.30
7.50 x 17	Eight-ply	2100	60	7.36
7.00 x 18	Eight-ply	1850	55	7.24

OPTIONS: [Dealer Accessories] Adjustable fabrikoid radiator cover. Left- and right-hand door arm rests for Cab, Panel, Pickup, and Canopy Express models. Defroster fan with two-speed electric motor. Dual horns. Gasoline filter. 20-in. high by 64-in. wide chrome-plated steel radiator grille guard for chrome bumpers. 20-in. high by 68-in. wide chrome-plated steel grille guard for channel-type bumpers. Heater shut-off valve. Fog lamps. DeLuxe heater and defroster. Load compartment light for Panel trucks. Under hood light. Back-up lamp for Sedan Delivery. Safety spot light. Outside rear view mirror, long or short arm types. Red Reflex reflector. Cigarette lighter. DeLuxe radio and whip antenna. Sun shades (visors). Tire traction mat assembly. Windshield washer. Rear axle magnetic filler plug. Transmission magnetic filler plug. Oil pan magnetic drain plug.

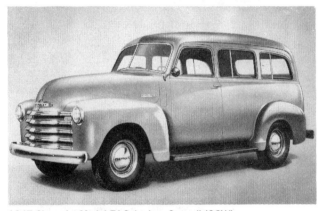

1947 Chevrolet Model EJ Suburban Carryall (OCW)

HISTORICAL: Production of all above models began May 1, 1947. Commercial model series production continued until March 31, 1948. It appears that the Sedan Delivery was built through August 1947. Calendar-year production was 335,343, but this included 1946 late-series models produced from Jan. 1, 1947 to May 1, 1947. It also does not include Advance-Design models built after Jan. 1, 1948. The EJ/EP/ER/ES models were titled as both 1947 and 1948 models, depending upon the calendar-year in which they were sold. Dealers and salesmen were unlikely to promote them as 1947 models in 1948. Calendar-year registrations: [All Series] 235,803. Calendar-year sales: [All Series] 259,533. Innovations: The all-new, completely restyled line featured "the cab that breathes," with 30 Advance-Design features and an alligator-jaw hood opening to make servicing easier. The capacity of Chevrolet's commercial body plant at Indianapolis, Ind. was expanded to double production capacity this year. A new assembly plant in Flint, Mich. was also opened. Late in the year, a large new plant in Los Angeles began operations. A new manufacturing plant at Cleveland was also opened.

1948 CHEVROLET

SEDAN DELIVERY — MODEL FJ — SIX-CYLINDER: A T-shaped vertical center bar was used to update the grille on the 1948 Sedan Delivery. A new hood mascot and emblem appeared. This model continued to be a commercial version of the passenger car sharing few engineering features with conventional Commercial trucks. It had a chrome grille, chrome front and rear bumpers, a bright metal windshield division bar and black rubber gravel shields. No body side moldings appeared. Short, spear-shaped hood side nameplates with a dark-finished center said Stylemaster. At the rear was a curb side-opening panel door (the same one used since 1941). The Sedan Delivery shared the windshield of the 1948

Chevrolet four-door Sport Sedan. The interior was trimmed in blue-black imitation leather, code 137. Chevrolet did not emphasize a tonnage class for the Sedan Delivery. A three-speed manual transmission was standard. A heavy-duty three-speed was optional. The Sedan Delivery had a 4,100-lb. GVW rating.

1948 Chevrolet Stylemaster Model FJ Sedan Delivery (OCW)

1948 Chevrolet 1/2-Ton Model FP Pickup (CMD)

1/2-TON LIGHT-DUTY COMMERCIAL — MODEL FP/SERIES 3100 — SIX-CYLINDER: The 1948 conventional trucks in the Light-Duty Commercial line again featured Advance-Design "Unisteel" cab styling. There were no significant changes from 1947 specifications. The grille had five broad horizontal bars topped by a broad hood ornament containing a blue bow tie and vermilion Chevrolet lettering. Rectangular parking lights were placed in chrome housings at the ends of the two uppermost grille bars. A painted grille was standard equipment. On all commercial trucks except Suburbans, the outer and inner grille bar assemblies were done in body color (Forester Green was standard). The outer bars had specific color pinstriping (Cream Medium was standard) with one stripe on each bar. On Suburbans, the outer bars were chrome-plated and the inner bar assemblies were finished in a grayish-green called Channel Green Baking Dulux. The chrome radiator grille package was a regular production option (RPO) on models other than the Suburban. Rear corner windows for cab models were optional. On trucks with the rear corner windows, a different rear roof panel section was used. A polished chrome Chevrolet Thriftmaster nameplate was installed near the rear edge of the "alligator" hood. Underscore lines and the word Thriftmaster were painted vermilion, while the background of the nameplate was set off with black finish. Chrome-plated curved-type front bumpers were standard on all 3100s. Similar rear bumpers were standard on most models. Chrome hubcaps with vermilion Chevrolet lettering were standard. A two-piece, flat windshield was used. It had a black rubber seal and polished stainless steel divider bar. Polished stainless steel windshield reveal moldings were standard on Suburbans and optional on other models. The filler tube for the under-frame-mounted gas tank came out the right-hand side of the body, ahead of the rear wheels. Cab models and single-unit body models had one belt molding stripe, which was Cream Medium with standard finishes. Forester Green was the standard truck color, but was not used on Suburbans. The Suburbans were finished with a Fathom Green upper body and Channel Green lower body. The following no-cost color options (pinstripe colors in parentheses) were offered on all models except the Suburban: Swift's Red (Argent Silver), Armour Yellow (Black), White (Emerald Green), Jet Black (Argent Silver), Omaha Orange (Black), Cape Maroon (Gold), Mariner Blue (Cream Medium), Windsor Blue (Cream Medium), Seacrest Green (Cream Medium), Sun Beige (Totem Scarlet), and Cream Medium (Black). The instrument panel featured electric type fuel and battery charge indicators and pressure-type fuel indicator and oil pressure gauge. The speedometer was driven by a flexible shaft. Interior panels were finished in slate gray enamel. The 3100 (FP model prefix) trucks had a base 4,600-lb. GVW rating.

1948 Chevrolet 1/2-Ton Model FP Suburban Carryall (CMD)

1948 Chevrolet 3/4-Ton Model FR Pickup (CMD)

3/4-TON LIGHT-DUTY COMMERCIAL — MODEL FR/SERIES 3600 — SIX-CYLINDER: The 3/4-ton trucks had the same Advance-Design styling, features and finish as other conventional trucks. They had a longer wheelbase than 3100s. The Pickup load box was longer and had six stake pockets. Long running boards were used. No Suburban or Panel was offered in this line. There were Platform and Stake models. The hubcaps were larger than the type used on 3100s, but looked the same and had vermilion Chevrolet lettering. Features and finish were similar to those for 3100 models. Curved-type chrome front bumpers were standard on all models. Base tires on 3600s were 15 in. six-ply rated on 15 x 5.50 semi-drop-center rims. The 15 in. rims had no stripe. Optional 17-in. rims had two Cream Medium stripes. Standard GVW rating for these trucks was 5,200-5,800 lb. depending upon tire options.

3/4-TON DUBL-DUTI — MODEL FT/SERIES 3700 — SIX-CYLINDER: Two Dubl-Duti Forward-Control chassis returned to the Chevrolet truck line. Model 3742 was the 3/4-ton version on a 125.25-in. wheelbase. Standard walk-in delivery truck bodies could be supplied by several factory-approved sources or the buyer could add his/her own body.

1-TON MEDIUM-DUTY COMMERCIAL — MODEL FS/SERIES 3800 — SIX-CYLINDER: The 1-ton had the same Advance-Design styling, features and finish as other conventional trucks. The basic model lineup was unchanged. It included single and dual rear wheel options for all except the Express, Canopy and Panel. The Express had a longer wheelbase than the 3600 Pickup, longer running boards, and a longer load box with eight stake pockets. A curved-type chrome front bumper was standard on all models. Regular equipment tires were 7.00 x 17 six-ply rated for trucks with single rear wheels or 7.00 x 18 eight-ply rated for trucks with dual rear wheel options. The hubcaps were identical to those used on 3600s. They had vermilion Chevrolet lettering. No hubcaps were used on the 18 x 5 in. wheels of the Chassis-and-Cab, Platform and Stake models, which had eight bolts and eight circular openings. The standard GVWs for trucks with single rear wheels were 5,700, 6,100, and 6,700 lb., depending on tire options. A base GVW of 8,800 lb. was listed for trucks with optional dual rear wheels. A four-speed manual transmission was standard.

1948 Chevrolet 1-Ton Model FS Platform Stake (K. Robbins)

1-TON DUBL-DUTI — MODEL FU/SERIES 3900 — SIX-CYLINDER: Two Dubl-Duti Forward-Control chassis returned to the Chevrolet truck line. Model 3942 was the 1-ton version on a 1137-in. wheelbase. Standard walk-in delivery truck bodies could be supplied by several factory-approved sources or the buyer could add his/her own body. Weight ratings up to 10,000 lb. were available. This is the first time a GVW of 5-tons was available with a 1-ton nominally rated truck. These Dubl-Dutis were introduced part way through the model-year, as early factory literature does not include them.

I.D. DATA: Serial number located: [All] on plate attached to rear face of left-hand door hinge pillar, on right side of cowl under hood. [Chassis models] on plate temporarily attached near steering column, with final location per body maker. The first symbol indicated the assembly plant: 1=Flint, Mich., 2=Tarrytown, N.Y., 3=St. Louis, Mo., 5=Kansas City, Kan., 6=Oakland, Calif., 8=Atlanta, Ga., 9=Norwood, Ohio, 14=Baltimore, Md., 20=Los Angeles, Calif., and 21=Janesville, Wis. The second and third symbols indicate model prefix/series as follows: FJ=Series 1500, FP=3100, FR=3600, FS=3800, FT=3700, FU=3900. The fourth symbol indicated month of assembly, A=Jan., B=Feb., etc. The following symbols indicated the sequential production number. Each series was separately numbered in sequence, starting with 1001 at each assembly plant: Serial numbers: [Series 1500] FJ-1001 and up, [Series 3100] FP-1001 and up, [Series 3600] FR-1001 and up, [Series 3700] FT-1001 and up, [Series 3800] FS-1001 and up, [Series 3900] FU-1001 and up. Engine numbers located: Stamped on boss on right side of cylinder block, to the rear of the distributor.

1948 Chevrolet 1/2-Ton Model FP Panel (CMD)

1948 Chevrolet 1-Ton Model FS Pickup/Express (CMD)

Model	Body Type	Price	Weight	Prod. Total
Sedan Delivery — Model FJ/Series 1500 — 116 in. w.b.				
FJ	Sedan Delivery	1361	3075	19,490
1/2-Ton Commercial — Model FP/Series 3100 — 116 in. w.b.				
3102	Chassis	890	2430	-
3103	Chassis & Cab	1113	2960	-
3104	Pickup	1180	3215	-
3105	Panel	1377	3425	-
3107	Canopy	1429	3415	-
3116	Suburban (gate)	1627	3515	-
3/4-Ton Commercial — Model FR/Series 3600 — 125.25 in. w.b.				
3602	Chassis	1004	2660	-
3603	Chassis & Cab	1227	3180	-
3604	Pickup	1315	3460	-
3608	Platform	1320	3655	-
3609	Stake	1378	3740	-
3/4-Ton Dubl-Duti — Model FT/Series 3700 — 125.25 in. w.b.				
3742	Chassis	1097	2465	-
1-Ton Commercial — Model FS/Series 3800 — 137 in. w.b.				
3802	Chassis	1087	3035	-
3803	Chassis & Cab	1310	3545	-
3804	Pickup	1425	3965	-
3805	Panel	1596	4220	-
3807	Canopy	1674	4210	-
3808	Platform	1440	4050	-
3809	Stake	1513	4300	-
1-Ton Dubl-Duti — Model FU/Series 3900 — 137 in. w.b.				
3942	Chassis	1125	2630	-

1948 Chevrolet 1/2-Ton Model FP Suburban Carryall (CMD)

ENGINE: Inline. OHV. Thriftmaster Six. Six-cylinder. Cast-iron block. Bore & stroke: 3-1/2 x 3-3/4 in. Displacement: 216.5 cid. Compression ratio: 6.5:1. Gross horsepower: 90 at 3300 rpm. Gross torque: 174 lb.-ft. at 1200-2000 rpm. NACC horsepower: 29.4. Four main bearings. Mechanical valve lifters. Carburetor: Carter downdraft one-barrel model W1-574S.
CHASSIS: [Model 1500] Wheelbase: 116 in. Overall length: 197.5 in. Front tread: 57.6 in. Rear tread: 60 in. Tires: 6.00 x 16 in.
CHASSIS: [Model 3100] Wheelbase: 116 in. Overall length: 196.6 in. Tires: 6.00 x 16 in.
CHASSIS: [Model 3600] Wheelbase: 125.25 in. Overall length: 206 in. Tires: 15 in. six- or eight-ply truck tires.
CHASSIS: [Model 3800] Wheelbase: 137 in. Overall length: 223.88 in. Tires: 7.00 x 17 in.

1948 Chevrolet 1-Ton Model FS Panel (CMD)

TECHNICAL: Manual transmission: [1500/3100/3600] 3F/1R column-mounted, [3800] [4F/1R] Floor-mounted gearshift. Single-disc, diaphragm spring clutch. [1500/3100] Semi-floating hypoid rear axle, [3600/3800] full-floating rear axle. Hydraulic, four-wheel brakes. Wheels: [1500/3100] One-piece drop center 16 in. wheels, [3600/3800] Multi-piece split rims. Standard rear axles: [1500] 4.11:1, 3.73:1, [3100] 4.11:1, [3600] 4.57:1, [3800] 5.14:1.

OPTIONS: [RPO] 1-1/2-in. hydraulic shock absorbers for series 300 trucks (No. 200). Economy rear axle for Sedan Delivery only (No. 201). Low-ratio rear axle (No. 204-A). Outside rear view mirror and bracket (No. 210). Oil-bath air cleaner (No. 216) Two-stage rear springs. Heavy-duty clutch for house-to-house delivery units (No. 227). Paint Options (No.234 for Commercial Trucks/No. 235 for Sedan Delivery):

Option No.	Body Color	DuPont No. (Air-Drying)	Wheel Stripe Color	DuPont Mo. (Air-Drying)
STD Suburban				
	Fathom Green (upper)	93-20953	Cream Medium	93-530
	Channel Green (lower)	93-20952		
STD Other 3000				
	Forester Green	93-62006	Cream Medium	93-530
234-A	Swift's Red	93-1863R	Argent Silver	165-5642
234-B	Armour Yellow	93-3421	Black	93-005
234-C	White	93-508	Emerald Green	93-2537
234-D	Jet Black	93-005	Argent Silver	165-5642
234-E	Omaha Orange	93-082	Black	93-005
234-F	Cape Maroon	93-64539	Gold Bronze	SM-1530AA
234-G	Mariner Blue	93-63203	Cream Medium	93-530
234-H	Windsor Blue	93-63225	Cream Medium	93-530
234-J	Seacrest Green	93-62201	Cream Medium	93-530
234-K	Sun Beige	93-61083	Totem Scarlet	93-2767
234-L	Cream Medium	93-530	Black	93-005

Truck Radiator Grille Inner Bar: Waldorf White 246-71052 or 93-71052
NOTE 1: The above color combinations were available for Commercial Truck models, as indicated, at all assembly plants. The 1948 Chevrolet trucks were finished in high-luster Dulux synthetic enamel which was baked on in thermostatically controlled ovens. To assist service managers and mechanics in obtaining matching colors when repairs were necessary, the air-drying Dulux number was listed, instead of the number of the Baking Dulux type paint.

1948 Chevrolet 1-Ton Model FS Pickup/Express (CMD)

Option No.	Body Color	DuPont No. (Duco)	Wheel Stripe Color	DuPont Mo. (Duco)
STD Sed. Dly.				
	Mayland Black	246-2048	Argent Silver	289-4202
235-A	Liveoak Green (Met.)	202-36777	Argent Silver	289-4202
235-B	Lake Como Blue	n.a.	n.a.	n.a.
235-C	Dove Gray	n.a.	n.a.	n.a.
235-D	Silver Gray Green	n.a.	n.a.	n.a.
235-E	Battleship Gray	202-54791	Argent Silver	289-4202
235-F	Oxford Maroon	207-39638	Argent Silver	289-4202
Sedan Delivery Two-Tones				
235-G	Satin Green	253-39814	French White	289-4202
	Marsh Brown			
235-H	Silver Gray Green	n.a.	n.a.	n.a.
	Liveoak Green	207-36777		
235-J	Dove Gray	n.a.	n.a.	n.a.
	Battleship Gray	202-54791		
235-K	Dove Gray	n.a.	n.a.	n.a.
	Lake Como Blue	n.a.	n.a.	n.a.

2-1/2-quart dry capacity oil filter (No. 237). Chrome-plated 13-gauge steel heavy-duty bumper guards for all models equipped with chrome bumpers (No. 245). Tail and stop lamp equipment for installation on Sedan Delivery, Carryall Suburban, Panel, and Canopy Express (No. 256). 17-1/2-quart heavy-duty cooling system, including heavy-duty radiator core and shroud for fan (No. 256). Right-hand auxiliary fold-forward front bucket seat for Panel and Canopy models (No. 268). Double-acting, "progressive" two-stage rear springs recommended for fragile loads (No. 268). Radiator overflow return tank (No. 271). Heavy-duty three-speed transmission for Sedan Delivery only (No. 316). Heavy-duty four-speed transmission (No. 318). Tru-Stop brake equipment (No. 348). Sign panel for advertising on Stake and Stake Express models. The panel is 36 x 28 in. for model 3809 and 35 x 38 in. for others (No. 351). 18-gallon inside-the-frame (not cab) fuel tank for models 3802/3803/3812/3822/and 3832 (No. 379). Wide running boards for model

3104 Pickup only (No. 389). Fresh-Air heater/defroster system (No. 385). Chrome radiator grille for all series 3000 (No. 386). Cab rear corner windows for all cab models (No. 387). DeLuxe Cab equipment consisting of rear corner windows, bright metal windshield and door window reveals, door window garnish molding, seat back trim panel, arm rest on driver's side door, and right-hand sun shade and chrome-plated radiator grille on 3000 series models (No. 390) DeLuxe Panel equipment, including bright metal reveals for side door windows, bright metal reveals for rear door windows, bright metal windshield reveals, garnish moldings for side door windows, arm rest for driver's side door, bright metal moldings for front and rear fenders, right-hand sun shade, and chrome-plated radiator grille (No. 390; not available on Canopy Express or Carryall Suburban). Various tire options, as follows:

Light Duty Truck Tire Options

Size	Ply Rating	Capacity (lb.)	PSI	Section (in.)
15 in.	Six-ply	1500	40	7.74
15 in.	Eight-ply	1700	48	7.74
6.00 x 16	Four-ply	990	32	6.25
6.00 x 16	Six-ply	1065	36	6.21
6.50 x 16	Six-ply	1290	40	6.65
7.00 x 17	Six-ply	1550	45	7.30
7.00 x 17	Eight-ply	1775	55	7.30
7.50 x 17	Eight-ply	2100	60	7.36
7.00 x 18	Eight-ply	1850	55	7.24

CANOPY EXPRESS
MODELS 3107, 116" WHEELBASE, 3807, 137" WHEELBASE

Waterproof side curtains and slam-gate. Screen sides are available at e

1948 Chevrolet 1-Ton Model FS Canopy Express (CMD)

OPTIONS: [Dealer Accessories] Adjustable fabrikoid radiator cover. Left- and right-hand door arm rests for Cab, Panel, Pickup, and Canopy Express models. Defroster fan with two-speed electric motor. Dual horns. Gasoline filter. 20-in. high by 64-in. wide chrome-plated steel radiator grille guard for chrome bumpers. 20-in. high by 68-in. wide chrome-plated steel grille guard for channel-type bumpers. Heater shut-off valve. Fog lamps. DeLuxe heater and defroster. Load compartment light for Panel trucks. Under hood light. Back-up lamp for Sedan Delivery. Safety spot light. Outside rear view mirror, long or short arm types. Red Reflex reflector. Cigarette lighter. DeLuxe radio and whip antenna. Sun shades (visors). Tire traction mat assembly. Windshield washer. Rear axle magnetic filler plug. Transmission magnetic filler plug. Oil pan magnetic drain plug. Tail and stop lamps for universal use (right-hand light mandatory for trucks registered in the State of Washington). Directional signal kit (includes "lollipop" lights). Underhood lamp. Package compartment light and switch. Front and rear directional signals. Cigarette lighter. Prismatic rear view mirror. Rear view mirror. Bracket for rear view mirror. Hood ornament. Ventilated seat pad. Utility pocket. Windshield scraper. Radiator insect screen. Electric shaver. Windshield frost shield. Right-hand sunshade. Radiator overflow tank. Thermostats (151-, 161- or 180-degrees). Heater shut off valve. Windshield washer. [All except Model 3116] Left-hand or right-hand Maroon door arm rest. [Model 3116 only] Brown right-hand door arm rest.

Finer-looking, more spacious Chevrolet panel trucks are designed for bigger loads—for greater durability, comfort, convenience. Merchandise is protected from weather and theft.

INTERIORS—Panel bodies are wider, more spacious, with over 13 per cent more cubic-foot capacity! Seat riser at the right of the driver is flush with the floor, increasing load space by 20¼ inches!

1948 Chevrolet 1-Ton Model FS DeLuxe Panel (CMD)

HISTORICAL: Introduced: [Sedan Delivery] Oct. 1, 1947, [Commercials] April 1, 1948. Calendar-year registrations: [All Series] 302,219. Calendar-year sales: [All Series] 323,648. Calendar-year production: [All Series] 389,690. Market share: 28.46 percent. Note: None of these totals or percentages include the Sedan Delivery. Innovations: Controls for three-speed transmission moved to steering column. New foot-type parking brake on 1/2-ton models. Four-speed synchromesh transmission (with helical cut gears) introduced. Upon the death of Nicholas Dreystadt, W.F. Armstrong was temporarily named general manager of Chevrolet Motor Division. Later, T.H. Keating was promoted from the general sales manager's post to take over from Armstrong.

1949 Chevrolet Styleline Model GJ Sedan Delivery (CMD)

SEDAN DELIVERY — MODEL GJ/SERIES 1500 — SIX-CYLINDER: For 1949 a major change was made in the Sedan Delivery. It had a new 115-in. wheelbase and shared a new lower, wider body with Chevrolet's first, true postwar passenger cars. The Sedan Delivery was a Styleline Special. Many historians say it is based on the Station Wagon, but that is an oversimplification of fact. The windshield glass was the same used on some passenger cars, but not wagons. Interestingly, tinted glass was not offered for the Sedan Delivery, though the tinted passenger car windshield should fit it. Doors were unique to the Sedan Delivery from 1949-1952. Front door window glass was the same used on 1949-1952 four-door Sedans, not Station Wagons. Lower rear quarter panel stampings were unique to the Sedan Delivery. However, the rear compartment floor panel was same one used for 1949-1952 Station Wagons. Rear bumper bars, ends and guards were also the same as wagon parts. The Sedan Delivery had a 92.5 cu. ft. load space that was 73 in. long and looked much more streamlined than the 1948 body. It had a curb side-opening rear panel door, the same door being used on all 1949-1954 models. The chrome grille had a bowed upper bar with Chevrolet lettering and a wide horizontal center bar. Round parking lamps were situated above the point where the curved and horizontal bars met. Seven short vertical bars divided the lower grille opening. Mayland Black was the standard color for the Sedan Delivery. The interior was trimmed with brown imitation leather, code 163. Standard equipment included front and rear chrome bumpers, single tail and stop lamps, a license plate lamp, dual windshield wipers, bright metal belt line moldings, bright headlamp rims, bright rocker sill moldings, chrome hubcaps, black rubber gravel shields, and five extra-low-pressure tires.

1949 Chevrolet 1/2-Ton Model GP Carryall Suburban (CMD)

1949 1/2-TON LIGHT-DUTY COMMERCIAL — MODEL GP/SERIES 3100 — SIX-CYLINDER: The 1949 conventional trucks had some noticeable changes from the prior Advance-Design models in appearance, features and trim. The unchanged grille again had five broad horizontal bars topped by a broad hood ornament with a cloisonné blue (metallic) bow tie emblem and vermilion Chevrolet lettering on a chrome background. Rectangular parking lights were again placed in chrome housings at the ends of the uppermost pair of grille bars. A painted grille was standard equipment on all models, except Suburban Carryalls. The outer grille bar assembly was again done in body color (Forester Green Baking Dulux remained standard). The inner bar assemblies were changed to Waldorf White Baking Dulux finish. The outer bars were not striped. A chrome radiator grille package was standard on the Suburban Carryall and optional on other models. The common option included non-striped chrome outer grille bars, while the inner grille bars remained Waldorf White Baking Dulux. Rear corner windows for cab models were again available, but now as part of the DeLuxe Cab and Equipment option package. On trucks with the rear corner windows, a different rear roof panel section was used. A polished chrome Chevrolet nameplate was installed near the rear edge of the "alligator" hood. Below it was a second nameplate indicating the series. It said 3100 on 1/2-ton models. The background of the Chevrolet nameplate was set off with black finish. Chrome-plated curved-type front bumpers were standard on all 3100s. Similar rear bumpers were standard on all models. Chrome hubcaps with vermilion Chevrolet lettering were standard. The 3100 wheels had three pinstripes in the striping colors bracketed below. A two-piece, flat windshield was used. It had a black rubber seal and polished stainless steel divider bar. The gas tank was now located inside the cab (on cab models). Its filler tube came out the rear right-hand corner of the cab, just behind the rotary type, chrome door handles. (The tank and filler location were unchanged on chassis and single-unit body models). Both cab models and single-unit body models had one belt molding stripe, which was Cream Medium with standard finishes. Forester Green was the standard truck color, except for Suburbans. The Suburban's standard two-tone paint scheme was Fathom Green upper/Channel Green lower body. The Suburban came with Fathom Green wheels, other models came with black wheels. The following no-cost color options (pinstripe colors in parentheses) were offered on all models except the Suburban: Swift's Red (Argent Silver), Armour Yellow (Black), White (Emerald Green), Jet Black (Argent Silver), Omaha Orange (Black), Cape Maroon (Gold), Mariner Blue (Cream Medium), Windsor Blue (Cream Medium), Seacrest Green (Cream Medium), Sun Beige (Totem Scarlet), and Cream Medium (Black). The interior was highlighted by wide seats, a large windshield, side and rear windows and an unchanged instrument panel. The instrument panel featured AC instruments: electric fuel gauge and ammeter, pressure-type heat indicator and oil pressure gauge, and dial speedometer driven by a flexible shaft from the transmission. Panel trucks offered optional polished stainless steel rear window reveals. Cab mountings were improved by removing a single rear cab-to-frame shackle and adding two shackles to the rear sides of the cab, creating a four-point cab mounting. Removing the associated gussets freed up space behind the seat to install the interior fuel tank. The 3100 (FP model prefix) trucks had a base 4,600-lb. GVW rating.

1949 Chevrolet 3/4-Ton Model GR Pickup (CMD)

3/4-TON LIGHT-DUTY COMMERCIAL — MODEL GR/SERIES 3600 — SIX-CYLINDER: The 3/4-ton trucks had the same Advance-Design styling, features and finish as other conventional trucks. There was a 3600 call-out below the Chevrolet nameplate on the hood. They had a longer wheelbase. The Pickup load box was longer and had six stake pockets. Long running boards were used. No Suburban, Panel, or Canopy Express was offered in this line. There were Platform and Stake models. The hubcaps were larger than those on 3100s. They looked the same with their vermilion Chevrolet lettering. They were also identical to 3800 series hubcaps. The standard black wheels were of a different design, with an eight-bolt attachment pattern. They were not pinstriped. Curved-type chrome front bumpers were standard on all models. Similar rear bumpers were standard on Models 3602/3603/3604/3612. Base tires on 3600s were 15 in. six-ply rated on 15 x 5.50 semi-drop-center rims. The 15 in. rims had no stripe. Optional 17 in. rims had two Cream Medium stripes. Standard GVW rating for these trucks was 5,200-5,800 lb. depending upon tire options.

1949 Chevrolet 1/2-Ton Model GP Carryall Suburban (CMD)

3/4-TON DUBL-DUTI — MODEL GT/SERIES 3700 — SIX-CYLINDER: Two Dubl-Duti Forward-Control chassis were available. Model 3742 was the 3/4-ton version on a 125.25-in. wheelbase. Standard walk-in delivery truck bodies could be supplied by several factory-approved sources or the buyer could add his/her own body. The wheels were of eight-bolt design.

1949 Chevrolet 1-Ton Model GS Express/Pickup (OCW)

1949 Chevrolet 1-Ton Model GS Express/Pickup (CMD)

1-TON MEDIUM-DUTY COMMERCIAL — MODEL GS/SERIES 3800 — SIX-CYLINDER: The 1-ton had the same Advance-Design styling, features and finish as other conventional trucks. The basic model lineup was unchanged. It included single and dual rear wheel options for all except the Pickup (called the Express), Canopy and Panel. The Pickup had a longer wheelbase than the 3600 Pickup, longer running boards, and a longer load box with eight stake pockets. A curved-type chrome front bumper was standard on all models. A similar rear bumper was standard on Models 3805/3807. Regular equipment tires were 7.00 x 17 six-ply rated for trucks with single rear wheels or 7.00 x 18 eight-ply rated for trucks with dual rear wheel options. The hubcap design was shared with 3100s, though the 3800 hubcaps were larger and identical to 3600 series hubcaps. They had vermilion Chevrolet lettering. The standard black wheels had two pinstripes. No hubcaps were used on the 18 x 5 in. wheels of the Chassis-and-Cab, Platform and Stake models, which had eight bolts and eight circular openings. The standard GVWs for trucks with single rear wheels were 5,700, 6,100, and 6,700 lb. depending on tire options. A base GVW of 8,800 lb. was listed for trucks with optional dual rear wheels. A four-speed manual synchromesh transmission was standard.

1-TON DUBL-DUTI — MODEL GU/SERIES 3900 — SIX-CYLINDER: Two Dubl-Duti Forward-Control chassis returned to the Chevrolet truck line. Model 3942 was the 1-ton version on a 137-in. wheelbase. Standard walk-in delivery truck bodies could be supplied by several factory-approved sources or the buyer could add his/her own body.

1949 Chevrolet 1/2-Ton Model GP Carryall Suburban (CMD)

I.D. DATA: Serial number located: [All] on plate attached to rear face of left-hand door hinge pillar, on right side of cowl under hood. [Chassis models] on plate temporarily attached near steering column, with final location per body maker. The first symbol indicated the assembly plant: 1=Flint, Mich., 2=Tarrytown, N.Y., 3=St. Louis, Mo., 5=Kansas City, Kan., 6=Oakland, Calif., 8=Atlanta, Ga., 9=Norwood, Ohio, 14=Baltimore, Md., 20=Los Angeles, Calif., and 21=Janesville, Wis. The second and third symbols indicate model prefix/series as follows: GJ=Series 1500, GP=3100, GR=3600, GS=3800, GT=3700, GU=3900. The fourth symbol indicates month of assembly, A=Jan., B=Feb., etc. The following symbols indicated the sequential production number. Each series was separately numbered in sequence, starting with 1001 at each assembly plant: Serial numbers: [GJ] GJ-1001 and up, [GP] GP-1001 and up, [GR] GR-1001 and up, [GT] GT-1001 and up, [GS] GS-1001 and up, [GU] GU-1001 and up. Engine numbers located: On crankcase at rear of distributor, right side of engine.

Model	Body Type	Price	Weight	Prod. Total
Sedan Delivery — Model GJ/Series 1508 — 115 in. w.b.				
1271	Sedan Delivery	1465	3050	9310
1/2-Ton Commercial — Model GP/Series 3100 — 116 in. w.b.				
3102	Chassis	961	2430	-
3103	Chassis & Cab	1185	2920	-
3104	Pickup	1253	3185	-
3105	Panel	1450	3425	-
3107	Canopy	1502	3385	-
3116	Suburban	1700	3710	-
3/4-Ton Commercial — Model GR/Series 3600 — 125.25 in. w.b.				
3602	Chassis	1060	2750	-
3603	Chassis & Cab	1284	3170	-
3604	Pickup	1372	3520	-
3608	Platform	1378	3550	-
3609	Stake	1435	3725	-
3/4-Ton Dubl-Duti — Model GT/Series 3700 — 125.25 in. w.b.				
3742	Chassis	1076	2465	-
1-Ton Commercial — Model GS/Series 3800 — 137 in. w.b.				
3802	Chassis	1134	3005	-
3803	Chassis & Cab	1357	3430	-
3804	Pickup	1471	3945	-
3805	Panel	1669	4220	-
3807	Canopy	1746	4180	-
3808	Platform	1487	3960	-
3809	Stake	1560	4215	-
1-Ton Dubl-Duti — Model GU/Series 3900 — 137 in. w.b.				
3942	Chassis	1169	2700	

1949 Chevrolet 1/2-Ton Model GP Panel (CMD)

ENGINE: Inline. OHV. Thriftmaster Six. Six-cylinder. Cast-iron block. Bore & stroke: 3-1/2 x 3-3/4 in. Displacement: 216.5 cid. Compression ratio: 6.6:1. Gross horsepower: 90 at 3300 rpm. Gross torque: 174 lb.-ft. at 1200-2000 rpm. NACC horsepower: 29.4. Four main bearings. Mechanical valve lifters. Carburetor: Carter downdraft one-barrel model WI-574S.

CHASSIS: [Model 1500] Wheelbase: 115 in. Overall length: 196-7/8 in. Height: 67-5/8 in. Front tread: 56-11/16 in. Rear tread: 58-3/4 in. Tires: 6.70 x 15 in. four-ply. GVW: 4,100 lb. Axles and wheels have a new five-lug design.

CHASSIS: [Model 3100] Wheelbase: 116 in. Overall length: 196.6 in. Tires: 6.00 x 16 in. six-ply. GVWs: 4,200 lb./4,500 lb./4,600 lb.

CHASSIS: [Model 3600] Wheelbase: 125.25 in. Overall length: 206 in. Tires: 15 in. six-ply. GVW: 5,200 lb./5,400 lb./5,800 lb.

CHASSIS: [Model 3700] Wheelbase: 125.25 in. Tires: 15 in. six-ply. Maximum GVW: 7,000 lb.

CHASSIS: [Model 3800] Wheelbase: 137 in. Overall length: 223.88 in. Tires: 7.00 x 17 in. six-ply. GVWs: 6,700 lb./8,800 lb.

CHASSIS: [Model 3900] Wheelbase: 137 in. Tires: 7.00 x 17 in. six-ply. Maximum GVW: 10,000 lb.

TECHNICAL: Manual, synchromesh transmission: [1500/3100/3600] 3F/1R column-mounted, [3800] [4F/1R] Floor-mounted gearshift. Single-disc, diaphragm spring clutch. [1500/3100] Semi-floating hypoid rear axle, [3600/3800] full-floating rear axle. Hydraulic, four-wheel brakes. Wheels: [1500] One-piece drop center 15-in. wheels. [3100] One-piece drop center 16 in. wheels, [3600/3800] Multi-piece split rims. Standard rear axles: [1500] 4.11:1, 3.73:1, [3100] 4.11:1, [3600] 4.57:1, [3800] 5.14:1.

1949 Chevrolet Styleline Model GJ Sedan Delivery (CHP)

OPTIONS: [RPO] 1-1/2-in. diameter front and rear double-acting shock absorbers for 3000 series trucks (No. 200). Economy rear axle for Sedan Delivery (No. 201). Long running boards and rear fenders for 3600/3800 Chassis-and-Cab (No 207). 5.14:1 rear axle ratio for 3600 models for house-to-house delivery service (No. 208A). 4.57:1 rear axle ratio for 3800s. Left- and right-hand rear view mirrors and brackets (No. 210). Oil-bath air cleaner for Sedan Delivery and all 3000 series trucks (No. 216). Heavy-duty clutch for 3100s for house-to-house delivery service (No. 227). Platform equipment for 3600 high-sill models (No. 230). Paint Options (No.234 for Commercial Trucks/No. 235 for Sedan Delivery):

1949 Chevrolet 1/2-Ton Model GP Ice Cream Vending Truck (JAG)

Option No. Body Color	DuPont No. (Air-Drying)	Wheel Stripe Color	DuPont Mo. (Air-Drying)
STD Suburban			
Fathom Green (upper)	93-20953	Cream Medium	93-530
Channel Green (lower)	93-20952		
STD Other 3000			
Forester Green	93-62006	Cream Medium	93-530
234-A Swift's Red	93-1863R	Argent Silver	165-5642
234-B Armour Yellow	93-3421	Black	93-005
234-C White	93-508	Emerald Green	93-2537
234-D Jet Black	93-005	Argent Silver	165-5642
234-E Omaha Orange	93-082	Black	93-005
234-F Cape Maroon	93-64539	Gold Bronze	SM-1530AA
234-G Mariner Blue	93-63203	Cream Medium	93-530
234-H Windsor Blue	93-63225	Cream Medium	93-530
234-J Seacrest Green	93-62201	Cream Medium	93-530
234-K Sun Beige	93-61083	Totem Scarlet	93-2767
234-L Cream Medium	93-530	Black	93-005

Truck Radiator Grille Inner Bar: Waldorf White 246-71052 or 93-71052

NOTE 1: The above color combinations were available for Commercial Truck models, as indicated, at all assembly plants. The 1949 Chevrolet trucks were finished in high-luster Dulux synthetic enamel which was baked on in thermostatically controlled ovens. To assist service managers and mechanics in obtaining matching colors when repairs were necessary, the air-drying Dulux number was listed, instead of the number of the Baking Dulux type paint.

1949 Chevrolet 1-Ton Model GS Canopy (ATC)

Option No. Body Color	DuPont No. (Duco)	Wheel Stripe Color	DuPont Mo. (Duco)
STD Sed. Dly.			
Mayland Black	253-2122	Argent Silver	289-4202
235-A Liveoak Green (Met.)	207-36777	Argent Silver	289-4202
235-B Grecian Gray	253-7869	Mayland Black	253-2122
235-C Vista Gray (Met.)	207-36307	Argent Silver	289-4202
235-D Monaco Blue (Met.)	207-39277	Argent Silver	289-4202
235-E Oxford Maroon (Met.)	207-39638	Argent Silver	289-4202
Sedan Delivery Two-Tones			
235-G Liveoak Green (Met.)	207-36777	Argent Silver	289-4202
Satin Green	253-39814		
235-H Vista Gray (Met)	207-36307	Argent Silver	289-4202
Grecian Gray	2253-7869		

NOTE 2: Color codes shown for Sedan Delivery are Duco paint numbers.

1949 Chevrolet 3/4-Ton Model GR Platform Stake (CMD)

NOTE 3: Dulux wheel colors for Sedan Delivery were: (STD) Black No. 505, (235-A) Liveoak Green No. 538, (235-B) Grecian Gray No. 551, (235-C) Monaco Blue No. 553, (235-E) Oxford Maroon No. 512.

Oil filter with 2-1/2-quart dry capacity (No. 237). Governor for standard 216 cid engine only (No. 241). Tail and stop lamp equipment for installation on Sedan Delivery, Carryall Suburban, Panel, and Canopy Express models (No. 249). Heavy-duty rear springs for 3100s (No. 254). 17-1/2-quart cooling system with heavy-duty radiator (No. 256). Right-hand front tilting auxiliary seat for Panel and Canopy Express models (No. 263). Heavy-duty three-speed manual transmission with steering column gear shift for Sedan Delivery (No. 316). Heavy-duty four-speed manual transmission for 3100/3600 (No. 318). School bus equipment for model 3802 (No. 329A). Fuel and vacuum pump for all except 3700/3900 (No.

340). True-Stop brake equipment, required on school bus in some states (No. 348). Genuine leather seat trim for single unit body models (No 361). Front bumper equipment 3700/3900 (No. 367). Spare wheel and tire carrier for 3700/3900 (No. 384). Chrome radiator grille for all 3000 except model 3116 (No. 386). Wide running boards for 3104 Pickup only (No. 389). DeLuxe Cab equipment consisting of rear corner windows, bright metal windshield and door window reveals, door window garnish molding, seat back trim panel, arm rest on driver's side door, and right-hand sun shade and chrome-plated radiator grille on 3000 series models (No. 390) DeLuxe Panel equipment, including bright metal reveals for side door windows, bright metal reveals for rear door windows, bright metal windshield reveals, garnish moldings for side door windows, arm rest for driver's side door, bright metal moldings for front and rear fenders, right-hand sun shade, and chrome-plated radiator grille (No. 390; not available on Canopy Express or Carryall Suburban). Stake and stock rack equipment (all Stake, Express Stake, and High-Rack models.) Various tire options as follows:

1949 Chevrolet 1-Ton Model GS Panel (CMD)

Light Duty Truck Tire Options

Option No.	Size	Ply Rating	Capacity (lb.)	PSI	Section (in.)
273	15 in.	Six-ply	1500	40	7.74
280	15 in.	Eight-ply	1700	48	7.74
n.a.	6.00 x 16	Six-ply	1065	36	6.21
282	6.50 x 16	Six-ply	1290	40	6.65
n.a.	6.70 x 15	Four-ply	920	24	n.a.
n.a.	6.70 x 15	Six-ply	920	30	n.a.
277	7.00 x 17	Six-ply	1575	45	7.30
n.a.	7.00 x 17	Eight-ply	1775	55	7.30
272	7.50 x 17	Eight-ply	2100	60	7.36
295	7.00 x 18	Eight-ply	1800	55	7.24

1949 Chevrolet 3/4-Ton Model GR Pickup (CMD)

DEALER ACCESSORIES: Rod type radio antenna. Adjustable fabrikoid radiator cover. Right- and left-hand door arm rests (maroon or brown). Dual horns. Auxiliary driving lamps. Gasoline filter. Outside air ventilator, heater, and defroster system. Dash recirculating heater and defroster unit. 20-1/2-in. high by 36-in. long truck grille guard to fit chrome or channel-type bumpers. Safety-Light spot lamp. Long-arm outside rear view mirror. Glare-Proof inside rear view mirror. Bracket for cowl-mounted rear view mirror. Radiator overflow condenser. Red reflex reflector. Running board safety tread plate. "Lollipop" style lights included in directional signal kit. Under hood light. Load compartment light for Panels only. Back-up lamp for attachment to rear of Sedan Delivery only. Cigarette lighter. Illuminated cigarette lighter. DeLuxe radio and antenna. Interior sun shades (visors). Tire traction mat assembly. Automatic, push-button start windshield washer. Locking gas cap. License plate frame. Curved bumper guard. Static eliminator. Powder for static eliminator. Magnetic plugs for rear axle filler, transmission drain and oil pan drain. Ventilated seat pad. Radiator insect screen. Electric shaver. Tool kit with bag and tools.

1949 Chevrolet 1/2-Ton Model GP Pickup (OCW)

HISTORICAL: Introduced to dealers January 1949. Calendar-year registrations: [All Commercial] 345,519. Calendar-year production: [All Commercial] 383,543, [All Commercial below 5,000-lb. GVW] 201,537, [All Commercials with 5,001-10,000-lb. GVWs] 97,678. Market share: [All Commercials] 33.88 percent. The Sedan Delivery was not in the Commercial Truck line. It was considered a Commercial Car. Innovations: All-new styling for Sedan Delivery. New four-point cab mountings. Cantrell wood-bodied station wagons and Olsen Kurbside delivery trucks were built on the Chevrolet chassis this year.

1950 Chevrolet 1/2-Ton Model HJ Panel (OCW)

SEDAN DELIVERY — MODEL HJ/SERIES 1500 — SIX-CYLINDER: The passenger car-based Sedan Delivery was part of Chevrolet's Styleline Special series. It had a new frontal treatment. The grille used the same upper and center molding bars and circular parking lamps as the 1949 grille. The outer vertical moldings were the same, but the five intermediate vertical moldings of 1949 were replaced with two inner moldings with three slots in them. A completely new grille reinforcement panel was used. There was a different hood ornament. The 73-in. load floor length gave a usable cargo area of 92.5 cu. ft. Many historians say the Sedan delivery is based on the Station Wagon, but that is an oversimplification of fact. The windshield glass (non-tinted only) was the same used on some passenger cars, but not Station Wagons. Doors were specific to the Sedan Delivery and not used on other cars. Front door window glass was the same used on 1949-1952 four-door Sedans, not Station Wagons. Lower rear quarter panel stampings were unique to the Sedan Delivery. However, the rear compartment floor panel was same one used for 1949-1952 Station Wagons. Rear bumper bars, ends and guards were also the same as wagon parts. Brown imitation leather trim Combination No. 163 was introduced in 1950.

1950 Chevrolet 1/2-Ton Model HP Pickup (P. Bachman)

1/2-TON LIGHT-DUTY COMMERCIAL — MODEL HP/SERIES 3100 — SIX-CYLINDER: The 1950 conventional trucks had some technical changes from the prior Advance-Design models. Appearance features and finish had only minor changes. All 3100s had improved seat cushion padding. A 56-in. wide bench seat was standard in cab models. The Suburban Carryall with panel rear doors was reintroduced. Forester Green was now the standard for all models, including Suburbans and Suburbans were now available in all 12 colors that Chevrolet offered for trucks. In 1/2-ton models, new direct double-acting shock absorbers with one-inch piston diameters were standard all around. There was an improved Rochester B carburetor, and a new circuit breaker lighting system. A revamped version of the Thriftmaster six was standard in 3100/3600/3800 models. It had a new "Power Jet" downdraft carburetor, larger exhaust valves and a straight-through muffler. The unchanged grille again had five broad horizontal bars topped by a broad hood ornament with a cloisonné blue (metallic) bow tie emblem and vermilion Chevrolet lettering on a chrome background. Rectangular parking lights were again placed in chrome housings between the ends of the top two grille bars. A painted grille was standard equipment on all models, except Suburban Carryalls. The outer grille bar assembly was again done in body color (Forester Green remained standard). The inner bar assemblies retained their Waldorf White finish. The outer bars were not striped. A chrome radiator grille package was standard on the Suburban Carryall and optional on other models. The chrome option included non-striped chrome outer grille bars, while the inner grille bars remained Waldorf White. Rear corner windows for cab models were again optional. On trucks with the rear corner windows, a different rear roof panel section was used. A polished chrome Chevrolet nameplate was installed near the rear edge of the "alligator" hood. Below it was a second nameplate indicating the series: 3100 for 1/2-tons.

The upper edge of the base of the Chevrolet nameplate was set off with Black Baking Dulux finish. Chrome-plated curved-type front bumpers were standard on all 3100s. Similar rear bumpers were standard on all models. Chrome hubcaps with vermilion Chevrolet lettering were standard. The 3100 wheels had three pinstripes in the striping colors bracketed below. Forester Green wheels were now standard on Suburbans, but the wheels were painted body color when paint options were ordered. On other trucks, black wheels were standard. When the RPO 390 DeLuxe Equipment package was ordered, the wheels were body color on trucks with hubcaps and black on others. Wheel striping varied with tires. There were three stripes when 6.70 x 15 tires were mounted, no stripes with the 15-in. wheel, three stripes with 16-in. rims and two stripes with 17-in. rims. A two-piece, flat windshield was used. It had a black rubber seal and polished stainless steel divider bar. The gas tank was again located inside cab models. Its filler tube came out rear right-hand corner of the cab, just behind the doors with rotary type chrome handles. The filler was just ahead of the rear wheels on single-unit body models. Both cab models and single-unit body models had one belt molding stripe, which was Cream Medium with standard finish. The following no-cost color options (pinstripe colors in parentheses) were offered on all models: Swift's Red (Argent Silver), Armour Yellow (Black), White (Emerald Green), Jet Black (Argent Silver), Omaha Orange (Black), Cape Maroon (Gold), Mariner Blue (Cream Medium), Windsor Blue (Cream Medium), Seacrest Green (Cream Medium), Sun Beige (Totem Scarlet), and Cream Medium (Black). The unchanged instrument panel featured AC instruments including an electric fuel gauge, an electric ammeter, a pressure-type heat indicator, an oil pressure gauge, and a dial speedometer driven by a flexible shaft from the transmission. Panel trucks offered optional polished stainless steel rear window reveals. The 3100 (HP model prefix) trucks had a base 4,600-lb. GVW rating.

1950 Chevrolet 3/4-Ton Model HR Pickup (CMD)

3/4-TON LIGHT-DUTY COMMERCIAL — MODEL HR/SERIES 3600 — SIX-CYLINDER: The 3/4-ton trucks had the same Advance-Design styling, features and finish as other conventional trucks. Eight-leaf front springs were made standard for these 3600 models. They had 3600 hood nameplates and a longer wheelbase. The Pickup load box was longer and had six stake pockets. Long running boards were used. No Suburban, Panel or Canopy Express was offered in this line. There were Platform and Stake models. The hubcaps were larger than the ones on 3100s with similar vermilion Chevrolet lettering. The standard black wheels were of eight-bolt design and not pinstriped. Curved-type chrome front bumpers were standard on all models. Similar rear bumpers were standard on Models 3602/3603/3604/3612. Base tires on 3600s were 15 in. six-ply rated on 15 x 5.50 semi-drop-center rims. The 15 in. rims had no stripe and 17 in. rims had two Cream Medium stripes. The GVW rating range for these trucks was 5,200-5,800 lb. depending upon tire options. The 3600s had the same new direct double-acting hydraulic shock absorbers as the 3100s.

3/4-TON DUBL-DUTI — MODEL HT/SERIES 3700 — SIX-CYLINDER: Two Dubl-Duti Forward-Control chassis remained in the Chevrolet truck line. Both had a new 235 cid "Loadmaster" six. Due to a less efficient updraft carburetor, this engine had the same horsepower rating as the 216 cid Thriftmaster six. Model 3742 was the 3/4-ton version on a 125.25-in. wheelbase. Standard walk-in delivery truck bodies could be supplied by several factory-approved sources or the buyer could add his/her own body. The wheels were of eight-bolt design. The 3700s had the same new direct double-acting hydraulic shock absorbers as the 3100s.

1950 Chevrolet 1-Ton Model HS Stake Bed (OCW)

1-TON MEDIUM-DUTY COMMERCIAL — MODEL HS/SERIES 3800 — SIX-CYLINDER: The 3800 Series had the same Advance-Design styling, features and finish as other conventional trucks. The call-out under the hood nameplate said 3800. These models were available with an optional power brake system. This Hydrovac brake booster reduced pedal effort by two-thirds. Panel and Canopy models had a one-piece floor made of 3/4-in. thick, five-ply laminated wood. The

basic model lineup was unchanged. It included single and dual rear wheel options for all except the Express, Canopy and Panel. The Pickup (or Express) had a longer wheelbase than the 3600 Pickup, longer running boards, and a longer load box with eight stake pockets. A curved-type chrome front bumper was standard on all models. A similar rear bumper was standard on Models 3805/3807. Regular equipment tires were 7.00 x 17 six-ply rated for trucks with single rear wheels or 7.00 x 18 eight-ply rated for trucks with dual rear wheel options. The hubcaps were the same ones used on 3600s. They had vermilion Chevrolet lettering. The standard black wheels had two pinstripes. No hubcaps were used on the 18 x 5 in. wheels of the Chassis-and-Cab, Platform and Stake models, which had eight bolts and eight circular openings. The standard GVWs for trucks with single rear wheels were 5,700, 6,100, and 6,700 lb. depending on tire options. A GVW of 8,800 lb. was listed for trucks with optional dual rear wheels. A four-speed manual synchromesh transmission was standard.

1950 Chevrolet 1-Ton Model HS Panel (OCW)

1-TON DUBL-DUTI — MODEL HU/SERIES 3900 — SIX-CYLINDER: Two Dubl-Duti Forward-Control chassis were again part of the Chevrolet truck line. Both had a new 235 cid "Loadmaster" six. Due to a less efficient updraft carburetor, this engine had the same horsepower rating as the 216 cid Thriftmaster six. Model 3942 was the 1-ton version on a 137-in. wheelbase. Standard walk-in delivery truck bodies could be supplied by several factory-approved sources or the buyer could add his/her own body.

1950 Chevrolet 1/2-Ton Model HP Pickup (OCW)

I.D. DATA: Serial number located: [Chassis models] on plate temporarily attached near steering column, with final location per body maker. [Others] On plate attached to rear face of left-hand door hinge pillar. The first symbol indicated the assembly plant: 1=Flint, Mich., 2=Tarrytown, N.Y., 3=St. Louis, Mo., 5=Kansas City, Kan., 6=Oakland, Calif., 8=Atlanta, Ga., 9=Norwood, Ohio, 14=Baltimore, Md., 20=Los Angeles, Calif., and 21=Janesville, Wis. The second and third symbols indicate model prefix/series as follows: HJ=Series 1500, HP=3100, HR=3600, HS=3800, HT=3700, HU=3900. The fourth symbol indicates month of assembly, A=Jan., B=Feb., etc. The following symbols indicated the sequential production number. Each series was separately numbered in sequence, starting with 1001 at each assembly plant. Serial numbers were as follows: [Series 1500] HJ-1001 to 49801, [Series 3100] HP-1001 to 37721, [Series 3600] HR-1001 to 12078, [Series 3742] HT-1001 to 1600, [Series 3800] HS-1001 to 5611 and [Series 3942] HU-1001 to 1408. Engine numbers stamped on crankcase near rear of distributor on right side of engine. Motor numbers were as follows: [Series 1500] HA-1001 to 1320152, [Series 3100] HB-1001 to 1320152, [Series 3600] HC-1001 to 1320152, [Series 3742/3800/3942] same as 3600 Series.

1950 Chevrolet 1/2-Ton Model HP Suburban (OCW)

1950 Chevrolet 1/2-Ton Model HP Pickup (OCW)

Model	Body Type	Price	Weight	Prod. Total
Sedan Delivery — Model HJ/Series 1500 — 115 in. w.b.				
1271	Sedan Delivery	1455	3105	-
1/2-Ton Commercial — Model HP/Series 3100 — 116 in. w.b.				
3103	Chassis & Cab	1175	2910	-
3104	Pickup	1243	3175	-
3105	Panel	1440	3375	-
3106	Suburban (doors)	1690	3670	-
3107	Canopy	1492	3335	-
3116	Suburban (gate)	1690	3675	-
3/4-Ton Commercial — Model HR/Series 3600 — 125.25 in. w.b.				
3602	Chassis	1050	2710	-
3603	Chassis & Cab	1274	3170	-
3604	Pickup	1302	3515	-
3608	Platform	1308	3560	-
3609	Stake	1425	3700	-
3/4-Ton Dubl-Duti — Model HT/Series 3700 — 125.5 in. w.b.				
3742	Chassis	1066	2475	-
1-Ton Commercial — Model HS/Series 3800 — 137 in. w.b.				
3802	Chassis	1124	2980	-
3803	Chassis & Cab	1347	3440	-
3804	Pickup	1461	3930	-
3805	Panel	1659	4190	-
3807	Canopy Express	1736	4145	-
3808	Platform	1477	4010	-
3809	Stake Bed	1550	4255	-
1-Ton Dubl-Duti — Model HU/Series 3900 — 137 in. w.b.				
3942	Chassis	1159	2640	-

1950 Chevrolet 1-Ton Model HS Express/Pickup (CMD)

1950 Chevrolet 1-Ton Model HS Panel (CMD)

ENGINE: [Standard Series 1500/3100/3600/3800] Inline. OHV. Thriftmaster. Six-cylinder. Cast-iron block. Bore & stroke: 3-1/2 x 3-3/4 in. Displacement: 216.5 cid. Compression ratio: 6.6:1. Gross horsepower: 92 at 3400 rpm. Net horsepower: 85 at 3300 rpm. Gross torque: 176 lb.-ft. at 1000-2000 rpm. Net torque: 170 at 1000 to 2000 rpm. NCCA horsepower: 29.4. Four main bearings. Mechanical valve lifters. Carburetor: Single one-barrel model Rochester Model B Power Jet downdraft.
ENGINE: [Standard Dubl-Duti] Inline. OHV. Loadmaster. Six-cylinder. Cast-iron block. Bore & stroke: 3-9/16 x 3-15/16 in. Displacement: 235.5 cid. Compression ratio: 6.7:1. Brake horsepower: 92 at 3400 rpm. Net horsepower: 30.4. Four main bearings. Mechanical valve lifters. Carburetor: Single one-barrel model Carter updraft.

CHASSIS: [Model 1500] Wheelbase: 115 in. Overall length: 196-7/8 in. Height: 67-5/8 in. Front tread: 56-11/16 in. Rear tread: 58-3/4 in. Tires: 6.70 x 15 in. GVW: 4,100 lb.
CHASSIS: [Model 3100] Wheelbase: 116 in. Overall length: 196.6 in. Tires: 6.00 x 16 in. six-ply. GVWs: 4,200 lb./4,500 lb./4,600 lb.
CHASSIS: [Model 3600] Wheelbase: 125.25 in. Overall length: 206 in. Tires: 15 in. six-ply. GVWs: 5,200 lb./5,400 lb./5,800 lb.
CHASSIS: [Model 3700] Wheelbase: 125.25 in. Tires: 15 in. six-ply. Maximum GVW: 7,000 lb.
CHASSIS: [Model 3800] Wheelbase: 137 in. Overall length: 223.88 in. Tires: 7.00 x 17 in. six-ply. GVWs: 6,700 lb./8,800 lb.
CHASSIS: [Model 3900] Wheelbase: 137 in. Tires: 7.00 x 17 in. six-ply. Maximum GVW: 10,000 lb.

1950 Chevrolet 1/2-Ton Model HP Pickup With DeLuxe Cab Equipment (OCW)

TECHNICAL: Manual, synchromesh transmission: [1500/3100/3600] 3F/1R column-mounted, [3800] [4F/1R] Floor-mounted gearshift. Single-disc, diaphragm spring clutch. [1500/3100] Semi-floating hypoid rear axle, [3600/3800] full-floating rear axle. Hydraulic, four-wheel brakes. Wheels: [1500] One-piece drop center 15 in. wheels. [3100] One-piece drop center 16 in. wheels, [3600/3800] Multi-piece split rims. Standard rear axles: [1500] 4.11:1, 3.73:1, [3100] 4.11:1, [3600] 4.57:1, [3800] 5.14:1.
OPTIONS: [RPO] Direct double-acting rear shock absorbers, except standard on 3100-3700 models (No. 200). Long running boards and rear fenders (No. 207). 5.14:1 rear axle ratio (No. 208). Rear view mirrors and brackets: short right-hand, long left-hand bracket only, long right-hand and short left-hand bracket only (No. 210). Rear shock absorber shield (No. 211). Hydrovac power brake (No. 213). Oil bath air cleaner (No. 216). Heavy-duty clutch (No. 227).
Paint Options 234-235

Option No.	Body Color	DuPont No. (Air-Drying)	Wheel Stripe Color	DuPont Mo. (Air-Drying)
STD Suburban				
	Fathom Green (upper)	93-20953	Cream Medium	93-530
	Channel Green (lower)	93-20952		
STD Other 3000				
	Forester Green	93-62006	Cream Medium	93-530
234-A	Swift's Red	93-1863R	Argent Silver	165-5642
234-B	Armour Yellow	93-3421	Black	93-005
234-C	White	93-508	Emerald Green	93-2537
234-D	Jet Black	93-005	Argent Silver	165-5642
234-E	Omaha Orange	93-082	Black	93-005
234-F	Cape Maroon	93-64539	Gold Bronze	SM-1530AA
234-G	Mariner Blue	93-63203	Cream Medium	93-530
234-H	Windsor Blue	93-63225	Cream Medium	93-530
234-J	Seacrest Green	93-62201	Cream Medium	93-530
234-K	Sun Beige	93-61083	Totem Scarlet	93-2767
234-L	Cream Medium	93-530	Black	93-005

Truck Radiator Grille Inner Bar: Waldorf White 246-71052 or 93-71052
NOTE 1: The above color combinations were available for Commercial Truck models, as indicated, at all assembly plants. The 1950 Chevrolet trucks were finished in high-luster Dulux synthetic enamel which was baked on in thermostatically controlled ovens. To assist service managers and mechanics in obtaining matching colors when repairs were necessary, the air-drying Dulux number was listed, instead of the number of the Baking Dulux type paint.

1950 Chevrolet 1/2-Ton Model HP Suburban (OCW)

1950 Chevrolet 1/2-Ton Model HP Suburban (OCW)

Option No. Body Color		DuPont No. (Duco)	Wheel Stripe Color	DuPont Mo. (Duco)
STD Sed. Dly.				
	Mayland Black	246-2048	Argent Silver	165-021
235-A	Mist Green	253-55504	Mayland Black	95-004
235-B	Grecian Gray	246-7869	Mayland Black	95-004
235-C	Falcon Gray	281-55501	Argent Silver	165-021
235-D	Windsor Blue	286-55498	Cream Medium	93-530
235-E	Crystal Green	287-55255	Argent Silver	165-021
235-F	Oxford Maroon	207-39638	Argent Silver	165-021
235-J	Rodeo Beige	281-55505	French White	28953561
Sedan Delivery Two-Tones				
235-G	Mist Green Crystal Green	253-55504	Mayland Black	95-004
235-H	Grecian Gray Falcon Gray	246-7869	Mayland Black	95-004

NOTE 2: Color codes shown for Sedan Delivery are Duco paint numbers.
NOTE 3: Dulux wheel colors for Sedan Delivery were: (STD) Black No. 505, (235-A) Liveoak Green No. 538, (235-B) Grecian Gray No. 551, (235-C) Falcon Gray No. 563, (235-D) Windsor Blue No. 564, (235-E) Crystal Green No. 554, (235-F) Oxford Maroon No. 512, (235-G) Mist Green No.565, (235-H) Grecian Gray No. 551, (235-J) Rodeo Beige No. 566.
Oil filter (No. 237). Governor (No. 241). Dual tail and stop light (No. 249). Heavy-duty rear springs (No. 254). Heavy-duty radiator (No. 256). Right-hand auxiliary seat (No. 263). Auxiliary rear springs (No. 267). Heavy-duty three-speed transmission for Sedan Delivery only (No. 316). Heavy-duty four-speed(No. 361). Front bumper for Forward-Control chassis (No. 367). Chrome radiator grille (No. 386). DeLuxe equipment package for all cab models and Panel (No. 390). transmission (No. 318). Combination fuel and vacuum pump (No. 340). Various tire options, as follows:

Light Duty Truck Tire Options

Option No.	Size	Ply Rating	Capacity (lb.)	PSI	Section (in.)
273	15 in.	Six-ply	1500	40	7.74
280	15 in.	Eight-ply	1700	48	7.74
n.a.	6.00 x 16	Six-ply	1065	36	6.21
282	6.50 x 16	Six-ply	1290	40	6.65
n.a.	6.70 x 15	Four-ply	920	24	n.a.
n.a.	6.70 x 15	Six-ply	1050	30	n.a.
277	7.00 x 17	Six-ply	1575	45	7.30
n.a.	7.00 x 17	Eight-ply	1775	55	7.30
272	7.50 x 17	Eight-ply	2100	60	7.36
295	7.00 x 18	Eight-ply	1800	55	7.24
n.a.	7.50 x 17	10-ply	2395	75	n.a.

1950 Chevrolet Styleline Special Model HJ Sedan Delivery (Modern Wheels)

DEALER ACCESSORIES: Rod type radio antenna (all). Right- or left-hand door arm rest, Maroon (all except Suburban). Right- or left-hand door arm rest, brown (Suburban only). Locking gas cap (all). Radiator cover (all). Maroon seat cover (all cab models). Fiber seat cover (all cab models). Gasoline filter (all). License plate frame (all). Curved bumper guard (all except Dubl-Duti). Radiator grille guard for curved type bumper (all except Dubl-Duti). Bumper guard for curved type bumper (all except Dubl-Duti). Outside air heater/defroster (all except Chassis & Cowl). Recirculated air type heater (all except Chassis & Cowl). Matched horns (all). Static eliminator injector (all). Powder for static eliminator injector (all). Guide dual sealed-beam

fog lights (all). Guide spotlight with bracket (all). Unity spotlight with bracket (all). Magnetic trouble lamp (all). Universal stop and taillamps (all). Load compartment lamp (Panel). Underhood lamp (all). Package compartment light and switch (all). Front and rear directional signals (all). Front signal lamps, single lens (all). Front signal lamps, double lens (all). Rear signal lamp with switch (all). Cigarette lighter (all). Two tire traction mats (all). Non-glare rear view mirror (all). Long-arm adjustable outside rear view mirror (all). Bracket unit for cowl-mounted rear view mirror (all). Hood ornament (all). Ventilated seat pad (all). Rear axle magnetic filler plug (all). Magnetic transmission drain plug (all). Magnetic oil pan drain plug, (all). Delco radio receiving set, plus antenna (all except Chassis & Cowl). Four-inch red Reflex reflector (all). Windshield scraper (all). Radiator insect screen (all). Electric shaver (all). Right-hand sun shade (all). Running board safety tread (all). Tool kit bag and tools (all). Windshield washer (all).
OPTIONS: [Authorized Aftermarket] A four-wheel drive (4x4) conversion by NAPCO Products, Co., of Minneapolis, Minn., was available for 1950-1954 Chevrolet trucks with open drive shafts, but not on 3100s featuring torque tube drive. It was merchandised through Chevrolet dealers for approximately $1,200. NAPCO literature describes it as a "Powr-Pak" four-wheel drive system that shifted in and out of four-wheel drive without stopping or declutching. It featured a two-speed transfer case (eight forward speeds and two in reverse) and full-engine-torque power-take-off. NAPCO also promoted a Chevrolet "Mountain Goat" 4x4 Pickup model.

1950 Chevrolet 1-Ton Model HS Panel (OCW)

HISTORICAL: Dealer introduction: January, 1950. Calendar-year registrations: [All Commercials] 414,496. Calendar-year production: [All Commercials] 494,573, [All Commercials 5,000 lb. and less GVW] 265,515. [All Commercials 5,001 lb.-10,000-lb. GVW] 102,669. The Sedan Delivery is not a Commercial model. Innovations: Improved engines. Suburban with panel doors reintroduced. Wider seats with improved padding. This was all-time record for sales of the Sedan Delivery to date. It was also a record year for production of Commercial models. In the month of August alone, 45,779 trucks were built.

1951 CHEVROLET

1951 Chevrolet Model 1508 Sedan Delivery (OCW)

SEDAN DELIVERY — MODEL JJ/SERIES 1500 — SIX-CYLINDER: The passenger car-based Sedan Delivery was still a member of Chevrolet's Styleline Special series. A completely new radiator grille was used in 1951. A narrow chrome upper molding had a Chevrolet script stamped into it. Below this was a ribbed horizontal deflector, a veed horizontal chrome molding, a plain deflector with nine tabs on its lower edge and another veed horizontal molding at the bottom. The veed chrome horizontal moldings were connected at each end by sideways U-shaped moldings. This gave the entire lower section of the grille a loop-like appearance. Parking lamp housings with five vertical slots fit inside the U-shaped moldings on either end. There was a different hood ornament. The 73-in. long load floor with a usable load space of 92.5 cu. ft. remained unchanged. The Sedan Delivery's windshield glass (non-tinted only) was the same used on some passenger cars, but not wagons. Doors were specific to this model and not used on other cars (although Sedan doors can be modified to fit). Front door window glass was the same used on 1949-1952 four-door Sedans, not wagons. Lower rear quarter panel stampings were unique to the Sedan Delivery. However, the rear compartment floor panel was same one used for 1949-1952 Station Wagons. Rear bumper bars, ends and guards were also the same as wagon parts. Standard equipment included front and rear bumpers and bumper guards, front license guard, hood ornament and emblem, chrome-plated headlamp rims with doors, dual windshield wipers, dual horns, outside key locks, front and rear bumper gravel deflectors, one combination tail/stop/license plate lamp, bright, full-length rear fender crown molding, bright metal windshield divider, bright windshield reveal molding, bright rear window reveal molding, Bonderized body and sheet metal, plain plastic control knob inserts, chrome-plated radio grille, three-position ignition switch, left-hand sun shade and dome light. Interior trim was still brown imitation leather, combination number 163. Mayland Black was the standard body color for Sedan Deliveries. Other choices included Aspen Green, Thistle Gray, Trophy Blue, Burgundy Red, and Waldorf White. Two-tone color combinations were no longer a regular production option, but could be special-ordered at extra cost.

1951 Chevrolet 1/2-Ton Series 3100 Pickup (OCW)

1/2-TON LIGHT-DUTY COMMERCIAL — MODEL JP/SERIES 3100 — SIX-CYLINDER: Conventional trucks looked the same overall, but had some easy-to-spot changes. The left side cowl vent was eliminated. New ventipanes (door vent windows) were used instead. Korean War material restrictions led to discontinuance of many bright metal parts. Chrome grilles were not available, even on Carryall Suburbans, due to the war. The unchanged grille again had five broad horizontal bars topped by a broad hood ornament with a Cloisonné Blue (metallic) bow tie emblem and vermilion Chevrolet lettering on a chrome background. Rectangular parking lights were again placed in housings between the ends of the uppermost pair of grille bars. The outer grille bar assembly was painted body color (Forester Green was standard). The inner bar assemblies were painted Waldorf White. The outer bars were not striped. A curved, chrome front bumper was standard on all 3100 models until at least August 1951. Curved chrome rear bumpers were standard for single-unit body conventional trucks, but were not factory-supplied for cab models. Chevrolet hood side nameplates were still used. New research by Bob Adler proves that 1951 models didn't have 3100 series designators under the Chevrolet hood side nameplates, despite the fact that they show in some factory illustrations and literature. A foot-operated parking brake was now used on all 3100 models. Front brake linings in 1/2-tons were larger and bonded. Brakes on 3100 models were now of the Bendix duo-servo self-energizing type, instead of the old Huck type. Rear corner windows for cab models were optional. On trucks with this option, a different rear roof section was used. Hubcaps and wheels looked the same. The 3100 wheels had three pinstripes in the striping colors bracketed below. The gas tank was inside cab models. Its filler tube came out the rear right-hand corner of the cab, just behind the rotary type, chrome door handles. The filler was just ahead of the rear wheels on single-unit body models. Both cab models and single-unit body models had one belt molding stripe, which was Cream Medium with standard finish. The unchanged no-cost color options (pinstripe colors in parentheses) were offered on all models: Swift's Red (Argent Silver), Armour Yellow (Black), White (Emerald Green), Jet Black (Argent Silver), Omaha Orange (Black), Cape Maroon (Gold), Mariner Blue (Cream Medium), Windsor Blue (Cream Medium), Seacrest Green (Cream Medium), Sun Beige (Totem Scarlet), and Cream Medium (Black). The unchanged instrument panel featured AC instruments: electric fuel gauge and ammeter, pressure-type heat indicator and oil pressure gauge, and dial speedometer driven by a flexible shaft from the transmission.

1951 Chevrolet 3/4-Ton Series 3600 Pickup (CMD)

3/4-TON LIGHT-DUTY COMMERCIAL — MODEL JR/SERIES 3600 — SIX-CYLINDER: The 3/4-ton trucks had the same Advance-Design styling, features and finish as other conventional trucks. A Chevrolet nameplate was on the sides of the hood. The *1958 Chevrolet Master Parts Catalog* also lists a 3600 nameplate for 1949-1954 Series 3600 trucks. There is anecdotal evidence that 1951 models didn't have these series designators, despite the fact that they appear in some factory illustrations. Eight-leaf front springs were standard. These trucks had a longer wheelbase than 1/2-tons. The Pickup load box was longer than the 3100 type and had six stake pockets. Long running boards were used. No Carryall Suburban, Panel or Canopy Express was offered in this line. There were Platform and Stake models. The 3600 hubcaps looked like the ones on 3100s, but were larger and identical to those used on 3800s. The standard black wheels were of eight-bolt design and not pinstriped. Curved-type chrome front bumpers were standard on all models. Brakes were still of the Huck type. The tires on 3600s were 15-in. six-ply rated on 15 x 5.50 semi-drop-center rims. The 15-in. rims had no pinstripe, and the 17-in. rims had two pinstripes.

3/4-TON DUBL-DUTI — MODEL JT/SERIES 3700 — SIX-CYLINDER: Two Dubl-Duti Forward-Control chassis were in the Chevrolet truck line. Both had the 235-cid Loadmaster six with an updraft carburetor. Due to the lower efficiency of the updraft carburetor, this engine had the same horsepower rating as the 216-cid Thriftmaster six. Model 3742 was the 3/4-ton version on a 125.25-in. wheelbase. Standard walk-in Delivery truck bodies could be supplied by several factory-approved sources or the buyer could add his/her own body. The wheels were of eight-bolt design. A painted, Anvil Gray channel type front bumper was a regular production option (RPO) on the 3700 Dubl-Duti truck chassis.

1-TON MEDIUM-DUTY COMMERCIAL — MODEL JS/SERIES 3800 — SIX-CYLINDER: The 3800 Series had the same Advance-Design styling, features and finish as other conventional trucks. A Chevrolet nameplate was on the sides of the hood. A hand-operated parking brake was still used on 3800 models. Huck type rear brakes were also still used on the 1-tons. These models were available with an optional power brake system. This Hydrovac brake booster reduced pedal effort by two-thirds. Panel and Canopy Express models had a one-piece floor made of 3/4-in. thick, five-ply laminated wood. The basic model lineup was unchanged. It included single and dual rear wheel options for all except the Pickup (or Express), the Canopy Express, and the Panel. The Pickup had a longer wheelbase than the 3600 Pickup, longer running boards, and a longer load box with eight stake pockets. A curved-type chrome front bumper was standard on all models. A similar rear bumper was standard on Models 3805 and 3807. Regular equipment tires were 7.00 x 17 six-ply rated for trucks with single rear wheels or 7.00 x 18 eight-ply rated for trucks with dual rear wheel options. The hubcap design was shared with 3100s, although the 3600/3800 style hubcaps were larger. The standard black wheels had two pinstripes. No hubcaps were used on the 18 x 5-in. wheels of the Chassis-and-Cab, Platform, and Stake models, which had eight bolts and eight circular openings. A four-speed transmission was standard.

1-TON DUBL-DUTI — MODEL JU/SERIES 3900 — SIX-CYLINDER: Two Dubl-Duti Forward-Control chassis returned to the Chevrolet truck line. Both had a new 235-cid Loadmaster six with an updraft carburetor. Due to the lower efficiency of the updraft carburetor, this engine had the same horsepower rating as the 216-cid Thriftmaster six. Model 3942 was the 1-ton version on a 1137-in. wheelbase. Standard walk-in Delivery truck bodies could be supplied by several factory-approved sources or the buyer could add his/her own body. A painted Anvil Gray channel type front bumper was standard on the 3900 Dubl-Duti truck chassis.

1951 Chevrolet 1/2-Ton Series 3100 Pickup (OCW)

I.D. DATA: Serial number located: [Chassis models] on plate temporarily attached near steering column, with final location per body maker. [All others] on plate attached to rear face of left-hand door hinge pillar, on right side of cowl under hood. The first symbol indicated the assembly plant: 1=Flint, Mich., 2=Tarrytown, N.Y., 3=St. Louis, Mo., 5=Kansas City, Kan., 6=Oakland, Calif., 8=Atlanta, Ga., 9=Norwood, Ohio, 14=Baltimore, Md., 20=Los Angeles, Calif., and 21=Janesville, Wis. The second and third symbols indicate model prefix/series as follows: JJ=Series 1500, JP=3100, JR=3600, JS=3800, JT=3700, JU=3900. The fourth symbol indicates month of assembly, A=Jan., B=Feb., etc. The following symbols indicated the sequential production number. Each series was separately numbered in sequence, starting with 1001 at each assembly plant. Starting numbers for 1951, by series, were: [1500] JJ-1001, [3100] JP-1001, [3600] JR-1001, [3742] JT-1001, [3800] JS-1001 and [3942] JU-1001. Engine numbers located on right side of block behind distributor. Engine numbers were numbered in sequence, at each plant. Starting at 00-1001. Engine numbers for 1951, by series, were: [1500] JA-1001, [3100] JB-1001, [3600/3742/3800/3942] JC-1001.

Model	Body Type	Price	Weight	Prod. Total
Sedan Delivery — Model JJ/Series 1500 — 115 in. w.b.				
1271	Sedan Delivery	1532	3070	20,817
1/2-Ton Commercial — Model JP/Series 3100 — 116 in. w.b.				
3102	Chassis & Cowl	1035	2435	-
3112	Chassis & W/S	1057	2525	-
3103	Chassis & Cab	1282	2880	-
3104	Pickup	1353	3120	-
3105	Panel	1556	3350	-
3107	Canopy	1610	3325	-
3106	Suburban (doors)	1818	3640	-
3116	Suburban (gate)	1818	3635	-
3/4-Ton Commercial — Model JR/Series 3600 — 125.25 in. w.b.				
3602	Chassis & Cowl	1170	2650	-
3612	Chassis & W/S	1190	2760	-
3603	Chassis & Cab	1417	3095	-
3604	Pickup	1508	3470	-
3608	Platform	1514	3510	-
3609	Stake	1578	3690	-
3/4-Ton Dubl-Duti — Model JT/Series 3700 — 125.5 in. w.b.				
3742	Chassis	1190	2465	-
1-Ton Commercial — Model JS/Series 3800 — 137 in. w.b.				
3802	Chassis & Cowl	1258	2995	-
3812	Chassis & W/S	1280	3070	-
3803	Chassis & Cab	1505	3390	-
3804	Pickup	1622	3930	-
3808	Platform	1638	3955	-
3809	Stake	1708	4205	-
3805	Panel	1836	4185	-
3807	Canopy	1916	4105	-
1-Ton Dubl-Duti — Model JU/Series 3942 — 137 in. w.b.				
3942	Chassis	1296	2670	-

ENGINE: [Standard Series 1500/3100/3600/3800] Inline. OHV. Thriftmaster. Six-cylinder. Cast-iron block. Bore & stroke: 3-1/2 x 3-3/4 in. Displacement: 216.5 cid. Compression ratio: 6.6:1. Gross horsepower: 92 at 3400 rpm. Net horsepower: 85 at 3300 rpm. Gross torque: 176 lb.-ft. at 1000-2000 rpm. Net torque: 170 lb.-ft. at 1000 to 2000 rpm. NCCA horsepower: 29.4. Four main bearings. Mechanical valve lifters. Carburetor: Single one-barrel model Rochester Model 1B number 7002050.

1951 Chevrolet 1/2-Ton Series 3100 Canopy Express (OCW)

ENGINE: [Standard Dubl-Duti] Inline. OHV. Loadmaster. Six-cylinder. Cast-iron block. Bore & stroke: 3-9/16 x 3-15/16 in. Displacement: 235.5 cid. Compression ratio: 6.7:1. Brake horsepower: 92 at 3400 rpm. Net horsepower: 30.4. Four main bearings. Mechanical valve lifters. Carburetor: Single one-barrel updraft Carter model BB1-745S.

CHASSIS: [Model 1500] Wheelbase: 115 in. Overall length: 196-7/8 in. Height: 67-5/8 in. Front tread: 56-11/16 in. Rear tread: 58-3/4 in. Tires: 6.70 x 15 in. four-ply (6.70 x 15 six-ply optional). Maximum GVW: 4,100 lb.

CHASSIS: [Model 3100] Wheelbase: 116 in. Overall length: 196.6 in. Tires: 6.00 x 16 in. six-ply. Maximum GVW: 4,800 lb. (Note: 4,200 lb. with 6.00 x 16 six-ply tires and 4,800 lb. with 6.50 x 16 six-ply tires.

CHASSIS: [Model 3600] Wheelbase: 125.25 in. Overall length: 206 in. Tires: 15 in. six-ply. Maximum GVW: 5,800 lb. (With optional 7.00 x 17 eight-ply tires.

CHASSIS: [Model 3700] Wheelbase: 125.25 in. Tires: 15 in. six-ply. Maximum GVW: 7,000 lb. (With optional 7.00 x 17 eight-ply tires.

CHASSIS: [Model 3800] Wheelbase: 137 in. Overall length: 223.88 in. Tires: 7.00 x 17 in. six-ply. Maximum GVW: [Single rear wheels] 7,000 lb. (With 7.50 x 17 eight-ply tires), [Dual rear wheels] 8,800 lb. (With optional 7.00 x 18 eight-ply tires.

CHASSIS: [Model 3900] Wheelbase: 137 in. Tires: 7.00 x 17 in. six-ply. Maximum GVW: [Dual rear wheels] 10,000 lb.

1951 Chevrolet 1/2-Ton Series 3100 DeLuxe Panel (OCW)

TECHNICAL: Manual transmission: [1500] 3F/1R synchromesh column gear shift. [3100/3600] 3F/1R synchromesh, floor-mounted gear shift, [3800] [4F/1R] non-synchromesh, floor-mounted gearshift. Single-disc, diaphragm spring clutch. [1500/3100] Semi-floating hypoid rear axle, [3600/3800] full-floating rear axle. Hydraulic, four-wheel brakes. Wheels: [1500] One-piece drop center 15-in. wheels, [3100] One-piece drop center 16-in. wheels, [3600/3800] Multi-piece split rims. Standard rear axles: [1500] 4.11:1, [3100] 4.11:1, [3600] 4.57:1, 5.14:1 [3800] 5.14:1.

OPTIONS: [RPO] Rear view mirror and bracket: short right-hand, long left-hand bracket only, long right-hand and short left-hand bracket only. Color combinations. Cab corner windows (without DeLuxe Equipment bright trim). Platform equipment for all Model 3600 high-sill platform models). Stake rack and equipment (all Stake, Stake Express and High-Rack models). Double acting rear shock absorbers (3800). Cam-and-lever double-acting shock absorbers (3900). 5.14:1 ratio rear axle (3600 models). Long running boards and rear fenders (3600/3800 model cab and chassis models). Spare wheel and tire carrier (Dubl-Duti). Heavy-duty radiator (3600/3800 models). Dual tail and stop lamps (Suburbans/Panels/Canopies). Heavy-duty rear springs (3100). Wide running boards (Model 3104). School bus chassis (Dubl-Duti chassis). Oil bath air cleaner, 1-lb. dirt capacity. Oil bath air cleaner, 2-lb. dirt capacity. Heavy-duty clutch (3100).

OPTIONS: [RPO] Double-acting shock absorbers for 3600/3800 (No. 200). Long running boards and rear fenders (No. 207). Optional 5.14:1 rear axle ratio for 3600 (No. 208). Rear view mirrors and brackets (No. 209). Rear shock absorber shield (No. 211). Hydrovac power brakes (No. 213). Oil bath air cleaner (No. 216). Rear bumper (No. 218). Heavy-duty clutch (No. 227). Paint Options (No. 234 for Commercial Trucks /No. 235 for Sedan Delivery).

Option No.	Body Color	DuPont No. (Dulux)	Wheel Stripe Color	DuPont Mo. (Dulux)
STD Suburban	Fathom Green (upper)	286-55658	Argent Silver	165-5642
STD Other 3000	Forester Green	93-62006	Cream Medium	93-530
234-A	Swift's Red	93-1863R	Argent Silver	165-5642
234-B	Armour Yellow	93-3421	Black	93-005
234-C	White	93-508	Emerald Green	93-2537
234-D	Jet Black	93-005	Argent Silver	165-5642
234-E	Omaha Orange	93-082	Black	93-005
234-F	Cape Maroon	93-64539	Gold Bronze	SM-1530AA
234-G	Mariner Blue	93-63203	Cream Mediu	93-530

Option No.	Body Color	DuPont No. (Dulux)	Wheel Stripe Color	DuPont Mo. (Dulux)
234-H	Windsor Blue	93-63225	Cream Mediu	93-530
234-J	Seacrest Green	93-62201	Cream Mediu	93-530
234-K	Sun Beige	93-61083	Totem Scarlet	93-2767
234-L	Cream Medium	93-530	Black	93-005

Truck Radiator Grille Inner Bar: Waldorf White 246-71052 or 93-71052

NOTE 1: The above color combinations were available for Commercial Truck models, as indicated, at all assembly plants. The 1951 Chevrolet trucks were finished in high-luster Dulux synthetic enamel which was baked on in thermostatically controlled ovens. To assist service managers and mechanics in obtaining matching colors when repairs were necessary, the air-drying Dulux number was listed, instead of the number of the Baking Dulux type paint.

Option No.	Body Color	DuPont No. (Duco)	Wheel Stripe Color	DuPont Mo. (Duco)
STD	Mayland Black	246-2048	Argent Silver	289-4202
235-A	Aspen Green	281-55657	Mayland Black	253-2122
235-B	Thistle Gray	253-7869	Mayland Black	253-2122
235-D	Trophy Blue	281-55656	Argent Silver	289-4202
235-F	Burgundy Red	282-85638	Argent Silver	289-4202
246	Waldorf White	246-71052	N/A.	N/A.

NOTE 2: Color codes for Sedan Delivery are Duco paint codes.

NOTE 3: Sedan Delivery wheel colors (Dulux) were: (STD) Black No. 505, (235-A) Aspen Green No. 576, (235-B) Thistle Gray No. 579, (235-D) Trophy Blue No. 575, (235-F) Burgundy Red No. 580.
Oil filter (No. 237). Governor (No. 241). Dual tail and stop light (No. 249). Heavy-duty rear springs (No. 254). Heavy-duty radiator (No. 256). Auxiliary seat (No. 263). Auxiliary rear springs (No. 267). Vacuum reserve tank (No. 281). Heavy-duty three-speed transmission (No. 316). Heavy-duty four-speed transmission (No. 318). High-output generators (No. 326). Stand-and-drive controls for Dubl-Duti (328). Combination fuel and vacuum pump (No. 340). Front bumper (No. 367). Spare wheel and carrier (No. 384). Chrome radiator grille (No. 386). Cab rear corner windows (No. 387). DeLuxe equipment for Cab and Panel models (No. 390). Various tire options, as follows:

Light Duty Truck Tire Options

Size	Ply Rating	Capacity (lb.)	PSI	Section (in.)
15 in.	Six	1500	40	7.74
6.00 x 16	Six	1065	36	6.21
6.50 x 16	Six	1290	40	6.65
6.70 x 15	Four	925	24	N/A.
6.70 x 15	Six	1055	30	N/A.
7.00 x 17	Six	1550	45	7.30
7.00 x 17	Eight	1775	55	7.30
7.50 x 17	Eight	2100	55	7.36
7.50 x 17	Ten	2395	75	7.36
7.00 x 18	Eight	1800	55	7.24

DEALER ACCESSORIES: Rod type radio antenna (all). Locking gas cap (all). Radiator cover (all). Seat cover (all cab models). Fiber seat cover (all cab models). Gasoline filter (all). License plate frame (all). Curved bumper guard (all except Dubl-Duti). Radiator grille guard for curved type bumper (all except Dubl-Duti). Bumper guard for curved type bumper (all except Dubl-Duti). Outside air heater/defroster (all except Chassis-and-Cowl). Recirculated air type heater (all except Chassis-and-Cowl). Matched horns (all). Static eliminator injector (all). Powder for static eliminator injector (all). Guide dual sealed-beam fog lights (all). Guide spotlight with bracket (all). Unity spotlight with bracket (all). Magnetic trouble lamp (all). Universal stop and taillamps (all). Load compartment lamp (Panel). Underhood lamp (all). Package compartment light and switch (all). Front and rear directional signals (all). Front signal lamps, single lens (all). Front signal lamps, double lens (all). Rear signal lamp with switch (all). Cigarette lighter (all). Two tire traction mats (all). Non-glare rear view mirror (all). Long-arm adjustable outside rear view mirror (all). Bracket unit for cowl-mounted rear view mirror (all). Hood ornament (all). Ventilated seat pad (all). Rear axle magnetic filler plug (all). Magnetic transmission drain plug (all). Magnetic oil pan drain plug, (all). Delco radio receiving set, plus antenna (all except Chassis-and-Cowl). Four-inch red Reflex reflector (all). Windshield scraper (all). Radiator insect screen (all). Electric shaver (all). Right-hand sun shade (all). Running board safety tread (all). Tool kit bag and tools (all). Windshield washer (all).

1951 Chevrolet 1/2-Ton Series 3100 Carryall Suburban (Owners: Trudy & Randy Vollmer)

OPTIONS: [Authorized Aftermarket] A four-wheel drive (4x4) conversion by NAPCO Products, Co., of Minneapolis, Minn., was available for 1950-1954 Chevrolet trucks with open drive shafts, but not on 3100s featuring torque tube drive. It was merchandised through Chevrolet dealers for approximately $1,200. NAPCO literature describes it as a "Powr-Pak" four-wheel drive system that shifted in and out of four-wheel drive without stopping or declutching. It featured a two-speed transfer case (eight forward speeds and two in reverse) and full-engine-torque power-take-off. NAPCO also promoted a Chevrolet "Mountain Goat" 4x4 Pickup model.

HISTORICAL: Introduced: January, 1951. Calendar-year registrations: [All Series, all models except Sedan Delivery] 350,344. Calendar-year production: [All models except Sedan Delivery] 426,115 (30.17 percent market share. Calendar-year production by GVW: [Commercial up to 5,000 lb.] 215,175, [5,0001 lb.-10,000 lb.] 76,659. The National Production Agency, which governed production restrictions during the Korean War gave Chevrolet a quota of 34.95 percent of the light-duty truck market. A pressure type radiator cap which regulated cooling system pressure at 3-1/2 to 4-1/2 psi was also now installed on all Chevrolet trucks, except forward-control models.

1952 CHEVROLET

1952 Chevrolet Series 1500 Sedan Delivery (OCW)

SEDAN DELIVERY — MODEL KJ/SERIES 1500 — SIX-CYLINDER: The passenger car-based Sedan Delivery was a Styleline Special model identified by Job Number 1508 and Fisher Body Style Number 1271. The grille was somewhat similar to the previous year, except that the upper deflector was no longer grooved and five chrome "fins" or "teeth" were widely spaced across the upper horizontal chrome molding. Also, the parking lamp housings, still in sideways U-shaped end moldings, had the slotted section removed so that they could accommodate larger lenses. There was a different hood ornament. The 73-in. cargo area floor length usable load space of 92.5 cu. ft. remained unchanged. The Sedan Delivery's windshield glass (non-tinted only) was the same used on two- and four-door Sedans, but not Station Wagons. Doors were specific to this model and not used on other cars (although 1952 Chevrolet Sedan doors can be modified to fit). Front door window glass was the same used on 1949-1952 four-door Sedans, not Station Wagons. Lower rear quarter panel stampings were unique to the Sedan Delivery. However, the rear compartment floor panel was same one used for 1949-1952 Station Wagons. Rear bumper bars, ends and guards were also the same as Station Wagon parts. Standard equipment included front and rear bumpers and bumper guards, front license guard, hood ornament and emblem, chrome-plated headlamp rims with doors, dual windshield wipers, dual horns, right- and left-hand outside key locks, front and rear bumper gravel deflectors, one combination tail/stop/license plate lamp, bright, full-length rear fender crown molding, bright metal windshield divider, bright windshield reveal molding, bright rear window reveal molding, "Bonderized" (a phosphate etching process) body and sheet metal, plain plastic control knob inserts, chrome-plated "waterfall" radio grille, three-position ignition switch, left-hand sun shade and dome light. Onyx Black was the standard body color for 1952 Sedan Deliveries. Options included Birch Gray, Spring Green, Admiral Blue, Dusk Gray, Emerald Green, Sahara Beige, Regal Maroon, and Waldorf White. Interior trim was switched to dark gray imitation leather, combination number 216.

1952 Chevrolet 1/2-Ton Series 3100 Windowed U.S. Navy Survey Panel (OCW)

1/2-TON LIGHT-DUTY COMMERCIAL — MODEL KP/SERIES 3100 — SIX-CYLINDER: Conventional trucks looked the same as 1951 models except that new push-button type door handles were used. Chrome grilles were not available. The unchanged grille had five broad horizontal bars topped by a broad hood ornament with a Cloisonné Blue (metallic) bow tie emblem and vermilion Chevrolet lettering on a chrome background. Rectangular parking lights were again placed in housings between the ends of the uppermost pair of grille bars. The outer grille bars were body color (Forester Green standard). The inner bars were Thistle Gray. The outer bars were not striped. A curved painted front bumper was standard on all 3100 models. Curved painted rear bumpers were standard for single-unit body conventional trucks, but not for cab models. Chevrolet hood side

nameplates were still used. There were no series designators below them. A foot-operated parking brake was used. Brake were Bendix's duo-servo self-energizing type. Rear corner windows for cab models were optional. On trucks with this option, a different rear roof section was used. The gas tank was inside cab models. Its filler tube came out the rear right-hand corner of the cab, just behind the push-button type, chrome door handles. The filler was just ahead of the rear wheels on single-unit body models. Both cab models and single-unit body models had one belt molding stripe, which was Cream Medium with standard finish. The following no-cost color options (pinstripe colors in parentheses) were offered on all models: Swift's Red (Argent Silver), Armour Yellow (Black), White (Emerald Green), Jet Black (Argent Silver), Omaha Orange (Black), Cape Maroon (Gold), Mariner Blue (Cream Medium), Windsor Blue (Cream Medium), Seacrest Green (Cream Medium), Sun Beige (Totem Scarlet), and Cream Medium (Black). The unchanged instrument panel featured AC instruments, electric fuel gauge and ammeter, pressure-type heat indicator and oil pressure gauge, and dial speedometer driven by a flexible shaft from the transmission.

3/4-TON LIGHT-DUTY COMMERCIAL — MODEL KR/SERIES 3600 — SIX-CYLINDER: The 3/4-ton trucks had the same Advance-Design styling, features and finish as other conventional trucks. Eight-leaf front springs were standard. The 3600s had a longer wheelbase than 1/2-tons. The Pickup load box was longer than the half-ton type and had six stake pockets. Long running boards were used. No Suburban, Panel, or Canopy Express was offered in this line. There were Platform and Stake models. Hubcaps looked like the ones on 3100s, but they were larger in size. The standard wheels were of different eight-bolt design and not pinstriped. Curved-type painted front bumpers were standard on all models. A similar rear bumper was optional on incomplete bodies and flat bed combinations. A foot-operated parking brake was used on all 3600 models. Huck type brakes were used for the last time. The tires on 3600s were 15 in. six-ply rated on 15 x 5.50 semi-drop-center rims. The 15-in. rims had no stripe, and the 17-in. rims had two pinstripes.

3/4-TON DUBL-DUTI — MODEL KT/SERIES 3700 — SIX-CYLINDER: Two Dubl-Duti Forward-Control chassis were in the Chevrolet truck line. Both had the 235 cid Loadmaster six with updraft carburetor. Model 3742 was the 3/4-ton version on a 125.25-in. wheelbase. Standard walk-in Delivery truck bodies could be supplied by several factory-approved sources or the buyer could add his/her own body. The wheels were of eight-bolt design. A painted, Anvil Gray channel type front bumper was optional (RPO 367) on the 3700 Dubl-Duti truck chassis.

1-TON MEDIUM-DUTY COMMERCIAL — MODEL KS/SERIES 3800 — SIX-CYLINDER: The 3800 Series had the same Advance-Design styling, features and finish as other conventional trucks. A foot-operated parking brake was used on all 3800 models. Huck type rear brakes were still used, but for the last year. These models were available with an optional power brake system. This Hydrovac brake booster reduced pedal effort by two-thirds. Panel and Canopy Express models had a one-piece floor made of 3/4-in. thick, five-ply laminated wood. The basic model lineup was unchanged. It included single and dual rear wheel options for all except the Pickup (Express), Canopy Express and Panel. The Pickup had a longer wheelbase than the 3600 Pickup, longer running boards, and a longer load box with eight stake pockets. A curved-type painted front bumper was standard on all models. A similar rear bumper was standard on Models 3805 and 3807. Regular equipment tires were 7.00 x 17 six-ply rated for trucks with single rear wheels or 7.00 x 18 eight-ply rated for trucks with dual rear wheel options. The hubcaps were the same used on 3600s. The standard black wheels had two pinstripes. No hubcaps were used on the 18 x 5-in. wheels of the Chassis-and-Cab, Platform and Stake models, which had eight bolts and eight circular openings. A four-speed manual synchromesh transmission was standard. Truck with this transmission had a new black rubber floor mat made especially for use with the floor-mounted four-speed gear-shifter.

1-TON DUBL-DUTI — MODEL KU/SERIES 3900 — SIX-CYLINDER: Two Dubl-Duti Forward-Control chassis returned to the Chevrolet truck line. Both had a new 235 cid Loadmaster six with updraft carburetor. Due to the lower efficiency of the updraft carburetor, this engine had the same horsepower rating as the 216 cid Thriftmaster six. Model 3942 was the 1-ton version on a 137-in. wheelbase. Standard walk-in delivery truck bodies could be supplied by several factory-approved sources or the buyer could add his/her own body. A painted, Anvil Gray channel type front bumper was optional (RPO 367) on the 3900 Dubl-Duti truck chassis.

1952 Chevrolet 1/2-Ton Series 3100 Pickup (OCW)

I.D. DATA: Serial number located: [Chassis models] on plate temporarily attached near steering column, with final location per body maker. [All others] on plate attached to rear face of left-hand door hinge pillar. The first symbol indicated the assembly plant: 1=Flint, Mich., 2=Tarrytown, N.Y., 3=St. Louis, Mo., 5=Kansas City, Kan., 6=Oakland, Calif., 8=Atlanta, Ga., 9=Norwood, Ohio, 14=Baltimore, Md., 20=Los Angeles, Calif., and 21=Janesville, Wis. The second and third symbols indicate model prefix/series as follows: KJ=Series 1500, KP=3100, KR=3600, KS=3800, KT=3700, KU=3900. The fourth symbol indicates month of assembly, A=Jan., B=Feb., etc. The following symbols indicated the sequential production number. Each series was separately numbered in sequence, starting with 1001 at each assembly plant. Serial numbers by series were: [1500] KJ-1001 to 19,286, [3100] KP-1001 to 27,704, [3600] KR-1001 to 8,132, [3742] KT-1001 to 1430, [3800] KS-1001 to 5409, and [3942] KU-1001 to 1,300. Engine numbers located on crankcase near rear of distributor on right side of engine. Engine numbers for 1952, by series, were: [1500] KA-1001 to 860,773, [3100] KB-1001 to 860,773, [3600/3742/3800/3942] KC-1001 to 860,773.

1952 Chevrolet 1/2-Ton Series 3100 Pickup (OCW)

Model No.	Body Type	Price	Weight	Prod. Total
Sedan Delivery — Model KJ/Series 1500 — 115 in. w.b.				
1508	Sedan Delivery	1648	3100	9175
1/2-Ton Commercial — Model KP/Series 3100 — 116 in. w.b.				
3102	Chassis & Cowl	1076	2435	-
3103	Chassis & Cab	1334	2880	-
3104	Pickup	1407	3120	-
3105	Panel	1620	3350	-
3107	Canopy	1676	3325	-
3112	Chassis & W/S	1099	2525	-
3106	Suburban (doors)	1933	3635	-
3116	Suburban (gate)	1933	3645	-
3/4-Ton Commercial — Model KR/Series 3600 — 125.25 in. w.b.				
3602	Chassis & Cowl	1216	2655	-
3603	Chassis & Cab	1474	3095	-
3604	Pickup	1569	3470	-
3608	Platform	1575	3510	-
3609	Stake	1642	3690	-
3612	Chassis & W/S	1238	2760	-
3/4-Ton Dubl-Duti — Model KT/Series 3700 — 125.25 in. w.b.				
3742	Chassis	1238	2470	-
1-Ton Commercial — Model KS/Series 3800 — 137 in. w.b.				
3802	Chassis & Cowl	1312	3000	-
3803	Chassis & Cab	1570	3395	-
3804	Pickup	1692	3915	-
3805	Panel	1916	4140	-
3807	Canopy	2000	4110	-
3808	Platform	1709	3960	-
3809	Stake	1782	4240	-
3812	Chassis & W/S	1335	3075	-
1-Ton Dubl-Duti — Model KU/Series 3900 — 137 in. w.b.				
3942	Chassis	1351	2670	-

ENGINE: [Standard Series 1500/3100/3600/3800] Inline. OHV. Thriftmaster. Six-cylinder. Cast-iron block. Bore & stroke: 3-1/2 x 3-3/4 in. Displacement: 216.5 cid. Compression ratio: 6.6:1. Gross horsepower: 92 at 3400 rpm. Net horsepower: 85 at 3300 rpm. Gross torque: 176 lb.-ft. at 1000-2000 rpm. Net torque: 170 at 1000 to 2000 rpm. NCCA horsepower: 29.4. Four main bearings. Mechanical valve lifters. Carburetor: [Early] Single one-barrel downdraft GM (Rochester) Model B "Power Jet" number 7004475, [Late] Same type, but various different model numbers.

ENGINE: [Standard Dubl-Duti] Inline. OHV. Loadmaster. Six-cylinder. Cast-iron block. Bore & stroke: 3-9/16 x 3-15/16 in. Displacement: 235.5 cid. Compression ratio: 6.7:1. Brake horsepower: 92 at 3400 rpm. NACC horsepower: 30.4. Four main bearings. Mechanical valve lifters. Carburetor: Carter single one-barrel updraft model BB1-871S.

1952 Chevrolet 1/2-Ton Series 3100 Panel (OCW)

CHASSIS: [Model 1500] Wheelbase: 115 in. Overall length: 197-7/8 in. Height: 67-1/8 in. Front tread: 57.6 in. Rear tread: 60 in. Tires: 6.70 x 15 in. Maximum GVW: 4,100 lb.

CHASSIS: [Model 3100] Wheelbase: 116 in. Overall length: 196.6 in. Tires: 6.00 x 16 in. six-ply. Maximum GVW: 4,800 lb. (Note: 4,200 lb. with 6.00 x 16 six-ply tires and 4,800 lb. with 6.50 x 16 six-ply tires).

CHASSIS: [Model 3600] Wheelbase: 125.25 in. Overall length: 206 in. Tires: 15 in. six-ply. Maximum GVW: 5,800 lb. (With optional 7.50 x 17 eight-ply tires).

CHASSIS: [Model 3700] Wheelbase: 125.25 in. Tires: 15 in. six-ply. Maximum GVW: 7,000 lb. (With optional 7.50 x 17 eight-ply tires.

CHASSIS: [Model 3800] Wheelbase: 137 in. Overall length: 223.88 in. Tires: 7.00 x 17 in. six-ply. Maximum GVW: [Single rear wheels] 7,000 lb. (With 7.50 x 17 eight-ply tires), [Dual rear wheels] 8,800 lb. (With optional 7.00 x 18 eight-ply tires).

CHASSIS: [Model 3900] Wheelbase: 137 in. Tires: 7.00 x 17 in. six-ply. Maximum GVW: [Dual rear wheels] 10,000 lb.

NOTE 3: Sedan Delivery wheel colors (Dulux) were: (STD) Black No. 505, (235-A) Birch Gray No. 600, (235-B) Dusk Gray No. 608, (235-C) Spring Green No. 602, (235-D) Emerald Green No. 601, (235-E) Admiral Blue No. 609, (235-F) Twilight Blue No. 604, (235-G) Sahara Beige No. 603, (235-H) Regal Maroon No. 599. Oil filter (No. 237). Governor (No. 241). Dual tail and stop light (No. 249). Heavy-duty rear springs (No. 254). Heavy-duty radiator (No. 256). Auxiliary seat (No. 263). Auxiliary rear springs (No. 267). Vacuum reserve tank (No. 281). Heavy-duty three-speed transmission (No. 316). Heavy-duty four-speed transmission (No. 318). High-output generators (No. 326). Solenoid starter (No. 327)0. Stand-and-drive controls for Dubl-Duti (328). Combination fuel and vacuum pump (No. 340). Cab rear corner windows (No. 387). Left-hand door key lock (No. 395). Various tire options as follows:

Light Duty Truck Tire Options

Size	Ply Rating	Capacity (lb.)	PSI	Section (in.)
15 in.	Six	1500	40	7.74
6.50 x 16	Six	1290	40	6.65
6.70 x 15	Four	925	24	N/A.
6.70 x 15	Six	1055	30	N/A.
7.00 x 17	Six	1550	45	7.30
7.00 x 17	Eight	1775	55	7.30
7.50 x 17	Eight	2100	60	7.36
7.50 x 17	Ten	2395	75	7.36
7.00 x 18	Eight	1800	55	7.24

DEALER ACCESSORIES: Rod type radio antenna (all). Locking gas cap (all). Radiator cover (all). Seat cover (all cab models). Fiber seat cover (all cab models). Gasoline filter (all). License plate frame (all). Curved bumper guard (all except Dubl-Duti). Painted radiator grille guard for curved type bumper (all). Painted bumper guard for curved type bumper (all except Dubl-Duti). Outside air heater/defroster (all except Chassis-and-Cowl). Recirculated air type heater (all except Chassis-and-Cowl). Matched horns (all). Static eliminator injector (all). Powder for static eliminator injector (all). Guide dual sealed-beam fog lights (all). Guide spotlight with bracket (all). Unity spotlight with bracket (all). Magnetic trouble lamp (all). Universal stop and taillamps (all). Load compartment lamp (Panel). Underhood lamp (all). Package compartment light and switch (all). Front and rear directional signals (all). Front signal lamps, single lens (all). Front signal lamps, double lens (all). Rear signal lamp with switch (all). Cigarette lighter (all). Two tire traction mats (all). Non-glare rear view mirror (all). Long-arm adjustable outside rear view mirror (all). Bracket unit for cowl-mounted rear view mirror (all). Hood ornament (all). Ventilated seat pad (all). Rear axle magnetic filler plug (all). Magnetic transmission drain plug (all). Magnetic oil pan drain plug, (all). Delco radio receiving set, plus antenna (all except Chassis-and-Cowl). Four-inch red Reflex reflector (all). Windshield scraper (all). Radiator insect screen (all). Electric shaver (all). Right-hand sun shade (all). Running board safety tread (all). Tool kit bag and tools (all). Windshield washer (all).

1952 Chevrolet 1/2-Ton Series 3100 Pickup (Owner: G. Landry)

TECHNICAL: Manual, synchromesh transmission: [1500/3100/3600] 3F/1R column-mounted, [3800] [4F/1R] Floor-mounted gearshift. Single-disc, diaphragm spring clutch. [1500/3100] Semi-floating hypoid rear axle, [3600/3800] full-floating rear axle. Hydraulic, four-wheel brakes. Wheels: [1500] One-piece drop center 15-in. wheels. [3100] One-piece drop center 16-in. wheels, [3600/3800] Multi-piece split rims. Standard rear axles: [1500] 4.11:1, [3100] 4.11:1, [3600] 4.57:1, 5.14:1 [3800] 5.14:1.

OPTIONS: [RPO] Double-acting rear shock absorbers for 3800 (No. 200). Rear cam-and-lever double-acting shock absorbers for 3900 (No. 201). Long running boards and rear fenders (No. 207). Optional 5.14:1 rear axle ratio for 3600 (No. 208). Rear view mirrors and brackets (No. 210). Rear shock absorber shield (No. 211). Hydrovac power brakes (No. 213). Oil bath air cleaner (No. 216). Positive crankcase ventilation (No. 217). Heavy-duty clutch (No. 227). Paint Options (No. 234-235):

Option No.	Body Color	DuPont No. (Dulux)	Wheel Stripe Color	DuPont Mo. (Dulux)
STD Suburban				
	Fathom Green (upper)	286-55658	Argent Silver	165-5642
STD Other 3000				
	Forester Green	93-62006	Cream Medium	93-530
234-A	Swift's Red	93-1863R	Argent Silver	165-5642
234-B	Armour Yellow	93-3421	Black	93-005
234-C	White	93-508	Emerald Green	93-2537
234-D	Jet Black	93-005	Argent Silver	165-5642
234-E	Omaha Orange	93-082	Black	93-005
234-F	Cape Maroon	93-64539	Gold Bronze	SM-1530AA
234-G	Mariner Blue	93-63203	Cream Medium	93-530
234-H	Windsor Blue	93-63225	Cream Medium	93-530
234-J	Seacrest Green	93-62201	Cream Medium	93-530
234-K	Sun Beige	93-61083	Totem Scarlet	93-2767
234-L	Cream Medium	93-530	Black	93-005

Truck Radiator Grille Inner Bar: Thistle Gray 253-70397

NOTE 1: The above color combinations were available for Commercial Truck models, as indicated, at all assembly plants. The 1952 Chevrolet trucks were finished in high-luster Dulux synthetic enamel which was baked on in thermostatically controlled ovens. To assist service managers and mechanics in obtaining matching colors when repairs were necessary, the air-drying Dulux number was listed, instead of the number of the Baking Dulux type paint.

Option No.	Body Color	DuPont No. (Duco)	Wheel Stripe Color	DuPont Mo. (Duco)
STD	Onyx Black	253-2247	Argent Silver	289-4202
235-A	Birch Green	253-55987	Onyx Black	253-2247
235-B	Dusk Gray	286-55988	Argent Silver	289-4202
235-C	Spring Green	253-55989	Onyx Black	253-2247
235-D	Emerald Green	286-55976	Argent Silver	289-4202
235-E	Admiral Blue	286-55991	Argent Silver	289-4202
235-F	Twilight Blue	253-55992	Onyx Black	253-2247
235-G	Sahara Beige	253-55979	Onyx Black	253-2247
235-H	Regal Maroon	207-55986	Argent Silver	289-4202
246	Waldorf White	246-71052	N/A.	N/A.

NOTE 2: Color codes for Sedan Delivery are Duco paint codes.
OPTIONS: [Authorized Aftermarket] A four-wheel drive (4x4) conversion by NAPCO Products, Co., of Minneapolis, Minn., was available for 1950-1954 Chevrolet trucks with open drive shafts. It was merchandised through Chevrolet dealers. NAPCO literature describes it as a "Powr-Pak" four-wheel drive system that shifted in and out of four-wheel drive without stopping or declutching. It featured a two-speed transfer case (eight forward speeds and two in reverse) and full-engine-torque power-take-off. NAPCO also promoted a Chevrolet "Mountain Goat" 4x4 Pickup model.
HISTORICAL: Introduced: January 1952. Calendar-year registrations: [All Commercials] 272,249. Innovations included new push-button door handles for conventional trucks, a slightly revised GM Rochester Model B carburetor, and use of a new four-pound pressure type radiator cap. Due to the Korean War, the radiators were made lighter, with air cells placed further apart. This increased cooling capacity. Warning: Do not use higher pressure radiator caps, as the lighter cellular radiators are built for a maximum pressure of four-pounds and do not stand up to excessive radiator pressure.

1953 CHEVROLET

SEDAN DELIVERY — MODEL D/SERIES 1500 — SIX-CYLINDER: The passenger car-based Sedan Delivery was totally new and redesigned. It was now called a One-Fifty (or 150) model, this being a shortened form of the old 1500 series designation. It could also be identified by the code 53-1271 on the Fisher Body tag under the hood. The grille consisted of a curvy upper chrome molding, with a dip in its center positioned above a deflector and a chrome support to which three large "teeth" were attached. Large round parking lamp housings attached to the end of the support. Below it was a second deflector and a veed horizontal molding. End moldings with six horizontally grooved impressions stamped into them attached to the round parking lamp housings. The new body featured a one-piece windshield. Doors were still specific to this model and not used on other cars. Front door window glass was the same used on 1953 (and 1954) four-door Sedans, not Station Wagons. Lower rear quarter panel stampings were unique to the Sedan Delivery. However, the rear compartment floor panel was again the same one used for Station Wagons. The rear panel door was the same part used since 1949. Rear bumper parts and guards were also the same as Station Wagon parts. Standard equipment included front and rear bumpers and bumper guards, front license guard, hood ornament and emblem, chrome-plated headlamp rims with doors, dual windshield wipers, dual horns, outside key locks, front and rear bumper gravel deflectors, one combination tail/stop/license plate lamp, chrome-plated radio grille, three-position ignition switch, left-hand sun shade, and dome light. Onyx Black remained the standard body color for 1953 Sedan Deliveries. Options included Driftwood Gray, Surf Green, Regatta Blue, Dusk Gray, Woodland Green, Sahara Beige, Madeira Maroon, Thistle Gray, and Moonstone Hysheen Gray. The interior was trimmed with beige imitation leather, combination number 276.

1953 Chevrolet 1/2-Ton Series 3100 Pickup (Owner: Dave Tesch)

1/2-TON LIGHT-DUTY COMMERCIAL — MODEL H/SERIES 3100 — SIX-CYLINDER: Conventional trucks looked the same as 1952 except for trim and finish. A new hood side nameplate appeared. It had the 3100 series designation above a broken loop of chrome shaped somewhat like a safety-pin. Chrome grilles were not available. The unchanged grille had five broad horizontal bars topped by a broad hood ornament with a Cloisonné Blue (metallic) bow tie emblem and vermilion Chevrolet lettering on a chrome background. Rectangular parking lights were again placed in housings between the ends of the uppermost pair of grille bars. The outer grille bars were body color (Juniper Green with Cream pinstripe standard). The inner bars were Thistle Gray. The outer bars were not striped. All bumpers were also painted. A curved type Anvil Gray front bumper was standard on all 3100 models. Curved painted rear bumpers were standard for single-unit body trucks only, not for cab models. When ordered as an option, bumper guards were painted, too. Hubcaps were painted, too. Cab corner windows were optional and did not include chromed gasket lock strips. On trucks with this option, a different rear roof section was used. A foot-operated parking

brake was used. Brake were Bendix's duo-servo self-energizing type. The gas tank was inside cab models. Its filler tube came out the rear right-hand corner of the cab, just behind the chrome door handles. The filler was just ahead of the rear wheels on single-unit body models. Both cab models and single-unit body models had one belt molding stripe, which was Cream Medium with standard finish. The following no-cost color options (pinstripe color in parenthesis) were offered: Commercial Red (Argent Silver), Jet Black (Argent Silver), Mariner Blue (Cream Medium), Cream Medium (Jet Black), Yukon Yellow (Jet Black), Ocean Green (Jet Black), Transport Blue (Cream Medium), Burgundy Maroon (Gold Bronze), Copper Tone Copper (Onyx Black or Shell White), Omaha Orange (Jet Black), Autumn Brown (Shell White), and Pure White (Juniper Green). The instrument panel featured AC instruments, electric fuel gauge and ammeter, pressure-type heat indicator and oil pressure, and dial speedometer driven by a flexible shaft from the transmission. Tinted glass was a new option. Even cab rear quarter windows could be ordered with tinted glass. Another new option was a side-mounted spare tire carrier. This assembly consisted of three 7/16 x 20 x 1-in. wheel mounting bolts, front and rear rail brackets measuring 1-3/16 x 2-1/2 x 17-1/2 in. and side and center wheel carrier cross braces. Also available was a wheel carrier locking mechanism. Incidentally, due to its short wheelbase the Model 3104 Pickup with side-mounted spare tire required a special left-hand welled rear fender (part number 3705885) to provide enough room for the fifth tire.

1953 Chevrolet 3/4-Ton Series 3600 Pickup (OCW)

3/4-TON LIGHT-DUTY COMMERCIAL — MODEL J/SERIES 3600 — SIX-CYLINDER: The 3/4-ton trucks had the same Advance-Design styling, features and finish as other conventional trucks. Eight-leaf front springs were standard. The 3600s had a longer wheelbase than 1/2-tons. The Pickup load box was longer than the 1/2-ton type and had six stake pockets. Running boards measuring 75-3/4 in. long were used. When a side-mounted spare tire carrier was used, dimpled rear fenders were not required. No Panel, Suburban or Canopy Express was offered in this line. There were Platform and Stake models. Hubcaps were also painted on 3600s. The standard wheels were of different eight-bolt design. Painted curved-type front bumpers were standard on all models. A similar rear bumper was optional on incomplete bodies and flat bed combinations. A foot-operated parking brake was used on all 3600 models. The brakes were Bendix's duo-servo self-energizing type. The standard tires on 3600s were 15 in. six-ply rated on 15 x 5.50 semi-drop-center rims.
3/4-TON DUBL-DUTI — MODEL K/SERIES 3700 — SIX-CYLINDER: Two Dubl-Duti Forward-Control chassis were in the Chevrolet truck line. Both had the 235 cid Loadmaster six with updraft carburetor. Model 3742 was the 3/4-ton version on a 125.25-in. wheelbase. Standard walk-in Delivery truck bodies could be supplied by several factory-approved sources or the buyer could add his/her own body. The wheels were of eight-bolt design.
1-TON MEDIUM-DUTY COMMERCIAL — MODEL L/SERIES 3800 — SIX-CYLINDER: The 3800 Series had the same Advance-Design styling, features and finish as other conventional trucks. A foot-operated parking brake was now used on all 3800 models. Bendix duo servo self-energizing brakes replaced the old Huck type on 3800 models. A Hydrovac brake booster was no longer optional. Panel and Canopy Express models had a one-piece floor made of 3/4-in. thick, five-ply laminated wood. The basic model lineup was unchanged. It included single and dual rear wheel options for all except the Pickup (Express), Canopy Express and Panel. The Pickup had a longer wheelbase than the 3600 Pickup, a longer load box with eight stake pockets, and very long running boards. When a side-mounted spare tire carrier was used, dimpled rear fenders were not required. A curved-type painted front bumper was standard on all models. A similar rear bumper was standard on Models 3805 and 3807. Regular equipment tires were 7.00 x 17 six-ply rated for trucks with single rear wheels or 7.00 x 18 eight-ply rated for trucks with dual rear wheel options. The hubcaps were painted. No hubcaps were used on the 18 x 5-in. wheels of the Chassis-and-Cab, Platform and Stake models, which had eight bolts and eight circular openings. A four-speed manual synchromesh transmission was standard. Trucks with this transmission had a black rubber floor mat made especially for use with the floor-mounted four-speed gear-shifter.

1953 Chevrolet 1/2-Ton Series 3100 Pickup (JCL)

1953 Chevrolet 3/4-Ton Series 3600 Pickup (OCW)

1-TON DUBL-DUTI — MODEL M/SERIES 3900 — SIX-CYLINDER: Two Dubl-Duti Forward-Control chassis returned to the Chevrolet truck line. Both had a new 235 cid Loadmaster six with updraft carburetor. Model 3942 was the 1-ton version on a 137-in. wheelbase. Standard walk-in Delivery truck bodies could be supplied by several factory-approved sources or the buyer could add his/her own body.

I.D. DATA: Serial number located: [Chassis models] on plate temporarily attached near steering column, with final location per body maker. [All others] on plate attached to rear face of left-hand door hinge pillar. The first symbol indicated the series: D=1500, H=3100, J=3600, K=3700, L=3800, M=3900. The second symbol indicated the model year: 3=1953. The third symbol indicated the assembly plant: A=Atlanta, Ga., B=Baltimore, Md., F=Flint, Mich., J=Janesville, Wis., K=Kansas City, Mo., L=Los Angeles, Calif., N=Norwood, Ohio, O=Oakland, Calif., S=St. Louis, Mo., T=Tarrytown, N.Y. Each series was separately numbered in sequence, starting with 000001 at each assembly plant. Serial numbers for 1953, by series, were as follows: [1500] D53-001001 to 228961, [3100] H53-001001 to 49126, [3600] J53-001001 to 49126, [3742] K53-001001 to 49126, [3800] L53-001001 to 49126 and [3942] M53-001001 to 49126. Engine numbers: On pad on crankcase rear of distributor on right side of engine. Each engine carried a letter code for model year, type and engine plant, plus a production unit number. All numbers were numbered at each source in sequence starting with 1001. Numbers used were: [1500] LA-1001 to LA-1183450, [3100] LB-1001 to LB-1183450, [3600] LC-1001 to LC-1183450, [3700] LC-1001 to LC-1183450, [3800] LC-1001 to LC-1183450, [3900] LC-1001 to LC-1183450.

1953 Chevrolet 1/2-Ton Series 3100 Panel (P. Bachman)

Model No.	Body Type	Price	Weight	Prod. Total
Sedan Delivery — Model D/Series 1500 — 115 in. w.b.				
1508	Sedan Delivery	1648	3160	15,523
1/2-Ton Commercial — Model H/Series 3100 — 116 in. w.b.				
3102	Chassis & Cowl	1076	2440	-
3112	Chassis & W/S	1099	2515	-
3103	Chassis & Cab	1334	2855	-
3104	Pickup	1407	3100	-
3105	Panel	1620	3335	-
3107	Canopy	1676	3305	-
3106	Suburban (doors)	1947	3625	-
3116	Suburban (gate)	1947	3635	-
3/4-Ton Commercial — Model J/Series 3600 — 125.25 in. w.b.				
3602	Chassis & Cowl	1216	2675	-
3612	Chassis & W/S	1238	2780	-
3603	Chassis & Cab	1474	3110	-
3604	Pickup	1569	3480	-
3608	Platform	1575	3515	-
3609	Stake	1642	3700	-
3/4-Ton Dubl-Duti — Model K/Series 3742 — 125.25 in. w.b.				
3742	Chassis	1238	2480	-
1-Ton Commercial — Model L/Series 3800 — 137 in. w.b.				
3802	Chassis & Cowl	1312	3000	-
3812	Chassis & W/S	1335	3080	-
3803	Chassis & Cab	1570	3405	-
3804	Pickup	1692	3920	-
3808	Platform	1709	3965	-
3809	Stake	1782	4210	-
3805	Panel	1916	4170	-
3807	Canopy	2000	4095	-
1-Ton Dubl-Duti — Model M/Series 3942 — 137 in. w.b.				
3942	Chassis	1351	2685	-

ENGINE: [Standard Series 1500/3100/3600/3800] Inline. OHV. Thriftmaster. Six-cylinder. Cast-iron block. Bore & stroke: 3-1/2 x 3-3/4 in. Displacement: 216.5 cid. Compression ratio: 6.6:1. Gross horsepower: 92 at 3400 rpm. Net horsepower: 85 at 3300 rpm. Gross torque: 176 lb.-ft. at 1000-2000 rpm. Net torque: 170 at 1000 to 2000 rpm. NCCA horsepower: 29.4. Four main bearings. Mechanical valve lifters. Carburetor: Single one-barrel downdraft GM (Rochester) Model B.

ENGINE: [Standard Dubl-Duti] Inline. OHV. Loadmaster. Six-cylinder. Cast-iron block. Bore & stroke: 3-9/16 x 3-15/16 in. Displacement: 235.5 cid. Compression ratio: 7.1:1. Brake horsepower: 107 at 3600 rpm. NACC horsepower: 30.4. Four main bearings. Mechanical valve lifters. Carburetor: Carter single one-barrel updraft model BB1.

CHASSIS: [Model 1500] Wheelbase: 115 in. Overall length: 195-1/2 in. Height: 67-1/8 in. Front tread: 62 in. Rear tread: 62 in. Tires: 6.70 x 15 in. Maximum GVW: 4,100 lb.

CHASSIS: [Series 3100] Wheelbase: 116 in. Overall length: [Pickup] 191.31 in., [Panel/Suburban] 195.31 in. Height: [Panel] 80.68 in., [Suburban] 79.5 in. Tires: 6.00 x 16 six-ply.

CHASSIS: [Series 3600] Wheelbase: 125.25 in. Overall length: [Pickup] 200-3/16 in., [Platform/Stake] 206 in. Tires: 15 in. six-ply.

CHASSIS: [Series 3800] Wheelbase: 137 in. Overall length: [Pickup] 221.5 in. [Panel] 229.57 in., [Platform/Stake] 224 in. Height: [Panel] 86.5 in. Tires: [front] 7.00 x 17 six-ply, [rear] eight-ply.

CHASSIS: [Series 3742] Wheelbase: 125.25 in. Overall length: 197-1/8 in. Front tread: 62 in. Rear tread: 62-3/8 in. Tires: 7.00 x 17 in.

CHASSIS: [Series 3942] Wheelbase: 137 in. Overall length: 221-7/8 in. Front tread: 61-3/8 in. Rear tread: 61-3/4 in. Tires: 7.50 x 17 eight-ply or 7.50 x 18 eight-ply (Dual rear wheels).

1953 Chevrolet 1/2-Ton Series 3100 Suburban (OCW)

TECHNICAL: Manual, synchromesh transmission: [1500/3100/3600] 3F/1R column-mounted, [3800] [4F/1R] Floor-mounted gear shift. Single-disc, diaphragm spring clutch. [1500/3100] Semi-floating hypoid rear axle, [3600/3800] full-floating rear axle. Hydraulic, four-wheel brakes. Wheels: [1500] One-piece drop center 15-in. wheels, [3100] One-piece drop center 16-in. wheels, [3600/3800] Multi-piece split rims. Standard rear axles: [1500] 4.11:1, [3100] 4.11:1, [3600] 4.57:1, 5.14:1 [3800] 5.14:1.

OPTIONS: [RPO] Double-acting rear shock absorbers for 3800 (No. 200). Rear cam-and-lever double-acting shock absorbers for 3900 (No. 201). Long running boards and rear fenders (No. 207). Optional 5.14:1 rear axle ratio for 3600 (No. 208). Rear view mirrors and brackets (No. 210). Rear shock absorber shield (No. 211). Oil bath air cleaner (No. 216). Positive crankcase ventilation — could be retro-fitted to 1950-1952 models (No. 217). Painted rear bumper (No. 218). Heavy-duty clutch (No. 227). Paint Options (No. 231 for Sedan Delivery and No. 234 for Commercial Trucks).

Option No.	Body Color	DuPont No. (Duco)	Wheel Stripe Color	DuPont Mo. (Duco)
STD	Onyx Black	253-2247	Argent Silver	289-4202
231-A	Driftwood Gray	253-57335	Onyx Black	253-2247
231-B	Dusk Gray	286-55988	Argent Silver	289-4202
231-C	Woodland Green	286-57497	Argent Silver	289-4202
231-D	Surf Green	253-57332	Onyx Black	253-2247
231-E	Regatta Blue	286-57497	Argent Silver	289-4202
231-F	Sahara Beige	253-55979	Onyx Black	253-2247
231-G	Madeira Maroon	281-57334	Argent Silver	289-4202
094	Thistle Gray	253-70397	Onyx Black	253-2247
202	Moonstone Hysheen Gray	N/A.	N/A.	N/A.
246	Sahara Beige	253-55979	Onyx Black	253-2247

NOTE 1: Color codes given for Sedan Delivery are Duco paint codes.
NOTE 2: Sedan Delivery wheel colors (Dulux) were: (STD) Black No. 505, (231-A) Driftwood Gray No. 623, (231-B) Dusk Gray No. 608, (231-C) Woodland Green No. 621, (231-D) Surf Green No. 620, (231-E) Regatta Blue No. 639, (231-F) Sahara Beige No. 603, (231-G) Madeira Maroon No. 622, (246) Sahara Beige No. 603.

Option No.	Body Color	Combination No.	Per-Max No.	Wheel Stripe Color
STD 3000	Juniper Green	518	2U389	Cream Medium
234-A	Commercial Red	411	2U502	Argent Silver
234-D	Jet Black	438	N/A.	Argent Silver
234-G	Mariner Blue	417	2U211	Cream Medium
234-L	Cream Medium	421	2U711	Jet Black
234-M	Yukon Yellow	495	2U723	Jet Black
234-N	Ocean Green	519	2U388	Jet Black
234-P	Transport Blue	520	2U255	Cream Medium
234-Q	Burgundy Maroon	521	2U610	N/A.
234-R	Coppertone	522	2U821	Shell White
234-S	Autumn Brown	523	2U822	Shell White
234-T	Pure White	N/A.	N/A.	Juniper Green
N/A.	Omaha Orange	439	U710	Jet Black

Truck Radiator Grille Inner Bar: Thistle Gray
NOTE 3: The above color combinations were available for Commercial Truck models, as indicated, at all assembly plants. The 1953 Chevrolet trucks were again finished in high-luster Dulux synthetic enamel which was baked on in thermostatically controlled ovens. To assist service managers and mechanics in obtaining matching colors when repairs were necessary, the air-drying Dulux was supplied, instead of the number of the Baking Dulux type paint. The colors in the chart above are for Per-Max colors, an aftermarket substitute for air-drying Dulux made by the Rinshed-Mason Paint Co.

Oil filter (No. 237). Governor (No. 241). Dual tail and stop light (No. 249). Heavy-duty rear springs (No. 254). Heavy-duty radiator (No. 256). Auxiliary seat (No. 263). Auxiliary rear springs (No. 267). Vacuum reserve tank (No. 281). Heavy-duty three-speed transmission (No. 316). Heavy-duty four-speed transmission (No. 318). High-output generators (No. 326). Solenoid starter (No. 327)0. Stand-and-drive controls for Dubl-Duti (328). Combination fuel and vacuum pump (No. 340). Cab rear corner windows (No. 387). Left-hand door key lock (No. 395). Various tire options as follows:

Light Duty Truck Tire Options

Size	Ply Rating	Capacity (lb.)	PSI	Section (in.)
15 in.	Six	1500		407.74
6.00 x 16	Six	1065	36	6.21
6.50 x 16	Six	1290	40	6.65
6.70 x 15	Four	925	24	N/A.
6.70 x 15	Six	1055	30	N/A.
7.00 x 17	Six	1550	45	7.30
7.00 x 17	Eight	1775	55	7.30
7.50 x 17	Eight	2100	60	7.36
7.50 x 17	Ten	2395	75	7.36
7.00 x 18	Eight	1850	55	7.24

1953 Chevrolet 1/2-Ton Series 3100 Pickup (Owner: Dallas F. Wyant)

DEALER ACCESSORIES: Rod type radio antenna (all). Locking gas cap (all). Radiator cover (all). Seat cover (all cab models). Fiber seat cover (all cab models). Gasoline filter (all). License plate frame (all). Curved bumper guard (all except Dubl-Duti). Radiator grille guard for curved type bumper (all). Bumper guard for curved type bumper (all except Dubl-Duti). Outside air heater/defroster (all except Chassis-and-Cowl). Recirculated air type heater (all except Chassis-and-Cowl). Matched horns (all). Static eliminator injector (all). Powder for static eliminator injector (all). Guide dual sealed-beam fog lights (all). Guide spotlight with bracket (all). Unity spotlight with bracket (all). Magnetic trouble lamp (all). Universal stop and taillamps (all). Load compartment lamp (Panel). Underhood lamp (all). Package compartment light and switch (all). Front and rear directional signals (all). Front signal lamps, single lens (all). Front signal lamps, double lens (all). Rear signal lamp with switch (all). Cigarette lighter (all). Two tire traction mats (all). Non-glare rear view mirror (all). Long-arm adjustable outside rear view mirror (all). Bracket unit for cowl-mounted rear view mirror (all). Hood ornament (all). Ventilated seat pad (all). Rear axle magnetic filler plug (all). Magnetic transmission drain plug (all). Magnetic oil pan drain plug, (all). Delco radio receiving set, plus antenna (all except Chassis-and-Cowl). Four-inch red Reflex reflector (all). Windshield scraper (all). Radiator insect screen (all). Electric shaver (all). Right-hand sun shade (all). Running board safety tread (all). Tool kit bag and tools (all). Windshield washer (all).

OPTIONS: [Authorized Aftermarket] A four-wheel drive (4x4) conversion by NAPCO Products, Co., of Minneapolis, Minn., was available for 1950-1954 Chevrolet trucks with open drive shafts. It was merchandised through Chevrolet dealers. NAPCO literature describes it as a "Powr-Pak" four-wheel drive system that shifted in and out of four-wheel drive without stopping or declutching. It featured a two-speed transfer case (eight forward speeds and two in reverse) and full-engine-torque power-take-off. NAPCO also promoted a Chevrolet "Mountain Goat" 4x4 Pickup model.

1953 Chevrolet 1/2-Ton Series 3100 Pickup (Owner: Robert Fries)

HISTORICAL: Introduced: January 1953. Calendar-year registrations: [All Commercials] 327,960. [Calendar-year production] (GVW up to 5,000 lb.) 203,242, (5,001 to 10,000 lb.) 71,517. Innovations: Completely new body style for Sedan Delivery. New side-mounted spare tire option for regular trucks. E-Z-Eye glass option introduced.

1954 Chevrolet Series One-Fifty Sedan Delivery (MVMA)

SEDAN DELIVERY — MODEL D/SERIES 1500 — SIX-CYLINDER: For 1954, the Sedan Delivery used the new-for-1953 body with a different treatment at front and rear. Up front, a new full-width grille had an upper chrome molding, with curved ends, above a large full-width horizontal molding. Five large "teeth" were spaced across this bar. Large parking lamp housings had a flattened-oval shape. They wrapped around the body corners and had inner extensions that bolted to the full-width molding. Below the grille was a large body-color sheet metal filler panel. This model was again in the One-Fifty series with code 54-1271 on the Fisher Body tag under the hood. Features included a one-piece windshield. Doors were still specific to this model and not used on other cars. Front door window glass was the same used on 1953 (and 1954) four-door Sedans. Lower rear quarter panel stampings were unique to the Sedan Delivery. However, the rear compartment floor panel was the same one used for Station Wagons. The rear panel door, used since 1949, was in its final year. Rear bumper parts and guards were also the same as Station Wagon parts. Standard equipment included front and rear bumpers and bumper guards, front license guard, hood ornament and emblem, chrome-plated headlamp rims with doors, dual windshield wipers, dual horns, outside key locks, front and rear bumper gravel deflectors, dual tail and stop lamps, license plate lamp, chrome-plated radio grille, three-position ignition switch, left-hand sun shade, and dome light. Onyx Black remained the standard body color for 1954 Sedan Deliveries. Options included most Chevrolet passenger car colors. The interior was trimmed with gray imitation leather, combination number 303. The Sedan Delivery was made available with automatic (Powerglide) transmission during 1954. It is described in the *Specification Supplement for 1954* revised on April 12, 1954. Powerglide transmission added 135 lb. to the weight of the truck.

1954 Chevrolet 1/2-Ton Series 3100 Panel (OCW)

1/2-TON COMMERCIAL — MODEL D/SERIES 3100 — SIX-CYLINDER: Conventional trucks had what was for them a major restyling. All-new was a one-piece windshield without vertical center molding. There was a new open radiator grille. The opening was filled with a massive cross-bar arrangement. The main horizontal bar extended the full-width of the body. Below it were rectangular parking lamps. The outer radiator grille bars were done in body color and the inner bars were Thistle Gray (except trucks painted Commercial Red had Argent Silver inner bars and trucks painted Pure White had Pure White inner bars). The word Chevrolet was stamped into the grille header bar and lettered in Waldorf White. Bumpers were finished in Anvil Gray. There was a new instrument panel with defroster openings that extended the full width of the windshield. The instruments, grouped in two clusters, were now recessed into the panel to minimize reflections. There was also a redesigned dispatch box (or glove compartment) and a restyled ash receiver. A revised steering wheel gave a full view of the instruments and incorporated finger-grips on the horizontal spokes. A new load box featured a two-inch lower loading height, flat side panel tops, deeper sides, and a grain-tight tailgate the same height as the sides. The 1954 taillights were round. When the optional rear bumper was ordered, the license plate was mounted in the center of the box under the tailgate. Some of the numerous technical changes included a more rugged three-speed manual transmission, a new optional Hydra-Matic transmission, a more durable clutch. Frame rigidity was increased by the use of a heavier cross member at the rear of the engine. Chrome fender bars were available as DeLuxe equipment on Panel trucks only. A switch to gray and maroon interiors was made for Suburbans. Juniper Green body finish with black wheels and Cream Medium wheel striping (16-in. wheels only) was standard finish for all models. Eleven other colors were optional at no extra cost. They included the following choices (wheel pinstripe color in parenthesis): Juniper Green (standard, with Cream Medium pinstripe), Commercial Red (Argent Silver), Jet Black (Argent Silver), Mariner Blue (Cream Medium), Cream Medium (Jet Black), Yukon Yellow (Jet Black), Ocean Green (Jet Black), Transport Blue (Cream Medium), Coppertone (Shell White), Omaha Orange (Jet Black), Autumn Brown (Shell White), and Pure White (Juniper Green). Standard wheels were black. On DeLuxe monotone and two-tone trucks, the wheels were the color of the lower body. On two-tone trucks, Shell White was used exclusively as the upper body color and the wheels were striped with the lower body color. Exceptions included trucks with the lower body done in Pure White, Cream Medium or Omaha Orange, in which cases the wheel striping was Jet Black or Onyx Black. As of about mid-February, 1954 Chevrolet introduced a new DeLuxe Cab option for all 3000 series trucks. It included two-tone interior trim that harmonized with the exterior color, stainless steel windshield and side window reveals, chrome-plated ventipane frames, right-hand sun shade, left-hand arm rest, cigar lighter, twin-tone horns, and cab rear corner windows. The two-tone interior colors were Light Green and Juniper Green, Light Blue and Dark Blue, Birch White and Brown, and Pearl Beige and maroon. This interior included a color-coordinated cloth seat, a color-coordinated rubber floor mat, color-coordinated windlacing, and special colored plastic arm rests. The option also included wheels painted lower body color, with triple striping on the 16-in. wheels.

1954 Chevrolet 3/4-Ton Series 3600 Stake Truck (OCW)

3/4-TON LIGHT-DUTY COMMERCIAL — MODEL J/SERIES 3600 — SIX-CYLINDER: The 3/4-ton trucks had the same Advance-Design styling, features and finish as other conventional trucks. New features included improved drive lines and universal joints. Eight-leaf front springs were standard. The 3600s had a longer wheelbase than 1/2-tons. The new grain-tight load box was longer than the 1/2-ton type and had six stake pockets. Running boards measuring 75-3/4 in. long were used. When a side-mounted spare tire carrier was used, dimpled rear fenders were not required. No Panel, Suburban or Canopy Express was offered in this line. There were Platform and Stake models on 3600s. The standard wheels were of different eight-bolt design. Painted curved-type front bumpers were standard on all models. A similar rear bumper was optional on Models 3602/3612/3603/3604 as RPO 218. A foot-operated parking brake was used on all 3600 models. The brakes were Bendix's duo-servo self-energizing type. The standard tires on 3600s were 15 in. six-ply rated on 15 x 5.50 semi-drop-center rims.

1954 Chevrolet 3/4-Ton Model 3742 Dubl-Duti With 10-Ft Forward Control Body

3/4-TON DUBL-DUTI — MODEL K/SERIES 3700 — SIX-CYLINDER: Two Dubl-Duti Forward-Control chassis were in the Chevrolet truck line. Both had the 235 cid Loadmaster six with updraft carburetor. Model 3742 was the 3/4-ton version on a 125.25-in. wheelbase. Standard walk-in delivery truck bodies could be supplied by several factory-approved sources or the buyer could add his/her own body. The wheels were of eight-bolt design. A painted, Anvil Gray channel type front bumper was optional on the 3700 Dubl-Duti truck chassis as RPO 367.

1-TON MEDIUM-DUTY COMMERCIAL — MODEL L/SERIES 3800 — SIX-CYLINDER: The 3800 Series had the same Advance-Design styling, features and finish as other conventional trucks. New features included improved drive lines and universal joints. A foot-operated parking brake was used on all 3800 models. Panel and Canopy Express models had a one-piece floor made of 3/4-in. thick, five-ply laminated wood. The basic model lineup was unchanged. It included single and dual rear wheel options for all except the Pickup (Express), Canopy Express and Panel. The Pickup had a longer wheelbase than the 3600 Pickup, a longer grain-tight load box with eight stake pockets, and very long running boards. When a side-

mounted spare tire carrier was used, dimpled rear fenders were not required. A curved-type painted front bumper was standard on all models. A similar rear bumper was standard on Models 3805 and 3807. Regular equipment tires were 7.00 x 17 six-ply rated for trucks with single rear wheels or 7.00 x 18 eight-ply rated for trucks with dual rear wheel options. The hubcaps were painted. No hubcaps were used on the 18 x 5-in. wheels of the Chassis-and-Cab, Platform and Stake models, which had eight bolts and eight circular openings. A four-speed manual synchromesh transmission was standard. Trucks with this transmission had a black rubber floor mat made especially for use with the floor-mounted four-speed gear shifter.

1954 Chevrolet 1-Ton Series 3800 Pickup-Express (OCW)

1-TON DUBL-DUTI — MODEL M/SERIES 3900 — SIX-CYLINDER: Two Dubl-Duti Forward-Control chassis returned to the Chevrolet truck line. Both had the 235 cid Loadmaster six with updraft carburetor. Model 3942 was the 1-ton version on a 137-in. wheelbase. Standard walk-in delivery truck bodies could be supplied by several factory-approved sources or the buyer could add his/her own body. A painted, Anvil Gray channel type front bumper was optional on the 3900 Dubl-Duti truck chassis.

1954 Chevrolet 1-Ton Series 3800 DeLuxe Panel (OCW)

I.D. DATA: Serial number located: [Chassis models] on plate temporarily attached near steering column, with final location per body maker. [All others] on plate attached to rear face of left-hand door hinge pillar. The first symbol indicated the series: D=1500, H=3100, J=3600, K=3700, L=3800, M=3900. The second symbol indicated the model year: 4=1954. The third symbol indicated the assembly plant: A=Atlanta, Ga., B=Baltimore, Md., F=Flint, Mich., J=Janesville, Wis., K=Kansas City, Mo., L=Los Angeles, Calif., N=Norwood, Ohio, O=Oakland, Calif., S=St. Louis, Mo., T=Tarrytown, N.Y. Each series was separately numbered in sequence, starting with 001001 at each assembly plant. Serial numbers, by series, were as follows: [1500] D54-001001 to 174684, [3100] H54-001001 to 52112, [3600] J54-001001 to 52112, [3700] K54-001001 to 52112, [3800] L54-001001 to 52112 and [3900] M54-001001 to 52112. Engine numbers located: On crankcase near rear of distributor on right side of engine. Each engine carried a letter code for model year, type and engine plant, plus a production unit number. All numbers were numbered at each source in sequence starting with 1001. Engine numbers by series were: [1500] 01001Z54 to 1024930, [3100] 01001X54 to 1024930, [3600] 01001X54 to 1024930, [3700] 01001T54 to 1024930, [3800] 01001T54 to 1024930, [3900] 01001T54 to 1024930. Engine numbers with X suffix indicated Thriftmaster 235 engine for 3100/3600/3800. Engine numbers with U suffix indicated Thriftmaster 235 with heavy-duty clutch for 3100/3600/3800. Engine numbers with M suffix indicated Thriftmaster 235 with Hydra-Matic for 3100/3600/3800. Engine numbers wit T suffix indicated Loadmaster 235 for 3700/3900. Engine numbers with L suffix indicated Loadmaster 235 with Hydra-Matic for 3700/3900.

1954 Chevrolet 1-Ton Series 3800 Panel (OCW)

Model No.	Body Type	Price	Weight	Prod. Total
Sedan Delivery — Model D-54/Series 1500 — 115 in. w.b				
1508	Sedan Delivery	1632	3195	8255
1/2-Ton Commercial — Model H-54/Series 3100 — 116 in. w.b.				
3102	Chassis & Cowl	1087	2430	-
3103	Chassis & Cab	1346	2870	-
3104	Pickup	1419	3145	-
3105	Panel Delivery	1631	3375	-
3107	Canopy	1688	3325	-
3112	Chassis & W/S	1109	-	-
3106	Suburban (doors)	1958	3655	-
3116	Suburban (gate)	1958	3660	-
3/4-ton Commercial — Model J-54/Series 3600 — 125.25 in. w.b.				
3602	Chassis & Cowl	1227	2685	-
3603	Chassis & Cab	1486	3120	-
3604	Pickup	1582	3525	-
3608	Platform	1587	3540	-
3609	Stake	1654	3700	-
3612	Chassis & W/S	1249	2780	-
3/4-Ton Dubl-Duti — Model K-54/Series 3700 — 125.25 in. w.b.				
3742	Chassis	1249	2460	-
1-Ton Commercial — Model L-54/Series 3800 — 137 in. w.b				
3802	Chassis & Cowl	1325	3015	-
3803	Chassis & Cab	1582	3435	-
3804	Pickup	1705	3880	-
3805	Panel Delivery	1929	4170	-
3807	Canopy	2012	4130	-
3808	Platform	1722	3950	-
3809	Stake	1794	4200	-
3812	Chassis & W/S	1347	3100	-
1-Ton Dubl-Duti — Model M-54/Series 3900 — 137 in. w.b.				
3942	Chassis	1364	2700	-

1954 Chevrolet 1/2-Ton Series 3100 Pickup (MVMA)

CHASSIS: [Series 3800] Wheelbase: 137 in. Overall length: [Pickup] 221.5 in., [Panel] 229.57 in., [Platform/Stake] 224 in. Height: [Panel] 86.5 in. Tires: [front] 7.00 x 17 six-ply, [rear] eight-ply.
CHASSIS: [Series 3742] Wheelbase: 125.25 in. Overall length: 197-1/8 in. Front tread: 62 in. Rear tread: 62-3/8 in. Tires: 7.00 x 17 in.
CHASSIS: [Series 3942] Wheelbase: 137 in. Overall length: 221-7/8 in. Front tread: 61-3/8 in. Rear tread: 61-3/4 in. Tires: 7.50 x 17 eight-ply or 7.50 x 18 eight-ply (Dual rear wheels).
TECHNICAL: Manual, synchromesh transmission: [1500/3100/3600] 3F/1R column-mounted, [3800] [4F/1R] Floor-mounted gearshift. Single-disc, diaphragm spring clutch. [1500/3100] Semi-floating hypoid rear axle, [3600/3800] full-floating rear axle. Hydraulic, four-wheel brakes. Wheels: [1500] One-piece drop center 15-in. wheels, [3100] One-piece drop center 16-in. wheels, [3600/3800] Multi-piece split rims. Standard rear axles: [1500] 3.70:1, [3100] 3.90:1, [3600] 4.57:1, 5.14:1 [3800] 5.14:1.

1954 Chevrolet Series One-Fifty Sedan Delivery (OCW)

ENGINE: [Sedan Delivery] Inline. OHV. Six-cylinder. Cast iron block. Bore & stroke: 3-9/16 x 3-15/16 in. Displacement: 235.5 cid. Compression ratio: 7.5:1. Gross horsepower: 115 at 3700 rpm. Net horsepower: 107 at 3600 rpm. SAE horsepower: 30.4. Gross torque: 200 lb.-ft. at 2000 rpm. Four main bearings. Solid valve lifters. Carburetor: One-barrel model GM/Rochester B. (Manual transmission only).
ENGINE: [All 3100/3600/3800] Inline. OHV. Six-cylinder. Cast iron block. Bore & stroke: 3-9/16 x 3-15/16 in. Displacement: 235.5 cid. Compression ratio: 7.5:1. Gross horsepower: 112 at 3700 rpm. Gross torque: 200 lb.-ft. at 2000 rpm. Four main bearings. Solid valve lifters. Carburetor: One-barrel model GM/Rochester B.
ENGINE: [Dubl-Duti] Inline. OHV. Six-cylinder. Cast iron block. Bore & stroke: 3-9/16 x 3-15/16 in. Displacement: 235.5 cid. Compression ratio: 7.5:1. Gross horsepower: 107 at 3600 rpm. Gross torque: 192 lb.-ft. at 2000 rpm. Four main bearings. Solid valve lifters. Carburetor: Updraft.
CHASSIS: [Model 1500] Wheelbase: 115 in. Overall length: 196 in. Height: 67-1/8 in. Front tread: 56.7 in. Rear tread: 58.8 in. Tires: 6.70 x 15 in. Maximum GVW: 4,100 lb.
CHASSIS: [Series 3100] Wheelbase: 116 in. Overall length: [Pickup] 191.31 in., [Panel/Suburban] 195.31 in. Height: [Panel] 80.68 in., [Suburban] 79.5 in. Tires: 6.00 x 16 six-ply.
CHASSIS: [Series 3600] Wheelbase: 125.25 in. Overall length: [Pickup] 200-3/16 in., [Platform/Stake] 206 in. Tires: 15 in. six-ply.

1954 Chevrolet Series One-Fifty Sedan Delivery (JAW)

OPTIONS: [Sedan Delivery] Directional signals (No. 100F/$15.75). Airflow heater (No. 101B/$72.80). Recirculating heater (No. 101C/$48.15). One-pint oil bath air cleaner (No. 216C/$5.40). Heavy-duty clutch (No. 227A/$3). One color paint options (No. 231A-H/No charge). One-quart capacity oil filter (No. 237B/$11). Governor adjusts 1,750 rpm to 2500 rpm (No. 241A/$17). Five-leaf heavy-duty rear springs (No 254W/$2.50). Six-leaf heavy-duty rear springs (No. 254X/$4). Auxiliary seat (No. 263B/n.a.). Overdrive, includes 4.11:1 rear axle ratio ($100). 30-ampere generator (No. 325P/$7). 40-ampere generator (No. 325Q/$75). E-Z-Eye glass, except rear door (No. 396P/$30). Positive crankcase ventilation (No. 417G/$12). Five 6.70 x 15 six-ply black sidewall tires (No./288A/$35). Five 6.70 x 15 six-ply white sidewall tires (No. 288L/$73.65). Five 6.70 x 15 four-ply white sidewall tires ($26.90)

1954 Chevrolet 1/2-Ton Series 3100 Pickup (DFW)

1954 Chevrolet 1/2-Ton Series 3100 Panel Door Suburban (OCW)

1954 Chevrolet 3/4-Ton Model 3742 Dubl-Duti With Forward-Control Body (GC)

OPTIONS: [All 3000 Series] Double-acting airplane type rear shock absorbers for all 3800s (No. 200M). Double-acting rear cam-and-lever type shock absorbers for model 3942 (No. 201). Long running boards and rear fenders for models 3602/3603/3612/3802/3803/3812 (No. 207L, 207M/$25-$30). Rear axle, 5.14:1 ratio for Series 3600 with 15-in. tires and standard or heavy-duty three-speed transmission, option 306N required (No. 208B/No charge). Rear axle, 5.14:1 ratio for Series 3600 with 17-in. tires and standard or heavy-duty three-speed transmission (No. 208B/No charge). Rear axle, 5.14:1 ratio for trucks with dual rear tires (208D/No charge). Short right-hand rear view mirror bracket for all Chassis-and-Cab, except Model 3103 (No. 210G/$3.25)). Long left-hand rear view mirror and bracket for all Chassis-and-Cabs, Pickups and single-unit body models (No. 210H/$1.70). Long right-hand rear view mirror and bracket for all cab models (No. 210J/$3.25). Short left-hand rear view mirror and bracket for all cab models (No. 210K/$1). Rear shock absorber shield for all, except Model 3942 (No. 211B, 211C/$2.50). Propeller shaft parking brake for 3800s (No. 214A, 214B, 214D, 214E/$6.50). One-pint oil bath air cleaner for all Commercial Trucks (216D or 216G/$3.70). One-quart oil bath air cleaner for all Series 3100/3600/3800 (No. 216E/$4.80). Positive crankcase ventilation system, including 1-qt. oil bath air cleaner, for all except Dubl-Duti (No. 217A, 217D, 217R, 217S/$12.50). Painted rear bumper for 3602/3603/3604/3612 models (No. 218B, 218D, 218E/$10). Chrome rear bumper (10/29/54) for models 3603/3604 (No. 218G, 218K or 218J/$13). Heavy-duty 11-in. diameter clutch with 123.7 sq. in. area (No. 227B/$5). High sills used on models 3808/3809 with 17-in. wheels and tires (No. 230A/$2.50) Monotone no-cost color options for all Sedan Deliveries (No. 231) and all Commercial Trucks (No. 234).

1954 Chevrolet 1/2-Ton Series 3100 End Gate Suburban (CMD)

Option No.	Body Color	DuPont No. (Duco)	Wheel Stripe Color	DuPont Mo. (Duco)
STD	Onyx Black	253-2247	Argent Silver	289-4202
231-A	Driftwood Gray	253-57335	Onyx Black	253-2247
231-B	Dusk Gray	286-55988	Argent Silver	289-4202
231-C	Woodland Green	286-57497	Argent Silver	289-4202
231-D	Surf Green	253-57332	Onyx Black	253-2247
231-E	Regatta Blue	286-57497	Argent Silver	289-4202
231-F	Sahara Beige	253-55979	Onyx Black	253-2247
231-G	Madeira Maroon	281-57334	Argent Silver	289-4202
094	Thistle Gray	253-70397	Onyx Black	253-2247
202	Moonstone Hysheen Gray	N/A.	N/A.	N/A.
246	Sahara Beige	253-55979	Onyx Black	253-2247

1954 Chevrolet 1-Ton Model 3802 16-Passenger School Bus (G. Carson)

1954 Chevrolet 1-Ton Series 3800 Canopy Express (OCW)

NOTE 1: Color codes given for Sedan Delivery are Duco paint codes.
NOTE 2: Sedan Delivery wheel colors (Dulux) were: (STD) Black No. 505, (231-A) Driftwood Gray No. 623, (231-B) Dusk Gray No. 608, (231-C) Woodland Green No. 621, (231-D) Surf Green No. 620, (231-E) Regatta Blue No. 639, (231-F) Sahara Beige No. 603, (231-G) Madeira Maroon No. 622, (246) Sahara Beige No. 603.

Option No.	Body Color	Combination No.	Per-Max No.	Wheel Stripe Color
STD 3000	Juniper Green	518	2U389	Cream Medium
234-A	Commercial Red	411	2U502	Argent Silver
234-D	Jet Black	438	N/A.	Argent Silver
N/A.	Omaha Orange	439	U710	Jet Black
234-G	Mariner Blue	417	2U211	Cream Medium
234-L	Cream Medium	421	2U711	Jet Black
234-M	Yukon Yellow	495	2U723	Jet Black
234-N	Ocean Green	519	2U388	Jet Black
234-P	Transport Blue	520	2U255	Cream Medium
234-R	Coppertone	522	2U821	Shell White
234-S	Autumn Brown	523	2U822	Shell White
234-T	Pure White	N/A.	N/A.	Juniper Green

Truck Radiator Grille Inner Bar: Thistle Gray

NOTE 2: The above color combinations were available for Commercial Truck models, as indicated, at all assembly plants. The 1953 Chevrolet trucks were again finished in high-luster Dulux synthetic enamel which was baked on in thermostatically controlled ovens. To assist service managers and mechanics in obtaining matching colors when repairs were necessary, the air-drying Dulux was supplied, instead of the number of the Baking Dulux type paint.

1954 Chevrolet 1/2-Ton Series 3100 Pickup (CMD)

1954 Chevrolet 1/2-Ton Series 3100 Chassis & Flat-Face Cowl (CMD)

1954 Chevrolet 1-Ton Series 3800 Stake (CMD)

NOTE 3: The colors in the chart above are for Per-Max colors, an aftermarket substitute for air-drying Dulux made by the Rinshed-Mason Paint Co.

One-quart oil filter with flexible lines for all Commercial Trucks (No. 237A/$10.57). Two-quart oil filter with flexible lines for all Commercial Trucks)No. 237K/$11.50). Governor to adjust 2300 to 3200 rpm for all except Dubl-Duti (No. 241G/$6). 17-quart, 2-1/2-in. thick heavy-duty radiator core for all 3600/3800 (No. 256L/$13.75). Ride Control seat for driver and two passengers for all cab models (No. 264B/$48). Dual tail and stop lights for 3800 (No. 249G, 249H/$10). Auxiliary seat for Panel and Canopy Express with imitation leather trim (No. 263A/$29). Auxiliary seat for Panel and Canopy Express with DeLuxe trim (No. 263C/$32). Auxiliary rear springs for 3800 (No. 267B/$14). Speedometer fittings for all 3600/3700/3800/3900 (No. 306N/$6.50). Speedometer fittings for all 3000 (No. 307/$6.50). Hydra-Matic four-speed automatic transmission for all 3000 series (No. 314G, 314H, 314U/$175). Heavy-duty three-speed transmission with column gear shift for all (No. 316D/$60). Four-speed synchromesh transmission with floor-mounted gear shift for all Series 3100/3600/3700 (No. 318C, 318D, 318H, 318J, 318N, 318P/$60). Two-speed electric windshield wipers for all Chassis-and-Cab/Pickup/single-unit body models except 3602 (No. 320A, 320B/$9.75)). 40-ampere generator for all (No. 326T/$7). 45-ampere generator for all (No. 326J,326K/$21). 55-ampere generator for all (No. 326B, 326D/$70). 55-amp. generator, normal and low cut-in for all except Dubl-Duti (No. 326G, 326L/$75). Solenoid starter (Model 3802). Junior school bus chassis for Model 3802 (No. 329A, 329B/$65-$90 depending on wheels and tires selected). Combination fuel and vacuum pump booster for all (No. 340A, 340M/$8.50). Side-mounted wheel carrier for Models 3104/3604/3804 (No. 342A, 342B, 342D, 342E, 342G, 342H/$6). Side-mount tire carrier teamed with No. 393 chrome package (No. 342C, 342F, 342J/$6.50). Lock for side-mount tire carrier only (No. 395F/$6). Rear quarter windows only, with clear glass (No. 387C, 387D/$25). Chrome grille, front bumper and hubcaps (No. 393C, 393F/$32). Left-hand door key lock (No. 395A/$1). Left-hand door and side-mount tire carrier lock (No. 395H/$7). E-Z Eye cab glass (No. 399A/$18). E-Z-Eye glass for rear corner window cab (No. 399B, 399F/$20). DeLuxe cab with monotone paint finish (No. 408B, 408H, 408J/$58). DeLuxe cab with two-tone paint finish (No. 430B, 430H, 430J, 438A, 438H, 438J, 438L/$70). DeLuxe Panel equipment with monotone paint (No. 430A/$35). DeLuxe Panel equipment with two-tone paint (439A, 439H, 439J, 439L/$55).

1954 Chevrolet 1/2-Ton Series 3100 Canopy Express (OCW)

1954 Chevrolet 1/2-Ton Series 3100 Pickup (CMD)

1954 Chevrolet 1/2-Ton Series 3100 Pickup (CMD)

1954 Chevrolet 3/4-Ton Dubl-Duti With 8-Ft. Forward-Control Body (G. Carson)

Light Duty Truck Tire Options

Size	Ply Rating	Capacity (lb.)	PSI	Section (in.)	Price
15 in.	Six	1500	40	7.74	$16.30
15 in.	Eight	1700	48	7.74	$29.45
6.00 x 16	Six	1065	36	6.21	$18.55
6.50 x 16	Six	1290	40	6.65	$108
6.70 x 15	Six	1055	30	N/A.	$37.90
7.00 x 17	Six	1550	45	7.30	$35
7.00 x 17	Eight	1775	55	7.30	$70.80
7.50 x 17	Eight	2100	60	7.36	$100.35
7.50 x 17	Ten	2395	75.	7.36	$77.35
7.00 x 18	Eight	1880	55	7.24	$61

NOTE 4: Tire prices are representative and vary per model and series or whether different sizes are fitted front and rear.

OPTION PACKAGE: [RPO 430/RPO/431] Discontinued for several years due to a shortage of materials, the DeLuxe Equipment option was again available in 1954. According to *Chevrolet Service News* (November 1953) it could be obtained in both Cab and Panel models. A two-tone interior color combination of gray and maroon is used on all, except Panel models. Gray paint is applied on the instrument panel, garnish moldings, lower door panels, and cowl side kick-panels. The seats were trimmed in leather fabric with gray cushion and backrest and maroon facings. In addition to the two-tone interiors, the following equipment was in the option: right-hand sun shade, arm rest on left-hand door, cigar lighter, dual horns, bright metal windshield and side door window reveal moldings (Panels also had rear window reveal moldings), rear corner windows on cab models, and front and rear fender moldings (bars) on Panels.

1954 Chevrolet 1/2-Ton Series 3100 Panel Door Suburban (CMD)

1954 Chevrolet 1-Ton Series 3800 Cantrell Commercial Station Wagon (G. Carson)

OPTIONS: [Dealer Accessories] Cowl mounted, rod type radio antenna (All). Brown arm rest for left- or right-hand door (All cab or single-unit body models). Locking gas tank filler cap (All). 16-in. stainless steel hubcaps (3100 only). Radiator overflow condenser (All except Dubl-Duti). Multi-color vertical stripe seat covers (All cab models). Rain deflectors (All). Gasoline filter (3100/3600/3800). Mud flaps (Platforms/Stakes). Guard for curved type bumper, painted or plated (Models 3100/3600). License plate frame (All). Outside air heater/defroster (All). Recirculating type heater/defroster (All). Second, high-note, horn (All). Tire static eliminator injector and powder for (All). Guide dual sealed beam fog lamps (All). Unity spot lamp with bracket mount (All with cigar lighter). Glove compartment lamp (All). Universal, right-hand tail and stop lamp (All except Dubl-Duti). Underhood lamp (All except Dubl-Duti). Directional signals

(All). Cigar/cigarette lighter (All). Rectangular floor mats, five colors (All). Door-mounted short-arm outside rear view mirror. (All) Five-inch round extendible arm outside rear view mirror. (All) Rectangular 5-1/2 x 7-1/2-in. extendible arm outside rear view mirror. (All) Non-glare outside rear view mirror with bracket mount (All). Hood ornament (All). Delco receiving set radio and antenna (All, except Chassis-and-Cowl). Reflex 4-in. red reflector (All). AC/DC electric shaver (All with cigar lighter). Rear step unit (All Platform and Stake models). Right-hand sun shade (All-standard on Suburbans). Tool kit with bag and tools (All). Outside mounted sun visor (All cab models). Foot-operated windshield wiper (All, except Dubl-Duti). Note: Option applications edited for 1/2- to 1-ton models only).

OPTIONS: [Authorized Aftermarket] A four-wheel drive (4x4) conversion by NAPCO Products, Co., of Minneapolis, Minn., was available for 1950-1954 Chevrolet trucks with open drive shafts. It was merchandised through Chevrolet dealers. NAPCO literature describes it as a "Powr-Pak" four-wheel drive system that shifted in and out of four-wheel drive without stopping or declutching. It featured a two-speed transfer case (eight forward speeds and two in reverse) and full-engine-torque power-take-off. NAPCO also promoted a Chevrolet "Mountain Goat" 4x4 Pickup model. Also available from Cantrell Body Co. was a wood station wagon body for the Chevrolet 3600/3800 Commercial chassis.

HISTORICAL: Introduced: December 1953. Calendar-year registrations: [All Commercials] 293,079. Calendar-year production [All Chevrolet Commercials] 325,515. Light-duty calendar year production by GVW: [Below 5,000 lb.] 170,824, [5,001 to 10,000 lb.] 64,599. Work on a 74,000 sq.-ft. extension to the Chevrolet truck factory in Indianapolis got underway this year. Innovations included: Hydra-Matic transmission. One-piece windshield. New front end styling for regular trucks.

1955 CHEVROLET
(First Series)

1955 Chevrolet "First Series" One-Fifty Sedan Delivery (DFW)

SEDAN DELIVERY — MODEL D/SERIES 1500 — SIX-CYLINDER: For 1955, General Motors planned the biggest revision of products it had ever attempted. At Chevrolet, all-new 1955 cars were introduced in the fall of 1954. However, the all-new trucks weren't quite ready at that time. Since the Sedan Delivery was based on the cars, it was completely changed in design. It had the all-new sheet metal of 1955 passenger cars with a slab-sided body and hooded headlamps. The front featured a narrow upper horizontal molding, curved end moldings and a narrow lower molding all connected to completely surround the 1955 Chevrolet passenger car grille insert. The one-piece insert had 15 vertical members and seven horizontal members intersecting to form 135 small rectangular openings. The upper center rectangle was open at the top, while the others were bordered by a thin grille surround. The parking lamps were wedge-shaped and not part of the grille itself. They attached to openings in the fenders. A body-color filler panel and right- and left-hand fender extensions completed the ensemble. The new Sedan Delivery was more directly based on a new two-door Handyman Station Wagon. The doors were the same as this model and the two-door Sedan. Front door glass was the same as the two-door Sedan. Both the rear compartment floor and the rear quarter panel sections were slightly unique to the Sedan Delivery. There was a new liftgate at the rear, instead of a panel door. This model was again in the One-Fifty series with code 55-1271 on the Fisher Body tag under the hood. Other new features included a wraparound windshield, ball joint suspension, a V-8 engine option, and Powerglide automatic transmission. Standard equipment included front and rear bumpers and bumper guards, front license guard, hood ornament and emblem, chrome-plated headlamp rims with doors, dual windshield wipers, dual horns, outside key locks, front and rear bumper gravel deflectors, dual tail and stop lamps, a license plate lamp, chrome-plated radio grille, three-position ignition switch, left-hand sun shade, and dome light. Onyx Black remained the standard body color for 1954 Sedan Deliveries. Options were India Ivory, Sea Mist Green, Glacier Blue, Shadow Gray, Neptune Green, Skyline Blue, and Gypsy Red. The interior was trimmed with straw brown imitation leather, combination number 501.

1/2-TON COMMERCIAL — MODEL D/SERIES 3100 — SIX-CYLINDER: The all-new trucks were supposed to be introduced along with the new passenger car line, but due to the size of GM's massive plan, Korean War contracts and sales pressure from Ford, truck-line development was delayed. When the totally new Sedan Delivery was introduced on Oct. 28, 1954, the Commercial models changed only very slightly from 1954 specifications. These "First Series 1955" trucks were available until March 25, 1955. Features again included a one-piece windshield and open radiator grille with cross-bars and rectangular parking lamps. All outer radiator grille bars were now done in Bombay Ivory and the inner bars were Onyx Black. The front hood ornament was the same as 1954, but striped with Bombay Ivory instead of Vermilion Red. The word Chevrolet was still stamped on the grille header bar, but the lettering color was changed to Onyx Black. Bumpers were Bombay Ivory on all trucks, except those painted Pure White, which had Pure White bumpers. There was a completely new winged hood side nameplate that said 3100 on the upper end and Chevrolet below. The background was painted black. The dashboard with defroster openings that extended the full width of the windshield and instruments grouped in two clusters was continued. So were the glove compartment, restyled ash tray, steering wheel, grain-tight load box/tailgate, and round taillights. When the optional rear bumper was ordered, the license plate was again mounted in the center of the box under the tailgate. An important technical change for 3100s was an open Hotchkiss drive shaft replacing the old torque tube type. Hydra-Matic transmission was optional. Chrome fender bars remained available as DeLuxe equipment on Panel trucks only. Body colors stayed the same, except for the two-toning color. Juniper Green body finish with Cream Medium wheel striping (16-in. wheels only) and Black wheels was standard finish for all models. Eleven other colors were optional at no extra cost. They included (pinstripe color in parenthesis): Commercial Red (Argent Silver), Jet Black (Argent Silver), Mariner Blue (Cream Medium), Cream Medium (Jet Black), Yukon Yellow (Jet Black), Ocean Green (Jet Black), Transport Blue (Cream Medium), Copper Tone Copper (Shell White), Omaha Orange (Jet Black), Autumn Brown (Shell White), and Pure White (Juniper Green). Standard wheels were Black. On DeLuxe monotone and two-tone trucks, the wheels were the color on the lower body. On two-tone trucks, Bombay Ivory was now used exclusively as the upper body color and the 16-in. wheels were usually striped with the lower body color. Exceptions included trucks with the lower body done in Pure White, Cream Medium or Omaha Orange, in which cases the wheel striping was Jet Black or Onyx Black. DeLuxe Cab models featured two-tone interior trim that harmonized with the exterior color, stainless steel windshield and side window reveals, chrome-plated ventipane frames, right-hand sun shade, left-hand arm rest, cigar lighter, twin-tone horns, and cab rear corner windows. The two-tone interior colors were light green and juniper green, light blue and dark blue, birch white and brown, and pearl beige and maroon. The latter interior included a color-coordinated cloth seat, a color-coordinated rubber floor mat, color-coordinated windlacing, and special colored plastic arm rests. The option also included wheels painted lower body color, with triple striping on the 16-in. wheels.

3/4-TON LIGHT-DUTY COMMERCIAL — MODEL J/SERIES 3600 — SIX-CYLINDER: The 3/4-ton trucks had the same Advance-Design styling, features and finish as other conventional trucks. New features included improved drive lines and universal joints. Eight-leaf front springs were standard. The 3600s had a longer wheelbase than 1/2-tons. The new grain-tight load box was longer than the 1/2-ton type and had six stake pockets. Running boards measuring 75-3/4 in. long were used. When a side-mounted spare tire carrier was used, dimpled rear fenders were not required. No Panel, Canopy Express or Suburban was offered in this line. There were Platform and Stake models. Hubcaps were also painted on 3600s. The standard wheels were of different eight-bolt design. Painted front bumpers were standard on all models. A similar rear bumper was optional on incomplete bodies and flat bed combinations. A foot-operated parking brake was used on all 3600 models. The brakes were Bendix's duo-servo self-energizing type. The standard tires on 3600s were 15 in. six-ply rated on 15 x 5.50 semi-drop-center rims.

3/4-TON DUBL-DUTI — MODEL K/SERIES 3700 — SIX-CYLINDER: Two Dubl-Duti Forward-Control chassis were in the Chevrolet truck line. Both had the 235 cid Loadmaster six with updraft carburetor. Model 3742 was the 3/4-ton version on a 125.25-in. wheelbase. Standard walk-in Delivery truck bodies could be supplied by several factory-approved sources or the buyer could add his/her own body. The wheels were of eight-bolt design. A painted channel type front bumper was an option on the 3700 Dubl-Duti truck chassis (RPO 367). Chevrolet did not make the body and could not be sure the factory style bumper would fit. The bumper was probably painted white this year.

1-TON MEDIUM-DUTY COMMERCIAL — MODEL L/SERIES 3800 — SIX-CYLINDER: The 3800 Series had the same Advance-Design styling, features and finish as other conventional trucks. New features included improved drive lines and universal joints. A foot-operated parking brake was used on all 3800 models. They had Bendix service brakes. Panel and Canopy Express models had a one-piece floor made of 3/4-in. thick, five-ply laminated wood. The basic model lineup was unchanged. It included single and dual rear wheel options for all except the Pickup (Express), Canopy Express and Panel. The Pickup had a longer wheelbase than the 3600 Pickup, a longer grain-tight load box with eight stake pockets, and very long running boards. When a side-mounted spare tire carrier was used, dimpled rear fenders were not required. A curved-type painted front bumper was standard on all models. A similar rear bumper was standard on Models 3805 and 3807. Regular equipment tires were 7.00 x 17 six-ply rated for trucks with single rear wheels or 7.00 x 18 eight-ply rated for trucks with dual rear wheel options. The hubcaps were painted. No hubcaps were used on the 18 x 5-in. wheels of the Chassis-and-Cab, Platform and Stake models, which had eight bolts and eight circular openings. A four-speed manual synchromesh transmission was standard. Trucks with this transmission had a black rubber floor mat made especially for use with the floor-mounted four-speed gear-shifter.

1955 Chevrolet First Series 1-Ton Model 3808 Platform (OCW)

1-TON DUBL-DUTI — MODEL M/SERIES 3900 — SIX-CYLINDER: Two Dubl-Duti Forward-Control chassis returned to the Chevrolet truck line. Both had a new 235 cid Loadmaster six with updraft carburetor. Model 3942 was the 1-ton version on a 137-in. wheelbase. Standard walk-in delivery truck bodies could be supplied by several factory-approved sources or the buyer could add his/her own body. A painted channel type front bumper was an option (RPO 367) on the 3900 Dubl-Duti truck chassis as Chevrolet did not make the body and could not be sure the factory style bumper would fit. The bumper was probably painted white this year.

I.D. DATA: Serial number located: [Chassis models] on plate temporarily attached near steering column, with final location per body maker. [All others] on plate attached to rear face of left-hand door hinge pillar. The first symbol indicated the series: D=1500, H=3100, J=3600, K=3700, L=3800, M=3900. The second symbol indicated the model year: 4=1954. The third symbol indicated the assembly plant: A=Atlanta, Ga., B=Baltimore, Md., F=Flint, Mich., J=Janesville, Wis., K=Kansas City, Mo., L=Los Angeles, Calif., N=Norwood, Ohio, O=Oakland, Calif., S=St. Louis, Mo., T=Tarrytown, N.Y. Each series was separately numbered in sequence, starting with 000001 at each assembly plant. Serial numbers for the 1955 First Series were a continuation of 1954 numbers. by series, were as follows: [1500] D55-001001 to 0017016, [3100] H55-001001 to 0017016, [3600] J55-001001 to 0017016, [3742] K55-001001 to 0017016, [3800] L53-001001 to 0017016 and [3942] M53-001001 to 0017016. Engine numbers located: On crankcase near rear of distributor on right side of engine. Each engine carried a letter code for model year, type and engine plant, plus a production unit number. All numbers were numbered at each source in sequence starting with 1001. Engine numbers by series were: [1500] 01001Z55 up, [3100/3600/3800] 01001X55 up, [3700/3900] 01001T55 up. Engine numbers with X suffix indicated Thriftmaster 235 engine for 3100/3600/3800. Engine numbers with U suffix indicated Thriftmaster 235 with heavy-duty clutch for 3100/3600/3800. Engine numbers with M suffix indicated Thriftmaster 235 with Hydra-Matic for 3100/3600/3800. Engine numbers with T suffix indicated Loadmaster 235 for 3700/3900. Engine numbers with L suffix indicated Loadmaster 235 with Hydra-Matic for 3700/3900.

Model No.	Body Type	Price	Weight	Prod. Total
Sedan Delivery — Model D-54/Series 1500 — 115 in. w.b				
1508	Sedan Delivery	1699	3110	8255
1/2-Ton Commercial — Model H-54/Series 3100 — 116 in. w.b.				
3102	Chassis & Cowl	1098	2455	-
3103	Chassis & Cab	1357	2845	-
3104	Pickup	1430	3125	-
3105	Panel	1642	3340	-
3107	Canopy	1699	3300	-
3112	Chassis & W/S	1120	2550	-
3106	Suburban (doors)	1968	3630	-
3116	Suburban (gate)	1968	3630	-
3/4-ton Commercial — Model J-54/Series 3600 — 125.25 in. w.b.				
3602	Chassis & Cowl	1238	2685	-
3603	Chassis & Cab	1497	3135	-
3604	Pickup	1593	3525	-
3608	Platform	1598	3550	-
3609	Stake	1665	3725	-
3612	Chassis & W/S	1260	2780	-
3/4-Ton Dubl-Duti — Model K-54/Series 3700 — 125.25 in. w.b.				
3742	Chassis	1260	2465	-
1-Ton Commercial — Model L-54/Series 3800 — 137 in. w.b				
3802	Chassis & Cowl	1336	3005	-
3803	Chassis & Cab	1593	3435	-
3804	Pickup	1716	3865	-
3805	Panel	1940	4170	-
3807	Canopy	2023	4105	-
3808	Platform	1733	3990	-
3809	Stake	1805	4255	-
3812	Chassis & W/S	1358	3100	-
1-Ton Dubl-Duti — Model M-54/Series 3900 — 137 in. w.b.				
3942	Chassis	1375	2725-	

ENGINE: [Sedan Delivery] Inline. OHV. Six-cylinder. Cast iron block. Bore & stroke: 3-9/16 x 3-15/16 in. Displacement: 235.5 cid. Compression ratio: 7.5:1. Gross horsepower: 123 at 3800 rpm. SAE horsepower: 30.4. Four main bearings. Solid valve lifters. Carburetor: One-barrel model GM/Rochester B.

ENGINE: [Commercials] Inline. OHV. Six-cylinder. Cast iron block. Bore & stroke: 3-9/16 x 3-15/16 in. Displacement: 235.5 cid. Compression ratio: 7.5:1. Gross horsepower: 112 at 3700 rpm. Brake horsepower: 105 at 3600 rpm. SAE horsepower: 30.4. Four main bearings. Solid valve lifters. Carburetor: One-barrel model GM/Rochester B.

ENGINE: [Dubl-Duti] Inline. OHV. Six-cylinder. Cast iron block. Bore & stroke: 3-9/16 x 3-15/16 in. Displacement: 235.5 cid. Compression ratio: 7.5:1. Gross horsepower: 107 at 3600 rpm. Gross torque: 192 lb.-ft. at 2000 rpm. Four main bearings. Solid valve lifters. Carburetor: Updraft.

CHASSIS: [Model 1500] Wheelbase: 115 in. Overall length: 197-1/8 in. Height: 62-1/8 in. Front tread: 58 in. rear tread: 58.8 in. Tires: 6.70 x 15 in. Maximum GVW: 4,100 lb.

CHASSIS: [Series 3100] Wheelbase: 116 in. Overall length: [Pickup] 191.31 in., [Panel/Suburban] 195.31 in. Height: [Panel] 80.68 in., [Suburban] 79.5 in. Tires: 6.00 x 16 six-ply.

CHASSIS: [Series 3600] Wheelbase: 125.25 in. Overall length: [Pickup] 200-3/16 in., [Platform/Stake] 206 in. Tires: 15 in., six-ply.

CHASSIS: [Series 3800] Wheelbase: 137 in. Overall length: [Pickup] 221.5 in., [Panel] 229.57 in., [Platform/Stake] 224 in. Height: [Panel] 86.5 in. Tires: [front] 7.00 x 17 six-ply, [rear] eight-ply.

CHASSIS: [Series 3742] Wheelbase: 125.25 in. Overall length: 197-1/8 in. Front tread: 62 in. Rear tread: 62-3/8 in. Tires: 15-in. six-ply.

CHASSIS: [Series 3942] Wheelbase: 137 in. Overall length: 221-7/8 in. Front tread: 61-3/8 in. Rear tread: 61-3/4 in. Tires: 7.50 x 17 eight-ply or 7.50 x 18 eight-ply (Dual rear wheels).

TECHNICAL: Manual, synchromesh transmission: [1500/3100/3600] 3F/1R with column-mounted gear shift, [3800] 4F/1R with floor-mounted gear shift. Single-disc, diaphragm spring clutch. [1500/3100] Semi-floating hypoid rear axle, [3600/3800] full-floating rear axle. Hydraulic, four-wheel brakes. Wheels: [1500] One-piece drop center 15-in. wheels, [3100] One-piece drop center 16-in. wheels, [3600/3800] Multi-piece split rims. Standard rear axles: [1500] 3.70:1, [3100] 3.90:1, [3600] 4.57:1, 5.14:1 [3800] 5.14:1.

OPTIONS: [Sedan Delivery] Directional signals (No. 100F/$15.75). Airflow heater (No. 101B/$72.80). Recirculating heater (No. 101C/$48.15). One-pint oil bath air cleaner (No. 216C/$5.40). Heavy-duty clutch (No. 227A/$3). One color paint options (No. 231A-H/No charge). One-quart capacity oil filter (No. 237B/$11). Governor adjusts 1,750 rpm to 2500 rpm (No. 241A/$17). Five-leaf heavy-duty rear springs (No 254W/$2.50). Six-leaf heavy-duty rear springs (No. 254X/$4). Auxiliary seat (No 263B/n.a.). Overdrive, includes 4.11:1 rear axle ratio ($100). 30-ampere generator (No. 325P/$7). 40-ampere generator (No. 325Q/$75). E-Z-Eye glass, except rear door (No. 396P/$30). Positive crankcase ventilation (No. 417G/$12). Five 6.70 x 15 six-ply black sidewall tires (No./288A$35). Five 6.70 x 15 six-ply white sidewall tires (No. 288L/$73.65). Five 6.70 x 15 four-ply white sidewall tires ($26.90)

OPTIONS: [All 3000 Series] Double-acting airplane type rear shock absorbers for all 3800s (No. 200M). Double-acting rear cam-and-lever type shock absorbers for model 3942 (No. 201). Long running boards and rear fenders for models 3602/3603/3612/3802/3803/3812 (No. 207L, 207M/$25-$30). Rear axle, 5.14:1 ratio for Series 3600 with 15-in. tires and standard or heavy-duty three-speed transmission, option 306N required (No. 208B/No charge). Rear axle, 5.14:1 ratio for Series 3600 with 17-in. tires and standard or heavy-duty three-speed transmission (No. 208B/No charge). Rear axle, 5.14:1 ratio for trucks with dual rear tires (208D/No charge). Short right-hand rear view mirror bracket for all Chassis-and-Cab, except Model 3103 (No. 210G/$3.25)). Long left-hand rear view mirror and bracket for all Chassis-and-Cabs, Pickups and single-unit body models (No. 210H/$1.70). Long right-hand rear view mirror and bracket for all cab models (No. 210J/$3.25). Short left-hand rear view mirror and bracket for all cab models (No. 210K/$1). Rear shock absorber shield for all, except Model 3942 (No. 211B, 211C/$2.50). Propeller shaft parking brake for 3800s (No. 214A, 214B, 214D, 214E/$6.50). One-pint oil bath air cleaner for all Commercial Trucks (216D or 216G/$3.70). One-quart oil bath air cleaner for all Series 3100/3600/3800 (No. 216E/$4.80). Positive crankcase ventilation system, including 1-qt. oil bath air cleaner, for all except Dubl-Duti (No. 217A, 217D, 217R, 217S/$12.50). Painted rear bumper for 3602/3603/3604/3612 models (No. 218B, 218D, 218E/$10). Chrome rear bumper (10/29/54) for models 3603/3604 (No. 218G, 218K or 218J/$13). Heavy-duty 11-in. diameter clutch with 123.7-sq. in. area (No. 227B/$5). High sills used on models 3808/3809 with 17-in. wheels and tires (No. 230A/$2.50) Monotone no-cost color options for all Sedan Deliveries (No. 231) and all Commercial Trucks (No. 234).

Option No.	Body Color	Combination No.	Per-Max No.	Wheel Stripe Color
STD	Onyx Black	253-2247	Argent Silver	289-4202
231-A	Driftwood Gray	253-57335	Onyx Black	253-2247
231-B	Dusk Gray	286-55988	Argent Silver	289-4202
231-C	Woodland Green	286-57497	Argent Silver	289-4202
231-D	Surf Green	253-57332	Onyx Black	253-2247
231-E	Regatta Blue	286-57497	Argent Silver	289-4202
231-F	Sahara Beige	253-55979	Onyx Black	253-2247
231-G	Madeira Maroon	281-57334	Argent Silver	289-4202
094	Thistle Gray	253-70397	Onyx Black	253-2247
202	Moonstone Hysheen Gray	N/A.	N/A.	N/A.
246	Sahara Beige	253-55979	Onyx Black	253-2247

NOTE 1: Color codes given for Sedan Delivery are Duco paint codes.

NOTE 2: Sedan Delivery wheel colors (Dulux) were: (STD) Black No. 505, (231-A) Driftwood Gray No. 623, (231-B) Dusk Gray No. 608, (231-C) Woodland Green No. 621, (231-D) Surf Green No. 620, (231-E) Regatta Blue No. 639, (231-F) Sahara Beige No. 603, (231-G) Madeira Maroon No. 622, (246) Sahara Beige No. 603.

Option No.	Body Color	DuPont No. (Duco)	Wheel Stripe Color	DuPont Mo. (Duco)
STD 3000	Juniper Green	518	2U389	Cream Medium
234-A	Commercial Red	411	2U502	Argent Silver
234-D	Jet Black	438	N/A.	Argent Silver
N/A.	Omaha Orange	439	U710	Jet Black
234-G	Mariner Blue	417	2U211	Cream Medium
234-L	Cream Medium	421	2U711	Jet Black
234-M	Yukon Yellow	495	2U723	Jet Black
234-N	Ocean Green	519	2U388	Jet Black
234-P	Transport Blue	520	2U255	Cream Medium
234-R	Coppertone	522	2U821	Shell White
234-S	Autumn Brown	523	2U822	Shell White
234-T	Pure White	N/A.	N/A.	Juniper Green

Truck Radiator Grille Inner Bar: Thistle Gray

NOTE 3: The above color combinations were available for Commercial Truck models, as indicated, at all assembly plants. The 1953 Chevrolet trucks were again finished in high-luster Dulux synthetic enamel which was baked on in thermostatically controlled ovens. To assist service managers and mechanics in obtaining matching colors when repairs were necessary, the air-drying Dulux was supplied, instead of the number of the Baking Dulux type paint.

NOTE 4: The colors in the chart above are for Per-Max colors, an aftermarket substitute for air-drying Dulux made by the Rinshed-Mason Paint Co.

One-quart oil filter with flexible lines for all Commercial Trucks (No. 237A/$10.57). Two-quart oil filter with flexible lines for all Commercial Trucks (No. 237K/$11.50). Governor to adjust 2300 to 3200 rpm for all except Dubl-Duti (No. 241G/$6). 17-quart, 2-1/2-in. thick heavy-duty radiator core for all 3600/3800 (No. 256L/$13.75). Ride Control seat for driver and two passengers for all cab models (No. 264B/$48). Dual tail and stop lights for 3800 (No. 249G, 249H/$10). Auxiliary seat for Panel and Canopy Express with imitation leather trim (No. 263A/$29). Auxiliary seat for Panel and Canopy Express with DeLuxe trim (No. 263C/$32). Auxiliary rear springs for 3800 (No. 267B/$14). Speedometer fittings for all 3600/3700/3800/3900 (No. 306N/$6.50). Speedometer fittings for all 3000 (No. 307/$6.50). Hydra-Matic four-speed automatic transmission for all 3000 series (No. 314G, 314H, 314U/$175). Heavy-duty three-speed transmission with column gear shift for all (No. 316D/$60)). Four-speed synchromesh transmission with floor-mounted gear shift for all Series 3100/3600/3700 (No. 318C, 318D, 318H, 318J, 318N, 318P/$60). Two-speed electric windshield wipers for all Chassis-and-Cab/Pickup/single-unit body models except 3602 (No. 320A, 320B/$9.75)). 40-ampere generator for all (No. 326H/$20). 45-ampere generator for all (No. 326T/$7). 50-ampere generator for all (No. 326J,326K/$21). 55-ampere generator for all (No. 326B, 326D/$70). 55-amp. generator, normal and low cut-in for all except Dubl-Duti (No. 326G, 326L/$75). Solenoid starter (Model 3802). Junior school bus chassis for Model 3802 (No. 329A, 329B/$65-$90 depending on wheels and tires selected). Combination fuel and vacuum pump booster for all (No. 340A, 340M/$8.50). Side-mounted wheel carrier for Models 3104/3604/3804 (No. 342A, 342B, 342D, 342E, 342G, 342H/$6). Side-mount tire carrier teamed with No. 393 chrome package (No. 342C, 342F, 342J/$6.50). Lock for side-mount tire carrier only (No. 395F/$6). Rear quarter windows only, with clear glass (No. 387C, 387D/$25). Chrome grille, front bumper and hubcaps (No. 393C, 393F/$32). Left-hand door key lock (No. 395A/$1). Left-hand door and side-mount tire carrier lock (No. 395H/$7). E-Z Eye cab glass (No. 399A/$18). E-Z-Eye glass for rear corner window cab (No. 399B, 399F/$20). DeLuxe cab with monotone paint finish (No. 408B, 408H, 408J/$58). DeLuxe cab with two-tone paint finish (No. 430B, 430H, 430J, 438A, 438H, 438J, 438L/$70). DeLuxe Panel equipment with monotone paint (No. 430A/$35). DeLuxe Panel equipment with two-tone paint (439A, 439H, 439J, 439L/$55).

1955 Chevrolet First Series 1/2-Ton Model 3104 Pickup (Greg Carson)

Size	Ply Rating	Capacity (lb.)	PSI	Section (in.)	Price
15 in.	Six	1500	40	7.74	$16.30
15 in.	Eight	1700	48	7.74	$29.45
6.00 x 16	Six	1065	36	6.21	$18.55
6.50 x 16	Six	1290	40	6.65	$108
6.70 x 15	Six	1055	30	N/A.	$37.90
7.00 x 17	Six	1550	45	7.30	$35
7.00 x 17	Eight	1775	55	7.30	$70.80
7.50 x 17	Eight	2100	60	7.36	$100.35
7.50 x 17	Ten	2395	75.	7.36	$77.35
7.00 x 18	Eight	1880	55	7.24	$61

NOTE 5: Tire prices are representative and vary per model and series or whether different sizes are fitted front and rear.

OPTION PACKAGE: [RPO 430/RPO/431] Discontinued for several years due to a shortage of materials, the DeLuxe Equipment option was again available in 1954. According to *Chevrolet Service News* (November, 1953) it could be obtained in both Cab and Panel models. A two-tone interior color combination of gray and maroon is used on all, except Panel models. Gray paint is applied on the instrument panel, garnish moldings, lower door panels, and cowl side kick-panels. The seats were trimmed in leather fabric with gray cushion and backrest and maroon facings. In addition to the two-tone interiors, the following equipment was in the option: right-hand sun shade, arm rest on left-hand door, cigar lighter, dual horns, bright metal windshield and side door window reveal moldings (Panels also had rear window reveal moldings, rear corner windows on cab models, and front and rear fender moldings (bars) on Panels.

OPTIONS: [Dealer Accessories] Cowl mounted, rod type radio antenna (All). Brown arm rest for left- or right-hand door (All cab or single-unit body models). Locking gas tank filler cap (All). 16-in. stainless steel hubcaps (3100 only). Radiator overflow condenser (All except Dubl-Duti). Multi-color vertical stripe seat covers (All cab models). Rain deflectors (All). Gasoline filter (3100/3600/3800). Mud flaps (Platforms/Stakes). Guard for curved type bumper, painted or plated (Models 3100/3600). License plate frame (All). Outside air heater/defroster (All). Recirculating type heater/defroster (All). Second, high-note, horn (All). Tire static eliminator injector and powder for (All). Guide dual sealed beam fog lamps (All). Unity spot lamp with bracket mount (All). Portable spot lamp (All with cigar lighter). Glove compartment lamp (All). Universal, right-hand tail and stop lamp (All except Dubl-Duti). Underhood lamp (All except Dubl-Duti). Directional signals (All). Cigar/cigarette lighter (All). Rectangular floor mats, five colors (All). Door-mounted short-arm outside rear view mirror. (All) Five-inch round extendible arm outside rear view mirror. (All) Rectangular 5-1/2 x 7-1/2-in. extendible arm outside rear view mirror. (All) Non-glare outside rear view mirror with bracket mount (All). Hood ornament (All). Delco receiving set radio and antenna (All, except Chassis-and-Cowl). Reflex 4-in. red reflector (All). AC/DC electric shaver (All with cigar lighter). Rear step unit (All Platform and Stake models). Right-hand sun shade (All, standard on Suburbans). Tool kit with bag and tools (All). Outside mounted sun visor (All cab models). Foot-operated windshield wiper (All, except Dubl-Duti). Note: Option applications edited for 1/2- to 1-ton models only).

1955 Chevrolet First Series 3/4-Ton Model 3602 Chassis-and-Cowl with Stand-and-Drive body (GC)

OPTIONS: [Authorized Aftermarket] A four-wheel drive (4x4) conversion by NAPCO Products, Co., of Minneapolis, Minn., was available for 1950-1954 Chevrolet trucks with open drive shafts. It was merchandised through Chevrolet dealers. NAPCO literature describes it as a "Powr-Pak" four-wheel drive system that shifted in and out of four-wheel drive without stopping or declutching. It featured a two-speed transfer case (eight forward speeds and two in reverse) and full-engine-torque power-take-off. NAPCO also promoted a Chevrolet "Mountain Goat" 4x4 Pickup model. Also available from Cantrell Body Co. was a wood station wagon body for the Chevrolet 3600/3800 Commercial chassis.

HISTORICAL: Introduced: Oct. 28, 1954. Produced through March 25, 1955, when all-new 1955 Second Series appeared. Calendar-year registrations and production included with 1954 or 1955 Second Series models. The change to open drive shaft is important for enthusiasts making non-original engine swaps in these trucks.

1955 CHEVROLET
(Second Series)

SEDAN DELIVERY — MODEL D/SERIES 1500 — SIX/V-8: Chevrolet's "Second Series" 1955 trucks were introduced on March 25, 1955. The Sedan Delivery was unchanged in appearance from the 1955 "First Series." The front featured a narrow upper horizontal molding, curved end moldings, and a narrow lower molding all connected to completely surround the 1955 Chevrolet passenger car grille insert. The one-piece insert had 15 vertical members and seven horizontal members intersecting to form 135 small rectangular openings. The upper center rectangle was open at the top, while the others were bordered by a thin grille surround. The parking lamps were wedge-shaped and not part of the grille itself. They attached to openings in the fenders. A body-color filler panel and right- and left-hand fender extensions completed the ensemble. The new Sedan Delivery was more directly based on a new two-door Handyman station wagon. The doors were the same as this model and the two-door Sedan. Front door glass was the same as the two-door Sedan. Both the rear compartment floor and the rear quarter panel

sections were slightly unique to the Sedan Delivery. There was a new liftgate at the rear, instead of a panel door. This model was again in the One-Fifty series with code 55-1271 on the Fisher Body tag under the hood. Other new features included a wraparound windshield, ball joint suspension, a V-8 engine option, and Powerglide automatic transmission. Standard equipment included front and rear bumpers and bumper guards, front license guard, hood ornament and emblem, chrome-plated headlamp rims with doors, dual windshield wipers, dual horns, outside key locks, front and rear bumper gravel deflectors, dual combination tail/stop/license plate lamp, chrome-plated radio grille, three-position ignition switch, left-hand sun shade, and dome light. Onyx Black remained the standard body color for 1954 Sedan Deliveries. Options were India Ivory, Sea Mist Green, Glacier Blue, Shadow Gray, Neptune Green, Skyline Blue, and Gypsy Red. The interior was trimmed with straw brown imitation leather, combination number 501.

1955 Chevrolet One-Fifty Sedan Delivery (D. Batten)

1/2-TON COMMERCIAL — MODEL H/SERIES 3100 — SIX/V-8: Chevrolet's new "Task Force" styling was characterized by lower, flatter hood and fender lines and roof lines. There was a Panoramic wraparound windshield and an eggcrate grille. The cabs and bodies were slab-sided. The standard Pickup still had short running boards and protruding rear fenders. A larger, winged Chevrolet emblem decorated the hood. The front fender sides had spear-shaped nameplates with Chevrolet lettering and the series designation. They were mounted behind and above the wheel openings. On trucks with the engine option, V-8 emblems were placed on the fender sides, just below the nameplates. Inside was a new dash with a fan-shaped instrument panel. Interiors were trimmed with "oakbark" woven plastic and breathable rayon fabric in color choices of black or beige for all models, plus brown and beige for cab models only. Floor mats were black rubber. Trucks with Custom Cab equipment had upgraded trims with foam padding, chrome dash knobs, cigar lighter, dual arm rests and sun shades, and extra chrome trim. This was available with either the standard 10-11/16 x 35-1/8-in. rear window or the optional Panoramic rear window that wrapped around the rear cab corners. Technical changes included a new Thriftmaster six, the optional V-8, shorter wheelbases, longer leaf springs, 12-volt electrics and tubeless tires on 1/2-ton (3100) models. For the second series trucks there were 13 solid and 13 two-tone color combinations. Solid colors (wheel stripe color in parenthesis) were: Juniper Green (Bombay Ivory), Commercial Red (Argent Silver), Sand Beige (Bombay Ivory), Jet Black (Bombay Ivory), Omaha Orange (Bombay Ivory), Granite Gray (Bombay Ivory), Empire Blue (Bombay Ivory), Cream Medium (Bombay Ivory), Yukon Yellow (Bombay Ivory), Ocean Green (Bombay Ivory), Crystal Blue (Bombay Ivory), Russet Brown (Bombay Ivory), Pure White. Two-tone color combinations came with the following lower body colors and Bombay Ivory upper body: Juniper Green, Commercial Red, Jet Black, Empire Blue, Cream Medium, Yukon Yellow, Ocean Green, Crystal Blue, Granite Gray, Sand Beige, and Omaha Orange. Wheel stripe colors were the same as with solid colors. Other choices were Sand Beige on top, Russet Brown on bottom (Bombay Ivory wheel stripe) or Commercial Red upper over Bombay Ivory lower body (Commercial Red wheel stripe). Wheels were painted lower body color on all 3000 Series trucks. DeLuxe exterior trim and two-tone options were no longer available for Suburbans. Only 15 x 5K or 16 x 5K wheels had pinstripes.

1955 Chevrolet 1/2-Ton Second Series 3100 Pickup (Lee Hoovler photo)

1955 Chevrolet 1/2-Ton Second Series Model 3124 Cameo Carrier (CMD)

1/2-TON COMMERCIAL (CAMEO) — Model H/Series 3100 — SIX/V-8: A new 1/2-ton model was the Suburban Pickup or Cameo Carrier. This was a limited-production, highly stylized 1/2-ton (Body Style No. 3124) based on the 3000 series chassis with a 114-in. wheelbase. General Motors stylist Chuck Jordan developed the Cameo Carrier's design based on military guided missile carriers he saw while in the service. Preliminary sketches were quickly translated into a production vehicle design. It was introduced on March 25, 1955. Special Cameo features included slab-sided rear fender skins made of fiberglass. These were made by Moulded Fiberglass Company of Ashtabula, Ohio. The fiberglass fenders were bolted on a standard cargo box to bring the exterior width of the cargo box out flush with the sides of the standard cab. Chrome moldings trimmed the gap between the cab and the box. A fiberglass tailgate panel over the steel tailgate hid the hinges, latches and restraining chain. There was a Chevrolet bow tie logo on the center of the tailgate. A hidden compartment below the endgate held the spare tire in a fiberglass well. It was accessible via a swing-down hinged rear bumper section. Unique taillights were seen. Standard equipment included DeLuxe Cab equipment and the Panoramic rear window. Cameos came finished in Bombay Ivory with Commercial Red accents around the side and rear windows. The inside of the cargo box was also done in red. The interior featured exclusive red and beige upholstery similar to that of a 1954 Chevrolet Bel Air passenger car. A red floor mat was used. A special red steering wheel had three spokes (the top two wider) and a flat horn button trimmed in black. Full wheelcovers from the 1955 Bel Air were used on ivory colored rims. Cameo Carriers had stripes on 16 x 5K wheels only.

1955 Chevrolet 1/2-Ton Second Series Model 3124 Cameo Carrier (Aftermarket wheels)

1/2-TON COMMERCIAL — MODEL M/SERIES 3200 — SIX/V-8: This was a new long wheelbase (LWB) 1/2-ton truck on the same frame as 3/4-ton models. It had a longer cargo box with longer running boards and more space between the cab and rear fenders. It had the same 5,000 lb. GVW rating as other 1/2-ton trucks.
1/2-TON DUBL-DUTI — MODEL F/SERIES 3400 — SIX/V-8: Three Dubl-Duti Forward-Control chassis were in the late-1955 Chevrolet truck line. A new model was the 1/2-ton Model 3442 a 104-in. wheelbase. Standard walk-in Delivery truck bodies could be supplied by several factory-approved sources or the buyer could add his/her own body.
3/4-TON COMMERCIAL — MODEL J/SERIES 3600 — SIX/V-8: This series included the medium-duty cab models on a 123.5-in. wheelbase. The Pickup had longer running boards and a longer cargo box. There were also Platform and Stake models. The GVW rating was 6,900 lb.
3/4-TON DUBL-DUTI — MODEL G/SERIES 3500 — SIX-CYLINDER: Model 3542 was the 3/4-ton Dubl-Duti on a 125-in. wheelbase. Standard walk-in delivery truck bodies could be supplied by several factory-approved sources or the buyer could add his/her own body. The wheels were of eight-bolt design. A painted, Anvil Gray channel type front bumper was optional on the 3700 Dubl-Duti truck chassis.
3/4-TON — DUBL-DUTI — MODEL K/SERIES 3700 — SIX-CYLINDER: Model 3742 was the 3/4-ton Dubl-Duti on a 137-in. wheelbase. Standard walk-in Delivery truck bodies could be supplied by several factory-approved sources or the buyer could add his/her own body. The wheels were of eight-bolt design. A painted, Anvil Gray channel type front bumper was optional on the 3700 Dubl-Duti truck chassis.
1-TON MEDIUM-DUTY COMMERCIAL — MODEL L/SERIES 3800 — SIX-CYLINDER: The 3800 Series had the same Task-Force styling as other conventional trucks. Panel and Canopy Express models had a one-piece floor made of 3/4-in. thick, five-ply laminated wood. The basic model lineup was unchanged. The 1-ton Pickup had a longer wheelbase than the 3600 Pickup, a longer grain-tight load box with extra stake pockets, and very long running boards. No hubcaps were used on the larger split-rim wheels of the Chassis-and-Cab, Platform and Stake models, which had eight bolts and eight circular openings. A four-speed manual synchromesh transmission was standard.

1955 Chevrolet 1/2-Ton Second Series 3100 Panel (DFW)

I.D. DATA: Serial number located: [Chassis models] on plate temporarily attached near steering column, with final location per body maker. [All others] on plate attached to rear face of left-hand door hinge pillar. The first symbol indicated the series: D=1500, H=3100, M=3200, F=3400, G=3500, J=3600, K=3700, L=3800. The second symbol was a 2 to indicate 1955 "Second Series." The third and fourth symbols indicated the model year: 55=1955. The fifth symbol indicated the assembly plant: A=Atlanta, Ga., B=Baltimore, Md., F=Flint, Mich., J=Janesville, Wis., K=Kansas City, Mo., L=Los Angeles, Calif., N=Norwood, Ohio, O=Oakland, Calif., S=St. Louis, Mo., T=Tarrytown, N.Y. Each series was separately numbered in sequence, starting with 000001 at each assembly plant. Serial numbers for 1955 second series trucks were as follows: [1500] D255-001001 to 256218, [3100] H255-001001 to 60351, [3200] M255-001001 to 60351, [3400] F255-001001 to 60351, [3500] G255-001001 to 60351, [3700] K255-001001 to 60351, [3600] J255-001001-60351 and [3800] L255-001001 to 60351. Engine numbers located on right side of engine on boss at rear of distributor. Engine numbers began with an F (Flint, Mich.) or T (Tonawanda, N.Y.) assembly plant code. On Sedan Deliveries, second symbol Z or Y indicated 235 cid six, G or F indicated 265 cid V-8. On Commercials, second symbol X, S, or M indicated 235 cid six, E indicated 265 V-8 (when available). Sequential production numbers for base 1955 engines were: [1500] 01001Z55 to 0905907, [3100] 01001X55 to 0905907, [3200] 01001X55 to 0905907, [3400/3500/3700] 01001T55 to 0905907 and [3600/3800] 01001X55 to 0905907. Transmission codes: M=Muncie three-speed or overdrive transmission, S=Saginaw three-speed or overdrive transmission, C=Cleveland Powerglide automatic transmission, T=Toledo four-speed synchromesh transmission, W=Borg-Warner heavy-duty three-speed transmission.

Model No.	Body Type	Price	Weight	Prod. Total
Sedan Delivery — Model D255/Series 1500 — 115 in. w.b.				
1508	Sedan Delivery	1699	3110	8811
1/2-Ton Commercial — Model H255/Series 3100 — 114 in. w.b.				
3102	Chassis & Cowl	1156	2335	-
3103	Chassis & Cab	1423	2850	-
3104	Pickup	1519	3210	-
3105	Panel	1801	3440	-
3106	Suburban (doors)	2150	3715	-
3112	Chassis & W/S	1193	2460	-
3116	Suburban (gate)	2150	3725	-
1/2-Ton Commercial (Cameo) — Model H255/Series 3100 — 114 in. w.b.				
3124	Suburban Pickup	1981	3355	5220
1/2-Ton Commercial — Model M255/Series 3200 — 123.25 in. w.b.				
3204	Pickup LWB	1540	3305	-
1/2-Ton Dubl-Duti — Model F255/Series 3400 — 104 in. w.b.				
3442	Chassis	1279	2600	-
3/4-Ton Dubl-Duti — Model G255/Series 3500 — 125 in. w.b.				
3542	Chassis	1317	2720	-
3/4 -Ton Dubl-Duti — Model K255/Series 3700 — 137 in. w.b.				
3742	Chassis	1350	2730	-
3/4-Ton Commercial — Model J255/Series 3600 — 123.25				
3602	Chassis & Cowl	1316	2730	-
3603	Chassis & Cab	1583	3205	-
3604	Pickup	1690	3625	-
3608	Platform	1711	3630	-
3609	Stake	1780	3815	-
3612	Chassis & W/S	1353	2815	-
1-Ton Commercial — Model L255/Series 3800 — 135 in. w.b.				
3802	Chassis & Cowl	1444	3050	-
3803	Chassis & Cab	1711	3535	-
3804	Pickup	1844	3985	-
3805	Panel	2135	4300	-
3808	Platform	1859	4075	-
3809	Stake	1944	4360	-
3812	Chassis & W/S	1481	3130	-

1955 Chevrolet 1/2-Ton Second Series Model 3124 Cameo Carrier (OCW)

1955 Chevrolet 1/2-Ton Second Series 3100 Pickup (DFW)

ENGINE: [1508/3100/3200/3600/3800] Inline. OHV. Six-cylinder. Cast iron block. Bore & stroke: 3-9/16 x 3-15/16 in. Displacement: 235.5 cid. Compression ratio: 7.5:1. Gross horsepower: 123 at 3800 rpm. Net horsepower: 109 at 3600 rpm. SAE horsepower: 30.4. Four main bearings. Solid valve lifters. Carburetor: Single-barrel downdraft. Model: Rochester B-7004468.
ENGINE: [1508 with Powerglide] Inline. OHV. Six-cylinder. Cast iron block. Bore & stroke: 3-9/16 x 3-15/16 in. Displacement: 235.5 cid. Compression ratio: 7.5:1. Gross horsepower: 136. SAE horsepower: 30.4. Four main bearings. Hydraulic valve lifters. Carburetor: Single-barrel downdraft Rochester model B.
ENGINE: [3400/3500/3700 only] Inline. OHV. Six-cylinder. Cast iron block. Bore & stroke: 3-9/16 x 3-15/16 in. Displacement: 235.5 cid. Compression ratio: 7.5:1. Gross horsepower: 119 at 3600 rpm. Net horsepower: 105 at 3600 rpm. SAE horsepower: 30.4. Four main bearings. Solid valve lifters. Carburetor: Single-barrel updraft Rochester model B.
ENGINE: [Optional 3100/3200/3600/3800] Vee-block. OHV. Eight-cylinders. Cast iron block. Bore & stroke: 3-3/4 x 3 in. Displacement: 265 cid. Compression ratio: 7.5:1. Gross horsepower: 154 at 4000 rpm. Net horsepower: 126 at 4000 rpm. Five main bearings. Solid/hydraulic (*) valve lifters. Carburetor: Two-barrel downdraft Rochester model 7008006.
ENGINE: [Optional 3100/3200/3600/3800] Vee-block. OHV. Eight-cylinders. Cast iron block. Bore & stroke: 3-3/4 x 3 in. Displacement: 265 cid. Compression ratio: 8.0:1. Gross horsepower: 162 at 4200 rpm. Five main bearings. Solid/hydraulic (*) valve lifters. Carburetor: Two-barrel.
ENGINE: [Optional 3100/3200/3600/3800] Vee-block. OHV. Eight-cylinders. Cast iron block. Bore & stroke: 3-3/4 x 3 in. Displacement: 265 cid. Compression ratio: 8.0:1. Gross horsepower: 180 at 4800 rpm. Five main bearings. Solid/hydraulic (*) valve lifters. Carburetor: Four-barrel Carter downdraft.
(*) The six was rated 123 hp with standard or overdrive transmission and 136 hp with Powerglide. The standard V-8 was rated 162 hp with all transmissions. In all cases, hydraulic valve lifters were used with Powerglide transmissions. In November 1955, *Chevrolet Service News* stated, "As a mid-season change, all V-8 engines were converted to hydraulic valve lifters. Since this same feature has been added to six-cylinder engines for the coming year, the need for periodic valve train adjustments to compensate for normal wear is now eliminated on all Chevrolet engines."

1955 Chevrolet 1/2-Ton Second Series 3100 Pickup (IMSC/Jack Martin)

CHASSIS: [Series 1500] Wheelbase: 115 in. Overall length: 200.8 in. Front tread: 58 in. Rear tread: 58.8 in. Tires: 7.15 x 14 four-ply. Maximum GVW: 4,100 lb.
CHASSIS: [Series 3100] Wheelbase: 114 in. Overall length: 185.687 in. Front tread: 60.5 in. Rear tread: 61.0 in. Tires: 6.70 x 15 four-ply. Maximum GVW: 5,000 lb. (4,500 lb. for Panel).
CHASSIS: [Series 3200] Wheelbase: 123.25 in. Overall length: 205.56 in. Tires: 6.70 x 15 four-ply. Maximum GVW: 5,000 lb.
CHASSIS: [Series 3442] Wheelbase: 104 in. Tires: 8 x 19.5 six-ply.
CHASSIS: [Series 3542] Wheelbase: 125 in. Tires: 8 x 19.5 six-ply.
CHASSIS: [Series 3742] Wheelbase: 137 in. Tires: 8 x 19.5 six-ply.
CHASSIS: [Series 3600] Wheelbase: 123.25 in. Overall length: 205.56 in. Tires: 7 x 17.5 six-ply. Maximum GVW: 6,900 lb.
CHASSIS: [Series 3800] Wheelbase: 135 in. Overall length: 215.81 in. Tires: [front] 8 x 17.5 six-ply, [rear] 8 x 17.5 eight-ply. Maximum GVW: 8,800 lb. (7,700 lb. Panel).
TECHNICAL: Selective synchromesh transmission. Speeds: [3800] 4F/1R, [others] 3F/1R. Column-mounted gear shift (floor-shift on 3800). Single-plate dry-disc clutch. [3600/3800] Full-floating rear axle, [Others] Semi-floating rear axle. Overall ratio: [3100/3200] 3.90:1, [3400/3500/3700] 5.14:1, [3600] 4.57:1. Four-wheel hydraulic brakes. Steel disc wheels. Options: Heavy-duty three-speed manual transmission. Overdrive transmission. Four-speed manual transmission. Hydra-Matic transmission. Rear axles. Heavy-duty clutch. Heavy-duty radiator. Oil bath air cleaner.
OPTIONS: [RPO] Directionals (No. 100). Heater/defroster (No. 101). Double-action shocks (No. 200). Rear view mirrors/brackets (No. 210). Rear shock absorber shield (No. 211). Hydrovac (No. 213). Prop shaft brake (No. 214). Oil bath air cleaner (No. 216). PCV system (No. 217). Painted or chrome rear bumper (No. 218). Turbo-Fire V-8 with manual transmission (No. 221). Turbo-Fire V-8 with overdrive transmission (No. 222). Turbo-Fire V-8 with Powerglide transmission (No. 223). Heavy-duty clutch (No. 227). High body sills (No. 230).) Monotone no-cost color options for all Sedan Deliveries (No. 231) and all Commercial Trucks (No. 234).

Option No.	Body Color	DuPont No. (Duco)	Wheel Stripe Color	DuPont Mo. (Duco)
STD	Onyx Black	253-2247	Argent Silver	289-4202
231-A	India Ivory	253-58458	Onyx Black	253-2247
231-B	Shadow Gray	286-57631	Argent Silver	289-4202
231-C	Neptune Green	281-57951	Argent Silver	289-4202
231-D	Sea Mist Green	253-57950	Onyx Black	253-2247
231-E	Glacier Blue	281-57921	Argent Silver	289-4202
231-H	Gypsy Red	253-57953	None	
231-J	Cashmere Blue	253-58455	Onyx Black	253-2247

NOTE 1: Color codes given for Sedan Delivery are Duco paint codes. Shadow Gray, Neptune Green, and Gypsy Red are special-order-only colors.
NOTE 2: Sedan Delivery wheel colors (Dulux) were: (STD) Black No. 505, (231-A) India Ivory No. 689, (235-B) Shadow Gray No. 654, (235-C) Neptune Green No. 671, (235-D) Sea Mist Green No. 670, (235-E) Glacier Blue No. 676, (235-H) Gypsy Red (No. 673), (235-J) Cashmere Blue No. 699.

1955 Chevrolet 1/2-Ton Second Series 3100 Panel (DFW)

Option No.	Body Color	Duco Code No.	Code No.	Dulux Combination No.
STD 3000	Juniper Green	246-72001-H	93-72001	634, 646 (L)
234-A	Commercial Red	246-9089-H	93-1863-H	636, 648 (L)
234-C	Sand Beige	246-57821	93-57821	724, 736 (L)
234-D	Jet Black	246-2048	93-005	637, 649 (L)
234-E.	Omaha Orange	246-6276	93-082	645, 652 (L)
234-G	Empire Blue	246-50633	93-2528	733, 744 (L) and Int.
234-L	Cream Medium	246-6596	93-530	639, 655 (L)
234-M	Yukon Yellow	246-34175	93-6578	635, 636 (L)
234-N	Ocean Green	246-72002-H	93-72002-H	640, 650 (L)
234-P	Crystal Blue	246-72889	93-72889	734, 745 (L)
234-S	Russet Brown	N.A.	N.A.	N.A.
234-T	Pure White	246-1497	93-21667	644
443-446	Bombay Ivory	246-72961	93-72961	646 (U), 647 (U), 648 (U), 649 (U), 650 (U), 651 (U), 652 (U), 653 (U), 654 (U), 655 (U), 656 (U)

NOTE 3: The above color combinations were available for Commercial Truck models, as indicated, at all assembly plants. The 1953 Chevrolet trucks were again finished in high-luster Dulux synthetic enamel which was baked on in thermostatically controlled ovens. To assist service managers and mechanics in obtaining matching colors when repairs were necessary, the air-drying Dulux was supplied, instead of the number of the Baking Dulux type paint.

1955 Chevrolet 1/2-Ton Second Series Model 3124 Cameo Carrier (Owner B. Wiggins/John Lee)

NOTE 4: The color codes in the chart above are for Duco and Dulux paints and Dulux two-tone combinations. Dulux made by the Rinshed-Mason Paint Co. Oil filter (No. 237). Governor (No. 241). Dual tail and stop lamps (No. 249). Heavy-duty rear springs (No. 254). Heavy-duty radiator (No. 256). Foam rubber seat cushion (No. 258). Auxiliary seat (No. 263). Auxiliary rear springs (No. 267). Airmatic seat (No. 269). Wide base wheels (No. 291). Speedometer fittings (No. 306). Speedometer fittings (No. 307). Powerglide transmission in Sedan Delivery (No. 313). Hydra-Matic transmission in Commercial trucks (No. 314). Overdrive (No. 315). Heavy-duty three-speed transmission (No. 316). Heavy-duty four-speed transmission (No. 318). Electric wipers (No. 320). Power steering (No. 350). High-output generator (No. 325). High-output generator (No. 326). Side-mounted spare tire carrier with "dimpled" rear fender required for 3100/3200/3600 (No. 341). Heavy-duty battery (No. 345). Power steering (No. 350). Channel type painted front bumper for Dubl-Duti (No. 367). Spare wheel carrier for Dubl-Duti (No. 384). Chrome equipment (No. 393). "Full-view" Panoramic rear window (No. 394). Left-hand door lock and lock for side-mounted spare (No. 395). E-Z-Eye tinted glass (No. 398). E-Z-Eye tinted glass for DeLuxe Cab (No. 399). Trademaster V-8 engine for 3100/3600 (No. 408). Trademaster V-8 engine for 3800 (No. 409). Four-barrel carburetor (No. 411). Hydrovac power brakes (No. 412). PCV system (No. 417). Running board (No. 423). DeLuxe Custom Cab equipment including Panoramic rear window, DeLuxe seat, chrome instrument knobs, cigarette lighter, dual visors, dual arm rests, two-tone upholstery and interior color scheme (No. 430). DeLuxe Custom Panel equipment including, DeLuxe seat, chrome instrument knobs, cigarette lighter, dual visors, dual arm rests, two-tone upholstery and interior color scheme (No. 431). Air conditioning (No. 450).

OPTIONS: [Dealer Accessories] Radio antenna. Heater (Standard/DeLuxe). Cigar lighter. Seat covers. External sun shade. Hubcaps. Directional signals. Front bumper guards (painted or chrome). Rear fold-down steps (Platform/Stake). Dual sun visors. Extendible outside mirrors. Spotlight with mirror. Windshield washer. External sun visor. Traffic viewer. Back-up lights (Sedan Delivery). Electric parking brake signal. Chrome hood ornament. Dual fog lamps. Red reflex reflectors. Portable spotlight. AC/DC shaver. Stainless steel door edge guards. Stainless steel door vent shades. Chrome door handle shields. Tool kit. Illuminated compass. Underhood light. Second (high-note) horn.

Light Duty Truck Tire Options (3100/3124 only)

Size	Ply Rating	Rim Width	Option No.	Capacity Frt. & Rear
6.70 x 15	Four	5-1/2K	Std.	1850 lb.
6.70 x 15 (5)	Four	5-1/2K	290	1850 lb.
6.70 x 15	Six	5-1/2 K	288	2110 lb.
6.70 x 15 (5)	Six	5-1/2 K	286	2110 lb.
6.50 x 16	Six	5 K	282	2430 lb.
7.00 x 17.5	Six	8.25-in.	285	3040 lb.

NOTE 5: White sidewall option.

1955 Chevrolet 1/2-Ton Second Series Model 3124 Cameo Carrier (Owner B. Wiggins/John Lee)

OPTIONS: [Authorized Aftermarket] A four-wheel drive (4x4) conversion by NAPCO Products Co., of Minneapolis, Minn., was available for 1955 Second Series Chevrolet trucks. It was merchandised through Chevrolet dealers. NAPCO literature describes it as a "Powr-Pak" four-wheel drive system that shifted in and out of four-wheel drive without stopping or declutching. It featured a two-speed transfer case (eight forward speeds and two in reverse) and full-engine-torque power-take-off. NAPCO also promoted a Chevrolet "Mountain Goat" 4x4 Pickup model. Also available from Cantrell Body Co. was a wood station wagon body for the Chevrolet 3600/3800 Commercial chassis.

HISTORICAL: Introduced: March 25, 1955. Calendar-year registrations: [All Commercial Series] 329,791. Calendar-year production by GVW class: [All Commercial up to 5,000 lb.] 219,805, [All Commercials, 5,001 lb. to 10,000 lb.] 64,589. Chevrolet was America's largest truck-maker with a 31.55 percent market share. Innovations: Completely restyled second series line. Panoramic windshield. New V-8 engine options. Limited-production Cameo Carrier with fiberglass body parts introduced. 12-volt electrical systems. Tubeless tires. Historical notes: This was a milestone year for Chevrolet light-duty trucks due to sweeping styling revisions, technical changes and introduction of a V-8 engine.

1956 CHEVROLET

1956 Chevrolet One-Fifty Sedan Delivery with modern tires (OCW)

1956 Chevrolet One-Fifty Sedan Delivery (DFW)

SEDAN DELIVERY — MODEL D56/SERIES 1500 — SIX/V-8: The Sedan Delivery was restyled along the lines of Chevrolet's passenger cars with squared-off fenders and more deeply hooded headlamps. Above the new grille was a narrow reinforcement. The grille insert had six thin horizontal members and 11 vertical members. This gave the impression of 68 narrow, horizontal rectangular openings with the grille installed on the Sedan Delivery. A one-piece sheet metal filler panel was below the grille. Parking lamp housings were massive chrome panels of a square shape with square lamps inserted into their center. A short chrome molding, curved on the outer end, sat on top of the large housing. Chrome extensions were attached to the outside of the housing. They had three grooves stamped in them. Side moldings were of the 150 Series style, stopping behind the side doors. The new Sedan Delivery remained based on the two-door Handyman Station Wagon. The doors were the same as this model and the two-door Sedan. Front door glass was the same as the two-door Sedan. Both the rear compartment floor and the rear quarter panel sections were slightly unique to the Sedan Delivery. The rear door was of liftgate design. This model was again in the One-Fifty series with code 56-1271 on the Fisher Body tag under the hood. Other features included a wraparound windshield, ball joint suspension, and optional Powerglide automatic transmission. The standard Chevrolet "Stovebolt" six had a higher 140-hp rating. The base rating for the 265-cid V-8 remained the same, but the four-barrel carburetor version now produced 205 hp and an increased compression ratio. Standard equipment included front and rear bumpers and bumper guards, front license guard, hood ornament and emblem, chrome-plated headlamp rims with doors, dual windshield wipers, dual horns, outside key locks, front and rear bumper gravel deflectors, dual combination tail/stop/license plate lamps, chrome-plated radio grille, three-position ignition switch, left-hand sun shade, and dome light. Onyx Black remained the standard color. Optional paint colors were India Ivory, Pinecrest Green, Sherwood Green, Nassau Blue, Harbor Blue, Calypso Cream, and Matador Red. The interior was trimmed with gold-striped charcoal gray imitation leather, combination number 615.

1956 Chevrolet 1/2-Ton Series 3100 Pickup (Owner: Roy Kaple)

1/2-TON COMMERCIAL — MODEL 3A56/SERIES 3100 — SIX/V-8: Changes for the regular Task-Force trucks were minor. The "handle-bar" hood emblem was smaller and redesigned so that the wings on it extended out from near the bottom, instead of the top. The emblem was finished in black to match the wheelcover trim. A large V-8 was added below the emblem to indicate V-8 models. Fender side nameplates kept the same basic shape, but had a raised blade portion and center crease line. They were moved above the main body feature line, instead of below it. V-8 emblems (when appropriate) were placed below the fender nameplates. Hydra-Matic equipped trucks had fender nameplates reading "Chevrolet 3100 Hydra-Matic." There were again 13 solid colors. New colors were Forest Green, Cardinal Red, Golden Yellow, Regal Blue, and Crystal Blue. Also available were Sand Beige, Jet Black, Omaha Orange, Granite Gray, Empire Blue, Yukon Yellow, Ocean Green, and Pearl White. Twelve two-tones were available on all models except Cameos and Carryall Suburbans. Nine combinations featured Arabian Ivory upper body finish in conjunction with colors listed above. New was a choice of Jet Black/Golden Yellow. Cardinal Red/Sand Beige was also available. DeLuxe equipment and two-tones were not available for Carryall Suburbans. Black wheels were standard. Two-toned models had the upper body color on the wheels. Cab models, except Cameo Carriers, had standard gray seat trim. Gray and black upholstery was standard in Panels and Carryall Suburbans. DeLuxe options included synthetic trim fabrics in blue, green, charcoal or gray.

1/2-TON Model 3A56/Series 3100 — SIX/V-8: COMMERCIAL (CAMEO) — SIX/V-8: The Cameo 1/2-ton Suburban Pickup continued as a limited-production model. This high-style truck, Fisher Body style number 3124, was based on the 3000 chassis with a 114-in. wheelbase. It had the same basic styling changes as other models. Special features included slab-sided rear fender skins made of fiberglass bolted onto a standard cargo box to bring the rear body width flush with the sides of the standard cab. Chrome moldings trimmed the gap between the cab and the box. Body side moldings were the same as 1955, but with black accents to match the new black-accented hubcaps. A fiberglass tailgate panel over the steel tailgate hid the hinges, latches and restraining chains. A hidden compartment below the endgate held the spare tire in a fiberglass well. It was accessible via a swing-down hinged rear bumper section. Unique taillights and a Chevrolet bow tie in the center of the tailgate were seen. Standard equipment included DeLuxe Cab equipment and the Panoramic rear window. This year's Cameo Pickup (or Suburban Pickup) came in eight two-tone combinations: Cardinal Red/Bombay Ivory, Cardinal Red/Sand Beige, Golden Yellow/Jet Black, Regal Blue/Arabian Ivory, Granite Gray/Arabian Ivory, Ocean Green/Arabian Ivory, and Crystal Blue/Arabian Ivory. The secondary color was used on the rear cab pillars and around the back window. The roof, windshield pillars and rest of the body were done in what was called the upper color, which is listed ahead of slashes above. The standard Cameo interior was done in beige imitation leather with red nylon inserts. Options were light and dark charcoal gray, light and dark blue, and light and dark green. The steering wheel horn button now had a slight hood at the top and was trimmed with the interior color. Wheel rims were painted the upper body color. Black-accented full wheelcovers from the 1956 Bel Air were optional on the standard 15-in. wheels. Cameo Carriers had stripes on the optional 16 x 5K wheels only.

1/2-TON COMMERCIAL — MODEL 3B56/SERIES 3200 — SIX/V-8: This was the long wheelbase (LWB) 1/2-ton truck on the same chassis as 3/4-ton models. It became known as the "Long Bed" or "Long Box" Pickup because it had a long 90-in. load box. Longer running boards were also used. There was more space between the cab and rear fenders. It still had the same 5,000-lb. maximum GVW rating as other 1/2-ton trucks.

3/4-TON DUBL-DUTI — MODEL 3C56/SERIES 3400 — SIX/V-8: Three Dubl-Duti Forward-Control chassis remained in the truck line. The Model 3442 had a 114-in. wheelbase. Standard walk-in delivery truck bodies could be supplied by several factory-approved sources or the buyer could add his/her own body.

3/4-TON DUBL-DUTI — MODEL 3D56/SERIES 3500 — SIX-CYLINDER: Model 3542 was the 3/4-ton Dubl-Duti on a 125-in. wheelbase. Standard walk-in delivery truck bodies could be supplied by several factory-approved sources or the buyer could add his/her own body. The wheels were of eight-bolt design. A painted, Anvil Gray channel type front bumper was optional on the 3500 Dubl-Duti truck chassis.

3/4-TON — DUBL-DUTI — MODEL F56/SERIES 3700 — SIX-CYLINDER: Model 3742 was the Dubl-Duti on a 137-in. wheelbase. Standard walk-in delivery truck bodies could be supplied by several factory-approved sources or the buyer could add his/her own body. The wheels were of eight-bolt design. A painted, Anvil Gray channel type front bumper was optional on the 3700 Dubl-Duti truck chassis.

3/4-TON COMMERCIAL — MODEL 3E56/SERIES 3600 — SIX/V-8: The 3600 Series Task-Force trucks had the same styling and trim changes as other conventional trucks. This series included the medium-duty cab models on a 123.5-in. wheelbase. Compared to 3100 Pickups, the 3600 Pickup had longer running boards and a longer cargo box with a horizontal support rib. There were also Platform and Platform/Stake models. The rail for the 3/4-ton Platform was 97-9/16 in. long. The maximum GVW rating was 6,900 lb.

1-TON MEDIUM-DUTY COMMERCIAL — MODEL 3G/SERIES 3800 — SIX-CYLINDER: The 3800 Series Task-Force trucks had the same styling and trim changes as other conventional trucks. Panel models had a one-piece floor made of 3/4-inch thick, five-ply laminated wood. The basic model lineup was unchanged. Compared to the 3600 Pickup, the 3800 Pickup had a longer wheelbase, a longer grain-tight load box with extra stake pockets and very long running boards. The 1-ton Platform and Platform/Stake trucks had a 115-9/16 in. long rail. No hubcaps were used on the larger split-rim wheels of the Chassis-and-Cab, Platform, and Stake models, which had eight bolts and eight circular openings. A four-speed manual synchromesh transmission was standard.

1956 Chevrolet 1/2-Ton Series 3100 Panel (C.H. Horst)

I.D. DATA: Serial number located: [Chassis models] On plate temporarily attached near steering column, with final location per body maker; [All others] on plate attached to rear face of left-hand door hinge pillar, on right side of cowl under hood. The first (Sedan Delivery) or first and second symbol(s) indicated the series: D=1500, 3A=3100, 3B=3200, 3C=3400, 3D=3500, 3E=3600, 3F=3700, 3G=3800. The next two symbols indicated the model-year: 56=1956. The fifth symbol indicated the assembly plant: A=Atlanta, Ga., B=Baltimore, Md., F=Flint, Mich., J=Janesville, Wis., K=Kansas City, Mo., L=Los Angeles, Calif., N=Norwood, Ohio, O=Oakland, Calif., S=St. Louis, Mo., T=Tarrytown, N.Y., W=Willow Run, Mich. Each series was separately numbered in sequence, starting with 000001 at each assembly plant. Serial numbers were: [Sedan Delivery] D56-001001 to 220555, [3100] 3A56-001001 to 033691, [3200] 3B56-001001 to 033691, [3600] 3E56-001001 to 033691, [3800] 3G56-001001 to 033691, [Dubl-Duti] 3C/D/F56-001001 to 033691. Engine numbers located on right side of engine on boss at rear of distributor. Engine numbers began with an F (Flint, Mich.) or T (Tonawanda, N.Y.) assembly plant code. Engine numbers consisted of an engine serial number, alphabetical factory code, two-digit model-year code and letter indicating the type of truck and type of engine. For example, an engine with the number 0068025F56X would be a 235 Thriftmaster in a 3100/3200/3600/3800 Series truck (code X) made in 1956 (code 56) at the Flint plant (code F) which had engine serial number 0068025. Other common codes for trucks in these series were: (XG) for the Thriftmaster 235 with Hydra-Matic, (V) for the Thriftmaster 235 with heavy-duty clutch, (A) for the Trademaster 265 V-8, (B) for the Trademaster 265 with Hydra-Matic, (W) for the Thriftmaster 235 Special and (WA) for the Thriftmaster 235 Special with Hydra-Matic. Codes for 3400/3500/3700 trucks were (D) for Trademaster 265 V-8, (DA) for Trademaster 265 V-8 with Hydra-Matic and (DB) for Trademaster 265 V-8 with heavy-duty clutch.

1956 Chevrolet 1/2-Ton Series 3100 Panel with modern tires (JLB)

Job No.	Body Type	Price	Weight	Prod. Total
Sedan Delivery — Model 3D56/Series 1500 — 115 in. w.b.				
1508	Sedan Delivery	1865	3145	-
1/2-Ton Commercial — Model 3A56/Series 3100 — 114 in. w.b.				
3102	Chassis & Cowl	1303	2374	-
3103	Chassis & Cab	1567	2872	-
3104	Pickup	1670	3217	-
3105	Panel	1966	3457	-
3106	Suburban (doors)	2300	3736	-
3112	Chassis & W/S	1341	2505	-
3116	Suburban (gate)	2300	3752	-
1/2-Ton Commercial (Cameo) — Model 3A56/Series 3100 — 114 in. w.b.				
3124	Cameo Pickup	2144	3373	1452
1/2-Ton Commercial (Long Box) — Model 3B56/Series 3200 — 123.25 in. w.b.				
3204	Pickup LWB	1692	3323	-
3/4-Ton Dubl-Duti — Model 3C56/Series 3400 — 114 in. w.b.				
3142	Chassis	1499	2716	-
3/4-Ton Dubl-Duti — Model 3D56/Series 3500 — 125 in. w.b.				
3542	Chassis	1537	2764	-
3/4-Ton Dubl-Duti — Model 3F56/Series 3700 — 137 in. w.b.				
3742	Chassis	1569	2784	-
3/4-Ton Commercial — Model 3E56/Series 3600 — 123.25 in. w.b.				
3602	Chassis & Cowl	1481	2736	-
3603	Chassis & Cab	1745	3252	-
3604	Pickup	1858	3633	-
3609	Platform & Stake	1950	3834	-
3612	Chassis & W/S	1519	2870	-
1-Ton Commercial — Model 3G56/Series 3800 — 135 in. w.b.				
3802	Chassis & Cowl	1611	2945	-
3803	Chassis & Cab	1875	3503	-
3804	Pickup	2009	3939	-
3805	Panel	2327	4243	-
3809	Platform & Stake	2122	4285	-
3812	Chassis & W/S	1649	3118	-

ENGINE: [All] Inline. OHV. Six-cylinder. Cast iron block. Bore & stroke: 3-9/16 x 3-15/16 in. Displacement: 235.5-cid. Compression ratio: 8.0:1. Gross horsepower: 140 at 3800 rpm. SAE horsepower: 30.4. Four main bearings. Hydraulic valve lifters. Carburetor: Single-barrel downdraft Rochester model B-7004468.

ENGINE: [Optional 3100/3200/3600/3800] V-block. OHV. Eight-cylinders. Cast iron block. Bore & stroke: 3-3/4 x 3 in. Displacement: 265-cid. Compression ratio: 7.5:1. Gross horsepower: 155 at 4000 rpm. Net horsepower: 126 at 4000 rpm. Five main bearings. Hydraulic valve lifters. Carburetor: Two-barrel downdraft Rochester model 7008006.

ENGINE: [Optional 1500] V-block. OHV. Eight-cylinders. Cast iron block. Bore & stroke: 3-3/4 x 3 in. Displacement: 265-cid. Compression ratio: 8.0:1. Gross horsepower: 162 at 4200 rpm. Five main bearings. Hydraulic valve lifters. Carburetor: Carter two-barrel.

ENGINE: [Optional 1500] V-block. OHV. Eight-cylinders. Cast iron block. Bore & stroke: 3-3/4 x 3 in. Displacement: 265-cid. Compression ratio: 9.25:1. Gross horsepower: 205 at 4800 rpm. Five main bearings. Hydraulic valve lifters. Carburetor: Four-barrel Carter downdraft.

1956 Chevrolet 1/2-Ton Series 3100 Cameo Carrier (Owner: Ken Whitcher)

CHASSIS: [Series 1500] Wheelbase: 115 in. Overall length: 200.8 in. Front tread: 58 in. Rear tread: 58.9 in. Tires: 7.15 x 14 four-ply. Maximum GVW: 4,100 lb.

CHASSIS: [Series 3100] Wheelbase: 114 in. Overall length: 185.7 in. Front tread: 60.5 in. Rear tread: 61.0 in. Tires: 6.70 x 15 four-ply. Maximum GVW: 5,000 lb..

CHASSIS: [Series 3200] Wheelbase: 123.25 in. Overall length: 205.56 in. Tires: 6.70 x 15 four-ply. Maximum GVW: 5,000 lb.
CHASSIS: [Series 3442] Wheelbase: 114 in. Tires: 8 x 19.5 six-ply. Maximum GVW: 7,000 lb.
CHASSIS: [Series 3542] Wheelbase: 125 in. Tires: 8 x 19.5 six-ply. Maximum GVW: 8,800 lb.
CHASSIS: [Series 3742] Wheelbase: 137 in. Tires: 8 x 19.5 six-ply. Maximum GVW: 10,000 lb.
CHASSIS: [Series 3600] Wheelbase: 123.25 in. Overall length: 205.56 in. Tires: 7 x 17.5 six-ply. Maximum GVW: 6,900 lb.
CHASSIS: [Series 3800] Wheelbase: 135 in. Overall length: 215.81 in. Tires: [Single rear wheels] 7.50 x 17.5, [Dual rear wheels] (front) 8 x 17.5 six-ply, (rear) 8 x 17.5 eight-ply. Maximum GVW: [Single rear wheels] 7,000 lb., [Dual rear wheels] 8,800 lb.
TECHNICAL: Selective synchromesh transmission. Speeds: [3800] 4F/1R, [Others] 3F/1R. Column-mounted gear shift (floor-shift on 3800). Single-plate dry-disc clutch. [3600/3800] Full-floating rear axle, [Others] Semi-floating rear axle. Overall ratio: [3100/3200] 3.90:1, [3400/3500/3700] 5.14:1, [3600] 4.57:1. Four-wheel hydraulic brakes. Steel disc wheels. Options: Heavy-duty three-speed manual transmission. Overdrive transmission. Four-speed manual transmission. Hydra-Matic transmission. Rear axles. Heavy-duty clutch. Heavy-duty radiator. Oil bath air cleaner.
OPTIONS: [RPO] Heater/defroster (No. 101). Directional signals (No. 105). Directional signals (No. 106). Air conditioning (No. 110). Air conditioning (No. 111). Double-action shocks (No. 200). Rear view mirrors/brackets (No. 210). Rear shock absorber shield (No. 211). Hydrovac power brakes (No. 213). Oil bath air cleaner (No. 216). PCV system (No. 217). Painted or chrome rear bumper (No. 218). Heavy-duty clutch (No. 227). Platform body (No. 230). Monotone no-cost color options for all Commercial Trucks (No. 234).

Option No.	Body Color	Duco Code No.	Dulux Code No.	Combination No.
STD 3000	Forest Green	246-59639	93-59639	723, 746 (L)
234-A	Cardinal Red	246-58209-H	93-58209-H	725, 736 (U) 737 (L), 748 (U)
234-B	Regal Blue	246-58184-H	93-58184	726, 740 (L)
234-C	Sand Beige (Called Oak Beige for interior use)	246-57821	93-57821	724, 736 (L)
234-D	Jet Black	246-2048	93-005.	729, 738 (U) 739 (L)
234-E.	Omaha Orange	246-6276	93-082	730, 742 (L)
234-F.	Granite Gray	246-72890	93-72890	728, 741 (L)
234-G	Empire Blue	246-50633	93-2528	733, 744 (L) and Int.
234-L	Golden Yellow	246-58199	93-58199	727, 738 (L) 739 (L)
234-M	Yukon Yellow	246-34175	93-6578	731, 743 (L)
234-N	Ocean Green (Called Crest Green for interior use)	246-72002-H	93-72002-H	735, 747 (L)
234-P	Crystal Blue (Called Iceberg Blue for interior use)	246-72889	93-72889	734, 745 (L)
234-T	Pure White (chrome trim)	246-1497	93-21667	732
234-U	Pure White (STD trim)	246-1497	93-21667	732
234-V	Pure White (STD 36/38)	246-1497	93-21667	732
2409	Arabian Ivory	246-58186	93-58186	737, 740, 741, 742, 743, 744, 745, 746, 747, (All U = Upper)

NOTE 1: The above color combinations were available for Commercial Truck models, as indicated, at all assembly plants. The Chevrolet trucks were again finished in high-luster Dulux synthetic enamel which was baked on in thermostatically controlled ovens. To assist service managers and mechanics in obtaining matching colors when repairs were necessary, the air-drying Dulux was supplied, instead of the number of the Baking Dulux type paint.

1956 Chevrolet 1/2-Ton Series 3100 Pickup (Photo: Lowell E. Eisenhour))

NOTE 2: The color codes in the chart above are for Duco and Dulux paints and Dulux two-tone combinations. Dulux made by the Rinshed-Mason Paint Co. Oil filter (No. 237). Governor (No. 241). Dual tail and stop lamps (No. 249). Heavy-duty rear springs (No. 254). Heavy-duty radiator (No. 256). Foam rubber seat cushion (No. 258). Auxiliary seat (No. 263). Auxiliary rear springs (No. 267). Speedometer fittings (No. 306). Speedometer fittings (No. 307). Powerglide transmission in Sedan Delivery (No. 313). Hydra-Matic transmission in Commercial trucks (No. 314). Overdrive (No. 315). Heavy-duty three-speed transmission (No. 316). Heavy-duty four-speed transmission (No. 318). Electric wipers (No. 320). Power steering (No. 324). High-output generator (No. 325). High-output generator (No. 326). Side-mounted spare tire carrier with "dimpled" rear fender required for 3100/3600 (No. 341). Power steering (No. 345). Power steering (No. 350). Power steering (No. 351). Heavy-duty seat trim (No. 357). Channel type painted front bumper for Dubl-Duti (No. 367). Spare wheel carrier for Dubl-Duti (No. 384). Chrome equipment (No. 393). "Full-view" panoramic rear window (No. 394). Left-hand door lock and lock for side-mounted spare (No. 395). E-Z-Eye tinted glass (No. 398). Trademaster V-8 engine for 3100/3600 (No. 408). Trademaster V-8 engine for 3800 (No. 409). Four-barrel

carburetor (No. 410). Hydrovac power brakes (No. 412). PCV system (No. 417). Auxiliary running board (No. 423). DeLuxe Custom Cab equipment including Panoramic rear window, DeLuxe seat, chrome instrument knobs, cigarette lighter, dual visors, dual arm rests, two-tone upholstery and interior color scheme (No. 431). DeLuxe Custom Panel equipment including DeLuxe seat, chrome instrument knobs, cigarette lighter, dual visors, dual arm rests, two-tone upholstery and interior color scheme (No. 434). Monotone no-cost color options for all Sedan Deliveries (No. 500-522).

Option No.	Body Color	DuPont No. (Duco)	Wheel Stripe Color	DuPont Mo. (Duco)
STD	Onyx Black	253-2247	Argent Silver	289-4202
500-A	India Ivory	253-58458	Onyx Black	253-2247
504-A	Pinecrest Green	286-58897	Onyx Black	253-2247
506-A	Sherwood Green	286-59525	Argent Silver	289-4202
508-A	Nassau Blue	253-58752	Onyx Black	253-2247
510-A	Harbor Blue	281-58812	Argent Silver	289-4202
522-A	Matador Red	253-59446	Onyx Black	253-2247

NOTE 3: Sedan Delivery wheel colors (Dulux) were: (STD) Black No. 505, (500-A) India Ivory No. 689, (504-A) Pinecrest Green No. 716, (506-A) Sherwood Green No. 717, (508-A) Nassau Blue No. 718, (No. 510-A) Harbor Blue No. 719, (522-A) Matador Red No. 738.

1956 Chevrolet 1/2-Ton Series 3100 Pickup (Photo: John Lee)

OPTIONS: [Dealer Accessories] Radio antenna. Heater (Standard/DeLuxe). Cigar lighter. Seat covers. External sun shade. Hubcaps. Directional signals. Front bumper guards (painted or chrome). Rear fold-down steps (Platform/Stake). Dual sun visors. Extendible outside mirrors. Spotlight with mirror. Windshield washer. External sun visor. Traffic viewer. Back-up lights (Sedan Delivery). Electric parking brake signal. Chrome hood ornament. Dual fog lamps. Red reflex reflectors. Portable spotlight. AC/DC shaver. Stainless steel door edge guards. Stainless steel door vent shades. Chrome door handle shields. Tool kit. Illuminated compass. Underhood light. Second (high-note) horn.

Light Duty Truck Tire Options (3100/3124 only)

Size	Ply Rating	Rim Width	Option No.	Capacity Frt. & Rear
6.70 x 15	Four	5-1/2K	Std.	1850 lb.
6.70 x 15 (*)	Four	5-1/2K	290	1850 lb.
6.70 x 15	Six	5-1/2 K	288	2110 lb.
6.70 x 15 (*)	Six	5-1/2 K	286	2110 lb.
6.50 x 16	Six	5 K	282	2430 lb.
7.00 x 17.5	Six	8.25-in.	285	3040 lb.

NOTE 4: (*) indicates white sidewall option.
OPTIONS: [Authorized aftermarket] A four-wheel drive (4x4) conversion by NAPCO Products Co., of Minneapolis, Minn., was available for Chevrolet trucks. It was merchandised through Chevrolet dealers. NAPCO literature describes it as a "Powr-Pak" four-wheel drive system that shifted in and out of four-wheel drive without stopping or declutching. It featured a two-speed transfer case (eight forward speeds and two in reverse) and full-engine-torque power-take-off. NAPCO also promoted a Chevrolet "Mountain Goat" 4x4 Pickup model.
HISTORICAL: Introduced: Fall 1955. Calendar-year production: [All Commercials] 353,509. Calendar-year production, all Commercials, by GVW class: [Up to 5,000 lb.] 194,015, [5,001 to 10,000 lb.] 59,182. The four millionth postwar Chevrolet truck was assembled during 1956. Innovations included new paint colors and two-tone combinations, a higher compression ratio and horsepower rating for the Thriftmaster 235 six-cylinder engine and the optional four-barrel Trademaster 265 V-8. The company sent a fleet of its larger Taskmaster trucks to special displays around the country this year.

1957 CHEVROLET

1957 Chevrolet One-Fifty Sedan Delivery (OCW)

1957 Chevrolet One-Fifty Sedan Delivery (H. Fries)

SEDAN DELIVERY — MODEL D/SERIES 1500 — SIX/V-8: The classic look for Chevrolet's 1957 cars included an oval front bumper grille with bomb type bumper guards, a flatter hood with windsplit bulges, screened headlamp housings and broad, flat tailfins. The 1957 passenger car grille used on the Sedan Delivery is one of the most famous designs. It had over 32 separate moldings, spacers, panels, supports, guards and lamp parts. The upper molding attached to the lip of the hood and was visually extended with curved moldings on either end. The delicate grille had a screen-like appearance and came with aluminum finish on Sedan Deliveries. A chrome horizontal bar with the Chevrolet emblem in a center housing and hooded parking lamp housings on either end was mounted in front of the grille insert. Round parking lamp assemblies fit inside the hooded housings. A body-color sheet metal filler panel was used below the grille. The massive bumper face bar below the grille consisted of center and separate end sections. Large, round guards attached to either end of the bumper. Round inserts bolted to the front of these guards. One-fifty style trim was used on the exterior of the body. The new Sedan Delivery remained based on the two-door Handyman Station Wagon. The doors were the same as this model and the two-door Sedan. Front door glass was the same as the two-door Sedan. Both the rear compartment floor and the rear quarter panel sections were slightly unique to the Sedan Delivery. The rear door was of liftgate design. Other features included a wraparound windshield, ball joint suspension, and optional Powerglide automatic transmission. The standard Chevrolet "Stovebolt" six again had 140 hp. The base rating for the 265-cid V-8 remained the same, but there were now 185-, 220-, 245-, 250- and 270-hp V-8 options with dual four-barrel carburetors or fuel-injection on the hotter engines. Standard equipment included front and rear bumpers and bumper guards, front license guard, hood ornament and emblem, chrome-plated headlamp rims with doors, dual windshield wipers, dual horns, outside key locks, front and rear bumper gravel deflectors, bright radio grille, three-position ignition switch, left-hand sunshade, and dome light. Onyx Black remained the standard color. Optional paint colors were Imperial Ivory, Surf Green, Highland Green, Lakespur Blue, Harbor Blue, and Matador Red. The interior was trimmed with a black and gray imitation leather and black imitation leather two-tone upholstery combination, number 651.

1957 Chevrolet 1/2-Ton Series 3100 Pickup with custom wheels (DFW)

1/2-TON COMMERCIAL — MODEL 3A/SERIES 3100 — SIX/V-8: Changes for Task-Force conventional trucks were minor. A new grille with an oval loop in the center was attached to a more massive, trapezoid-shaped grille surround. Between the outer surround and the inner open loop, there were four short bars on both the top and bottom. Painted grilles were standard, a chrome grille was optional. Fender side nameplates were now oval-shaped with the brand name and series number in a sculpted center depression. Trucks with Hydra-Matic transmission had this denoted on the trim. The nameplates were positioned above the feature line on the sides of the cowl. V-8 emblems were added when this option was ordered. The front hood badge was of the same general "handle-bar" shape, but larger. It had a Chevrolet bow tie in the center. On V-8 trucks, a chrome V was placed below the hood front ornament. The hood had two small windsplits sculpted into its top surface. The 3100 Pickup had short running boards. Single-unit body models included the Carryall Suburban and Panel. Brewster Green was the standard exterior body color. Options included Cardinal Red, Indian Turquoise, Sand Beige, Jet Black, Omaha Orange, Granite Gray, Royal Blue, Golden Yellow, Yukon Yellow, Ocean Green, Alpine Blue, Pure White, and Sandstone Beige. The 13 two-tones included Bombay Ivory upper body with all colors except Brewster Green or Golden Yellow, plus Ocean Green/Brewster Green, Alpine Blue/Royal Blue, or Jet Black/Golden Yellow. (Custom two-tones were not available for

Carryall Suburbans and the combinations were somewhat different for Cameo Carriers.) Standard interiors were gray synthetic fabric. Trucks with DeLuxe interiors had a non-glare satin-finish charcoal gray paint on the upper dash and light gray on the instrument panel. Doors were finished in light gray metal with charcoal gray metal door insert panels. A charcoal fiberboard top lining panel was used. The seats had light gray bolsters and rose-and-gray colored fabric on the cushions and back panels. Standard wheels were black. Custom Cab equipment was available for double-unit body models and included bright metal dashboard knobs, arm rests, DeLuxe steering trim, bright window frames and chrome equipment. The wheels of two-tone trucks were done in the lower body color, except when the exterior colors were Bombay Ivory/Jet Black or Cardinal Red/Bombay Ivory, in which cases the wheels were Bombay Ivory and Cardinal Red, respectively. DeLuxe equipment was optionally available for 3100s, except Carryall Suburbans. A factory 4x4 system was optionally available on most Chevrolet Commercial Trucks starting in 1957.

1957 Chevrolet 1/2-Ton Series 3100 Cameo Carrier (Owner: Marshall Whitt)

1/2-TON COMMERCIAL (CAMEO) — MODEL 3A/SERIES 3100 — SIX/V-8: The Cameo Carrier got the chrome version of the new grille, DeLuxe cab equipment and a Panoramic rear window as standard equipment. A new feature was a pair of horizontal rear quarter panel moldings with a contrast band between them. This trim ran horizontally from behind the cab to the area between the rear bumper and taillights. It carried bright metal decorations with a Chevrolet bow tie badge and a Cameo script on the contrast band. The oval-shaped fender side nameplates said 3124 and Chevrolet in a sculpted center depression. Trucks with Hydra-Matic transmission had this denoted on the trim. The nameplates were positioned above the feature line on the sides of the cowl. V-shaped emblems were added on the doors, on the feature line, when this option was ordered. Special Cameo features again included slab-sided rear fender skins made of fiberglass bolted onto a standard cargo box to bring the rear body width flush with the sides of the standard cab. Chrome moldings trimmed the gap between the cab and the box. A fiberglass tailgate panel over the steel tailgate hid the hinges, latches and restraining chains. A hidden compartment below the endgate held the spare tire in a fiberglass well. It was accessible via a swing-down hinged rear bumper section. Unique taillights and a Chevrolet bow tie in the center of the tailgate were seen. The 1957 Cameo's standard two-tone finish was Cardinal Red/Bombay Ivory. Also available were Bombay Ivory/Sand Beige, Bombay Ivory/Cardinal Red, Jet Black/Golden Yellow, Bombay Ivory/Indian Turquoise, Bombay Ivory/Granite Gray, Bombay Ivory/Ocean Green, Bombay Ivory/Alpine Blue, and Bombay Ivory/Sandstone Beige. The secondary color was used on the rear cab pillars and around the back window. The roof, windshield pillars and rest of the body were done in the upper color, which is listed first above. The standard Cameo interior had the same upholstery material as 1956-1957 models. Beige imitation leather with red nylon inserts was the standard color scheme. Options were light and dark charcoal gray, light and dark blue, and light and dark green. The steering wheel had a new recessed horn button and same-size spokes. It now had gray finish on the sides and top. Small chrome hubcaps and wheel trim rings were standard. The wheels were done in the lower body color, except when the exterior colors were Bombay Ivory/Jet Black or Cardinal Red/Bombay Ivory, in which cases the wheels were Bombay Ivory and Cardinal Red, respectively. Black-accented full wheelcovers from the 1956 Bel Air (the '57 Bel Air had 14-in. wheels) were optional on the limited-edition truck's standard 15-in. wheels. Cameo Carriers had stripes only on the optional 16 x 5K wheels.

1957 Chevrolet 1/2-Ton Series 3100 Cameo Carrier (Owner: Ken Whitcher)

1957 Chevrolet 1/2-Ton Series 3100 Pickup (Owner: Pete Scovronski)

1/2-TON COMMERCIAL — MODEL 3B/SERIES 3200 — SIX/V-8: The 3200 Series Task-Force trucks had the same basic styling and trim changes as other conventional trucks. This was the long wheelbase (LWB) 1/2-ton truck on the same chassis as 3/4-ton models. It became known as the "Long Bed" or "Long Box" Pickup because it had a longer load box. Chevrolet parts catalogs indicated that a 90-in. box was used for 1955-1957 Models 3200/3600 and that a 98-in. box was used for 1957-1958 Models 3200/3600, indicating a midyear change. Longer running boards were also used. There was more space between the cab and rear fenders. It still had the same 5,000-lb. maximum GVW rating as other 1/2-ton trucks.

3/4-TON DUBL-DUTI — MODEL 3C/SERIES 3400 — SIX/V-8: Three Dubl-Duti Forward-Control chassis remained in the truck line. The Model 3442 had a 114-in. wheelbase. Standard walk-in delivery truck bodies could be supplied by several factory-approved sources or the buyer could add his/her own body.

3/4-TON DUBL-DUTI — MODEL 3D/SERIES 3500 — SIX-CYLINDER: Model 3542 was the 3/4-ton Dubl-Duti on a 125-in. wheelbase. Standard walk-in delivery truck bodies could be supplied by several factory-approved sources or the buyer could add his/her own body. The wheels were of eight-bolt design. A painted, Anvil Gray channel type front bumper was optional on the 3500 Dubl-Duti truck chassis.

3/4-TON — DUBL-DUTI — MODEL F/SERIES 3700 — SIX-CYLINDER: Model 3742 was the Dubl-Duti on a 137-in. wheelbase. Standard walk-in delivery truck bodies could be supplied by several factory-approved sources or the buyer could add his/her own body. The wheels were of eight-bolt design. A painted, Anvil Gray channel type front bumper was optional on the 3700 Dubl-Duti truck chassis.

3/4-TON COMMERCIAL — MODEL 3E56/SERIES 3600 — SIX/V-8: The 3600 Series Task-Force trucks had the same styling and trim changes as other conventional trucks. This series included the medium-duty cab models on a 123.5-in. wheelbase. Compared to 3100 Pickups, the 3600 Pickup had longer running boards and a longer cargo box with a horizontal support rib. Chevrolet parts catalogs indicated that a 90-in. box was used for 1955-1957 Models 3600 and that a 98-in. box was used for 1957-1958 Models 3600, indicating a midyear change. There were also Platform and Platform/Stake models. The rail for the 3/4-ton Platform was 97-9/16 in. long. The maximum GVW rating was 6,900 lb.

1-TON MEDIUM-DUTY COMMERCIAL — MODEL 3G/SERIES 3800 — SIX-CYLINDER: The 3800 Series Task-Force trucks had the same styling and trim changes as other conventional trucks. Panel models had a one-piece floor made of 3/4-inch thick, five-ply laminated wood. The basic model lineup was unchanged. Compared to the 3600 Pickup, the 3800 Pickup had a longer wheelbase, a longer grain-tight load box with extra stake pockets and very long running boards. The 1-ton Platform and Platform/Stake trucks had a 115-9/16-in. long rail. No hubcaps were used on the larger split-rim wheels of the Chassis-and-Cab, Platform and Stake models, which had eight bolts and eight circular openings. A four-speed manual synchromesh transmission was standard.

1957 Chevrolet 1/2-Ton Model 3100 Panel (MLC)

I.D. DATA: Serial number located: [Chassis models] On plate temporarily attached near steering column, with final location per body maker; [All others] on plate attached to rear face of left-hand door hinge pillar, on right side of cowl under hood. The first (Sedan Delivery) or first and second symbol(s) indicated the series: D=1500, 3A=3100, 3B=3200, 3C=3400, 3D=3500, 3E=3600, 3F=3700, 3G=3800. The next two symbols indicated the model-year: 57=1957. The fifth symbol indicated the assembly plant: A=Atlanta, Ga., B=Baltimore, Md., F=Flint, Mich., J=Janesville, Wis., K=Kansas City, Mo., L=Los Angeles, Calif.,

N=Norwood, Ohio, O=Oakland, Calif., S=St. Louis, Mo., T=Tarrytown, N.Y., W=Willow Run, Mich. Each series was separately numbered in sequence, starting with 000001 at each assembly plant. Serial numbers were: [Sedan Delivery] D57-001001 to 314393, [3100] 3A57-001001 to 144196, [3200] 3B57-001001-144196, [3600] 3E57-001001 to 144196, [3800] 3G57-001001 to 144196, [Dubl-Duti] 3C/D/F57-001001 to 144196. Engine numbers located on right side of engine on boss at rear of distributor. Engine numbers began with an F (Flint, Mich.) or T (Tonawanda, N.Y.) assembly plant code. [Sedan Delivery] Second or second and third symbols A or B=235-cid/140 hp, C=265-cid/162 hp, F or G=283-cid/185 hp, E, FC, FE or FG=283-cid/220 hp, EA or GD=283-cid/245 hp, GF or EJ=283-cid/250 hp and EB or EK=283 cid 283 hp. [Commercials] Second or second and third symbols H or HE=235 cid/140 hp, L, LA or LB=265 cid/162 hp.

1957 Chevrolet 1/2-Ton Series 3100 Pickup (Owner: Pete Scovronski)

1957 Chevrolet 1/2-Ton Series 3100 Panel (DFW)

Job No.	Body Type	Price	Weight	Prod. Total
Sedan Delivery — Model D57/Series 1500 — 115 in. w.b.				
1508/1271 7273	Sedan Delivery	2020	3254	
1/2-Ton Commercial — Model 3A/Series 3100 — 114 in. w.b.				
3102	Chassis & Cowl	1433	2374	-
3103	Chassis & Cab	1697	2871	-
3104	Pickup	1800	3217	-
3105	Panel	2101	3458	-
3106	Suburban (doors)	2435	3738	-
3112	Chassis & W/S	1471	2514	-
3116	Suburban (gate)	2435	3752	-
1/2-Ton Commercial (Cameo) — Model 3A/Series 3100 — 114 in. w.b.				
3124 2244	Cameo Pickup	2273	3373	-
1/2-Ton Commercial (Long Box) — Model 3B/Series 3200 — 123.25 in. w.b.				
3204	Pickup LWB	1838	3322	-
3/4-Ton Dubl-Duti — Model 3C/Series 3400 — 114 in. w.b.				
3442	Chassis	1613	2722	-
3/4-Ton Dubl-Duti — Model 3D/Series 3500 — 125 in. w.b.				
3542	Chassis	1651	2764	-
3/4-Ton Dubl-Duti — Model 3F/Series 3700 — 137 in. w.b.				
3742	Chassis	1683	2784	-
3/4-Ton Commercial — Model 3E/Series 3600 — 123.25 in. w.b.				
3602	Chassis & Cowl	1616	2741	-
3603	Chassis & Cab	1880	3252	-
3604	Pickup	1993	3632	-
3609	Platform & Stake	2085	3876	-
3612	Chassis & W/S	1654	2881	-
1-Ton Commercial — Model 3G/Series 3800 — 135 in. w.b.				
3802	Chassis & Cowl	1763	2945	-
3803	Chassis & Cab	2027	3496	-
3804	Pickup	2160	3938	-
3805	Panel	2489	4243	-
3809	Platform & Stake	2274	4286	-
3812	Chassis & W/S	1801	3079	-

ENGINE: [All] Inline. OHV. Six-cylindr. Cast iron block. Bore & stroke: 3.562 x 3.937 in. Displacement: 235.5 cid. Compression ratio: 8.0:1. Brake horsepower: 140 at 4200 rpm. Four main bearings. Hydraulic valve lifters. Carburetor: Rochester one-barrel model 7007181.
ENGINE: [Optional All] V-type. OHV. Eight-cylinder. Cast iron block. Bore & stroke: 3.75 x 3 in. Displacement: 265 cid. Compression ratio: 8.0:1. Brake horsepower: 162 at 4400 rpm. Five main bearings. Hydraulic valve lifters. Carburetor: Rochester two-barrel model 7009909.
ENGINE: [Optional 1500] V-type. OHV. Eight-cylinder. Cast iron block. Bore & stroke: 3.875 x 3 in. Displacement: 283 cid. Compression ratio: 8.5:1. Brake horsepower: 185 at 4600 rpm. Five main bearings. Hydraulic valve lifters. Carburetor: Rochester two-barrel model 7012133.

1957 Chevrolet 1/2-Ton Series 3100 Cameo Carrier (OCW)

1957 Chevrolet 1/2-Ton Series 3100 Cameo Carrier (Photo: John Lee)

1957 Chevrolet 1/2-Ton Series 3100 Cameo Carrier (OCW)

1957 Chevrolet 1/2-Ton Series 3100 Cameo Carrier (Photo: Jerry Heasley

1957 Chevrolet 1/2-Ton Series 3100 Cameo Carrier (OCW)

1957 Chevrolet 1/2-Ton Series 3100 Cameo Carrier
(Owners: Del & Donna Hansen)

1957 Chevrolet 1/2-Ton Series 3100 Cameo Carrier (DFW)

1957 Chevrolet 1/2-Ton Series 3100 Cameo Carrier with custom wheels
(Photo: John Lee)

Standard Catalog of Chevrolet Trucks

1957 Chevrolet 1/2-Ton Series 3100 Carryall Suburban (Photo: John Lee)

ENGINE: [Optional 1500] V-type. OHV. Super Turbo-Fire. Eight-cylinder. Cast iron block. Bore & stroke: 3.875 x 3 in. Displacement: 283 cid. Compression ratio: 9.5:1. Brake horsepower: 220 at 4800 rpm. Five main bearings. Hydraulic valve lifters. Carburetor: Rochester four-barrel.
ENGINE: [Optional 1500] V-type. OHV. Super Turbo-Fire. Eight-cylinder. Cast iron block. Bore & stroke: 3.875 x 3 in. Displacement: 283 cid. Compression ratio: 9.5:1. Brake horsepower: 245. Five main bearings. Carburetors: Two Rochester four-barrels.
ENGINE: [Optional 1500] V-type. OHV. Super Turbo-Fire. Eight-cylinder. Cast iron block. Bore & stroke: 3.875 x 3 in. Displacement: 283 cid. Compression ratio: 9.5:1. Brake horsepower: 250 at 4800 rpm. Five main bearings. Fuel injection.
ENGINE: [Optional 1500] V-type. OHV. Super Turbo-Fire. Eight-cylinder. Cast iron block. Bore & stroke: 3.875 x 3 in. Displacement: 283 cid. Compression ratio: 10.5:1. Brake horsepower: 270 at 5600 rpm. Five main bearings. Two four-barrel carburetors.
CHASSIS: [Series 1500] Wheelbase: 115 in. Overall length: 200 in. Front tread: 58 in. Rear tread: 58.9 in. Tires: 7.50 x 14 four-ply. Maximum GVW: 4,100 lb.
CHASSIS: [Series 3100] Wheelbase: 114 in. Overall length: [Cameo] 193.56 in., [Others] 185.7 in. Front tread: 60.5 in. Rear tread: 61.0 in. Tires: 6.70 x 15 four-ply. Maximum GVW: 5,000 lb.
CHASSIS: [Series 3200] Wheelbase: 123.25 in. Overall length: [Early] 205.56, [Late] 215.81 in. Tires: 7 x 7.5 six-ply. Maximum GVW: 5,000 lb.
CHASSIS: [Series 3442] Wheelbase: 104 in. Tires: 8 x 19.5 six-ply. Maximum GVW: 7,000 lb.
CHASSIS: [Series 3542] Wheelbase: 125 in. Tires: 8 x 19.5 six-ply. Maximum GVW: 8,800 lb.
CHASSIS: [Series 3742] Wheelbase: 137 in. Tires: 8 x 19.5 six-ply. Maximum GVW: 10,000 lb.
CHASSIS: [Series 3600] Wheelbase: 123.25 in. Overall length: [Early] 205.56, [Late] 215.81 in. Tires: 7 x 17.5 six-ply. Maximum GVW: 6,900 lb.
CHASSIS: [Series 3800] Wheelbase: 135 in. Overall length: 215.81 in. Tires: [Single rear wheels] 7.50 x 17.5, [Dual rear wheels] (front) 8 x 17.5 six-ply, (rear) 8 x 17.5 eight-ply. Maximum GVW: [Single rear wheels] 7,000 lb., [Dual rear wheels] 9,600 lb.
TECHNICAL: Selective synchromesh transmission. Speeds: [3800] 4F/1R, [others] 3F/1R. Column-mounted gear shift (floor-shift on 3800). Single-plate dry-disc clutch. [3600/3800] Full-floating rear axle, [Others] Semi-floating rear axle. Overall ratio: [3100/3200] 3.90:1, [3400/3500/3700] 5.14:1, [3600] 4.57:1. Four-wheel hydraulic brakes. Steel disc wheels. Options: Heavy-duty three-speed manual transmission. Overdrive transmission. Four-speed manual transmission. Hydra-Matic transmission. Rear axles. Heavy-duty clutch. Heavy-duty radiator. Oil bath air cleaner.

1957 Chevrolet 1/2-Ton Series 3100 Panel (CMD)

OPTIONS: [RPO] Heater/defroster (No. 101). Directional signals (No. 105). Directional signals (No. 106). Air conditioning for Sedan Delivery (No. 110). Directional signals (No. 113). Double-action shocks (No. 200). Rear view mirrors/brackets (No. 210). Rear shock absorber shield (No. 211). Hydrovac power brakes (No. 213). Oil bath air cleaner (No. 216). PCV system (No. 217). Painted or chrome rear bumper (No. 218). Turbo-Fire 265-cid V-8 (No. 221). Turbo-Fire 283-cid V-8 for Sedan Delivery only (No. 223). Heavy-duty clutch (No. 227). Platform body (No. 230). Monotone no-cost color options for all Commercial Trucks: (STD) Brewster Green, (234-A) Cardinal Red, (234-B) Indian Turquoise, (234-C) Sand Beige, (234-D) Jet Black, (234-E) Omaha Orange, (234-F) Granite Gray, (234-G) Royal Blue, (234-L) Golden Yellow, (234-M) Yukon Yellow, (234-N) Ocean Green, (234-P) Alpine Blue, (234-U) Pure White, (234-V) Pure White, and (234-W) Sandstone Beige. Oil filter (No. 237). Governor (No. 241). Heavy-

duty front springs (No. 253). Heavy-duty rear springs (No. 254). Heavy-duty radiator (No. 256). Foam rubber seat cushion (No. 258). Auxiliary seat (No. 263). Auxiliary rear springs (No. 267). Turboglide transmission (No. 302). Speedometer fittings (No. 306). Speedometer fittings (No. 307). Powerglide transmission in Sedan Delivery (No. 313). Hydra-Matic transmission in Commercial trucks (No. 314). Overdrive transmission (No. 315). Heavy-duty three-speed transmission (No. 316). Heavy-duty four-speed transmission (No. 318). Electric wipers (No. 320). Power steering (No. 324). High-output generator (No. 325). High-output generator (No. 326). Side-mounted spare tire carrier with "dimpled" rear fender required for 3100/3200/3600 (No. 341). Heavy-duty battery (No. 345). Power steering with six-cylinder engines (No. 350). Power steering with V-8 engines (No. 351). Chrome exterior trim package (No. 393). Full-view rear window (No. 394). Left-hand door lock and lock for side-mounted spare (No. 395). E-Z-Eye tinted glass (No. 398). Trademaster V-8 engine for 3100/3600 (No. 408). Trademaster V-8 engine for 3800 (No. 409). Four-barrel carburetor (No. 410). Hydrovac power brakes (No. 412). PCV system (No. 417). Auxiliary running board (No. 423). DeLuxe Custom Cab equipment including Panoramic rear window, DeLuxe seat, chrome instrument knobs, cigarette lighter, dual visors, dual arm rests, two-tone upholstery and interior color scheme (No. 431). DeLuxe Custom Panel equipment including, DeLuxe seat, chrome instrument knobs, cigarette lighter, dual visors, dual arm rests, two-tone upholstery and interior color scheme (No. 434). Full-width seat (No. 482). Monotone color options for all Sedan Deliveries (No. 500-522).

Option No.	Body Color	DuPont Duco No.	Wheel Color	DuPont Dulux No.
STD	Onyx Black	253-2247	Black	505
500-A	Imperial Ivory	885-59931	Imperial Ivory	799
504-A	Surf Green	253-90147	Surf Green	807
505-A	Highland Green	286-59775	Highland Green	822
508-A	Larkspur Blue	253-90114	Larkspur Blue	808
510-A	Harbor Blue	281-58812	Harbor Blue	719
522-A	Matador Red	253-59446	Matador Red	738

Positraction rear axle (No. 675). Positraction rear axle (No. 676). Positraction rear axle (No. 678). Four-wheel-drive (No. 690).

1957 Chevrolet 1/2-Ton Series 3100 Carryall Suburban (Photo: John Lee)

OPTIONS: [Dealer Accessories] Radio antenna. Heater (Standard/DeLuxe). Cigar lighter. Seat covers. External sun shade. Hubcaps. Directional signals. Front bumper guards (painted or chrome). Rear fold-down steps (Platform/Stake). Dual sun visors. Extendible outside mirrors. Spotlight with mirror. Windshield washer. External sun visor. Traffic viewer. Back-up lights (Sedan Delivery). Electric parking brake signal. Chrome hood ornament. Dual fog lamps. Red reflex reflectors. Portable spotlight. AC/DC shaver. Stainless steel door edge guards. Stainless steel door vent shades. Chrome door handle shields. Tool kit. Illuminated compass. Underhood light. Second (high-note) horn.

HISTORICAL: Introduced: October 1956. Model-year production: [All Series] 359,098. Innovations: New 283-cid V-8 available as optional equipment. Sedan Delivery redesigned like passenger cars. Regular trucks have new grille styling. Expanded solid color choices and two-tone color schemes. Factory-built 4x4 trucks were available for the first time from Chevrolet this year.

1958 CHEVROLET

1958 Chevrolet Del Ray Sedan Delivery (DFW)

SEDAN DELIVERY — MODEL G/SERIES 1171 (SIX) — MODEL H/SERIES 1271 (V-8): The new Sedan Delivery was part of the Del Ray passenger car series. General styling updates included dual headlamps in each hooded front fender, a screen-like grille and gull-wing rear fender treatment with concave sculptured upper side panels. There was a single mid body molding that extended back along the lower edge of the concave rear side panel. The Sedan Delivery had revised six-cylinder and V-8 series/model coding to reflect its totally revised appearance and chassis. The grille was an elaborate assembly of about 40 separate parts. The upper chrome molding had center and outer sections. The grille "screen" had five full-width horizontal sections divided by tightly-spaced vertical members. Dual round parking lamps were housed in binocular-shaped ornaments that mounted to the grille insert on either side. A filler panel was below the insert. The bumper had massive chrome "wings" on either end and an upside-down-U shaped license plate frame molding in the center. A reinforcement and ribbed lower bar bolted into the license plate frame molding. Exterior paint colors included Honey Beige, Onyx Black, Cashmere Blue, Fathom Blue, Forest Green, Glen Green, Rio Red, and Snowcrest White. The interior was trimmed in a two-tone combination of gun metal gray imitation leather and metallic silver imitation leather, code number 801. The truck was based on the new two-door, six-passenger Yeoman Station Wagon and used that model's door, window glass and bumper parts. Rear quarter panels were exclusive to the Sedan Delivery, but the rear compartment floor was the same as the six-passenger Yeoman's floor. A rear liftgate was used again. An all-new Safety Girder X-type frame with coil springs at all four corners was featured. The six-cylinder (1100 Series) Sedan Delivery could be ordered with manual or Powerglide transmission. The V-8 (1200 Series) version could be ordered with manual or Turboglide transmission with all engines or with Powerglide on engines up to 250 hp. Manual overdrive transmission was offered with 185- or 230-hp V-8s. The 283-cid V-8 came with two-barrel or four-barrel carburetors and fuel-injection. The new 348-cid V-8 came with a single four-barrel carburetor or three two-barrel carburetors.

1958 Chevrolet 1/2-Ton 31 Apache Fleetside with custom wheels (RVM)

1/2-TON — MODEL 3A/SERIES 3100 — SIX/V-8: The new Task-Force Commercial Truck models had dual headlamps, a new grille, new trim, and technical changes. Styling-wise, the new grille consisted of narrow horizontal bars just below the hood and a more massive "barbell-shaped" lower molding extending out and under the headlamps. This molding had the Chevrolet name lettered across it and its rectangular outboard extensions surrounded the similarly-shaped parking lamp lenses. Base-level Apaches also had a cream-painted grille, bumper and headlamp buckets and cream-colored hubcaps. Chrome-plated parts could be substituted at extra cost. A rather large, jet-plane-shaped ornament, above the front fender feature line, carried the Apache name and series identification. Two significant merchandising innovations took place this year. First, the promotional designation Apache was applied to all models. Second, by the end of the year, buyers were presented with a choice of two types of pickups: The traditional type with exposed rear fenders and standard width box (called the Step-Side) and a new type with slab-sided rear steel fenders and extra-wide box, which was called the Fleetside. Fleetside models had a missile-shaped bulge along the slab-sided bed exterior. Their boxes were 75 in. wide versus the Cameo Carrier's 48-in. box. Although the general appearance of both was similar, the Fleetline did not use bolt-on plastic panels and fiberglass parts to achieve its slab-sided look. It replaced the Cameo Carrier at a point during the year. The optional 4x4 drive system was also available for 3100 models. Color choices for the year were: Jet Black, Dawn Blue, Marine Blue, Kodiak Brown, Granite Gray, Glade Green, Oriental Green, Polar Green, Omaha Orange, Cardinal Red, Tartan Turquoise, Pure White, Golden Yellow, and Yukon Yellow. There were 13 two-tone combinations for 1958 Chevrolet 30 Series trucks, except Cameos. They were [main color first]: (No. 727) Tartan Turquoise/Jet Black with Tartan Turquoise wheels, (No. 728) Jet Black/Cardinal Red with Cardinal Red wheels, (No. 729) Golden Yellow/Jet Black with Golden Yellow wheels, (No. 731) Oriental Green/Bombay Ivory with Oriental Green wheels, (No. 732) Glade Green/Polar Green with Polar Green wheels, (No. 733) Polar Green/Glade Green with Polar Green wheels, (No. 735) Marine Blue/Dawn Blue with Dawn Blue wheels, (No. 736) Dawn Blue/Marine Blue with Dawn Blue wheels, (No. 738) Kodiak Brown/Bombay Ivory with Kodiak Brown wheels, (No. 740) Cardinal Red/Bombay Ivory with Cardinal Red wheels, (No. 742) Omaha Orange/Bombay Ivory with Omaha Orange wheels, (No. 744) Yukon Yellow/Bombay Ivory with Yukon Yellow wheels, and (No. 746) Granite Gray/Bombay Ivory with Granite Gray wheels. This year the main (first) color covered the entire roof (instead of only the pillars) except for a strip below the rub rail. Carryall Suburbans were not available with DeLuxe trim or two-tone paint. Wheels were black with solid colors. Chevrolet's hard-wearing upholstery included new color combinations, with charcoal gray and metallic silver two-tone combinations in either all-vinyl DeLuxe (now base-level) or cloth-and-vinyl Custom (extra cost option) trims. Also featured was an 18-in. diameter deep-dish steering wheel and No-Glare instrument panel. Custom chrome and Custom cab equipment were separate options. Custom cab models had two arm rests, two sun visors, a cigarette lighter, foam rubber seat cushions and back rests, bright control knobs, and chrome window moldings. The Panoramic rear window was an option. New options included Cool-Pack air-conditioning and seat belts. Maximum GVW was [4x2] 5,000 lb., [4x4] 5,600 lb.

1958 Chevrolet 1/2-Ton 3124 Cameo Carrier Pickup (OCW)

1/2-TON COMMERCIAL (CAMEO) — Model 3A/SERIES 3124 — SIX/V-8: The Cameo had the new 1958 dual headlights. The outside of the box was trimmed like the 1957 model. Only nine two-tone color choices were used on Cameos. They were [main color first]: (No. 701) Bombay Ivory/Cardinal Red with Cardinal Red wheels for Cameos only, (No. 727) Tartan Turquoise/Jet Black with Tartan, (No. 729) Golden Yellow/Jet Black, (No. 731) Oriental Green/Bombay Ivory, (No. 733) Polar Green/Glade Green, (No. 736) Dawn Blue/Marine Blue, (No. 738) Kodiak Brown/Bombay Ivory, (No. 740) Cardinal Red/Bombay Ivory, and (No. 746) Granite Gray/Bombay Ivory. This year the main (first) color covered the entire roof (instead of only the pillars) except for a strip below the rub rail. Wheels were painted the main color, except for combination No. 701, with Cardinal Red wheels and a Bombay Ivory main color. The seat cloth changed from star design to a charcoal horizontal stripe. Red seat material with silver trim was used with the "standard" Cardinal Red/Bombay Ivory paint option. In this case the steering wheel, mast and top of the dash were red and door panels were Metallic Silver. Other interior combinations were optional. Standard production wheels were Cardinal Red. The Cameo again had the 114-in. wheelbase and 196.5-in. overall length. The box was 78.5 in. long. It had a 77-in. maximum outside width, but was only 50 in. wide on its interior. With standard 6.70 x 15 tires, the Cameo had a 4,600 lb. GVW rating and could handle payloads up to about 450 lb. With a simple change to six-ply tires, the numbers went to 4,300 lb. and 750 lb. With 1,550 lb. rear springs and 6.50 x 16 six-ply tires, the GVW was 4,600 lb. and the payload rating 1,050 lb. Combining the heavy springs with 7 x 17.5 six-ply tires upped the numbers to 5,000 lb. and 1,450 lb. Standard equipment included: A 1-pint oil bath air cleaner, 2200-lb. capacity I-beam front axle, 3300-lb. capacity hypoid semi-floating rear axle with 3.90:1 gear ratio, a 12-volt 54-plate 53 amp.-hr. battery, hydraulic four-wheel brakes, rear-wheel parking brake, chrome front bumper, painted rear bumper, chrome bumperettes, Custom cab equipment, 10-in. diameter diaphragm spring clutch, 17-quart cooling system, a hand throttle and choke, a headlamp and dome lamp switch, a headlight beam control switch, a speedometer, an ammeter, gauges for engine fuel, oil pressure and temperature, a 145-hp Thriftmaster six engine with road-draft type ventilation system, single exhaust system and muffler, front and integral rear fenders, a five-cross member channel section frame, carburetor fuel filter, a 17-1/2-gallon fuel tank behind seat, 12-volt 30-ampere generator, headlamps, parking lights and dual stop/taillamps, left side mirror with eight-inch fixed bracket, two-tone baked enamel paint, front and rear direct double-acting shock absorbers, semi-elliptic front springs, semi-elliptic two-stage rear springs, ball gear steering with 21.3 ratio, 18-in. diameter steering wheel, 6.70 x 15 four-ply tubeless tires, jack and wheel wrench, Full-View rear window, dual vacuum windshield wipers, and three-speed synchromesh transmission with steering column gear shift. Transmission options included Hydra-Matic, heavy-duty three-speed synchromesh, and heavy-duty four-speed synchromesh. The Cameo was listed in the *Chevrolet Truck Data Book* issued Oct. 1, 1957. The Fleetside was later phased in to replace it. The Cameo did not come with the 4x4 option. Maximum GVW was 5,000 lb.

1958 Chevrolet 1/2-Ton 31 Apache Fleetside Pickup (CMD)

1/2-TON COMMERCIAL — MODEL 3B/SERIES 3200 — SIX/V-8: The 3200 Series Task-Force trucks had the same basic styling and trim changes as other conventional trucks. A new Fleetside edition was introduced, as well as a Chassis-and-Cab. These were the long wheelbase (LWB) 1/2-ton trucks on the same chassis as 3/4-ton models. They are known as "Long Bed" or "Long Box" Pickups because they had a longer load box. Chevrolet parts catalogs indicated that a 98-in. box was used for 1957-1958 Models 3200/3600. Longer running boards were also needed because there was more space between the cab and rear fenders. It still had the same 5,000 lb. maximum GVW rating as other 1/2-ton trucks.

3/4-TON DUBL-DUTI — MODEL 3C/SERIES 3400 — SIX/V-8: Three Dubl-Duti Forward-Control chassis remained in the truck line. The Model 3442 had a 104-in. wheelbase. Standard walk-in delivery truck bodies could be supplied by several factory-approved sources or the buyer could add his/her own body.

3/4-TON DUBL-DUTI — MODEL 3D/SERIES 3500 — SIX-CYLINDER: Model 3542 was the 3/4-ton Dubl-Duti on a 125-in. wheelbase. Standard walk-in delivery truck bodies could be supplied by several factory-approved sources or the buyer could add his/her own body. The wheels were of eight-bolt design. A painted, Anvil Gray channel type front bumper was optional on the 3500 Dubl-Duti truck chassis.

3/4-TON — DUBL-DUTI — MODEL F/SERIES 3700 — SIX-CYLINDER: Model 3742 was the Dubl-Duti on a 137-in. wheelbase. Standard walk-in delivery truck bodies could be supplied by several factory-approved sources or the buyer could add his/her own body. The wheels were of eight-bolt design. A painted, Anvil Gray channel type front bumper was optional on the 3700 Dubl-Duti truck chassis.

1958 Chevrolet 3/4-Ton Apache 36 Fleetside Pickup (OCW)

3/4-TON COMMERCIAL — MODEL 3E56/SERIES 3600 — SIX/V-8: The 3600 Series Task-Force trucks had the same styling and trim changes as other conventional trucks. A Fleetside Pickup was added to this series of medium-duty cab models on a 123.5-in. wheelbase. Compared to 3100 Pickups, the 3600 Pickup had longer running boards and a longer cargo box with a horizontal support rib. Chevrolet parts catalogs indicated that a 98-in. box was used for 1957-1958 Models 3600. There were also Platform and Platform/Stake models. The rail for the 3/4-ton Platform was 97-9/16 in. long. The maximum GVW rating was: [4x2] 6,900 lb., [4x4] 7,300 lb.

1-TON MEDIUM-DUTY COMMERCIAL — MODEL 3G/SERIES 3800 — SIX-CYLINDER: The 3800 Series Task-Force trucks had the same styling and trim changes as other conventional trucks. There was no Fleetside Pickup in this line. Panel models had a one-piece floor made of 3/4-inch thick, five-ply laminated wood. The basic model lineup was unchanged. Compared to the 3600 Pickup, the 3800 Pickup had a longer wheelbase, a longer grain-tight load box with extra stake pockets and very long running boards. The 1-ton Stake trucks had a 115-9/16 in. long rail. No hubcaps were used on the larger split-rim wheels of the Chassis-and-Cab and Stake models, which had eight bolts and eight circular openings. A four-speed manual synchromesh transmission was standard. GVW: [4x2] 7,400, [4x4] 9,600, [Dual rear wheel, 4x2] 10,000 lb.

**1958 Chevrolet 1/2-Ton 3124 Cameo Carrier Pickup
(Owner: Bob Maul/John Lee Photo)**

**1958 Chevrolet 1/2-Ton 3124 Cameo Carrier Pickup
(Owner: Bob Maul/John Lee Photo)**

I.D. DATA: Serial number located: [Chassis models] On plate temporarily attached near steering column, with final location per body maker; [All others] on plate attached to rear face of left-hand door hinge pillar. The first (Sedan Delivery) or first and second symbol(s) indicated the series: G/H=1500, 3A=3100, 3B=3200, 3C=3400, 3D=3500, 3E=3600, 3F=3700, 3G=3800. The next two symbols indicated the model-year: 58=1958. The fifth symbol indicated the assembly plant: A=Atlanta, Ga., B=Baltimore, Md., F=Flint, Mich., J=Janesville, Wis., K=Kansas City, Mo., L=Los Angeles, Calif., N=Norwood, Ohio, O=Oakland, Calif., S=St. Louis, Mo., T=Tarrytown, N.Y., W=Willow Run, Mich. Each series was separately numbered in sequence, starting with 001001 at each assembly plant. Ending serial numbers not available. Engine numbers located on right side of engine on boss at rear of distributor. Engine numbers began with an F (Flint, Mich.) or T (Tonawanda, N.Y.) assembly plant code.

Job No.	Body Type	Price	Weight	Prod. Total
Sedan Delivery — Model D58/Series 1500 — 117.5 in. w.b.				
1171	Sedan Delivery	2123	3529	-
1/2-Ton Commercial — Model 3A/Series 3100 — 114 in. w.b.				
3102	Chassis	1517	2401	-
3103	Chassis & Cab	1770	2910	-
3104	Step-Side Pickup	1884	3273	-
3105	Panel	2185	3495	-
3106	Suburban (door)	2518	3794	-
3116	Suburban (gate)	2518	3799	-
3134	Fleetside Pickup	1900	-	-
1/2-Ton Commercial (Cameo) — Model 3A/Series 3100 — 114 in. w.b.				
3124	Cameo Carrier	2231	3423	-
1405				
1/2-Ton Commercial (Long Box) — Model 3B/Series 3200 — 123.25 in. w.b.				
3203	Chassis & Cab	1808	3102	-
3204	Step-Side Pickup LWB	1922	3342	-
3234	Fleetside Pickup LWB	1938	-	-
3/4-Ton Dubl-Duti — Model 3C/Series 3400 — 104 in. w.b.				
3442	Chassis	1652	2687	-
3445	Walk-in Delivery	3047	4698	-
3/4-Ton Dubl-Duti — Model 3D/Series 3500 — 125 in. w.b.				
3542	Chassis	1690	2754	-
3545	Walk-in Delivery	3132	4975	-
3/4-Ton Dubl-Duti — Model 3F/Series 3700 — 137 in. w.b.				
3742	Chassis	1722	2762	-
3745	Walk-in Delivery	3243	5223	-
3/4-Ton Dubl-Duti — Model 3E/Series 3600 — 123.25 in. w.b.				
3602	Chassis	1689	2751	-
3603	Chassis & Cab	1953	3270	-
3604	Step-Side Pickup	2066	3674	-
3634	Fleetside Pickup	2082	-	-
3609	Stake Bed	2158	3894	-
1-Ton Commercial — Model 3G/Series 3800 — 135 in. w.b.				
3802	Chassis	1836	3030	-
3803	Chassis & Cab	2100	3496	-
3804	Step-Side Pickup	2233	3973	-
3805	Panel	2561	4265	-
3809	Stake Bed	2346	4321	-

NOTE 1: The 4x4 option was available on all 3100/3600/3800 Series trucks, except Cameo Carrier.

ENGINE: [Standard, All] Inline. OHV. Six-cylinder. Cast iron block. Bore & stroke: 3-9/16 x 3-15/16 in. Displacement: 235.5 cid. Compression ratio: 8.25:1. Brake horsepower: 145 at 4200 rpm. Torque: 215 lb.-ft. at 2400 rpm. SAE horsepower: 125 at 4000 rpm. Four main bearings. Hydraulic valve lifters. Carburetor: Rochester one-barrel model 7012133.

ENGINE: [Optional All, except Dubl-Duti] V-block. OHV. Eight-cylinder. Cast iron block. Bore & stroke: 3-7/8 x 3 in. Displacement: 283 cid. Compression ratio: 8.5:1. Brake horsepower: 160 at 4200 rpm. Torque: 275 lb.-ft. at 2400 rpm. SAE horsepower: 137 at 3800 rpm. Five main bearings. Hydraulic valve lifters. Carburetor: Rochester two-barrel model 7012133.8.

ENGINE: [1200] V-block. OHV. Eight-cylinder. Cast iron block. Bore & stroke: 3-7/8 x 3 in. Displacement: 283 cid. Compression ratio: 8.5:1. Brake horsepower: 185 at 4500 rpm. Five main bearings. Hydraulic valve lifters. Carburetor: Rochester two-barrel model 7012133.

1958 Chevrolet 1/2-Ton 31 Apache Fleetside Pickup (CMD)

ENGINE: [1200] V-block. OHV. Eight-cylinder. Cast iron block. Bore & stroke: 3-7/8 x 3 in. Displacement: 283 cid. Compression ratio: 9.5:1. Brake horsepower: 230 at 4800 rpm. Five main bearings. Hydraulic valve lifters. Carburetor: Rochester four-barrel.

ENGINE: [1200] V-block. OHV. Eight-cylinder. Cast iron block. Bore & stroke: 3-7/8 x 3 in. Displacement: 283 cid. Compression ratio: 9.5:1. Brake horsepower: 250 at 5200 rpm. Five main bearings. Hydraulic valve lifters. Carburetor: Rochester fuel-injection.

ENGINE: [1200] V-block. OHV. Eight-cylinder. Cast iron block. Bore & stroke: 3-7/8 x 3 in. Displacement: 283 cid. Compression ratio: 9.5:1. Brake horsepower: 230 at 4800 rpm. Five main bearings. Hydraulic valve lifters. Carburetor: Two Carter four-barrels.

1958 Chevrolet 1/2-Ton Apache 10 Fleetside Pickup (OCW)

CHASSIS: [Series 1500] Wheelbase: 117.5 in. Overall length: 209.1 in. Height: 57.4 in. Tires: 7.50 x 14 four-ply. Maximum GVW: 4,100 lb.
CHASSIS: [Series 3100] Wheelbase: 114 in. Overall length: [Cameo] 196.50 in., [Others] 185.7 in. Front tread: 60.5 in. Rear tread: 61.0 in. Tires: 6.70 x 15 four-ply. Maximum GVW: 5,000 lb.
CHASSIS: [Series 3200] Wheelbase: 123.25 in. Overall length: [Early] 205.56, [Late] 215.81 in. Tires: 7 x 7.5 six-ply. Maximum GVW: 5,000 lb.
CHASSIS: [Series 3442] Wheelbase: 104 in. Tires: 8 x 19.5 six-ply. Maximum GVW: 7,000 lb.
CHASSIS: [Series 3542] Wheelbase: 125 in. Tires: 8 x 19.5 six-ply. Maximum GVW: 8,800 lb.
CHASSIS: [Series 3742] Wheelbase: 137 in. Tires: 8 x 19.5 six-ply. Maximum GVW: 10,000 lb.
CHASSIS: [Series 3600] Wheelbase: 123.25 in. Overall length: [Early] 205.56, [Late] 215.81 in. Tires: 7 x 17.5 six-ply. Maximum GVW: 6,900 lb.
CHASSIS: [Series 3800] Wheelbase: 135 in. Overall length: 215.81 in. Tires: [Single rear wheels] 7.50 x 17.5, [Dual rear wheels] (front) 8 x 17.5 six-ply, (rear) 8 x 17.5 eight-ply. Maximum GVW: [Single rear wheels] 7,000 lb., [Dual rear wheels] 9,600 lb.

1958 Chevrolet 3/4-Ton Apache 36 Step-Side Pickup (OCW)

OPTIONS: [Sedan Delivery RPO] Radio (No. 103). Heater (No. 112). Air cleaner (No. 216). Dual exhaust system (No. 220). Heavy-duty clutch (No. 227). Oil filter (No. 237). Governor (No. 241). Auxiliary seat (No. 263). Turboglide automatic transmission (No. 302). Powerglide automatic transmission (No. 313). Overdrive transmission (No. 315). Electric windshield wipers (No. 320). Power steering (No. 324). 45-amp. generator (No. 325). 35-amp. generator (No. 338). Heavy-duty battery (No. 345). DeLuxe steering wheel (No. 348). E-Z-Eye tinted glass (No. 398). V-8 engine (No. 410). Vacuum power brake (No. 412). Engine ventilation (No. 417). Padded instrument panel (No. 427). Full width seat (No. 482). Coil rear springs (No. 593). Optional rear axle ratios (No. 676).

1958 Chevrolet 1/2-Ton 31 Apache Fleetside Pickup (CMD)

TECHNICAL: Selective synchromesh transmission. Speeds: [3800] 4F/1R, [others] 3F/1R. Column-mounted gear shift (floor-shift on 3800). Single-plate dry-disc clutch. [3600/3800] Full-floating rear axle, [Others] Semi-floating rear axle. Overall ratio: [3100/3200] 3.90:1, [3400/3500/3700] 5.14:1, [3600] 4.57:1. Four-wheel hydraulic brakes. Steel disc wheels. Options: Heavy-duty three-speed manual transmission. Overdrive transmission. Four-speed manual transmission. Hydra-Matic transmission. Rear axles. Heavy-duty clutch. Heavy-duty radiator. Oil bath air cleaner.

1958 Chevrolet 3/4-Ton Step-Van (CMD)

OPTIONS: [Commercial Trucks RPO] Heater/defroster (No. 112). Recirculating heater (No. 115). Rear shocks (No. 200). Rear axle (No. 210). Exterior mirror (No. 210). Shock absorber shields (No. 211). Hydrovac power brakes (No. 212). Oil bath air cleaner (No. 216). PCV system (No. 217). Painted or chrome rear bumper (No. 218). Heavy-duty clutch (No. 227). Platform body (No. 230). Oil filter 1-qt. (No. 237). Governor (No. 241). Eight-leaf rear springs (No. 254). Heavy-duty radiator (No. 256). Foam rubber seat cushion (No. 258). Auxiliary seat (No. 263). Auxiliary rear springs (No. 267). Hydra-Matic transmission in 3100/3200/3600 Commercial trucks (No. 314). Heavy-duty three-speed transmission (No. 316). Heavy-duty four-speed transmission (No. 318). Electric windshield wipers (No. 320). Hydra-Matic transmission in 3800 Commercial trucks (No. 321). 45-ampere high-output generator (No. 325). 35-ampere high-output generator (No. 338). Side-mounted spare tire carrier with "dimpled" rear fender required for 3100 except Cameo/3200/3600 (No. 341). Heavy-duty battery (No. 345). Power steering with six-cylinder engines (No. 350). Chrome exterior trim package (No. 393). Full-view rear window (No. 394). Left-hand door lock and lock for side-mounted spare (No. 395). Right-hand door lock (No. 396). State of Pennsylvania serial number plate (No. 399K). Trademaster V-8 engine for 3100/3600 (No. 408). Running board (No. 423). DeLuxe Custom Cab equipment including Panoramic rear window, DeLuxe seat, chrome instrument knobs, cigarette lighter, dual visors, dual arm rests, two-tone upholstery and interior color scheme (No. 431). DeLuxe Custom Panel equipment including, DeLuxe seat, chrome instrument knobs, cigarette lighter, dual visors, dual arm rests, two-tone upholstery and interior color scheme (No. 431). 45-ampere heavy-duty generator (No. 587). Oil bath air cleaner (No. 591). Two-quart oil filter (No. 592). Right-hand door and tire lock (No. 599). Freewheeling hubs for trucks with 4x4 (No. 683). Positraction rear axle (No. 675). Positraction rear axle (No. 676). Positraction rear axle (No. 678). Four-wheel-drive (No. 690). Bostrom seat (No. 695). Monotone color options for all Sedan Deliveries (No. 900-938).

Option No.	Body Color	DuPont Duco No.	Wheel Color	DuPont Dulux No.
900-A	Onyx Black	44	Onyx Black	93-005
903-A	Glen Green	2289	Glen Green	93-58897
905-A	Forest Green	2629-H	Forest Green	181-15394-H
910-A	Cashmere Blue	2690	Cashmere Blue	93-91407
912-A	Fathom Blue	2699-H	Fathom Blue	2699-H
923-A	Rio Red	2698-H	Rio Red	93-91051-H
936-A	Snowcrest White	2697-L	Snowcrest White	93-91249
938-A	Honey Beige	2701	Honey Beige	93-91875

OPTIONS: [Dealer Accessories] Radio antenna. Heater (Standard/DeLuxe). Cigar lighter. Seat covers. External sun shade. Hubcaps. Directional signals. Front bumper guards (painted or chrome). Rear fold-down steps (Platform/Stake). Dual sun visors. Extendible outside mirrors. Spotlight with mirror. Windshield washer. External sun visor. Traffic viewer. Back-up lights (Sedan Delivery). Electric parking brake signal. Chrome hood ornament. Dual fog lamps. Red reflex reflectors. Portable spotlight. AC/DC shaver. Stainless steel door edge guards. Stainless steel door vent shades. Chrome door handle shields. Tool kit. Illuminated compass. Underhood light. Second (high-note) horn.

1958 Chevrolet 1/2-Ton 3124 Cameo Carrier Pickup
(Owner: Ken Whitcher

Standard Catalog of Chevrolet Trucks

Introduced: October 1957. Model-year production: [All Chevrolet Commercial Series] 278,632. Innovations: First year for dual headlights. All-new Fleetside Pickup with double-wall cargo-box construction introduced to replace the Cameo Carrier during the model-year. This was Chevrolet's 40th year of manufacturing trucks. Chevrolet's long association with Union Body Co., of Union City, Ind., began with the introduction of Step-Van forward-control (Walk-in delivery van) models.

1959 CHEVROLET

1959 Chevrolet Series 1200 1/2-Ton El Camino Sedan-Pickup (OCW)

EL CAMINO — MODEL G/SERIES 1100 (SIX) — MODEL H/SERIES 1200 (V-8): The big news from Chevrolet in 1959 was the all-new El Camino, the company's first Coupe-Pickup since 1941. Replacing the (1955-57) Cameo Pickup as a super-styled pickup, it was a vehicle which Chevrolet depicted as, "More than a car.... More than a truck." The El Camino had the general styling of Chevrolet's passenger sedan models, while possessing a load capacity of 1,150 pounds. The box was over 6 ft. long and nearly 5-1/2 ft. wide. It had a load volume of nearly 34 cu. ft. and was of double wall design. Its steel floor had built-in skid strips over a ribbed and embossed sub-floor supported by four cross members. Standard for the El Camino was a six-cylinder engine, but two V-8s were available along with Powerglide, Turboglide and overdrive transmissions as alternatives to the standard three-speed manual gearbox. Trim was of the Bel Air level with a full-length side molding with painted inserts and front fender ornaments. The front fender side scripts said El Camino. Features included all-vinyl trim, a Bel Air style steering wheel, and chrome window frames. The El Camino was offered in 13 solid and 10 two-tone color combinations. Colors were Tuxedo Black, Frost Blue, Harbor Blue, Gothic Gold, Aspen Green, Highland Green, Roman Red, Snow Crest White, Satin Beige, Cameo Coral, Classic Cream, Grecian Gray, and Crown Sapphire. The two-tone designs consisted of one color on the roof, upper pillar area and upper rear deck, with the rest of the vehicle in the second color. The spare tire was located behind the hinged passenger seat and the tailgate lowered to bed floor level for carrying extended loads. The maximum GVW was 4,900 lb.
SEDAN DELIVERY — MODEL G/SERIES 1100 (SIX) — MODEL H/SERIES 1200 (V-8): The 1959 Sedan Delivery was based on the Station Wagon. It had Biscayne level trim with a solid bright metal molding across the front fenders that extended to the middle of the doors. It grew two inches longer and was two inches lower. However, the completely redesigned "Slimline" body was wider and roomier. Styling features included increased glass area, "Spread Wing" rear styling, new taillights, and a full-width rear door that swung up to protect the user unloading during rain or snow. Standard equipment included a single bucket seat, auxiliary passenger seat, cargo interior with tempered Masonite panels, and car-style cab trimmings. Colors were Tuxedo Black, Frost Blue, Harbor Blue, Gothic Gold, Aspen Green, Highland Green, Roman Red, and Snow Crest White.

1959 Chevrolet 1/2-Ton Apache 31 Fleetside Pickup (OCW)

1/2-TON — MODEL 3A/SERIES 3100 — SIX/V-8: The new Task-Force Commercial models kept the dual headlamps, new grille, and basic technical features of 1958 models. The new grille consisted of narrow horizontal bars just below the hood and a more massive "barbell-shaped" lower molding extending out and under the headlamps. This molding had the Chevrolet name lettered across it and its rectangular outboard extensions surrounded the similarly-shaped parking lamp lenses. Base-level Apaches had a cream-painted grille, bumper and headlamp buckets and cream-colored hubcaps. The front hood emblem had an ornament with a somewhat "squashed T" shape. Fender side nameplates changed from a jet plane to a rocket ship shape and were moved just behind the headlamps. They said Chevrolet Apache 31 on the 3100s. Four-wheel drive was

optional. Colors included Frontier Beige, Jet Black, Baltic Blue, Dawn Blue, Cadet Gray, Galway Green, Glade Green, Sherwood Green, Omaha Orange, Cardinal Red, Tartan Turquoise, Pure White, Golden Yellow, and Yukon Yellow. All colors were available as the main color in two-tone combination with Bombay Ivory. "Color-Break" two-toning was new for Fleetside Pickups. This meant that everything above the hood-level feature line, except the rear of the cab, was finished in a contrasting color. Standard wheels were black and the wheels on two-toned trucks were the main body color. Buyers were again presented with a choice of two types of pickups: The Step-Side model had exposed rear fenders and a standard width box. Fleetsides had slab-sided rear steel fenders and an extra-wide box. Fleetside models had a missile-shaped bulge along the slab-sided bed exterior. Their boxes were 75 in. wide. Custom chrome and Custom cab equipment were separate options. Custom cab models had two arm rests, two sun visors, a cigarette lighter, foam rubber seat cushions and back rests, bright control knobs, and chrome window moldings. The Panoramic rear window was a separate option. Maximum GVWs were: [4x2] 5,000 lb., [4x4] 5,600 lb.

1959 Chevrolet 1/2-Ton Apache 32 Fleetside Long Box Pickup (Owner: William C. Samuelson)

1959 Chevrolet 1/2-Ton Apache 32 Fleetside Long Box Pickup (Owner: William C. Samuelson)

1/2-TON COMMERCIAL — MODEL 3B/SERIES 3200 — SIX/V-8: The 3200 Series Task-Force trucks had the same basic styling and trim changes as other conventional trucks. A new Step-Side Pickup with a 9-ft. box was introduced, as well as a Chassis-and-Cab. These were the long wheelbase (LWB) 1/2-ton trucks on the same chassis as 3/4-ton models. They are known as "Long Bed" or "Long Box" Pickups because they had a longer 98-in. load box. Longer running boards were needed because there was more space between the cab and rear fenders. These trucks were not available with four-wheel drive. They had the same 5,000 lb. maximum GVW rating as other 1/2-ton trucks.
3/4-TON DUBL-DUTI — MODEL 3C/SERIES 3400 — SIX/V-8: Three Dubl-Duti Forward-Control chassis remained in the truck line. The Model 3442 had a 104-in. wheelbase. Standard walk-in delivery truck bodies could be supplied by several factory-approved sources or the buyer could add his/her own body. A popular use for the Dubl-Duti chassis was as a platform for the Step-Van walk-in delivery trucks made by Union City Body Co., of Union City, Ind.
3/4-TON DUBL-DUTI — MODEL 3D/SERIES 3500 — SIX-CYLINDER: Model 3542 was the 3/4-ton Dubl-Duti on a 125-in. wheelbase. Standard walk-in delivery truck bodies, such as the Step-Van, could be supplied by several factory-approved sources or the buyer could add his/her own body. The wheels were of eight-bolt design. A painted, Anvil Gray channel type front bumper was optional on the 3500 Dubl-Duti truck chassis.
3/4-TON — DUBL-DUTI — MODEL F/SERIES 3700 — SIX-CYLINDER: Model 3742 was the Dubl-Duti on a 137-in. wheelbase. Standard walk-in delivery truck bodies, such as the Step-Vans, could be supplied by several factory-approved sources or the buyer could add his/her own body. The wheels were of eight-bolt design. A painted, Anvil Gray channel type front bumper was optional on the 3700 Dubl-Duti truck chassis.
3/4-TON COMMERCIAL — MODEL 3E/SERIES 3600 — SIX/V-8: The 3600 Series Task-Force trucks had the same styling and trim changes as other conventional trucks. Step-Side and Fleetside Pickups were in this series. Compared to 3100 Pickups, the 3600 Pickup had slightly longer running boards and a longer cargo box with a horizontal support rib. A 98-in. box was used. There were also Platform and Platform/Stake models. The rail for the 3/4-ton Platform was 97-9/16 in. long. The maximum GVW rating was: [4x2] 6,900 lb., [4x4] 7,300 lb.
1-TON MEDIUM-DUTY COMMERCIAL — MODEL 3G/SERIES 3800 — SIX-CYLINDER: The 3800 Series Task-Force trucks had the same styling and trim changes as other conventional trucks. There was no Fleetside Pickup in this line. Panel models had a one-piece floor made of 3/4-inch thick, five-ply laminated wood. The basic model lineup was unchanged. Compared to the 3600 Pickup, the 3800 Pickup had a longer wheelbase, a longer grain-tight load box with extra stake pockets and very long running boards. The 1-ton Stake used a 115-9/16 in. long rail. No hubcaps were used on the larger split-rim wheels of the Chassis-and-Cab and Stake models, which had eight bolts and eight circular openings. A four-speed manual synchromesh transmission was standard. GVW: [4x2] 7,400, [4x4] 9,600.

**1959 Chevrolet 3/4-Ton Apache 36 Step-Side Pickup
(Owner: Steve & Mary Huntington)**

I.D. DATA: Serial number located: [Chassis models] On plate temporarily attached near steering column, with final location per body maker; [All others] on plate attached to rear face of left-hand door hinge pillar, on right side of cowl under hood. The first (El Camino/Sedan Delivery) or first and second symbol(s) indicated the series: G=1100, H=1200, 3A=3100, 3B=3200, 3C=3400, 3D=3500, 3E=3600, 3F=3700, 3G=3800. The next two symbols indicated the model-year: 59=1959. The fifth symbol indicated the assembly plant: A=Atlanta, Ga., B=Baltimore, Md., F=Flint, Mich., J=Janesville, Wis., K=Kansas City, Mo., L=Los Angeles, Calif., N=Norwood, Ohio, O=Oakland, Calif., P=Pontiac, Mich., S=St. Louis, Mo., T=Tarrytown, N.Y., W=Willow Run, Mich. Each series was separately numbered in sequence, starting with 001001 at each assembly plant. Ending serial numbers not available. Engine numbers located on right side of engine on boss at rear of distributor. Engine numbers began with an F (Flint, Mich.) or T (Tonawanda, N.Y.) assembly plant code.

1959 Chevrolet Series 1200 1/2-Ton El Camino Sedan-Pickup (OCW)

Job No.	Body Type	Price	Weight	Prod. Total
El Camino — Series 1100/Model G — 119 in. w.b. — Six				
1180	El Camino	2352	3605	-
Sedan Delivery — Series 1100/Model G — 119 in. w.b. — Six				
1170	Sedan Delivery	2363	3590	-
El Camino — Series 1200/Model H — 119 in. w.b. — V-8				
1180	El Camino	-	-	-
Sedan Delivery — Series 1200/Model G — 119 in. w.b. — V-8				
1170	Sedan Delivery	-	-	-
1/2-Ton Commercial — Model 3A/Series 3100 — 114 in. w.b.				
3102	Chassis	1580	2421	-
3103	Chassis & Cab	1834	2909	-
3104	Step-Side Pickup	1948	3260	-
3105	Panel	2249	3490	-
3106	Suburban (doors)	2583	3778	-
3116	Suburban (gate)	2616	3796	-
3134	Fleetside Pickup	1964	3304	-
1/2-Ton Commercial (Long Bed) — Model 3B/Series 3200 — 123.25 w.b.				
3203	Chassis & Cab	1872	2988	-
3204	Step-Side Pickup	1986	3386	-
3234	Fleetside Pickup	2002	3381	-
3/4-Ton Dubl-Duti — Model 3C/Series 3400 — 104 in. w.b.				
3442	Chassis	1716	2700	-
3445	Step-Van	3112	5042	-
3/4-Ton Dubl-Duti — Model 3D/Series 3500 — 125 in. w.b.				
3542	Chassis	1754	2795	-
3545	Step-Van	3197	5247	-
3/4-Ton Dubl-Duti — Model 3F/Series 3700 — 137 in. w.b.				
3742	Chassis	1786	2823	-
3745	Step-Van	3308	5416	-
3/4-Ton Commercial — Model 3E/Series 3600 — 123.25 in. w.b.				
3602	Chassis	1753	2780	-
3603	Chassis & Cab	2018	3275	-
3604	Step-Side Pickup	2132	3669	-
3634	Fleetside Pickup	2148	3664	-
3609	Stake	2223	3844	-
1-Ton Commercial — Model 3G/Series 3800 — 135 in. w.b.				
3802	Chassis	1899	3020	-
3803	Chassis & Cab	2164	3501	-
3804	Step-Side Pickup	2298	3954	-
3805	Panel	2626	4270	-
3809	Stake	2411	4294	-

ENGINE: [Standard all except 1200] Inline. OHV. Six-cylinder. Cast iron block. Bore & stroke: 3.562 x 3.937 in. Displacement: 235.5 cid. Compression ratio: 8.25:1. Brake horsepower: 135 at 4000 rpm. Torque: 215 lb.-ft. at 2400 rpm. Four main bearings. Hydraulic valve lifters. Carburetor: Rochester two-barrel model 7013003. Name: Thriftmaster Six. Thriftmaster Special engine with lower horsepower and torque ratings available for Dubl-Duti.
ENGINE: [Standard 1200, Optional 3100/3200/3600/3800] V-type. OHV. Eight-cylinder. Cast iron block. Bore & stroke: 3.875 x 3 in. Displacement: 283 cid. Compression ratio: 8.5:1. Brake horsepower: 185. Five main bearings. Carburetor: Rochester two-barrel model 7013007. Name: Turbo-Fire V-8.
ENGINE: [Optional 1200] V-type. OHV. Eight-cylinder. Cast iron block. Bore & stroke: 3.875 x 3 in. Displacement: 283 cid. Compression ratio: 9.5:1. Brake horsepower: 230 at 4800 rpm. Maximum torque: 300 lb.-ft. at 3000. Five main bearings. Hydraulic valve lifters. Carburetor: Rochester four-barrel. Name: Super Turbo-Fire V-8.
ENGINE: [Optional 1200] V-type. OHV. Eight-cylinder. Cast iron block. Bore & stroke: 3.875 x 3 in. Displacement: 283 cid. Compression ratio: 9.5:1. Brake horsepower: 250. Five main bearings. Fuel-injection.
ENGINE: [Optional 1200] V-type. OHV. Eight-cylinder. Cast iron block. Bore & stroke: 3.875 x 3 in. Displacement: 283 cid. Compression ratio: 10.5:1. Brake horsepower: 290. Five main bearings. Fuel-injection.

1959 Chevrolet Series 1200 1/2-Ton El Camino Sedan-Pickup (JCL)

ENGINE: [Optional 1200] V-type. OHV. Eight-cylinder. Cast iron block. Bore & stroke: 4.125 x 3.25 in. Displacement: 348 cid. Compression ratio: 9.5:1. Brake horsepower: 250. Five main bearings. Carburetor: Four-barrel.
ENGINE: [Optional 1200] V-type. OHV. Eight-cylinder. Cast iron block. Bore & stroke: 4.125 x 3.25 in. Displacement: 348 cid. Compression ratio: 9.5:1. Brake horsepower: 280. Five main bearings. Carburetor: Three two-barrels.
ENGINE: [Optional 1200] V-type. OHV. Eight-cylinder. Cast iron block. Bore & stroke: 4.125 x 3.25 in. Displacement: 348 cid. Compression ratio: 11.0:1. Brake horsepower: 300. Five main bearings. Carburetor: Four-barrel.

**1959 Chevrolet 1/2-Ton Apache 31 Fleetside NAPCO 4x4 Pickup
(Owner: Dave Stevens)**

**1959 Chevrolet 1/2-Ton Apache 31 Fleetside NAPCO 4x4 Pickup
(Owner: Dave Stevens)**

1959 Chevrolet Series 1200 1/2-Ton El Camino Sedan-Pickup (Owner: Ed Plazek)

ENGINE: [Optional 1200] V-type. OHV. Eight-cylinder. Cast iron block. Bore & stroke: 4.125 x 3.25 in. Displacement: 348 cid. Compression ratio: 11.0:1. Brake horsepower: 305. Five main bearings. Carburetor: Four-barrel.
ENGINE: [Optional 1200] V-type. OHV. Eight-cylinder. Cast iron block. Bore & stroke: 4.125 x 3.25 in. Displacement: 348 cid. Compression ratio: 11.0:1. Brake horsepower: 315. Five main bearings. Carburetor: Three two-barrels.
ENGINE: [Optional 1200] V-type. OHV. Eight-cylinder. Cast iron block. Bore & stroke: 4.125 x 3.25 in. Displacement: 348 cid. Compression ratio: 11.25:1. Brake horsepower: 320. Five main bearings. Carburetor: Four-barrel.
ENGINE: [Optional 1200] V-type. OHV. Eight-cylinder. Cast iron block. Bore & stroke: 4.125 x 3.25 in. Displacement: 348 cid. Compression ratio: 11.25:1. Brake horsepower: 335. Five main bearings. Carburetor: Three two-barrels.
CHASSIS: [1100/1200] Wheelbase: 119 in. Overall length: 210.9 in. Height: 56.3 in. Tires: 8.00 x 14 four-ply. Maximum GVW: 4,900 lb.
CHASSIS: [Series 3100] Wheelbase: 114 in. Overall length: [Cameo] 193.56 in., [Others] 185.7 in. Front tread: 60.5 in. Rear tread: 61.0 in. Tires: 6.70 x 15 four-ply. Maximum GVW: 5,000 lb.
CHASSIS: [Series 3200] Wheelbase: 123.25 in. Overall length: [Early] 205.56, [Late] 215.81 in. Tires: 7 x 7.5 six-ply. Maximum GVW: 5,000 lb.
CHASSIS: [Series 3442] Wheelbase: 104 in. Tires: 8 x 19.5 six-ply. Maximum GVW: 7,000 lb.
CHASSIS: [Series 3542] Wheelbase: 125 in. Tires: 8 x 19.5 six-ply. Maximum GVW: 8,800 lb.
CHASSIS: [Series 3742] Wheelbase: 137 in. Tires: 8 x 19.5 six-ply. Maximum GVW: 10,000 lb.
CHASSIS: [Series 3600] Wheelbase: 123.25 in. Overall length: [Early] 205.56, [Late] 215.81 in. Tires: 7 x 17.5 six-ply. Maximum GVW: 6,900 lb.
CHASSIS: [Series 3800] Wheelbase: 135 in. Overall length: 215.81 in. Tires: [Single rear wheels] 7.50 x 17.5, [Dual rear wheels] (front) 8 x 17.5 six-ply, (rear) 8 x 17.5 eight-ply. Maximum GVW: [Single rear wheels] 7,000 lb., [Dual rear wheels] 9,600 lb.

1959 Chevrolet 1/2-Ton Apache 31 Step-Side Pickup (DFW)

TECHNICAL: Selective synchromesh transmission. Speeds: [3800] 4F/1R, [others] 3F/1R. Column-mounted gear shift (floor-shift on 3800). Single-plate dry-disc clutch. [3600/3800] Full-floating rear axle, [Others] Semi-floating rear axle. Overall ratios: [1100/1200] Four from 3.08 to 4.11, [3100/3200] Five from 3.38 to 4.11, [3400/3500/3700] 4.7:1 [3600] 4.57:1., [3800] 5.14:1. Four-wheel hydraulic brakes. Steel disc wheels. Options: Heavy-duty three-speed manual transmission. Overdrive transmission. Four-speed manual transmission. Hydra-Matic transmission. Rear axles. Heavy-duty clutch. Heavy-duty radiator. Oil bath air cleaner.

1959 Chevrolet Series 1200 1/2-Ton El Camino Sedan-Pickup (CMD)

OPTIONS: [El Camino and Sedan Delivery RPO] Heater (No. 101). Radio (No. 103). Windshield washers (No. 109). Air conditioning for El Camino only (No. 110). Recirculating heater (No. 116). Full wheel discs (No. 117). Six-cylinder oil bath air cleaner (No. 216). Dual exhaust system for V-8 models (No. 220). Heavy-duty clutch with six-cylinder engine (No. 227). One-quart oil filter (No. 237). Auxiliary seat for Sedan Delivery (No. 263). Turboglide automatic transmission for V-8 models only (No. 302). Powerglide automatic transmission (No. 313). Overdrive transmission (No. 315). Electric windshield wipers (No. 320). Power steering (No. 324). 45-ampere generator (No. 325). 40-ampere generator (No. 326). Foam rubber seat for El Camino (No. 335). 35-ampere generator (No. 338). Heavy-duty battery (No. 345). DeLuxe equipment (No. 347). DeLuxe steering wheel (No. 348). E-Z-Eye tinted glass (No. 398). Vacuum power brake (No. 412). Padded instrument panel (No. 427). Full width seat for Sedan Delivery (No. 482). Six-cylinder economy carburetor (No. 581). Coil rear springs (No. 593). Positraction rear axle (No. 675). Optional rear axle ratios (No. 676). Four-speed manual synchromesh transmission for El Camino (No. 685).

1959 Chevrolet Series 1200 1/2-Ton El Camino Sedan-Pickup

OPTIONS: [Commercial Trucks RPO] Heater (No. 101). Radio (No. 103). Heater/defroster (No. 112). Recirculating heater (No. 115). Rear axle (No. 208). Exterior mirror (No. 210). Shock absorber shields (No. 211). Painted or chrome rear bumper (No. 218). Heavy-duty clutch (No. 227). Platform body (No. 230). Oil filter 1-qt. (No. 237). Governor (No. 241). Eight-leaf rear springs (No. 254). Heavy-duty radiator (No. 256). Foam rubber seat cushion (No. 258). Auxiliary seat (No. 263). Hydra-Matic transmission in 3100/3200/3600 Commercial trucks (No. 314). Heavy-duty three-speed transmission (No. 316). Heavy-duty four-speed transmission (No. 318). Electric windshield wipers (No. 320). 40-ampere generator (No. 336). 35-ampere high-output generator (No. 338). Side-mounted spare tire carrier with "dimpled" rear fender required for 3100 except 3200/3600 (No. 341). Heavy-duty battery (No. 345). Power steering with six-cylinder engines (No. 350). Maximum economy option (No. 371). 50-ampere generator (No. 378). 50-ampere heavy-duty generator (No. 379). Chrome exterior trim package (No. 393). Full-view rear window (No. 394). Right-hand door lock and lock for side-mounted spare (No. 395). E-Z-Eye tinted glass (No. 398). Spare tire carrier lock (No. 396). Serial number plate (No. 399K). Trademaster V-8 (No. 408). Running board (No. 423). DeLuxe Custom Cab equipment including Panoramic rear window, DeLuxe seat, chrome instrument knobs, cigarette lighter, dual visors, dual arm rests, two-tone upholstery and interior color scheme (No. 431). DeLuxe Custom Panel equipment including, DeLuxe seat, chrome instrument knobs, cigarette lighter, dual visors, dual arm rests, two-tone upholstery and interior color scheme (No. 431). Oil bath air cleaner (No. 591). Two-quart oil filter (No. 592). Right-hand door and tire lock (No. 599). Positraction rear axle (No. 675). Freewheeling hubs for trucks with 4x4 (No. 683). Four-wheel-drive (No. 690). Bostrom seat (No. 695). Monotone color options for Commercial Trucks: (No. 700) Jet Black, (No. 703) Galway Green, (No. 704) Sherwood Green, (No. 705) Glade Green, (No. 707) Dawn Blue, (No. 708) Baltic Blue, (No. 710) Tartan Turquoise, (No. 712) Frontier Beige, (No. 714) Cardinal Red, (No. 716) Omaha Orange, (No. 718) Golden Yellow, (No. 719) Yukon Yellow, (No. 721) Pure White, (No. 723) Cadet Gray. Monotone color options for all Sedan Deliveries: (No. 900) Tuxedo Black, (No.903) Aspen Green, (No. 905) Highland Green, (No. 910) Frost Blue, (No. 912) Harbor Blue, (No. 914) Crown Sapphire, (No. 920) Gothic Gold, (No. 923) Roman Red, (No. 925) Classic Cream, (No. 936) Snowcrest White, (No. 938) Satin Beige, (No. 940) Grecian Gray, (No. 942) Cameo Coral.

1959 Chevrolet 1/2-Ton Apache 31 Step-Side Pickup (OCW)

OPTIONS: [Dealer Accessories] Radio antenna. Seat covers. External sun shade. Directional signals. Front bumper guards (painted or chrome). Rear fold-down steps (Platform/Stake). Extendible outside mirrors. Spotlight with mirror. Windshield washer. External sun visor. Traffic viewer. Back-up lights (Sedan Delivery and El Camino). Electric parking brake signal. Chrome hood ornament. Dual fog lamps. Red reflex reflectors. Portable spotlight. AC/DC shaver. Stainless steel door edge guards. Stainless steel door vent shades. Chrome door handle shields. Tool kit. Illuminated compass. Underhood light. Second (high-note) horn.
HISTORICAL: Introduced: October 1958. Calendar-year registrations: [All Commercial Series] 306,237. Calendar-year production: [All Commercial Series] 326,102. Innovations: El Camino personal Pickup introduced. Positraction rear axle option made available. Longer 119-in. wheelbase for Sedan Delivery and El Camino. Chevrolet sold its seventh millionth truck since 1918 during the 1959 model run.

1960 CHEVROLET

1960 Chevrolet El Camino (John Lee)

EL CAMINO — SERIES 1100 (SIX)/SERIES 1200 (V-8) — SIX/V-8: Both the El Camino and Sedan Delivery adopted the 1960 passenger car appearance changes. The grille was oval-shaped with two free-floating headlights at either end. A cross-bar arrangement of moldings held the bow-tie emblem in a smaller oval at the center. The cross bars were backed by full-width horizontal bars. Parking lamps were underneath the redesigned bumper. The rear had more angular gull-wing fins than 1959 models. Below them was a horizontal full-width oval with two round taillamps at each end. The El Camino had an integral cargo bed and cab roof with rear overhang. Exterior trim for the El Camino was similar to the Bel Air level.

1960 Chevrolet 1/2-Ton Del Ray Series 1100 (OCW)

SEDAN DELIVERY — SERIES 1100 (SIX)/SERIES 1200 (V-8) — SIX/V-8: — The Sedan Delivery, adopted the 1960 passenger car appearance changes. The grille was oval-shaped with two free-floating headlights at either end. A cross-bar arrangement of moldings held the bow-tie emblem in a smaller oval at the center. They were backed by full-width horizontal bars. Parking lamps were underneath the redesigned bumper. The rear had more angular gull-wing fins than 1959 models. Below them was a horizontal full width oval with two round taillamps at each end. Sedan Deliveries looked a bit plain this year.

1960 Chevrolet 1/2-Ton Apache 10 Fleetside Custom Cab Pickup (OCW)

1/2-TON COMMERCIAL — MODEL C10 (4x2), K10 (4x4)/SERIES 1000 — SIX/V-8: Chevrolet offered 185 trucks on 18 different wheelbases. The Apache 10 models in the Series 1000 (1/2-ton) line came with C10/K10/C14 model prefixes. All-new design features included an elongated grille and headlamps where parking lamps were previously. The low-mounted grille consisted of full-width surround of rectangular oval shape housing dual headlamps at each end, plus four horizontal blades between them. The bumpers, grille and inner faces of the grille surround were ivory-colored on base-level Apaches. Chevrolet lettering on the grille was black. At each end of the front hood face were "jet pod" air inlets with elongated parking lamps inside. The fender sides had chrome engine call-outs. A red bow tie in the middle of the hood's front face identified sixes. A red Chevrolet bow tie with a V-shaped molding below was substituted on V-8 powered trucks. At the rear of the front fenders, below the main feature line near the front door seam, was a Chevrolet Apache 10 nameplate. The body was indented or "pinched-in" at the mid-belt level. The panels then flared out, creating a sculptured crease along the upper belt line level. The entire upper belt line seemed to have a flattened bulge to it. In front, the fenders had a flat, bulged look which ended with "jet pods" at the

front. The center hood panel was somewhat lower and flatter than the outer panels. The cab looked wider, lower and flatter than in the past, but still had a wraparound windshield and side ventipanes. At the front was a massive, but plain, full-width wraparound bumper. Step-Side Pickups had running boards between the cab and "pontoon" style rear fenders. On these models, the pinched-in waist ended behind the cab doors and a separate crease line decorated the rear fender sides. A Custom Cab option was available. It included a bright radiator grille, bright hubcaps, bright window frames, and bright black-accented "Custom" scalp moldings on the rear upper quarter of the cab. A chrome front bumper was a separate option, as was a Full-View rear window. Paint colors were Jet Black, Brigade Blue, Marlin Blue, Klondike Gold, Garrison Gray, Hemlock Green, Neptune Green, Omaha Orange, Cardinal Red, Grenadier Red, Tartan Turquoise, Pure White, Golden Yellow, and Yukon Yellow. Two-toned pickups had the contrasting color on all panels above the middle of the pinched-in body crease except the roof and rear roof areas. Cab interiors were finished in metallic silver with a charcoal gray and metallic silver dashboard. The seats had silver coverings with charcoal gray facings. A silver left-hand sun shade was used with the base DeLuxe interior. Custom Cab interiors had charcoal upper door embossments, a silver and charcoal gray left-hand door arm rest, silver right-hand sun visor, silver pattern cloth upholstery (with charcoal gray vinyl facings and bolsters), chrome knobs, a cigar lighter, and chrome Chevrolet nameplates. Two-toning on Carryall Suburbans was done with the contrast color on the lower body, under the pinched-in waist, and on the rear of the roof. This made them look somewhat like a pickup with a camper shell on back. Carryall Suburbans again came with either panel doors or an end-gate.

1960 Chevrolet 1/2-Ton Apache 10 Fleetside Pickup (DFW)

1/2-TON COMMERCIAL — MODELS C14/SERIES 1000 (4x2) — SIX/V-8: The C14 trucks in the Apache 10 Series 1000 line used a C14 model prefix. They had the same basic styling and trim changes as other conventional trucks. These were the long wheelbase (LWB) 1/2-ton trucks on the same chassis as 3/4-ton models. They are known as "Long Bed" or "Long Box" Pickups because they had a longer load box. Longer running boards were needed on Step-Sides because there was more space between the cab and rear fenders. These trucks were not available with four-wheel drive.

3/4-TON DUBL-DUTI — MODEL P20/SERIES 2000 — SIX/V-8: Six Dubl-Duti Forward-Control chassis remained in the 2000 Series 3/4-ton truck line. The P23/P25/P26 models had wheelbases of 104 in./125 in./137 in., respectively. Standard walk-in delivery truck bodies could be supplied by several factory-approved sources. Popular models were the Step-Van walk-in delivery trucks made by Union City Body Co., of Union City, Ind. A channel type front bumper was optional on Dubl-Duti trucks.

1960 Chevrolet 3/4-Ton Series C2500 Step-Side Pickup (IMSC)

3/4-TON COMMERCIAL — MODEL C25/SERIES 2000 — SIX/V-8: The Apache 20 Series 2000 (3/4-ton) trucks had the same styling and trim changes as other conventional trucks. Step-Side and Fleetside Pickups were in this series. Compared to 3100 Pickups, the 3600 Pickup had slightly longer running boards and a longer cargo box with a horizontal support rib. A 98-in. box was used. There were also Platform and Platform/Stake models. The rail for the 3/4-ton Platform was 97-9/16 in. long.

1-TON DUBL-DUTI — MODEL P30/SERIES 3000 — SIX/V-8: Six Dubl-Duti Forward-Control chassis were in a new 3000 Series (1-ton) truck line. The P33/P35/P36 models had wheelbases of 104 in./125 in./137 in., respectively. Standard walk-in delivery truck bodies could be supplied by several factory-approved sources. Popular models were the Step-Van walk-in delivery trucks made by Union City Body Co., of Union City, Ind. A channel type front bumper was optional on Dubl-Duti trucks.

1-TON MEDIUM-DUTY COMMERCIAL — MODEL C36/SERIES 3000 — SIX-CYLINDER: The Apache 30 Series 3000 (1-ton) trucks had the same styling and trim changes as other conventional trucks. There was no Fleetside Pickup in this line. Panel models had a one-piece floor made of 3/4-inch thick, five-ply laminated wood. The basic model lineup was unchanged. Compared to the 3600 Pickup, the 3800 Pickup had a longer wheelbase, a longer box with extra stake pockets, and very long running boards. The 1-ton Stake trucks had a 115-9/16-in. long rail. No hubcaps were used on the larger split-rim wheels of the Chassis-and-Cab and Stake models, which had eight bolts and eight circular openings. A four-speed manual synchromesh transmission was standard.

I.D. DATA: Serial number located: [Chassis models] On plate temporarily attached near steering column, with final location per body maker; [All others] on plate attached to rear face of left-hand door hinge pillar, on right side of cowl under hood. The first symbol indicated model-year, 0=1960. The second symbol indicated type: C=Conventional, K=4x4, G=El Camino/Sedan Delivery (six), H=El Camino/Sedan Delivery (V-8). The third and fourth symbols indicated the model prefix: El Camino/Sedan Delivery=11, El Camino/Sedan Delivery (V-8)=12, 1/2-ton standard wheelbase=14, 1/2-ton long wheelbase=15, 3/4-ton=25, 1-ton=36. The fifth symbol indicated body style: 2=Chassis & Cowl, 3=Chassis-and-Cab, 4=Pickup, 5=Panel, 6=Carryall Suburban, 9=Platform/Stake. The sixth symbol indicated the assembly plant: A=Atlanta, Ga., B=Baltimore, Md., F=Flint, Mich., J=Janesville, Wis., K=Kansas City, Mo., L=Los Angeles, Calif., N=Norwood, Ohio, O=Oakland, Calif., S=St. Louis, Mo., T=Tarrytown, N.Y., and W=Willow Run, Mich. Remaining symbols were the sequential production number starting with 100001 at each plant. Ending serial numbers not available. The Chevrolet engine had the source, date and type stamped on a serial number pad. Source codes were: F=Flint, Mich., T=Tonawanda, N.Y., C=Canada. Month codes were 1=Jan., 2=Feb., etc. Date codes were 01=first of month, etc. El Camino/Sedan Delivery prefix codes began with A/B/C/D/E/F/G/H (some plus second letter). Commercial model engine prefix codes were: [Thriftmaster 235] J/JB/JC/JD, [Thriftmaster 235 Special] K/KA, [Trademaster 283] M/MA. Engine serial numbers: [Six] Right side of block behind distributor, [V-8] Front of block below right-hand cylinder head. Engine serial numbers not available.

1960 Chevrolet 1/2-Ton Apache 10 Fleetside Custom Cab Pickup (CMD)

Model No.	Body Type	Price	Weight	Prod. Total
El Camino — Series 1100 — 119 in. w.b. — (six)				
1180	El Camino	2366	3545	-
Sedan Delivery — Series 1100 — 119 in. w.b. — (six)				
1170	Sedan Delivery	2361	3605	-
El Camino — Series 1100 — 119 in. w.b. — (V-8)				
1180	El Camino	-	-	-
Sedan Delivery — Series 1100 — 119 in. w.b. — (V-8)				
1170	Sedan Delivery	-	-	-
1/2-Ton Commercial — Model C14,K14/Series 1000 — 115 in. w.b. [Apache 10]				
C1402	Chassis	1623	2505	-
C1403	Chassis & Cab	1877	3035	-
C1404	Step-Side	1991	3395	-
C1405	Panel	2308	3615	-
C1406	Suburban (doors)	2690	3960	-
C1416	Suburban (gate)	2723	3975	-
C1434	Fleetside	2007	3425	-
NOTE 1: K14 indicates Apache 10 4x4 trucks.				
1/2-Ton Commercial (Long Bed) — Model C15/Series 1000 — 127 in. w.b. [Apache 10]				
C1503	Chassis & Cab	1914	3090	-
C1504	Step-Side	2028	3505	-
C1534	Fleetside	2044	3565	-
3/4-Ton Dubl-Duti — Model P23/Series 2000 — 104 in. w.b.				
P2342	Chassis	1687	2690	-
P2345	Step-Van	3083	5030	-
3/4-Ton Dubl-Duti — Model P25/Series 2000 — 125 in. w.b.				
P2542	Chassis	1725	2740	-
P2545	Step-Van	3168	5185	-
3/4-Ton Dubl-Duti — Model P26/Series 2000 — 137 in. w.b.				
P2642	Chassis	1758	2770	-
P2645	Step-Van	3279	5365	-
3/4-Ton Commercial — Model C25,K25/Series 2000 — 127 in. w.b. [Apache 20]				
C2502	Chassis	1795	2785	-
C2503	Chassis & Cab	2059	3370	-
C2504	Step-Side	2173	3790	-
C2509	Stake 8 ft.	2264	4000	-
C2534	Fleetside	2189	3845	-
NOTE 2: K25 indicates Apache 20 4x4 trucks.				
1-Ton Commercial — Model C36/Series 3000 — 133 in. w.b. [Apache 30]				
C3602	Chassis	1952	3095	-
C3603	Chassis & Cab	2216	3665	-
C3604	Step-Side	2350	4120	-
C3605	Panel	2775	4405	-
C3609	Stake 9 ft.	2463	4485	-
1-Ton Dubl-Duti — Model P33/Series 3000 — 104 in. w.b.				
P3342	Chassis	1877	2865	-
P3345	Step-Van	3273	5205	-
1-Ton Dubl-Duti — Model P35/Series 3000 — 125 in. w.b.				
P3542	Chassis	1915	2930	-
P3545	Step-Van	3358	5375	-
1-Ton Dubl-Duti — Model P36/Series 3000 — 137 in. w.b				
P3642	Chassis	1948	2960	-
P3645	Step-Van	3469	5550	-

1960 Chevrolet 1/2-Ton Series 1100 Del Ray (OCW)

ENGINE: [Standard All except 1200] Inline. OHV. Six-cylinder. Cast iron block. Bore & stroke: 3.562 x 3.937 in. Displacement: 235.5 cid. Compression ratio: 8.25:1. Brake horsepower: 135 at 4000 rpm. Torque: 215 lb.-ft. at 2400 rpm. Four main bearings. Hydraulic valve lifters. Carburetor: Rochester two-barrel model 7013003. (Thriftmaster Special engine with lower horsepower and torque ratings available for Dubl-Duti.)
ENGINE: [Optional 1000/2000/3000] V-type. OHV. Eight-cylinder. Cast iron block. Bore & stroke: 3.875 x 3 in. Displacement: 283 cid. Compression ratio: 8.25:1. Brake horsepower: 160. Five main bearings. Carburetor: Two-barrel.
ENGINE: [Standard 1200] V-type. OHV. Eight-cylinder. Cast iron block. Bore & stroke: 3.875 x 3 in. Displacement: 283 cid. Compression ratio: 8.5:1. Brake horsepower: 170. Five main bearings. Carburetor: Two-barrel.
ENGINE: [Optional 1200] V-type. OHV. Eight-cylinder. Cast iron block. Bore & stroke: 3.875 x 3 in. Displacement: 283 cid. Compression ratio: 8.5:1. Brake horsepower: 230 at 4800 rpm. Maximum Torque: 300 lb.-ft. at 3000. Five main bearings. Hydraulic valve lifters. Carburetor: Four-barrel.
ENGINE: [Optional 1200] V-type. OHV. Eight-cylinder. Cast iron block. Bore & stroke: 3.875 x 3 in. Displacement: 283 cid. Compression ratio: 9.5:1. Brake horsepower: 250. Five main bearings. Carburetor: Four-barrel.
ENGINE: [Optional 1200] V-type. OHV. Eight-cylinder. Cast iron block. Bore & stroke: 4.125 x 3.25 in. Displacement: 348 cid. Compression ratio: 9.5:1. Brake horsepower: 250. Five main bearings. Carburetor: Four-barrel.
ENGINE: [Optional 1200] V-type. OHV. Eight-cylinder. Cast iron block. Bore & stroke: 4.125 x 3.25 in. Displacement: 348 cid. Compression ratio: 9.5:1. Brake horsepower: 280. Five main bearings. Carburetor: Three two-barrels.
ENGINE: [Optional 1200] V-type. OHV. Eight-cylinder. Cast iron block. Bore & stroke: 4.125 x 3.25 in. Displacement: 348 cid. Compression ratio: 11.25:1. Brake horsepower: 320. Five main bearings. Carburetor: Four-barrel.
ENGINE: [Optional 1200] V-type. OHV. Eight-cylinder. Cast iron block. Bore & stroke: 4.125 x 3.25 in. Displacement: 348 cid. Compression ratio: 11.25:1. Brake horsepower: 335. Five main bearings. Carburetor: Three two-barrels.

1960 Chevrolet El Camino (BQR)

CHASSIS: [1100/1200] Wheelbase: 119 in. Overall length: 210.9 in. Height: 56.3 in. Tires: 8.00 x 14 four-ply. Maximum GVW: 4,900 lb.
CHASSIS: [C14] Wheelbase: 115 in. Overall length: [Pickup] 186.75, [Carryall Suburban] 199.5 in. Tires: 6.70 x 15 four-ply. Maximum GVW: 5,200 lb.
CHASSIS: [C15] Wheelbase: 127 in. Overall length: 206.25 in. Tires: 6.75 x 15 four-ply. Maximum GVW: 5,600 lb.
CHASSIS: [P23] Wheelbase: 104 in. Tires: 7 x 17.5 six-ply.
CHASSIS: [P25] Wheelbase: 125 in. Tires: 7 x 17.5 six-ply.
CHASSIS: [P26] Wheelbase: 137 in. Tires: 7 x 17.5 six-ply.
CHASSIS: [Series C25] Wheelbase: 127 in. Overall length: 210.75 in. Tires: 7 x 17.5 six-ply.
CHASSIS: [Series C36] Wheelbase: 133 in. Overall length: 211.75 in. Tires: (front) 8 x 17.5 six-ply, (rear) 8 x 17.5 eight-ply.
CHASSIS: [P33] Wheelbase: 104 in. Tires: 8 x 19.5 six-ply.
CHASSIS: [P35] Wheelbase: 125 in. Tires: 8 x 19.5 six-ply.
CHASSIS: [P36] Wheelbase: 137 in. Tires: 8 x 17.5 six-ply.

1960 Chevrolet 1/2-Ton C10 Apache DeLuxe Panel (DFW)

1960 Chevrolet El Camino (Doug Howard)

TECHNICAL: Selective synchromesh transmission. Speeds: [1-ton] 4F/1R, [Others] 3F/1R. Column-mounted gear shift (except four-speed). 10 or 11 in. diaphragm spring type clutch. [1-ton] Full-floating rear axle, [Others] Semi-floating rear axle. Base overall ratio: [1100/1200] 3.55:1, [C14/C15/K14/K15] 3.90:1, [C25/K25] 4.57:1, [C36] 5.14:1. Four-wheel hydraulic brakes.

1960 Chevrolet El Camino (Doug Howard)

OPTIONS: [El Camino and Sedan Delivery RPO] Delco AM radio (No. 103). Electric windshield wipers (No. 109). Air conditioning (No. 110). Heater (No. 116). Full wheel discs (No. 117). Inside rear view mirror (No. 129). Oil bath air cleaner (No. 216). Dual exhaust system (No. 220). Heavy-duty clutch (No. 227). Oil filter (No. 237). Powerglide automatic transmission (No. 313). Overdrive transmission (No. 315). Power steering (No. 324). Electric windshield wipers (No. 333). Foam rubber seat (No. 335). Heavy-duty generator (No. 338). Heavy-duty battery (No. 345). DeLuxe steering wheel (No. 348). E-Z-Eye glass (No. 398). Vacuum power brakes (No. 412). Padded instrument panel (No. 427). Economy carburetor (No. 581). Auxiliary rear springs (No. 593). Positraction rear axle (No. 675). Monotone color options for all Sedan Deliveries: (No. 900) Tuxedo Black, (No.903) Cascade Green, (No. 905) Jade Green, (No. 910) Horizon Blue, (No. 912) Royal Blue, (No. 915) Tasco Turquoise, (No. 920) Suntan Copper, (No. 923) Roman Red, (No. 925) Crocus Cream, (No. 938) Fawn Beige, (No. 940) Sateen Silver, (No. 941) Shadow Gray. (Note: Fawn Beige, Suntan Copper, Crocus Cream, Sateen Silver, and Tasco Turquoise were available on El Caminos only.)

OPTIONS: [Commercials RPO] Air cleaner. Positraction. Special rear axle ratio. Heavy-duty battery. Spare wheel carrier. Painted rear bumper. Heavy-duty clutch. Directionals. Trademaster 283 V-8. Heavy-duty radiator fan. Ammeter. Oil pressure gauge. Generator. Alternator. Laminated glass. Engine governor. Heater and defroster. Towing hooks. Outside rearview mirror. Oil filter. Heavy-duty radiator. Delco AM radio and antenna. Bostrom seat. Shock absorbers. Rear springs. Tachometer. Fuel tank. Powerglide transmission. Heavy-duty three-speed transmission. Four-speed transmission. Positive crankcase ventilation system. Full-View rear window. Windshield washers. Electric windshield wipers. Alternator. Ammeter. Thriftmaster Special economy engine.). Monotone color options for Commercial Trucks: (No. 700) Jet Black, (No. 703) Neptune Green, (No. 705) Hemlock Green, (No. 707) Brigade Blue, (No. 708) Marlin Blue, (No. 710) Tartan Turquoise, (No. 713) Klondike Gold, (No. 714) Cardinal Red, (No. 715) Grenadier Red, (No. 716) Omaha Orange, (No. 718) Golden Yellow, (No. 719) Yukon Yellow, (No. 721) Pure White, (No. 723) Garrison Gray.

1960 Chevrolet 1/2-Ton Series 32 Apache Fleetside Pickup (DFW)

OPTION PACKAGES: [Custom Appearance Equipment] Includes silver anodized radiator grille and headlamp door assembly, chrome-plated windshield reveal moldings, bright metal cab upper rear quarter panel trim plates, chrome horn ring steering wheel, chrome trimmed instrument panel knobs, and two-tone inside front door panels. [Custom Comfort and Convenience Equipment] Includes left door armrest, outside key lock, chrome cigar lighter, full foam rubber seat cushion, special seat trim (cab models and Suburban), and added sound insulation. [Custom Chrome Equipment] Chrome hubcaps. Not available with 4x4 or dual rear wheel options. [Side Trim Moldings] Bright body side moldings for Fleetside models.

1960 Chevrolet 1/2-Ton C10 Apache Carryall Suburban (BOR)

HISTORICAL: Introduced: Fall 1959. Calendar-year production: [All Chevrolet Commercials] 394,017. Innovations: All-new styling for Pickups, Panels and Carryall Suburbans. First independent front suspension system for trucks. Light-duty models featured torsion bars in front and coil springs at rear. Chevrolet was America's number one truck-maker. This was the last year for a Sedan Delivery. It was also the last year for the full-size El Camino.

1961 CHEVROLET

1961 Chevrolet Corvair 95 Loadside Pickup (DFW)

CORVAIR 95 — MODEL R12/SERIES 1000 — SIX: Chevrolet's answer to the Volkswagen van was the all-new Corvair 95. These were driver-forward models built on the Corvair platform, with a rear-mounted air-cooled engine and transaxle. Dual headlamps, a small front grille with a Chevrolet emblem, and a concave, sculptured contrast panel along the front and sides were among styling characteristics. The panel model had steel sides in place of three side windows. There were two side load doors and double rear panel doors. It was merchandised as the Corvan and had Corvair 95 scripts on the front doors. A pickup was made by adding a cab panel-back and removing the upper sheet metal at the rear. It had a cargo box that was 105 in. long and 43-7/8 in. wide. It was called the Loadside model and featured fixed, double-wall box-side panel doors just behind the cab. Also available was the Rampside version, which had a unique door in the side of the box that dropped to the ground to make a cargo loading ramp. Standard equipment on all Corvair 95s included: An air-cooled six-cylinder engine, three-speed synchromesh transmission, electric wipers, directional signals and five tubeless tires. Chrome hubcaps, chrome bumpers and a Custom interior/exterior appearance package were available.

1961 Chevrolet Corvan 95 Panel Delivery Truck (CMD)

1961 Chevrolet 1/2-Ton Apache K14 Carryall Suburban 4x4 (RCA)

1/2-TON COMMERCIAL — MODEL C14 (4x2), K14 (4x4)/SERIES 1000 — SIX/V-8: For Chevrolet's regular light-duty Commercial Trucks the most notable exterior change involved a revised front end appearance. Each "jet pod" front fender opening contained a Cameo white embossed "spinner" housing the parking lamps. The slotted rear face of the housings were black-finished. The spinners and slots allowed air to enter the pods for under hood ventilation. The horizontal-bars grille of 1960 was changed. The grille now had a silver anodized main insert. There was only one horizontal bar through the center, with Chevrolet lettering on it. The background of the center bar with Chevrolet lettering was painted low gloss black. The rest of the grille was Cameo White. Fender side nameplates were raised to the upper belt line crease, just ahead of the hood's upper rear seam. The nameplates said Apache 10 on a red bar for Series 1000 trucks. Exterior colors were Jet Black, Balboa Blue, Brigade Blue, Woodsmoke Blue, Tahiti Coral, Neptune Green, Woodland Green, Romany Maroon, Omaha Orange, Cardinal Red, Tampico Turquoise, Cameo White, Pure White, Flaxen Yellow, and Yukon Yellow. Cameo White could be teamed with one of the eight new colors for "Color-Break" two-toning on cab models, Fleetside Pickups, Panels, and Suburban Carryalls. The Step-Side Pickups were two-toned the same way they were in 1960. Exterior rear view mirrors were finished in Jet Black with body-color arms and brackets. There were four separate Custom equipment options. They are listed as options below. They no longer included chrome vent window and side window frames or glove box door nameplates. New were full foam rubber seat cushions, additional insulation, and a horn-ring steering wheel. All C14/K14 trucks had a new lower transmission tunnel. New hubcaps were also seen. They were finished in Cameo White with a red Chevrolet bow tie. Chrome hubcaps were optional, as part of the chrome bumper package. Torsion-Spring Ride was one of Chevrolet's highly-promoted selling features for 1961. With this type of IFS (independent front suspension) system each wheel flexed independently, helping to keep the trucks level with the road at all times. "They work harder because they ride easier," Chevrolet said in its ads. Offered again were Step-Side Pickups (with pontoon rear fenders) and Fleetside Pickups (with slab type rear fenders) with 6-1/2-ft. boxes. Both featured rugged tailgates with anti-rattle latches and support chains, plus select wood floors with steel cargo skid strips. All conventional Chevrolet Pickups gave the smooth ride and sure handling of independent front suspension chassis design, plus the bonus features of extra room and comfort in the cab and a lower loading height. Pickups featured bodies with double-walled side panels to protect the exterior surfaces against dents caused by shifting cargo. A separate front panel protected the back of the cab. Step-Sides offered a 50-in.-wide unobstructed load space (without wheel wells), plus handy running boards for easy access to cargo from either side. Fleetsides were preferred by buyers concerned with looks and extra load space, as they were a full 6-feet wide, with wheel wells on either side. Other models included the Panel, Carryall Suburban, and Chassis-and-Cab trucks. Chevrolet cabs featured extra-quality construction to keep them solid and tight through their long, hard-working lives. A deep-sculptured double-panel roof added rigidity to the entire cab structure. Reinforced box-section pillars supported the roof and frame doorways to help keep the doors working right and sealing tight for life. Massive double-walled cowl arches bridged the front of the cab structure, uniting the door frames, dash and floor panels in an integrated, high-strength assembly. The rugged floor panel assembly was double-braced with massive cross members, plus front and rear sills. The reinforced cab mounting points rode on new floating-action mounts for better isolation from frame vibration. The Apache 10 four-wheel-drive trucks had a K14 model prefix, even though Apache 10 nameplates decorated the fender sides.

1961 Chevrolet 1/2-Ton Series C10 Apache Fleetside Pickup (CMD)

1/2-TON COMMERCIAL — MODEL C15 (4x2)/SERIES 1000 — SIX/V-8: The C15 trucks in the Apache 10 Series 1000 line used a C15 model prefix. Apache 10 nameplates decorated the fender sides. They had the same basic styling and trim changes as other conventional trucks. These were the long wheelbase (LWB) 1/2-ton trucks on the same chassis as 3/4-ton models. They are known as "Long Bed" or "Long Box" Pickups because they had a longer 8-ft. load box. Longer running boards were needed on Step-Side Pickups because there was more space between the cab and rear fenders. This series could now be had with four-wheel-drive. The Apache 10 Long Bed four-wheel-drive models had a K15 model prefix.
1/2-TON DUBL-DUTI — MODEL P13/SERIES 1000 — SIX/V-8: A 1/2-ton Dubl-Duti model resurfaced in 1961. The P13 had a 102-in. wheelbase. An approved Step-Van walk-in delivery truck made by Union City Body Co., of Union City, Ind. was most commonly mounted on the Dubl-Duti chassis. Buyers could order other bodies, too. A channel type front bumper was optional on Dubl-Duti trucks, which continued to use the Special Thriftmaster Six with less horsepower than the Commercial Series base engine.

1961 Chevrolet 3/4-Ton Apache K15 Fleetside 4x4 Pickup (RCA)

3/4-TON COMMERCIAL — MODEL C25/SERIES 2000 — SIX/V-8: The Apache 20 Series 2000 (3/4-ton) trucks had the same styling and trim changes as other conventional trucks. The fender side nameplates said Apache 20. Step-Side and Fleetside Pickups were in this series. Compared to 3100 Pickups, the 3600 Pickup had slightly longer running boards and a longer cargo box with a horizontal support rib. An 8-ft. bed was used. There were also Platform and Platform/Stake models. The rail for the 3/4-ton Platform was about 8 ft. long. The rugged Chevrolet Stake Rack body was designed and built for maximum cargo convenience and a long, hard working life. Platforms of tough 1-1/4-in. select wood planking were built on high-strength frameworks of steel cross sills, and shock-cushioning wood sub-sills. Round-cornered steel rub rails edged the platform for protection against docking damage and injury. Wear-resistant steel-lined stake pockets supported racks of top-quality hardwood, with assembly hardware recessed to leave interior surfaces smooth and snag-free. The Apache 20 four-wheel-drive 3/4-ton models had a K25 model prefix.
3/4-TON DUBL-DUTI — MODEL P23, P25, P26/SERIES 2000 — SIX/V-8: Three 3/4-ton Dubl-Duti Forward-Control chassis remained in the 3000 Series (1-ton) truck line. The P23/P25/P26 models had wheelbases of 104 in./125 in./137 in., respectively. Standard walk-in delivery truck bodies could be supplied by several factory-approved sources. Popular models were the Step-Van walk-in delivery trucks made by Union City Body Co., of Union City, Ind. A channel type front bumper was optional on Dubl-Duti trucks.

1961 Chevrolet 1/2-Ton Apache 10 Step-Side Pickup (Owner: Fred & Gayle Lossman)

1-TON MEDIUM-DUTY COMMERCIAL — MODEL C36/SERIES 3000 — SIX-CYLINDER: The Apache 30 Series 3000 (1-ton) trucks had the same styling and trim changes as other conventional trucks. The fender side nameplates said Apache 30. There was no Fleetside Pickup in this line. Panel models had a one-piece floor made of 3/4-in. thick, five-ply laminated wood. The basic model lineup was unchanged. Compared to the 3600 Pickup, the 3800 Pickup had a longer wheelbase, a longer 9-ft. box with extra stake pockets, and very long running boards. The 1-ton Stake trucks had a rail about 9-1/2 ft. long. The rugged Chevrolet Stake Rack body was designed and built for maximum cargo convenience and a long, hard working life. Platforms of tough 1-1/4-in. select wood planking were built on high-strength frameworks of steel cross-sills, and shock-cushioning wood sub-sills. Round-cornered steel rub rails edged the platform for protection against docking damage and injury. Wear-resistant steel-lined stake pockets supported racks of top-quality hardwood, with assembly hardware recessed to leave interior surfaces smooth and snag-free. No hubcaps were used on the larger split-rim wheels of the Chassis-and-Cab and Stake models, which had eight bolts and eight circular openings. A four-speed manual synchromesh transmission was standard. No four-wheel-drive option was offered.

1961 Chevrolet 1/2-Ton Apache C10 Step-Side Pickup (Owner: Fred & Gayle Lossman)

1-TON DUBL-DUTI — MODEL P33, P35, P36/SERIES 3000 — SIX/V-8: Three Dubl-Duti Forward-Control chassis were in the 3000 Series (1-ton) truck line. The P33/P35/P36 models had wheelbases of 104 in./125 in./137 in., respectively. Standard walk-in delivery truck bodies could be supplied by several factory-approved sources. Popular models were the Step-Van walk-in delivery trucks made by Union City Body Co., of Union City, Ind. A channel type front bumper was optional on Dubl-Duti trucks.

1961 Chevrolet 1/2-Ton Apache C10 Custom Fleetside Pickup (CMD)

I.D. DATA: Serial number located: [Chassis models] On plate temporarily attached near steering column, with final location per body maker. [All others] on plate attached to rear face of left-hand door hinge pillar, on right side of cowl under hood. The first symbol indicated model year, 1=1961. The second symbol indicated type: C=Conventional, K=4x4, R=Corvair 95. The third and fourth symbols indicated the model prefix: Corvair 95=12, 1/2-ton standard wheelbase=14, 1/2-ton long wheelbase=15, 3/4-ton=25, 1-ton=36. The fifth symbol indicated body style: 2=Chassis & Cowl, 3=Chassis-and-Cab, 4=Pickup, 5=Panel, 6=Suburban Carryall, 9=Platform/Stake. The sixth symbol indicated the assembly plant: A=Atlanta, Ga., B=Baltimore, Md., F=Flint, Mich., J=Janesville, Wis., K=Kansas City, Mo., L=Los Angeles, Calif., N=Norwood, Ohio, O=Oakland, Calif., S=St. Louis, Mo., T=Tarrytown, N.Y., and W=Willow Run, Mich. Remaining symbols were the sequential production number starting with 100001 at each plant. Ending serial numbers not available. The Chevrolet engine had the source, date and type stamped on a serial number pad. Source codes were: F=Flint, Mich., T=Tonawanda, N.Y., C=Canada. Month codes were 1=Jan., 2=Feb., etc. Date codes were 01=first of month, etc. Corvair 95 prefix codes were V, W. Commercial model engine prefix codes were: [Thriftmaster 235] J/JB/JC, [Thriftmaster 235 Special] K, [Trademaster 283] M/MA. Engine serial numbers: [Six] Right side of block behind distributor, [V-8] Front of block below right-hand cylinder head. Engine serial numbers not available.

1961 Chevrolet Corvair 95 Rampside Pickup (John Lee Photo)

Model	Body Type	Price	Weight	Prod. Total
1/2-Ton Corvair 95 — Model R12/Series 1000 — 95 in. w.b.				
R1205	Corvan	2289	2695	15,806
R1244	Loadside	2079	2595	2,475
R1254	Rampside	2133	2605	10,787
1/2 Ton Commercial (4x2) — Model C14/Series 1000 — 115 in. w.b.				
[Apache 10]				
C1403	Chassis & Cab	1877	3030	-
C1434	Fleetside	2007	3425	-
C1404	Step-Side	1991	3390	-
C1405	Panel	2308	3665	-
C1406	Suburban (doors)	2669	3970	-
C1416	Suburban (gate)	2702	4000	-
1/2 Ton Commercial (4x4) — Model K14/Series 1000 — 115 in. w.b.				
[Apache 10]				
K1434	Fleetside	2684	-	-
K1404	Step-Side	2668	-	-
K1405	Panel	2985	-	-
K1406	Suburban (doors)	3346	-	-
K1416	Suburban (gate)	3379	-	-

Model	Body Type	Price	Weight	Prod. Total
1/2 Ton Commercial (4x2) — Model C15/Series 1000 — 127 in. w.b.				
[Apache 10]				
C1503	Chassis & Cab	-	-	-
C1534	Fleetside	2007	3425	-
C1504	Step-Side	1991	3390	-
1/2 Ton Commercial (4x4) — Model K15/Series 1000 — 127 in. w.b.				
[Apache 10]				
K1503	Chassis & Cab	2554	3430	-
K1534	Fleetside	2684	3825	-
K1504	Step-Side	2668	3790	-
1/2-Ton Dubl-Duti — Model P23/Series 1000 — 102 in. w.b.				
P1345	Package Delivery	2546	3904	-
3/4-Ton Commercial (4x2) — Model C25/Series 2000 — 127 in. w.b.				
[Apache 20]				
C2539	Fleetside	2189	3855	-
C2504	Step-Side	2173	3810	-
C2503	Chassis & Cab	2059	3395	-
C2509	Stake 8 ft.	2264	4020	-
3/4-Ton Commercial (4x4) — Model K25/Series 2000 — 127 in. w.b.				
[Apache 20]				
K2539	Fleetside	2866	-	-
K2504	Step-Side	2850	-	-
3/4-Ton Dubl-Duti — Model P23,P25,P26/Series 2000 — 104-137 in. w.b.				
P2345	Package Delivery	3083	5030	-

NOTE 1: Data for 104 in. w.b. Dubl-Duti, 123 in./137 in. w.b. optional.

Model	Body Type	Price	Weight	Prod. Total
1-Ton Commercial (4x2) — Model C36/Series 3000 — 133 in. w.b.				
[Apache 30]				
C3605	Panel	2775	4490	-
C3604	Step-Side	2350	4110	-
C3603	Chassis & Cab	2216	3655	-
C3609	Stake	2463	4485	-
1-Ton Dubl-Duti — Model P33,P35,P36/Series 3000 — 104-137 in. w.b.				
P3345	Package Delivery	3273	5185-	-

NOTE 2: Data for 104 in. w.b. Dubl-Duti, 123.25 in./137 in. w.b. optional.

1961 Chevrolet Corvair 95 Rampside Pickup (CMD)

ENGINE: [Corvair 95] Opposed. OHV. Turbo-Air. Six-cylinder. Aluminum block. Bore & stroke: 3.437 in. x 2.60 in. Displacement: 144.8 cid. Compression ratio: 8.0:1. Brake horsepower: 80 at 4400 rpm. Maximum torque: 128 lb.-ft. at 2300 rpm. Four main bearings. Hydraulic valve lifters. Carburetor: Two Rochester one-barrel model 7019101.
ENGINE: [All except Corvair 95 and Dubl-Duti] Inline. OHV. Thriftmaster. Six-cylinder. Cast iron block. Bore & stroke: 3-9/16 in. x 3-15/16 in. Displacement: 235.5 cid. Compression ratio: 8.25:1. Brake horsepower: 135 at 4000 rpm. Maximum torque: 217 lb.-ft. at 2000 rpm. Four main bearings. Hydraulic valve lifters. Carburetor: Rochester one-barrel model B7015011.
ENGINE: [Optional, Except Corvair 95 and P models] V-type. OHV. Trademaster. Eight-cylinder. Cast iron block. Bore & stroke: 3-7/8 in. x 3 in. Displacement: 283 cid. Compression ratio: 8.5:1. Brake horsepower: 160 at 4200 rpm. Maximum torque: 270 lb.-ft. at 2000 rpm. Five main bearings. Hydraulic valve lifters. Carburetor: Rochester two-barrel model 2G7015017.
CHASSIS: [Corvair 95] Wheelbase: 95 in. Overall length: 179.7 in. Height: 68.5 in. Front tread: 58 in. Rear tread: 58 in. Tires: 7.00 x 14 in. Maximum GVW: 4,600 lb.
CHASSIS: [C14/K14] Wheelbase: 115 in. Overall length: [Pickup] 186-3/4 in., [Chassis-and-Cab] 180-1/4 in. Bed length: [Pickup] 78-1/8 in. Cab to rear axle on Chassis-and-Cab: 42 in. Cab to end of frame on Chassis-and-Cab: 75-1/2 in. Front tread: 63.1 in. Rear tread: 61 in. Tires: 6.70 x 15 in. Maximum GVW: [4x2] 4,600 lb., [4x4] 5,300 lb.
CHASSIS: [C15/K15] Wheelbase: 127 in. Overall length: [Pickup] 206-in., [Chassis-and-Cab] 200-1/4 in. Bed length: [Pickup] 98 in. Cab to rear axle on Chassis-and-Cab: 54 in. Cab to end of frame on Chassis-and-Cab: 95-1/2 in Front tread: 63.1 in. Rear tread: 61.1 in. Tires: 6.70 x 15 in. Maximum GVW: [4x2] 4,600 lb., [4x4] 5,600 lb.

FLEETSIDE PICKUP—powered by the most popular truck 6 ever built.

1961 Chevrolet 1/2-Ton Apache C10 Custom Fleetside Pickup (CMD)

Standard Catalog of Chevrolet Trucks

1961 Chevrolet Corvair 95 Rampside Pickup (OCW)

CHASSIS: [C25/K25] Wheelbase: 127 in. Overall length: [Pickup] 206 in., [Stake] 210-3/4 in., [Chassis-and-Cab] 211-3/4 in. Bed length: [Pickup] 98 in., [Stake] 98 in. Bed width: [Stake] 85 in. Cab to rear axle on Chassis-and-Cab: 54 in. Cab to end of frame on Chassis-and-Cab: 95-1/2 in. Tires: 7 x 17.5 in. Maximum GVW: [4x2] 6,000 lb., [4x4] 6,800 lb.
CHASSIS: [C36] Wheelbase: 133 in. Overall length: [1-ton Step-Side Pickup] 216-1/4 in., [Stake] 221-3/8 in., [Chassis-and-Cab] 199-3/4 in.] Bed length: [1-ton Step-Side Pickup] 108-1/4 in., [Stake] 109 in. Bed width: [Stake] 85 in. Tires: 8 x 17.5 in. Maximum GVW: 7,800 lb.
CHASSIS: [C36] Wheelbase: 157 in. Overall length: [Stake] 256-1/2 in.,[Chassis-and-Cab] 200-1/4 in.] Bed length: [Stake] 144 in. Bed width: 85 in. Cab to rear axle on Chassis-and-Cab: 60 in. Cab to end of frame on Chassis-and-Cab: 107 in. Tires: 8 x 17.5 in. Maximum GVW: 7,800 lb.
CHASSIS: [P10] Wheelbase: 102 in. Tires: 6.70 x 15 in.
CHASSIS: [P20] Wheelbase: 137 in. Tires: 7 x 17.5 in.
CHASSIS: [P30] Wheelbase: 104-137 in. Tires: 8 x 19.5 in.
TECHNICAL: Manual. Synchromesh. Speeds: 3F/1R. Column-mounted gear shift lever. Single-plate dry-disc clutch. Rear axle: [1-ton] Full-floating, [Others] semi-floating. Standard axle ratio: [R12] 3.89:1, [C14/C15/K14/K15] 3.90:1, [C25/K25] 4.57:1, [C36] 5.14:1. Hydraulic four-wheel brakes. Pressed steel wheels.
OPTIONS: [Corvair 95] Positraction. Front and rear chrome bumpers. Custom Equipment package. Left-hand door (Corvan). Level Pickup box floor. Gasoline heater/defroster. Direct-Air heater/defroster. Chrome hubcaps. Two-tone exterior. Radio. Full-width front seat. Single right-hand auxiliary seat. Whitewall tires. Six-ply rated tires. Four-speed manual transmission. Powerglide automatic transmission. Two-speed electric wipers and washers. Rear bumper. Radio. Heater. Clock. Cigar lighter. Radio antenna. Seat covers.
OPTIONS: [Commercials RPO] Directionals (No. 105). Heater and defroster (No. 112). Towing hooks (No. 114). Delco AM radio and antenna (No. 123). Heavy-duty radiator fan (No. 124). Windshield washers (No. 130). Outside rear view mirror (No. 210). Shock absorbers (No. 213). Special rear axle ratio (No. 215). Painted rear bumper (No. 218). Heavy-duty clutch (No. 223). Oil filter (No. 239). Engine governor (No. 241). Positive crankcase ventilation system (No. 243). Rear springs (No. 254). Heavy-duty radiator (No. 256). Tachometer (No. 266). Ammeter and oil pressure gauge (No. 301). Powerglide transmission (No. 311). Heavy-duty three-speed transmission (No. 313). Four-speed transmission (No. 315). Spare wheel carrier (No. 341). Heavy-duty battery (No. 345). Generator (No. 351). Electric windshield wipers (No. 355). Laminated glass (No. 370). Thriftmaster Special economy engine (No. 371). Full-View rear window (No. 394). Trademaster 283 V-8 (No. 408). Fuel tank (No. 472). Air cleaner (No. 591). Positraction (No. 680). Monotone paint options: (No. 700) Jet Black, (NO. 703) Neptune Green, (No. 705) Woodland Green, (No. 707) Brigade Blue, (No. 708) Balboa Blue, (No. 718) Flaxen Yellow, (No. 719) Yukon Yellow, (No. 721) Pure White, (No. 723) Woodsmoke Blue, (No. 724) Romany Maroon, (No. 725) Tahiti Coral, (No. 726) Cameo White, (No. 727) Tampico Turquoise, (No. 740) Cardinal Red, (No. 742) Omaha Orange. Bostrom seat (No. 1001). Ammeter (No. 1003). Alternator (No. 1055)

1961 Chevrolet 1/2-Ton Series C10 Apache Fleetside Pickup (JLC)

OPTION PACKAGES: [Custom Appearance Equipment] Includes silver anodized radiator grille and headlamp door assembly, chrome-plated windshield reveal moldings, bright metal cab upper rear quarter panel trim plates, chrome horn ring steering wheel, chrome trimmed instrument panel knobs, and two-tone inside front door panels. [Custom Comfort and Convenience Equipment] Includes left

door arm rest, outside key lock, chrome cigar lighter, full foam rubber seat cushion, special seat trim (cab models and Suburban), and added sound insulation. [Custom Chrome Equipment] Chrome hubcaps. Not available with 4x4 or dual rear wheel options. [Side Trim Moldings] Bright body side moldings for Fleetside models.

1961 Chevrolet Corvair 95 Rampside Pickup (John Lee Photo)

HISTORICAL: Introduced: Fall 1960. Commercial model calendar-year production: [All six-cylinder] 294,194, [All V-8] 48,391, [Total] 342,658. Commercial model calendar-year registrations: [6000 lb. or less] 202,697, [6001-10,000 lb.] 44,903. Innovations: All-new Corvair truck-line. Alternators available (instead of generator) in electrical system. Optional heavy-duty front suspension introduced. Diesel options introduced for medium-duty series (and heavy-duties). Public acceptance of the styling and economy of the Corvair trucks was enthusiastic, but the lack of a single, smooth cargo load floor (due to rear engine location) proved to be a drawback to sales of these models. A fourth type of Corvair Van (Model R1206 Greenbrier) was merchandised as a passenger car (station wagon). It had a price of $2,651 and a 2,895 lb. curb weight. Production of this model, at 18,489, was the highest of all Corvair 95s (total output was 47,557). Chevrolet was America's number one truck-maker in 1961, but only by the narrow margin of 3,670 units. Its 30.39 percent market share represented the production of 342,658 Commercial and Dubl-Duti models, down from 1960's total of 394,014 units. This was in contrast to production of 494,575 trucks in 1950. The company's great strength at this time was in the six-cylinder category. The six-cylinder-powered Chevrolet truck outsold its nearest competitor by nearly 100,000 units. J.E. Conlan was assistant general sales manager of the Chevrolet Truck Division.

1962 CHEVROLET

1962 Chevrolet 1/2-Ton Corvair 95 Rampside Pickup
(Owner: Dr. George Johnson)

CORVAIR 95 — MODEL R12/SERIES 10 — SIX: The Corvair 95 trucks were virtually unchanged, except for serial numbers. A new option was a positraction rear axle. These driver-forward models had a Corvair platform, a rear-mounted air-cooled engine and a transaxle. Dual headlamps, a small front grille with Chevrolet emblem and a sculptured contrast panel around the body were styling characteristics. The Corvan had steel panel sides, two side load doors, and double rear panel doors. It had Corvair 95 scripts on the front doors. A Loadside Pickup was made by adding a cab back panel and removing the upper sheet metal at the rear. The cargo box was 105 in. long and 43-7/8 in. wide. It featured a double-wall box. Also available was the Rampside Pickup which had a unique door in the side of the box. It dropped to the ground to make a cargo loading ramp. Standard equipment on all Corvair 95s included: An air-cooled six-cylinder engine, three-speed synchromesh transmission, electric wipers, directional signals, and five tubeless tires. Chrome hubcaps, chrome bumpers and a Custom interior/exterior appearance package were available.

K1534 FLEETSIDE PICKUP

1962 Chevrolet 1/2-Ton K10 Fleetside 4x4 Pickup (CMD)

1/2-TON COMMERCIAL — MODEL C14 (4x2), K14 (4x4)/SERIES 10 — SIX/V-8: The Apache name disappeared on conventional trucks and the 1000 Series description gave way to the 10-20-30 model prefixes, still used today. A restyled hood panel gave the 1962 Chevrolet 10 series 1/2-ton trucks a new appearance. It was lower and flatter than the "jet pod" style hood and had a bevel around its perimeter to mate with the previous lines. Rectangular parking lamps were set into the bevel at each front corner. Rectangular air slot openings were punched into the bevel on either side of center. The grille had two horizontal members and two vertical members crossing to form nine rectangular openings. Large, rectangular headlamp housings sat outside each end of the grille. The standard grille was done in Cameo White with black Chevrolet lettering on the lower molding of the grille surround. Standard hubcaps were also Cameo White. Chrome equipment was optional. The hood side nameplates were moved slightly back to the sides of the cowl. The badge had vertical grooves and a black background with a red-accented Chevrolet bow tie at the front and a 10 (for C10 or 10 series) at the rear. Custom Fleetsides got a new silver anodized aluminum body side molding with white accents. Colors for the year were Desert Beige, Jet Black, Balboa Blue, Brigade Blue, Georgian Gray, Seamist Jade, Glenwood Green, Woodland Green, Omaha Orange, Cardinal Red, Crystal Turquoise, Cameo White, Pure White, and Yukon Yellow. All colors, except the two whites, were used as lower body colors in the 12 two-tone color options. They were teamed with Cameo White on the upper body. Interiors were painted in two shades of Fawn Beige with Cameo White accenting the steering wheel and mast. There were wide, deep-cushioned seats inside with plenty of room for three passengers. Standard seats had medium fawn (tan) embossed vinyl with light fawn facings. Custom interiors had color-keyed nylon pattern cloth and pin-seal vinyl upholstery with red trim in Cameo White trucks, georgian gray trim in Cardinal Red trucks, and medium fawn trim in all other cases. A full six-inch foam seat was a separate option. There were four separate Custom equipment options, which are listed as below. Offered again were Step-Side (with pontoon rear fenders) and Fleetside (with slab type rear fenders) Pickups with 6-1/2-ft. boxes. Both featured rugged tailgates with anti-rattle latches and support chains, plus select wood floors with steel cargo skid strips. All Chevrolet conventional pickups gave the smooth ride and sure handling of independent front suspension chassis design, plus the bonus features of extra room and comfort in the cab and a lower loading height. Pickups featured bodies with double-walled side panels to protect the exterior surfaces against dents caused by shifting cargo. A separate front panel protected the back of the cab. Step-Sides offered a 50-in.-wide unobstructed load space (without wheel wells), plus handy running boards for easy access to cargo from either side. Fleetsides were preferred by buyers concerned with looks and extra load space, as they had a full 6-feet wide, with wheel wells on either side. Other models included the Panel, Carryall Suburban, and Chassis-and-Cab trucks. Chevrolet cabs featured extra-quality construction to keep them solid and tight through their long, hard-working lives. A deep-sculptured double-panel roof added rigidity to the entire cab structure. Reinforced box-section pillars supported the roof and frame doorways to help keep the doors working right and sealing tight for life. Massive double-walled cowl arches bridged the front of the cab structure, uniting the door frames, dash and floor panels in an integrated, high-strength assembly. The rugged floor panel assembly was double-braced with massive cross members, plus front and rear sills. The reinforced cab mounting points rode on new floating-action mounts for better isolation from frame vibration. Four-wheel-drive 1/2-ton models in the K10 Series had a K14 model prefix.

1962 Chevrolet 1/2-Ton Series C15 Fleetside Long Bed Pickup (OCW)

1/2-TON COMMERCIAL — MODELS C15 (4x2)/SERIES 10 — SIX/V-8: The C15 trucks in the 10 Series used a C15 model prefix. Their fender side nameplates had a red Chevrolet bow tie and the number 10. They had the same basic styling and trim changes as other conventional trucks. These were the long wheelbase (LWB) 1/2-ton trucks on the same chassis as 3/4-ton models. They are known as "Long Bed" or "Long Box" Pickups because they had a longer 8-ft. load box. Longer running boards were needed on Step-Side Pickups because there was more space between the cab and rear fenders. The Apache 10 Long Bed four-wheel-drive models had a K15 model prefix.

1962 Chevrolet 1/2-Ton C10 Endgate DeLuxe Carryall Suburban (OCW)

1/2-TON DUBL-DUTI — MODEL P13/SERIES 10 — SIX/V-8: The 1/2-ton Dubl-Duti returned again in 1962. The P13 had a 102-in. wheelbase. An approved Step-Van walk-in delivery truck made by Union City Body Co., of Union City, Ind. was most commonly mounted on the Dubl-Duty chassis. Buyers could order other bodies, too. A channel type front bumper was optional on Dubl-Duti trucks. The P10/P13 model used the regular Thriftmaster Six.

3/4-TON COMMERCIAL — MODEL C25/SERIES 20 — SIX/V-8: The 20 Series (3/4-ton) trucks had the same styling and trim changes as other conventional trucks. The fender side nameplates had a red Chevrolet bow tie emblem and the number 20. Step-Side and Fleetside Pickups were in this series. Compared to C10-14 Pickups, the C20 Pickup had slightly longer running boards and a longer cargo box with a horizontal support rib. An 8-ft. long box was used. There were also Platform and Platform/Stake models. The rail for the 3/4-ton Platform was about 8 ft. long. The rugged Chevrolet Stake Rack body was designed and built for maximum cargo convenience and a long, hard working life. Platforms of tough 1-1/4-in. select wood planking were built on high-strength frameworks of steel cross sills, and shock-cushioning wood sub-sills. Round-cornered steel rub rails edged the platform for protection against docking damage and injury. Wear-resistant steel-lined stake pockets supported racks of top-quality hardwood, with assembly hardware recessed to leave interior surfaces smooth and snag-free. The 20 Series four-wheel-drive 3/4-ton models had a K25 model prefix.

P2545 STEP-VAN

1962 Chevrolet 3/4-Ton P25 Step-Van (CMD)

3/4-TON DUBL-DUTI — MODEL P23, P25, P26/SERIES 20 — SIX/V-8: Three 3/4-ton Dubl-Duti Forward-Control chassis remained in the 20 Series (3/4-ton) truck line. The P23/P25/P26 models had wheelbases of 104 in./125 in./137 in., respectively. Standard walk-in delivery truck bodies could be supplied by several factory-approved sources. Popular models were the Step-Van walk-in delivery trucks made by Union City Body Co., of Union City, Ind. A channel type front bumper was optional on Dubl-Duti trucks. The P20 and P30 Dubl-Duti trucks used a Trademaster Special six with slightly different horsepower rating.

1-TON MEDIUM-DUTY COMMERCIAL — MODEL C36/SERIES 30 — SIX-CYLINDER: The 30 Series (1-ton) trucks had the same styling and trim changes as other conventional trucks. The fender side nameplates had a red Chevrolet bow tie logo and number 30. There was no Fleetside Pickup in this line. Panel models had a one-piece floor made of 3/4-in. thick, five-ply laminated wood. The basic model lineup was unchanged. Compared to the C20-C25 Pickup, the C30-C36 Pickup had a longer wheelbase, a longer box with extra stake pockets and very long running boards. The 1-ton Stake trucks had a long rail nearly 9-1/2 ft. long. The rugged Chevrolet Stake Rack body was designed and built for maximum cargo convenience and a long, hard working life. Platforms of tough 1-1/4-in. select wood planking were built on high-strength frameworks of steel cross sills, and shock-cushioning wood sub-sills. Round-cornered steel rub rails edged the platform for protection against docking damage and injury. Wear-resistant steel-lined stake pockets supported racks of top-quality hardwood, with assembly hardware recessed to leave interior surfaces smooth and snag-free. No hubcaps were used on the larger split-rim wheels of the Chassis-and-Cab and Stake models, which had eight bolts and eight circular openings. A four-speed manual synchromesh transmission was standard. No four-wheel-drive option was offered.

1-TON DUBL-DUTI — MODEL P33, P35, P36/SERIES 30 — SIX/V-8: Three Dubl-Duti Forward-Control chassis were in the 30 Series (1-ton) truck line. The P33/P35/P36 models had wheelbases of 104 in./125 in./137 in., respectively. Standard walk-in delivery truck bodies could be supplied by several factory-approved sources. Popular models were the Step-Van walk-in delivery trucks made by Union City Body Co., of Union City, Ind. A channel type front bumper was optional on Dubl-Duti trucks. The P20 and P30 Dubl-Duti trucks used a Trademaster Special six with slightly different horsepower rating.

1962 Chevrolet 1-Ton C35 Chassis-and-Cab with dual rear wheels and Special Van Body (CMD)

I.D. DATA: Serial number located: [Chassis models] On plate temporarily attached near steering column, with final location per body maker. [All others] on plate attached to rear face of left-hand door hinge pillar, on right side of cowl under hood. The first symbol indicated model year, 2=1962. The second symbol indicated type: C=Conventional, K=4x4, R=Corvair 95. The third and fourth symbols indicated the model prefix: Corvair 95=12, 1/2-ton standard wheelbase=14, 1/2-ton long wheelbase=15, 3/4-ton=25, 1-ton=36. The fifth symbol indicated body style: 2=Chassis & Cowl, 3=Chassis-and-Cab, 4=Pickup, 5=Panel, 6=Suburban Carryall, 9=Platform/Stake. The sixth symbol indicated the assembly plant: A=Atlanta, Ga., B=Baltimore, Md., F=Flint, Mich., G=Framingham, Mass., J=Janesville, Wis., K=Kansas City, Mo., L=Los Angeles, Calif., N=Norwood, Ohio, O=Oakland, Calif., S=St. Louis, Mo., T=Tarrytown, N.Y., and W=Willow Run, Mich. Remaining symbols were the sequential production number starting with 100001 at each plant. Ending serial numbers not available. The Chevrolet engine had the source, date and type stamped on a serial number pad. Source codes were: F=Flint, Mich., T=Tonawanda, N.Y., C=Canada. Month codes were 1=Jan., 2=Feb., etc. Date codes were 01=first of month, etc. Corvair 95 prefix codes were V, W. Commercial model engine prefix codes were: [Thriftmaster 235] J/JB/JC, [Thriftmaster 235 Special] K/KA, [Trademaster 283] M/MA. Engine serial numbers: [Six] Right side of block behind distributor, [V-8] Front of block below right-hand cylinder head. Engine serial numbers not available.

1962 Chevrolet 1-Ton C30 Chassis-and-Crew-Cab With Fleetside Box (J. Gunnell Photo)

Model	Body Type	Price	Weight	Prod. Total
1/2-Ton Corvair 95 — Model R12/Series 10 — 95 in. w.b.				
R1205	Corvan	2294	2820	13,491
R1244	Loadside	2084	2580	369
R1254	Rampside	2138	2660	4,102
1/2 Ton Commercial (4x2) — Model C14/Series 10 — 115 in. w.b.				
C1403	Chassis & Cab	1897	3020	-
C1434	Fleetside	2027	3440	-
C1404	Step-Side	2011	3385	-
C1405	Panel	2328	3650	-
C1406	Suburban (doors)	2623	3980	-
C1416	Suburban (gate)	2656	3990	-
1/2 Ton Commercial (4x4) — Model K14/Series 10 — 115 in. w.b.				
K1434	Fleetside	2678	-	-
K1404	Step-Side	2678	-	-
K1405	Panel	2979	-	-
K1406	Suburban (doors)	3274	-	NEW (CT61-63-#17)-
K1416	Suburban (gate)	3307	-	-
1/2 Ton Commercial (4x2) — Model C15/Series 10 — 127 in. w.b.				
C1503	Chassis & Cab			-
C1534	Fleetside	2027	3440	-
C1504	Step-Side	2011	3385	-
1/2 Ton Commercial (4x4) — Model K15/Series 10 — 127 in. w.b.				
K1503	Chassis & Cab	2585	3430	-
K1534	Fleetside	2715	3825	-
K1504	Step-Side	2699	3790	-
1/2-Ton Dubl-Duti — Model P23/Series 10 — 102 in. w.b.				
P1345	Package Delivery	2546	3695	-
3/4-Ton Commercial (4x2) — Model C25/Series 20 — 127 in. w.b.				
C2534	Fleetside	2209	3905	-
C2504	Step-Side	2193	3845	-
C2503	Chassis & Cab	2080	3405	-
C2509	Stake 8 ft.	2284	4035	-
3/4-Ton Commercial (4x4) — Model K25/Series 20 — 127 in. w.b.				
K2539	Fleetside	2886	-	-
K2504	Step-Side	2870	-	-

Model	Body Type	Price	Weight	Prod. Total
3/4-Ton Dubl-Duti — Model P23,P25,P26/Series 20 — 104-137 in. w.b.				
P2345	Package Delivery	3083	4945	-
NOTE 1: Data for 104 in. w.b. Dubl-Duti, 123 in./137 in. w.b. optional.				
1-Ton Commercial (4x2) — Model C36/Series 30 — 133 in. w.b.				
C3605	Panel	2797	4525	-
C3604	Step-Side	2372	4155	-
C3603	Chassis & Cab	2238	3700	-
C3609	Stake	2485	4530	-
1-Ton Dubl-Duti — Model P33,P35,P36/Series 30 — 104-137 in. w.b.				
P3345	Package Delivery	3275	5140	-
NOTE 2: Data for 104-in. w.b. Dubl-Duti, 123.25-in./137-in. w.b. optional.				

1962 Chevrolet 1/2-Ton Corvan 95 Panel Delivery Truck (CMD)

Corvair 95 Corvan

1962 Chevrolet 1/2-Ton Corvan 95 Panel Delivery Truck (CMD)

1962 Chevrolet Corvair 95 Rampside Pickup with Traville "Campside" camping unit

ENGINE: [Corvair 95] Opposed. OHV. Turbo-Air. Six-cylinder. Aluminum block. Bore & stroke: 3.437 in. x 2.60 in. Displacement: 144.8 cid. Compression ratio: 8.0:1. Brake horsepower: 80 at 4400 rpm. Maximum torque: 128 lb.-ft. at 2300 rpm. Four main bearings. Hydraulic valve lifters. Carburetor: Two Rochester one-barrel model 7019101.
ENGINE: [All except Series 95 and P20/P30 Dubl-Duti] Inline. OHV. Thriftmaster. Six-cylinder. Cast iron block. Bore & stroke: 3-9/16 in. x 3-15/16 in. Displacement: 235.5 cid. Compression ratio: 8.25:1. Brake horsepower: 135 at 4000 rpm. Maximum torque: 217 lb.-ft. at 2000 rpm. Four main bearings. Hydraulic valve lifters. Carburetor: Rochester one-barrel model B7015011. (The P20/P30 Dubl-Duti trucks had a Thriftmaster Special six with slightly less horsepower).

1962 Chevrolet 1/2-Ton K10 4x4 Panel Door Carryall Suburban (CMD)

ENGINE: [Optional, except Corvair 95 and P models] V-type. OHV. Trademaster. Eight-cylinder. Cast iron block. Bore & stroke: 3-7/8 in. x 3 in. Displacement: 283 cid. Compression ratio: 8.5:1. Brake horsepower: 160 at 4200 rpm. Maximum torque: 270 lb.-ft. at 2000 rpm. Five main bearings. Hydraulic valve lifters. Carburetor: Rochester two-barrel model 2G7015017.

R1254 RAMPSIDE PICKUP

1962 Chevrolet Corvair 95 Rampside Pickup (CMD)

CHASSIS: [Corvair 95] Wheelbase: 95 in. Overall length: 179.7 in. Height: 68.5 in. Front tread: 58 in. Rear tread: 58 in. Tires: 7.00 x 14 in. Maximum GVW: 4,600 lb. **CHASSIS:** [C14/K14] Wheelbase: 115 in. Overall length: [Pickup] 186-3/4 in., [Chassis-and-Cab] 180-1/4 in. Bed length: [Pickup] 78-1/8 in. Cab to rear axle on Chassis-and-Cab: 42 in. Cab to end of frame on Chassis-and-Cab: 75-1/2 in. Front tread: 63.1 in. Rear tread: 61 in. Tires: 6.70 x 15 in. Maximum GVW: [4x2] 4,600 lb., [4x4] 5,300 lb.

1962 Chevrolet 1/2-Ton P10 Step-Van 7 (CMD)

CHASSIS: [C15/K15] Wheelbase: 127 in. Overall length: [Pickup] 206-in., [Chassis-and-Cab] 200-1/4 in. Bed length: [Pickup] 98 in. Cab to rear axle on Chassis-and-Cab: 54 in. Cab to end of frame on Chassis-and-Cab: 95-1/2 in Front tread: 63.1 in. Rear tread: 61.1 in. Tires: 6.70 x 15 in. Maximum GVW: [4x2] 4,600 lb., [4x4] 5,600 lb.

1962 Chevrolet 1/2-Ton C10 Panel Truck with Franklin Body Co. Ambulance conversion (CMD)

1962 Chevrolet Corvair 95 Rampside Pickup (OCW)

CHASSIS: [C25/K25] Wheelbase: 127 in. Overall length: [Pickup] 206 in., [Stake] 210-3/4 in., [Chassis-and-Cab] 211-3/4 in. Bed length: [Pickup] 98 in., [Stake] 98 in. Bed width: [Stake] 85 in. Cab to rear axle on Chassis-and-Cab: 54 in. Cab to end of frame on Chassis-and-Cab: 95-1/2 in. Tires: 7 x 17.5 in. Maximum GVW: [4x2] 6,000 lb., [4x4] 6,800 lb.
CHASSIS: [C36] Wheelbase: 133 in. Overall length: [1-ton Step-Side Pickup] 216-1/4 in., [Chassis-and-Cab] 199-3/4 in. Bed length: [1-ton Step-Side Pickup] 108-1/4 in., [Stake] 109 in. Bed width: [Stake] 85 in. Tires: 8 x 17.5 in. Maximum GVW: 7,800 lb.
CHASSIS: [C36] Wheelbase: 157 in. Overall length: [Stake] 256-1/2 in.,[Chassis-and-Cab] 200-1/4 in.] Bed length: [Stake] 144 in. Bed width: 85 in. Cab to rear axle on Chassis-and-Cab: 60 in. Cab to end of frame on Chassis-and-Cab: 107 in. Tires: 8 x 17.5 in. Maximum GVW: 7,800 lb.
CHASSIS: [P10] Wheelbase: 102 in. Tires: 6.70 x 15 in.
CHASSIS: [P20] Wheelbase: 137 in. Tires: 7 x 17.5 in.
CHASSIS: [P30] Wheelbase: 104-137 in. Tires: 8 x 19.5 in.
TECHNICAL: Manual. Synchromesh. Speeds: 3F/1R. Column-mounted gear shift lever. Single-plate dry-disc clutch. Rear axle: [1-ton] Full-floating, [Others] semi-floating. Standard axle ratio: [R12] 3.89:1, [C14/C15/K14/K15] 3.90:1, [C25/K25] 4.57:1, [C36] 5.14:1. Hydraulic four-wheel brakes. Pressed steel wheels.
OPTIONS: [Corvair 95] Custom chrome, R1200 without wheelcovers ($25.10). Custom Equipment, R1205 with standard seat ($17.56). Custom Equipment, R1205 with full-width seat ($19.23). Custom Equipment, R1206 ($167.20). Custom Equipment, R1244/1254 ($19.23). Left side body doors, R1205/1206 ($62.70). Floor level Pickup box, R1244/1254 ($37.65). Laminated front door glass ($4.20). Direct Air heater ($57.69). Gasoline operated heater ($71.10). Outside rear view mirror, left or right ($3.77). Two-tone paint ($20.90). Two-tone paint, 1200 Pickups ($25.10). Full-width seat, R1205 ($31.78). Full-width seat, R1205 ($20.90). Third seat, R1206 ($29.30). Heavy-duty front springs ($8.40). Heavy-duty shock absorbers ($5.87). Whitewall tires, four-ply ($24.60). Blackwall tires, six-ply ($34.46). Whitewall tires, six-ply ($67.47). Full wheelcovers, R1206 with Custom equipment packages($6.73). Two-speed washers and wipers ($12.55).

1962 Chevrolet 1-Ton Series C30 Fleetside Pickup (DFW)

OPTIONS: [C10/C20/C30] Engine: 150 hp 261 High-Torque L-6 RPO 293 ($50.20). Trademaster 283-cid V-8 RPO 408 ($92). Oil bath air cleaner RPO 591, six-cylinder with governor ($1.72), without governor ($5.06). Positraction axle RPO 680, C1400/1500 ($50.20). No-Spin rear axle RPO 677, C2500 ($104.50). Optional rear axle ratios: 3.38:1 with manual transmission RPO 215 ($5.06), 4.11:1 with manual transmission, 4.11:1 with Powerglide RPO 205 ($25.10). Heavy-duty battery RPO 356 ($5.87). Eleven-inch heavy-duty clutch, six-cylinder only RPO 223 ($4.20). Custom Appearance package RPO 432, Panel truck ($33.45), others ($40.13). Custom Chrome option RPO 393, all with chrome front bumper ($16.75), Pickups with both bumpers chromed ($41.80), Panel truck with chrome bumpers ($25.10). Custom Comfort option RPO 433, Panel truck ($9.21), other models ($42.66). Custom side moldings RPO 393, Fleetsides ($16.75). Temperature control radiator fan RPO 124 ($16.75). 35-ampere generator RPO 355 ($5.87). 42-ampere Delcotron RPO 320 ($22.62). 52-ampere Delcotron RPO 443 ($29.30). All glass tinted RPO 411 ($11.74). Tinted windshield RPO 411 ($10.07). DeLuxe heater RPO 112 ($53.11). Recirculating heater RPO 115 ($37.22). 17.5-in. outside rear view mirror RPO 210, except Panel truck, left-hand ($1.72), right-hand ($3.77). Eight-inch outside rear view mirror, right-hand RPO 210 ($3.77). Oil filter, with standard six-cylinder RPO 592 ($2.96). Two-tone [called "Tu-Tone"] paint, Panel truck ($20.90), others ($12.55). Heavy-duty radiator, except with Powerglide RPO 256 ($16.75). Radio RPO 123 ($37.22). Auxiliary seat, Panel truck RPO 264 ($31.78). Full-depth foam seat, except Panel truck RPO 258 ($25.10). Heavy-duty shock absorbers RPO 213, rear ($6.73), front [requires rears] ($5.87). Heavy-duty springs RPO 254, C2500 front ($2.53), all models, rear ($5.06).

Heavy-duty three-speed manual transmission RPO 316, C1400 ($58.55), C1500 ($62.70) and C2500 ($71.10). Heavy-duty four-speed manual transmission RPO 318, C1400 ($62.70), C1500 ($66.90) and C2500 ($72.25). Powerglide transmission, all models RPO 311 ($146.30). Full-View rear window RPO 394 , except Panel truck ($33.45). Two-speed windshield wipers and washers RPO 355 ($12.55).
NOTE 3: Prices above are dealer cost for 1962 options.
COMMERCIAL MONOTONE COLOR OPTIONS [RPO]: (No. 500) Jet Black, (No. 502) Seamist Jade, (No. 503) Glenwood Green, (No. 505) Woodland Green, (No. 507) Brigade Blue, (No. 508) Balboa Blue, (No. 510) Crystal Turquoise, (No. 514) Cardinal Red, (No. 516) Omaha Orange, (No. 519) Yuma Yellow, (No. 521) Pure White, (No. 522) Georgian Gray, (No. 526) Cameo White, (No. 528) Desert Beige.
OPTION PACKAGES: [Custom Appearance Equipment RPO 432] Includes silver anodized radiator grille and headlamp door assembly, chrome-plated windshield reveal moldings, bright metal cab upper rear quarter panel trim plates, chrome horn ring steering wheel, chrome trimmed instrument panel knobs, and two-tone inside front door panels. [Custom Comfort and Convenience Equipment RPO 433] Includes left door arm rest, outside key lock, chrome cigar lighter, full foam rubber seat cushion, special seat trim (cab models and Suburban), and added sound insulation. [Custom Chrome Equipment RPO 393] Chrome hubcaps. Not available with 4x4 or dual rear wheel options. [Side Trim Moldings] Bright body side moldings for Fleetside models. (Package prices are given above).

1962 Chevrolet 1/2-Ton C10 Step-Side Pickup (DFW)

HISTORICAL: Introduced: Fall 1961. Calendar-year registrations: [All Chevrolet Commercials] 425,406. Calendar-year production: [All Chevrolet Commercials] 396,819. Of this total, 82 percent were six-cylinder models. Innovations: New styling for C Series models. First diesels in big Chevrolet trucks. Chevrolet was America's number one truck-maker in 1962. The eight millionth Chevrolet truck since 1918 was sold this season. J.E. Conlan remained in charge of Chevrolet's Truck and Fleet Sales Department. Model-year production: 396,940.

1963 CHEVROLET

1963 Chevrolet Corvair 95 Rampside Pickup (OCW)

CORVAIR 95 — MODEL R12/SERIES 1000 — SIX: The Corvair 95 trucks were again virtually unchanged. These driver-forward models had a Corvair platform, a rear-mounted air-cooled engine, and a transaxle. Dual headlamps, a small front grille with a Chevrolet bow tie emblem, and a sculptured contrast panel around the body were styling characteristics. The Corvan had steel body sides, two side load doors, and double rear panel doors. It had Corvair 95 scripts on the front doors. A Loadside Pickup was made by adding a cab back panel and removing the upper sheet metal at the rear. It dropped to the ground to make a cargo loading ramp. Standard equipment on all Corvair 95s included: An air-cooled six-cylinder engine, three-speed synchromesh transmission, electric wipers, directional signals and five tubeless tires. Chrome hubcaps, chrome bumpers and a Custom The 1962 style hood interior/exterior appearance package were available.

1963 Chevrolet 1/2-Ton Series C10 Fleetside Custom Cab Pickup (OCW)

1/2-TON COMMERCIAL — MODEL C14 (4x2), K14 (4x4)/SERIES 10 — SIX/V-8: was carried over for 1963 Chevrolet 10 Series 1/2-ton trucks: A new technical improvement was a coil spring front suspension, replacing the 1960-1962 torsion bar type. A new radiator grille had an eggcrate appearance with round parking lamp housings at either end. The standard grille was made of steel painted Cameo White. The headlamp bezels and the Chevrolet lettering on the lower grille surround was accented in black. An anodized aluminum grille was part of the Custom Appearance Equipment package. Satin-finished chrome fender side name badges were mounted on the cowl, behind the front wheel opening. They were rectangular in shape and had a red 10 on top and red Chevrolet bow tie emblem near the bottom. Exterior colors for the year were Desert Beige, Jet Black, Balboa Blue, Brigade Blue, Georgian Gray, Seamist Jade, Glenwood Green, Woodland Green, Omaha Orange, Cardinal Red, Crystal Turquoise, Cameo White, Pure White, and Yukon Yellow. All colors, except the two whites, were used as lower body colors in the 12 two-tone color options. They were teamed with Cameo White on the upper body. Interiors were done in two shades of fawn beige with cameo white accenting the steering wheel and mast. Standard seats had medium fawn (tan) embossed vinyl with light fawn facings. Custom interiors had color-keyed nylon pattern cloth and pin-seal vinyl upholstery. They featured red trim in Cameo White trucks, georgian gray trim in Cardinal Red trucks, and medium fawn trim in others. There were four separate Custom equipment options, which are listed as options below. Offered again were Step-Side (with pontoon rear fenders) and Fleetside (with slab type rear fenders) Pickups with 6-1/2-ft. boxes. Both featured rugged tailgates with anti-rattle latches and support chains, plus select wood floors with steel cargo skid strips. All Chevrolet conventional pickups gave the smooth ride and sure handling of independent front suspension chassis design, plus the bonus features of extra room and comfort in the cab and a lower loading height. Pickups featured bodies with double-walled side panels to protect the exterior surfaces against dents caused by shifting cargo. A separate front panel protected the back of the cab. Step-Sides offered a 50-in.-wide unobstructed load space (without wheel wells), plus handy running boards for easy access to cargo from either side. Fleetsides were preferred by buyers concerned with looks and extra load space, as they were a full 6-feet wide, with wheel wells on either side. Other models included the Panel, Carryall Suburban, and Chassis-and-Cab trucks. Chevrolet cabs featured extra-quality construction to keep them solid and tight through their long, hard-working lives. A deep-sculptured double-panel roof added rigidity to the entire cab structure. Reinforced box-section pillars supported the roof and frame doorways to help keep the doors working right and sealing tight for life. Massive double-walled cowl arches bridged the front of the cab structure, uniting the door frames, dash and floor panels in an integrated, high-strength assembly. The rugged floor panel assembly was double-braced with massive cross members, plus front and rear sills. The reinforced cab mounting points rode on new floating-action mounts for better isolation from frame vibration. The 10 Series four-wheel-drive 1/2-ton models had a K14 model prefix.

1963 Chevrolet 1/2-Ton Series C10 Step-Side Pickup (OCW)

1/2-TON COMMERCIAL — MODELS C15 (4x2)/SERIES 10 — SIX/V-8: The C15 trucks in the Chevrolet 10 series long-wheelbase line used a C15 model prefix. Their fender side nameplates had a red Chevrolet bow tie and the number 10. They had the same basic styling and trim changes as other conventional trucks. These were the long wheelbase (LWB) 1/2-ton trucks on the same chassis as 3/4-ton models. They are known as "Long Bed" or "Long Box" Pickups because they had a longer 8-ft. load box. Longer running boards were needed on Step-Sides because there was more space between the cab and rear fenders. The Apache 10 Long Bed four-wheel-drive models had a K15 model prefix.
1/2-TON DUBL-DUTI — MODEL P13/SERIES 10 — FOUR/SIX/V-8: The 1/2-ton Dubl-Duti returned again in 1963. It had a 102-in. wheelbase. An approved Step-Van walk-in delivery truck made by Union City Body Co., of Union City, Ind. was most commonly mounted on the Dubl-Duty chassis. A channel type front bumper was optional on Dubl-Duti trucks. The P10 now featured the four-cylinder High-Torque 153-cid/90-hp (Chevy II) engine as standard equipment.

1963 Chevrolet 3/4-Ton C25 Fleetside Pickup (CMD)

3/4-TON COMMERCIAL — MODEL C25/SERIES 20 — SIX/V-8: The C25 trucks in the Chevrolet 20 Series 3/4-ton line had the same styling and trim changes as other conventional trucks. The fender side nameplates had a red Chevrolet bow tie emblem and the number 20. Step-Side and Fleetside Pickups were in this series. Compared to C10-C14 Pickups, the C20-C25 had slightly longer running boards and an 8-ft. long box was used. There were also Platform and Platform/Stake models. The rail for the 3/4-ton Platform was about 8 ft. long. The rugged Chevrolet Stake Rack body was designed and built for maximum cargo convenience and a long, hard working life. Platforms of tough 1-1/4-in. select wood planking were built on high-strength frameworks of steel cross sills, and shock-cushioning wood sub-sills. Round-cornered steel rub rails edged the platform for protection against docking damage and injury. Wear-resistant steel-lined stake pockets supported racks of top-quality hardwood, with assembly hardware recessed to leave interior surfaces smooth and snag-free. The four-wheel-drive 3/4-ton models in the 20 Series had a K25 model prefix.

3/4-TON DUBL-DUTI — MODEL P23, P25, P26/SERIES 20 — SIX/V-8: Three 3/4-ton Dubl-Duti Forward-Control chassis remained in the 20 Series (3/4-ton) truck line. The P23/P25/P26 models had wheelbases of 104 in./125 in./137 in., respectively. A channel type front bumper was optional on Dubl-Duti trucks. New this year was use of a High-Torque 230 cid/140 hp six-cylinder engine as standard equipment in P20/P30 models.

1-TON MEDIUM-DUTY COMMERCIAL — MODEL C36/SERIES 30 — SIX-CYLINDER: The Chevrolet 30 Series 1-ton trucks had the same styling and trim changes as other conventional trucks. The fender side nameplates had a red Chevrolet bow tie and number 30. There was no Fleetside Pickup in this line. Panel models had a one-piece floor made of 3/4-in. thick, five-ply laminated wood. The basic model lineup was unchanged. Compared to the C20-C25 Pickup, the C30-C36 Pickup had a longer wheelbase, a longer box with extra stake pockets, and very long running boards. The 1-ton Stake trucks had a long rail nearly 9-1/2 ft. long. The rugged Chevrolet Stake Rack body was designed and built for maximum cargo convenience and a long, hard working life. Platforms of tough 1-1/4-in. select wood planking were built on high-strength frameworks of steel cross sills, and shock-cushioning wood sub-sills. Round-cornered steel rub rails edged the platform for protection against docking damage and injury. Wear-resistant steel-lined stake pockets supported racks of top-quality hardwood, with assembly hardware recessed to leave interior surfaces smooth and snag-free. No hubcaps were used on the larger split-rim wheels of the Chassis-and-Cab and Stake models, which had eight bolts and eight circular openings. A four-speed manual synchromesh transmission was standard. No four-wheel-drive option was offered.

1-TON DUBL-DUTI — MODEL P33, P35, P36/SERIES 30 — SIX/V-8: Three Dubl-Duti Forward-Control chassis were in the 30 Series (1-ton) truck line. The P33/P35/P36 models had wheelbases of 104 in./125 in./137 in., respectively. A channel type front bumper was optional on Dubl-Duti trucks. New this year was use of a High-Torque 230 cid/140 hp engine as standard equipment in P20/P30 models.

1963 Chevrolet 1/2-Ton Series C10 Step Side Pickup (CMD)

I.D. DATA: Serial number located: [Chassis models] On plate temporarily attached near steering column, with final location per body maker. [All others] on plate attached to rear face of left-hand door hinge pillar, on right side of cowl under hood. The first symbol indicated model year, 3=1963. The second symbol indicated type: C=Conventional, K=4x4, R=Corvair 95. The third and fourth symbols indicated the model prefix: Corvair 95=12, 1/2-ton standard wheelbase=14, 1/2-ton long wheelbase=15, 3/4-ton=25, 1-ton=36. The fifth symbol indicated body style: 2=Chassis & Cowl, 3=Chassis-and-Cab, 4=Pickup, 5=Panel, 6=Suburban Carryall, 9=Platform/Stake. The sixth symbol indicated the assembly plant: A=Atlanta, Ga., B=Baltimore, Md., F=Flint, Mich., G=Framingham, Mass., J=Janesville, Wis., K=Kansas City, Mo., L=Los Angeles, Calif., N=Norwood, Ohio, O=Oakland, Calif., P=Pontiac, Mich., S=St. Louis, Mo., T=Tarrytown, N.Y., and

W=Willow Run, Mich. Remaining symbols were the sequential production number starting with 100001 at each plant. Ending serial numbers not available. The Chevrolet engine had the source, date and type stamped on a serial number pad. Source codes were: F=Flint, Mich., T=Tonawanda, N.Y., C=Canada. Month codes were 1=Jan., 2=Feb., etc. Date codes were 01=first of month, etc. Corvair 95 prefix codes were: [Turbo Air 145 cid/80 hp six] V, W. Commercial model engine prefix codes were: [Hi-Torque 153 cid/90 hp L-4] F/FA, [Hi-Torque 235 cid/135 hp L-6] J/JC, [Hi-Torque 261 cid/150 hp L-6] N/ND/NE/NK/NL/NM/NQ/NS/NU, [High-Torque 292 cid/165 hp L-6] PG/PK, [High-Torque 283 cid/175 hp V-8] M/MA. Engine serial numbers: [Six] Right side of block behind distributor, [V-8] Front of block below right-hand cylinder head. Engine serial numbers not available.

1963 Chevrolet 1/2-Ton Series C10 Step Side Pickup (CMD)

Model	Body Type	Price	Weight	Prod. Total
1/2-Ton Corvair 95 — Model R12/Series 10 — 95 in. w.b.				
R1205	Corvan	2212	2800	11,161
R1254	Rampside	2212	2800	2,046
1/2 Ton Commercial (4x2) — Model C14/Series 10 — 115 in. w.b.				
C1403	Chassis & Cab	1895	2820	-
C1434	Fleetside	2025	3235	-
C1404	Step-Side	2009	3190	-
C1405	Panel	2326	3440	-
C1406	Suburban (doors)	2620	3720	-
C1416	Suburban (gate)	2653	3735	-
1/2 Ton Commercial (4x4) — Model K14/Series 10 — 115 in. w.b.				
K1434	Fleetside	2676	-	
K1404	Step-Side	2676	-	
K1405	Panel	2977	-	
K1406	Suburban (doors)	3272	-	
K1416	Suburban (gate)	3305	-	
1/2 Ton Commercial (4x2) — Model C15/Series 10 — 127 in. w.b.				
C1503	Chassis & Cab			
C1534	Fleetside	2025	3235	-
C1504	Step-Side	2660	3190	-
1/2 Ton Commercial (4x4) — Model K15/Series 10 — 127 in. w.b.				
K1534	Fleetside	2676	-	
K1504	Step-Side	2660	-	
1/2-Ton Dubl-Duti — Model P23/Series 10 — 102 in. w.b.				
P1345	Package Delivery	2544	3450	-
3/4-Ton Commercial (4x2) — Model C25/Series 20 — 127 in. w.b.				
C2534	Fleetside	2207	3760	-
C2504	Step-Side	2193	3710	-
C2503	Chassis & Cab	2079	3280	-
C2509	Stake 8 ft.	2284	3895	-
3/4-Ton Commercial (4x4) — Model K25/Series 20 — 127 in. w.b.				
K2539	Fleetside	2884	-	
K2504	Step-Side	2868	-	
3/4-Ton Dubl-Duti — Model P23,P25,P26/Series 20 — 104-137 in. w.b.				
P2345	Package Delivery	3082	4805	-
NOTE 1: Data for 104 in. w.b. Dubl-Duti, 123 in./137 in. w.b. optional.				
1-Ton Commercial (4x2) — Model C36/Series 30 — 133 in. w.b.				
C3605	Panel	2797	4523	-
C3604	Step-Side	2371	3900	-
C3603	Chassis & Cab	2236	3430	-
C3609	Stake	2483	4230	-
1-Ton Dubl-Duti — Model P33,P35,P36/Series 30 — 104-137 in. w.b.				
P3345	Package Delivery	3274	5020	-
NOTE 2: Data for 104 in. w.b. Dubl-Duti, 123.25 in./137 in. w.b. optional.				

1963 Chevrolet 1/2-Ton Series C10 Step-Side Pickup
(Lowell E. Eisenhour photo)

1963 Chevrolet Corvair 95 Rampside Pickup (Owner/photographer: Jean A. Allen)

1963 Chevrolet Corvair 95 Rampside Pickup (Owner: Bill Fuss)

1963Chevrolet Corvair 95 Rampside Pickup with Traville "Campside" camping unit (Jean A. Allen)

ENGINE: [Standard P10] Inline. Overhead valve. High-Torque 153. Four-cylinder. Bore and stroke: 3-7/8 x 3-1/4 in. Displacement: 153 cid. Brake horsepower: 90 at 4000 rpm. Torque: 152 lb.-ft at 2400 rpm.
ENGINE: [Corvair 95] Opposed. OHV. Turbo-Air. Six-cylinder. Aluminum block. Bore & stroke: 3.437 in. x 2.60 in. Displacement: 144.8 cid. Compression ratio: 8.0:1. Brake horsepower: 80 at 4400 rpm. Maximum torque: 128 lb.-ft. at 2300 rpm. Four main bearings. Hydraulic valve lifters. Carburetor: Two Rochester one-barrel model 7019101.
ENGINE: [Standard C10/C20/P20/P30, Optional P10] Inline. OHV. High-Torque 230. Six-cylinder. Cast iron block. Bore and stroke: 3-7/8 x 3-1/4 in. Displacement: 230 cid. Brake horsepower: 140 at 4400 rpm. Torque: 220 lb.-ft. at 1600 rpm.
ENGINE: [Standard K10/K20] Inline. OHV. High-Torque 235. Six-cylinder. Cast iron block. Bore & stroke: 3-9/16 in. x 3-15/16 in. Displacement: 235.5 cid. Compression ratio: 8.25:1. Brake horsepower: 135 at 4000 rpm. Maximum torque: 217 lb.-ft. at 2000 rpm. Four main bearings. Hydraulic valve lifters. Carburetor: Rochester one-barrel model B7015011.

1963 Chevrolet 1/2-Ton Corvan 95 Panel Delivery (CMD)

ENGINE: [Optional K10/K20] Inline. OHV. High-Torque 261. Six-cylinder. Cast iron block. Bore and stroke: 3-3/4 x 3-15/16. Displacement: 261 cid. Brake horsepower: 150 at 4000 rpm. Torque: 235 lb.-ft. at 2000 rpm.
ENGINE: [Optional C10/C20/C30] Inline. OHV. High-Torque 292. Six-cylinder. Cast iron block. Bore and stroke: 3-7/8 x 4-1/8. Displacement: 292 cid. Brake horsepower: 165 at 3800 rpm. Torque: 280 lb.-ft. at 1600 rpm.
ENGINE: [Optional, Except Corvair 95 and P models] V-type. OHV. High-Torque 283. Eight-cylinder. Cast iron block. Bore & stroke: 3-7/8 in. x 3 in. Displacement: 283 cid. Compression ratio: 8.5:1. Brake horsepower: 160 at 4200 rpm. Maximum torque: 270 lb.-ft. at 2000 rpm. Five main bearings. Hydraulic valve lifters. Carburetor: Rochester two-barrel model 2G7015017.

1963 Chevrolet 1/2-Ton Series C10 Fleetside Custom Cab Pickup (DFW)

CHASSIS: [Corvair 95] Wheelbase: 95 in. Overall length: 179.7 in. Height: 68.5 in. Front tread: 58 in. Rear tread: 58 in. Tires: 7.00 x 14 in. Maximum GVW: 4,600 lb.
CHASSIS: [C14/K14] Wheelbase: 115 in. Overall length: [Pickup] 186-3/4 in., [Chassis-and-Cab] 180-1/4 in. Bed length: [Pickup] 78-1/8 in. Cab to rear axle on Chassis-and-Cab: 42 in. Cab to end of frame on Chassis-and-Cab: 75-1/2 in. Front tread: 63.1 in. Rear tread: 61 in. Tires: 6.70 x 15 in. Maximum GVW: [4x2] 4,600 lb., [4x4] 5,300 lb.
CHASSIS: [C15/K15] Wheelbase: 127 in. Overall length: [Pickup] 206-1/4 in., [Chassis-and-Cab] 200-1/4 in. Bed length: [Pickup] 98 in. Cab to rear axle on Chassis-and-Cab: 54 in. Cab to end of frame on Chassis-and-Cab: 95-1/2 in Front tread: 63.1 in. Rear tread: 61.1 in. Tires: 6.70 x 15 in. Maximum GVW: [4x2] 4,600 lb., [4x4] 5,600 lb.
CHASSIS: [C25/K25] Wheelbase: 127 in. Overall length: [Pickup] 206 in., [Stake] 210-3/4 in., [Chassis-and-Cab] 211-3/4 in. Bed length: [Pickup] 98 in., [Stake] 98 in. Bed width: [Stake] 85 in. Cab to rear axle on Chassis-and-Cab: 54 in. Cab to end of frame on Chassis-and-Cab: 95-1/2 in. Tires: 7 x 17.5 in. Maximum GVW: [4x2] 6,000 lb., [4x4] 6,800 lb.
CHASSIS: [C36] Wheelbase: 133 in. Overall length: [1-ton Step-Side Pickup] 216-1/4 in., [Chassis-and-Cab] 199-3/4 in.] Bed length: [1-ton Step-Side Pickup] 108-1/4 in., [Stake] 109 in. Bed width: [Stake] 85 in. Tires: 8 x 17.5 in. Maximum GVW: 7,800 lb.
CHASSIS: [C36] Wheelbase: 157 in. Overall length: [Stake] 256-1/2 in., [Chassis-and-Cab] 200-1/4 in.] Bed length: [Stake] 144 in. Bed width: 85 in. Cab to rear axle on Chassis-and-Cab: 60 in. Cab to end of frame on Chassis-and-Cab: 107 in. Tires: 8 x 17.5 in. Maximum GVW: 7,800 lb.
CHASSIS: [P10] Wheelbase: 102 in. Tires: 6.70 x 15 in.
CHASSIS: [P20] Wheelbase: 137 in. Tires: 7 x 17.5 in.
CHASSIS: [P30] Wheelbase: 104-137 in. Tires: 8 x 19.5 in.

1963 Chevrolet 1/2-Ton Series C10 Fleetside Cab Pickup (CMD)

TECHNICAL: Manual. Synchromesh. Speeds: 3F/1R. Column-mounted gear shift lever. Single-plate dry-disc clutch. Rear axle: [1-ton] Full-floating, [Others] semi-floating. Standard axle ratio: [R12] 3.89:1, [C14/C15/K14/K15] 3.90:1, [C25/K25] 4.57:1, [C36] 5.14:1. Hydraulic four-wheel brakes. Pressed steel wheels.
OPTIONS: [Corvair 95] Custom chrome, R1200 without wheel covers ($25.10). Custom Equipment, R1205 with standard seat ($17.56). Custom Equipment, R1205 with full-width seat ($19.23). Custom Equipment, R1206 ($167.20). Custom Equipment, R1244/1254 ($19.23). Left side body doors, R1205/1206 ($62.70). Floor level Pickup box, R1244/1254 ($37.65). Laminated front door glass ($4.20). Direct Air heater ($57.69). Gasoline operated heater ($71.10). Outside rear view mirror, left or right ($3.77). Two-tone paint ($20.90). Two-tone paint, 1200 Pickups ($25.10). Auxiliary front seat, R1205 ($31.78). Full-width seat, R1205 ($20.90). Third seat, R1206 ($29.30). Heavy-duty front springs ($8.40). Heavy-duty shock absorbers ($5.87). Whitewall tires, four-ply ($24.60). Blackwall tires, six-ply ($34.46). Whitewall tires, six-ply ($67.47). Full wheelcovers, R1206 with Custom ($6.73). Two-speed washers and wipers ($12.55).

OPTIONS: [C10/C20/C30] Engine: 150 hp 261 High-Torque L-6 ($50.20). Trademaster 283 V-8 ($92). Oil bath air cleaner, six-cylinder with governor ($1.72), without governor ($5.06). Positraction axle, C1400/1500 ($50.20). No-Spin rear axle, C2500 ($104.50). Optional rear axle ratios: 3.38:1 with manual transmission ($5.06), 4.11:1 with manual transmission, 4.11:1 with Powerglide ($25.10). Heavy-duty battery ($5.87). Eleven-inch heavy-duty clutch, six-cylinder only ($4.20). Custom Appearance package, Panel truck ($33.45), others ($40.13). Custom Chrome option, all with chrome front bumper ($16.75). Pickups with both bumpers chromed ($41.80), Panel truck with chrome bumpers ($25.10). Custom Comfort option, Panel truck ($9.21), other models ($42.66). Custom side moldings, Fleetsides ($16.75). Temperature control radiator fan ($16.75). 35-ampere generator ($5.87). 42-ampere Delcotron ($22.62). 52-ampere Delcotron ($29.30). All glass tinted ($11.74). Tinted windshield ($10.07). DeLuxe heater ($53.11). Recirculating heater ($37.22). 17.5-in. outside rear view mirror, except Panel truck, left-hand ($1.72), right-hand ($3.77). Eight-inch outside rear view mirror, right-hand ($3.77). Oil filter, with standard six-cylinder ($2.96). Two-tone [called Tu-tone] paint, Panel truck ($20.90), others ($12.55). Heavy-duty radiator, except with Powerglide ($16.75). Radio ($37.22). Auxiliary seat, Panel truck ($31.78). Full-depth foam seat, except Panel truck ($25.10). Heavy-duty shock absorbers, rear ($6.73), front [requires rears] ($5.87). Heavy-duty springs, C2500 front ($2.53), all models, rear ($5.06). Heavy-duty three-speed manual transmission, C1400 ($58.55), C1500 ($62.70) and C2500 ($71.10). Heavy-duty four-speed manual transmission, C1400 ($62.70), C1500 ($66.90) and C2500 ($72.25). Powerglide transmission, all models ($146.30). Full-View rear window, except Panel truck ($33.45). Two-speed windshield wipers and washers ($12.55). [Prices above are dealer cost for 1962 options.]

OPTION PACKAGES: [Custom Appearance Equipment] Includes silver anodized radiator grille and headlamp door assembly, chrome-plated windshield reveal moldings, bright metal cab upper rear quarter panel trim plates, chrome horn ring steering wheel, chrome-trimmed instrument panel knobs, and two-tone inside front door panels. [Custom Comfort and Convenience Equipment] Includes left door arm rest, outside key lock, chrome cigar lighter, full foam rubber seat cushion, special seat trim (cab models and Suburban), and added sound insulation. [Custom Chrome Equipment] Chrome hubcaps. Not available with 4x4 or dual rear wheel options. [Side Trim Moldings] Bright body side moldings for Fleetside models. (Package prices are given above.)

HISTORICAL: Introduced: Sept. 28, 1962. Calendar-Year Production Total: 483,119. (This was 33.01 percent of total industry.) In round numbers, the total included 500 four-cylinder-powered trucks, 2,200 diesels, 378,000 six-cylinder models, and 102,400 trucks with V-8 power plants. Calendar-year registrations: 425,406. Corvair, total production for model year: 26,968 (including Greenbrier Sports Wagon). Innovations: New High-Torque 230-cid and 292-cid six-cylinder engines. Light-duty trucks adopt ladder-type frame. Chevrolet commanded its largest share, ever, of the U.S. truck market in 1983. Over one-third of all trucks built this year had Chevrolet bow tie badges. It was also the first time since 1950 that truck deliveries went above 400,000 units. Leafing through a *Chevrolet Silver Book* for 1963 reveals some of the unusual vocational equipment available in the factory-approved aftermarket. This included roll-up doors for walk-in deliveries (from Overhead Door Corp., of Marion, Ohio), a Crew-Cab conversion (from Orrville Metal Specialty Co., of Orrville, Ohio), a fan-belt-driven automatic snow plow from Monarch Road Machinery Co. (of Grand Rapids, Mich.) and pickup truck extension boom wrecker units from Canfield Tow Bar Co.) of Detroit, Mich. Winnebago Industries and Wolverine Camper Co. were among firms offering slide-in campers for Pickups. Perhaps the ultimate conversion, however, was the Go-Home mobile home (based on Corvair running gear) made by Ultra-Van Mfg. Co., of Oakland, Calif.

1964 CHEVROLET

1964 Chevrolet 1/2-Ton El Camino Custom Sedan-Pickup (OCW)

EL CAMINO — MODEL A/SERIES 53-56 — SIX/V-8: Returning after a four-year hiatus was the El Camino, which Chevrolet described as a "personal pickup." Built on the mid-size Chevelle's 115-in. wheelbase, the El Camino was available with many passenger-car options. It came with two trim levels. El Caminos in the 53 (six-cylinder) and 54 (V-8) series were the base models, with trim and appointments comparable to the Chevelle 300. Custom El Caminos in the 55 (six-cylinder) and 56 (V-8) series had trim and appointments comparable to the Chevelle Malibu. Customs had additional moldings around the wheel openings and the load box, chrome window/windshield frames, and a windsplit molding on the center of the hood. The 1964 El Caminos came in Tuxedo Black, Meadow Green, Bahama Green, Silver Blue, Daytona Blue, Azure Aqua, Lagoon Aqua, Almond Fawn, Ember Red, Saddle Tan, Ermine White, Desert Beige, Satin Silver, and Palomar Red. Color-keyed all-vinyl seats and sidewall trim were available in almond fawn, lagoon aqua or ember red for base models. The standard interior also included an embossed vinyl headliner, dual sun visors, arm rests, color-keyed vinyl floor mats, a cigar lighter, lockable glove compartment, bright instrument panel facing, and foam seat

cushions. Customs featured color-keyed pattern cloth and leather-grain vinyl upholstery and had deep-twist floor carpeting, a bright glove compartment facing, two-tone steering wheel and electric clock. The El Camino had an outside width of 73-1/4 in. The pickup box inside width was 59-3/4 in. behind the cab, and 64-3/4 in. near the tailgate. There was 46 in. between the wheelhousings. The bed of the box was 78-1/2 in. long. The tailgate measured 55-1/2 in. x 23 in. With the bed-level tailgate lowered, the overall bed length was 101.6 in. This box was larger than the one used on full-size 1959-1960 El Caminos.

1964 Chevrolet 1/2-Ton G10 Chevy Van Commercial Panel (CMD)

1/2-TON CHEVY VAN — MODEL G/SERIES 10 — FOUR: A low-priced, front-engine Chevy Van was released early in calendar 1964. Styling characteristics included five-segment vents on the front with a bow-tie underneath, and an oval, horizontal-bar grille near the bottom of the front single headlights. It had the same general characteristics configuration and 90-in. wheelbase as the Corvan, but utilized a water-cooled 153-cid four-cylinder Chevy II engine. It was available in two models called the Carryall and Panel. The Carryall was marketed as a passenger vehicle with windows. Auxiliary passenger seats were available. The Commercial Panel had double right-hand side cargo doors. It was considered a truck.

1964 Chevrolet 1/2-Ton Corvair 95 Rampside Pickup (OCW)

CORVAIR 95 — MODEL R12/SERIES 1000 — SIX: The Corvair 95 trucks were driver-forward models on a Corvair platform, with a rear-mounted air-cooled engine, and a transaxle. Dual headlamps, a small front grille with Chevrolet emblem and a sculptured contrast panel around the body were styling characteristics. The 1964 models were virtually unchanged, except for serial numbers and new paint schemes. Colors included Meadow Green, Bahama Green, Daytona Blue, Lagoon Aqua, Desert Beige, and Goldwood Yellow. The slow-selling Loadside Pickup was gone. Back again was the Corvan with steel panel sides, two side load doors, and double rear panel doors. It had Corvair 95 scripts on the front doors. Also available was the Rampside Pickup. It was made by adding a cab back panel and removing the upper sheet metal at the rear. The double-wall cargo box was 105 in. long and 43-7/8 in. wide. A unique door in the side of the box dropped to the ground to make a cargo loading ramp. Standard equipment on all 1964 Corvair 95s included: An air-cooled six-cylinder engine that grew from 145 cid to 164 cid and gained more horsepower, a three-speed synchromesh transmission, electric windshield wipers, directional signals, and five tubeless tires. Chrome hubcaps, chrome bumpers, and a Custom interior/exterior appearance package were available.

1964 Chevrolet 1/2-Ton Series C10-C14 Fleetside Pickup (OCW)

110

1964 Chevrolet 1/2-Ton Series C10-C14 Fleetside Long Bed Pickup (OCW)

1/2-TON COMMERCIAL — MODEL C14 (4x2), K14 (4x4)/SERIES 10 — SIX/V-8: The 1963 style hood was carried over for 1964 Chevrolet 10 series 1/2-ton trucks, but a lot of other cab sheet metal was changed due to the elimination of a wraparound windshield. The front roof pillars now slanted backwards, instead of slightly forward. This gave the door window frames a totally new shape. These rather drastic alterations were neatly integrated to the previous body, however, so overall styling was much the same. The grille also looked basically similar to the previous design with small changes. The vertical and horizontal elements were slimmer, and more tightly cross-hatched. The black-accented Chevrolet lettering was on the top (instead of bottom) bar. The headlamp surrounds were square-shaped. The standard grille was made of steel painted off-white, as were bumpers and hubcaps. An anodized aluminum grille was part of the Custom Appearance Equipment package. Fender side name badges were mounted in the same location on the cowl, behind the front wheel opening. They looked like red squares framed in chrome with a chrome "10" in the center and a chrome Chevrolet bow tie above. Exterior colors for the year were Tuxedo Black, Dark Blue, Light Blue, Fawn, Gray, Gray Green, Dark Green, Light Green, Orange, Red, Turquoise, White, Off-White, and Yellow. All colors (except the two whites) were used as lower body colors in the 12 two-tone color options. They were teamed with Off-White on the upper body. Interiors were done in two shades of fawn beige with off-white accenting the steering wheel and mast. Standard seats had medium fOwn embossed vinyl with light fawn (beige) facings. Custom interiors had color-keyed nylon-faced pattern cloth inserts and vinyl bolsters. The striped inserts were mostly medium fawn beige. Contrasting bolsters were red or fawn, depending upon the color of the truck, with a white bottom bolster. An all-new dashboard was inside the 1964 trucks. It had a redesigned instrument cluster, glove compartment, ash tray and trim plates. Control knobs were angle-mounted at the bottom of the cluster, which was recessed to hood the instruments from glare. There were four separate Custom Equipment options, which are listed in the options section below. Offered again were Step-Side (with pontoon rear fenders) and Fleetside (with slab type rear fenders) Pickups. Both had with 6-1/2-ft. boxes. Other models included the 7-1/2-ft. Panel, the Carryall Suburban, and three chassis models. The 10 series Short Box four-wheel-drive 1/2-ton models had a K14 model prefix.

1964 Chevrolet 1/2-Ton Series C10-C14 Custom Fleetside Pickup (OCW)

1/2-TON COMMERCIAL — MODELS C15 (4x2)/SERIES 10 — SIX/V-8: The C15 trucks in the Chevrolet 10 series long-wheelbase line used a C15 model prefix. Their fender side nameplates were square red badges with a chrome bow tie and number 10. They had the same basic styling and trim changes as other conventional trucks. These were the long wheelbase (LWB) 1/2-ton trucks on the same chassis as 3/4-ton models. They had a longer 8-ft. load box. Longer running boards were needed on Step-Sides because there was more space between the cab and rear fenders. The 10 series Long Bed four-wheel-drive models had a K15 model prefix.

1964 Chevrolet 1/2-Ton Series C10-C14 Step-Side Pickup w/custom wheels (OCW)

1964 Chevrolet 1/2-Ton Series C10-C14 Custom Fleetside Pickup (OCW)

1/2-TON DUBL-DUTI — MODEL P13/SERIES 10 — SIX/V-8: The 1/2-ton Dubl-Duti returned again. It had a 102-in. wheelbase. An approved 7-ft. Step-Van walk-in delivery truck made by Union City Body Co., of Union City, Ind. was most commonly mounted on this Dubl-Duti chassis. A channel type front bumper was optional and 153 High-Torque four-cylinder engine was standard.

3/4-TON COMMERCIAL — MODEL C25/SERIES 20 — SIX/V-8: The C25 trucks in the Chevrolet 20 series 3/4-ton line had the same styling and trim changes as other conventional trucks. The fender side nameplates were square red badges with a chrome bow tie emblem and chrome number 20. Step-Side and Fleetside Pickups were in this series. Compared to C10-C14 pickups, the C20-C25 pickup had slightly longer running boards and an 8-ft. Long Box was used. There were also 8-ft. Platform and Platform/Stake models. The four-wheel-drive 3/4-ton models in the 20 series had a K25 model prefix.

1964 Chevrolet 3/4-Ton Series P20 Step-Van (CMD)

3/4-TON DUBL-DUTI — MODEL P23, P25, P26/SERIES 20 — SIX/V-8: Three 3/4-ton Dubl-Duti Forward-Control chassis remained in the 20 series (3/4-ton) truck line. The P23/P25/P26 models had wheelbases of 104 in./125 in./137 in., respectively. The 104-in. wheelbase was recommended for 7-ft. to 8-1/2-ft. bodies, the 125-in. wheelbase was recommended for 9-1/2 to 10-1/2-ft. long bodies and the 137-in. wheelbase was recommended for 11-1/2-ft. to 12-1/2-ft. long bodies. Bodies could be sourced from factory approved firms or independent suppliers. A channel type front bumper was optional. A High-Torque 230 six-cylinder engine was standard.

1-TON MEDIUM-DUTY COMMERCIAL — MODEL C36/SERIES 30 — SIX-CYLINDER: The Chevrolet 30 series 1-ton trucks had the same styling and trim changes as other conventional trucks. The fender side nameplates were square red badges with a chrome Chevrolet bow tie and number 30. There was no Fleetside Pickup in this line. Panel models had a one-piece floor made of 3/4-in. thick, five-ply laminated wood. The basic model lineup was unchanged. Compared to the C20-C25 Pickup, the C30-C36 Pickup had a longer wheelbase, a longer box with extra stake pockets, and very long running boards. The 1-ton Stake trucks had a long rail some 9 ft. long. No hubcaps were used on the larger split-rim wheels of the Chassis-and-Cab and Stake models, which had eight bolts and eight circular openings. A four-speed manual synchromesh transmission was standard. No four-wheel-drive option was offered.

1-TON DUBL-DUTI — MODEL P33, P35, P36/SERIES 30 — SIX/V-8: Three Dubl-Duti Forward-Control chassis were in the 30 series (1-ton) truck line. The P33/P35/P36 models had wheelbases of 104 in./125 in./137 in., respectively. The 104-in. wheelbase was recommended for 7-ft. to 8-1/2-ft. bodies, the 125-in. wheelbase was recommended for 9-1/2 to 10-1/2-ft. long bodies, and the 137-in. wheelbase was recommended for 11-1/2-ft. to 12-1/2-ft. long bodies. Bodies could be sourced from factory approved firms or independent suppliers. A High-Torque 230 six-cylinder engine was standard equipment.

1964 Chevrolet 1/2-Ton Series C10-C14 Step-Side Pickup (OCW)

1964 Chevrolet 1/2-Ton El Camino Pickup (LC)

I.D. DATA: Serial number located: [Chassis models] On plate temporarily attached near steering column, with final location per body maker. [All others] On plate attached to rear face of left-hand door hinge pillar, on right side of cowl under hood. The first symbol indicated model-year, 4=1964. The second symbol (except El Caminos) indicated type: C=Conventional, K=4x4, R=Corvair 95, G=Chevy Van. The next two indicated the model prefix: Corvair 95=12, El Camino six=53, El Camino V-8=54, Custom El Camino six=55, Custom El Camino V-8=56, 1/2-ton standard wheelbase=14, 1/2-ton long wheelbase=15, 3/4-ton=25, 1-ton=36. The next symbol (or pair of symbols for El Caminos) indicated body style: 2=Chassis-and-Cowl, 3=Chassis-and-Cab, 4=Pickup, 5=Panel, 6=Carryall Suburban Carryall, 9=Platform/Stake, 80=Sedan-Pickup. The next symbol indicated the assembly plant: A=Atlanta, Ga., B=Baltimore, Md., C=Atlanta, Ga. BOP, F=Flint, Mich., G=Framingham, Mass., H=Fremont, Calif., J=Janesville, Wis., K=Kansas City, Mo., L=Los Angeles, Calif., N=Norwood, Ohio, O=Oakland, Calif., P=Pontiac, Mich., S=St. Louis, Mo., T=Tarrytown, N.Y., V=Southgate, Calif., W=Willow Run, Mich., Y=Wilmington, Del. (El Caminos were made at the A/B/H/K/L factories). Remaining symbols were the sequential production number starting with 100001 at each plant. Ending serial numbers not available. The Chevrolet engine had the source, date and type stamped on a serial number pad. Source codes were: F=Flint, Mich., T=Tonawanda, N.Y., C=Canada. Month codes were 1=Jan., 2=Feb., etc. Date codes were 01=first of month, etc. Corvair 95 prefix codes were: [Turbo Air 164 cid/95 hp] V/W, [Turbo Air 164 cid/110 hp] VB/WB. Commercial model engine prefix codes were: [High-Torque 153-cid/90-hp L4] F/FA, [High-Torque 230-cid/140-hp L6] N/ND/NE/NK/NL/NM/NQ/NU, [High-Torque 292-cid/165-hp L6] PG/PK/PV/PL, High-Torque 283-cid/175-hp V-8] M/MA. Engine serial numbers: [Six] Right side of block behind distributor, [V-8] Front of block below right-hand cylinder head. Engine serial numbers not available.

1964 Chevrolet 1/2-Ton Corvair 95 Rampside Pickup (CMD)

Model	Body Type	Price	Weight	Prod. Total
El Camino — Series 53/Series 55 — 115 in. w.b. — Six				
5380	Pickup	2267	2935	-
5580	Custom Pickup	2342	2935	-
El Camino — Series 54/Series 56 — 115 in. w.b. — V-8				
5480	Pickup	2367	2935	-
5680	Custom Pickup	2442	2935	-
NOTE 1: Total El Camino production was 36,615.				
Chevy Van — Model G/Series 10 — 90 in. w.b. — Four				
G1205	Panel	2067	2735	-
Corvair 95 — Model R12/Series 10 — 95 in. w.b. — Six				
R1254	Rampside	2136	2665	851
R1205	Corvan	2212	2800	8147
1/2-Ton Commercial — Model C14/Series 10 — 115 in. w.b.				
C1403	Chassis & Cab	1893	2810	-
C1434	Fleetside	2023	3205	-
C1404	Step-Side	2007	3175	-
C1405	Panel 7.5 ft.	2324	3405	-
C1406	Suburban (doors)	2629	3695	-
C1416	Suburban (gate)	2662	3705	-
1/2-Ton Commercial (4x4) — Model K14/Series 10 — 115 in. w.b.				
K1434	Fleetside	2674	-	-
K1404	Step-Side	2658	-	-
K1405	Panel 7.5 ft.	2975	-	-
K1406	Suburban (doors)	3280	-	-
K1416	Suburban (gate)	3313	-	-
1/2-Ton Commercial (Long Bed) — Model C15/Series 10 — 127 in. w.b.				
C1503	Chassis & Cab			-
C1534	Fleetside	2023	3205	-
C1504	Step-Side	2007	3175	-
1/2-Ton Comm. (Long Bed/4x4) — Model K15/Series 10 — 127 in. w.b.				
K1503	Chassis & Cab	2582	3430	-
K1534	Fleetside	2711	3825	-
K1504	Step-Side	2695	3790	-
1/2-Ton Dubl-Duti — Model P/Series 10 — 102 in. w.b.				
P1345	Step-Van	2477	3475	-
3/4-Ton Commercial — Model C25/Series 20 — 127 in. w.b.				
C2503	Chassis & Cab	2078	3230	-
C2534	Fleetside	2208	3710	-
C2504	Step-Side	2192	3665	-
C2509	Stake	2283	3855	-

Model	Body Type	Price	Weight	Prod. Total
1-Ton Commercial — Model C36/Series 30 — 133 in. w.b.				
C3603	Chassis & Cab	2235	3410	-
C3604	Step-Side	2370	3880	-
C3609	Stake 9 ft.	2482	4240	-
C3605	Panel 10.5 ft.	2794	4240	-
1-Ton — Model P/Series 30 — 104-137 in. w.b.				
P3345	Step-Van	3274	5030	-

1964 Chevrolet 1/2-Ton Series C10-C14 Custom Fleetside Pickup (CMD)

ENGINE: [Standard El Camino, Optional G10] Inline. OHV. Six-cylinder. Cast iron block. Bore & stroke: 3-9/16 in. x 3-1/4 in. Displacement: 194 cid. Compression ratio: 8.5:1. Brake horsepower: 120 at 4400 rpm. Maximum torque: 177 lb.-ft. at 2400 rpm. Seven main bearings. Hydraulic valve lifters. Carburetor: Rochester one-barrel model 7023105.
ENGINE: [Standard P10/G10] Inline. OHV. Four-cylinder. Cast iron block. Bore & stroke: 3-7/8 in. x 3-1/4 in. Displacement: 153.1 cid. Compression ratio: 8.5:1. Brake horsepower: 90 at 4000 rpm. Maximum torque: 152 lb.-ft. at 2400 rpm. Net horsepower: 75 at 4000 rpm. Five main bearings. Hydraulic valve lifters. Carburetor: Rochester one-barrel model 7020103.

1964 Chevrolet Corvair 95 Commercial Panel Truck (OCW)

ENGINE: [Standard Corvair 95] Opposed. OHV. Six-cylinder. Aluminum block. Bore & stroke: 3.437 in. x 2.938 in. Displacement: 163.6 cid. Compression ratio: 8.25:1. Brake horsepower: 95 at 3600 rpm. Four main bearings. Hydraulic valve lifters. Carburetor: Two Rochester one-barrel model 7019101.
ENGINE: [Optional Corvair 95] Opposed. OHV. Six-Cylinder. Aluminum block. Bore & Stroke: 3.437 in. x 2.938 in. Displacement: 163.6 cid. Compression ratio: 9.0:1. Brake horsepower: 110 at 3600 rpm. Four main bearings. Hydraulic valve lifters. Carburetor: Two Rochester single-barrel. (This engine available with three- or four-speed manual transmissions only).

1964 Chevrolet 1/2-Ton Series P10 Step-Van (CMD)

1964 Chevrolet 1/2-Ton Series C10-C14 Step-Side Pickup w/custom wheels (Lowell E. Eisenhour)

ENGINE: [Standard C-K10/C-K15/C-K20/C30/P20/P30/Optional P10/El Camino] Inline. OHV. Six-cylinder. Cast iron block. Bore & stroke: 3-7/8 in. x 3-1/4 in. Displacement: 230 cid. Compression ratio: 8.5:1. Brake horsepower: 140 at 4400 rpm. Maximum torque: 220 lb.-ft. at 1600 rpm. Net horsepower: 120 at 3600 rpm. Seven main bearings. Hydraulic valve lifters. Carburetor: Rochester model B-7023017.
ENGINE: [Optional C-K10/C-K15/C-K20/C30/P20/P30] Inline. OHV. Six-cylinder. Cast iron block. Bore & stroke: 3-7/8 in. x 4-1/4 in. Displacement: 292 cid. Compression ratio: 8.0:1. Brake horsepower: 165 at 3800 rpm. Maximum torque: 280 lb.-ft. at 1600 rpm. Net horsepower: 147 at 3600 rpm. Seven main bearings. Hydraulic valve lifters. Carburetor: Rochester one-barrel model B-7023013.

1964 Chevrolet 1/2-Ton Series C10-C14 Carryall Suburban and Panel (CMD)

ENGINE: [Optional C-K10/C-K15/C-K20/C30] V-type. OHV. Eight-cylinder. Cast iron block. Bore & stroke: 3-7/8 in. x 3 in. Displacement: 283 cid. Compression ratio: 9.0:1. Brake horsepower: 175 at 4400 rpm. Maximum torque: 275 lb.-ft. at 2400 rpm. Net horsepower: 145 at 4200 rpm. Five main bearings. Hydraulic valve lifters. Carburetor: Rochester model 2G-7023010.
ENGINE: [Optional El Camino] V-type. OHV. Eight-cylinder. Cast iron block. Bore & stroke: 3.875 in. x 3.0 in. Displacement: 283 cid. Compression ratio: 9.25:1. Brake horsepower: 195 at 4800 rpm. Five main bearings. Hydraulic valve lifters. Carburetor: Rochester two-barrel model 7024101.
ENGINE: [Optional El Camino] V-type. OHV. Eight-cylinder. Cast iron block. Bore & stroke: 4 x 3.25 in. Displacement: 327 cid. Compression ratio: 10.5:1. Brake horsepower: 250 at 4400 rpm. Maximum torque: 350 lb.-ft. at 2800 rpm. Carburetor: Four-barrel.
CHASSIS: [El Camino] Wheelbase: 115 in. Overall length: 198-1/4 in. Front tread: 58 in. Rear tread: 58 in. Tires: 7.00 x 14 in.
CHASSIS: [G10] Wheelbase: 90 in. Tires: 6.50 x 13 in.
CHASSIS: [95] Wheelbase: 95 in. Overall length: 179.7 in. Height: 68.5 in. Front tread: 58 in. Rear tread: 58 in. Tires: 7.00 x 14 in.

1964 Chevrolet 3/4-Ton Series C20-C15 Fleetside Pickup (OCW)

CHASSIS: [C14/K14] Wheelbase: 115 in. Overall length: [Pickup] 186-3/4 in., [Chassis-and-Cab] 180-1/4 in. Bed length: [Pickup] 78-1/8 in. Cab to rear axle on Chassis-and-Cab: 42 in. Cab to end of frame on Chassis-and-Cab: 75-1/2 in. Front tread: 63.1 in. Rear tread: 61 in. Tires: 6.70 x 15 in. Maximum GVW: [4x2] 4,600 lb., [4x4] 5,300 lb.
CHASSIS: [C15/K15] Wheelbase: 127 in. Overall length: [Pickup] 206-in., [Chassis-and-Cab] 200-1/4 in. Bed length: [Pickup] 98 in. Cab to rear axle on Chassis-and-Cab: 54 in. Cab to end of frame on Chassis-and-Cab: 95-1/2 in. Height: 71 in. Front tread: 63.1 in. Rear tread: 61.1 in. Tires: [C15] 6.70 x 15 in., [K15] 7 x 17.5 in. Maximum GVW: [4x2] 4,600 lb., [4x4] 5,600 lb.
CHASSIS: [C20/K20] Wheelbase: 127 in. Overall length: [Pickup] 206 in., [Stake] 210-3/4 in., [Chassis-and-Cab] 211-3/4 in. Bed length: [Pickup] 98 in., [Stake] 98 in. Bed width: [Stake] 85 in. Cab to rear axle on Chassis-and-Cab: 54 in. Cab to end of frame on Chassis-and-Cab: 95-1/2 in. Tires: 7 x 17.5 in. Maximum GVW: [4x2] 6,000 lb., [4x4] 6,800 lb.
CHASSIS: [C36] Wheelbase: 133 in. Overall length: [1-ton Step-Side Pickup] 216-1/4 in., [Stake] 221-3/8 in. [Chassis-and-Cab] 199-3/4 in. Bed length: [1-ton Step-Side Pickup] 108-1/4 in., [Stake] 109 in. Bed width: [Stake] 85 in. Tires: 8 x 17.5 in. Maximum GVW: 7,800 lb.
CHASSIS: [C36] Wheelbase: 157 in. Overall length: [Stake] 256-1/2 in. [Chassis-and-Cab] 200-1/4 in. Bed length: [Stake] 144 in. Bed width: [Stake] 85 in. Cab to rear axle on Chassis-and-Cab: 60 in. Cab to end of frame on Chassis-and-Cab: 107 in. Tires: 8 x 17.5 in. Maximum GVW: 7,800 lb.

1964 Chevrolet 1/2-Ton G10 Chevy Van Commercial Panel (CMD)

CHASSIS: [C10/K10] Wheelbase: 115 in. Overall length: 206 in. (115-in. wheelbase). Height: 71 in. Front tread: 63.1 in. Rear tread: 61.1 in.
CHASSIS: [P10] Wheelbase: 102 in. Tires: 6.70 x 15 in.
CHASSIS: [P20/P30] Wheelbase: 104 in.-137 in. Tires: 7 x 17.5 in.
TECHNICAL: Chevrolet three-speed manual transmission (Borg-Warner heavy-duty three-speed optional). [C30] 4F/1R, [Others] 3F/1R. Column-mounted gear shift lever. Single-plate, dry-disc clutch. Rear axle: [1/2-ton] semi-floating, [3/4-ton/1-Ton] full-floating. Base rear axles: [El Camino] 3.08:1, [Corvair 95] 3.55:1, [C-K10] 3.73:1, [C-K20] 4.11:1, [C30] 5.14:1. Four-wheel hydraulic, drum brakes. Brake linings: [Corvair 95] 11 x 2 in. [C-K10] 11 x 2.75 in., [C-K20/C30] 12 x 2 in., [El Camino] 9-1/2 x 2-1/2 in. Kelsey-Hayes pressed steel wheels.

1964 Chevrolet 1/2-Ton El Camino Pickup (CMD)

EL CAMINO OPTIONS: 230-cid/140-hp Turbo-Thrift six-cylinder engine for 13380 and 13580 models. 327-cid/ 250-hp Turbo-Fire V-8 engine for 13480 and 13680 models. Overdrive transmission. Four-speed synchromesh transmission. Powerglide transmission with six-cylinder engine. Powerglide transmission with V-8 engines. Power brakes. Power steering. Power windows. 3.36:1 ratio rear axle. Positraction rear axle. 66-plate 70-amp.-hr. heavy-duty battery. Metallic brake linings. Heavy-duty front and rear suspension. Temperature-controlled fan for 195-hp V-8 (included with Four Season air conditioner or optional V-8). 42-ampere Delcotron generator. 55-ampere Delcotron generator (included with air conditioning). 62-ampere Delcotron generator. 62-ampere Delcotron generator for use with air conditioner. Car-to-trailer plug-in electrical harness. Heavy-duty radiator. Electric tachometer. Speed and Cruise Control. Four Season air conditioning (includes 55-ampere Delcotron generator, heavy-duty radiator, and temperature-controlled fan. Soft-Ray tinted glass (all windows). Soft-Ray tinted glass in windshield only. Padded instrument panel. Driver and passenger seat belts, Custom, Custom Deluxe or Custom Deluxe with retractors. Bucket seats for models 13580 and 13680 only. Compass with integral battery and switch. Clock. Type A Comfort and Convenience equipment including outside rear view mirror, inside non-glare mirror, two-speed electric wiper/washer system for 13380 and 13560 models or 13480 and 13680 models. Type B Comfort and Convenience equipment including remote-control outside rear view mirror, inside non-glare mirror, two-speed electric wiper/washer system for 13380 and 13560 models or 13480 and 13680 models. Front bumper guard. Rear bumper guard. Low "D" note horn to supplement standard horn. Simulated wood trim steering wheel. AM/FM push-button radio. AM manual radio. AM push-button radio. Full wheelcovers. Simulated wire wheelcovers. 7.35 x 14 4-ply white sidewall tires. 7.75 x 14 4-ply black sidewall tires. 7.75 x 14 4-ply white sidewall tires. 7.75 x 14 8-ply black sidewall tires.
CORVAIR OPTIONS: (dealer prices): Custom Equipment Group, includes windshield molding, door inserts, nylon-and-vinyl seat, two-tone doors and steering wheel, right visor, left door arm rest, cigar lighter and dispatch box trim plate: R1205 with standard seat ($17.56), R1205 with full-length seat

($19.23), R1254 ($19.23). 110-hp engine ($20.90). Four-speed manual transmission ($71.10). Powerglide ($127.60). Gas heater ($71.10). Direct Air heater ($57.69). Manual radio ($37.22). Passenger car type tires: 7.00x14 four-ply rated whitewall ($24.70), 7.00 x 14 six-ply rated black sidewall ($34.16), 7.00x14 six-ply rated whitewall ($54.65), 7.00 x 14. Custom Chrome Trim, with wheelcovers ($16.75), without wheelcovers ($25.10). Two-tone paint: Pickups ($25.10), all others ($20.90). Wheelcovers for R1254 ($8.40), Greenbrier Custom ($6.73), standard Greenbrier ($8.40). Auxiliary seat, R1205 ($31.78). Air cleaner ($5.06). Positraction ($29.30). Body doors, R1205 ($62.70). Level pickup box floor, R1254 ($37.65). 35 amp. generator ($29.30). Laminated front glass ($4.20). Rear door glass ($10.07). Dual outside rear view mirrors ($7.54). Left- or right-hand fixed mirror ($3.77). Wire-control outside rear view mirror ($4.20). Heavy-duty shocks, except R1206 ($5.87). Heavy-duty front springs, includes heavy-duty shocks, except R1206 ($8.40). Windshield washer and two-speed wipers ($12.55).

NOTE 2: The prices above indicate dealer cost for the Corvair options.

1964 Chevrolet 1/2-Ton Series C10-C14 Custom Fleetside Pickup (OCW)

COMMERCIAL TRUCK OPTIONS: 292-cid six-cylinder engine ($75.25). 230-cid/120-hp six-cylinder engine in Step-Van ($50.20). 283-cid V-8 in C models and K20s ($92.00). Powerglide with heavy-duty radiator ($146.30). Step-Van, Borg-Warner three-speed manual transmission ($60 average). Four-speed manual transmission ($68 average). Heavy-duty battery ($5.87). Air cleaner with 230-cid six-cylinder engine ($5.06). Air cleaner with 292-cid six-cylinder engine ($1.72). Custom Appearance Group: C10/30 and K10 ($33.45), C10/20/30 and K10/20 ($40.13). No-Spin axle ($104.50). Positraction axle ($50.20). Vacuum power brakes ($35.12). Painted rear bumper ($16.75). Painted front bumper ($4.20). Spare wheel carrier (average $11). Custom chrome package ($41.80). Custom Comfort package ($42.66). Economy equipment ($5.87). Fuel filter ($5.87). Gauge package ($5.87). 42-ampere generator ($16.75). 55-ampere generator ($23.43). 62-ampere generator ($69.43). Laminated glass, except Step-Vans ($4.20). Soft-Ray windshield, except Carryall/Step-Van ($10.07). E-Z-Eye windshield, P10 ($15.08). Soft-Ray glass in all windows, except Step-Van ($11.74). E-Z-Eye windshield, P20/30 ($16.75). Soft-Ray glass, all Carryall Suburban windows ($15.08). Deluxe heater/defroster, except Step-Van ($53.11). Standard heater and defroster, except Step-Van ($41.80). Towing hooks ($10.07). Freewheeling hubs ($61.03). Lamp group ($20.90). Optional locks: Right-hand door ($1.29), side spare wheel ($5.06), Both ($5.87). 17-in. mirrors: left ($1.72), right-extended type ($3.77). 6 x 11-in. mirrors ($4.20 each). 7 x 16-in. mirrors ($12.55 each). C10 Custom side moldings ($25.10). Two-tone paint: pickup/cab ($12.55), Panel/Carryall Suburban ($20.90), 8-ft. Platform/Stake ($117.05). 9-ft. Platform/Stake ($142.15). 12-ft. Platform/Stake ($167.20). Heavy-duty radiator ($16.75). Radio ($37.22). Folding auxiliary seat for Panel ($31.78). Bostrom seat, except Step-Vans ($96.15). Tachometer ($37.65). Wipers and washers ($12.55).

NOTE 3: The prices above indicate dealer cost for the Commercial Truck options.

COLOR OPTIONS: [CHEVROLET 1964-1969]

Name	Ditzler Code	Model-Year(s)				
Argent Silver (Int.)	8568		67	66		
Anniversary Gold Poly	23048	68				
Balboa Blue	12409					64
Black (Exterior & Interior)	9000	69 68 67				
Black (Interior)	9248		68 67			
Black (Interior-flat)	9317	69				
Cameo White	8290		67	66	65	64
Cardinal Red	70704					64
Charcoal (Interior)	32325				65	
Charcoal Gray Poly (Interior)	32189	69 68 67	66	65	64	
Dark Aqua Poly	13184			66		
Dark Aqua Poly	43658		67			
Dark Blue	12409	69 68 67	66	65		
Dark Blue (Interior)	13823	69				
Dark Blue Poly (Interior)	13224		68			
Dark Blue Poly Suede (Interior)	13398		68 67			
Dark Fawn Suede (Interior)	22862		68 67			
Dark Green (Exterior/Interior)	42850	69 68 67				
Dark Green (Interior)	44041	69				
Dark Green Poly (Interior)	43622			66		
Dark Green Poly Suede (Interior)	43693		67			
Dark Green Poly (Interior)	43860		68			
Dark Red Suede (Interior)	71594		68 67			
Dark Red (Interior-flat)	71486	69				
Dark Red (Interior)	71670		68			
Dark Red (Interior)	71756	69				
Dark Saddle (Interior)	23201	69				
Dark Saddle Poly (Interior)	22974	69				
Dark Turquoise Poly (Interior)	13822	69				
Dark Turquoise Poly (Interior-flat)	13824	69				
Fawn	22567				65	
Fawn	22425					64
Fawn Poly (Interior)	22125			66	65	64
Fawn Poly (Interior)	22743			66		
Gray Green Poly	43277					64

Name	Ditzler Code	Model-Year(s)				
Ivory	8290		68 67			
Ivory (Interior)	8319		67	66	65	64
Light Blue	12846	69 68 67	66	65	64	
Light Gray	32374			66	65	64
Light Green (Interior/Exterior)	43523	69 68 67	66			
Light Green	42344				65	64
Light Yellow	81503		68			
Maroon Poly	2099	69				
Maroon Poly	50703				65	
Medium Blue Poly	13363		68 67			
Medium Blue Poly (Interior)	13391		67			
Medium Fawn Poly (Interior)	22151		67			
Medium Fawn Poly (Interior)	22858		67			
Medium Green Poly (Interior)	43687		67			
Medium Green Poly (Interior)	43861		68			
Omaha Orange	60156		67	66	65	64
Orange	61056	69 68				
Pure White	8080		67	66	65	64
Red (Exterior/Interior)	70704	69 68 67	66	65	64	
Red (Interior)	71671		68			
Red Poly (Interior)	21571			66		
Saddle Poly	2101	69				
Saddle Poly	26683		68	66		
Silver Fawn Poly (Interior)	23026		68			
Silver Poly (Interior/Exterior)	32537	69 68 67	66			
Tangier Gold Poly	22158					64
Turquoise Poly	2098	69				
Turquoise Poly	43276			66	65	64
Vermilion Poly	71581		68 67			
White	8080	69 68 67				
Woodland Green	42850		67	66	65	64
Yellow	81503		67	65		
Yellow-Green Poly	2097	69				
Yuma Yellow	81348		67	66	65	64

Specify DQE for alkyd enamel, DDL for acrylic lacquer, DAR for acrylic enamel, DL or DIA for interior.

OPTION PACKAGES: [Custom Appearance Equipment] Includes silver anodized radiator grille and headlamp door assembly, chrome-plated windshield reveal moldings, bright metal cab upper rear quarter panel trim plates, chrome horn ring steering wheel, chrome-trimmed instrument panel knobs, and two-tone inside front door panels. [Custom Comfort and Convenience Equipment] includes left door arm rest, outside key lock, chrome cigar lighter, full foam rubber seat cushion, special seat trim (cab models and Suburban), and added sound insulation. [Custom Chrome Equipment] chrome hubcaps. Not available with 4x4 or dual rear wheel options. [Side Trim Moldings] bright body side moldings for Fleetside models. (Package prices are given above).

HISTORICAL: Introduced Sept. 29, 1963. Model-year production: [All commercial] 523,791. Calendar-year registrations: [All commercial] 483,853. Innovations: Compact van series introduced midyear. El Camino reintroduced on Chevelle platform. New features of full-size trucks include self-adjusting brakes and 6,000 mile chassis lube intervals. The nine millionth Chevrolet truck of all time was produced this season. Model-year output of Corvair trucks was 15,199 units. This included 6,201 Greenbrier Sport Wagons, which were merchandised as a station wagon in the passenger car line and had a price of $2,666 and weight of 2,990 lb.

1965 CHEVROLET

1965 Chevrolet 1/2-Ton El Camino Sedan-Pickup (CMD)

EL CAMINO — MODEL A/SERIES 13000 — SIX/V-8: The intermediate-sized El Camino had a new vehicle-wide lattice-type silver-anodized radiator grille with new central emblem and bright moldings. It had a finer pattern and heavier horizontal center bar. Chevrolet's red, white and blue emblem was in the bar's mid-section. A massive new chrome wraparound front bumper was slotted. The front parking lamps were relocated into long, horizontal slots. Newly styled front fenders featured new engine emblems in front of the wheel openings. A newly styled hood featured Chevrolet lettering along its lip. Built on the mid-size Chevelle's 115-in. wheelbase, the El Camino was available with many passenger-car options. The low, sleek lines of the Sedan-Pickup were accented by curved side windows. All models had new rear quarter panel El Camino nameplates, bright body side lower moldings with black paint fill, chrome hubcaps, and bright vent window frames and posts. Bright moldings also adorned the pickup box, and the roof. El Caminos came with two trim levels. El Caminos in the 53 (six-cylinder) and 54 (V-8) series were the base models, with trim and appointments comparable to the Chevelle 300. Custom El Caminos in the 55 (six-cylinder) and 56 (V-8) series had trim and appointments comparable to the Chevelle Malibu. Custom El Caminos also had a new bright body sill molding, front and rear wheel opening moldings, a roof drip gutter molding, windshield pillar moldings, bright door frame moldings, and a chrome hood windsplit molding. All models had an all-steel perimeter frame with 12 body mounting points, box-section roof pillars, headers, and rails, a heavily ribbed underbody, a double-wall cowl, flush-and-dry rocker panels, protective inner fender skirts, and 6-month/6,000-mile chassis lubrication. The 1965 El Caminos came in 12 Mirror Magic acrylic lacquer finishes, 10 of which were new. Color choices included Tuxedo Black, Ermine White, Mist Blue, Danube Blue, Willow Green, Cypress Green, Artesian Turquoise, Tahitian Turquoise, Madeira Maroon, Evening Orchid, Regal Red, Sierra Tan, Cameo Beige, Glacier Gray, and Crocus Yellow. Color-keyed all-vinyl seats and sidewall trim were featured as standard equipment, along with an instrument cluster trim plate, steering wheel hub emblem, chrome door hardware, and two-key locking system. The standard interior also included an embossed vinyl headliner, dual sun visors, left- and right-hand arm rests, color-keyed vinyl floor mats, a cigar lighter, a dome lamp with door jamb switches, a horn ring, a lockable glove compartment, seat belts, and foam seat cushions. Fawn, aqua, or red interior trims were available according to the exterior finish color. Customs featured color-keyed pattern cloth and leather-grain vinyl upholstery with bright back rest trim plates, plus luxury carpeting, a bright glove box door trim plate and light, and a two-tone steering wheel, and an electric clock. A new vinyl bucket seat option included a vinyl spare wheel and tire cover and wheel trim disks. Other new options were an AM/FM radio and simulated wire wheel covers. The 1964-1967 El Camino style pickup box was used again. It featured rigid double-panel all-steel construction, a tailgate, and an all-steel box floor. There was an emblem and Chevrolet lettering in the center of the tailgate. The inside width of the pickup box was 59-3/4 in. behind the cab and 64-3/4 in. near the tailgate. There was 46 in. between the wheelhousings. The bed of the box was 78-1/2 in. long. The tailgate measured 55-1/2 in. x 23 in. With the bed-level tailgate lowered, the overall bed length was 101.6 in. At the rear was a massive chrome wraparound bumper with new integral back-up lamp provisions, plus bright rear roof peak, rear window, and tailgate moldings. Under the hood, El Camino buyers could get standard or optional six-cylinder engines, plus a standard 283-cid V-8 or choice of two optional 327-cid Turbo-Fire V-8s. All engines had automatic chokes, overhead valves, full-flow oil filters, 4-quart oil changes, Delcotron AC generators, a 54-plate battery, a positive crankcase ventilation system, and 6,000-mile/60-day oil change intervals. New engine features included oil-wetted paper air cleaner elements for V-8s and new oil pumps with thicker flanges for sixes.

1965 Chevrolet 1/2-Ton G10 Chevy Van Commercial Panel (CMD)

1/2-TON CHEVY VAN — MODEL G/SERIES 10 — FOUR: The compact, front-engine Chevy Van was now the only van Chevrolet offered. The Corvair 95 series was gone, taking with it the Corvan and the Rampside Pickup. Chevy Van styling characteristics again included five-segment vents on the front with a bow-tie underneath, and an oval, horizontal-bar grille near the bottom of the front single headlights. The Chevy Van had the same general characteristics, cab-over-engine configuration and 90-in. wheelbase as the Corvan, but it utilized a water-cooled 153-cid four-cylinder Chevy II engine as its base power plant. The 194-cid and 230-cid sixes were both available at extra-cost this year. Two models called the Panel and Sportvan were offered. The Sportvan was marketed as a truck, although it was available with windows and auxiliary passenger seats. Also offered were Sportvan Custom editions. The Commercial Panel had double right-hand side cargo doors. This was clearly a truck.

1965 Chevrolet 1/2-Ton K10 Standard 4x4 Fleetside Pickup (CMD)

1/2-TON COMMERCIAL — MODEL C14 (4x2), K14 (4x4)/SERIES 10 — SIX/V-8: The conventional trucks were unchanged in styling, trim or appointments, except for repositioning the identification badges higher on the cowl sides, above the main feature line. New on the option list this year was a factory air conditioning system. A new 327-cid V-8 was available in some trucks, too. An auxiliary hot water heater was available for the rear compartment of Carryall Suburbans. Even the grille was unchanged. It had thin vertical and horizontal elements in a tightly cross-hatched pattern. Black-accented Chevrolet lettering was on the top bar and the headlamp surrounds were square-shaped. The standard grille was made of steel painted off-white, as were bumpers and hubcaps. An anodized aluminum grille and body side moldings were part of several Custom Appearance Equipment packages. The cowl badges resembled a square and a rectangle separately framed in chrome. The square had a small Chevrolet bow tie. The rectangle had the series designation on a red background with vertical ribbing. Exterior colors for the year were Black, Dark Blue, Light Blue, Fawn Tan, Gray, Dark Green, Light Green, Maroon, Turquoise, White, Off-White, Dark Yellow, and Light Yellow. Colors (except the two whites) were used as lower body colors in two-tone color options. They were teamed with off-white on the upper body. Interiors were again done in two shades of fawn beige with off-white accenting the steering wheel and mast. Standard seats had medium fawn (beige)

embossed vinyl with light fawn facings. Custom interiors had color-keyed nylon-faced pattern cloth inserts and vinyl bolsters. The striped inserts were mostly medium fawn beige. Contrasting bolsters were red or fawn, depending upon the color of the truck, with a white bottom bolster. There were four separate Custom equipment options, which are listed in the options section below. Offered again were Step-Side Pickups (with pontoon rear fenders) and Fleetside Pickups (with slab type rear fenders) with 6-1/2-ft. boxes. Other models included the 7-1/2-ft. Panel and the Carryall Suburban with end gate or panel door options. Three chassis models were available, too. The 10 series Short Box four-wheel-drive 1/2-ton models had a K14 model prefix. The 1/2-ton trucks came with GVWs from 4,100 lb. to 5,000 lb. Up front was an independent front suspension with a 2,500-lb. axle. At the rear was a 3,500-lb. axle or a 3,500-lb. optional positraction rear axle. Self-adjusting four-wheel brakes were 11 x 2 in. front and rear with a total lining area of 167 in. A 10-in. clutch was standard. Engine choices included a 230-cid six, 292-cid six or 283-cid V-8. A 2.98-in. frame section modulus was standard. An 18-1/2-gallon fuel tank was standard, with a 21-gallon tank optional. Front and rear shock absorbers were provided. Up front were 1,250-lb. coil springs. In the rear were 1,250 lb. two-stage coil springs. A 17-in. steering wheel was used with a 24.0:1 ratio steering gear. Transmission choices included three-speed synchromesh, heavy-duty three-speed synchromesh, four-speed synchromesh or two-speed Powerglide. The standard 6.70 x 15 4-ply tires rode on 15 x 5.5-in. six-stud disc wheels.

1965 Chevrolet 1/2-Ton C10 Custom Fleetside Pickup (JAG)

1/2-TON COMMERCIAL — MODELS C15, K15/SERIES 10 — SIX/V-8: The C15 trucks in the Chevrolet 10 series long-wheelbase line used a C15 model prefix. Their cowl side nameplates were chrome and red badges with a bow tie and number 10. They had the same basic styling and trim changes as other conventional trucks. These were the long wheelbase (LWB) 1/2-ton trucks on the same chassis as 3/4-ton models. They are known as "Long Bed" or "Long Box" Pickups because they had a longer 8-ft. load box. Longer running boards were needed on Step-Sides because there was more space between the cab and rear fenders. The 10 series Long Bed four-wheel-drive models had a K15 model prefix. The 1/2-ton trucks came with GVWs from 4,100 lb. to 5000 lb. Up front was an independent front suspension with a 2500-lb. axle. At the rear was a 3500-lb. rear axle or a 3500-lb. optional positraction rear axle. Self-adjusting four-wheel brakes were 11 x 2 in. front and rear with a total lining area of 167 in. A 10-in. clutch was standard. Engine choices included a 230-cid six, 292-cid six or 283-cid V-8. A 2.98-in. frame section modulus was standard. An 18-1/2-gallon fuel tank was standard, with a 21-gallon tank optional. Front and rear shock absorbers were provided. Up front were 1,250-lb. coil springs. In the rear were 1,250 lb. two-stage coil springs. A 17-in. steering wheel was used with a 24.0:1 ratio steering gear. Transmission choices included three-speed synchromesh, heavy-duty three-speed synchromesh, four-speed synchromesh or two-speed Powerglide. The standard 6.70 x 15 4-ply tires rode on 15 x 5.5-in. six-stud disc wheels.

1965 Chevrolet 1/2-Ton C10 Custom Fleetside Pickup (JAG)

1/2-TON DUBL-DUTI — MODEL P13/SERIES 10 — SIX/V-8: The 1/2-ton Dubl-Duti returned again. It had a 102-in. wheelbase. An approved 7-ft. Step-Van walk-in delivery truck made by Union City Body Co., of Union City, Ind. was most commonly mounted on the Dubl-Duti chassis. A High-Torque 153 four-cylinder engine was standard equipment.
3/4-TON COMMERCIAL — MODEL C25/SERIES 20 — SIX/V-8: The C25 trucks in the Chevrolet 20 series 3/4-ton line had the same styling and trim changes as other conventional trucks. The cowl side nameplates were chrome and red badges with a bow tie emblem and chrome number 20. Step-Side and Fleetside Pickups were in this series. Compared to C10-C14 pickups, the C20-C25 pickup had slightly longer running boards and an 8-ft. Long Box was used. There were also Platform and Platform/Stake models. The rail for the 3/4-ton Platform was about

8-ft. long. The four-wheel-drive 3/4-ton models in the 20 series had a K25 model prefix. In midyear, a truck camper package (with chassis beefed-up for camper use) was released. These trucks had distinctive "Camper Special" badges. The 3/4-ton trucks came with GVWs from 5,500 lb. to 7,500 lb. Up front was an independent front suspension with a 3000-lb. axle. At the rear was a 5200-lb. rear axle or a 5200-lb. optional No-Spin rear axle. Self-adjusting four-wheel brakes were 11 x 2-3/4 in. front and rear with a total lining area of 239 sq. in. A 10-in. clutch was standard. Engine choices included a 230-cid six, 292-cid six or 283-cid V-8. A 3.71-in. frame section modulus was standard. An 18-1/2-gallon fuel tank was standard, with a 21-gallon tank optional. Front and rear shock absorbers were provided. Up front were 1,250-lb. coil springs. In the rear were 2,000 lb. two-stage coil springs. A 17-in. steering wheel was used with a 24.0:1 ratio steering gear. Transmission choices included three-speed synchromesh, heavy-duty three-speed synchromesh, four-speed synchromesh or two-speed Powerglide. The standard 17.5 x 5.25 6-ply tires rode on 17.5 x 5.25-in. eight-stud disc wheels.

1965 Chevrolet 3/4-Ton C20 Stake with dual rear wheels (CMD)

3/4-TON DUBL-DUTI — MODEL P23, P25, P26/SERIES 20 — SIX/V-8: Three 3/4-ton Dubl-Duti Forward-Control chassis remained in the 20 series (3/4-ton) truck line. The P23/P25/P26 models had wheelbases of 104 in./125 in./137 in., respectively. The 104-in. wheelbase was recommended for 7-ft. to 8-1/2-ft. bodies, the 125-in. wheelbase was recommended for 9-1/2 to 10-1/2-ft. long bodies and the 137-in. wheelbase was recommended for 11-1/2-ft. to 12-1/2-ft. long bodies. Bodies could be sourced from factory approved firms or independent suppliers. A High-Torque 230 six was standard equipment.

1-TON MEDIUM-DUTY COMMERCIAL — MODEL C36, C38/SERIES 30 — SIX-CYLINDER: The Chevrolet 30 series 1-ton trucks had the same styling and trim changes as other conventional trucks. The fender side nameplates were chrome and red badges with a Chevrolet bow tie and number 30. There was no Fleetside Pickup in this line. The 10-ft. Panel model had a one-piece floor made of 3/4-in. thick, five-ply laminated wood. The basic model lineup was unchanged. Compared to the C20-C25 Pickup, the C30-C36 Pickup had a longer wheelbase, a longer 9-ft. box and very long running boards. The 1-ton Stake trucks had a long rail some 9-ft. long. No hubcaps were used on the larger split-rim wheels of the Chassis-and-Cab and Stake models, which had eight bolts and eight circular openings. There was a new midyear Camper Special package with "Camper Special" badges in place of 30 series call-outs. There was also a C38 model 1-ton Chassis-and-Cab with a long 157-in. wheelbase. It was perfectly suited for use a recreational vehicle (RV) chassis. No four-wheel-drive option was offered. The 1-ton trucks came with GVWs from 6,700 lb. to 10,000 lb. Up front was an independent front suspension with a 3500-lb. axle. At the rear was a 7200-lb. rear axle or a 7200-lb. optional No-Spin rear axle. Self-adjusting four-wheel brakes were 11 x 2-1/4 in. in front and 13 x 2-1/2-in. in the rear with a total lining area of 252 sq. in. An 11-in. clutch was standard. Engine choices included a 230-cid six, 292-cid six or 283-cid V-8. A 5.05-in. (3600) or 7.29-in. (3800) frame section modulus was standard. An 18-1/2-gallon fuel tank was standard, with a 21-gallon tank optional. Front shock absorbers were standard and heavy-duty front and rear shock absorbers were available. Up front were 1500-lb. coil springs. In the rear were 2,400-lb. leaf springs 52 in. long. A 2-1/2 in. wide. A 17-in. steering wheel was used with a 24.0:1 ratio steering gear. A four-speed synchromesh transmission was standard and the heavy-duty three-speed synchromesh gear box was optional. The standard 8 x 17.5 (6-ply front/8-ply rear) tires rode on 17.5 x 5.25-in. eight-stud disc wheels.

1-TON DUBL-DUTI — MODEL P33, P35, P36/SERIES 30 — SIX/V-8: Three Dubl-Duti Forward-Control chassis were in the 30 series (1-ton) truck line. The P33/P35/P36 models had wheelbases of 104 in./125 in./137 in., respectively. The 104-in. wheelbase was recommended for 7-ft. to 8-1/2-ft. bodies, the 125-in. wheelbase was recommended for 9-1/2 to 10-1/2-ft. long bodies and the 137-in. wheelbase was recommended for 11-1/2-ft. to 12-1/2-ft. long bodies. Bodies could be sourced from factory approved firms or independent suppliers. A High-Torque 230 six was standard equipment.

1965 Chevrolet 1/2-Ton C10 Standard Fleetside Pickup with custom wheels (DFW)

1965 Chevrolet 1/2-Ton C10 Custom Fleetside Long Box Pickup (CMD)

I.D. DATA: Serial number located: [Chassis models] on plate temporarily attached near steering column, with final location per body maker. [All others] on plate attached to rear face of left-hand door hinge pillar, on right side of cowl under hood. The first symbol (first three El Camino) indicated truck type: 133/134/135/136=El Camino, C=Conventional Cab, K=4x4, G=Chevy Van, P=Dubl-Duti Package Delivery, G=Chevy Van. The next two symbols on El Caminos indicated model (80=Sedan-Pickup), next two symbols on other trucks indicated the series: 14=1/2-ton, 15=1/2-ton LWB, 25=3/4-ton, 36=1-ton, 38=1-ton LWB. The next symbol indicated body type: 2=Chassis-and-Cowl, 3=Chassis-and-Cab, 4=Pickup, 5=Panel, 6=Carryall Suburban, 9=Stake. The next symbol (all) indicated model-year: 5=1965. The next symbol (all) identified assembly plant: [Commercial] A=Atlanta, Ga., B=Baltimore, Md., F=Flint, Mich., J=Janesville, Wis., N=Norwood, Ohio, P=Pontiac, Mich., S=St. Louis, Mo., T=Tarrytown, N.Y., Z=Fremont, Calif. [El Camino] A=Lakewood, Atlanta, Ga., B=Baltimore, Md., G=Framingham, Mass., K=Leeds, Kansas City, Mo., Z=Fremont, Calif. Remaining symbols were the sequential production number starting with 100001 at each plant. Ending serial numbers not available. The Chevrolet engine had the source, date and type stamped on a serial number pad. Source codes were: F=Flint, Mich., T=Tonawanda, N.Y., C=Canada. Month codes were 1=Jan., 2=Feb., etc. Date codes were 01=first of month, etc. Commercial model engine prefix codes were: [Hi-Torque 153-cid/90-hp L4] SA/SB/SC/SE, [High-Torque 194-cid/120-hp L6] SG/SI, [High-Torque 230-cid/140-hp Chevy Vans] SK/SL, [High-Torque 230-cid/140-hp L6 C/K/P] TA/TE/TF/TH/TI/TJ/TK/UH/UI/UU/UV, High-Torque 283-cid/175-hp V-8] WA/WE/WC/WF., [327-cid/185-hp V-8 (after midyear)] YD/YC/YR/YS/YH. Engine serial numbers: [Six] Right side of block behind distributor, [V-8] front of block below right-hand cylinder head. Engine serial numbers not available.

1965 Chevrolet 1/2-Ton El Camino Sedan-Pickup (CMD)

Model	Body Type	Price	Weight	Prod. Total
El Camino — Model A/Series 13000 — 115 in. w.b. — Six				
13380	Pickup	2272	2925	Note 1
13580	Custom Pickup	2353	2935	Note 1
El Camino — Model A/Series 13000 — 115 in. w.b. — V-8				
13480	Pickup	2380	3060	Note 1
13680	Custom Pickup	2461	3060	Note 1
NOTE 1: Total El Camino production was 36,316.				
Chevy Van — Model G/Series 10 — 90 in. w.b. — Four				
G1205	Panel	2105	2610	-
G1206	Sportvan	2355	2870	-
G1226	Custom Sportvan	2492	2970	-
G1236	Deluxe Sportvan	2717	3115	-
1/2-Ton Commercial — Model C14/Series 10 — 115 in. w.b.				
C1403	Chassis & Cab	1894	2830	-
C1434	Fleetside	2023	3205	-
C1404	Step-Side	2007	3190	-
C1405	Panel 7.5 ft.	2324	3420	-
C1406	Suburban (door)	3281	3680	-
C1416	Suburban (gate)	3314	3710	-
1/2-Ton Commercial (4x4) — Model K14/Series 10 — 115 in. w.b.				
K1434	Fleetside	2675	3825	-
K1404	Step-Side	2659	3805	-
K1405	Panel 7.5 ft	2976	4080	-
K1406	Suburban (door)	3270	4385	-
K1416	Suburban (gate)	3303	4415	-
1/2-Ton Commercial (Long Bed) — Model C15/Series 10 — 127 in. w.b.				
C1503	Chassis & Cab			-
C1534	Fleetside	2060	3315	-
C1504	Step-Side	2044	3300	-
1/2-Ton Comm. (Long Bed/4x4) — Model K15/Series 10 — 127 in. w.b.				
K1503	Chassis & Cab	2584	3445	-
K1534	Fleetside	2713	3840	-
K1504	Step-Side	2697	3805	-

Model	Body Type	Price	Weight	Prod. Total
1/2-Ton Dubl-Duti — Model P/Series 10 — 102 in. w.b.				
P1345	Step-Van	2477	3475	-
3/4-Ton Commercial — Model C25/Series 20 — 127 in. w.b.				
C2503	Chassis & Cab	2078	3230	-
C2534	Fleetside	2208	3710	-
C2504	Step-Side	2192	3665	-
C2509	Stake	2283	3855	-
3/4-Ton Commercial (4x4) — Model K25/Series 20 — 127 in. w.b.				
K2503	Chassis & Cab	2756	3805	-
K2534	Fleetside	2885	4270	-
K2504	Step-Side	2869	4225	-
3/4-Ton Dubl-Duti — Model P/Series 20 — 104-137 in. w.b.				
P2345	Step-Van	3081	4825	-
1-Ton Commercial — Model C36/Series 30 — 133 in. w.b.				
C3603	Chassis & Cab	2235	3410	-
C3604	Step-Side	2370	3880	-
C3609	Stake 9 ft.	2482	4240	-
C3605	Panel 10.5 ft.	2794	4240	-
1-Ton — Model P/Series 30 — 104-137 in. w.b.				
P3345	Step-Van	3274	5030	-

1965 Chevrolet 1/2-Ton El Camino Sedan-Pickup with modern wheels (DFW)

ENGINE: [Standard El Camino, Optional G10] Inline. OHV. Six-cylinder. Cast iron block. Bore & stroke: 3-9/16 in. x 3-1/4 in. Displacement: 194 cid. Compression ratio: 8.5:1. Brake horsepower: 120 at 4400 rpm. Maximum torque: 177 lb.-ft. at 2400 rpm. Seven main bearings. Hydraulic valve lifters. Carburetor: Rochester one-barrel model 7023105.
ENGINE: [Standard P10/G10] Inline. OHV. Four-cylinder. Cast iron block. Bore & stroke: 3-7/8 in. x 3-1/4 in. Displacement: 153.1 cid. Compression ratio: 8.5:1. Brake horsepower: 90 at 4000 rpm. Maximum torque: 152 lb.-ft. at 2400 rpm. Net horsepower: 75 at 4000 rpm. Five main bearings. Hydraulic valve lifters. Carburetor: Rochester one-barrel model 7020103.
ENGINE: [Standard C-K10/C-K15/C-K20/C30/P20/P30/Optional P10/El Camino] Inline. OHV. Six-cylinder. Cast iron block. Bore & stroke: 3-7/8 in. x 3-1/4 in. Displacement: 230 cid. Compression ratio: 8.5:1. Brake horsepower: 140 at 4400 rpm. Maximum torque: 220 lb.-ft. at 1600 rpm. Net horsepower: 120 at 3600 rpm. Seven main bearings. Hydraulic valve lifters. Carburetor: Rochester model B-7023017.
ENGINE: [Optional C-K10/C-K15/C-K20/C30/P20/P30] Inline. OHV. Six-cylinder. Cast iron block. Bore & stroke: 3-7/8 in. x 4-1/4 in. Displacement: 292 cid. Compression ratio: 8.0:1. Brake horsepower: 165 at 3800 rpm. Maximum torque: 280 lb.-ft. at 1600 rpm. Net horsepower: 147 at 3600 rpm. Seven main bearings. Hydraulic valve lifters. Carburetor: Rochester one-barrel model B-7023013.
ENGINE: [Optional C-K10/C-K15/C-K20/C30] V-type. OHV. Eight-cylinder. Cast iron block. Bore & stroke: 3-7/8 in. x 3 in. Displacement: 283 cid. Compression ratio: 9.0:1. Brake horsepower: 175 at 4400 rpm. Maximum torque: 275 lb.-ft. at 2400 rpm. Net horsepower: 145 at 4200 rpm. Five main bearings. Hydraulic valve lifters. Carburetor: Rochester model 2G-7023010.
ENGINE: [Optional El Camino] V-type. OHV. Eight-cylinder. Cast iron block. Bore & stroke: 3.875 in. x 3.0 in. Displacement: 283 cid. Compression ratio: 9.25:1. Brake horsepower: 195 at 4800 rpm. Five main bearings. Hydraulic valve lifters. Carburetor: Rochester two-barrel model 7024101.
ENGINE: [Optional El Camino] V-type. OHV. Eight-cylinder. Cast iron block. Bore & stroke: 4 x 3.25 in. Displacement: 327 cid. Compression ratio: 10.5:1. Brake horsepower: 250 at 4400 rpm. Maximum torque: 350 lb.-ft. at 2800 rpm. Carburetor: Four-barrel.
ENGINE: [Optional El Camino] V-type. OHV. Eight-cylinder. Cast iron block. Bore & stroke: 4 x 3.25 in. Displacement: 327 cid. Compression ratio: 10.5:1. Brake horsepower: 300 at 5000 rpm. Maximum torque: 360 lb.-ft. at 3200 rpm. Carburetor: Four-barrel.
ENGINE: [Optional El Camino] V-type. OHV. Eight-cylinder. Cast iron block. Bore & stroke: 4 x 3.25 in. Displacement: 327 cid. Compression ratio: 11.0:1. Brake horsepower: 350 at 5800 rpm. Torque: 360 lb.-ft. at 3200 rpm. Carburetor: Four-barrel. (Special order option)

1965 Chevrolet 1/2-Ton C10 Standard Fleetside Pickup (CMD)

ENGINE: [Optional El Camino] V-type. OHV. Eight-cylinder. Cast iron block. Bore & stroke: 4.09 x 3.76 in. Displacement: 396 cid. Compression ratio: 11.0:1. Brake horsepower: 375. Carburetor: Four-barrel.
CHASSIS: [El Camino] Wheelbase: 115 in. Overall length: 201.3 in. Overall width: 73.2 in. Loaded overall height: 54.1 in. Tailgate opening at floor: 55.5 in. Tailgate to ground (open and loaded): 15.1 in. Box length at floor with tailgate open: 101.5 in. Box length at floor with tailgate closed: 78.5 in. Box capacity: 38.5 cu.-ft. Front tread: 58 in. Rear tread: 58 in. Tires: 7.35 x 14 in. GVW rating: 4,200 lb.
CHASSIS: [G10] Wheelbase: 90 in. Tires: 6.50 x 13 in.
CHASSIS: [C14/K14] Wheelbase: 115 in. Overall length: [Pickup] The 1/2-ton trucks came with GVWs from 4,100 lb. to 5000 lb. Up front was an independent front suspension with a 2500-lb. axle. At the rear was a 3500-lb. rear axle or a 3500-lb. optional positraction rear axle. Self-adjusting four-wheel brakes were 11 x 2 in. front and rear with a total lining area of 167 in. A 10-in. clutch was standard. Engine choices included a 230-cid six, 292-cid six or 283-cid V-8. A 2.98-in. frame section modulus was standard. An 18-1/2-gallon fuel tank was standard, with a 21-gallon tank optional. Front and rear shock absorbers were provided. Up front were 1,250-lb. coil springs. In the rear were 1,250 lb. two-stage coil springs. A 17-in. steering wheel was used with a 24.0:1 ratio steering gear. Transmission choices included three-speed synchromesh, heavy-duty three-speed synchromesh, four-speed synchromesh or two-speed Powerglide. The standard 6.70 x 15 4-ply tires rode on 5.5-in. six-stud disc wheels.
CHASSIS: [C15/K15] Wheelbase: 127 in. Overall length: [Pickup] 206-in., [Chassis-and-Cab] 200-1/4 in. Bed length: [Pickup] 98 in. Cab to rear axle on Chassis-and-Cab: 54 in. Cab to end of frame on Chassis-and-Cab: 95-1/2 in. Height: 71 in. Front tread: 63.1 in. Rear tread: 61.1 in. Tires: [C15] 6.70 x 15 in., [K15] 7 x 17.5 in. Maximum GVW: [4x2] 4,600 lb., [4x4] 5,600 lb.
CHASSIS: [C20/K20] Wheelbase: 127 in. Overall length: [Pickup] 206 in., [Stake] 210-3/4 in., [Chassis-and-Cab] 211-3/4 in. Bed length: [Pickup] 98 in., [Stake] 98 in. Bed width: [Stake] 85 in. Cab to rear axle on Chassis-and-Cab: 54 in. Cab to end of frame on Chassis-and-Cab: 95-1/2 in. Tires: 7 x 17.5 in. Maximum GVW: [4x2] 6,000 lb., [4x4] 6,800 lb.
CHASSIS: [C36] Wheelbase: 133 in. Overall length: [1-ton Step-Side Pickup] 216-1/4 in., [Stake] 221-3/8 in., [Chassis-and-Cab] 199-3/4 in. Bed length: [1-ton Step-Side Pickup] 108-1/2 in., [Stake] 109 in. Bed width: [Stake] 85 in. Tires: 8 x 17.5 in. Maximum GVW: 7,800 lb.
CHASSIS: [C36] Wheelbase: 157 in. Overall length: [Stake] 256-1/2 in. [Chassis-and-Cab] 200-1/4 in. Bed length: [Stake] 144 in. Bed width: [Stake] 85 in. Cab to rear axle on Chassis-and-Cab: 60 in. Cab to end of frame on Chassis-and-Cab: 107 in. Tires: 8 x 17.5 in. Maximum GVW: 7,800 lb.
CHASSIS: [P10] Wheelbase: 102 in. Tires: 7.75 x 15 in.
CHASSIS: [P20/P30] Wheelbase: 104 in. Tires: 7.75 x 15 in.

1965 Chevrolet 1/2-Ton C10 Standard Fleetside Pickup (CMD)

TECHNICAL: Chevrolet three-speed manual transmission (Borg-Warner heavy-duty three-speed optional). [C30] 4F/1R, [Others] 3F/1R. Column-mounted gear shift lever. Single-plate, dry-disc clutch. Rear axle: [1/2-ton] semi-floating, [3/4-ton/1-Ton] full-floating. Base rear axles: [El Camino] 3.08:1, [Corvair 95] 3.55:1, [C-K10] 3.73:1, [C-K20] 4.11:1, [C30] 5.14:1. Four-wheel hydraulic, drum brakes. Brake linings: [Corvair 95] 11 x 2 in. [C-K10] 11 x 2.75 in., [C-K20/C30] 12 x 2 in., [El Camino] 9-1/2 x 2-1/2 in. Kelsey-Hayes pressed steel wheels.
EL CAMINO OPTIONS: 230-cid/140-hp Turbo-Thrift six-cylinder engine for 13380 and 13580 models. 327-cid/ 250-hp Turbo-Fire V-8 engine for 13480 and 13680 models. 327-cid/300-hp Turbo-Fire V-8 for 13480 and 13680 models. Overdrive transmission. Four-speed synchromesh transmission. Powerglide transmission with six-cylinder engine. Powerglide transmission with V-8 engine. Power brakes. Power steering. 3.36:1 ratio rear axle. Positraction rear axle. 66-plate 70-amp.-hr. heavy-duty battery. Metallic brake linings. Heavy-duty front and rear suspension. Temperature-controlled fan for 195-hp V-8 (included with Four Season air conditioner or optional V-8). 42-ampere Delcotron generator. 55-ampere Delcotron generator (included with air conditioning). 62-ampere Delcotron generator. 62-ampere Delcotron generator for use with air conditioner. Car-to-trailer plug-in electrical harness. Heavy-duty radiator. Electric tachometer. Speed and Cruise Control. Four Season air conditioning (includes 55-ampere Delcotron generator, heavy-duty radiator, and temperature-controlled fan. Soft-Ray tinted glass (all windows). Soft-Ray tinted glass in windshield only. Padded instrument panel. Driver and passenger seat belts, Custom, Custom Deluxe or Custom Deluxe with retractors. Bucket seats for models 13580 and 13680 only. Compass with integral battery and switch. Clock. Type A Comfort and Convenience equipment including outside rear view mirror, inside non-glare mirror, two-speed electric wiper/washer system for 13380 and 13560 models or 13480 and 13680 models. Type B Comfort and Convenience equipment including remote-control outside rear view mirror, inside non-glare mirror, two-speed electric wiper/washer system for 13380 and 13560 models or 13480 and 13680 models. Front bumper guard. Rear bumper guard. Low "D" note horn to supplement standard horn. Simulated wood trim steering wheel. AM/FM push-button radio. AM manual radio. AM push-button radio. Full wheelcovers. Simulated wire wheelcovers. 7.35 x 14 4-ply white sidewall tires. 7.75 x 14 4-ply black sidewall tires. 7.75 x 14 4-ply white sidewall tires. 7.75 x 14 8-ply black sidewall tires.
CORVAIR 95 OPTIONS: 164-cid/110-hp P-6 Turbo-Air engine. Powerglide automatic transmission. Four-speed synchromesh transmission. Forced-air heater and defroster. Aircraft-type gasoline heater and defroster. Deluxe equipment including anodized aluminum glove box trim plate, chrome front and rear bumpers, chrome hubcaps, cigarette lighter, front and rear dome lamp, red inserts

for rear door cove, right-hand sun shade, stainless steel windshield reveal moldings, vinyl spare tire cover, special roof panel paint treatment, left- and right-hand front door arm rests, rear ash tray in front seat back, two-tone steering wheel, vinyl seat trim, vinyl-coated rubber floor covering, vinyl door and sidewall trim pads, four interior colors keyed to exterior color and foam pad for seat back rest. Rear seat. Seat belts with retractors. Double left-hand side doors. Chrome front and rear bumpers. Wheel trim covers. Laminated safety glass in front door windows. 7.00 x 14 white sidewall tires. Two-speed electric windshield wiper and washer. Outside rear view mirror. West Coast type outside rear view mirror. Two-tone finish. Manual radio and antenna. Heavy-duty front springs. Positraction rear axle. Oil bath air cleaner. 12-47-ampere AC generator. Hazard warning switch. Camper unit. Window screens. Car top sleeper and ladder. Table 2x4-ft. Pop-up tent. Type A Comfort and Convenience equipment including outside rear view mirror, inside non-glare mirror, two-speed electric wiper/washer system for 13380 and 13560 models or 13480 and 13680 models.

1965 Chevrolet 1/2-Ton C10 Standard Step-Side Pickup (CMD)

COMMERCIAL TRUCK OPTIONS:: 293-cid V-8 ($92). 292-cid six-cylinder $75.25. Oil bath air cleaner ($5.06). Positraction ($50.20). No-Spin rear axle ($104.50). Rear axle, 3.07:1 ratio, with stick ($10.07). Rear axle, 4.11:1 ratio, with stick ($6.73). Heavy-duty battery ($5.87). Painted rear bumper on C/K Pickups with painted front bumper ($16.75). Heavy-duty 11-in. clutch with six-cylinder engine only ($4.20). Custom Appearance option: Panel ($33.45), others ($40.13). Custom Chrome option: Pickup with chrome front bumper ($16.75), Pickup with two chrome bumpers ($41.80), Panel with two chrome bumpers ($25.10). Custom Comfort option, Panel ($9.21), others ($42.66). Fleetside Custom side moldings ($25.10). Delcotron alternators: 42-amp. ($16.75), 52-amp. ($23.43). Tinted glass ($11.74). Tinted windshield ($10.07). Deluxe heater ($53.11). Thrift-Air heater ($41.80). Outside rear view mirrors: 17-1/4 in. left, except Panel ($1.72), right, except Panel ($3.77), 6-1/4 in. ($3.77). Tu-tone paint: Panel ($20.90), other trucks ($12.55). Heavy-duty radiator, except with Powerglide ($16.75). Radio ($37.22). Auxiliary Panel truck seat ($31.78). Foam seat ($16.75). Heavy-duty front shocks (average $6). Heavy-duty rear shocks ($6.73). Heavy-duty front springs, C25 ($2.53). Heavy-duty rear springs, all ($5.06). Heavy-duty three-speed transmission: C14 ($58.55), C15 ($62.70) and C25 ($71.10). Heavy-duty four-speed transmission: C14 ($62.70), C15 ($66.90) and C25 ($75.25). Powerglide, all ($146.30). Full-View rear window, except Panel ($33.45). Two-speed windshield washers and wipers ($12.55).
COLOR OPTIONS: See 1964 options section for complete chart of 1964-1969 Chevrolet Commercial Truck colors.
OPTION PACKAGES: [Custom Appearance Equipment] Includes silver anodized radiator grille and headlamp door assembly, chrome-plated windshield reveal moldings, bright metal cab upper rear quarter panel trim plates, chrome horn ring steering wheel, chrome-trimmed instrument panel knobs, and two-tone inside front door panels. [Custom Comfort and Convenience Equipment] includes left door arm rest, outside key lock, chrome cigar lighter, full foam rubber seat cushion, special seat trim (cab models and Suburban), and added sound insulation. [Custom Chrome Equipment] chrome hubcaps. Not available with 4x4 or dual rear wheel options. [Side Trim Moldings] bright body side moldings for Fleetside models.
NOTE 2: Package prices are given under "options" above.

1965 Chevrolet 1/2-Ton C10 End Gate Carryall Suburban (CMD)

HISTORICAL: Introduced: Sept. 24, 1964. Model-year production: [All Commercials] 619,685. Commercial model (not El Camino) calendar-year registrations: 567,473. Commercial model calendar-year factory shipments by GVW class: [6,000 lb. and less] 427,100, [6,001-10,000 lb.] 111,600. Retail sales: 574,120 units (up 15.6 percent). Innovations: Larger six-cylinder engine for vans. 327-cid V-8 released at midyear. New midyear truck-camper options. First year for factory air conditioning. Chevrolet showcased the Turbo Titan III, a gas-turbine powered experimental truck, in 1965. Chevy called it the "Truck of Tomorrow." The 1965 Chevrolet commercial vehicles were advertised as "Work Power" trucks. This was an all-time record season for America's number one truck-maker and the first in which registrations broke the 500,000 level. Chevrolet claimed that, by the end of 1965, there were 4,751,127 Chevrolet trucks operating in the U.S.

EL CAMINO — MODEL A/SERIES 13000 — SIX/V-8: An all-new Chevelle body was used for the El Camino, although the pickup box was unchanged. It had a slanted front end. The front fenders had a wraparound design. A new grille was lower and wider. It had multiple horizontal blades and wider-spaced vertical blades with a Chevrolet emblem in its center. There were two slots inside the bumper that were shorter and wider than in 1968. Following the Chevelle's every-other-year pattern, the parking lights were moved to a position inside the bumper slots below the headlamps. There was a new dashboard and new hubcaps, too. Redesigned full wheelcovers had a spoked, rather than finned, look. There were engine designation badges on the front fender, El Camino nameplates on the rear fenders, and a tailgate with a bright latch and Chevrolet lettering. Even the standard model had bright windshield frames and a chrome hood windsplit molding. The El Camino Custom added bright side and rear window frames, moldings on the upper edge of the pickup box and wide rocker panel moldings with rear quarter panel extensions. There was no official Super Sport option this year, although the 396-cid V-8 was available as a separate option. Exterior colors for 1966 were Tuxedo Black, Ermine White, Mist Blue, Danube Blue, Marina Blue, Willow Green, Artesian Turquoise, Tropic Turquoise, Aztec Bronze, Madeira Maroon, Regal Red, Sandalwood Tan, Cameo Beige, Chateau Slate, and Lemonwood Yellow. The standard interior trims were fawn (beige), blue or red vinyl. Custom interiors came with still richer all-vinyl trims in black, fawn or red. Bucket seats were optional. The pickup box inside width was 59-3/4 in. behind the cab and 64-3/4 in. near the tailgate. There was 46 in. between the wheelhousings. The bed of the box was 78-1/2 in. long. The tailgate measured 55-1/2 in. x 23 in. With the bed-level tailgate lowered, the overall bed length was 101.6 in.

1966 Chevrolet 1/2-Ton El Camino "SS-396" Sedan-Pickup (CMD)

1/2-TON CHEVY VAN — MODEL G/SERIES 10 — FOUR: The compact, front-engine Chevy Van was basically unchanged for 1966. Styling characteristics again included five-segment vents on the front with a bow-tie underneath and an oval, horizontal-bar grille near the bottom of the front single headlights. It had the same general characteristics and 90-in. wheelbase. The 153-cid four-cylinder Chevy II engine was dropped. A 194-cid six-cylinder engine was standard equipment. The 230-cid six was available at extra-cost. It was available in two models called the Panel and Sportvan. The Sportvan was marketed as a truck, although it was available with windows and auxiliary passenger seats. Also offered were Sportvan Custom and Sportvan Deluxe editions. The Commercial Panel had double right-hand side cargo doors and was clearly a truck. There was a new pop-up camper option.
1/2-TON COMMERCIAL — MODEL C14 (4x2), K14 (4x4)/SERIES 10 — SIX/V-8: Front end sheet metal was unchanged for 1966. Designation plates were moved below the feature line, behind the front wheel opening. They had a rectangular shape with two rectangular plaques on the surface. The narrower rectangle on top. It was satin-finished and carried a blue bow tie. The larger bottom rectangle had a chrome "10" and red background with horizontal grooves. Standard equipment on all light-duty trucks included seat belts, dual long-arm mirrors, two-speed wiper washers, and back-up lamps. Exterior colors were Dark Aqua Metallic, Black, Dark Blue, Light Blue, Gray Metallic, Dark Green, Light Green, Orange, Red, Saddle Metallic, Silver Metallic, White, Off-White, and School Bus Yellow. All metal interior parts were medium fawn. Non-glare dark fawn was on the instrument panel, which had a silver face plate. The steering column was medium fawn and the steering wheel had a chrome, half-circle horn ring. The glove box door was silver gray with black Chevrolet lettering. Standard upholstery was medium fawn textured vinyl with embossed surfaces and fawn seat belts. A black rubber floor mat was used. The Custom Comfort interior option included nylon-faced cloth upholstery in a medium and dark brown two-tone pattern with white vinyl back rest inserts. Custom trim also included a left arm rest, right-hand sun shade, chrome cigar lighter, foam seats, insulation, and right door lock. A Custom Appearance package included bright windshield frames, "Custom" embossed roof pillar trim plates, a silver anodized aluminum grille, a medium fawn steering wheel with chrome horn ring, bright dashboard knobs, and two-tone door panels. A chrome front bumper was part of the Custom Chrome option. Silver anodized, chrome double body side moldings were available for Fleetside pickups. The center of the molding was accented with off-white (or white on white trucks). Offered again were Step-Side (with pontoon rear fenders) and Fleetside (with slab type rear fenders) Pickups with 6-1/2-ft. boxes. Other models included the 7-1/2-ft. Panel and the 7-1/2-ft. Carryall Suburban with panel door or tailgate. There were also Chassis-and-Cowl, Chassis-Cowl-and-Windshield, and Chassis-and-Cab models. The 10 series Short Box four-wheel-drive 1/2-ton models had a K14 model prefix.
1/2-TON COMMERCIAL — MODELS C15 (4x2)/SERIES 10 — SIX/V-8: The C15 trucks in the Chevrolet 10 series long-wheelbase line again used a C15 model prefix. They had the same trim changes as C14s. Designation plates were moved below the feature line, behind the front wheel opening. They had a rectangular shape with two rectangular plaques on the surface. The narrower rectangle on top was satin-finished and carried a blue bow tie. The larger bottom rectangle had a chrome 10 and red background with horizontal grooves. These were long

wheelbase (LWB) 1/2-ton trucks on the same chassis as 3/4-ton models. They are known as "Long Bed" or "Long Box" Pickups because they had a longer 8-ft. load box. Longer running boards were needed on Step-Sides because there was more space between the cab and rear fenders. The 10 series Long Bed four-wheel-drive models had a K15 model prefix.

1/2-TON DUBL-DUTI — MODEL P13/SERIES 10 — SIX/V-8: The 1/2-ton Dubl-Duti returned again. It had a 102-in. wheelbase. The small Step-Van walk-in delivery truck with a 7-ft. long body was approved for this chassis. It was made by Union City Body Co., of Union City, Ind. A 194-cid High-Torque six-cylinder engine was standard equipment.

1966 Chevrolet 1/2-Ton C10 Fleetside Pickup (OCW)

3/4-TON COMMERCIAL — MODEL C25/SERIES 20 — SIX/V-8: The C25 trucks in the Chevrolet 20 series 3/4-ton line had the same styling and trim changes as other conventional trucks. The designation plates here had a bow tie emblem and chrome number 20. Step-Side and Fleetside Pickups were in this series. They featured the 8-ft. pickup box. There were also Platform and Platform/Stake models. The rail for the 3/4-ton Platform was 8 ft. long. The four-wheel-drive 3/4-ton models in the 20 series had a K25 model prefix. In midyear, a truck camper package (with chassis beefed-up for camper use) was released.

3/4-TON DUBL-DUTI — MODEL P23, P25, P26/SERIES 20 — SIX/V-8: Three 3/4-ton Dubl-Duti Forward-Control chassis remained in the 20 series (3/4-ton) truck line. The P23/P25/P26 models had wheelbases of 104 in./125 in./137 in., respectively. The 104-in. wheelbase was recommended for bodies 7 ft. to 8-1/2 ft. long, the 125-in. wheelbase was recommended for bodies 9-1/2 to 10-1/2 ft. long. The 137-in. wheelbase was recommended for bodies 11-1/2 to 12-1/2 ft. long. Bodies were available from factory-authorized suppliers or buyers could order them locally.

1-TON MEDIUM-DUTY COMMERCIAL — MODEL C36, C38/SERIES 30 — SIX-CYLINDER: The Chevrolet 30 series 1-ton trucks had the same styling and trim changes as other conventional trucks. The fender side nameplates had a Chevrolet bow tie and number 30. There was no Fleetside Pickup in this line. The 10-ft. Panel had a one-piece floor made of 3/4-in. thick, five-ply laminated wood. The basic model lineup was unchanged. Compared to the C20-C25 Pickup, the C30-C36 Pickup had a longer wheelbase and 9-ft. Long Box. The 1-ton Stake trucks were also 9 ft. long. No hubcaps were used on the larger split-rim wheels of the Chassis-and-Cab and Stake models, which had eight bolts and eight circular openings. The Camper Special package continued. Camper Specials had their own designation plates with a Chevrolet bow tie and "Camper Special" in chrome script. The C38 model 1-ton Chassis-and-Cab with a long 157-in. wheelbase for use as an RV chassis was offered again. A four-speed manual synchromesh transmission was standard. No four-wheel-drive option was offered.

1-TON DUBL-DUTI — MODEL P33, P35, P36/SERIES 30 — SIX/V-8: Three Dubl-Duti Forward-Control chassis were in the 30 series (1-ton) truck line. The P33/P35/P36 models had wheelbases of 104 in./125 in./137 in., respectively. The 104-in. wheelbase was recommended for bodies 7 ft. to 8-1/2 ft. long, the 125-in. wheelbase was recommended for bodies 9-1/2 to 10-1/2 ft. long. The 137-in. wheelbase was recommended for bodies 11-1/2 to 12-1/2 ft. long. Bodies were available from factory-authorized suppliers or buyers could order them locally. A High-Torque 230 six was standard equipment.

1966 Chevrolet 1/2-Ton El Camino Sedan-Pickup (OCW)

I.D. DATA: Serial number located: [Chassis models] on plate temporarily attached near steering column, with final location per body maker. [All others] on plate attached to rear face of left-hand door hinge pillar, on right side of cowl under hood. The first symbol (first three El Camino) indicated truck type: 133/134/135/136=El Camino, C=Conventional Cab, K=4x4, G=Chevy Van, P=Dubl-Duti Package Delivery, G=Chevy Van. The next two symbols on El Caminos indicated series (80=Sedan-Pickup), next two symbols on other trucks indicated the series: 14=1/2-ton, 15=1/2-ton LWB, 25=3/4-ton, 36=1-ton, 38=1-ton LWB. The next symbol indicated body type: 2=Chassis-and-Cowl, 3=Chassis-and-Cab, 4=Pickup, 5=Panel, 6=Carryall Suburban, 9=Stake. The next symbol (all) indicated model-year: 6=1966. The next symbol (all) identified assembly plant: The next symbol indicated the assembly plant: [Commercial] A=Atlanta, Ga., B=Baltimore, Md., F=Flint, Mich., J=Janesville, Wis., N=Norwood, Ohio,

P=Pontiac, Mich., S=St. Louis, Mo., T=Tarrytown, N.Y., Z=Fremont, Calif. [El Camino] A=Lakewood, Atlanta, Ga., B=Baltimore, Md., G=Framingham, Mass., K=Leeds, Kansas City, Mo., Z=Fremont, Calif. Remaining symbols were the sequential production number starting with 100001 at each plant. Ending serial numbers not available. The Chevrolet engine had the source, date and type stamped on a serial number pad. Source codes were: F=Flint, Mich., T=Tonawanda, N.Y., C=Canada. Month codes were 1=Jan., 2=Feb., etc. Date codes were 01=first of month, etc. Prefix codes for Commercial and Dubl-Duti models were [194-cid/120-hp High-Torque six] SC/SD/SO/SP/SG/SI/SE/SF, [230-cid/140-hp High-Torque six] SR/SS/ST/SU/SK/SL/TH/TI, [250-cid/150-hp High-Torque six] SV/SW/SX/TA/TE/TF/TJ/TK/VQ/VR/UR/UT/UU/UV, [283-cid/175-hp High-Torque V-8] WF/WH/WA/WE, [327-cid/185-hp High-Torque V-8] YC/YD/YR/YS/YH.

Model	Body Type	Price	Weight	Prod. Total
El Camino — Model A/Series 13000 — 115 in. w.b. — Six				
13380	Pickup	2318	2930	Note 1
13580	Custom Pickup	2396	2930	Note 1
El Camino —— Model A/Series 13000 — 115 in. w.b. — V-8				
13480	Pickup	2426	3075	Note 1
13680	Custom Pickup	2504	3075	Note 1
NOTE 1: Total El Camino production was 35,119.				
Chevy Van — Model G/Series 10 — 90 in. w.b. — Four				
G1205	Panel	2141	2755	28,180
G1206	Sportvan	2388	2965	4,209
G1226	Custom Sportvan	2521	3065	2,674
G1236	Deluxe Sportvan	2747	3125	2,341
1/2-Ton Commercial — Model C14/Series 10 — 115 in. w.b.				
C1403	Chassis & Cab	1927	2835	40
C1434	Fleetside	2066	3220	57,386
C1404	Step-Side	2050	3195	59,947
C1405	Panel 7.5 ft.	2361	3420	-
C1406	Suburban (door)	2598	3710	6,717
C1416	Suburban (gate)	2629	3735	5,334
1/2-Ton Ton Commercial (4x4) — Model K14/Series 10 — 115 in. w.b.				
K1434	Fleetside	2718	3825	678
K1404	Step-Side	2702	3810	1,123
K1405	Panel 7.5 ft.	3013	4085	170
K1406	Suburban (door)	3270	4385	530
K1416	Suburban (gate)	3303	4415	418
1/2-Ton Commercial (Long Bed) — Model C15/Series 10 — 127 in. w.b.				
C1503	Chassis & Cab	-	-	1,155
C1534	Fleetside	2104	3225	178,752
C1504	Step-Side	2087	3290	26,456
1/2-Ton Comm. (Long Bed/4x4) — Model K15/Series 10 — 127 in. w.b.				
K1503	Chassis & Cab	-	-	30
K1534	Fleetside	2756	3845	1,976
K1504	Step-Side	2739	3810	457
1/2-Ton Dubl-Duti — Model P/Series 10 — 102 in. w.b.				
P1345	Step-Van	2658	3480	3,202
3/4-Ton Commercial — Model C25/Series 20 — 127 in. w.b.				
C2503	Chassis & Cab	2112	3265	6,520
C2534	Fleetside	2252	3700	55,855
C2504	Step-Side	2236	3700	9,905
C2509	Stake	2328	3890	1,499
3/4-Ton Commercial (4x4) — Model K25/Series 20 — 127 in. w.b.				
K2503	Chassis & Cab	-	-	-
K2534	Fleetside	2904	4270	1,796
K2504	Step-Side	2888	4225	924
3/4-Ton Dubl-Duti — Model P/Series 20 — 104-137 in. w.b.				
P2345	Step-Van	3432	4835	192
1-Ton Commercial — Model C36/Series 30 — 133 in. w.b.				
C3603	Chassis & Cab	2269	3455	11,852
C3604	Step-Side	2414	3930	3,646
C3609	Stake 9 ft.	2527	4285	3,651
C3605	Panel 10.5 ft.	2832	4265	3,560
1-Ton — Model P/Series 30 — 104-137 in. w.b.				
P3345	Step-Van	3432	5040	61

ENGINE: [Standard P10/G10] Inline. OHV. Six-cylinder. Cast iron block. Bore & stroke: 3-9/16 in. x 3-1/4 in. Displacement: 194 cid. Compression ratio: 8.5:1. Brake horsepower: 120 at 4400 rpm. Maximum torque: 220 lb.-ft. at 1600 rpm. Seven main bearings. Hydraulic valve lifters. Carburetor: Rochester one-barrel model 7023105.

ENGINE: [Standard C10, Optional P10/G10/El Camino] Inline. OHV. Six-cylinder. Cast iron block. Bore & stroke: 3-7/8 in. x 3-1/4 in. Displacement: 230 cid. Compression ratio: 8.5:1. Brake horsepower: 140 at 4400 rpm. Maximum torque: 220 lb.-ft. at 1600 rpm. Net horsepower: 120 at 3600 rpm. Seven main bearings. Hydraulic valve lifters. Carburetor: Rochester one-barrel model B-7023017.

ENGINE: [Standard C10/K10/P20/C20/K20/P30/C30] Inline. OHV. Six-cylinder. Cast iron block. Bore & stroke: 3.875 in. x 3.53 in. Displacement: 250 cid. Compression ratio: 8.5:1. Brake horsepower: 155 at 4200 rpm. Seven main bearings. Hydraulic valve lifters. Carburetor: Downdraft two-barrel.

ENGINE: [C10/K10/P20/C20/K20/P30/C30] Inline. OHV. Six-cylinder. Cast iron block. Bore & stroke: 3-7/8 in. x 4-1/2 in. Displacement: 292 cid. Compression ratio: 8.0:1. Brake horsepower: 170 at 4000 rpm. Maximum torque: 275 lb.-ft. at 1600 rpm. Net horsepower: 153 at 3600 rpm. Seven main bearings. Hydraulic valve lifters. Carburetor: Rochester model B-7024009.

ENGINE: [Optional C10/C20/C30/K10/K20] V-type. OHV. Eight-cylinder. Cast iron block. Bore & stroke: 3-7/8 in. x 3 in. Displacement: 283 cid. Compression ratio: 9.0:1. Brake horsepower: 175 at 4400 rpm. Maximum torque: 275 lb.-ft. at 2400 rpm. Five main bearings. Hydraulic valve lifters. Carburetor: Rochester two-barrel model 7024101.

1966 Chevrolet 1/2-Ton El Camino "327" Sedan-Pickup (Duffy's)

ENGINE: [Optional El Camino] V-type. OHV. Eight-cylinder. Cast iron block. Bore & stroke: 3-7/8 in. x 3 in. Displacement: 283 cid. Compression ratio: 9.25:1. Brake horsepower: 195 at 4800 rpm. Maximum torque: 285 lb.-ft. at 2400 rpm. Five main bearings. Hydraulic valve lifters. Carburetor: Rochester two-barrel model 7024101.
ENGINE: [Optional El Camino] V-type. OHV. Eight-cylinder. Cast iron block. Bore & stroke: 3-7/8 in. x 3 in. Displacement: 283 cid. Compression ratio: 9.25:1. Brake horsepower: 220 at 4800 rpm. Maximum torque: 285 lb.-ft. at 2400 rpm. Five main bearings. Hydraulic valve lifters. Carburetor: Rochester four-barrel.
ENGINE: [C10/C20/C30] V-type. OHV. Eight-cylinder. Cast iron block. Bore & stroke: 4 in. x 3-1/4 in. Displacement: 327 cid. Compression ratio: 9.25:1. Brake horsepower: 220 at 4400 rpm. Maximum torque: 320 lb.-ft. at 2800 rpm. Five main bearings. Hydraulic valve lifters. Carburetor: Rochester four-barrel model 4G.
ENGINE: [Optional El Camino] V-type. OHV. Eight-cylinder. Cast iron block. Bore & stroke: 4 in. x 3-1/4 in. Displacement: 327 cid. Compression ratio: 9.25:1. Brake horsepower: 275 at 4800 rpm. Maximum torque: 355 lb.-ft. at 3200 rpm. Five main bearings. Hydraulic valve lifters. Carburetor: Rochester four-barrel.
ENGINE: [Optional El Camino] V-type. OHV. Eight-cylinder. Cast iron block. Bore & stroke: 4.094 in. x 3.76 in. Displacement: 396 cid. Compression ratio: 10.25:1. Brake horsepower: 325 at 4800 rpm. Maximum torque: 410 lb.-ft. at 3200 rpm. Five main bearings. Carburetor: Downdraft four-barrel.
ENGINE: [Optional El Camino] V-type. OHV. Eight-cylinder. Cast iron block. Bore & stroke: 4.094 in. x 3.76 in. Displacement: 396 cid. Compression ratio: 10.25:1. Brake horsepower: 360 at 5200 rpm. Maximum torque: 420 lb.-ft. at 3600 rpm. Five main bearings. Carburetor: four-barrel.
ENGINE: [Optional El Camino] V-type. OHV. Eight-cylinder. Cast iron block. Bore & stroke: 4.094 in. x 3.76 in. Displacement: 396 cid. Compression ratio: 11.25:1. Brake horsepower: 375. Five main bearings. Carburetor: four-barrel

1966 Chevrolet 1/2-Ton C10 Custom Fleetside Pickup with custom wheels (OCW)

CHASSIS: [El Camino] Wheelbase: 115 in. Overall length: 197 in. Front tread: 58 in. Rear tread: 58 in. Tires: 7.35 x 14. GVW: 4,300 lb.
CHASSIS: [G10] Wheelbase: 90 in. Tires: 6.50 x 13 in. GVW: 3,900 to 5,000 lb.
CHASSIS: [C14/K14] Wheelbase: 115 in. Overall length: [Pickup] 186-3/4 in., [Chassis-and-Cab] 180-1/4 in. Bed length: [Pickup] 78-1/8 in. Cab to rear axle on Chassis-and-Cab: 42 in. Cab to end of frame on Chassis-and-Cab: 75-1/2 in. Front tread: 63.1 in. Rear tread: 61 in. Tires: 6.70 x 15 in. Maximum GVW: [4x2] 4,600 lb., [4x4] 5,300 lb.
CHASSIS: [C15/K15] Wheelbase: 127 in. Overall length: [Pickup] 206-in., [Chassis-and-Cab] 200-1/4 in. Bed length: [Pickup] 98 in. Cab to rear axle on Chassis-and-Cab: 54 in. Cab to end of frame on Chassis-and-Cab: 95-1/2 in. Height: 71 in. Front tread: 63.1 in. Rear tread: 61.1 in. Tires: [C15] 6.70 x 15 in., [K15] 7 x 17.5 in. Maximum GVW: [4x2] 4,600 lb., [4x4] 5,600 lb.
CHASSIS: [C20/K20] Wheelbase: 127 in. Overall length: [Pickup] 206 in., [Stake] 210-3/4 in., [Chassis-and-Cab] 211-3/4 in. Bed length: [Pickup] 98 in., [Stake] 98 in. Bed width: [Stake] 85 in. Cab to rear axle on Chassis-and-Cab: 54 in. Cab to end of frame on Chassis-and-Cab: 95-1/2 in. Tires: 7 x 17.5 in. Maximum GVW: [4x2] 6,000 lb., [4x4] 6,800 lb.
CHASSIS: [C36] Wheelbase: 133 in. Overall length: [1-ton Step-Side Pickup] 216-1/4 in., [Stake] 221-3/8 in., [Chassis-and-Cab] 199-3/4 in. Bed length: [1-ton Step-Side Pickup] 108-1/4 in., [Stake] 109 in. Bed width: [Stake] 85 in. Tires: 8 x 17.5 in. Maximum GVW: 7,800 lb.
CHASSIS: [C36] Wheelbase: 157 in. Overall length: [Stake] 256-1/2 in., [Chassis-and-Cab] 200-1/4 in. Bed length: [Stake] 144 in. Bed width: [Stake] 85 in. Cab to rear axle on Chassis-and-Cab: 60 in. Cab to end of frame on Chassis-and-Cab: 107 in. Tires: 8 x 17.5 in. Maximum GVW: 7,800 lb.
CHASSIS: [P10] Wheelbase: 102 in. Tires: 7.75 x 15 in. GVW: 4,600 to 5,400 lb.
CHASSIS: [P20] Wheelbases: (P2300) 104 in., (P2500) 125 in., (P2600) 137 in. Base tires: 7 x 17.5. GVW: 7,000 lb.
CHASSIS: [P30] Wheelbases: (P3300) 104 in., (P3500) 125 in., (P3600) 137 in. Base tires: 8 x 19.5. GVW: 7,500 to 14,000 lb.

1966 Chevrolet 1/2-Ton El Camino Sedan-Pickup with custom wheels (DFW)

1966 Chevrolet 1/2-Ton El Camino "327" Sedan-Pickup (CMD)

TECHNICAL: Chevrolet three-speed manual transmission (Borg-Warner heavy-duty three-speed optional). [C30] 4F/1R, [Others] 3F/1R. Column-mounted gear shift lever. Single-plate, dry-disc clutch. Rear axle: [1/2-ton] semi-floating, [3/4-ton/1-Ton] full-floating. Base rear axles: [El Camino] 3.08:1, [Corvair 95] 3.55:1, [C-K10] 3.73:1, [C-K20] 4.11:1, [C-K30] 5.14:1. Four-wheel hydraulic, drum brakes. Brake linings: [Corvair 95] 11 x 2 in. [C-K10] 11 x 2.75 in., [C-K20/CK-30] 12 x 2 in., [El Camino] 9-1/2 x 2-1/2 in. Kelsey-Hayes pressed steel wheels.
EL CAMINO OPTIONS: Oil bath air cleaner. No-Spin rear axle. Heavy-duty battery. Two-tone paint. Heavy-duty cooling. Heavy-duty front shocks. Heavy-duty rear shocks. Heavy-duty three-speed transmission. Four-speed transmission. Turbo-Hydramatic transmission (with V-8). Powerglide transmission (with six). Engine, 230 High-Torque six. Engine, 283-cid V-8 ($108). Engine, 327 cid/250-275 hp. Power steering ($86). Engine, 396 cid/325 hp. Engine, 396 cid/360 hp. Engine, 396 cid/375 hp. Full wheel discs. Custom interior. Bucket seats (Custom). Power windows. 3.36:1 ratio rear axle. Positraction rear axle. 66-plate 70-amp.-hr. heavy-duty battery. Metallic brake linings. Heavy-duty front and rear suspension. Temperature-controlled fan for 195-hp V-8 (included with Four Season air conditioner or optional V-8). 42-ampere Delcotron generator. 55-ampere Delcotron generator (included with air conditioning). 62-ampere Delcotron generator. 62-ampere Delcotron generator for use with air conditioner. Car-to-trailer plug-in electrical harness. Heavy-duty radiator. Electric tachometer. Speed and Cruise Control. Four Season air conditioning (includes 55-ampere Delcotron generator, heavy-duty radiator, and temperature-controlled fan). Soft-Ray tinted glass (all windows). Soft-Ray tinted glass in windshield only. Padded instrument panel. Driver and passenger seat belts, Custom, Custom Deluxe or Custom Deluxe with retractors. Bucket seats for models 13580 and 13680 only. Compass with integral battery and switch. Clock. Type A Comfort and Convenience equipment including outside rear view mirror, inside non-glare mirror, two-speed electric wiper/washer system for 13380 and 13560 models or 13480 and 13680 models. Type B Comfort and Convenience equipment including remote-control outside rear view mirror, inside non-glare mirror, two-speed electric wiper/washer system for 13380 and 13560 models or 13480 and 13680 models. Front bumper guard. Rear bumper guard. Low "D" note horn to supplement standard horn. Simulated wood trim steering wheel. AM/FM push-button radio. AM manual radio. AM push-button radio. Full wheelcovers. Simulated wire wheelcovers. 7.35 x 14 4-ply white sidewall tires. 7.75 x 14 4-ply black sidewall tires. 7.75 x 14 4-ply white sidewall tires. 7.75 x 14 8-ply black sidewall tires.

1966 Chevrolet 1/2-Ton C10 Fleetside Pickup (OCW)

COMMERCIAL AND DUBL-DUTI OPTIONS: 293-cid V-8 ($92). 292-cid six-cylinder $75.25. Oil bath air cleaner ($5.06). Positraction ($50.20). No-Spin rear axle ($104.50). Rear axle, 3.07:1 ratio, with stick ($10.07). Rear axle, 4.11:1 ratio, with stick ($6.73). Heavy-duty battery ($5.87). Painted rear bumper on pickups with painted front bumper ($16.75). Heavy-duty 11-in. clutch with six-cylinder only ($4.20). Custom Appearance option: Panel ($33.45), others ($40.13). Custom Chrome option: Pickup with chrome front bumper ($16.75), Pickup with two chrome bumpers ($41.80), Panel with two chrome bumpers ($25.10). Custom Comfort option ($9.21), others ($42.66). Fleetside Custom side moldings ($25.10). Delcotron alternators: 42-amp. ($16.75), 52-amp. ($23.43). Tinted glass ($11.74). Tinted windshield ($10.07). Deluxe heater ($53.11). Thrift-Air heater ($41.80). Outside rear view mirrors: 17-1/4-in. left, except Panel ($1.72), right, except Panel ($3.77), 6-1/4-in. right ($3.77). Tu-tone paint: Panel ($20.90), other trucks ($12.55). Heavy-duty radiator, except with Powerglide ($16.75). Radio ($37.22). Auxiliary Panel truck seat ($31.78). Foam seat ($16.75). Heavy-duty front shocks (average $6). Heavy-duty rear shocks ($6.73). Heavy-duty front springs, C25 ($2.53). Heavy-duty rear springs, all ($5.06). Heavy-duty three-speed transmission: C14 ($58.55), C15 ($62.70) and C25 ($71.10). Heavy-duty four-speed transmission: C14 ($62.70), C15 ($66.90) and C25 ($75.25). Powerglide, all ($146.30). Full-View rear window, except Panel ($33.45). Two-speed windshield washers and wipers ($12.55).

OPTION PACKAGES: [Custom Appearance Equipment] includes silver anodized radiator grille and headlamp door assembly, chrome-plated windshield reveal moldings, bright metal cab upper rear quarter panel trim plates, chrome horn ring steering wheel, chrome-trimmed instrument panel knobs, and two-tone inside front door panels. [Custom Comfort and Convenience Equipment] includes left door arm rest, outside key lock, chrome cigar lighter, full foam rubber seat cushion, special seat trim (cab models and Suburban), and added sound insulation. [Custom Chrome Equipment] chrome hubcaps. Not available with 4x4 or dual rear wheel options. [Side Trim Moldings] bright body side moldings for Fleetside models. (Package prices are given above).

COLOR OPTIONS: See 1964 options section for complete chart of 1964-1969 Chevrolet Commercial Truck colors.

HISTORICAL: Model-year [All El Camino] 35,119. Model-year production: [All Chevy Commercials] 621,354. Commercial model-year production by GVW class: [G Vans] 37,403, [C10-C14] 115-in. wheelbase] 140,783, [K10-K14] 2,959, [K10-K15] 2,463, [P10] 3,309, [C20] 73,825, [K20] 3,151, [P20] 4,793, [C30] 23,223, [P30/157-in. wheelbase] 7,032. Light-Duty model-year output by marketing category: [Domestic] 461,774, [U.S. built for export] 11,120, [U.S. built for Canada] 31,885, [Total] 504,779. Innovations: Safety equipment made standard in light-duty trucks. Expanded heavy-duty line made available. Chevy clinched its 10 millionth truck sale, of all time, this season.

1967 CHEVROLET

1967 Chevrolet 1/2-Ton El Camino Sedan-Pickup V-8 (JAG)

EL CAMINO — MODEL A/SERIES 13000 — SIX/V-8: The last of the second-generation El Caminos had a new radiator grille, front bumpers, fenders and hood, plus restyled wraparound taillights. The front fenders had more of a vertical downward curve. The grille again had horizontal and vertical elements, but the horizontal moldings were brighter and wider and stood out more. The widest molding, just below the hood lip, had a satin finished look and a Chevrolet emblem in its center. Dual headlamps were used. There was one wide horizontal slot, and the parking lamps were in other openings at either end. At the rear, the three-slot-styled taillights wrapped around the body corners. An El Camino script decorated the rear fenders. The front fender, just behind the headlamps, had an engine call-out. It was a shield with a 250 on top for sixes, a V with flags for 283 V-8s, a V-with flags and 327 numbers for a bigger V-8, and an open center V with flags and a Turbo-Jet 396 plaque for the biggest V-8, a high-performance big-block engine. The Custom models had a thin chrome molding along the lower body feature line, a rear beauty panel between two moldings running across the tailgate, and hubcaps with Chevrolet bow ties. This was the first year for an official SS-396 "model," although it was an option rather than a series. The SS-396 featured a blacked-out grille with SS emblems at its center. Chevelle 300 style all-vinyl upholstery, with all-vinyl embossed side panels, door arm rests and vinyl-coated color-keyed floor mats were standard. The Custom interior added horizontal pleats embossed into the vinyl seat coverings, and door panels with horizontal ribs. Bucket seats were available in Customs, including those with the SS-396 option. Exterior body colors were Tuxedo Black, Ermine White, Nantucket Blue, Deepwater Blue, Marina Blue, Granada Gold, Mountain Green, Emerald Turquoise, Tahoe Turquoise, Royal Plum, Madiera Maroon, Bolero Red, Sierra Fawn, Capri Cream, and Butternut Yellow. The 1964 type pickup box was also in its last appearance. It was 59-3/4 in. wide behind the cab and 64-3/4 in. wide near the tailgate. There was 46 in. between the wheelhousings. The bed of the box was 78-1/2 in. long. The tailgate measured 55-1/2 in. x 23 in. With the bed-level tailgate lowered, the overall bed length was 101.6 in.

1967 Chevrolet 1/2-Ton El Camino Sedan-Pickup (OCW)

1/2-TON CHEVY VAN — MODEL G/SERIES 10 — FOUR: Chevy Vans had a more rounded configuration with a larger windshield. An additional 12 models with V-8 engines were offered in the Chevy Van and Sportvan series. Replacing the 194-cid six as base engine in G10s was the 230-cid six. The 250-cid six and 307-cid V-8 were optional. The compact 90-in. wheelbase G10 Chevy Van was basically unchanged, but there was a new G10 model line added. This new sub-series featured the same four models on a longer 108-in. wheelbase. Their bodies were 18 in. longer than the 90-in. wheelbase models. Styling characteristics again included five-segment vents on the front with a bow-tie underneath and an oval, horizontal-bar grille near the bottom of the front single headlights. Both lines offered Panel, Sportvan, Sportvan Custom and Sportvan Deluxe models.

3/4-TON CHEVY VAN — MODEL G/SERIES 10 — FOUR: The new 108-in. wheelbase forward-control vans also came in a 3/4-ton C20 series. Styling characteristics were the same as long wheelbase C10s. The front had a bow-tie underneath and an oval and a horizontal-bar grille near the bottom of the front single headlights. Panel, Sportvan, Sportvan Custom and Sportvan Deluxe models were included. Engines were the same used for G10s.

1967 Chevrolet 1/2-Ton C10 Step-Side Pickup (RCA)

1/2-TON COMMERCIAL — MODEL C (4x2), K (4x4)/SERIES 10 — SIX/V-8: The 1967 conventional trucks were described by Chevrolet as possessing "the most significant cab and sheet metal styling change in Chevrolet history." The new styling reflected the importance of an attractive appearance in the light-duty truck field, as more and more were purchased for personal transportation and camper use. The major styling themes on the Pickup combined an inner slant above the belt line with a side body feature line nearly dividing the wheel wells into equal sections. A new lower cab with increased glass area featured a new rigid roof designed for extra strength. The front end was very attractive with single headlights recessed into square receptacles at either end of a grille with a single wide center bar. The front sheet metal also featured greatly improved protection against corrosion. The use of smooth surfaced, undercoated, full fender skirts protected the fenders and other sheet metal from mud, water and salt. In addition, minimal use of coach joints and liberal use of spot weld sealers provided additional corrosion resistance. Standard equipment included safety belts, two padded sun visors, two-speed electric wipers, rubber floor mat, dome light, new padded dash, left-hand outside mirror (right-hand mirror on chassis and Stake models), back-up lights (except chassis), turn signals, and hazard flashers. There was a new Fleetside box with double-wall side panels, flat-top wheelwells, and a one-hand, quick-release tailgate. Designation plates were mounted high on the sides of the cowl. Exterior body colors included Black, Light Green, Dark Green, Medium Blue Poly, Light Blue, Dark Blue, Dark Aqua Poly, Red, Vermilion Poly, Omaha Orange, Yellow, White, Silver Poly, and Ivory. The two-tone paint scheme was white above the belt line with the second color below. Another version used white only on the roof panel, with the windshield pillars and window frames and lower body done in the second color. The standard interior featured color-keyed vinyl upholstery, foam cushions, and steel spring seats. White bumpers and a white grille background were standard. A chrome front bumper was part of the Custom Chrome option. Custom equipment included a full-depth foam-padded seat, color-keyed woven fabric and vinyl trim, two door arm rests, cigar lighter, cowl insulation, undercoating, and embossed vinyl door panels. There was also a new Custom Sport Truck (CST) option that included CST plaques on the window sills, bucket seats, a center console/seat, chrome front bumper, bright pedal trim, chrome dash knobs, chrome horn button, silver anodized grille background, and headlamp and windshield bright trim. This year's Panel and Carryall Suburban were switched to a 127-in. wheelbase. Both had new, longer bodies with one entry door on the driver's side, and two on the passenger's side. The Carryall Suburban again offered options of a tailgate or rear panel doors. Offered again were Step-Side (with pontoon rear fenders) and Fleetside (with slab type rear fenders) Pickups with 6-1/2-ft. boxes. Other offerings included the Chassis-and-Cowl, Chassis-Cowl-and-Windshield, and Chassis-and-Cab models. The 10 series Short Box four-wheel-drive 1/2-ton models had a K14 model prefix. There was no longer separate C10-C15 and K10-K15 series for long wheelbase models. Instead, the 127-in. wheelbase 1/2-tons were simply coded differently under a new system that indicated cab-to-axle dimensions. An 07 code in the VIN indicated 115-in. wheelbase, an 09 indicated 127-in. wheelbase.

1967 Chevrolet 1/2-Ton C10 Fleetside Pickup (OCW)

1/2-TON FORWARD-CONTROL — MODEL P/SERIES 10 — SIX/V-8: The 1/2-ton Forward-Control returned again. It had a 102-in. wheelbase. A small Step-Van walk-in delivery truck with a 7-ft. long body was approved for this chassis. It was made by Union City Body Co., of Union City, Ind. A channel type front bumper was optional.

1967 Chevrolet 3/4-Ton C20 Custom Camper Special Fleetside Pickup (CMD)

3/4-TON COMMERCIAL — MODEL C, K/SERIES 20 — SIX/V-8: Carryover trucks in the Chevrolet 20 series 3/4-ton line had the same styling and trim changes as other conventional trucks. The big news for 1967 was the introduction of Carryall Suburbans and Panels in this line. These had the same dimensions as comparable 1/2-ton models, but heavier chassis components. The designation plates had a bow tie emblem and chrome number 20. Step-Side and Fleetside Pickups were in this series. They featured the 8-ft. pickup box. There was also an 8-ft. Stake model. The four-wheel-drive 3/4-ton models in the 20 series had a K25 model prefix.

3/4-TON FORWARD-CONTROL — MODEL P/SERIES 20 — SIX/V-8: Three 3/4-ton Forward-Control chassis remained in the 20 series (3/4-ton) truck line. The P23/P25/P26 models had wheelbases of 104 in./125 in./137 in., respectively. The 104-in. wheelbase was recommended for bodies 7 to 8-1/2 ft. long, the 125-in. wheelbase was recommended for bodies 9-1/2 to 10-1/2 ft. long. The 137-in. wheelbase was recommended for bodies 11-1/2 to 12-1/2 ft. long. Bodies were available from factory-authorized suppliers or buyers could order them locally. New this year was an optional three-cylinder diesel engine.

1-TON MEDIUM-DUTY COMMERCIAL — MODEL C/SERIES 30 — SIX-CYLINDER: The Chevrolet 30 series 1-ton trucks had the same styling and trim changes as other conventional trucks. The fender side nameplates had a Chevrolet bow tie and number 30. There was no Fleetside Pickup in this line and the Panel was dropped this year. There were chassis models, plus a 9-ft. Pickup and 9-ft. Stake. No hubcaps were used on the larger split-rim wheels of the Chassis-and-Cab and Stake models, which had eight bolts and eight circular openings. The Camper Special package continued. Camper models had their own designation plates with a Chevrolet bow tie and 'Camper Special' chrome script. The C38 model 1-ton Chassis-and-Cab with a long 157-in. wheelbase for use as an RV chassis was also offered again. A four-speed manual synchromesh transmission was standard. No four-wheel-drive option was offered.

1-TON FORWARD-CONTROL — MODEL P/SERIES 30 — SIX/V-8: Three Forward-Control chassis were in the 30 series (1-ton) truck line. The P33/P35/P36 models had wheelbases of 104 in./125 in./137 in., respectively. The 104-in. wheelbase was recommended for bodies 7 ft. to 8-1/2 ft. long, the 125-in. wheelbase was recommended for bodies 9-1/2 to 10-1/2 ft. long. The 137-in. wheelbase was recommended for bodies 11-1/2 to 12-1/2 ft. long. Bodies were available from factory-authorized suppliers or buyers could order them locally. A High-Torque 230 six was standard equipment. New this year was an optional three-cylinder diesel engine.

1967 Chevrolet 1/2-Ton C10 Carryall Suburban (OCW)

I.D. DATA: Serial number located: [Chassis models] on plate temporarily attached near steering column, with final location per body maker. [All others] on plate attached to rear face of left-hand door hinge pillar, on right side of cowl under hood. [El Camino] The first symbol indicated manufacturer: 1=Chevrolet. The second and third symbols indicated series: 33=six/34=V-8/36=Custom six/36=Custom V-8. The fourth and fifth symbols indicated body type: 80=Sedan-Pickup. The sixth symbol indicated model-year: 7=1967. The seventh symbol indicated assembly plant: A=Atlanta/Lakewood, B=Baltimore, Md., G=Framingham, Mass., K=Kansas City, Mo. (Leeds), Z=Fremont, Calif.. The remaining symbols were the sequential production number starting with 100001 at each plant. Ending serial numbers not available. The Chevrolet engine had the source, date and serial stamped on a serial number pad. Various source codes were used. Month codes were 1=Jan., 2=Feb., etc. Date codes were 01=first of month, etc. The were numerous prefix codes to indicate engines and transmission attachments. [Other models] The first symbol indicated truck type: C=Conventional Cab, K=4x4, G=Chevy Van, P=Forward-Control Package Delivery. The second symbol indicated type of engine: S=six, E=eight, T=diesel. The third symbol indicated the GVW range: [GVW] 1=3,600 to 5,500 lb., 2=5,500 to

8,100 lb., 3=6,700 to 10,000 lb., 4=Over 10,000 lb. The fourth and fifth symbols indicated the cab-to-axle dimension: 07=42 to 47 in., 09=54-59 in., 10=60-65 in., 14=84-89 in. The sixth symbol indicated body type: 02=Chassis-and-Cowl, 03=Chassis-and-Cab, 04=Step-Side Pickup, 05=Panel or Panel Van, 06=Carryall Suburban (doors) or Sportvan, 09=Platform/Stake, 12=Chassis-and-Cowl, 12=Cab with air brakes, 16=Carryall Suburban (gate), 26=Custom Sportvan, 34=Fleetside, 36=Deluxe Sportvan, 35=Forward-Control. The seventh symbol indicates model-year: 7=1967. The eighth symbol indicates assembly plant: A=Atlanta, Ga., B=Baltimore, Md., F=Flint, Mich., J=Janesville, Wis., K=Kansas City, Mo., S=St. Louis, Mo., T=Tarrytown, N.Y., Z=Fremont, Calif. 1=Oshawa, Canada.

Model	Body Type	Price	Weight	Prod. Total
El Camino — Model A/Series 13000 — 115 in. w.b.				
13480	Pickup	2613	3193	Note 1
13680	Custom Pickup	2694	3210	Note 1
NOTE 1: Total El Camino production was 34,830				
1/2-Ton Chevy Van — Model G/Series 100 — 90 in. w.b.				
GS11005	Panel	2331	2849	17,956
GS11006	Sportvan	2571	3035	2398
GS11026	Custom Sportvan	2699	3138	777
GS11036	Deluxe Sportvan	2890	3174	535
1/2-Ton Chevy Van — Model G/Series 100 — 108 in. w.b.				
GS11005	Panel	-	-	13,644
GS11006	Sportvan	-	-	2,568
GS11026	Custom Sportvan	-	-	1,603
GS11036	Deluxe Sportvan	-	-	1,665
3/4-Ton Chevy Van 20 — 3/4Ton — 108 in. w.b.				
GS21305	Panel	2618	3109	6013
GS21306	Sportvan	2848	3241	930
GS21326	Custom Sportvan	2975	3365	501
GS21336	Deluxe Sportvan	3166	3409	508
1/2-Ton Commercial — Model C/Series 10 — 127 in. w.b.				
CS10903	Chassis & Cab	-	-	39
CS10934	Fleetside 8 ft.	2408	3440	165,973
CS10904	Step-Side 8 ft.	2371	3345	19,969
CS10905	Panel	2742	3502	3827
CS10906	Suburban	2986	3670	5164
1/2-Ton Commercial (4x4) — Model K/Series 10 — 115 in. w.b.				
KS10703	Chassis & Cab	2903	-	32
KS10734	Fleetside 6.5 ft.	3051	-	1046
KS10704	Step-Side 6.5 ft.	3013	-	1,229
1/2-Ton Commercial (4x4) — Model K/Series 10 — 127 in. w.b.				
KS10903	Chassis & Cab	-	-	41
KS10934	Fleetside 8 ft.	3088	-	2,715
KS10904	Step-Side 8 ft.	3051	-	500
KS10905	Panel	3422	-	30
KS10906	Suburban	3666	3670	166
1/2-Ton Forward-Control — Model P/Series 10 — 102 in. w.b.				
PS10535	Step-Van	2864	3559	2374
3/4-Ton Commercial — Model C/Series 20 — 127 in. w.b.				
CS20903	Chassis & Cab	2403	3346	6320
CS20934	Fleetside 8 ft.	2550	3848	50,413
CS20904	Step-Side 8 ft.	2513	3753	785
CS20905	Stake	2606	3973	1415
CS20905	Panel	2884	3917	940
CS20906	Suburban	3170	4093	709
Long Horn Pickup				
CS21034	Pickup 8.5 ft.	2614	-	-
3/4-Ton Commercial (4x4) — Model K/Series 20 — 127 in. w.b.				
KS20903	Chassis & Cab	3083	-	498
KS20934	Fleetside 8 ft.	3230	-	2,773
KS20904	Step-Side 8 ft.	3193	-	-
KS20905	Panel	3286	-	8
KS20906	Suburban	3850	-	120
Long-Horn Pickup				
KS21034	Fleetside 8.5 ft.	-	-	-
3/4-Ton Forward-Control — Model P/Series 20 — 104/125/137 in. w.b.				
PS20835	Step-Van (125 in.)	3626	4970	203
1-Ton Commercial — Model C/Series 30 — 133 in. w.b.				
CS31003	Chassis & Cab	2561	3556	11,304
CS31034	Fleetside 8.5 ft.	2755	-	-
CS31004	Step-Side 9 ft.	2695	3995	4026
CS31009	Stake 9 ft.	2875	4390	3236
1-Ton Forward-Control — Model P/Series 30 — 104/125/127 in. w.b.				
PT30835	Step-Van (diesel)	5648	5931	10

NOTE 2: Production totals from Chevrolet records are for model-year through July 31, 1967 and include all trucks built in U.S. factories for domestic/export/Canadian markets.

NOTE 3: Additional production: [C10] Chassis-Cowl-and-Windshield=15, Chassis-and-Cowl=6, Chassis-and-Cab/127-in. wheelbase=1,066, Chassis-only=140. [K20] Chassis-and-Cab=498, Panel=8, Carryall Suburban=120. [P20] Chassis-only=151, Step-Van/104-in. wheelbase=143, Step-Van/125-in. wheelbase=1,313, Chassis-only/125-in. wheelbase=400, Step-Van/137-in. wheelbase=652, Chassis-only/137-in. wheelbase=240, Panel/137-in. wheelbase=76. [C30] Chassis-and-Cowl= 366, Chassis-Cowl-and-Windshield=8, Chassis-and-Cab/157-in. wheelbase=4,488. [P30] Step-Van: Total gas=6, 777, Total diesel=117.

1967 Chevrolet 1/2-Ton C10 Fleetside Pickup (OCW)

1967 Chevrolet 1/2-Ton El Camino Sedan-Pickup with custom wheels (DFW)

ENGINE: [Standard El Camino G10/P10/G20] Inline. OHV. Six-cylinder. Cast iron block. Bore & stroke: 3-7/8 in. x 3-1/4 in. Displacement: 230 cid. Compression ratio: 8.5:1. Brake horsepower: 140 at 4400 rpm. Torque: 220 lb.-ft. at 1600 rpm. Net horsepower: 120 at 3600 rpm. Seven main bearings. Hydraulic valve lifters. Carburetor: Rochester one-barrel model 7028006/7028010.
ENGINE: [Standard C10/C20/K10/K20/P30, Optional G10/P10/El Camino] Inline. OHV. Six-cylinder. Cast iron block. Bore & stroke: 3-7/8 in. x 3.53 in. Displacement: 250 cid. Compression ratio: 8.5:1. Brake horsepower: 155 at 4200 rpm. Torque: 235 lb.-ft. at 1600 rpm. Seven main bearings. Hydraulic valve lifters. Carburetor: Rochester one-barrel model 7028007/7028011.
ENGINE: [Optional C10/C20/C30/P10/P20/P30] Inline. OHV. Six-cylinder. Cast iron block. Bore & stroke: 3-7/8 in. x 4-1/2 in. Displacement: 292 cid. Compression ratio: 8.1:1. Brake horsepower: 170 at 4000 rpm. Torque: 275 lb.-ft. at 1600 rpm. Seven main bearings. Hydraulic valve lifters. Carburetor: Rochester one-barrel model 7028012/7028013.
ENGINE: [Optional: K Series/C10/C20/C30] V-block. OHV. Eight-cylinder. Cast iron block. Bore & stroke: 3-7/8 in. x 3 in. Displacement: 283 cid. Brake horsepower: 175 at 4400 rpm. Torque: 275 lb.-ft. at 2400 rpm. Five main bearings. Hydraulic valve lifters.
ENGINE: [Optional El Camino] V-type. OHV. Eight-cylinder. Cast iron block. Bore & stroke: 3-7/8 in. x 3 in. Displacement: 283 cid. Compression ratio: 9.25:1. Brake horsepower: 195 at 4800 rpm. Maximum torque: 285 lb.-ft. at 2400 rpm. Five main bearings. Hydraulic valve lifters. Carburetor: Rochester two-barrel model 7024101.
ENGINE: [Optional: C10/C20/C30/K10/K20] V-block. OHV. Eight-cylinder. Cast iron block. Bore & stroke: 4 in. x 3.25 in. Displacement: 327 cid. Compression ratio: 9.25:1. Brake horsepower: 220. Five main bearings. Hydraulic valve lifters. Carburetor: Rochester four-barrel model 4G.
ENGINE: [El Camino/standard SS-396] V-block. OHV. Eight-cylinder. Cast iron block. Bore & stroke: 4.09 in. x 3.76 in. Displacement: 396 cid. Compression ratio: 10.25:1. Brake horsepower: 325 at 4800 rpm. Torque: 410 lb.-ft. at 3200 rpm. Five main bearings. Hydraulic valve lifters. Carburetor: Rochester four-barrel model Quadra-Jet.
ENGINE: [Optional El Camino SS-396] V-block. OHV. Eight-cylinder. Cast iron block. Bore & stroke: 4.09 in. x 3.76 in. Displacement: 396 cid. Compression ratio: 10.25:1. Brake horsepower: 350 at 5200 rpm. Torque: 415 lb.-ft. at 3400 rpm. Five main bearings. Hydraulic valve lifters. Carburetor: Rochester four-barrel model Quadra-Jet.
ENGINE: [Optional El Camino] V-type. OHV. Eight-cylinder. Cast iron block. Bore & stroke: 4.094 in. x 3.76 in. Displacement: 396 cid. Compression ratio: 11.25:1. Brake horsepower: 375. Five main bearings. Carburetor: four-barrel.
CHASSIS: [El Camino] Wheelbase: 115 in. Overall length: 197 in. Front tread: 58 in. Rear tread: 58 in. Tires: 7.35 x 14 in. GVW: 4,300 lb.
CHASSIS: [G10] Wheelbase: 90 in. Overall length: 6.95 x 14 in. GVW: 3,900 to 5,000 lb.
CHASSIS: [C10/K10] Wheelbase: 115 in. Overall length: 186-3/4 in. Height: 71 in. Front tread: 63.1 in. Rear tread: 61.1 in. Tires: Tires: [4x2] 7.75 x 15 in., [Carryall Suburban] 8.15 x 15 in., [4x4] 17.5 x 17 four-ply. GVW: [4x2] 4,400 to 5,000 lb., [4x4] 5,600 lb.
CHASSIS: [C10/K10] Wheelbase: 127 in. Overall length: 206-1/4 in. Height: 71 in. Front tread: 63.1 in. Rear tread: 61.1 in. Tires: [4x2] 7.75 x 15 in. four-ply, [4x4] 17.5 x 17. GVW: [4x2] 4,400 to 5,000 lb., [4x4] 5,600 lb.
CHASSIS: [P10] Wheelbase: 102 in. Tires: 7.75 x 15 in. GVW: 4,600 to 5,400 lb.
CHASSIS: [C20/K20] Wheelbase: 127 in. Overall length: 206-1/4 in. Tires: [4x2] 7 x 17.5 in., [4x4] 7 x 17.5 six-ply. GVW: [4x2] 5,500 to 7,500 lb.], [4x4] 5,700 to 7,600 lb.
CHASSIS: [P20] Wheelbases: (P2300) 104 in., (P2500) 125 in., (P2600) 137 in. Base tires: 7 x 17.5. GVW: 7,000 lb.
CHASSIS: [C30] Wheelbase: 133 in. Tires: 8 x 17.5. GVW: 6,700 to 14,000 lb.
CHASSIS: [P30] Wheelbases: (P3300) 104 in., (P3500) 125 in. (P3600) 137 in. Base tires: 8 x 19.5. GVW: 7,500 to 14,000 lb.

1967 Chevrolet 1/2-Ton CST 10 Fleetside Pickup (Photo/Owner: Michael Grant))

TECHNICAL: Chevrolet three-speed manual transmission (Borg-Warner heavy-duty three-speed optional). [C30] 4F/1R, [Others] 3F/1R. Column-mounted gearshift lever. Single-plate, dry-disc clutch. Rear axle: [1/2-ton] semi-floating, [3/4-ton/1-ton] full-floating. Base rear axles: [El Camino] 3.08:1, [Corvair 95] 3.55:1, [C-K10] 3.73:1, [C-K20] 4.11:1, [C30] 5.14:1. Four-wheel hydraulic, drum brakes. Brake linings: [Corvair 95] 11 x 2 in. [C-K10] 11 x 2.75 in., [C-K20/C30] 12 x 2 in., [El Camino] 9-1/2 x 2-1/2 in. Kelsey-Hayes pressed steel wheels.

EL CAMINO OPTIONS: Tinted glass. Tinted windshield. Power windows. Custom Deluxe front seat belts. Strato-bucket bucket seats. Strato-Ease headrest. Regular headrest. Safety harness. Front and rear floor mats. Deluxe foam front seat cushion. Door edge guards. Black or beige vinyl roof. Delete heater/defroster. Air conditioning. Remote control outside rear view mirror. Console. Heavy-duty suspension. Positraction. Rear axle ratios: 3.70, 3.36, 3.08, 3.31, 3.55, 2.73, 3.07, 3.73. Vacuum power brakes. Front disc brakes. Brake linings. Radiator fan. Air injector reactor. Cruise Control. 61-amp. Delcotron alternator. 42-amp. Delcotron alternator. Heavy-duty clutch. Overdrive transmission. Four-speed transmission. Close-ratio four-speed transmission. Powerglide transmission (with six). Three-speed Turbo-Hydramatic transmission (with V-8s). Dual exhausts. Deluxe steering wheel. Comfortilt steering wheel. Woodgrain steering wheel. Power steering. Mag style wheelcovers. Wheel trim covers. Simulated wire wheels. Heavy-duty battery. Tri-volume horn. Instrument panel gauges. Speed warning indicator. Tachometer. Underhood lamp. Glove box lamp. Ash tray lamp. Instrument panel courtesy lamps. Electric clock. Push-button AM radio and antenna. Push-button AM/FM radio and antenna. Heavy-duty radiator. Front bumper guards. SS-396 equipment.

COMMERCIAL TRUCK OPTIONS: Oil bath air cleaner. Heavy-duty air cleaner. Air conditioning. Positraction. Rear axle ratios. Heavy-duty battery. Vacuum power brakes. Chrome front bumper. Chrome hubcaps. Side-mounted spare wheel carrier. Heavy-duty clutch. Heavy-duty cooling. Custom side molding package. Pickup box floor. Fuel filter. Gauges. Generator. Soft-Ray tinted glass. Air injector reactor. Engine governor. Safety harness. Heater and defroster. Towing hooks. Rear side marker lights. Right-hand door lock. Exterior rear view mirror. Camper Special package with custom "Camper Special" nameplates. Fuel and vacuum pump booster. Heavy-duty radiator. AM radio and antenna. Auxiliary seat in Panel. Heavy-duty shock absorbers. Speed warning indicator. Auxiliary rear springs. Heavy-duty front springs. Heavy-duty rear springs. Front stabilizer bar. Heavy-duty starter. Power steering. Tachometer. Throttle control. Positive crankcase ventilation system. Full wheelcovers, Full-View rear window. Custom interior equipment. Custom chrome equipment. Custom Sport Truck equipment.

1967 Chevrolet 3/4-Ton C20 Camper Special Fleetside Pickup with Wolverine Camper (WCC)

COLOR OPTIONS: See 1964 options section for complete chart of 1964-1969 Chevrolet Commercial Truck colors.
OPTION INSTALLATION RATES: Heavy-duty seat (6 percent). Rear seat (44 percent). Panoramic Cab (12 percent). Tinted glass (13 percent). Bucket seats. Level-Ride seat. One-passenger auxiliary seat (61 percent). Rear center seat belt (6 percent). Center and rear seat (59 percent). Deluxe shoulder harness (1 percent). Spare wheel lock (1 percent). Side rails (1 percent). Side molding (34 percent). Single-speed wipers. Deluxe heater (88 percent). Air conditioning (3 percent). Junior West Coast mirror (32 percent). Senior West Coast mirror (12 percent). Long or short outside rear view mirror (4 percent). Front crossview mirror. Platform and stake rack (3 percent). Platform equipment (1 percent). Pickup box mounting (7 percent). Floorboard (44 percent). Special heavy-duty frame (23 percent). 9,000 lb. front axle (16 percent). 5,000-4,000 lb. front axle (26 percent). 5,000-7,000 lb. front axle (14 percent). Heavy-duty front axle (16 percent). Front wheel locking hub (75 percent). Heavy rear springs (70 percent). Auxiliary springs (33 percent). Positraction (11 percent). No-Spin rear axle (8 percent). 3.07:1 rear axle (1 percent). 4.11:1 rear axle (3 percent). Vacuum gauge (74 percent). Heavy-duty air cleaner (17 percent). Oil bath air cleaner (17 percent). Transistor ignition. 327-cid. V-8 (21 percent). Overdrive (1 percent). Four-speed transmission (21 percent). Heavy-duty four-speed transmission (2 percent). Powerglide transmission (10 percent). Three-speed automatic transmission (3 percent). Wheel trim cover (7 percent). Chrome hubcaps (9 percent). Roof marker lamps (9 percent). Whitewall tires (8 percent). Speed warning indicator (2 percent). Speed warning indicator (2 percent). Tachometer (2 percent). Push-button radio (23 percent). Chrome bumper (17 percent). Rear painted bumpers (26 percent). Rear step bumper (9 percent). Custom Appearance equipment (17 percent). Custom Comfort and Convenience equipment (21 percent). Camper Special equipment (2 percent). Custom Sport Truck (CST) option package (3 percent). Two-tone paint (25 percent).
NOTE 4: The percentage figures after each option are from Chevrolet records. They indicate what percentage of 1/2-ton to 2-ton trucks which qualified for the particular option were factory-equipped with the option. For example, the figure of 75 percent for front wheel locking hubs means 75 percent of 4 x 4 models only.
HISTORICAL: Introduced Sept. 11, 1966. Innovations: First year power steering was available for 4x4 models. New three-door Carryall Suburban styling. All trucks adopt 15 safety-related product improvements including dual cylinder brake systems, hazard lights, brake system warning lamp, energy-absorbing steering column, padded instrument panel, padded sun visors, folding front seat back latch, and thicker laminated windshield glass. Extensively restyled El Camino. First year for Chevy Vans with two wheelbase lengths. First year for V-8 power in vans. R.M. O'Connor was assistant general sales manager, truck & fleet sales, for Chevrolet Motor Div. Commercials, model-year production by series: [1/2-ton] (G10) 42,133, (C10) 288,356, (K10) 6,055 and (P10) 2,514. [3/4-ton] (G20) 8,032, (C20) 67,681 (K20) 4,271 (P20/gas) 3,178 and (P20/diesel) 10. [1-ton] (C30) 23,428, (P30) 6,777 and (P30/diesel) 117. Commercials, model-year production by engine type: [1/2-ton] (six) 207,720, (V-8) 131,338. [3/4 Ton] (six) 41,583, (V-8) 41,589. 1-ton: [six] 20,805, (V-8) 9,517. [Grand Total] 452,552.
NOTE 5: Model-year series production totals immediately above do not include El Caminos.

1968 CHEVROLET

1968 Chevrolet 1/2-Ton El Camino SS-396 Sedan-Pickup (OCW)

EL CAMINO — MODEL A/SERIES 13000 — SIX/V-8: For 1968, the El Camino was totally restyled. The cab had a more streamlined, "flying buttress" rear roof line. A new 116-in. wheelbase, the same used for Chevelle four-door Sedans and Station Wagons, was featured. Overall length grew from 197 in. (1964-1967) to 207 in. (1968-1972). The new pickup box, which would also be used through 1972, had different dimensions. Outside width increased to 75-1/2 in. Inside width behind the cab was down slightly to 59 in. Inside width near the tailgate remained at 64-1/2 in. The width between the wheelhousings fell to 44 in. The bottom bed length increased slightly to 79-1/4 in. However, tailgate measurements changed to 54-1/2 x 22-1/2 in., so lowering the tailgate added slightly less extra load length. The front end was patterned along the lines of the 1968 Chevelle passenger cars. Features included a front bumper that was slotted behind the license plate only. The parking lights were relocated to the ends of the bumper. Two headlamps on each side were set into squarish, bright metal housings. A fine, screen-like mesh grille ran the full width of the front. It had a horizontal Chevrolet badge in its center. All El Caminos had front side markers with the engine's cubic inch displacement on the front marker bezel. The base model had a chrome front bumper, Chevrolet grille badge, chrome-framed side marker lamps, an El Camino rear fender script, a bright tailgate latch, and a chrome Chevrolet script on the right-hand side of the tailgate. Added on El Camino Customs were bright window frames, pickup box upper edge moldings, rear body corner moldings, and wide rocker panel accent moldings. The SS-396 was a distinct model-option this year. On SS-396 versions, the grille was blacked out and an SS grille center badge was added. This option also included a special power dome hood, fat Wide-Oval tires on 6-in. JK rims, black out lower body perimeter finish, chrome moldings on lower body feature lines, special styled wheels, and SS tailgate moldings. The 396-cid/325-hp engine was standard. A 350-hp version of the big-block with a high-lift camshaft and dual exhausts was optional at extra cost. Rear side markers were optional, at least late in the model-year. Hide-Away headlamps were optional and body accent striping was available, at extra cost, for SS-396s only. Exterior body colors were Tuxedo Black, Ermine White, Grotto Blue, Fathom Blue, Island Teal, Ash Gold, Grecian Green, Tripoli Turquoise, Teal Blue, Cordovan Maroon, Seafrost Green, Matador Red, Palomino Ivory, Sequoia Green, and Butternut Yellow.

1/2-TON CHEVY VAN — MODEL G/SERIES 10 — FOUR: Chevy Vans were basically unchanged. The 90-in. and 108-in. Chevy Vans and Sportvans were offered in the G10 model line. The 18-in. longer body used with the longer wheelbase matched the dimensions of G20s. The grille had six horizontal bars divided into four segments by three vertical bars. The center bar was widest. The remaining vertical bars were narrower. Single, large round headlamps were at either end of the grille. Rectangular parking/directional lights were next to the headlamps. Under the windshield, five segmented vents continued to appear. Below the center vent segment was a Chevrolet bow tie emblem. There were large, rectangular side marker lamps. Standard models came with bumper, grille and hubcaps done in white. Chrome trim was optional. Both lines offered a Commercial Panel with double cargo doors available on the passenger side and at the rear. Both also offered window models in three levels of trim. The Sportvan was the base model. Sportvan Customs were in the middle. Sportvan Deluxe models were the fanciest. A 230-cid six was the base engine.

3/4-TON CHEVY VAN — MODEL G/SERIES 20 — SIX/V-8: The 108-in. wheelbase forward-control vans also came as 3/4-ton G20 models. Styling characteristics were the same as long wheelbase G10s. Models included the Commercial Panel with double cargo doors available on the passenger side and at the rear. There were also window models in three levels of trim: base Sportvan, Sportvan Custom, and Sportvan Deluxe. G20 line offered a 307-cid V-8.

1968 Chevrolet 3/4-Ton CST 20 Fleetside Long Box Pickup (CMD)

1/2-TON COMMERCIAL — MODEL C, K/SERIES 10 — SIX/V-8: Safety side marker lamps were added to the front fenders of Pickups, Panels and Suburbans. A modestly revamped body had slightly more bright work. Badges on the side of the cowl carried C10 designations for 1/2-ton models. The C10 (and K10 four-wheel-drive) chassis models and Pickups came on 115- or 127-in. wheelbases. The Chassis-Cowl-and-Windshield version was dropped. Panels and Suburbans came only on the longer wheelbase. The Suburban again had two doors on the passenger side and one on the driver's side. Surburbans were available with a tailgate or Panel truck style double rear doors. Pickups on the shorter wheelbase had a 6-1/2 ft. cargo box. Those on the long wheelbase featured an 8-ft. box. Both sizes came in Step-Side or Fleetside models. Standard equipment included a painted front bumper, directional signals, Deluxe Air heater/defroster, back-up lights, exterior left and right mirrors, full-width seat with vinyl interior trim, seat belts with retractors, and two-speed wipers and washers. Chrome front and rear bumpers were a separate option. The standard "pie plate" hubcaps had a wide color stripe and a Chevrolet bow tie in the center. Custom wheelcovers had a "gear sprocket" look with color-keyed finish and a bow tie in the center. The Custom Chrome option included chrome trim on the radiator grille, window frames, cab interior, steering wheel, etc. Custom equipment included Custom interior trim, right-hand sun shade, cigar lighter, bright hubcaps, bright dash knobs, dual horns, a Deluxe steering wheel, and other features. There was also the Custom Comfort & Appearance option. It included bright windshield trim, rear window moldings and ventipane frames, Custom front fender nameplates, color-keyed vinyl-coated floor mats, foam seats with color-keyed vinyl trim, a cigarette lighter, bright dash knobs, cowl insulation, and full-depth arm rests. On approximately four percent of production, the badges read CST10, indicating the buyer had selected the Custom Sport Truck package. This was a notch higher. The CST option had most items listed above, plus a chrome front bumper, CST plaques, full-width Western style vinyl seats, pedal trim, roof rim molding, carpeting, and extra insulation. CST equipment cost $161.40 extra. Bucket seats were $113 extra in CSTs and $139 in other cab models. Colors offered for the year were Black, Light Green, Dark Green, Medium Blue Poly, Clematis (Light) Blue, Dark Blue, Red, Metallic Vermilion Poly, Orange, Dark Yellow, Light Yellow, White, Silver Poly, Saddle Poly, and Ivory. Two-tone finishes were done using Off-White as the second (upper) color. It could be applied to all sheet metal above the belt line or to only the top and rear of the cab, leaving the windshield pillar painted main body color. This was the 50th anniversary of Chevrolet trucks and a special Anniversary Gold and Off-White two-tone paint option was available for $49.50 on Fleetside pickups and $31.25 on Step-Sides. Interiors were available in a choice of white or black.

1968 Chevrolet 1/2-Ton C10 Fleetside Long Box Pickup (CMD)

1/2-TON FORWARD-CONTROL — MODEL P/SERIES 10 — SIX/V-8: The 1/2-ton Forward-Control returned again. It had a 102-in. wheelbase. A small Step-Van walk-in delivery truck with a 7-ft. long body was approved for this chassis. It was made by Union City Body Co., of Union City, Ind. A channel type front bumper was optional.

3/4-TON COMMERCIAL — MODEL C, K/SERIES 20 — SIX/V-8: Carryover trucks in the Chevrolet 20 Series 3/4-ton line had the same styling, trim changes and options as other conventional trucks. The big news for 1968 was the introduction of a new "Longhorn" Fleetside Pickup with a 133-in. wheelbase and 8-1/2-ft. box. The Chassis-Cowl-and-Windshield model was dropped. Suburbans and Panels continued in this line. These had the same dimensions as comparable 1/2-ton models, but heavier chassis components. The designation plates had a number 20. Step-Side and Fleetside Pickups were also in this series. They featured an 8-ft. box. There was also an 8-ft. Stake model. The four-wheel-drive 3/4-ton models in the 20 Series had a K25 model prefix.

3/4-TON FORWARD-CONTROL — MODEL P/SERIES 20 — SIX/V-8: Just two 3/4-ton Forward-Control chassis remained in the 20 Series (3/4-ton) truck line. The 104-in. wheelbase was dropped. Remaining were the 125-in. wheelbase recommended for bodies 9-1/2 to 10-1/2 ft. long, and the 137-in. wheelbase recommended for bodies 11-1/2 to 12-1/2 ft. long. Bodies were available from factory-authorized suppliers or buyers could order them locally. There was an optional three-cylinder diesel engine. Also new was a coil spring front suspension, as the Step-Van chassis was now starting to find its way into the growing RV market.

1-TON MEDIUM-DUTY COMMERCIAL — MODEL C/SERIES 30 — SIX-CYLINDER: The Chevrolet 30 Series 1-ton trucks had the same styling and trim changes and options as other conventional trucks. The fender side nameplates had a number 30. The Chassis-Cowl-and-Windshield model was dropped. There were Chassis-and-Cowl and Chassis-and-Cab models, plus a new Fleetside Longhorn Pickup with an 8.5-ft box, a Step-Side Pickup with a 9-ft. box and a Stake with 9-ft. rail. No hubcaps were used on the larger split-rim wheels of the Chassis-and-Cab and Stake models, which had eight bolts and eight circular openings. The Camper Special package continued. Camper models had their own designation plates with a Chevrolet bow tie and "Camper Special" chrome script. The C38 model C30 1-ton Chassis-and-Cab with a long 157-in. wheelbase designed for use as an RV chassis was also offered again. A four-speed manual synchromesh transmission was standard. No four-wheel-drive option was offered in this series.

1-TON FORWARD-CONTROL — MODEL P/SERIES 30 — SIX/V-8: Three Forward-Control chassis were in the 30 Series (1-ton) truck line, but the 104-in. wheelbase was dropped. Offered were wheelbases of 125 in., 133 in., and 157 in. respectively. The 125-in. wheelbase was recommended for bodies 9-1/2 to 10-1/2 ft. long. The 137-in. wheelbase was recommended for bodies 11-1/2 to 12-1/2 ft. long. The new 157-in. wheelbase was used for a large Step-Van King model with a 14-1/2 ft. aluminum body. It was also suitable for RV use. Bodies were available from factory-authorized suppliers or buyers could order them locally. A channel type front bumper was optional. A High-Torque 230-cid six was standard equipment. There was an optional three-cylinder diesel engine. A coil spring front suspension was featured, as the Step-Van chassis was now starting to find its way into the growing RV market.

124

1968 Chevrolet 1/2-Ton CST 10 Fleetside Long Box Pickup (CMD)

I.D. DATA: Serial Number located: [Chassis models] on plate temporarily attached near steering column, with final location per body maker. [All others] on plate attached to rear face of left-hand door hinge pillar, on right side of cowl under hood. [El Camino] The first symbol indicated manufacturer: 1=Chevrolet. The second and third symbols indicated series: 33=six/34=V-8/35=Custom six/36=Custom V-8/38=SS=-396. The fourth and fifth symbols indicated body type: 80=Sedan-Pickup. The sixth symbol indicated model-year: 8=1968. The seventh symbol indicated assembly plant: A=Atlanta (Lakewood), B=Baltimore, Md., G=Framingham, Mass., K=Kansas City, Mo. (Leeds), Z=Fremont, Calif. The remaining symbols were the sequential production number starting with 100001 at each plant. Ending serial numbers not available. The Chevrolet engine had the source, date and type stamped on a serial number pad. Various source codes were used. Month codes were 1=Jan., 2=Feb., etc. Date codes were 01=first of month, etc. The were numerous prefix codes to indicate engines and transmission attachments. The collectible 396s had the following codes: [325 hp] EK/ET/ED, [350 hp] EF/EU/EL, [375 hp] EG. [Other models] The first symbol indicated truck type: C= Conventional Cab, K=4x4, G=Chevy Van, P=Forward-Control. The second symbol indicated type of engine: S=six, E=eight, T=diesel. The third symbol indicated the GVW range: [GVW] 1=3,600 to 5,600 lb., 2=5,500 to 8,100 lb., 3=6,700 to 10,000 lb., 4=Over 10,000 lb. The fourth and fifth symbols indicated the cab-to-axle dimension: 07=42 to 47 in., 09=54-59 in., 10=60-65 in., 14=84-89 in. The sixth symbol indicated body type: 02=Chassis & Cowl, 03=Chassis & Cab, 04=Step-Side Pickup, 05=Panel or Panel Van, 06=Suburban (doors) or Sportvan, 09=Platform/Stake, 12=Chassis & Cowl, 12=Cab with air brakes, 16=Suburban (gate), 26=Custom Sportvan, 34=Fleetside, 36=Deluxe Sportvan, 35=Forward-Control. The eighth symbol indicates model-year: 8=1968. The ninth symbol indicates assembly plant: A=Atlanta, Ga., B=Baltimore, Md., F=Flint, Mich., J=Janesville, Wis., K=Kansas City, Mo., S=St. Louis, Mo., T=Tarrytown, N.Y., Z=Fremont, Calif., 1=Oshawa, Canada.

1968 Chevrolet 1/2-Ton C10 Carryall Suburban (JAG)

Model	Body Type	Price	Weight	Prod. Total
El Camino — Model A/Series 13000 — 116 in. w.b. — Six				
13380	Pickup	2523	3169	Note 1
13580	Custom Pickup	2603	3181	Note 1
El Camino — Model A/Series 13000 — 116 in. w.b. — V-8				
13480	Pickup	2613	3193	Note 1
13680	Custom Pickup	2694	3210	Note 1
El Camino SS — Model A/Series 13000 — 116 in. w.b. — V-8				
13880	SS-396 Pickup	3138	- 5,190	

NOTE 1: Total El Camino production was 41,791.

Model	Body Type	Price	Weight	Prod. Total
1/2-Ton Chevy Van — Model G/Series 100 — 90 in. w.b.				
GS11005	Panel	2458	3005	18,617
GS11006	Sportvan	2634	3191	2153
GS11026	Custom Sportvan	2758	3295	685
GS11036	Deluxe Sportvan	2945	3331	403
1/2-Ton Chevy Van — Model G/Series 100 — 108 in. w.b.				
GS11005	Panel	2522	3122	17,569
GS11006	Sportvan	2706	3241	2,961
GS11026	Custom Sportvan	2828	3359	2,158
GS11036	Deluxe Sportvan	3020	3399	1,681
3/4-Ton Chevy Van — Model G/Series 20 — 108 in. w.b.				
GS21305	Panel	2737	3262	5,504
GS21306	Sportvan	2904	3390	715
GS21326	Custom Sportvan	3028	3514	325
GS21336	Deluxe Sportvan	3215	3558	363
1/2-Ton Commercial — Model C/Series 10 — 115 in. w.b.				
CE10703	Chassis & Cab	2320	3048	2735
CE10734	Fleetside 6.5 ft.	2468	3467	46,483
CE10704	Step-Side 6.5 ft.	2430	3389	46,322

Model	Body Type	Price	Weight	Prod. Total
1/2-Ton Commercial — Model C/Series 10 — 127 in. w.b.				
CE10902	Chassis & Cowl			14
CE10903	Chassis & Cab	2358	3136	1,197
CE10934	Fleetside 8 ft.	2506	3572	204,286
CE10904	Step-Side 8 ft.	2468	3477	18,632
CE10905	Panel	2839	3641	4,801
CE10906	Suburban	3081	3809	11,004
1/2-Ton Commercial 4x4 — Model K/Series 10 — 115 in. w.b.				
KE10703	Chassis & Cab	2874	3435	43
KE10734	Fleetside 6.5 ft.	3022	3851	1,449
KE10704	Step-Side 6.5 ft.	2985	3771	1,706
1/2-Ton Commercial 4x4 — Model K/Series 10 — 127 in. w.b.				
KE10903	Chassis & Cab	2911	3512	41
KE10934	Fleetside 8 ft.	3060	4024	-
KE10904	Step-Side 8 ft.	3022	3916	552
KE10905	Panel	3393	4123	59
KS10906	Suburban	3667	4212	4,259
1/2-Ton Forward Control — Model P/Series 10 — 102 in. w.b.				
PE10535	Chassis			125
PE10535	Step-Van	2864	3559	2,767
3/4-Ton Commercial — Model C/Series 20 — 127 in. w.b.				
CE20903	Chassis & Cab	2499	3458	6,636
CE20902	Chassis & Cowl			12
CE20934	Fleetside 8 ft.	2547	3960	60,646
CS20904	Step-Side 8 ft.	2610	3865	7,666
CE20909	Stake 8 ft.	2702	4085	1,103
CE20905	Panel	2981	4035	1,572
CE20906	Suburban	3264	4217	1,047
KE20905	Panel	3534	4111	68
KE20906	Suburban	3611	4215	299
3/4-Ton Forward Control — Model P/Series 20 — 125 in. w.b.				
PS20842	Chassis	1915	2749	404
PS20835	Steel Step-Van	3723	5070	2,314
PS20835	Aluminum Step-Van	-	-	44
PT20835	Diesel Step-Van	-	-	4
3/4-Ton Forward Control — Model P/Series 20 — 133 in. w.b.				
PS21842	Chassis	1950	2765	188
PS21835	Step-Van	3723	5070	2314
PS21835	Steel Step-Van	-	-	735
PS21835	Aluminum Step-Van	-	-	32
PT21835	Diesel Step-Van	-	-	1
1-Ton Commercial — Model C/Series 30 — 133 in. w.b.				
CE31003	Chassis & Cab	2657	3665	11,948
CE31034	Fleetside 8.5 ft.	2852	4158	213
CE31004	Step-Side 9 ft.	2791	4104	2,836
CE31009	Stake 9 ft.	2971	4499	3,272
1-Ton Forward Control — Model P/Series 30 — 125 in. w.b.				
PS30842	Chassis	3925	3764	759
PS30835	Step-Van	3902	5288	733
PS30835	Step-Van Aluminum	-	-	16
PT30835	Diesel Step-Van	-	-	2
1-Ton Forward Control — Model P/Series 30 — 133 in. w.b.				
PS31842	Chassis	3960	3784	1,043
PS31843	Chassis & Cowl			238
PS31835	Steel Step-Van			˙ 1,401
PS31835	Aluminum Step-Van	-	-	73
1-Ton Step-Van King — Model P/Series 30 — 157 in. w.b.				
PE38835	Step-Van King			853

NOTE 2: Second letter in model code indicates engine: S=Six, E=V-8, T=3-cyl. diesel.

NOTE 3: Production totals from Chevrolet records are for model-year through Aug. 1, 1968 and include all trucks made in U.S. factories for domestic/export/Canadian markets. Where no production total is shown, records were incomplete.

ENGINE: [Standard El Camino G10/P10/G20] Inline. OHV. Six-cylinder. Cast iron block. Bore & stroke: 3-7/8 in. x 3-1/4 in. Displacement: 230 cid. Compression ratio: 8.5:1. Brake horsepower: 140 at 4400 rpm. Torque: 220 lb.-ft. at 1600 rpm. Net horsepower: 120 at 3600 rpm. Seven main bearings. Hydraulic valve lifters. Carburetor: Rochester one-barrel model 7028006/7028010.

ENGINE: [Standard C10/C20/C30/K10/K20, Optional G10/G20/P10/El Camino] Inline. OHV. Six-cylinder. Cast iron block. Bore & stroke: 3-7/8 in. x 3.53 in. Displacement: 250 cid. Compression ratio: 8.5:1. Brake horsepower: 155 at 4200 rpm. Torque: 235 lb.-ft. at 1600 rpm. Seven main bearings. Hydraulic valve lifters. Carburetor: Rochester one-barrel model 7028007/7028011.

ENGINE: [Optional C10/C20/C30, Standard P20/P30] Inline. OHV. Six-cylinder. Cast iron block. Bore & stroke: 3-7/8 in. x 4-1/2 in. Displacement: 292 cid. Compression ratio: 8.1:1. Brake horsepower: 170 at 4000 rpm. Torque: 275 lb.-ft. at 1600 rpm. Seven main bearings. Hydraulic valve lifters. Carburetor: Rochester one-barrel model 7028012/7028013.

1968 Chevrolet 1/2-Ton CST 10 Fleetside Long Box Pickup (CMD)

ENGINE: [Optional G10/G20/P10/P20/P30/C10/C20/C30/K10/K20/El Camino): V-type. OHV. Eight-cylinder. Cast iron block. Bore & stroke: 3-7/8 in. x 3.25 in. Displacement: 307 cid. Compression ratio: 9.0:1. Brake horsepower: 200 at 4800 rpm. Five main bearings. Hydraulic valve lifters. Carburetor: Rochester two-barrel model 26 (numbers vary).

ENGINE: [Optional: C10/C20/C30/K10/K20] V-block. OHV. Eight-cylinder. Cast iron block. Bore & stroke: 4 in. x 3.25 in. Displacement: 327 cid. Compression ratio: 8.5:1. Brake horsepower: 220 at 4800 rpm. Five main bearings. Hydraulic valve lifters. Carburetor: Rochester four-barrel model 4G.

ENGINE: [Optional: El Camino] V-block. OHV. Eight-cylinder. Cast iron block. Bore & stroke: 4 in. x 3.25 in. Displacement: 327 cid. Compression ratio: 8.75:1. Brake horsepower: 250. Five main bearings. Hydraulic valve lifters. Carburetor: Rochester four-barrel model 4G.

ENGINE: [Optional: El Camino] V-block. OHV. Eight-cylinder. Cast iron block. Bore & stroke: 4 in. x 3.25 in. Displacement: 327 cid. Compression ratio: 10.0:1. Brake horsepower: 275. Five main bearings. Hydraulic valve lifters. Carburetor: Rochester four-barrel model 4G.

ENGINE: [Optional: El Camino] V-block. OHV. Eight-cylinder. Cast iron block. Bore & stroke: 4 in. x 3.25 in. Displacement: 327 cid. Compression ratio: 11.0:1. Brake horsepower: 325. Five main bearings. Hydraulic valve lifters. Carburetor: Rochester four-barrel model 4G.

ENGINE: [El Camino/standard SS-396] V-block. OHV. Eight-cylinder. Cast iron block. Bore & stroke: 4.09 in. x 3.76 in. Displacement: 396 cid. Compression ratio: 10.25:1. Brake horsepower: 325 at 4800 rpm. Torque: 410 lb.-ft. at 3200 rpm. Five main bearings. Hydraulic valve lifters. Carburetor: Rochester four-barrel model Quadra-Jet.

ENGINE: [Optional: El Camino SS-396] V-block. OHV. Eight-cylinder. Cast iron block. Bore & stroke: 4.09 in. x 3.76 in. Displacement: 396 cid. Compression ratio: 10.25:1. Brake horsepower: 350 at 5200 rpm. Torque: 415 lb.-ft. at 3400 rpm. Five main bearings. Hydraulic valve lifters. Carburetor: Rochester four-barrel model Quadra-Jet.

ENGINE: [Optional El Camino] V-type. OHV. Eight-cylinder. Cast iron block. Bore & stroke: 4.094 in. x 3.76 in. Displacement: 396 cid. Compression ratio: 11.25:1. Brake horsepower: 375. Five main bearings. Carburetor: four-barrel.

ENGINE: [Optional P20/P30] Diesel. Model 3-53N. Three-cylinder. Bore and stroke: 3.875 x 4.5 in. Displacement: 159.2 cid. Brake horsepower: 94 at 2800 rpm. Torque: 205 lb.-ft. at 1500 rpm.

1968 Chevrolet 1/2-Ton CST 10 Fleetside Long Box Pickup (CMD)

CHASSIS: [El Camino] Wheelbase: 116 in. Overall length: 206 in. Front tread: 59 in. Rear tread: 59 in. Tires: 7.35 x 14 in. GVW: 4,300 lb.
CHASSIS: [C10] Wheelbase: 115 in. Overall length: 188-1/2 in. Height: 74.5 in. Inside length of pickup box: 78-1/2 in. Front tread: 63.1 in. Rear tread: 61.1 in. Tires: Tires: [4x2] 8.25 x 14 in., [Suburban] 8.15 x 15 in. GVW: [4x2] 4,400 to 5,000 lb.
CHASSIS: [K10] Wheelbase: 115 in. Overall length: 188-1/4 in. Inside length of pickup box: 78-1/2 in. Front tread: 63.1 in. Rear tread: 61.1 in. Tires: Tires: [4x4] 17.5 x 17 four-ply. GVW: [4x4] 5,600 lb.
CHASSIS: [C10] Wheelbase: 127 in. Overall length: 207-3/4 in. Height: 71 in. Inside length of pickup box: 98 in. Front tread: 63.1 in. Rear tread: 61.1 in. Tires: [4x2] 7.75 x 15 in. four-ply. GVW: [4x2] 4,400 to 5,000 lb.
CHASSIS: [K10] Wheelbase: 127 in. Overall length: 208 in. Inside length of pickup box: 98 in. Front tread: 63.1 in. Rear tread: 61.1 in. Tires: [4x4] 17.5 x 17. GVW: [4x4] 5,600 lb.
CHASSIS: [P10] Wheelbase: 102 in. Tires: 7.75 x 15 in. GVW: 4,600 to 5,400 lb.
CHASSIS: [C20] Wheelbase: 127 in. Overall length: 206-1/4 in. Tires: [4x2] 8.00 x 16.5 six-ply. GVW: [4x2] 5,500 to 7,500 lb.
CHASSIS: [K20] Wheelbase: 127 in. Overall length: 208 in. Tires: [4x4] 7 x 17.5 six-ply. GVW: [4x4] 5,700 to 7,600 lb.
CHASSIS: [P20] Wheelbases: (P2300) 104 in., (P2500) 125 in., (P2600) 137 in. Base tires: 7 x 17.5. GVW: 7,000 lb.
CHASSIS: [C21] Wheelbase: 133 in. Overall length: 213-3/4 in. Inside length of pickup box: 104 in. Tires: 8 x 17.5 in. GVW: 6,700 to 14,000 lb.
CHASSIS: [C30] Wheelbase: 133 in. Overall length: 217-3/4 in. Inside length of pickup box: 108-1/4 in. Tires: 8 x 17.5 in. GVW: 6,700 to 14,000 lb.
CHASSIS: [P30] Wheelbases: (P3300) 104 in., (P3500) 125 in., (P3600) 137 in. Base tires: 8 x 19.5. GVW: 7,500 to 14,000 lb.

1968 Chevrolet 1/2-Ton CST 10 Fleetside Long Box Pickup (CMD)

TECHNICAL: Standard transmission: Chevrolet three-speed manual (Borg-Warner heavy-duty three-speed optional). Type transmission: [C30] 4F/1R, [Others] 3F/1R. Column-mounted gearshift lever. Single-plate, dry-disc clutch. Rear axle: [1/2-ton] semi-floating, [3/4-ton/1-ton] full-floating. Base rear axles: [El Camino] 3.08:1, [C10/K10] 3.73:1, [C20/K20] 4.11:1, [C30] 5.14:1. Brakes: Four-wheel hydraulic drums. Brake linings: [C10/K10] 11 x 2.75 in., [C20/K20/C30] 12 x 2 in., [El Camino] 9-1/2 x 2-1/2 in. Kelsey-Hayes pressed steel wheels.

1968 Chevrolet 1/2-Ton Custom 10 Fleetside Long Box Pickup (CMD)

EL CAMINO OPTIONS: Air conditioning. Heavy-duty battery. Custom seat belts. Tinted glass. Tinted windshield. Power windows. Front bumper guards. Custom Deluxe front seat belts. Strato bucket seats. Strato Ease headrest. Regular headrest. Safety harness. Front and rear floor mats. Underhood trouble light. Deluxe foam front seat cushion. Door edge guards. Black or beige vinyl roof. Delete heater/defroster. Air conditioning. Remote-control outside rear view mirror. Console. Heavy-duty suspension. Positraction. Rear axle ratios: 3.70, 3.36, 3.08, 3.31, 3.55, 2.73, 3.07, 3.73. Vacuum power brakes. Front disc brakes. Brake linings. Radiator fan. Air injector reactor. Cruise Control. 61-ampere Delcotron alternator. 42-ampere Delcotron alternator. Heavy-duty clutch. Overdrive transmission. Four-speed transmission. Close-ratio four-speed transmission. Powerglide transmission (with six). Three-speed Turbo-Hydramatic transmission (with V-8s). Dual exhausts. Deluxe steering wheel. Comfortilt steering wheel. Woodgrain steering wheel. Power steering. Mag style wheelcovers. Wheel trim covers. Simulated wire wheels. Heavy-duty battery. Tri-volume horn. Special instrumentation. Auxiliary lighting. Speed warning indicator. Tachometer. Glove box lamp. Ash tray lamp. Instrument panel courtesy lamps. Electric clock. Push-button AM radio and antenna. Push-button AM/FM radio and antenna. Heavy-duty radiator. Front bumper guards. SS-396 equipment. Vinyl roof. Deluxe front seat cushions. Concealed windshield wipers. [SS-396] Front Strato Bucket seats. Accent striping. Engine: 396-cid/350-hp V-8. Engine: 396-cid/375-hp V-8. Special mag style wheelcovers. Rally wheel rims.

TRUCK OPTIONS: Oil bath air cleaner. Heavy-duty air cleaner. Air conditioning. Arm rests. Positraction. Rear axle ratios. Heavy-duty battery. Seat belts. Vacuum power brakes. Chrome front bumper. Chrome hubcaps. Side-mounted spare wheel carrier. Heavy-duty clutch. Heavy-duty cooling. Custom side molding package. Fuel filter. Gauges. Generator. Soft-Ray tinted glass. Engine governor. Door edge guards. Towing wire harness. Safety harness. Heater and defroster package. Towing hooks. Rear side marker lights. Right-hand door lock. Exterior rear view mirror. Ship-to-Shore power outlet. Camper Special package with custom "Camper Special" nameplates. Fuel and vacuum pump booster. AM radio and antenna. Heavy-duty shock absorbers. Speed warning indicator. Heavy-duty front springs. Heavy-duty rear springs. Front stabilizer bar. Heavy-duty starter. Power steering. Body side paint stripes. Throttle control. Full wheelcovers. One-passenger auxiliary seat. Panoramic rear window. Custom interior equipment. Custom chrome equipment. Custom Sport Truck equipment. Bucket seats. Trailering Special equipment.

COLOR OPTIONS: See 1964 options section for complete chart of 1964-1969 Chevrolet Commercial Truck colors.

OPTIONS AND INSTALLATION RATES: Heavy-duty seat (6 percent). Front center seat belt (2 percent). Rear seat (40 percent). Shoulder harness (1 percent). Panoramic cab (19 percent). Bucket seats (2 percent). Custom bench seat (1 percent). One-passenger auxiliary seat (55 percent). Rear center seat (10 percent). Center and rear seat (41 percent). Shoulder harness (not available/a). Spare wheel lock (2 percent). Upper body side molding (not available/a). Door edge guards (6 percent). Side trim molding (36 percent). Heater deletion (12 percent). Air conditioning (3 percent). Roof-mounted air conditioning (not available). Front door arm rest (2 percent). Jr. West Coast mirror (32 percent). Sr. West Coast mirror (3 percent). Non-glare inside mirror (16 percent). Body paint stripe (5 percent). Platform equipment (3 percent). Pickup box mounting (9 percent). Floorboard (28 percent). Front stabilizer (20 percent). Heavy front springs (18 percent). Front wheel locking hub (75 percent). Heavy rear spring (65 percent). Heavy shocks (11 percent). Heavy front axle (12 percent). Auxiliary springs (22 percent). Heavy-duty rear shocks (4 percent). Leaf springs (2 percent). Positraction (11 percent). No-Spin rear axle (7 percent). Pow-R-Lock rear axle (not available). Optional gear axle (16 percent). Cruise control (not available). Oil bath air cleaner (10 percent). 327-cid V-8 engine (26 percent). 396-cid four-barrel engine (3 percent). 396-cid two-barrel engine (1 percent). Overdrive (1 percent). Heavy-duty three-speed manual transmission (9 percent). Four-speed manual transmission (21 percent). Powerglide transmission (9 percent). Three-speed automatic transmission (16 percent). Wheel trim covers (10 percent). Chrome hubcaps (12 percent). Whitewall tires (9 percent). Roof marker lamps (2 percent). Speed warning indicator (not available). Tachometer (1 percent). Push-button radio (25 percent). Camper Special equipment (3 percent). Custom Sport Truck option (4 percent). Two-tone paint (32 percent). Full gauge package (55 percent). Custom Appearance package (3 percent). Custom Comfort & Convenience package (26 percent).

NOTE 4: Partial list of options and installation rates based on Chevrolet cumulative model-year records for 1/2-ton to 2-ton trucks built through Aug. 1, 1968. Figures do not include El Camino, which was considered a Chevelle passenger car for record-keeping purposes. The installation rate (percent) shows the percent option usage in those trucks qualifying for the particular option. For example, front wheel locking hubs were used on 75 percent of Chevy's four-wheel-drive trucks, not 75 percent of total production. The notation not available indicates percentage installation rate not available.

HISTORICAL: Calendar-year production [All Chevrolet commercials] 680,499. Chevrolet Commercials, model-year production by tonnage class and engine: [1/2-ton] (six-cylinder) 202,962, (V-8) 190,413, [Total] 393,375. [3/4-ton] (six-cylinder) 35,645, (V-8) 62,731, [Total] 98,376. [1-ton] (six-cylinder) 14,556, (V-8) 15,179, (Total) 29,735. (Grand Total) 521,486. Innovations: First year for front and rear safety side markers. New models included 3/4- and 1-ton Forward-Control Step-Vans equipped with independent front suspension, coil springs, power steering and V-8 engines. New 327-cid/200-hp and 396-cid/310-hp engines. Chevrolet celebrated its 50th year of truck manufacturing in 1968. Special Anniversary Gold with Off-White paint was optional. Record sales and production marked Chevrolet's truck operations this season. Dealers delivered 843,990 trucks of all sizes. Most Chevrolet trucks were built at St. Louis, Mo. The home plant, at Flint, Mich., was the second highest source. However, the Fremont, Calif. factory was challenging for second place. This was the first year that production of V-8 powered trucks (410,178 units) outpaced production of sixes (269,291 units). T.L. Pritchett, assistant general sales manager, was head of the truck division.

1969 CHEVROLET

1969 Chevrolet 1/2-Ton El Camino SS-396 Sedan-Pickup (CMD)

EL CAMINO — MODEL A/SERIES 13000 — SIX/V-8: For 1969, the El Camino had a mild, but handsome facelift. A new fine-finned grille insert was dominated by a bright horizontal moldings at its top, center and bottom. The center molding had a Chevrolet badge in the middle. The center bumper slot was larger. Following an every-other-year Chevelle tradition, the parking lamps were moved back inside the slot, which was widened just enough to accommodate the lenses. At the rear, all El Caminos had large back-up lamps set into the tailgate on either side of the Chevrolet nameplate in the center. The rear bumper indentations filled by back-up lamps on passenger cars had red reflectors on the Sedan-Pickup. Accenting base models was a Chevrolet script on the left fender top, front side marker engine call-outs, rear side marker lamps, rear fender El Camino nameplates, bright windshield frames, bright tailgate latch, Chevrolet nameplate on tailgate, and narrow rocker panel moldings. Custom models had bright window frames, pickup box upper edge moldings, rear body corner moldings, two moldings across the tailgate at taillight top and bottom height, a bright rear window frame, bright moldings on lower body feature line, and silver anodized lower body perimeter finish. The SS-396 reverted to an option this year. On SS-396 versions, the grille had black out finish. The grille center and middle of the tailgate had SS-396 badges. The engine call-outs on the front side marker lamp housings said Turbo-Jet 396. This option also included a special power dome hood, fat G70-14 Red Stripe tires on 14 x 7-in. rims, black out style lower body perimeter finish, chrome moldings on the lower body feature line, special styled wheels, suspension upgrades, power disc brakes, wheel opening moldings, and SS tailgate moldings. The 396-cid/325-hp engine with chrome accents was standard. A 350-hp version of the big-block with a high-lift camshaft and dual exhausts was optional at extra cost. The "flying buttress" roof line was retained. The pickup box, used through 1972, had an outside width of 75-1/2 in. Inside width behind the cab was 59 in. Inside width near the tailgate was 64-1/2 in. The width between the wheelhousings was 44 in. The bottom bed length measured 79-1/4 in. Tailgate measurements were 54-1/2 x 22-1/2 in. El Camino exterior body colors included Tuxedo Black, Butternut Yellow, Dover White, Dark Blue, Garnet Red, Glacier Blue, Azure Turquoise, Fathom Green, Frost Green, Burnished Brown, Champagne, Olympic Gold, Burgundy, Cortez Silver, LeMans Blue, and (for SS-396s only) Orange and Daytona Yellow.

1969 Chevrolet 1/2-Ton G10 Chevy Van 108 Panel Truck (CMD)

1/2-TON CHEVY VAN — MODEL G/SERIES 10 — SIX/V-8: Only the 1/2-ton G10 line offered the compact van body with 209-cu. ft. of payload space on a 90-in. wheelbase. The larger 256-cu. ft. body, mounted on a 108-in. wheelbase, could be ordered, too. It was 18 in. longer. Four G10 models were offered in the two lengths with six-cylinder or V-8 power plants. Standard features included Stay-Tight integral body-frame construction and durable, tapered leaf springs.

Styling was basically unchanged. The grille had six horizontal bars divided into four segments by three vertical bars. The center bar was widest. The remaining vertical bars were narrower. Single, large round headlamps were at either end of the grille. Rectangular parking/directional lights were next to the headlamps. Under the windshield, five segmented vents continued to appear. Below the center vent segment was a Chevrolet bow tie emblem. There were large, rectangular side marker lamps. Standard models came with bumper, grille and hubcaps done in white. Chrome trim was optional. Both lines offered a Commercial Panel with double cargo doors available on the passenger side and at the rear. Both also offered window models in three levels of trim. The Sportvan was the base model. Sportvan Customs were in the middle. Sportvan Deluxe models were the fanciest. A 230-cid six was the base engine. A 307-cid V-8 was optional.
3/4-TON CHEVY VAN — MODEL G/SERIES 20 — SIX/V-8: The 108-in. wheelbase driver-forward vans also came as 3/4-ton G20 models. Styling characteristics were the same as long wheelbase G10s. Models included the Commercial Panel with double cargo doors available on the passenger side and at the rear. There were also window models in three levels of trim: base Sportvan, Sportvan Custom, and Sportvan Deluxe. The G20 line offered the same engines as G10s.

1969 Chevrolet 1/2-Ton K10 Blazer Open 4x4 Sport Utility Vehicle (CMD)

1/2-TON BLAZER — MODEL K/SERIES 5 — SIX/V-8: Attracting considerable attention was Chevrolet's entry into the expanding 4x4 off-road vehicle field. It was called the Blazer. Its suspension system consisted of single-leaf tapered front springs with a combination of multi-leaf and tapered springs at the rear. The ball-type steering unit had a 24:1 ratio and its standard engine was Chevrolet's 155-hp six. The Blazer's single-unit body was joined to a heavy channel steel frame. The rear-mounted 23.5-gallon fuel tank was located inside the frame. Numerous options were offered for the Blazer including four-speed manual and automatic transmissions, V-8 engines, power steering, power brakes and a completely removable fiberglass top. Colors, exterior trim, upholstery and equipment were very similar or the same as used on the conventional K10 models.

1969 Chevrolet 1/2-Ton Custom/10 Fleetside Pickup (CW)

1/2-TON COMMERCIAL — MODEL C, K/SERIES 10 — SIX/V-8: Pickups had a frontal redesign. An aluminum center piece, in the grille, was embossed with the Chevrolet name. It had integral, rectangular parking lamps at each end, next to its square headlamp housings. A large Chevrolet bow tie was at the front center of the hood. Inside was a new low-profile steering wheel, new seat back construction and new foot-operated parking brake. Standard equipment on all Pickups included: six-cylinder engine, self-adjusting four-wheel brakes, dual brake master cylinder, back-up lights, Panoramic rear window, side marker reflectors, left-and right-hand outside rear view mirrors, heater and defroster, padded dash, non-glare front instrument panel finish, padded sun visors, ash tray, seat belts with retractors, push-button seat belt buckles, low-profile control knobs, two-speed electric washer/wipers, windshield defrosters, safety glass, flexible fuel filler neck, deep-dish steering wheel with telescoping shaft, and thick laminate safety glass windshield, full-width seat with vinyl interior trim, and painted front bumper. Chrome front and rear bumpers were a separate option. The standard C10 had no side trim, plain black rubber window gaskets, and painted bumpers. The grille shell had bright metal finish. The hubcaps were also painted. The vent window pillars and frames were painted flat black. The standard "pie plate" hubcaps were painted. Rear moldings around the taillamps and tailgate were not available on standard C10. Upper and lower belt moldings were optional. Trucks equipped with the lower belt molding had the center of the molding painted black. Chrome-plated "gear sprocket" wheelcovers with color-keyed finish and a bow tie in the center were optional. The Custom C10 was designated by Custom/10 nameplates on the front fenders. There was bright metal trim around the windshield, rear window, and vent window pillar and frame. Base bumpers and hubcaps were still painted, however. Upper and lower belt moldings were both optional and the center of the lower molding is painted. When equipped with lower side moldings, the Custom/10 also got taillamp moldings and twin tailgate moldings. These moldings were positioned above and below the Chevrolet lettering on the back. The Custom/10 grille came in bright metal with a plastic grid design for the insert. (The grille was the same for all models). Chrome hubcaps were optional on Custom/10 models. The top-of-the-line was the Custom Sport Truck, which said CST/10 on its front fender sides. The CST had all Custom/10 features, plus more. The lower belt molding was standard and had an exclusive woodgrain center insert. The upper belt molding was still optional. The CST also had special front side marker lamps with chrome trim, which were not available on other models. Taillight and tailgate moldings (with a woodgrain appliqué and chrome Chevrolet lettering) were standard on CSTs, too. Chrome pie plate hubcaps were standard, full wheelcovers were optional. A cab-mounted cargo lamp also came standard on CSTs. There were Custom Interior Convenience, Custom Appearance, and Custom Comfort & Convenience options. Bucket seats were extra in all cab models. Fifteen paint colors were available: Black, Light Green, Yellow Green, Dark Green, Light Blue, Dark Blue, Turquoise, Red, Orange, Maroon, Dark Yellow, Yellow, White, Silver, and Saddle. Seat colors were saddle, blue, green, red, black and turquoise. The C10 (and K10 four-wheel-drive) Chassis models and Pickups came on 115- or 127-in. wheelbases. The Chassis-and-Cowl model was dropped. Both Fleetside and Step-Side Pickups offered a 6-1/2-ft. box or 8-ft. box. Panels and Suburbans came only on the longer wheelbase. The Suburban again had two-doors on the passenger side and one on the driver's side. Suburbans were available with a tailgate or Panel truck style double rear doors. Both single-unit body models had coil springs on all four wheels. Optional seats, in the Suburban, converted the 181-cu. ft. payload space into a passenger compartment. Pickups on the shorter wheelbase had a 6-1/2-ft. cargo box. Those on the long wheelbase featured an 8-ft. box. Both sizes came in Step-Side or Fleetside models. Two-toning was done using Off-White as the second (upper) color. It was applied to all sheet metal above the belt line.

1969 Chevrolet 1/2-Ton P10 Step-Van 7 (CMD)

1/2-TON FORWARD-CONTROL — MODEL P/SERIES 10 — SIX/V-8: The 1/2-ton Forward-Control returned again. It had a 102-in. wheelbase. The Forward-Control chassis and Step-Van were designed for door-to-door delivery service. Body lengths ranged from seven to eight feet for this Step-Van 7 series. Features included independent coil spring front suspension and two six-cylinder engines. Buyers could also get full-height doors, sliding side doors and double rear doors.
3/4-TON COMMERCIAL — MODEL C, K/SERIES 20 — SIX/V-8: Carryover trucks in the Chevrolet 20 Series 3/4-ton line had the same styling, trim changes and options as other conventional trucks. The Step-Side Pickup had the 8-ft. box. The "Longhorn" Fleetside pickup had a 133-in. wheelbase and 8-1/2-ft. box. The Chassis-and-Cowl model and 4x4 Panel were dropped. The Chassis-and-Cab, two Suburbans and the 4x2 Panel continued in this line. These had the same dimensions as comparable 1/2-ton models, but heavier chassis components. The designation plates had a number 20. Step-Side and Fleetside Pickups were also in this series. They featured the 8-ft. pickup box. There was also an 8-ft. Stake model. The four-wheel-drive 3/4-ton models in the 20 Series had a K20 model prefix.

1969 Chevrolet 3/4-Ton Custom Camper C20 Longhorn Fleetside extended box Pickup (CMD)

1969 Chevrolet 1-Ton C-30 Chassis-and-Cab with Open Road frame-mounted camper body. (CMD)

3/4-TON FORWARD-CONTROL — MODEL P/SERIES 20 — SIX-V-8: Just two 3/4-ton Forward-Control chassis remained in the 20 Series (3/4-ton) truck line, but they were the basis for numerous steel, aluminum, and round and square styled bodies, and a number of engine choices. The P20 Forward-Control chassis and Step-Van were designed for door-to-door delivery service. Features included independent coil spring front suspension, three six-cylinder engines, two optional V-8s, plus a three-cylinder Detroit diesel engine. Buyers could also get full-height doors, sliding side doors and double rear doors. Remaining in the 3/4-ton series were the 125-in. wheelbase chassis recommended for bodies 9-1/2 to 10-1/2 ft. long and the 137-in. wheelbase recommended for bodies 11-1/2 to 12-1/2 ft. long. Bodies were available from factory-authorized suppliers or buyers could order them locally. The coil spring suspension reflected the fact that the Forward-Control chassis was now starting to find its way into the growing RV market.
1-TON MEDIUM-DUTY COMMERCIAL — MODEL C/SERIES 30 — SIX-CYLINDER: The Chevrolet 30 Series 1-ton trucks had the same styling and trim changes and options as other conventional trucks. The fender side nameplates had a number 30. The Stake with 9-ft. rail was dropped. There were four 133-in. wheelbase models: Chassis-and-Cowl, Chassis-and-Cab, Longhorn Pickup with 8.5-ft box, and a Step-Side Pickup with 9-ft. box. The Stake was dropped. No hubcaps were used on the larger split-rim wheels of the Chassis-and-Cab models, which had eight bolts and eight circular openings. The Camper Special package continued. Camper models had their own designation plates with a Chevrolet bow tie and "Camper Special" chrome script. The C38 model 1-ton Chassis-and-Cab with a long 157-in. wheelbase for use as an RV chassis was also offered again. A four-speed manual synchromesh transmission was standard. No four-wheel-drive option was offered.

1969 Chevrolet 1-Ton P-30 Step-Van King w/ Parson Mobile Products motorhome conversion (CMD)

1-TON FORWARD-CONTROL — MODEL P/SERIES 30 — SIX/V-8: Three Forward-Control chassis were in the 30 Series (1-ton) truck line. The Forward-Control chassis and Step-Van were designed for door-to-door delivery service. Body lengths ranged up to 14-1/2 ft. for the 1-ton Step-Van King. Features included independent coil spring front suspension, three six-cylinder engines, two optional V-8s, plus a three-cylinder Detroit diesel engine. Buyers could also get full-height doors, sliding side doors and double rear doors. P30s were offered were wheelbases of 125 in., 133 in., and 157 in. respectively. The 125-in. wheelbase chassis recommended for bodies 9-1/2 to 10-1/2 ft. long. The 137-in. wheelbase was recommended for bodies 11-1/2 to 12-1/2 ft. long. The new 157-in. wheelbase was used for the large aluminum-bodied Step-Van King model, as well as for RV conversions. Bodies were available from factory-authorized suppliers or buyers could order them locally. A High-Torque 230 six was standard equipment.
I.D. DATA: Serial Number located: [Chassis models] on plate temporarily attached near steering column, with final location per body maker. [All others] on plate attached to rear face of left-hand door hinge pillar, on right side of cowl under hood. [El Camino] The first symbol indicated manufacturer: 1=Chevrolet. The second and third symbols indicated series: 33=six/34=V-8/35=Custom six/36=Custom V-8. The fourth and fifth symbols indicated body type: 80=Sedan-Pickup. The sixth symbol indicate model-year: 9=1969. The seventh symbol indicated assembly plant: A=Atlanta (Lakewood), B=Baltimore, Md., G=Framingham, Mass., K=Kansas City, Mo. (Leeds), Z=Fremont, Calif., The remaining symbols were the sequential production number starting with 100001 at each plant. Ending serial numbers not available. The Chevrolet engine had the source, date and type stamped on a serial number pad. Various source codes were

used. Month codes were 1=Jan., 2=Feb., etc. Date codes were 01=first of month, etc. The were numerous prefix codes to indicate engines and transmission attachments. The collectible 396s had the following codes: [325 hp] JA/JK/JV/ KG/KH/KI, [350 hp] JC/JE/KB, [375 hp] JD/KF/KD. [Other models] The first symbol indicated truck type: C=Conventional Cab, K=4x4, G=Chevy Van, P=Forward-Control. The second symbol indicated type of engine: S=six, E=eight, T=diesel. The third symbol indicated the GVW range: [GVW] 1=3,600 to 5,600 lb., 2=5,500 to 8,100 lb., 3=6,700 to 10,000 lb., 4=Over 10,000 lb. The fourth and fifth symbols indicated the cab-to-axle dimension: 07=42 to 47 in., 09=54-59 in., 10=60-65 in., 14=84-89 in. The sixth symbol indicated body type: 02=Chassis & Cowl, 03=Chassis & Cab, 04=Step-Side Pickup, 05=Panel or Panel Van, 06=Suburban (doors) or Sportvan, 09=Platform/Stake, 12=Chassis & Cowl, 12=Cab with air brakes, 14=Blazer, 16=Suburban (gate), 26=Custom Sportvan, 34=Fleetside, 36=Deluxe Sportvan, 35=Forward-Control. The eighth symbol indicates model-year: 9=1969. The ninth symbol indicates assembly plant: A=Atlanta, Ga., B=Baltimore, Md., F=Flint, Mich., J=Janesville, Wis., K=Kansas City, Mo., S=St. Louis, Mo., T=Tarrytown, N.Y., Z=Fremont, Calif. 1=Oshawa, Canada.

1969 Chevrolet 1/2-Ton El Camino Custom Sedan-Pickup (DFW)

Model	Body Type	Price	Weight	Prod. Total
El Camino — Model A/Series 13000 — 116 in. w.b. — Six				
13380	Pickup	2552	3192	Note 1
13580	Custom Pickup	2632	3219	Note 1
El Camino — Model A/Series 13000 — 116 in. w.b. — V-8				
13480	Pickup	2642	3216	Note 1
13680	Custom Pickup	2723	3248	Note 1
NOTE 1: Total El Camino production was 48,385.				
1/2-Ton Chevy Van — Model G/Series 100 — 90 in. w.b.				
GS11005	Panel	2531	3072	18,456
GS11006	Sportvan	2738	3266	1,730
GS11026	Custom Sportvan	2863	3375	526
GS11036	Deluxe Sportvan	3050	3415	270
1/2-Ton Chevy Van — Model G/Series 100 — 108 in. w.b.				
GS11005	Panel	2595	3189	20,730
GS11006	Sportvan	2810	3316	3,065
GS11026	Custom Sportvan	2935	3439	2,598
GS11036	Deluxe Sportvan	3125	3586	382
GS21336	Deluxe Sportvan	3294	3629	306
1/2-Ton Blazer — Model K/Series 5 — 104 in. w.b.				
KE10514	Open Utility	2852	2947	4935
1/2-Ton Commercial — Model C/Series 10 — 115 in. w.b.				
CE10703	Chassis & Cab	2383	3116	2,343
CE10734	Fleetside 6.5 ft.	2532	3531	54,211
CE10704	Step-Side 6.5 ft.	2494	3450	49,147
1/2-Ton Commercial — Model C/Series 10 — 127 in. w.b.				
CE10903	Chassis & Cab	2421	3189	1,203
CE10934	Fleetside 8 ft.	2569	3623	268,233
CE10904	Step-Side 8 ft.	2532	3523	18,179
CE10905	Pane	2960	3724	5,492
CE10906	Suburban	3194	3815	14,056
1/2-Ton Commercial 4x4 — Model K/Series 10 — 115 in. w.b.				
KE10703	Chassis & Cab	2936	3316	58
KE10734	Fleetside 6.5 ft.	3085	3732	1,649
KE10704	Step-Side 6.5 ft.	3047	3652	1,698
1/2-Ton Commercial 4x4 — Model K/Series 10 — 127 in. w.b.				
KE10903	Chassis & Cab	2973	3522	35
KE10934	Fleetside 8 ft.	3123	3836	4937
KE10904	Step-Side 8 ft.	3085	36512	521
KE10905	Panel	3513	3935	-
KS10906	Suburban	3749	4024	-
1/2-Ton Forward-Control — Model P/Series 10 — 102 in. w.b.				
PE10535	Chassis	-	-	125
PE10535	Step-Van	2944	3702	2,819
3/4-Ton Commercial — Model C/Series 20 — 127 in. w.b.				
CE20903	Chassis & Cab	2614	3506	8,440
CE20934	Fleetside 8 ft.	2762	4013	74,894
CS20904	Step-Side 8 ft.	2724	3907	8,090
CE20909	Stake 8 ft.	2832	4138	-
CE20905	Panel	3172	4093	1,779
CE20906	Suburban	3447	4199	2,736
Long Horn Pickup				
CE21034	Pickup 8.5 ft.	2826	4066	8,797-
3/4-Ton Commercial 4x4 — Model K/Series 20 — 127 in. w.b.				
KE20903	Chassis & Cab	3205	3626	556
KE20934	Fleetside 8 ft.	3353	4131	6,124
KE20904	Step-Side 8 ft.	3315	4025	1,071
KE20906	Suburban	4040	4316	545
3/4-Ton Forward-Control — Model P/Series 20 — 125 in. w.b.				
PS20842	Chassis	1980	2749	616
PS20835	Step-Van	3819	5175	1,843
PS20855	Aluminum Step-Van	-	-	68
3/4-Ton Forward Control — Model P/Series 20 — 133 in. w.b.				
PS21842	Chassis	2015	2765	233
PS21835	Step-Van	3930	5410	950
PS21835	Aluminum Step-Van	4900	4760	79
1-Ton Commercial — Model C/Series 30 — 133 in. w.b.				
CE31002	Chassis & Cowl	-	-	236
CE31003	Chassis & Cab	2724	3689	16,828
CE31034	Fleetside 8.5 ft.	2919	4276	2457
CE31004	Step-Side 9 ft.	2858	4120	1,300
CE31009	Stake 9 ft.	3063	4617	-

Model	Body Type	Price	Weight	Prod. Total
1-Ton Commercial — Model C/Series 30 — 157 in. w.b.				
CE31103	Chassis & Cab	2839	4066	8,290
1-Ton Forward Control — Model P/Series 30 — 125 in. w.b.				
PS30842	Chassis	2140	2968	3,447
PS30835	Step-Van King	3900	5394	855
PS30835	Step-Van Aluminum	-	-	46
PT30835	Step-Van Diesel	4020	3764	Note 2
PT30835	Step-Van King Diesel	5775	6170	Note 2
1-Ton Forward Control — Model P/Series 30 — 133 in. w.b.				
PS31842	Chassis	2175	2987	1,170
PS31843	Chassis & Cowl	-	-	236
PS31835	Steel Step-Van	4010	5630	1,600
PS31835	Aluminum Step-Van	-	-	126
PT31042	Chassis (Diesel)	4050	3784	Note 2
PT31035	Step-Van King	5885	6405	Note 2:
1-Ton Step-Van King — Model P/Series 30 — 157 in. w.b.				
PE38842	Chassis	-	-	1,607
PE38835	Steel Step-Van	-	-	924
PE38835	Aluminum Step-Van	-	-	86

1969 Chevrolet 1/2-Ton C10 Carryall Suburban (CMD)

NOTE 2: Total production of diesel-powered Forward-Control models was 53.
NOTE 3: Second letter in model code indicates engine: S=Six, E=V-8, T=3-cyl. diesel.
NOTE 4: Production totals from Chevrolet records are for model-year through Aug. 1, 1969 and include all trucks made in U.S. factories for domestic/export/Canadian markets. Where no production total is shown, records were not complete.

1969 Chevrolet 1/2-Ton C10 Fleetside Pickup (OCW)

ENGINE: [Standard El Camino G10/P10/G20] Inline. OHV. Six-cylinder. Cast iron block. Bore & stroke: 3-7/8 in. x 3-1/4 in. Displacement: 230 cid. Compression ratio: 8.5:1. Brake horsepower: 140 at 4400 rpm. Torque: 220 lb.-ft. at 1600 rpm. Net horsepower: 120 at 3600 rpm. Seven main bearings. Hydraulic valve lifters. Carburetor: Rochester one-barrel model 7028006/7028010.
ENGINE: [Standard C10/C20/C30/K10/K20/P30, Optional G10/G20/P10/El Camino] Inline. OHV. Six-cylinder. Cast iron block. Bore & stroke: 3-7/8 in. x 3.53 in. Displacement: 250 cid. Compression ratio: 8.5:1. Brake horsepower: 155 at 4200 rpm. Torque: 235 lb.-ft. at 1600 rpm. Seven main bearings. Hydraulic valve lifters. Carburetor: Rochester one-barrel model 7028007/7028011.

1969 Chevrolet 3/4-Ton K20 Step-Side 4x4 Pickup with Sheldon Vacationeer shell (CMD)

1969 Chevrolet 1/2-Ton CST 10 Fleetside long-box Pickup (CMD)

1969 Chevrolet 1/2-Ton CST 10 Fleetside long-box Pickup with shell camper (CMD)

1969 Chevrolet 1/2-Ton CST 10 Fleetside short-box Pickup (CMD)

1969 Chevrolet 3/4-Ton C20 Fleetside Pickup with cab-over camper (CMD)

1969 Chevrolet 3/4-Ton Custom K20 Fleetside 4x4 Long Box Pickup with shell camper (CMD)

1969 Chevrolet 1/2-Ton CST 10 Fleetside Pickup (CMD)

1969 Chevrolet 1/2-Ton Custom K10 Fleetside long-box 4x4 Pickup (CMD)

1969 Chevrolet 1/2-Ton Custom/10 Fleetside Long Box Pickup (CMD)

1969 Chevrolet Commercial Truck standard bench seat interior with CST trim (CMD)

ENGINE: [Optional C10/C20/C30, Standard P20/P30] Inline. OHV. Six-cylinder. Cast iron block. Bore & stroke: 3-7/8 in. x 4-1/2 in. Displacement: 292 cid. Compression ratio: 8.1:1. Brake horsepower: 170 at 4000 rpm. Torque: 275 lb.-ft. at 1600 rpm. Seven main bearings. Hydraulic valve lifters. Carburetor: Rochester one-barrel model 7028012/7028013.
ENGINE: [Optional G10/G20/P10/P20/P30/C10/C20/C30/K10/K20/El Camino): V-type. OHV. Eight-cylinder. Cast iron block. Bore & stroke: 3-7/8 in. x 3.25 in. Displacement: 307 cid. Compression ratio: 9.0:1. Brake horsepower: 200 at 4800 rpm. Five main bearings. Hydraulic valve lifters. Carburetor: Rochester two-barrel model 26 (numbers vary).
ENGINE: [Optional C10/C20/C30/K10/K20/El Camino] V-type. OHV. Eight-cylinder. Cast iron block. Bore & stroke: 4.0 in. x 3.48 in. Displacement: 350 cid. Compression ratio: 9.1. Brake horsepower: 255 at 4400 rpm. Five main bearings. Hydraulic valve lifters. Carburetor: Rochester model 4MV.
ENGINE: [Optional C10/C20/C30/K10/K20] V-type. OHV. Eight-cylinder. Cast iron block. Bore & stroke: 4.0 in. x 3.48 in. Displacement: 350 cid. Compression ratio: 10.25.1. Brake horsepower: 300 at 4800 rpm. Five main bearings. Hydraulic valve lifters. Carburetor: Rochester model 4MV.
ENGINE: [Optional C10/C20/C30/K10/K20/El Camino] V-type. OHV. Eight-cylinder. Cast iron block. Bore & stroke: 4.0 in. x 3.48 in. Displacement: 350 cid. Compression ratio: 11.0:1. Brake horsepower: 350 at 5000 rpm. Five main bearings. Hydraulic valve lifters. Carburetor: Rochester model 4MV.
ENGINE: [Optional C10/C20/C30/K10/K20] V-type. OHV. Eight-cylinder. Cast iron block. Bore & stroke: 4.09 in. x 3.76 in. Displacement: 396 cid. Compression ratio: 9.1. Brake horsepower: 310 at 4800 rpm. Maximum torque: 400 lb.-ft. at 3200 rpm. Five main bearings. Hydraulic valve lifters. Carburetor: Rochester model 4MV 7028211.
ENGINE: [Standard: El Camino With SS-396] V-block. OHV. Eight-cylinder. Cast iron block. Bore & stroke: 4.09 in. x 3.76 in. Displacement: 396 cid. Compression ratio: 10.25:1. Brake horsepower: 325 at 4800 rpm. Torque: 410 lb.-ft. at 3200 rpm. Five main bearings. Hydraulic valve lifters. Carburetor: Rochester four-barrel model Quadra-Jet.

1969 Chevrolet Commercial Truck optional bucket seat interior with CST trim (CMD)

1969 Chevrolet Commercial Truck standard bench seat interior with Custom trim (CMD)

ENGINE: [Optional: El Camino With SS-396] V-block. OHV. Eight-cylinder. Cast iron block. Bore & stroke: 4.09 in. x 3.76 in. Displacement: 396 cid. Compression ratio: 10.25:1. Brake horsepower: 350 at 5200 rpm. Torque: 415 lb.-ft. at 3400 rpm. Five main bearings. Hydraulic valve lifters. Carburetor: Rochester four-barrel model Quadra-Jet.
ENGINE: [Optional: El Camino With SS-396] V-type. OHV. Eight-cylinder. Cast iron block. Bore & stroke: 4.094 in. x 3.76 in. Displacement: 396 cid. Compression ratio: 11.25:1. Brake horsepower: 375. Five main bearings. Carburetor: four-barrel
ENGINE: [Optional P20/P30] Diesel. Model 3-53N. Three-cylinder. Bore and stroke: 3.875 x 4.5 in. Displacement: 159.2 cid. Brake horsepower: 94 at 2800 rpm. Torque: 205 lb.-ft. at 1500 rpm.

1969 Chevrolet 1-Ton C-30 Chassis-and-Cab with Open Road frame-mounted camper body. (CMD)

1969 Chevrolet Commercial Truck standard bench seat interior with standard trim (CMD)

1969 Chevrolet 1/2-Ton C10 Panel (CMD)

CHASSIS: [El Camino] Wheelbase: 116 in. Overall length: 201 in. Front tread: 59 in. Rear tread: 59 in. Tires: 7.35 x 14 in. GVW: 4,300 lb.
CHASSIS: [G10] Wheelbase: 90 in. Tires: 6.95 x 14 in. GVW: 3,900 to 5,000 lb.
CHASSIS: [C10] Wheelbase: 115 in. Overall length: 188-1/2 in. Height: 74.5 in. Inside length of pickup box: 78-1/2 in. Front tread: 63.1 in. Rear tread: 61.1 in. Tires: [4x2] 8.25 x 14 in., [Suburban] 8.15 x 15 in. GVW: [4x2] 4,400 to 5,000 lb.
CHASSIS: [K10] Wheelbase: 115 in. Overall length: 188-1/4 in. Inside length of pickup box: 78-1/2 in. Front tread: 63.1 in. Rear tread: 61.1 in. Tires: Tires: [4x4] 17.5 x 17 four-ply. GVW: [4x4] 5,600 lb.
CHASSIS: [C10] Wheelbase: 127 in. Overall length: 207-3/4 in. Height: 71 in. Inside length of pickup box: 98 in. Front tread: 63.1 in. Rear tread: 61.1 in. Tires: [4x2] 7.75 x 15 in. four-ply. GVW: [4x2] 4,400 to 5,000 lb.
CHASSIS: [K10] Wheelbase: 127 in. Overall length: 208 in. Inside length of pickup box: 98 in. Front tread: 63.1 in. Rear tread: 61.1 in. Tires: [4x4] 17.5 x 17. GVW: [4x4] 5,600 lb.
CHASSIS: [P10] Wheelbase: 102 in. Tires: 7.75 x 15 in. GVW: 4,600 to 5,400 lb.
CHASSIS: [C20] Wheelbase: 127 in. Overall length: 206-1/4 in. Tires: [4x2] 8.00 x 16.5 six-ply. GVW: [4x2] 5,500 to 7,500 lb.
CHASSIS: [K20] Wheelbase: 127 in. Overall length: 208 in. Tires: [4x4] 7 x 17.5 six-ply. GVW: [4x4] 5,700 to 7,600 lb.
CHASSIS: [P20] Wheelbases: (P2300) 104 in., (P2500) 125 in., (P2600) 137 in. Base tires: 7 x 17.5. GVW: 7,000 lb.
CHASSIS: [C21] Wheelbase: 133 in. Overall length: 213-3/4 in. Inside length of pickup box: 104 in. Tires: 8 x 17.5 in. GVW: 6,700 to 14,000 lb.
CHASSIS: [C30] Wheelbase: 133 in. Overall length: 217-3/4 in. Inside length of pickup box: 108-1/4 in. Tires: 8 x 17.5 in. GVW: 6,700 to 14,000 lb.
CHASSIS: [P30] Wheelbases: (P3300) 104 in., (P3500) 125 in., (P3600) 137 in. Base tires: 8 x 19.5. GVW: 7,500 to 14,000 lb.

1969 Chevrolet 1/2-Ton G10 Chevy Van 108 Panel Truck (CMD)

TECHNICAL: Standard transmission: Chevrolet three-speed manual (Borg-Warner heavy-duty three-speed optional). Type: [C30] 4F/1R, [Others] 3F/1R. Column-mounted gearshift lever. Single-plate, dry-disc clutch. Rear axle: [1/2-ton] semi-floating, [3/4-ton/1-Ton] full-floating. Base rear axles: [El Camino] 3.08:1, [C10/K10] 3.73:1, [C20/K20] 4.11:1, [C30] 5.14:1. Brakes: Four-wheel hydraulic, drum brakes. Brake linings: [C10/K10] 11 x 2.75 in., [C20/K20/C30] 12 x 2 in., [El Camino] 9-1/2 x 2-1/2 in. Kelsey-Hayes pressed steel wheels.
EL CAMINO OPTIONS: Strato-bucket seats. Speed and cruise control. Comfortilt steering wheel. Deluxe steering wheel. Wheelcovers. Mag-style wheelcovers. Simulated wire wheelcovers. Rally wheels and trim. Concealed windshield wipers. Deluxe seat and shoulder belts. Appearance guard group. Console. Power door locks. Tinted glass. Tri-volume horn. Special instrumentation. Auxiliary lighting. Vinyl roof cover.

1969 Chevrolet 1/2-Ton G10 Chevy Van with Red-E-Kamp conversion (CMD)

CHEVY VAN OPTIONS: Tinted windshield (15 percent). One-passenger auxiliary seat (27 percent). Heater deletion (2 percent). Jr. West Coast mirror (72 percent). R-Hide door (94 percent). Body paint stripe (1 percent). Non-glare inside mirror (not available). Front stabilizer (68 percent). Heavy front springs (73 percent). Heavy rear springs (85 percent). Positraction (9 percent). Optional rear axles (27 percent). Hydraulic brake booster (10 percent). Ignition block heater (2 percent). Emission controls (9 percent). Oil bath air cleaner (4 percent). 250-cid six-cylinder engine (16 percent). Powerglide transmission (19 percent). Three-speed automatic transmission (16 percent). Whitewall tires (12 percent). Heavy-duty battery (16 percent). Dual electric horns (1 percent). Speed warning indicator (not available). Heavy-duty radiator (5 percent). Chrome bumper (7 percent). Gauge package (30 percent). Custom equipment (3 percent). Two-tone paint (14 percent). Cargo door lock (8 percent). Swing-out rear door glass (7 percent). Tinted side door glass (26 percent). Tinted rear door glass (77 percent). Center seat (28 percent). Center and rear seat (26 percent). Stationary auxiliary seat (53 percent).

1969 Chevrolet 3/4-Ton Custom Camper C20 Longhorn Fleetside extended box Pickup (CMD)

C/K TRUCK OPTIONS: Heavy-duty seats (3 percent). Custom Sport Truck Option (6 percent). Chrome bumper (18 percent). Custom Comfort & Appearance option (28 percent). Blazer removable top, white (94 percent). Blazer removable top, black (6 percent). Full-foam seat (23 percent). Painted rear bumper (16 percent). Rear step bumper (16 percent). Heavy-duty cooling (1 percent). Chrome rear bumper (2 percent). Courtesy lights (99 percent). Push-button radio (41 percent). Tachometer (1 percent). Speed warning indicator (not available). Side marker lamps (not available). Cargo lamps (not available). Camper wiring (2 percent). Roof marker lamps (2 percent). Whitewall tires (13 percent). Step-Van dual rear wheel conversion (71 percent). Side-mounted wheel carrier (11 percent). Chrome hubcaps (11 percent). Wheel trim cover (19 percent). Hydraulic steering (21 percent). 350-cid medium-duty V-8 (8 percent). 350-cid light-duty V-8 (32 percent). 292-cid six-cylinder (14 percent). SS-396 four-barrel V-8 (4 percent). Heavy-duty clutch (28 percent). Overdrive (1 percent). Four-speed manual transmission (17 percent). Type N heavy-duty four-speed manual transmission (1 percent). Powerglide transmission (5 percent). 300 Deluxe three-speed automatic transmission (10 percent). Hydraulic brake booster (14 percent). Positraction (7 percent). Pow-R-Lock rear axle (1 percent). No-Spin rear axle (6 percent). Positraction (7 percent).

1969 Chevrolet 1-Ton P-30 Step-Van King (CMD)

NOTE 5: Option use rates based on Chevrolet records for model-year through Dec. 31, 1969. Figures show percentage of option usage on truck qualified for the option. For example, Step-Van dual rear wheel option was used on 71 percent of all Step-Vans offering this equipment, not 71 percent of total Chevrolet production.
CUSTOM OPTION PACKAGE: An optional Custom Comfort and Appearance package included bright metal windshield moldings, rear window trim and ventipane frames, Custom (CS) nameplates on front fenders, color-keyed vinyl-coated rubber floor mats, full-depth foam seat with color-keyed fabric and vinyl trim, vinyl trim door panels with bright upper retainers, a cigar lighter, Chevrolet Custom nameplate on dispatch box (glove compartment) door, bright metal control knob inserts, cowl insulation and full-depth armrests.
CST OPTION PACKAGE: The top trim level was the Custom Sport Truck option. It included most equipment in the CS package, plus a chrome front bumper, full-width vinyl seats, bright pedal frames, bright roof drip moldings, extra insulation, matching carpets and CST nameplates for the front fenders. Bucket seats with a center console were available on CST models.

1969 Chevrolet 1/2-Ton El Camino Sedan-Pickup (DFW)

COLOR OPTIONS: See 1964 options section for complete chart of 1964-1969 Chevrolet Commercial Truck colors.

HISTORICAL: Introduced: Fall 1968. Model-year production [All Chevrolet Commercials] 684,748. Model-year Commercial production by tonnage and engine type: [1/2-ton] (six) 199,256, (V-8) 281,172, (Total) 480,428. [3/4-ton] (six) 30,991, (V-8) 93,178, (Total) 124,169. [1-ton] (six) 16,617, (V-8) 22,408, (Total) 39,025. [Grand Total] 643,622. Production of Custom Sport Truck (CST) option: 29,942. Production of CS option: 147,311. Innovations: All-new Blazer. New hinged hood on Step-Vans. New 350-cid V-8 option. New LP gas engine conversions available. Historical notes: Chevrolet production records show a model number and listing for a 4x2 Blazer, but indicate that none were built in this model-year. In 1969, Chevrolet became a full-line truck-maker sharing GMC's heavy over-the-road product line with Chevrolet nameplates.

1970 CHEVROLET

EL CAMINO — MODEL A/SERIES 13000 — SIX/V-8: The 1970 El Camino had a blunter, heftier front end replacing the 1968-1969 wrap-over look. The dual headlamps were placed in square bezels outside the grille. A cross-hatch pattern grille insert was divided into four sections by wider chrome cross-bars. There was a bow tie in the center. Following the every-other-year pattern used since 1964, the rectangular parking lights were moved from inside the bumper air slot to the outer ends of the bumper. Regular El Caminos featured a new dash with a wide rectangular-shaped speedometer and gauges. The SS dash used circular units. At the rear, all El Caminos had large back-up lamps set into the tailgate, on either side of the Chevrolet nameplate in the center. The rear bumper indentations filled by back-up lamps on passenger cars had red reflectors on the sedan-pickup. Accenting base models were a Chevrolet script on the upper left grille section, El Camino nameplates and engine plaques above the feature line behind the front wheel openings, bright tailgate latch, and Chevrolet nameplate on tailgate. Custom models had lower body side and wheel opening moldings, silver anodized lower body perimeter finish, pickup box edge and rear body corner moldings, moldings running across the tailgate at top and bottom of taillamps, and a contrasting rear beauty panel with Chevrolet nameplate. There was an SS-396 option (RPO Z25). In midyear, the 396-cid engine was actually enlarged to 402 cid, though the well-known SS-396 name was still used in sales promotion. About the same time (January, 1970) a new SS-454 option was released. Technically, it came in RPO Z15/LS5 and RPO Z15/LS6 versions. The first had a high-lift camshaft and 10.25:1 compression for 360 hp. The second had a special camshaft and 11.25:1 compression to produce 450 hp. A cowl-induction hood was available for SS models at $124. A popular option was the hood racing stripes, which were $43 extra. Super Sports included a black-accented grille with SS grille badges, special hood with locking pins, styled wheels, suspension upgrades, power disc brakes, wheel opening moldings, and SS tailgate emblems. The lower body perimeter was also blacked-out. The flying buttress roof line was retained for all El Caminos. The pickup box, used through 1972, had an outside width of 75-1/2 in. Inside width behind the cab was 59 in. Inside width near the tailgate was 64-1/2 in. The width between the wheelhousings was 44 in. The bottom bed length measured 79-1/4 in. Tailgate measurements were 54-1/2 x 22-1/2 in. El Camino exterior body colors included Tuxedo Black, Classic White, Cortez Silver, Cranberry Red, Black Cherry, Champagne Gold, Autumn Gold, Gobi Beige, Desert Sand, Green Mist, Forest Green, Misty Turquoise, Astro Blue, and Fathom Blue. Upholstery in a choice of coated plain vinyl or coated patterned fabrics came in black, medium metallic blue, and medium metallic saddle.

1970 Chevrolet 1/2-Ton El Camino SS Sport Sedan-Pickup (OCW)

1/2-TON CHEVY VAN — MODEL G/SERIES 10 — SIX/V-8: Chevy Vans continued to feature Chevrolet's so-called "Easy-Access" body design, which was popular with highly mobile businessmen. A three-range Turbo-Hydramatic transmission could be ordered. The styling, now in its last appearance, was unchanged from 1969. The grille had six horizontal bars divided into four segments by three vertical bars. The center bar was widest. The remaining vertical

bars were narrower. Single, large round headlamps were at either end of the grille. Rectangular parking/directional lights were next to the headlamps. Under the windshield, five segmented vents continued to appear. Below the center vent segment was a Chevrolet bow tie emblem. There were large, rectangular side marker lamps. Standard models came with bumper, grille and hubcaps done in white. Chrome trim was optional. Only the 1/2-ton G10 line offered the compact van body with 209 cu. ft. of payload space on a 90-in. wheelbase. The larger 256-cu.-ft. body, mounted on a 108-in. wheelbase, could be ordered, too. It was 18 in. longer. Four G10 models were offered in the two lengths with six-cylinder or V-8 power plants. Standard features included Stay-Tight integral body frame construction and durable, tapered leaf springs. Both lines offered a Commercial Panel with double cargo doors available on the passenger side and at the rear. Both also offered window models in three levels of trim. The Sportvan was the base model. Sportvan Customs were in the middle. Sportvan Deluxe models were the fanciest. A 230-cid six was the base engine. A 307-cid V-8 was optional.

3/4-TON CHEVY VAN — MODEL G/SERIES 20 — SIX/V-8: The 108-in. wheelbase driver-forward vans also came as 3/4-ton G20 models. Styling characteristics were the same as long wheelbase G10s. Models included the Commercial Panel with double cargo doors available on the passenger side and at the rear. There were also window models in three levels of trim: base Sportvan, Sportvan Custom, and Sportvan Deluxe. The G20 line offered the same engines as G10s.

1970 Chevrolet 1/2-Ton K5 Blazer 4x4 Sport Utility Vehicle (RCA)

1/2-TON BLAZER — MODEL K/SERIES 10 — SIX/V-8: Blazers had a new grille with six groups of silver "dashes" above and below the horizontal aluminum center bar with Chevy's name across it. A 4x2 Blazer was produced this season, but less than 1,000 were made. The 4x4 version was more than 10 times as popular. The Blazer's suspension system consisted of single-leaf tapered front springs with a combination of multi-leaf and tapered springs at the rear. The ball-type steering unit had a 24:1 ratio and its standard engine was Chevrolet's 155-hp six. The single-unit body was joined to a heavy channel steel frame. The rear-mounted 23.5-gallon fuel tank was located inside the frame. Numerous options were offered for the Blazer including four-speed manual and automatic transmissions, V-8 engines, power steering, power brakes and a completely removable fiberglass top. Colors, exterior trims, upholstery and equipment were very similar or the same as used on the conventional K10 models.

1970 Chevrolet 1/2-Ton CST/10 Fleetside short box Pickup (OCW)

1/2-TON COMMERCIAL — MODEL C, K/SERIES 10 — SIX/V-8: The C10s continued with the general 1969 styling. The outer grille was the same as 1969. It featured a horizontal aluminum center bar. This bar was embossed with the Chevrolet name and had integral rectangular parking lamps at each end, next to the square headlamp housings. The plastic grille insert was modified. It had a more rectangular grillwork with silver horizontal dashes against a black background. A large bow tie was at the front center of the hood. Inside was a low-profile steering wheel, full-width bench seat and foot-operated parking brake. Standard equipment on all Pickups included: six-cylinder engine, self-adjusting four-wheel brakes, dual brake master cylinder with warning lights, back-up lights, directional signals and four-way flashers, Panoramic rear window, left- and right-hand outside rear view mirrors, non-glare inside mirror, heater and defroster, padded dash, non-glare front instrument panel finish, padded sun visors, ash tray, seat belts with retractors, push-button seat belt buckles, low-profile control knobs, two-speed electric washer/wipers, windshield defrosters, safety glass, flexible fuel filler neck, deep-dish steering wheel with telescoping shaft, thick laminate safety glass windshield, front and rear side markers, and painted front bumper. Chrome front and rear bumpers were a separate option. The standard C10 had no side trim, plain black rubber window gaskets, and painted bumpers. The grille shell had bright metal finish. The hubcaps were also painted. The vent window pillars and frames were flat black. The standard "pie plate" hubcaps were painted. Rear moldings around the taillamps and tailgate were not available on standard C10. Upper and lower belt moldings were optional. Trucks equipped with the lower belt molding had the center of the molding painted black. Chrome-plated "gear sprocket" wheelcovers with color-keyed finish and a bow tie in the center were optional. The Custom C10 was designated by Custom/10 nameplates on the front fenders. There was bright metal trim around the windshield, rear window, and vent window pillar and frame. Base bumpers and hubcaps were still painted, however. Upper and lower belt moldings were both optional and the center of the lower molding was painted. When equipped with lower side moldings, the Custom/10 also got taillamp moldings and two tailgate moldings. These moldings were positioned above and below the Chevrolet lettering on the back. The Custom/10 grille came in bright metal with a plastic grid design for the insert. (The grille was the same for all models). Chrome hubcaps were optional on Custom/10 models. The top-of-the-line was the Custom Sport Truck, which said CST/10 on its front fender sides. The CST had all Custom/10 features, plus more. The lower belt molding was standard and had an exclusive wood-grain center insert. The upper belt molding was still optional. The CST also had special front side marker lamps with chrome trim, which was not available on other models. Taillight and tailgate moldings (with a wood-grain appliqué and chrome Chevrolet lettering) was standard on CSTs, too. Chrome "pie plate" hubcaps were standard, full wheelcovers were optional. A cab-mounted cargo lamp also came standard on CSTs. There were Custom Interior Convenience, Custom Appearance, and Custom Comfort & Convenience options, too. Bucket seats were extra in all cab models. Exterior colors were Black, Medium Blue, Yellow Green, Dark Green, Dark Olive, Dark Blue, Medium Blue, Dark Blue Green, Flame Red, Red, Orange, Medium Green, Yellow, Light Yellow, White, Copper, Red Orange, Medium Gold, Dark Gold, Dark Bronze, Medium Blue-Green, and Dark Blue. The standard interior featured a three-passenger bench seat, foam padding, dome light, rubber floor mat, two door arm rests, and all-vinyl trim in saddle, blue, green, red, black or turquoise. The Custom interior added color-keyed floor mats, full-depth seat with color-keyed fabric-and-vinyl trim (same colors), vinyl trim door panels, cigar lighter, Custom plaque on glove compartment, and added cowl insulation. The C10 (and K10 four-wheel-drive) Chassis and Pickups came on 115- or 127-in. wheelbases. Both Fleetside and Step-Side Pickups offered a 6-1/2-ft. box or 8-ft. box. Panels and Carryall Suburbans came only on the longer wheelbase. The Carryall Suburban again had two-doors on the passenger side and one on the driver's side. Suburbans were available with a tailgate or Panel truck style double rear doors. Both of these single-unit body models had coil springs on all four wheels. Optional seats in the Carryall Suburban converted the 181-cu.-ft. payload space into a passenger compartment. Pickups on the shorter wheelbase had the 6-1/2-ft. cargo box. Two-toning was done using white as the second (upper) color. It was applied to all sheet metal above the belt line. On CSTs the body side between the upper and lower belt line moldings could also be done in white. For the first time a 402-cid V-8 (advertised as a 396-cid V-8) was available.

1/2-TON FORWARD-CONTROL — MODEL P/SERIES 10 — SIX/V-8: The 1/2-ton Forward-Control returned again. It had a 102-in. wheelbase. A small Step-Van walk-in delivery truck was approved for this chassis. It was made by Union City Body Co., of Union City, Ind. A channel type front bumper was optional equipment. The Forward-Control chassis and Step-Van were designed for door-to-door delivery service. Body lengths ranged from seven to eight feet for this Step-Van 7 series. Features included independent coil spring front suspension, and three six-cylinder engines. Buyers could also get full-height doors, sliding side doors and double rear doors.

3/4-TON COMMERCIAL — MODEL C, K/SERIES 20 — SIX/V-8: Carryover trucks in the Chevrolet 20 Series 3/4-ton line had the same styling, trim changes and options as other conventional trucks. The Step-Side Pickup had the 8-ft. box. The "Longhorn" Fleetside Pickup had a 133-in. wheelbase and 8-1/2-ft. box. The Chassis-and-Cowl model and 4x4 Panel were dropped. The Chassis-and-Cab, two Carryall Suburbans and the 4x2 Panel continued in this line. These had the same dimensions as comparable 1/2-ton models, but heavier chassis components. The designation plates had a number 20. Step-Side and Fleetside Pickups were also in this series. They featured the 8-ft. pickup box. The 8-ft. Stake model was dropped this year. The four-wheel-drive 3/4-ton models in the 20 Series had a K20 model prefix.

1970 Chevrolet 1-Ton C30 "Camper Special" Fleetside Pickup (CMD)

1-TON MEDIUM-DUTY COMMERCIAL — MODEL C/SERIES 30 — SIX-CYLINDER: The Chevrolet 30 Series 1-ton trucks had the same styling and trim changes and options as other conventional trucks. The fender side nameplates had a number 30. There were four 133-in. wheelbase models: Chassis-and-Cowl, Chassis and Cab, Longhorn Pickup with 8.5-ft box and a Step-Side Pickup with 9-ft. box. No hubcaps were used on the larger split-rim wheels of the Chassis-and-Cab models, which had eight bolts and eight circular openings. The Camper Special package continued. Camper models had their own designation plates with a Chevrolet bow tie and "Camper Special" chrome script. The C38 model 1-ton Chassis-and-Cab with a long 157-in. wheelbase for use as an RV chassis was also offered again. A four-speed manual synchromesh transmission was standard. No four-wheel-drive option was offered.

1-TON FORWARD-CONTROL — MODEL P/SERIES 30 — SIX/V-8: Three Forward-Control chassis were in the 30 Series (1-ton) truck line. The Forward-Control chassis and Step-Van were designed for door-to-door delivery service. Body lengths ranged up to 14-1/2 ft. for the 1-ton Step-Van King. Features included independent coil spring front suspension, three six-cylinder engines, two optional V-8s, plus a three-cylinder Detroit diesel engine. Buyers could also get full-height doors, sliding side doors and double rear doors. Offered were wheelbases of 125 in., 133 in., and 157 in. respectively. The 125-in. wheelbase chassis was recommended for bodies 9-1/2 to 10-1/2 ft. long. The 137-in. wheelbase was recommended for bodies 11-1/2 to 12-1/2 ft. long. The 157-in. wheelbase was used for the large aluminum body Step-Van King model, as well as for RV conversions. Bodies were available from factory-authorized suppliers or buyers could order them locally. A High-Torque 230 six was standard equipment.

1970 Chevrolet 3/4-Ton CST/20 Fleetside long box Pickup (CW)

3/4-TON FORWARD-CONTROL — MODEL P/SERIES 20 — SIX/V-8: Just two 3/4-ton Forward-Control chassis remained in the 20 Series (3/4-ton) truck line, but they were the basis for numerous steel, aluminum, and round and square styled bodies, plus a number of engine choices. The Forward-Control chassis and Step-Van were designed for door-to-door delivery service. Body lengths ranged up to over 12 ft. for the P20 Step-Vans. Features included independent coil spring front suspension, three six-cylinder engines, two optional V-8s, plus a three-cylinder Detroit diesel engine. Buyers could also get full-height doors, sliding side doors and double rear doors. Remaining in the 3/4-ton series were the 125-in. wheelbase chassis recommended for bodies 9-1/2 to 10-1/2 ft. long and the 137-in. wheelbase recommended for bodies 11-1/2 to 12-1/2 ft. long. Bodies were available from factory-authorized suppliers or buyers could order them locally. The coil spring front suspension reflected the fact that the Forward-Control was now starting to find its way into the growing RV market.

1970 Chevrolet 1/2-Ton CST/10 Fleetside long box Pickup (OCW)

I.D. DATA: Serial number located: [Chassis models] on plate temporarily attached near steering column, with final location per body maker. [All others] on plate attached to rear face of left-hand door hinge pillar, on right side of cowl under hood. [El Camino] The first symbol indicated manufacturer: 1=Chevrolet. The second and third symbols indicated series: 33=six/34=V-8/35=Custom V-8/36=Custom V-8. The fourth and fifth symbols indicated body type: 80=Sedan-Pickup. The sixth symbol indicated model-year: 0=1970. The seventh symbol indicated assembly plant: A=Atlanta (Lakewood), B=Baltimore, Md., F=Flint, Mich., K=Kansas City, Mo. (Leeds), L=Los Angeles (Van Nuys), Calif., R=Arlington, Texas. The remaining symbols were the sequential production number starting with 100001 at each plant. Ending serial numbers not available. The Chevrolet engine had the source, date and type stamped on a serial number pad. Various source codes were used. Month codes were 1=Jan., 2=Feb., etc. Date codes were 01=first of month, etc. The were numerous prefix codes to indicate engines and transmission attachments. The collectible 396-cid V-8s had the following codes: [350 hp] CTW/CTX/CTZ, [375 hp] CTY/CKN/CKO/CKD/CKP/CKQ/CKT/CKU. The collectible 454-cid V-8s had the following prefixes: [360 hp] CRN/CGT/CRQ/CRM/CRT/CGU/CRU, [450 hp] CRR/CRS/CRY/CRV/CRW/CRX. [Other models] The first symbol indicated truck type: C=Conventional Cab, K=4x4, G=Chevy Van, P=Forward-Control. The second symbol indicated type of engine: S=six, E=eight, T=diesel. The third symbol indicated the GVW range: [GVW] 1=3,600 to 5,600 lb., 2=5,500 to 8,100 lb., 3=6,700 to 10,000 lb., 4=Over 10,000 lb. The fourth and fifth symbols indicated the cab-to-axle dimension: 05=30-35 in., 07=42 to 47 in., 09=54-59 in., 10=60-65 in., 14=84-89 in. The sixth symbol indicated body type: 02=Chassis & Cowl, 03=Chassis-and-Cab, 04=Step-Side Pickup, 05=Panel or Panel Van, 06=Carryall Suburban (doors) or Sportvan, 14=Blazer, 18=Carryall Suburban (gate), 26=Custom Sportvan, 34=Fleetside, 36=Deluxe Sportvan, 35=Forward-Control. The eighth symbol indicates model-year: 0=1970. The ninth symbol indicates assembly plant: A=Atlanta, Ga., B=Baltimore, Md., F=Flint, Mich., J=Janesville, Wis., P=Pontiac, Mich., S=St. Louis, Mo., T=Tarrytown, N.Y., Z=Fremont, Calif. 1=Oshawa, Canada. The remaining symbols were the sequential production number starting with 100001 at each plant. Ending serial numbers not available. The Chevrolet engine had the source, date and type stamped on a serial number pad. Various source codes were used. Month codes were 1=Jan., 2=Feb., etc. Date codes were 01=first of month, etc. The were numerous prefix codes to indicate engines and transmission attachments.

1970 Chevrolet 1/2-Ton El Camino Sedan-Pickup (DFW)

Model	Body Type	Price	Weight	Prod. Total
El Camino — Model A/Series 13000 — 116 in. w.b. — Six				
13380	Pickup	2676	3302	Note 1
13580	Custom Pickup	2760	3324	Note 1
El Camino — Model A/Series 13000 — 116 in. w.b. — V-8				
13480	Pickup	2770	3418	Note 1
13680	Custom Pickup	2850	3442	Note 1

NOTE 1: Total El Camino production was 47,707.

Model	Body Type	Price	Weight	Prod. Total
1/2-Ton Chevy Van — Model G/Series 100 — 90 in. w.b.				
GS11005	Panel	2490	3059	3,933
GS11006	Sportvan	2725	3255	134
GS11026	Custom Sportvan	2850	3362	57
GS11036	Deluxe Sportvan	3035	3400	42
1/2-Ton Chevy Van — Model G/Series 100 — 108 in. w.b.				
GS11005	Panel	2675	3210	3,069
GS11006	Sportvan	2850	3350	422
GS11026	Custom Sportvan	2975	3480	303
GS11036	Deluxe Sportvan	3160	3425	158
3/4-Ton Chevy Van — Model G/Series 20 — 108 in. w.b.				
GS21305	Panel	2745	3281	1,195
GS21306	Sportvan	2970	3414	134
GS21326	Custom Sportvan	3095	3538	61
GS21336	Deluxe Sportvan	3280	3582	45

NOTE 2: Van production was low due to a strike and model changeover.

Model	Body Type	Price	Weight	Prod. Total
1/2-Ton Blazer 4x2 — Model C/Series 5 — 104 in. w.b.				
CS10514	Open Utility	2385	3375	Note 2
CE10514	Open Utility	2852	2947	Note 2

NOTE 3: 4x2 Blazer production: 985 includes CS (six) and CE (V-8) models.

Model	Body Type	Price	Weight	Prod. Total
1/2-Ton Blazer 4x4 — Model K/Series 5 — 104 in. w.b.				
KS10514	Open Utility	2955	3677	Note 3
KE10514	Open Utility	3050	3807	Note 3

NOTE 4: 4x4 Blazer production: 11,527 includes KS (six) and KE (V-8) models.

Model	Body Type	Price	Weight	Prod. Total
1/2-Ton Commercial — Model C/Series 10 — 115 in. w.b.				
CS10703	Chassis & Cab	2405	3090	2,084
CS10734	Fleetside 6.5 ft.	2560	3506	40,754
CS10704	Step-Side 6.5 ft.	2520	3426	40,754
1/2-Ton Commercial — Model C/Series 10 — 127 in. w.b.				
CS10903	Chassis & Cab	2445	3107	7,277
CS10934	Fleetside 8 ft.	2595	3605	234,904
CS10904	Step-Side 8 ft.	2560	3510	11,857
CS10905	Panel	3040	3730	3,965
CS10906	Suburban (doors)	3250	3862	11,332
1/2-Ton Commercial 4x4 — Model K/Series 10 — 115 in. w.b.				
KS10703	Chassis & Cab	2975	3295	64
KS10734	Fleetside 6.5 ft.	3158	3711	2,554
KS10704	Step-Side 6.5 ft.	3090	3631	1,629
1/2-Ton Commercial 4x4 — Model K/Series 10 — 127 in. w.b.				
KS10903	Chassis & Cab			26
KS10934	Fleetside 8 ft.	3165	3810	7,348
KS10904	Step-Side 8 ft.	3158	3715	464
KS10905	Panel	3641	3923	-
KS10906	Suburban	3849	4055	-
1/2-Ton Forward-Control — Model P/Series 10 — 102 in. w.b.				
PS10535	Chassis	1835	2120	211
PS10535	Step-Van	3139	3674	2,526
3/4-Ton Commercial — Model C/Series 20 — 127 in. w.b.				
CS20903	Chassis & Cab	2650	3496	7,277
CS20934	Fleetside 8 ft.	2790	3871	70,880
CS20904	Step-Side 8 ft.	2752	3776	5,856
CS20905	Panel	3269	3991	1,032
CS20906	Suburban	3441	4113	2,246
Long Horn Pickup				
CE21034	Pickup 8.5 ft.	2854	3912	5,281

Model	Body Type	Price	Weight	Prod. Total
3/4-Ton Commercial 4x4 — Model K/Series 20 — 127 in. w.b.				
KS20903	Chassis & Cab	3402	3606	582
KS20934	Fleetside 8 ft.	3540	4101	6,124
KS20904	Step-Side 8 ft.	3502	4006	953
KS20902	Panel	4019	4221	-
KS20906	Suburban	4190	4343	541
3/4-Ton Forward Control — Model P/Series 20 — 125 in. w.b.				
PS20842	Chassis	2160	2819	421
PS20835	Step-Van	3905	5206	1,520
PS20855	Aluminum Step-Van	-		60
3/4-Ton Forward Control — Model P/Series 20 — 133 in. w.b.				
PS21842	Chassis	2195	2841	184
PS21835	Step-Van	4015	5437	872
PS21855	Aluminum Step-Van	4985	4638	64
1-Ton Commercial — Model C/Series 30 — 133 in. w.b.				
CS31002	Chassis & Cowl	-		138
CS31003	Chassis & Cab	2735	3641	14,873
CS31034	Fleetside 8.5 ft.	2935	4157	1,404
CS31004	Step-Side 9 ft.	2875	4071	2,101
1-Ton Commercial — Model C/Series 30 — 157 in. w.b.				
CS31103	Chassis & Cab	2775	3788	-
1-Ton Forward Control — Model P/Series 30 — 125 in. w.b.				
PS30842	Chassis	2320	2992	446
PS30835	Step-Van	4080	5379	1,520
(Diesel)				
PT30835	Step-Van King	5780	6101	3
PT30855	Step-Van King Alum.	6570	5439	35
1-Ton Forward Control — Model P/Series 30 — 133 in. w.b.				
PS31042	Chassis	2350	3015	1,758
PS31035	Step-Van	4190	5611	1,624
PS31035	Step-Van King	5895	6338	-
PS31055	Step-Van King Alum.	6860	5537	68
1-Ton Forward Control — Model P/Series 30 — 157 in. w.b.				
PS31442	Chassis	2350	-	2,608
PS31435	Step-Van King	6040	6677	1,207
PS31455	Step-Van King Alum.	7170	5714	76

NOTE 5: All prices/weights above are for sixes (except El Camino/Blazer V-8s)
NOTE 6: Total production of diesel-powered Forward-Control models was 37-38.
NOTE 7: Production totals from Chevrolet records are for model-year through Aug. 31, 1970 and include all trucks made in U.S. factories for domestic/export/Canadian markets. Models with no production indicated due to incomplete records.

1970 Chevrolet 1/2-Ton K5 Blazer 4x4 Sport Utility Vehicle (CMD)

ENGINE: [Optional P20/P30] Diesel. Model 3-53N. Three-cylinder. Bore and stroke: 3.875 x 4.5 in. Displacement: 159.2 cid. Brake horsepower: 94 at 2800 rpm. Torque: 205 lb.-ft. at 1500 rpm.
ENGINE: [Standard all models] Inline. OHV. Six-cylinder. Cast iron block. Bore & stroke: 3.875 in. x 3.53 in. Displacement: 250 cid. Compression ratio: 8.5:1. Brake horsepower: 155 at 4200 rpm. Seven main bearings. Hydraulic valve lifters. Carburetor: Rochester one-barrel model M: 7028007/7028011.
ENGINE: [Optional P20/C10/C20/C30/K10/K20] Inline. OHV. Six-cylinder. Cast iron block. Bore & stroke: 3-7/8 in. x 4.12 in. Displacement: 292 cid. Compression ratio: 8.1:1. Brake horsepower: 170 at 4000 rpm. Maximum torque: 275 lb.-ft. at 1600 rpm. Seven main bearings. Hydraulic valve lifters. Carburetor: Rochester one-barrel model M: 7028012/7028013.
ENGINE: [Optional El Camino/K10/G10/G20/P10/P20/C10/C20/C30/K20] V-type. OHV. Eight-cylinder. Cast iron block. Bore & stroke: 37/8- in. x 31/4- in. Displacement: 307 cid. Compression ratio: 9.0:1. Brake horsepower: 200 at 4800 rpm. Five main bearings. Hydraulic valve lifters. Carburetor: Rochester two-barrel.
ENGINE: [Optional El Camino] V-type. OHV. Eight-cylinder. Cast iron block. Bore & stroke: 4 in. x 3.48 in. Displacement: 350 cid. Compression ratio: 9.0:1. Brake horsepower: 250 at 4600 rpm. Five main bearings. Hydraulic valve lifters. Carburetor: Rochester two-barrel.
ENGINE: [Optional C10/K10/C20/K20/C30/G10/G20/G30/P30] V-type. OHV. Eight-cylinder. Cast iron block. Bore & stroke: 4 in. x 3.48 in. Displacement: 350 cid. Compression ratio: 9.0:1. Brake horsepower: 255 at 4800 rpm. Maximum torque: 365 lb.-ft. at 3200 rpm. Five main bearings. Hydraulic valve lifters. Carburetor: Rochester four-barrel.

1970 Chevrolet 3/4-Ton K20 Fleetside 4x4 Pickup (RCA)

1970 Chevrolet 1/2-Ton CST/10 Fleetside long box Pickup (OCW)

ENGINE: [Optional El Camino] V-type. OHV. Eight-cylinder. Cast iron block. Bore & stroke: 4 in. x 3.48 in. Displacement: 350 cid. Compression ratio: 10.25:1. Brake horsepower: 300. Five main bearings. Hydraulic valve lifters. Carburetor: Rochester four-barrel.
ENGINE: [Optional El Camino] V-type. OHV. Eight-cylinder. Cast iron block. Bore & stroke: 4.126 in. x 3.76 in. Displacement: 400 cid. Compression ratio: 9.0:1. Brake horsepower: 250. Five main bearings. Hydraulic valve lifters. Carburetor: Two-barrel.
ENGINE: [Optional C5/K5/C10/C20/C30] V-type. OHV. Eight-cylinder. Cast iron block. Bore & stroke: 4.126 in. x 3.76 in. Displacement: 400 cid. Compression ratio: 9.0:1. Brake horsepower: 310. Five main bearings. Hydraulic valve lifters. Carburetor: Four-barrel.
ENGINE: [Optional El Camino] V-type. OHV. Eight-cylinder. Cast iron block. Bore & stroke: 4.126 in. x 3.76 in. Displacement: 400 cid. Compression ratio: 10.25:1. Brake horsepower: 330. Five main bearings. Hydraulic valve lifters. Carburetor: Two-barrel.
ENGINE: [Standard El Camino SS-396] V-type. OHV. Eight-cylinder. Cast iron block. Bore & stroke: 4.09 in. x 3.76 in. Displacement: 396 cid. Compression ratio: 10.25:1. Brake horsepower: 350 at 5200 rpm. Maximum torque: 445 lb.-ft. at 3400 rpm. Five main bearings. Hydraulic valve lifters. Carburetor: Rochester four-barrel model Quadra-Jet.
ENGINE: [Optional: El Camino With SS-396] V-type. OHV. Eight-cylinder. Cast iron block. Bore & stroke: 4.094 in. x 3.76 in. Displacement: 396 cid. Compression ratio: 11.25:1. Brake horsepower: 375. Five main bearings. Carburetor: four-barrel.
ENGINE: [Optional El Camino] V-type. OHV. Eight-cylinder. Cast iron block. Bore & stroke: 4.251 in. x 3.76 in. Displacement: 454 cid. Compression ratio: 10.25:1. Brake horsepower: 360 at 4400 rpm. Maximum torque: 500 lb.-ft. at 3200 rpm. Five main bearings. Hydraulic valve lifters. Carburetor: Rochester four-barrel model Quadra-Jet.
ENGINE: [Optional El Camino] V-type. OHV. Eight-cylinder. Cast iron block. Bore & stroke: 4.251 in. x 4.0 in. Displacement: 454 cid. Compression ratio: 11.0:1. Brake horsepower: 450. Carburetor: Rochester four-barrel model Quadra-Jet.
CHASSIS: [Series K10 Blazer] Wheelbase: 104 in. Overall length: 177.5 in. Height: 68.7 in. Front tread: 60.4 in. Rear tread: 60.4 in. Tires: E78-15B. GVW: 4,600-5,000 lb.
CHASSIS: [El Camino] Wheelbase: 116 in. Overall length: 206.8 in. Height: 54.4 in. Front tread: 60.2 in. Rear tread: 59.2 in. Tires: F78-14. GVW: 4,100 lb.
CHASSIS: [G10] Wheelbase: 90 in. Tires: 6.95 x 14 in. GVW: 3,900 to 5,000 lb.
CHASSIS: [Series G20] Wheelbase: 108 in. Tires: 7.75 x 15. GVW: 5,200-6,200 lb.
CHASSIS: [C10/K10] Wheelbase: 115 in. Overall length: 186-3/4 in. Height: 74.5 in. Front tread: 63.1 in. Rear tread: 61.1 in. Tires: Tires: [4x2] G78-14, [4x4] G78-15. GVW: [4x2] 4,400 to 5,400 lb., [4x4] 5,200-5,600 lb.
CHASSIS: [C10/K10] Wheelbase: 127 in. Overall length: 206-1/4 in. Height: 71 in. Front tread: 63.1 in. Rear tread: 61.1 in. Tires: [4x2] H78-15, [4x4] G78-15. GVW: [4x2] 4,400 to 5,400 lb., [4x4] 5,200-5,600 lb.
CHASSIS: [P10] Wheelbase: 102 in. Tires: G78-15. GVW: 4,600 to 5,400 lb.

1970 Chevrolet 1/2-Ton Custom 10 Fleetside short box Pickup (JAG)

CHASSIS: [C20/K20] Wheelbase: 127 in. Overall length: 206-1/4 in. Tires: [4x2] 7 x 17.5 in., [4x4] 7 x 17.5 six-ply. GVW: [4x2] 6,200-7,500 lb.], [4x4] 6,400-7,500 lb. (Longhorn Pickup has 133-in. wheelbase).
CHASSIS: [P20] Wheelbases: 125 in., 137 in. Base tires: 8.75 x 16.5. GVW: 6,500-7,500 lb.
CHASSIS: [C30] Wheelbase: 133 in. Tires: 8.75 x 16.5 in. GVW: 6,600 to 14,000 lb. (Chassis-and-Cab available with 157-in. wheelbase).
CHASSIS: [P30] Wheelbases: 125 in., 133 in., 157 in. Base tires: 8.75 x 16.5. GVW: 7,300-14,000 lb.
TECHNICAL: Chevrolet manual transmission standard. Type of transmission: [C30] 4F/1R, [Others] 3F/1R (Borg-Warner heavy-duty three-speed optional). Column-mounted gear shift lever standard. Clutch: Single-plate, dry-disc type. Rear axle: [1/2-ton] semi-floating, [3/4-ton/1-ton] full-floating. Base rear axles: [El Camino] 3.08:1, [C10/K10] 3.73:1, [C20] 4.10:1, [K20] 4.57:1, [C30] 5.14:1. Brakes: Four-wheel hydraulic, front disc/rear drum. Kelsey-Hayes pressed steel wheels.
C5/K5/C10/K10/C20/K20 OPTIONS: 292-cid six-cylinder engine ($95). 307-cid V-8 engine ($120). 307-cid V-8 engine ($120). 400-cid V-8 engine (average $160). 350-cid V-8 engine, for El Camino ($70). Four-speed manual transmission ($190). Powerglide transmission (average $195). Turbo-Hydramatic transmission ($280). Power brakes ($50). Power steering (average $115). Four-wheel-drive system ($570). (3/4-ton): 292-cid six-cylinder engine ($95). 307-cid V-8 engine ($95). 400-cid V-8 engine ($160). Powerglide transmission (average $190). Turbo-Hydramatic transmission (average $230). Power steering (average $130). Four-speed manual transmission (average $100). Four-wheel-drive system ($705).
C30 OPTIONS: 307-cid V-8 engine ($100). 292-cid six-cylinder engine ($95). 350-cid V-8 engine ($40). 400-cid V-8 engine ($160). LPG kit ($80). Turbo-Hydramatic transmission ($230). New Process transmission ($30). Nine-foot platform ($310). 12-foot platform ($370). 157-in. wheelbase ($40).

1970 Chevrolet 1/2-Ton Custom 10 Fleetside short box Pickup (JAG)

COMMERCIAL TRUCK OPTIONS: [1/2-ton to 1-ton with usage rates] Rear seat (57 percent). Front center seat belt (1 percent). Tinted glass (28 percent). Body side belt molding (14 percent). Wide lower body side molding (46 percent). Door edge guards (12 percent). Air conditioning (16 percent). Roof-mounted air conditioning (15 percent). Painted camper mirror (1 percent). Stainless camper mirror (2 percent). Jr. West Coast mirror, stainless (10 percent). Dual Sr. West Coast mirrors (3 percent). Jr. painted West Coast mirror (21 percent). Body paint stripe (5 percent). Heavy-duty shocks (14 percent). Front stabilizer (28 percent). Heavy-duty front springs (24 percent). 4x4 front locking hubs (79 percent). Heavy rear springs (65 percent). Auxiliary springs (20 percent). Leaf spring suspension (20 percent). Positraction (10 percent). No-Spin rear axle (6 percent). Optional rear axles (11 percent). Hydraulic brake booster (23 percent). Oil bath air cleaner (5 percent). Engine block heater (3 percent). Manual throttle (3 percent). 292-cid six-cylinder engine (15 percent). 396-cid four-barrel V-8 (9 percent). Heavy-duty clutch (21 percent). Four-speed manual transmission (17 percent). Heavy-duty close-ratio four-speed manual transmission (1 percent). Powerglide transmission (2 percent). Turbo-Hydramatic transmission (38 percent). Three-speed manual transmission (4 percent). 4x4 auxiliary fuel tank (1 percent). Hydraulic power steering (33 percent). G78x15 whitewall tires (15 percent). H78x15B whitewall tires (3 percent). Wheel trim covers (25 percent). Chrome hubcaps (11 percent). Tachometer (1 percent). Push-button radio (48 percent). Two-tone paint (30 percent). Special two-tone paint (15 percent). Custom Sport Truck option (10 percent). Special camper equipment (4 percent). Custom Comfort and Convenience option (24 percent). Chrome rear bumper (4 percent). Chrome bumper (6 percent). Painted rear bumper (11 percent). Rear step bumper (17 percent). Chrome front bumper (20 percent).
NOTE 8: Option use rates based on Chevrolet records for model-year through Dec. 31, 1970. Figures show percentage of option usage on truck qualified for the option. For example, Step-Van dual rear wheel option was used on 71 percent of all Step-Vans offering this equipment, not 71 percent of total Chevrolet production).
CUSTOM OPTION PACKAGE: An optional Custom Comfort and Appearance package included bright metal windshield moldings, rear window trim and ventipane frames, Custom (CS) nameplates on front fenders, color-keyed vinyl-coated rubber floor mats, full-depth foam seat with color-keyed fabric and vinyl trim, vinyl trim door panels with bright upper retainers, a cigar lighter, Chevrolet Custom nameplate on dispatch box door, bright metal control knob inserts, cowl insulation and full-depth arm rests.
CST OPTION PACKAGE: The top trim level was the Custom Sport Truck option. It included most equipment in the CS package, plus a chrome front bumper, full-width vinyl seats, bright pedal frames, bright roof drip moldings, extra insulation, matching carpets and CST nameplates for the front fenders. Bucket seats with a center console were available on CST models.
OTHER OPTION PACKAGES: [Custom Appearance Equipment] includes silver anodized radiator grille and headlamp door assembly, chrome-plated windshield reveal moldings, bright metal cab upper rear quarter panel trim plates, chrome horn ring steering wheel, chrome-trimmed instrument panel knobs, and two-tone inside front door panels. [Custom Comfort and Convenience Equipment] includes left door arm rest, outside key lock, chrome cigar lighter, full foam rubber seat cushion, special seat trim (cab models and Carryall Suburban), and added sound insulation. [Custom Chrome Equipment] chrome hubcaps. Not available with 4x4 or dual rear wheel options. [Side Trim Moldings] bright body side moldings for Fleetside models.
NOTE 9: Package prices are shown above.

1970-1974 CHEVROLET TRUCK COLOR OPTIONS

Name	Ditzler Code	75	74	73	72	71	70
Acanthus Blue (Dark) [L]	14448		74	73	72		
Adonis Yellow [L]	82025		74	73	72		
Argent Silver (Interior)	8568				72	71	
Avocado (Interior)	44738		74	73			
Avocado (Interior)	44742		74	73			
Black (Exterior & Interior) [L]	9000		74	73	72	71	70
Black (Interior)	9248		74				
Black (Interior-flat)	9317		74		72	71	70
Black (Interior)	9387		74				
Blue [V]	2329				72		
Blue	14715			73			
Blue Gray Poly (Interior) [L]	33041			73	72		
Bright Green Poly	2676		74				
Bright Red	2258		74				
Bright Yellow Poly	2570			73			
Bright Yellow	2681		74				
Burnt Orange Poly	2565			73			
Bronze	2671		74				
Charcoal (Interior)	33048		74	73			
Charcoal (Interior)	33049		74	73			
Clematis Blue (Light) [L]	14449	75	74	73	72		
Copper Poly	2202				72	71	70
Crimson Red [L]	72096	75	74				
Dark Argent [L]	33042			73	72		
Dark Blue	2366			73			
Dark Blue	2169						70
Dark Blue (Exterior/Interior)	2366			73	72	71	
Dark Blue	12409						70
Dark Blue (Interior)	13823		74				
Dark Blue Poly (Exterior/Interior)	2169						70
Dark Blue-Green Poly	2206						70
Dark Bright Blue Poly	2564			73			
Dark Bright Blue Poly	2672		74				
Dark Bronze [V]	2451				72		
Dark Bronze Poly	2203						70
Dark Gold Poly	2204						70
Dark Green [V]	2439				72		
Flat Dark Green (Interior)	44224						70
Dark Green (Interior)	44392				72	71	
Dark Green Poly (Interior)	2206						70
Dark Green Poly	2207				72		70
Flat Dark Olive (Interior)	44225						70
Dark Olive (Interior)	44384					71	
Dark Olive (Interior)	44390					71	
Dark Olive Poly (Exterior/Interior)	2207				72		70
Dark Saddle (Interior)	23453				72	71	
Dark Saddle (Interior)	23519				72	71	
Dark Sandalwood	2368						70
Dark Sandalwood (Interior)	23374				72	71	70
Flat Dark Sandalwood (Interior)	23375				72	71	70
Flat Dark Red (Interior)	71809						70
Dark Red	2673		74				
Dark Yellow [V]	2463				72		
Desert Sand	2568		74	73			
Flame Red	2258			73			70
Gold [V]	2448				72		
Horizon Blue [L]	14719		74				
Hugger Orange	2212				72	71	70
Ivory	8290		74				
Jasmine Yellow [L]	82162		74				
Light Blue	2563		74	73			
Light Green [V]	2437				72		
Light Olive	2571		74	73			
Light Sandalwood	2370						70
Light Turquoise Poly	2572			73			
Lime Poly	2674		74				
Madder Red [L]	71993		74	73	72		
Matte Black [L]	9222			73	72		
Matte Black [L]	9396			73	72		
Matte Black [L]	9371			73	72		
Meadow Green	2208		74				
Medium Blue (Exterior/Interior)	2188		74		72	71	70
Medium Blue Poly (Exterior/Int.)	2163						70
Medium Blue-Green Poly	2205						70
Medium Gold Poly	2176				72		70
Medium Green (Exterior/Interior)	2208				72	71	70
Medium Green	2369				72	71	
Medium Olive Poly	2097				72	71	
Midnight Black [L]	9000		74				
New Saddle (Interior)	23825		74	73			
New Saddle (Interior)	23820		74	73			
Ochre	2323		74	73	72	71	
Ochre [L]	82056			73	72		
Orange [V]	2450				72		
Orange	61056				72	71	70
Palm Green [L]	44935		74				
Parchment (Interior)	23128				72	71	
Pearl (Interior)	33047		74	73			
Red [V]	2189				72		
Red (Interior)	2209						70
Red (Exterior/Interior)	70704		74		72	71	70
Red-Orange	2212						70
Sandalwood (Interior)	23373				72		
Silver [V]	2429				72		
Silver [L]	8593			73	72		
Silver Poly (Exterior/Interior)	32537		74	73			
Slate Blue (Exterior/Interior)	14520		74	73			
Slate Blue (Exterior/Interior)	14523		74	73			
Slate Green (Exterior/Interior)	44737		74	73			
Strato White [L]	0883		74				
Tan	2569			73			
Walnut Beige [L]	23735		74	73	72	71	
Weldenia White [L]	0831		74				
Westway Tan [L]	24003		74				
Wheatland Yellow	81348			73	72		
White [L]	0844			73	72		
White [V]	2058				72		
White	2185		74	73	72	71	70
Yellow	2324				72		
Yellow	81348				72	71	70
Yellow Gold	2567		74	73			
Yellow Green Poly	2097						70

Specify DQE for alkyd enamel, DDL for acrylic lacquer, DAR for acrylic enamel, DL or DIA for interior.

[L] = LUV Mini-Pickup truck color.

[V] = Vega Panel Express color.

HISTORICAL: Model-year production [All Chevrolet Commercial] 492,607. Model-year production, Commercial light-duty, by tonnage and engine type: [1/2-ton] (six) 115,286, (V-8) 259,348, (Total) 374,634. [3/4-Ton] (six) 18,644, (V-8) 88,893, (Total) 107,537. [1-Ton] (six) 10,350, (V-8) 25,552, (Total) 35,902. (Grand Total) 518,073. [RPO Production] (Custom Sport Truck) 49,717, (Custom/10) 126,848, (Camper Special) 20,900.

1971 CHEVROLET

1971 Chevrolet 1/2-Ton Vega Panel Express (OCW)

1/2-TON VEGA PANEL — MODEL HV/SERIES 14000 — FOUR: New for 1971 was a Panel Express version of the sub-compact Vega. It was based on the Kammback wagon, with the rear side windows blanked out. Chevy described it as, "the kinky way to haul around your surfboard." It came only with the standard all-vinyl interior, less the Station Wagon's passenger bucket seat, and only with black or green upholstery. The Vega wagon's Custom interior option was not available. Standard equipment included the four-cylinder aluminum block engine, three-speed manual transmission, front disc brakes, two separate stowage compartments below the floor, many safety features, and a choice of 10 colors. It had a 67.4-in. floor length, with 42.6 in. between the wheelhousings. Its cargo volume was 68.7-cu.-ft. The payload capacity was 650 lb.

1971 Chevrolet 1/2-Ton El Camino SS Sport Sedan-Pickup (Photo: John Lee)

1/2-TON EL CAMINO — MODEL AC, AD/SERIES 13000 — SIX/V-8: The El Camino models had a new look due to the use of single-unit Power Beam headlamps in square bezels. The grille had a "ice cube tray" insert and Chevrolet bow tie in its center. The front parking lamps were double-deck rectangles that angled around the body corners to double as side marker lights. El Camino nameplates and designation badges were mounted on the front fender sides, behind the wheel opening. The rear end appearance had hardly any changes. For the first time, the front bumper had no air slots or parking lamps in it. Standard models had bright windshield frames, back-up lights on the tailgate, and a base six-cylinder engine. Customs added a V-8 as base engine, body side moldings, wheelhouse moldings, pickup box rim moldings, rear body corner moldings, two moldings on the tailgate, and silver anodized lower body perimeter. Super Sport equipment (RPO Z15) was available for all Custom models with V-8s other than the base 307-cid V-8. You could get an SS-350, SS-396 (it actually had a 402-cid V-8), or SS-454. The basic SS package was $365 extra and the engine selections were separate options. The performance and appearance package included a black-accented grille with SS emblems, SS badges behind the front wheel cutouts, sport suspension, power front disc brakes, domed hood with lock pins, and 15 x 7 sport wheels with F60-15 raised white-letter tires. By the end of the year, the 454-cid V-8 replaced the 396-cid completely. A plain cloth and vinyl interior was standard. The colors were black, dark blue, dark jade green and sandalwood. The Custom interior had vinyl seats with ribbed insert panels, color-keyed carpeting and imitation wood-grain trim. It came in black, light sandalwood, antique saddle knit-vinyl, dark saddle, dark blue or antique dark jade. Exterior colors were Antique White, Nevada Silver, Tuxedo Black, Ascot Blue, Mulsanne Blue, Cottonwood Green, Lime Green, Antique Green, Sunflower, Placer Gold, Sandalwood, Burnt Orange, Classic Copper, Cranberry Red, and Rosewood. The flying buttress roof line was retained for all El Caminos. The pickup box, used through 1972, had an outside width of 75-1/2 in. The inside width behind the cab was 59 in. and the inside width near the tailgate was 64-1/2 in. The width between the wheelhousings was 44 in. The bottom bed length measured 79-1/4 in. Tailgate measurements were 54-1/2 x 22-1/2 in.

1971 Chevrolet 3/4-Ton G20 108 Chevy Van with Trailwagon
camper conversion (CMD)

1/2-TON CHEVY VAN/SPORTVAN — MODEL G/SERIES 10 — SIX/V-8: The Chevrolet van models were attractively restyled. They had new 110-in. and 125-in. wheelbases, plus an extended front hood that made 26 service areas readily accessible. Van grilles consisted of seven horizontal bars with a center-mounted Chevrolet emblem. The Sportvan Deluxe became the Beauville. This fancy new model offered travel space for 12 passengers and featured a 307-cid V-8 as standard equipment. Other innovations included independent front suspension and a sliding door option. A Custom Appearance package was available, as well as Custom & Convenience interior equipment.

3/4-TON CHEVY VAN/SPORTVAN — MODEL G/SERIES 20 — SIX/V-8: The 108-in. wheelbase driver-forward vans also came as 3/4-ton G20 models. Styling characteristics were the same as G10s. Models included the Panel with double cargo doors available on the passenger side and at the rear. There were also window models in two levels of trim: base Sportvan or Beauville. The G20 line offered the same engines as G10s and a V-8 was standard in the Beauville model.

1-TON CHEVY VAN/SPORTVAN — MODEL G/SERIES 30 — SIX/V-8: For the first time ever, buyers could order a G30 (1-ton) van. Styling characteristics were the same as G10s and G20s. Models included the Panel with double cargo doors available on the passenger side and at the rear. There were also window models in two levels of trim called (base) Sportvan or (fancier) Beauville. Officially, the G30 Sportvan and Beauville were available only on the longer 125-in. wheelbase, which was different than in the other series. However, Chevrolet production records show that nine Sportvans and eight Beauvilles were built on the 110-in. wheelbase.

1971 Chevrolet 1/2-Ton Blazer K5 Sport Utility Vehicle (CMD)

1/2-TON BLAZER — MODEL C, K/SERIES 5 — SIX/V-8: Chevy's Blazer had a new, eggcrate grille. Some sources say that the 4x2 version was introduced this year, although factory records show nearly 1,000 of these were made in model-year 1970. This year production of the 4x2 version crept up slightly to just under 1,300 units. The 4x4 version was more than 10 times as popular. The Blazer's suspension system consisted of single-leaf tapered front springs with a combination of multi-leaf and tapered springs at the rear. The ball-type steering unit had a 24:1 ratio and its standard engine was Chevrolet's 155-hp six. The single-unit body was joined to a heavy channel steel frame. The rear-mounted 23.5-gallon fuel tank was located inside the frame. Numerous options were offered for the Blazer, including four-speed manual and automatic transmissions, V-8 engines, power steering, power brakes and a completely removable fiberglass top. Colors, exterior trims, upholstery and equipment were very similar or the same as those offered on the C10/K10 conventional models.

1971 Chevrolet 1/2-Ton C10 Step-Side Pickup with Vacationeer
shell camper (CMD)

1/2-TON COMMERCIAL — MODEL C, K/SERIES 10 — SIX/V-8: Pickups, Panels and Carryall Suburbans featured a new eggcrate grille. It had five horizontal blades and 15 vertical members. A painted black stripe appeared around the outer edge of the grille. The Chevrolet bow tie moved from the hood to the grille center. The parking/directional lights were moved from their previous location in the grille to positions within the front bumper. Inside was a low-profile steering wheel, full-width bench seat and foot-operated parking brake. Standard equipment on all Pickups included: six-cylinder engine, side terminal battery, self-adjusting four-wheel brakes (front discs), dual brake master cylinder with warning lights, back-up lights, directional signals and four-way flashers, Panoramic rear window, left- and right-hand outside rear view mirrors, non-glare inside mirror, heater and defroster, padded dash, non-glare front instrument panel finish, padded sun visors, ash tray, seat belts with retractors, push-button seat belt buckles, low-profile control knobs, two-speed electric washer/wipers, windshield defrosters, safety glass, flexible fuel filler neck, deep-dish steering wheel with telescoping shaft, thick laminate safety glass windshield, right-hand coat hook, front and rear side markers, and painted front bumper. Chrome front and rear bumpers were a separate option. There were new names for different trim levels. The standard C10 became the Custom. It had no side trim, plain black rubber window gaskets, and white-painted bumpers. The grille shell had bright metal finish. The hubcaps were also painted. The vent window pillars and frames were flat black. The standard hubcaps were painted. Rear moldings around the taillamps and tailgate were not available on Customs. Upper and lower belt moldings were optional. Customs equipped with the lower belt molding, should have the center of the molding painted black. A new Custom Deluxe trim level became what the Custom/10 had been. Custom Deluxe equipment included a full-width bench seat with comfortably padded seat cushions and back rest, vinyl upholstery and door panels, steel roof panel painted in main exterior color, black rubber floor mat extending to firewall, padded arm rests, padded sun shades, courtesy lamp, prismatic rear view mirror, foam-padded instrument panel, bright upper and lower grille outline moldings, bright headlamp bezels, bright outside rear view mirrors, bright door handles, white-painted front bumper, hubcaps and wheels, and bright Custom Deluxe nameplates. Upper and lower belt moldings were both optional. Unlike 1970, when the lower belt molding was black-accented, the center of the 1971 lower molding had a wood-grain insert. When equipped with lower body side moldings, the Custom Deluxe also got taillamp and two tailgate moldings. These moldings were positioned above and below the Chevrolet lettering on the back. Chrome hubcaps were optional on Custom Deluxe models. A new Cheyenne trim level was comparable to the previous Custom Sport Truck option. The Cheyenne package included a bench seat with full-depth foam cushions and back rests, Custom-grained vinyl upholstery or nylon and vinyl upholstery, special door trim panels, cab headliner, deep-twist nylon carpeting extending to firewall, color-keyed garnish moldings, ash tray-mounted cigar lighter, Custom steering wheel, Cheyenne dashboard nameplates, door or manually-operated courtesy lights, extra acoustical insulation, and all Custom Deluxe exterior items, plus cab-mounted cargo lamp, bright metal cab trim and moldings, bright upper body side and tailgate moldings, and central lighted appliqués for Fleetside and Cheyenne nameplates. When equipped with a lower body side molding, the Cheyenne also got wood-grain molding inserts. Bucket seats were optional for Cheyennes with the vinyl interior. A Cheyenne Super option package was introduced at midyear in 1971. This model took up where the Cheyenne left off, adding both upper and lower (wood-grain) body side moldings and a chrome-plated tailgate release. There were Custom Appearance, and Custom Comfort & Convenience options, too. Exterior colors were Black, Dark Blue, Medium Blue, Medium Bronze, Dark Green, Medium Green, Yellow, Ochre, Dark Olive, Medium Olive, Red Orange, Orange, White, Dark Yellow, and Yellow. The standard interior featured a three-passenger bench seat, foam padding, dome light, rubber floor mat, two door arm rests, and all-vinyl trim in green, blue, black or parchment. The Custom and Cheyenne interiors came black, blue, parchment or olive patterned cloth and vinyl. The C10 (and K10 four-wheel-drive) Chassis-and-Cab and Pickups came on 115-in. or 127-in. wheelbases. Both Fleetside and Step-Side Pickups offered a 6-1/2-ft. box or 8-ft. box. Pickups on the shorter wheelbase had the 6-1/2-ft. cargo box. The Panel was discontinued. Carryall Suburbans came only on the longer wheelbase. The Carryall Suburban again had two-doors on the passenger side and one on the driver's side. Surburbans were available with tailgates or double rear doors. They had a floor space that was 9 ft. long. With second and third seats removed, cargo space totaled 190 cu.-ft. Four-wheel-drive was available for a price of just over $500. Both of these single-unit body models had coil springs on all four wheels. Two-toning was done using white as the second (upper) color. It was applied to all sheet metal above the belt line. On Cheyennes, the body side, between the upper and lower belt line moldings was usually done in white.

1/2-TON FORWARD-CONTROL — MODEL P/SERIES 10 — SIX/V-8: The 1/2-ton Forward-Control returned again. It had a 102-in. wheelbase. A small Step-Van walk-in delivery truck was approved for this chassis. It was made by Union City Body Co., of Union City, Ind. A channel type front bumper was standard equipment. The Forward-Control chassis and Step-Van were designed for door-to-door delivery service. Body lengths ranged from seven to eight feet for this Step-Van 7 series. Features included independent coil spring front suspension, and three six-cylinder engines. Buyers could also get full-height doors, sliding side doors and double rear doors.

1971 Chevrolet 3/4-Ton K20 Fleetside long box 4x4 Pickup (RCA)

3/4-TON COMMERCIAL — MODEL C, K/SERIES 20 — SIX/V-8: Carryover trucks in the Chevrolet 20 Series 3/4-ton line had the same styling, trim changes and options as other conventional trucks. Fleetside and Step-Side Pickups had an 8-ft. box. Also available was the "Longhorn" Fleetside with a 133-in. wheelbase and 8-1/2-ft. box. The Chassis-and-Cab and two Carryall Suburbans continued in this line. These had the same dimensions as comparable 1/2-ton models, but heavier chassis components. The designation plates had a number 20. The 8-ft. Stake model was available as an extra on the platform option for the Chassis-and-Cab. It cost about $400 for the platform option. The four-wheel-drive 3/4-ton models in the 20 Series had a K20 model prefix. Longhorns were not built with four-wheel-drive.

138

1971 Chevrolet 1-Ton Fleetside "Camper Special" Pickup with Open Road camper unit (CMD)

3/4-TON FORWARD-CONTROL — MODEL P/SERIES 20 — SIX/V-8: Just two 3/4-ton Forward-Control chassis remained in the 20 Series (3/4-ton) truck line, but they were the basis for numerous steel and aluminum body models. A number of power plants could be had, including three six-cylinder engines, two optional V-8s, plus a three-cylinder Detroit diesel. The Forward-Control chassis and Step-Van were designed for door-to-door delivery service. Body lengths ranged up to over 12 ft. for the P20 Step-Vans. Features included independent coil spring front suspension. Buyers could also get full-height doors, sliding side doors and double rear doors. Remaining in the 3/4-ton series were the 125-in. wheelbase chassis recommended for bodies 9-1/2 to 10-1/2 ft. long and the 137-in. wheelbase recommended for bodies 11-1/2 to 12-1/2 ft. long. Bodies were available from factory-authorized suppliers or buyers could order them locally. The coil spring front suspension reflected the fact that the Forward-Control chassis was now starting to find its way into the growing RV market.

1-TON MEDIUM-DUTY COMMERCIAL — MODEL C/SERIES 30 — SIX-CYLINDER: The Chevrolet 30 Series 1-ton trucks had the same styling and trim changes and options as other conventional trucks. The fender side nameplates had a number 30. There were four 133-in. wheelbase models: Chassis-and-Cowl, Chassis and Cab, Longhorn Pickup with 8.5-ft box and a Step-Side Pickup with a 9-ft. box. No hubcaps were used on the larger split-rim wheels of the Chassis-and-Cab models, which had eight bolts and eight circular openings. The Camper Special package continued. The C38 model 1-ton Chassis-and-Cab with a long 157-in. wheelbase for use as an RV chassis was also offered again. Nearly 12,000 of these were sold. A four-speed manual synchromesh transmission was standard. No four-wheel-drive option was offered.

1-TON FORWARD-CONTROL — MODEL P/SERIES 30 — SIX/V-8: Three Forward-Control chassis were in the 30 Series (1-ton) truck line. The Forward-Control chassis and Step-Van were designed for door-to-door delivery service. Body lengths ranged up to 14-1/2 ft. for the 1-ton Step-Van King. Features included independent coil spring front suspension, three six-cylinder engines, two optional V-8s, plus a three-cylinder Detroit diesel engine. Buyers could also get full-height doors, sliding side doors and double rear doors. Offered for P30 buyers were wheelbases of 125 in., 133 in., and 157 in. respectively. The 125-in. wheelbase chassis was recommended for bodies 9-1/2 to 10-1/2 ft. long. The 137-in. wheelbase was recommended for Step-Van King bodies 11-1/2 to 12-1/2 ft. long. The 157-in. wheelbase was also used for the large aluminum body Step-Van King models, as well as for RV constructions. Bodies were available from factory-authorized suppliers or buyers could order them locally. A High-Torque 230 six was standard equipment. Chevrolet also began producing special P30 1-ton motorhome chassis on 137-in. and 157-in. wheelbases. Almost 1,600 were constructed in 1971.

1971 Chevrolet 1/2-Ton Custom/10 Carryall Suburban (Owners: Randy & Trudy Vollmer)

I.D. DATA: Serial number located: [Chassis models] on plate temporarily attached near steering column, with final location per body maker. [All others] on plate attached to rear face of left-hand door hinge pillar, on right side of cowl under hood. [El Camino] The first symbol indicated manufacturer: 1=Chevrolet. The second and third symbols indicated series: 33=six/34=V-8/36=Custom V-8. The

fourth and fifth symbols indicated body type: 80=Sedan-Pickup. The sixth symbol indicated model-year: 1=1971. The seventh symbol indicated assembly plant: B=Baltimore, Md., K=Kansas City, Mo. (Leeds), L=Los Angeles (Van Nuys), Calif., R=Arlington, Texas. The remaining symbols were the sequential production numbers starting with 100001 at each plant. Ending serial numbers not available. The Chevrolet engine had the source, date and type stamped on a serial number pad. Various source codes were used. Month codes were 1=Jan., 2=Feb., etc. Date codes were 01=first of month, etc. The were numerous prefix codes to indicate engines and transmission attachments. The collectible 396-cid (actually 402-cid) V-8s had the following codes: [300 hp] CLP/CLB/CLL/CLR/CLS. The collectible 454-cid V-8s had the following prefixes: [365 hp] CPA/CPG/CPD, [425 hp] CPP/CPR/CPZ. [Other models] The first symbol indicated truck type: C=Conventional Cab, K=4x4, G=Chevy Van, P=Forward-Control. The second symbol indicated type of engine: S=six, E=eight, T=diesel. The third symbol indicated the GVW range: [GVW] 1=3,900 to 5,800 lb., 2=5,200 to 7,500 lb., 3=6,600 to 14,000 lb. The fourth and fifth symbols indicated the cab-to-axle dimension: 05=30-35 in., 07=42 to 47 in., 09=54-59 in., 10=60-65 in., 14=84-89 in. The sixth symbol indicated body type: 02=Chassis & Cowl, 03=Chassis-and-Cab, 04=Step-Side Pickup, 05=Panel Van, 06=Carryall Suburban (doors)/Sportvan, 14=Blazer, 16=Carryall Suburban (gate), 32=Motorhome chassis, 34=Fleetside, 36=Beauville Van, 35=Forward-Control (steel Step-Van body), 42=Forward-Control chassis, 55=Forward-Control (aluminum Step-Van body). The eighth symbol indicates model-year: 1=1971. The ninth symbol indicates assembly plant: A=Atlanta (Lakewood), Ga., B=Baltimore, Md., F=Flint, Mich., J=Janesville, Wis., K=Kansas City (Leeds), Mo., L=Los Angeles (Van Nuys), Calif., P=Pontiac, Mich., R=Arlington, Texas, S=St. Louis, Mo., T=Tarrytown, N.Y., U=Lordstown, Ohio, Z=Fremont, Calif. 1=Oshawa, Canada. The remaining symbols were the sequential production number starting with 100001 at each plant. Ending serial numbers not available. The Chevrolet engine had the source, date and type stamped on a serial number pad. Various source codes were used. Month codes were 1=Jan., 2=Feb., etc. Date codes were 01=first of month, etc. There were numerous prefix codes to indicate engines and transmission attachments.

1971 Chevrolet 1/2-Ton C10 Fleetside long box Pickup customized (OCW)

Model	Body Type	Price	Weight	Prod. Total
1/2-Ton Vega — Model HV/Series 14000 — 97 in. w.b. -Four				
14105	Panel Express	2138	2152	7,800
El Camino — Model A/Series 13000 — 116 in. w.b. — Six				
13380	Sedan-Pickup	2886	3302	Note 1
El Camino — Model A/Series 13000 — 116 in. w.b. — V-8				
13480	Sedan-Pickup	2983	3418	Note 1
13680	Custom Sedan-Pickup	3069	3442	Note 1
NOTE 1: Total El Camino production was 41,606.				
1/2-Ton Chevy Van — Model G/Series 10 — 110 in. w.b.				
GS11005	Panel	2881	3460	15,012
GS11006	Sportvan	3304	3694	1,846
1/2-Ton Chevy Van — Model G/Series 10 — 110 in. w.b. — V-8				
GE11036	Beauville	3738	3936	481
1/2-Ton Chevy Van — Model G/Series 10 — 125 in. w.b.				
GS11305	Panel	3010	3615	15,013
GS11306	Sportvan	3430	3856	2,011
1/2-Ton Chevy Van — Model G/Series 10 — 125 in. w.b. — V-8				
GS11336	Beauville	3865	4136	1,146
3/4-Ton Chevy Van — Model G/Series 20 — 110 in. w.b.				
GS21005	Panel	2976	3489	5,901
GS21006	Sportvan	3350	3761	1,774
3/4-Ton Chevy Van — Model G/Series 20 — 110 in. w.b.				
GS21036	Beauville	3817	4094	345
3/4-Ton Chevy Van — Model G/Series 20 — 125 in. w.b.				
GS21305	Panel	3105	3653	14,027
GS21306	Sportvan	3471	3929	2,796
3/4-Ton Chevy Van — Model G/Series 20 — 125 in. w.b.				
GS21336	Beauville	3943	4296	3,568
1-Ton Chevy Van — Model G/Series 30 — 110 in. w.b.				
GS31005	Panel	3087	3781	624
GS31006	Sportvan	-	-	9
GS31006	Beauville	-	-	8
1-Ton Chevy Van — Model G/Series 30 — 110 in. w.b.				
GS31305	Chevy Van	3236	3948	9,518
GS31306	Sportvan	3594	4117	1,834
1-Ton Chevy Van — Model G/Series 30 — 125 in. w.b.				
GS31336	Beauville	4060	4590	1,552
1/2-Ton Blazer 4x2 — Model C/Series 5 — 104 in. w.b.				
CS10514	Open Utility	2659	3375	1,277
1/2-Ton Blazer 4x4 — Model K/Series 5 — 104 in. w.b.				
KS10514	Open Utility	3234	3677	17,220
1/2-Ton Commercial — Model C/Series 10 — 115 in. w.b.				
CS10703	Chassis & Cab	2656	3090	1,476
CS10704	Step-Side 6.5 ft.	2816	3426	19,041
CS10734	Fleetside 6.5 ft.	2816	3506	32,865
1/2-Ton Commercial — Model C/Series 10 — 127 in. w.b.				
CS10903	Chassis & Cab	2689	3107	588
CS10904	Step-Side 8 ft.	2854	3510	7,269
CS10934	Fleetside 8 ft.	2854	3605	206,313
CS10906	Suburban (doors)	3599	3862	4,550
CS10916	Suburban (gate)	3631	3870	5,395
1/2-Ton Commercial 4x4 — Model K/Series 10 — 115 in. w.b.				
KS10704	Step-Side 6.5 ft.	3414	3739	1,438
KS10734	Fleetside 6.5 ft.	3414	3824	3,068

Model	Body Type	Price	Weight	Prod. Total
1/2-Ton Commercial 4x4 — Model K/Series 10 — 127 in. w.b.				
KS10904	Step-Side 8 ft.	3451	3832	364
KS10934	Fleetside 8 ft.	3451	3927	9,417
KS10906	Suburban (doors)	4226	4191	631
KS10916	Suburban (gate)	4256	4191	994
1/2-Ton Forward-Control — Model P/Series 10 — 102 in. w.b.				
PS10542	Chassis	2119	2120	229
PS10535	Steel Step-Van	3425	3781	1.905
3/4-Ton Commercial — Model C/Series 20 — 127 in. w.b.				
CS20903	Chassis & Cab	2897	3496	4,523
CS20903	Chassis & Cab With Stake	3319	-	Note 2
CS20904	Step-Side 8 ft.	3058	3896	3,406
CS20934	Fleetside 8 ft.	3058	3991	62,465
CS20906	Suburban (doors)	3760	4245	1,343
CS20916	Suburban (gate)	3791	4253	1,203
NOTE 2: Stake option included with C20 Chassis & Cab production.				
3/4-Ton Long Horn — Model C/Series 20 — 133 in. w.b.				
CE21034	Pickup 8.5 ft.	3236	4100	3,331
3/4-Ton Commercial 4x4 — Model K/Series 20 — 127 in. w.b.				
KS20903	Chassis & Cab	3641	3659	509
KS20904	Step-Side 8 ft.	3804	4061	674
KS20934	Fleetside 8 ft.	3804	4156	10,066
KS20906	Suburban (doors)	4530	4414	256
KS20916	Suburban (gate)	4538	4414	353
3/4-Ton Forward Control — Model P/Series 20 — 125 in. w.b.				
PS20842	Chassis	2378	2819	288
PS20835	Steel Step-Van	4198	5206	819
PS20855	Aluminum Step-Van	-	-	48
3/4-Ton Forward Control — Model P/Series 20 — 133 in. w.b.				
PS21042	Chassis	2411	2841	167
PS21035	Steel Step-Van	4311	5437	654
PS21035	Aluminum Step-Van	5192	4638	37
1-Ton Commercial — Model C/Series 30 — 133 in. w.b.				
CS31002	Chassis & Cowl	-	-	139
CS31003	Chassis & Cab	2735	3641	11,438
CS31003	Chassis & Cab w/Stake	3530	-	Note 3
CS31004	Step-Side 9 ft.	2875	4071	1,557
CS31034	Fleetside 8.5 ft.	2935	4157	1,479
NOTE 3: Stake option included with C30 Chassis & Cab production.				
1-Ton Commercial — Model C/Series 30 — 157 in. w.b.				
CS31103	Chassis & Cab	2775	3788	6,071
1-Ton Forward Control — Model P/Series 30 — 125 in. w.b.				
PS30842	Chassis	2320	2992	278
PS30835	Steel Step-Van	4080	5379	561
PS30855	Aluminum Step-Van	-	-	71
1-Ton Forward Control (King) — Model P/Series 30 — 133 in. w.b.				
PS31042	King Chassis	2350	3015	853
PS31035	Steel Step-Van King	4190	5611	1,378
PS31055	Alum. Step-Van King	6860	5537	107
1-Ton Forward Control — Model P/Series 30 — 157 in. w.b.				
PS31442	Chassis	2350		1,669
PS31435	Steel Step-Van King	6040	6677	1,052
PS31455	Alum. Step-Van King	7170	5714	70
1-Ton Motorhome — Model P/Series 30 — 137 in. w.b. — V-8				
PE31132	Motorhome Chassis	3353	3219	788
1-Ton Motorhome — Model P/Series 30 — 157 in. w.b. — V-8				
PE31132	Motorhome Chassis	3391	3307	821

NOTE 4: Model codes, prices and weights on charts are for sixes, except where model is in a V-8 only series.
NOTE 5: Detailed Chevrolet records show above production totals with separate breakouts for country of origin and type of engine. To put these in a convenient format, the totals above show combined U.S. output, plus imports from Canada, through Aug. 31, 1971. They include both six-cylinder and V-8 trucks, although most model codes in chart are six-cylinder codes.
NOTE 6: Platform/stake options, big-block V-8s, diesel engines, and LPG conversions were options. See the options section below for partial data on options usage.

1971 Chevrolet 1/2-Ton C10 Cheyenne Fleetside short box Pickup (JLC)

ENGINE: [Standard Vega] Inline. OHV. Four-cylinder. Aluminum block. Bore & stroke: 3.501 in. x 3.625 in. Displacement: 140 cid. Compression ratio: 8.0:1. Brake horsepower: 90 at 4600 rpm. Net horsepower: 72 at 4200 rpm. Maximum torque: 136 lb.-ft. at 2400 rpm. Five main bearings. Hydraulic valve lifters. Carburetor: one-barrel.
ENGINE: [Standard: All except Vega/P20/P30] Inline. OHV. Six-cylinder. Cast iron block. Bore & stroke: 3.9 in. x 4.5 in. Displacement: 250 cid. Compression ratio: 8.5:1. Brake horsepower: 145 at 4200 rpm. Maximum torque: 235 lb.-ft. at 1600 rpm. Net horsepower: 110 at 4000 rpm. Seven main bearings. Mechanical valve lifters. Carburetor: Rochester one-barrel.
ENGINE: [Optional P Series] Inline. OHV. Three-cylinder. Diesel. Cast iron block. Bore & stroke: 3.875 x 4.5 in. Displacement: 159.2 cid. Horsepower: 94 at 2800 rpm. Torque: 205 at 1500. Taxable horsepower: 18.02. Induction: Fuel-injection.

1971 Chevrolet 1-Ton Fleetside "Camper Special" Pickup with Eagle Custom camper unit (CMD)

ENGINE: [Standard P20/P30, optional C5/K5/C10/K10/C20/K20/C30/G10/G20/G30] Inline. OHV. Six-cylinder. Cast iron block. Bore & stroke: 3-7/8 in. x 4-1/8 in. Displacement: 292 cid. Compression ratio: 8.0:1. Brake horsepower: 165 at 4000 rpm. Maximum torque: 270 lb.-ft. at 1600 rpm. Net horsepower: 125 at 3600 rpm. Seven main bearings. Hydraulic valve lifters. Carburetor: Rochester one-barrel.
ENGINE: [Standard Beauville, optional El Camino/C5/K5/C10/K10/P10/P20/G10] V-block. OHV. Eight-cylinder. Cast iron block. Bore & stroke: 3.875 in. x 3.25 in. Displacement: 307 cid. Compression ratio: 8.5:1. Brake horsepower: 200 at 4600 rpm. Maximum torque: 300 lb.-ft. at 2400 rpm. Net horsepower: 135 at 4000 rpm. Five main bearings. Hydraulic valve lifters. Carburetor: Rochester two-barrel.

1971 Chevrolet 3/4-Ton C20 Carryall Suburban with Airstream travel trailer (CMD)

ENGINE: [Optional C20/K20/P20/C30/P30/G20/G30] V-block. OHV. Eight-cylinder. Cast iron block. Bore & stroke: 3.875 in. x 3.25 in. Displacement: 307 cid. Compression ratio: 8.5:1. Brake horsepower: 215 at 4800 rpm. Maximum torque: 305 lb.-ft. at 2800 rpm. Net horsepower: 135 at 4000 rpm. Five main bearings. Hydraulic valve lifters. Carburetor: Rochester two-barrel.
ENGINE: [Optional C5/K5/C10/K10/C20/K20/P20/C30/P30/G20/G30] V-block. OHV. Eight-cylinder. Cast iron block. Bore & stroke: 4.0 in. x 3.5 in. Displacement: 350 cid. Compression ratio: 8.5:1. Brake horsepower: 250 at 4600 rpm. Maximum torque: 350 lb.-ft. at 3000 rpm. Net horsepower: 170 at 3600 rpm. Five main bearings. Hydraulic valve lifters. Carburetor: Rochester four-barrel.
ENGINE: [El Camino] V-block. OHV. Eight-cylinder. Cast iron block. Bore & stroke: 4.0 in. x 3.5 in. Displacement: 350 cid. Compression ratio: 8.5:1. Brake horsepower: 245 at 4400 rpm. Five main bearings. Hydraulic valve lifters. Carburetor: Rochester two-barrel.
ENGINE: [El Camino] V-block. OHV. Eight-cylinder. Cast iron block. Bore & stroke: 4.0 in. x 3.5 in. Displacement: 350 cid. Compression ratio: 8.5:1. Brake horsepower: 270 at 4800 rpm. Five main bearings. Hydraulic valve lifters. Carburetor: Rochester four-barrel.

1971 Chevrolet 3/4-Ton C20 Fleetside Pickup with El Dorado slide-in camper unit (CMD)

1971 Chevrolet 1-Ton C30 Chassis-and-Cab with Open Road camper body (CMD)

ENGINE: [Optional 400-cid V-8] V-block. OHV. Eight-cylinder. Cast iron block. Bore & stroke: 4.125 in. x 3.75 in. Displacement: 402 cid. Compression ratio: 8.5:1. Brake horsepower: 300 at 4800 rpm. Net horsepower: 240 at 4400 rpm. Torque: 410 at 3200 rpm. Five main bearings. Hydraulic valve lifters. Carburetor: Rochester four-barrel.
ENGINE: [Optional El Camino/SS] V-block. OHV. Eight-cylinder. Cast iron block. Bore & stroke: 4.251 in. x 4.00 in. Displacement: 454 cid. Compression ratio: 8.5:1. Brake horsepower: 365 at 4800 rpm. Maximum torque: 465 lb.-ft. at 3200 rpm. Net horsepower: 285. Five main bearings. Hydraulic valve lifters. Carburetor: four-barrel.
ENGINE: [SPO El Camino/SS] V-block. OHV. Eight-cylinder. Cast iron block. Bore & stroke: 4.251 in. x 4.00 in. Displacement: 454 cid. Compression ratio: 9.0:1. Brake horsepower: 425 at 5600 rpm. Maximum torque: 475 lb.-ft. at 4000 rpm. Five main bearings. Hydraulic valve lifters. Carburetor: four-barrel.
CHASSIS: [Vega] Wheelbase: 97 in. Overall length: 176 in. Height: 51.8 in. Front tread: 54.8 in. Rear tread: 53.6 in. Tires: 6.00-13B. GVW: 3,300 lb.
CHASSIS: [El Camino] Wheelbase: 116 in. Overall length: 206.8 in. Height: 54.4 in. Front tread: 60.2. Rear tread: 59.2 in. Tires: E78-14B. GVW: 4,100 lb.
CHASSIS: [G10] Wheelbase: 110/125 in. Overall length: 178/202.2 in. Height 80 in. Tires: F78-14B. GVW: 4,000-5,100 lb.
CHASSIS: [G20] Wheelbase: 110/125 in. Overall length: 178/202.2 in. Height: 80 in. Tires: G78-15B. GVW: 5,600-5,900 lb.
CHASSIS: [G30] Wheelbase: 110/125 in. Overall length: 178/202.2 in. Height: 80 in. Tires: 8 x 16.5. GVW: 6,100-8,000 lb.
CHASSIS: [Blazer] Wheelbase: 104 in. Overall length: 177.5 in. Height: 68.7 in. Front tread: 60.4 in. Rear tread: 60.4 in. Tires: E78-15B. GVW: 4,100 lb.
CHASSIS: [C10] Wheelbase: 115/127 in. Tires: [115-in. wheelbase] G78-15B, [127-in. wheelbase] H78-15B. GVW: 4,400-5,100 lb.
CHASSIS: [K10] Wheelbase: 115/127 in. Tires: [115-in. wheelbase] G78-15B, [127-in. wheelbase] H78-15B. GVW: 5,200-5,600 lb.
CHASSIS: [P10] Wheelbase: 102 in. Height: 75 in. Tires: G78-15B. GVW: 4,600-5,400 lb.
CHASSIS: [C20] Wheelbase: 127/133 in. Tires: [127-in. wheelbase] G78-15, [133 in. Longhorn] 8.75 x 16.5 six-ply. GVW: 6,200-7,500 lb.
CHASSIS: [K20] Wheelbase: 127 in. Tires: [127-in. wheelbase] G78-15, [133 in. Longhorn] 8.75 x 16.5, six-ply. GVW: 6,400-7,500 lb.
CHASSIS: [P20] Wheelbase: 125/133 in. Overall length: 220.75/244.75 in. Tires: 8.75 x 16.5. GVW: 6,500-7,500 lb.
CHASSIS: [C30] Wheelbase: 133 in./157 in. Tires: 8.75 x 16.5. GVW: 6,600-14,000 lb.
CHASSIS: [P30] Wheelbase: 133/157 in. Overall length: 220.75/265.75 in. Tires: 8.75 x 16.5. GVW: 7,300-14,000 lb.

1971 Chevrolet 1/2-Ton El Camino SS Sport Sedan-Pickup (Photo: John Lee)

TECHNICAL: Saginaw manual, fully-synchronized, transmission. Speeds: 3F/1R. Column-mounted gear shift lever. Single-plate dry-disc clutch (250-cid engine), coil spring single-dry-plate (292/307/350/402/454-cid engines). Rear axle: [1/2-ton] semi-floating, [3/4-ton/1-ton] full-floating rear axle. Hydraulic, four-wheel brakes. Kelsey-Hayes pressed steel wheels.
OPTIONS: Rear bumper ($53.80). Radio ($69.95). Clock. Air conditioning. Deluxe heater. Gauge package (ammeter, oil, temperature). Tilt wheel. Shoulder belts. Tinted glass ($19.40). Dual outside mirrors ($21.00). Dome light switch ($4.35). Side wheel carrier ($15.10). Full foam seat ($30.15). [1/2-ton] 292-cid six-cylinder engine ($95). 307-cid V-8 engine ($120). 400-cid V-8 engine (average $160). 350-cid V-8 in El Camino ($70). Four-speed transmission ($190). Powerglide transmission ($195). Turbo-Hydramatic transmission (average $280). Power brakes (average $50). Power steering (average $115). Four-wheel-drive system (average $570). [3/4-ton] 292-cid six-cylinder engine ($95). 307-cid V-8, over base six ($120). 400-cid V-8 over 307-cid V-8 ($175). Powerglide (average $210). Turbo-Hydramatic transmission (average $245). Four-wheel-drive transmission (average $120). Power steering (average $140). Four-wheel-drive system ($680). [1-ton] 307-cid V-8 over base six ($120). 292-cid six-cylinder engine ($95). 350-cid V-8 over 307 ($45). 400-cid V-8 engine, over 350. LPG kit ($95). Turbo-Hydramatic transmission ($245). New Process transmission ($30). Vacuum brakes ($45). Power steering (average $135). Nine-foot platform equipment ($425). 12-ft. platform equipment ($484). 157-in. wheelbase ($30).

OPTIONS: [With usage rate] Tinted glass, van (27 percent). Cargo door lock, van (8 percent). Body glass, van (10 percent). Right side glass, van (7 percent). Side door window glass, panel van (1 percent). All tinted glass, light trucks (30 percent). Rear door glass, van (64 percent). Sliding rear window, light truck (3 percent). Bucket seats, light truck (3 percent). Custom bench seat (used on 967 light trucks). Body side belt molding, light truck ($27 percent). Wide lower body side molding, light truck (28 percent). Upper body side molding, light truck (37 percent). Door edge guards, light truck (12 percent). Body side molding, van (1 percent). Deluxe air conditioning, light truck (25 percent). Roof air conditioning, light truck (25 percent). Front air conditioning, van (3 percent). Rear air conditioning, van (1 percent). Painted camper mirror, light truck (3 percent). Stainless camper mirror, light truck (3 percent). Stainless steel West Coast Jr. mirror: light truck (10 percent), van (13 percent). Dual West Coast Sr. mirror, light truck (41 percent). Painted West Coast Jr. mirror: light truck (19 percent), van (50 percent). Body paint stripe, light truck (8 percent). Platform and Stake equipment, light truck (14 percent). Positraction: light truck (11 percent), van (12 percent), Step-Van (7 percent). Oil bath air cleaner: light truck (3 percent), van (5 percent). 350 light-duty V-8 engine: light truck (65 percent), van (49 percent). 292-cid six-cylinder engine: light truck (14 percent), van (68 percent). 396 V-8 engine: Step-Van (8 percent), light truck (6 percent). LPG engine package (used on only 387 light trucks and six vans.) Four-speed transmission: light truck (14 percent), van (24 percent). Heavy-duty, close-ratio, four-speed manual transmission (used on 1,122 light trucks). Powerglide transmission: light truck (1 percent), van (7 percent), Step-Van (6 percent). M-38 Turbo-Hydramatic transmission: light truck (45 percent), van (49 percent), Step-Van (22 percent). M-49 Turbo-Hydramatic transmission: light truck (6 percent), Step-Van (17 percent). Tilt steering wheel, light truck (2 percent). Power steering: light truck (43 percent), van (9 percent), Step-Van (17 percent). Wheel trim cover: light truck (53 percent), van (37 percent). AM/FM push-button radio, light truck (1 percent). Chrome rear bumper, light truck (3 percent). Chrome front bumper, light truck (22 percent). Cheyenne Super package, light truck (2 percent). Removable hardtop, Blazer/light truck: black (78 percent), white (21 percent). Custom Appearance package, van (9 percent). Custom Comfort and Convenience package: light truck (21 percent), van (10 percent). Camper Special package, light truck (18 percent). Cheyenne package, light truck (16 percent). Notes: A total of 72,609 light trucks were equipped with the Cheyenne trim package. A total of 7,190 vans were equipped with Custom Appearance features. A total of 20,501 Pickups got the Camper Special option. A total of 9,867 trucks were Cheyenne Super models. Custom Deluxe equipment was added to 8,686 vans and 98,895 light trucks. Over 50 percent of the light-duty trucks were two-toned in standard colors or special colors. One two-tone paint combination ending with code 73 was used on only three trucks.
COLOR OPTIONS: See 1970 options section for complete chart of 1970-1974 Chevrolet Commercial Truck colors.

1971 Chevrolet 1/2-Ton El Camino SS Sport Sedan-Pickup (Photo: John Lee)

HISTORICAL: Introduction: The 1971 Chevy Vans and Sportvans were introduced in May, 1970. Production start-up date for other 1971 models was Aug. 21, 1970. They hit the showrooms one month and eight days later [Sept. 29, 1970]. Calendar-year Commercial model registrations, by weight class: [6000-lb. and less] 450,354, [6,001 to 10,000-lb.] 145,358. Calendar-year Commercial production was 739,478 units, outpacing the previous record of 683,694 set in 1969. The 1971 total included 599,207 trucks with V-8 engines, 128,660 with inline six-cylinder engines, 345 with V-6s, 9,120 Vega Panels with the four-cylinder engine and 2,146 diesels. El Caminos are not included in such production totals, as they were counted with Chevelle passenger cars. Also, 15,670 vans were considered Nova Sportvans and their output was included with passenger car production totals. Innovations: All 1971 Chevrolet truck engines were modified to operate on unleaded gasoline. Front disc brakes were standard on all conventional light-duty models and Step-Vans. Independent front suspension was adopted for vans. The fuel evaporative system, formerly optional in California, became standard in all 1/2-tons. A big recovery from strike-year 1970 made this a banner season. Several truck factories ran six days a week, all year, to keep up with demand. A.T. Olson was assistant general sales manager of the truck division.

1972 CHEVROLET

1/2-TON LUV MINI-PICKUP — MODEL L/SERIES 82 — FOUR: An all-new LUV Pickup truck was introduced in March 1972 as a captive import sourced from Isuzu Motors of Japan. The 1972 model is readily identifiable by its 1955 Chevrolet-like eggcrate grille and total of eight round reflectors and lights on the rear end. The name LUV stood for Light Utility Vehicle. A total of 21,098 of these trucks were sold from March to December 1972.
1/2-TON VEGA — MODEL V/SERIES 14000 — FOUR: The Vega Panel Express was available, again, in 1972. Its grille was finished in a manner that made the vertical elements slightly less prominent. A model emblem was seen on the cowl. Otherwise, there was very little change. It was again based on the Kammback Station Wagon, with the rear side windows blanked out. It came only with the standard all-vinyl interior, less passenger bucket seat. Standard equipment included the four-cylinder aluminum block engine, three-speed manual transmission, front disc brakes, two separate stowage compartments below the floor, many safety features and a choice of colors. It had a 67.4-in. floor length, 42.6 in. between the wheelhousings, and a 68.7-cu.-ft. cargo volume. Payload capacity was 650 lb.

1972 Chevrolet 1/2-Ton El Camino Sedan-Pickup (DFW)

1/2-TON EL CAMINO — MODEL AC, AD/SERIES 13000 — SIX/V-8: Larger, one-piece corner lights were seen on the El Camino. They bent around the body corners to double as side markers. The grille had a cross-hatch pattern, but four horizontal moldings with bright finish stood out the most. They split the grille into three horizontal segments. The center bow tie emblem of 1971 was replaced with Chevrolet letters at the left-hand side of the lower grille segment. El Camino nameplates and designation badges were mounted on the front fender sides, behind the wheel opening. The rear end appearance had hardly any changes. The front bumper had no air slots or parking lamps in it. Standard models had bright windshield frames, back-up lights on the tailgate, and a base six-cylinder engine. Customs added a V-8 as base engine, all bright window frames, body side moldings, wheelhouse moldings, pickup box rim moldings, rear body corner moldings, two moldings on the tailgate, and silver anodized lower body perimeter. Super Sport equipment (RPO Z15) was available for all Custom models with V-8s other than the base 307-cid V-8. You could get an SS-350, SS-396 (actually a 402-cid one), or SS-454. The basic SS (Super Sport) package cost less than last year. It was a $350 option. The engine selected by the buyer was a separate option. The basic SS package included a black-accented grille with SS badges, cowl badges, hood locking pins, styled wheels, special vertically pleated door panels, round instrument panel gauges, sport suspension, power front disc brakes, and 15 x 7 sport wheels with F60-15 raised white-letter tires. The 396-cid engine was gone, although the 402-cid V-8-powered trucks were promoted as SS-396 models. An unusual dealer option costing about $65 extra was a "Flame Chevy '73" decal kit. The exterior colors for the year were Antique White, Pewter Silver, Ascot Blue, Mulsanne Blue, Spring Green, Gulf Green, Sequoia Green, Covert Tan, Placer Gold, Cream Yellow, Golden Brown, Mojave Gold, Orange Flame, Midnight Bronze, and Cranberry Red. Interiors came in black, antique covert tan vinyl, and cloth-and-vinyl combinations, as well as pinta fabric combinations. The "flying buttress" roof line was retained for all El Caminos. The pickup box still had an outside width of 75-1/2 in. Inside width behind the cab was 59 in. Inside width near the tailgate was 64-1/2 in. The width between the wheelhousings was 44 in. The bottom bed length measured 79-1/4 in. Tailgate measurements were 54-1/2 x 22-1/2 in. This was the last year for this pickup box.

1972 Chevrolet 1/2-Ton G10 Chevy Van Panel (CMD)

1/2-TON VAN — MODEL G/SERIES 10 — SIX/V-8: Chevrolet vans continued to come in three basic models: Chevy Van (panel), Sportvan and Beauville. The Beauville model offered travel space for 12 passengers. All G10 models could be had with 110- or 125-in. wheelbases. Panels and Sportvans used the 250-cid/145-hp inline six as base power plant. Base engine in the 1/2-ton Beauville was the 307-cid/200-hp V-8. An extended front hood made 26 service areas readily accessible. Van grilles consisted of seven horizontal bars with a center-mounted Chevrolet emblem. Other innovations included independent front suspension and a sliding door option. A Custom Appearance package was available, as well as a Custom and Convenience interior option.
3/4-TON VAN — MODEL G/SERIES 20 — SIX/V-8: The 108-in. wheelbase driver-forward vans also came as 3/4-ton G20 models. Styling characteristics were the same as G10s. Models included the Chevy Van with double panel doors available on the passenger side and at the rear. There were also window models in two levels of trim: base Sportvan or Beauville. The G20 line offered the same engines as G10s, but a 350-cid V-8 was standard in the Beauville.
1-TON VAN — MODEL G/SERIES 30 — SIX/V-8: In the 1-ton (G30) line, only the Chevy Van panel was available with the shorter wheelbase, while the G30 Sportvan and Beauville were available only on the longer 125-in. wheelbase, which was different than in the other series. Chevrolet production records show that no 1972 Sportvans or Beauvilles were built on the 110-in. wheelbase. Only the G30 Chevy Van came with a six. In the 3/4- and 1-ton lines the 350-cid/250-hp V-8 was standard.
1/2-TON BLAZER — MODEL C, K/SERIES 5 — SIX/V-8: Light trucks, including Blazers, looked similar to the previous year's model, except that the border of the grille surround was no longer black-finished. Factory records show nearly 3,500 of the 4x2 Blazers were made in model-year 1971. The 4x4 version was now nearly 15 times as popular. The Blazer's suspension system consisted of single-leaf tapered front springs with a combination of multi-leaf and tapered springs at the rear. The ball-type steering unit had a 24:1 ratio and its standard engine was Chevrolet's 155-hp six. The single-unit body was joined to a heavy channel steel frame. The rear-mounted 23.5-gallon fuel tank was located inside the frame. Numerous options were offered for the Blazer including four-speed manual and automatic transmissions, V-8 engines, power steering, power brakes and a completely removable fiberglass top. Colors, exterior trims, upholstery and equipment were very similar or the same as used on the conventional C10/K10 models.

1972 Chevrolet 1/2-Ton C10 Fleetside long box Pickup (OCW)

1/2-TON COMMERCIAL — MODEL C, K/SERIES 10 — SIX/V-8: Pickups, Panels and Carryall Suburbans looked similar to the previous year's models, except that the borders of the grille surrounds were no longer black-finished. There were new molded door panels with integral arm rests. A new Highlander interior package was available. Featured again was an eggcrate grille with five horizontal blades and 15 vertical members. A Chevrolet bow tie was on grille's center. The parking/directional lights were in the front bumper. Inside was a low-profile steering wheel, full-width bench seat, and foot-operated parking brake. Standard equipment on all Pickups included: A six-cylinder engine, side terminal battery, self-adjusting four-wheel brakes (front discs), dual brake master cylinder with warning lights, back-up lights, directional signals and four-way flashers, Panoramic rear window, left- and right-hand outside rear view mirrors, non-glare inside mirror, heater and defroster, padded dash, non-glare front instrument panel finish, padded sun visors, ash trays with retractors, push-button seat buckles, low-profile control knobs, two-speed electric washer/wipers, windshield defrosters, safety glass, flexible fuel filler neck, deep-dish steering wheel with telescoping shaft, thick laminate safety glass windshield, right-hand coat hook, front and rear side markers, and painted front bumper. Chrome front and rear bumpers were a separate option. There were different trim levels. The base Custom had no side trim, plain black rubber window gaskets, and white-painted bumpers. The grille shell had bright metal finish. The hubcaps were also painted. The vent window pillars and frames were flat black. The standard hubcaps were painted. Rear moldings around the taillamps and tailgate were not available on Customs. Upper and lower belt moldings were optional. Customs equipped with the lower belt molding should have the center of the molding painted black. Custom Deluxe equipment included a full-width bench seat with comfortably padded seat cushions and back rest, vinyl seat upholstery and door panels, steel roof panel painted in main exterior color, black rubber floor mat extending to firewall, padded arm rests, padded sun shades, courtesy lamp, prismatic rear view mirror, foam-padded instrument panel, bright upper and lower grille outline moldings, bright headlamp bezels, bright outside rear view mirrors, bright door handles, white-painted front bumper, hubcaps and wheels, and bright Custom Deluxe nameplates. Upper and lower belt moldings were both optional. The center of the 1972 lower molding had a wood-grain insert. When equipped with lower body side molding, the Custom Deluxe also got taillamp and two tailgate moldings. These moldings were positioned above and below the Chevrolet lettering on the back. Chrome hubcaps were optional on Custom Deluxe models. The Cheyenne trim package included a bench seat with full-depth foam cushions and back rests, Custom-grained vinyl upholstery or nylon and vinyl upholstery, special door trim panels, cab headliner, deep-twist nylon carpeting extending to firewall, color-keyed garnish moldings, ash tray-mounted cigar lighter, Custom steering wheel, Cheyenne dashboard nameplates, door-operated or manually-operated courtesy lights, extra acoustical insulation, and all Custom Deluxe exterior items, plus a cab-mounted cargo lamp, bright metal cab trim and moldings, bright upper body side and tailgate moldings, and central taillight appliqués for Fleetside and Cheyenne nameplates. When equipped with a lower body side molding, the Cheyenne also got wood-grain molding inserts. Bucket seats were optional for Cheyennes with the vinyl interior. A Cheyenne Super option package took up where the Cheyenne left off, adding both upper and lower (wood-grain) body side moldings, and a chrome-plated tailgate release. There were Custom Appearance, and Custom Comfort & Convenience options, too. Exterior colors were Midnight Black, Hawaiian Blue, Mariner Blue, Classic Bronze, Spanish Gold, Glenwood Green, Meadow Green, Spruce Green, Willow Green, Firebolt Orange, Tangier Orange, Crimson Red, Frost White, Grapefruit Yellow, and Wheatland Yellow. The standard interior featured a three-passenger bench seat, foam padding, dome light, rubber floor mat, two door arm rests, and all-vinyl trim in green, blue, black or parchment. The Custom and Cheyenne interiors came with black pinta coated fabric, antique medium tan pinta coated fabric or antique light covert coated fabric. The C10 (and K10 four-wheel-drive) Chassis-and-Cab and Pickup models came on 115- or 127-in. wheelbases. Both Fleetside and Step-Side Pickups offered a choice of 6-ft. or 8-ft. boxes. Pickups on the shorter wheelbase had the 6-1/2 ft. cargo box. Carryall Suburbans came only on the longer wheelbase. The Carryall Suburban no longer came with the 292-cid six. It again had two-doors on the passenger side and one on the driver's side. A tailgate or double rear doors were available. They had a floor space that was 9 ft. long. With second and third seats removed, cargo space totaled 190 cu.-ft. Four-wheel-drive was available for a price of just over $500. Both of these single-unit body models had coil springs on all four wheels. Two-toning was done using white as the second (upper) color. It was applied to all sheet metal above the belt line or just the upper and rear cab panels. On Cheyennes, the body side, between the upper and lower belt line moldings was usually done in white.

1972 Chevrolet 1/2-Ton C10 Fleetside long box Pickup (OCW)

142

1/2-TON FORWARD-CONTROL — MODEL P/SERIES 10 — SIX/V-8: The Forward-Control chassis was designed for door-to-door delivery service. Body lengths ranged from seven to eight feet for the P10 series. Step-Vans looked identical to 1971 versions. The P10 models were sold in chassis and steel panel models on a 102-in. wheelbase. These were advertised as Step Van 7 models (due to their seven-foot-long bodies). The grilles had single round headlights in the top of the housings, with rectangular parking lamps below. Features included independent coil spring front suspension, and three six-cylinder engines. Buyers could also get full-height doors, sliding side doors and double rear doors.

1972 Chevrolet 3/4-Ton C20 Fleetside long box Pickup (CMD)

3/4-TON COMMERCIAL — MODEL C, K/SERIES 20 — SIX/V-8: Carryover trucks in the Chevrolet 20 Series 3/4-ton line had the same styling, trim changes and options as other conventional trucks. Fleetside and Step-Side Pickups had 8-ft. boxes. Also available was the "Longhorn" Fleetside with a 133-in. wheelbase and 8-1/2-ft. box. The Chassis-and-Cab and two Carryall Suburbans continued to be offered in this line. They had the same dimensions as comparable 1/2-ton models, but heavier chassis components. The designation plates had a number 20. The 8-ft. Stake model was available as an extra on the platform option for the Chassis-and-Cab. It cost about $400 for the platform option. The four-wheel-drive 3/4-ton models in the 20 Series had a K20 model prefix. Longhorns were not built with four-wheel-drive.

3/4-TON FORWARD-CONTROL — MODEL P/SERIES 20 — SIX/V-8: The Forward-Control chassis was designed for door-to-door delivery service. The 3/4-ton P20 models offered two wheelbases. They came in Step-Van chassis form or as Step-Van King models with steel or aluminum panel bodies. Remaining in the series were the 125-in. wheelbase chassis recommended for bodies 9-1/2 to 10-1/2 ft. long and the 137-in. wheelbase recommended for bodies 11-1/2 to 12-1/2 ft. long. Step-Van King did not refer to the wheelbase, but to the body height and width. The Kings had their round headlamps below the rectangular parking lamps. A number of power plants could be had, including three six-cylinder engines and two optional V-8s. The three-cylinder Detroit diesel was not listed. Features included independent coil spring front suspension. Buyers could also get full-height doors, sliding side doors and double rear doors. The coil spring front suspension reflected the fact that the Forward-Control chassis had found popularity among recreational vehicle builders.

1972 Chevrolet 1-Ton C30 Chassis & Cab with slide-in camper body (CMD)

1-TON MEDIUM-DUTY COMMERCIAL — MODEL C/SERIES 30 — SIX-CYLINDER: The Chevrolet 30 Series 1-ton trucks had the same styling and trim changes and options as other conventional trucks. The fender side nameplates had a number 30. There were four 133-in. wheelbase models: Chassis-and-Cowl, Chassis-and-Cab, Longhorn Pickup with 8.5-ft box, and Step-Side Pickup with a 9-ft. box. No hubcaps were used on the larger split-rim wheels of the Chassis-and-Cab models, which had eight bolts and eight circular openings. The Camper Special package continued. The C38 model 1-ton Chassis-and-Cab with a long 157-in. wheelbase for use as an RV chassis was also offered again. Nearly 9,000 of these were sold. A four-speed manual synchromesh transmission was standard. No four-wheel-drive option was offered.

1-TON FORWARD-CONTROL — MODEL P/SERIES 30 — SIX/V-8: Two P30 models were the same sizes as P20s, but had much higher GVW ratings of 7,300-14,000 lb. versus the 3/4-ton's 6,500-7,500 lb. The third model featured a 157-in. wheelbase and accommodated body lengths up to 14-1/2 ft. for the 1-ton Step-Van King. More and more of these Forward-Control chassis were being used for motorhome conversions. Features included independent coil spring front suspension, three six-cylinder engines and two optional V-8s. Some Step-Vans had Liquid Petroleum Gas conversions. Buyers could also get full-height doors, sliding side doors, and double rear doors. Chevrolet also produced the special P30 1-ton motorhome chassis on 137-in. and 157-in. wheelbases. Almost 5,200 were constructed in 1972.

I.D. DATA: Serial number located: [Chassis models] on plate temporarily attached near steering column, with final location per body maker. [All others] on plate attached to rear face of left-hand door hinge pillar, on right side of cowl under hood. [LUV] The VIN consists of 10 symbols. The first three symbols are the model name. The fourth and fifth symbols are the plant code. The last five symbols are the sequential production number. [El Camino] The first symbol indicated manufacturer: 1=Chevrolet. The second symbol indicated series: C=base, D=Custom. The third and fourth symbols indicated body style: 80=Sedan-Pickup. The fifth symbol indicated engine: D=250-cid six, F=307-cid V-8, H=350-cid V-8, J=350-cid V-8, K=350-cid V-8, L=350-cid V-8, R=400-cid V-8, S=402-cid V-8, U=402-cid V-8, V=454-cid V-8, W=454-cid V-8.: C=base, D=Custom. The sixth symbol indicated model-year: 2=1972. The seventh symbol indicated assembly plant: B=Baltimore, Md., K=Kansas City, Mo. (Leeds), L=Los Angeles (Van Nuys), Calif., R=Arlington, Texas. The remaining symbols were the sequential production number starting with 100001 at each plant. Ending serial numbers not available. The Chevrolet engine had the source, date and type stamped on a serial number pad. Various source codes were used. Month codes were 1=Jan., 2=Feb., etc. Date codes were 01=first of month, etc. There were numerous prefix codes to indicate engines and transmission attachments. [C/K/G/P Series] The first symbol indicated truck type: C=Conventional Cab, K=4x4, G=Chevy Van, P=Forward-Control, Z=Motorhome. The second symbol indicated type of engine: S=six, E=eight, T=diesel. The third symbol indicated the GVW range: [GVW] 1=3,900 to 5,800 lb., 2=5,200 to 7,500 lb., 3=6,600 to 14,000 lb. The fourth and fifth symbols indicated the cab-to-axle dimension: 05=30-35 in., 07=42 to 47 in., 09=54-59 in., 10=60-65 in., 14=84-89 in. The sixth symbol indicated body type: 02=Chassis & Cowl, 03=Chassis-and-Cab, 04=Step-Side Pickup, 05=Panel Van, 06=Carryall Suburban (doors)/Sportvan, 14=Blazer, 16=Carryall Suburban (gate), 32=Motorhome chassis, 34=Fleetside, 36=Beauville Van, 35=Forward-Control (steel Step-Van body), 42=Forward-Control chassis, 55=Forward-Control (aluminum Step-Van body). The eighth symbol indicates model-year: 2=1972. The ninth symbol indicates assembly plant: A=Atlanta (Lakewood), Ga., B=Baltimore, Md., F=Flint, Mich., G=Framingham, Mass., J=Janesville, Wis., K=Kansas City (Leeds), Mo., L=Los Angeles (Van Nuys), Calif., P=Pontiac, Mich., R=Arlington, Texas, S=St. Louis, Mo., T=Tarrytown, N.Y., U=Lordstown, Ohio, Z=Fremont, Calif. 1=Oshawa, Canada. The remaining symbols were the sequential production number starting with 100001 at each plant. Ending serial numbers not available. The Chevrolet engine had the source, date and type stamped on a serial number pad. Various source codes were used. Month codes were 1=Jan., 2=Feb., etc. Date codes were 01=first of month, etc. The were numerous prefix codes to indicate engines and transmission attachments.

1972 Chevrolet 1/2-Ton C10 Fleetside long box Pickup (CMD)

Model	Body Type	Price	Weight	Prod. Total
1/2-Ton LUV — Model L/Series 82 — 102.4 in. w.b.				
82	Mini-Pickup	2196	2360	21,098
1/2-Ton Vega — Model V/Series 14000 — 97 in. w.b. -Four				
14105	Panel Express	2080	2152	4,114
El Camino — Model A/Series 13000 — 116 in. w.b. — Six				
13380	Sedan-Pickup	2790	3302	Note 1
El Camino — Model A/Series 13000 — 116 in. w.b. — V-8				
13480	Sedan-Pickup	2880	3418	Note 1
13680	Custom Sedan-Pickup	2960	3442	Note 1
NOTE 1: Total El Camino production was 57,147.				
1/2-Ton Van — Model G/Series 10 — 110 in. w.b.				
GS11005	Panel	2775	3460	12,205
GS11006	Sportvan	3285	3694	1,346
1/2-Ton Van — Model G/Series 10 — 110 in. w.b. — V-8				
GE11036	Beauville	3685	3936	433
1/2-Ton Van — Model G/Series 10 — 125 in. w.b.				
GS11305	Panel	2910	3615	14,044
GS11306	Sportvan	3410	3856	1,593
1/2-Ton Van — Model G/Series 10 — 125 in. w.b. — V-8				
GS11336	Beauville	3805	4136	997
3/4-Ton Van — Model G/Series 20 — 110 in. w.b.				
GS21005	Panel	2890	3489	4,618
GS21006	Sportvan	3335	3761	605
3/4-Ton Van — Model G/Series 20 — 110 in. w.b.				
GS21036	Beauville	3760	4094	345
3/4-Ton Van — Model G/Series 20 — 125 in. w.b.				
GS21305	Panel	3020	3653	16,084
GS21306	Sportvan	3460	3929	3,310
3/4-Ton Van — Model G/Series 20 — 125 in. w.b.				
GS21336	Beauville	3880	4296	5,581
1-Ton Van — Model G/Series 30 — 110 in. w.b.				
GS31005	Panel	2996	3781	623
1-Ton Van — Model G/Series 30 — 125 in. w.b.				
GS31305	Van	3130	3948	12,545
GS31306	Sportvan	3575	4117	2,036
1-Ton Van — Model G/Series 30 — 125 in. w.b.				
GS31336	Beauville	3995	4590	2,020
1/2-Ton Blazer 4x2 — Model C/Series 5 — 104 in. w.b.				
CS10514	Open Utility	2585	3375	3,357
1/2-Ton Blazer 4x4 — Model K/Series 5 — 104 in. w.b.				
KS10514	Open Utility	3145	3677	44,266
1/2-Ton Commercial — Model C/Series 10 — 115 in. w.b.				
CS10703	Chassis & Cab	2530	3090	1,640
CS10704	Step-Side 6.5 ft.	2680	3426	22,042
CS10734	Fleetside 6.5 ft.	2680	3506	39,730

Model	Body Type	Price	Weight	Prod. Total
1/2-Ton Commercial — Model C/Series 10 — 127 in. w.b.				
CS10903	Chassis & Cab	2560	3107	717
CS10904	Step-Side 8 ft.	2715	3510	7,538
CS10934	Fleetside 8 ft.	2715	3605	273,249
CS10906	Suburban (doors)	3495	3862	6,748
CS10916	Suburban (gate)	3525	3870	10,757
1/2-Ton Commercial 4x4 — Model K/Series 10 — 115 in. w.b.				
KS10704	Step-Side 6.5 ft.	3251	3766	1,736
KS10734	Fleetside 6.5 ft.	3251	3836	6,069
1/2-Ton Commercial 4x4 — Model K/Series 10 — 127 in. w.b.				
KS10904	Step-Side 8 ft.	3287	3846	407
KS10934	Fleetside 8 ft.	3287	3926	18,431
KS10906	Suburban (doors)	4273	4206	993
KS10916	Suburban (gate)	4305	4206	2,145
1/2-Ton Forward-Control — Model P/Series 10 — 102 in. w.b.				
PS10542	Chassis	2015	2120	196
PS10535	Steel Step-Van	3260	3781	2,063
3/4-Ton Commercial — Model C/Series 20 — 127 in. w.b.				
CS20903	Chassis & Cab	2760	3496	5,974
CS20903	Chassis & Cab w/ Stake	3168	4163	Note 2
CS20904	Step-Side 8 ft.	2915	3896	3,973
CS20934	Fleetside 8 ft.	2915	3991	94,458
CS20906	Suburban (doors)	3650	4245	2,136
CS20916	Suburban (gate)	3680	4253	3,141

NOTE 2: Stake option included with C20 Chassis & Cab production.

Model	Body Type	Price	Weight	Prod. Total
3/4-Ton Long Horn — Model C/Series 20 — 133 in. w.b.				
CE21034	Pickup 8.5 ft.	3088	3950	3,328
3/4-Ton Commercial 4x4 — Model K/Series 20 — 127 in. w.b.				
KS20903	Chassis & Cab	3415	3651	676
KS20904	Step-Side 8 ft.	3567	4051	755
KS20934	Fleetside 8-ft.	3567	4141	19,648
KS20906	Suburban (doors)	4275	4541	503
KS20916	Suburban (gate)	4308	4585	879
3/4-Ton Forward Control — Model P/Series 20 — 125 in. w.b.				
PS20842	Chassis	2265	2819	343
PS20835	Steel Step-Van	4000	5206	1,706
PS20855	Aluminum Step-Van	-	-	92
3/4-Ton Forward Control — Model P/Series 20 — 133 in. w.b.				
PS21042	Chassis	2295	2841	189
PS21035	Steel Step-Van	4605	5437	989
PS21035	Aluminum Step-Van	4770	4638	42
1-Ton Commercial — Model C/Series 30 — 133 in. w.b.				
CS31002	Chassis & Cowl	-	-	127
CS31003	Chassis & Cab	2845	3641	14,988
CS31003	Chassis & Cab w/Stake	2370	4488	Note 3
CS31004	Step-Side 9 ft.	2990	4071	1,542
CS31034	Fleetside 8.5 ft.	3050	4157	2,450

NOTE 3: Stake option included with C30 Chassis-and-Cab production.

Model	Body Type	Price	Weight	Prod. Total
1-Ton Commercial — Model C/Series 30 — 157 in. w.b.				
CS31103	Chassis & Cab	2885	3788	8,944
1-Ton Forward Control — Model P/Series 30 — 125 in. w.b.				
PS30842	Chassis	2435	2992	441
PS30835	Steel Step-Van	4165	5379	559
PS30855	Aluminum Step-Van	-	-	125
1-Ton Forward Control (King) — Model P/Series 30 — 133 in. w.b.				
PS31042	King Chassis	2470	3015	967
PS31035	Steel Step-Van King	4270	5611	1,710
PS31055	Alum. Step-Van King	-	-	127
1-Ton Forward Control — Model P/Series 30 — 157 in. w.b.				
PS31442	Chassis	2350		1,899
PS31435	Steel Step-Van King	6040	6677	1,702
PS31455	Alum. Step-Van King	7170	5714	231
1-Ton Motorhome — Model P/Series 30 — 137 in. w.b. — V-8				
PE31132	Motorhome Chassis	3190	3219	2,267
1-Ton Motorhome — Model P/Series 30 — 157 in. w.b. — V-8				
PE31132	Motorhome Chassis	3225	3307	2,942

NOTE 4: Models, prices and weights on charts are for sixes, except where model is in a V-8 only series.

NOTE 5: Detailed Chevrolet records show above production totals with separate breakouts for country of origin and type of engine. To put these in a convenient format, the totals above show combined U.S. output, plus imports from Canada, through Aug. 31, 1972. They include both six-cylinder and V-8 trucks, although most model codes in chart are six-cylinder codes.

NOTE 6: Platform/stake options, big-block V-8s, diesel engines, and LPG conversions were options. See the options section below for partial data on options usage.

ENGINE: [Standard LUV] Inline. OHV. Four-cylinder. Cast iron block. Bore & stroke: 3.31 in. x 3.23 in. Displacement: 110.8 cid. Compression ratio: 8.5:1. Net horsepower: 75 at 5000 rpm. Maximum torque: 88 lb.-ft at 3000 rpm. Five main bearings. Hydraulic valve lifters. Carburetor: two-barrel.

ENGINE: [Standard Vega] Inline. OHV. Four-cylinder. Aluminum block. Bore & stroke: 3.501 in. x 3.625 in. Displacement: 140 cid. Compression ratio: 8.0:1. Brake horsepower: 90 at 4600-4800 rpm. Net horsepower: 72 at 4200 rpm. Maximum torque: 115 lb.-ft. at 2400 rpm. Five main bearings. Hydraulic valve lifters. Carburetor: one-barrel.

1972 Chevrolet 1/2-Ton C10 Carryall Suburban (CMD)

1972 Chevrolet 1/2-Ton LUV Mini-Pickup (OCW)

ENGINE: [Standard El Camino, all C/K, P10] Inline. OHV. Six-cylinder. Cast iron block. Bore & stroke: 3.9 in. x 4.5 in. Displacement: 250 cid. Compression ratio: 8.5:1. Brake horsepower: 145 at 4200 rpm. Maximum torque: 230 lb.-ft. at 1600 rpm. Net horsepower: 110 at 4000 rpm. Seven main bearings. Hydraulic valve lifters. Carburetor: Rochester one-barrel model 1.

ENGINE: [Standard P20/P30, optional C20/C30] Inline. OHV. Six-cylinder. Cast iron block. Bore & stroke: 3-7/8 in. x 4-1/8 in. Displacement: 292 cid. Compression ratio: 8.0:1. Brake horsepower: 165 at 4000 rpm. Maximum torque: 270 lb.-ft. at 1600 rpm. Net horsepower: 125 at 3600 rpm. Seven main bearings. Hydraulic valve lifters. Carburetor: Rochester one-barrel.

ENGINE: [Optional El Camino, G10] V-block. OHV. Eight-cylinder. Cast iron block. Bore & stroke: 3.875 in. x 3.25 in. Displacement: 307 cid. Compression ratio: 8.5:1. Net horsepower: 130 at 4000 rpm. Five main bearings. Hydraulic valve lifters. Carburetor: Rochester two-barrel.

1972 Chevrolet 1/2-Ton El Camino Sedan-Pickup (OCW)

ENGINE: [Optional C/K] V-block. OHV. Eight-cylinder. Cast iron block. Bore & stroke: 3.875 in. x 3.25 in. Displacement: 307 cid. Compression ratio: 8.5:1. Brake horsepower: 200 at 4600 rpm. Maximum torque: 300 lb.-ft. at 2400 rpm. Net horsepower: 135 at 4000 rpm. Five main bearings. Hydraulic valve lifters. Carburetor: Rochester two-barrel.

ENGINE: [El Camino, standard in California] V-block. OHV. Eight-cylinder. Cast iron block. Bore & Stroke: 4.0 x 3.5 in. Displacement: 350 cid. Compression ratio: 8.5:1. Net horsepower: 165 at 3400 rpm. Five main bearings. Hydraulic valve lifters. Carburetor: Rochester two-barrel.

ENGINE: [Optional El Camino, C, K, G, P20, P30] V-block. OHV. Eight-cylinder. Cast iron block. Bore & Stroke: 4.0 x 3.5 in. Displacement: 350 cid. Compression ratio: 8.5:1. Brake horsepower: 250 at 4600 rpm. Torque: 350 lb.-ft. at 3000 rpm. Net horsepower: 175 at 3600 rpm. Five main bearings. Hydraulic valve lifters. Carburetor: Rochester two-barrel. Note: Standard in G20/G30 Beauville model).

ENGINE: [Optional: El Camino, C5, K5, C10, C20, K20, C30, P20, P30] V-block. OHV. Eight-cylinder. Cast iron block. Bore & Stroke: 4.125 in. x 3.75 in. Displacement: 402 cid. Compression ratio: 8.5:1. Brake horsepower: 300 at 4800 rpm. Net horsepower: 240 at 4400 rpm. Five main bearings. Hydraulic valve lifters. Carburetor: Rochester four-barrel.

1972 Chevrolet 1/2-Ton K5 Blazer 4x4 Sport Utility Vehicle (OCW)

1972 Chevrolet 1/2-Ton C10 Fleetside long box Pickup (Owner: Ken Buttolph)

ENGINE: [Optional El Camino SS only, RPO LS5] V-block. OHV. Eight-cylinder. Cast iron block. Bore & stroke: 4.251 in. x 4.00 in. Displacement: 454 cid. Compression ratio: 8.5:1. Net horsepower: 270 at 4000 rpm. Maximum torque: 390 lb.-ft. at 3200 rpm. Five main bearings. Hydraulic valve lifters. Carburetor: Rochester four-barrel.

CHASSIS: [LUV] Wheelbase: 102.4 in. Overall length: 173.8 in. Height: 59.3 in. Front tread: 54 in. Rear tread: 52.2 in. Tires: 6.00-14C.

CHASSIS: [Vega] Wheelbase: 97 in. Overall length: 176 in. Height: 51.8 in. Front tread: 54.8 in. Rear tread: 53.6 in. Tires: E78-14A.

CHASSIS: [El Camino] Wheelbase: 116 in. Overall length: 206.8 in. Height: 54.4 in. Front tread: 60.2 in. Rear tread: 59.2 in. Tires: E78-14B.

CHASSIS: [G10] Wheelbase: 110 in./125 in. Overall length: 178 in./202.2 in. Height 80 in. Tires: E78-14B.

CHASSIS: [G20] Wheelbase: 110 in./125 in. Overall length: 178 in./202.2 in. Height: 80 in. Tires: G78-15B.

CHASSIS: [G30] Wheelbase: 110 in./125 in. Overall length: 178 in./202.5 in. Height: 80 in. Tires: 8.75 x 16.5C.

CHASSIS: [Blazer] Wheelbase: 104 in. Overall length: 177.5 in. Height: 67.7 in. Front tread: 60.4 in. Rear tread: 60.4 in. [4x4] Tires: E78-15B.

CHASSIS: [C10] Wheelbase: 115 in./127 in. Overall length: 200.5 in. Height: 74.5 in. [115-in. wheelbase] G78-15B, [127-in. wheelbase] H78-15B.

CHASSIS: [K10] Wheelbase: 115 in./127 in. Tires: [115-in. wheelbase] G78-15B, [127-in. wheelbase] H78-15B.

CHASSIS: [P10] Wheelbase: 102 in. Height: 75 in. Tires: G78-15B.

CHASSIS: [C20] Wheelbase: 127/133 in. Overall length: 200.5 in. Height: 74.5 in. Tires: 8.75 x 16.5C.

CHASSIS: [K20] Wheelbase: 127 in. Tires: 8.75 x 16.5.

CHASSIS: [P20] Wheelbase: 125 in./133 in. Overall length: 220.75 in./244.75 in. Tires: 8.75 x 16.5C.

CHASSIS: [C30] Wheelbase: 133 in. Tires: 8.75 x 16.5.

CHASSIS: [P30] Wheelbase: 125 in./157 in. Overall length: 220.75 in./265.75 in. Tires: 8.75 x 16C.

TECHNICAL: Transmission: Three-speed synchromesh. Gears: [1-ton] 4F/1R, [Others] 3F/1R. Column-mounted gear shift lever. Single-plate, dry-disc clutch [250-cid engine], coil-spring single-dry-plate (292/307/350/402-cid engines). Rear axle: [1/2-ton] semi-floating, [3/4-ton and 1-ton] full-floating. Hydraulic four-wheel brakes. Kelsey-Hayes pressed steel wheels.

OPTIONS: [1/2-ton] 292-cid six-cylinder engine ($90). 307-cid V-8 engine ($120). 400-cid V-8 engine (average $173). 350-cid V-8 engine, El Camino ($70). Four-speed transmission ($190). Powerglide transmission (average $195). Turbo-Hydramatic transmission ($242). Power brakes ($50). Power steering (average $140). Four-wheel-drive ($575). [3/4-ton] 292-cid six-cylinder engine ($90). 307-cid V-8 engine, over six-cylinder ($120). 400-cid V-8 engine over 307 ($170). Powerglide transmission (average $210). Turbo-Hydramatic transmission (average $210). Four-speed manual transmission (average $105). Power steering (average $140). Four-wheel-drive ($660). [1-ton] 307-cid V-8 engine over six-cylinder ($120). 292-cid six-cylinder engine ($97). 350-cid V-8 engine over 307 ($45). 400-cid V-8 engine ($177). Liquid Petroleum Gas kit ($97). Turbo-Hydramatic transmission ($248). Power steering ($135). 9-ft. platform ($425). 12-ft. platform ($487). 157-in. wheelbase ($40).

C/K SERIES OPTIONS WITH FACTORY INSTALLATION RATES: Body side belt molding (33 percent). Wide lower belt molding (54 percent). Upper body side molding (46 percent). Door edge guards (17 percent). Deluxe air conditioning (33 percent). Roof-mounted air conditioning (34 percent). Custom Comfort & Appearance group (24 percent). Camper Special package (19 percent). Removable top for Blazer: black (23 percent), white (76 percent). Gauge package (81 percent). Cheyenne Super package (7 percent). Custom Sport Truck (Cheyenne) option (22 percent). [Note: The factory records say CST, even though CST wasn't merchandised in 1972. Most likely, the records were compiled after the CST name arrived and it was used to designate the same trim level]. Chrome front bumper (22 percent). V37 chrome bumper (7 percent). Rear step bumper (20 percent). Full foam seat (21 percent). Painted rear bumper (7 percent). Tachometer (2 percent). Push-button radio (60 percent). AM/FM radio (3 percent). VF1 rear chrome bumper (3 percent). Tool and storage box (6 percent). Camper wiring harness (4 percent). Cargo lamp (5 percent). Wheel trim cover (31 percent). Chrome hubcaps (16 percent). Tilt steering (9 percent). Blazer and C/K 4x4 skid plate (26 percent). Power steering (58 percent). Deluxe wheelcovers (8 percent). M38 Turbo-Hydramatic transmission (55 percent). M49 Turbo-Hydramatic transmission (28 percent). Four-speed manual transmission (13 percent). Liquid Petroleum Gas engine kit (used on 1,429 trucks). 396-V-8 engine (8 percent). 292-cid six-cylinder engine (8 percent). 350-cid V-8 engine (79 percent). 4x4 front locking hubs (86 percent). Positraction (15 percent). Bucket seats (4 percent). Front stabilizer (35 percent). Body paint stripe (6 percent). Platform and stake rack (13 percent).

G SERIES VAN OPTIONS WITH FACTORY INSTALLATION RATES: Body side trim molding (1 percent). Front air conditioning (12 percent). Rear air conditioning (4 percent). Camper conversion (113 units). Custom Appearance package (9 percent). Custom Comfort & Appearance Option (11 percent). Gauge package (60 percent). Rear chrome bumper (14 percent). Push-button radio (42 percent). Chrome hubcaps (4 percent). Tilt steering (3 percent). M38 Turbo-Hydramatic transmission (65 percent). 350-cid V-8 engine (33 percent). Positraction (12 percent). Front stabilizer (57 percent). Stainless steel Jr. West Coast mirror (14 percent). Painted Jr. West Coast mirror (50 percent). Rear door glass (57 percent). Side door glass (28 percent). Swing-out rear door glass (22 percent). Stationary auxiliary seat (87 percent). Side rear door trim panel (used on 13 units). Rear door trim panel (used on 14 units). Heavy-duty rear springs (64 percent). No-Spin rear axle (8 percent). 3.73:1 rear axle (3 percent). 3.40:1 rear axle (32 percent).

STEP-VAN OPTIONS WITH FACTORY INSTALLATION RATES: Body insulation (6 percent). Roof insulation (5 percent). Gauge package (96 percent). Cargo lamp (37 percent). Dual rear wheel conversion (88 percent). Roof marker clearance lamps (10 percent). Roof marker cluster bar (5 percent). M38 Turbo-Hydramatic transmission (7 percent). M49 Turbo-Hydramatic transmission (15 percent). Four-speed manual transmission (19 percent). Liquid Petroleum Gas engine kit (nine units). 396 V-8 engine (51 percent). 292-cid six-cylinder engine (79 percent). 350-cid V-8 engine (100 percent). Positraction (3 percent). 74 in. rear doors with piano hinges (4 percent), with straps (7 percent).

NOTE 7: All production and option use information in this section is based on Chevrolet records covering cumulative model-year through July 31, 1972. Figures indicate what percentage of trucks eligible for an option were built with it. For example, the 396-cid V-8 was not available in all Step-Vans so the 77 percent figure does not apply to total Step-Van output, only to those Step-Vans available with the 396 V-8. The production total for LUV Pickups is actually the number sold between March and December 1972.

COLOR OPTIONS: See 1970 options section for complete chart of 1970-1974 Chevrolet Commercial Truck colors.

HISTORICAL: Introduced: [LUV] March 1972, [Others] Sept. 21, 1971. Calendar-year registrations: [Nova Sportvan] 16,839. [Others] 774,871 including 165,829 Chevy Van/El Caminos/Blazer/Vega/LUV. Calendar-year registrations by weight class: [6,000 lb. and less] 539,242, [6,000-10,000 lb.] 722,379. Calendar-year production: 770,773 units or 31.10 percent share of total truck market. Calendar-year sales: 748,478. Model-year production by tons and engine: [1/2-ton] (four/six) 85,120, (V-8) 387,582, (both) 472,702. [3/4-ton] (four/six) 15,952, (V-8) 153,383, (both) 169,335. [1-ton] (four/six) 8,316, (V-8) 49,929, (both) 58,245. [Grand total] 700,282 units. Additional production breakouts: [Camper Special] 32,226, [Light truck with Custom Comfort & Convenience] 156,391, [Van with Custom Comfort & Convenience] 8,993, [Van with Custom Appearance package] 7,379. [Factory van-campers] 113, [Custom Sport Truck/Cheyenne] 142,636, [Cheyenne Supers] 40,636. Innovations: Front disc brakes made standard in light-duty trucks. Sliding load door made standard on vans. New cab trim and stain-resistant acrylic enamel paint finish. Stellite-faced exhaust valves in 350-cid and 400-cid engines. Exhaust valve rotators added to 307/350/400-cid V-8s. Four-barrel 350-cid V-8 optional in 1/2-ton vans. All-new LUV Pickup introduced. Record highs of 828,961 units produced and 845,000 units sold for 1972 broke 1971's record. During 1972, Chevrolet predicted that it would have its first one-million unit truck year in 1973. A.T. Olson was assistant general sales manager, the top spot in the truck division.

1973 CHEVROLET

1/2-TON LUV — MODEL L/SERIES 82 — FOUR: The LUV was a badge-engineered product sourced from Izusu Motors of Japan. It put Chevrolet in the mini-truck market until the arrival of the S-10 in mid-1981. Beginning early in 1973, the LUV model adopted rectangular-shaped headlamps in place of the circular units used since its 1972 introduction. The grille appeared to have a slightly finer grillwork. A unique (at the time) feature of this Mini-Pickup was a crank-down spare lowered by a chain-and-winch system.

1/2-TON VEGA — MODEL V/SERIES 14000 — FOUR: The Vega Panel Express was available again. Its grille was finished in a manner that made the vertical elements slightly less prominent. There was very little change. It was again based on the Kammback Station Wagon, with the rear side windows blanked out. It came only with the standard all-vinyl interior, less the Station Wagon's passenger bucket seat. Standard equipment included the four-cylinder aluminum block engine, three-speed manual transmission, front disc brakes, two separate stowage compartments below the floor, many safety features and a choice of colors. It had a 67.4-in. floor length, 42.6 in. between the wheelhousings, and a 68.7-cu.-ft. cargo volume. Payload capacity was 650 lb.

1972 Chevrolet cab models Highlander luxury interior (CMD)

1973 Chevrolet 1/2-Ton El Camino Sedan-Pickup (CP)

1/2-TON EL CAMINO — MODEL C, D/SERIES 13000 — SIX/V-8: The El Camino received its first new body since 1968. Accentuating its appearance, which was essentially that of the Chevelle, were two new trim packages called Estate and Conquista. The former was available on the standard El Camino and included a two-tone paint scheme and special moldings. The Estate version could be ordered only on the Classic model. It consisted of full body side and tailgate accents with a wood-grain vinyl trim. In addition, the base El Camino had its own body side, tailgate, drip rail, and wheel opening moldings.

1/2-TON, 3/4-TON, 1-TON CHEVY VAN — MODEL G/SERIES 10, 20, 30 — SIX/V-8: Chevy Vans had no exterior changes except that the blue Chevy badge was now painted ochre. The G10s and G20s had rubber bushings on the inner pivots of their front suspension for a quieter ride. The G30s had a new 5,700-lb. Salisbury axle. All series included 110-in. and 125-in. wheelbases. A V-8 was standard in Beauvilles.

1/2-TON BLAZER UTILITY — MODEL C, K/SERIES 5 — SIX/V-8: The 1973 Blazers had a full-time 4x4 system. Those with Cheyenne trim had a chrome circle on the rear fender. The tailgate came two ways. With the Open Utility it was like the Fleetside Pickup's gate. When the optional hardtop was ordered, the gate had a manually-operated roll-up window. This eliminated the lift-gate that had been used in older tops

1973 Chevrolet 3/4-Ton C20 Cheyenne Carryall Suburban (CP)

1/2-TON, 3/4-TON, 1-TON CONVENTIONAL — MODEL C, K/SERIES 10, 20, 30 — SIX/V-8: The 1973 Chevrolet light trucks were radically changed in appearance from previous models. Major styling features consisted of curved side glass, doors that opened into the roof line, and the elimination of roof drip rails. Running along the belt line was a sculptured cove. Along with the very wide and flat load box, it gave the new model very clean and distinctive lines. Also contributing to the Chevrolet's good looks was a simple eggcrate grille suggestive of the classic 1955 Chevrolet passenger car grille. A wider interior featured a powered, flow-through ventilation system. A redesigned dash, with all instruments and controls placed in a semi-circular cluster within easy reach and view of the driver, was adopted. The steering wheel was also reduced in diameter. All models had longer wheelbases. The C10/K10 Pickups with a 6-1/2-ft. box came on the standard 117-1/2-in. wheelbase, which was used only for these models and small chassis models. The C10/K10 Pickups with an 8-ft. box featured a 131-1/2-in. wheelbase. This wheelbase was also used for 1/2-ton chassis models and all basic C30 models. The C20/K20 trucks, except Carryall Suburbans, were on a 127-in. wheelbase. All Carryall Suburbans, both 1/2-ton and 3/4-ton, were on a 129.5-in. wheelbase. Longer wheelbases were provided for Chassis-and-Cab and the new Crew-Cab trucks. Crew-Cab bodies that seated six could be had as an option on all 3/4-ton and 1-ton Pickups. The Crew-Cab was actually an option costing about $1,000. The box used for factory-made Crew-Cab Pickups was the 8-ft. Fleetside box. There were numerous other technical changes. C10 models used rubber control arm bushings for a quieter and smoother ride. Leaf-springs replaced the rear coil springs used in 1972 on C10/C20 models. Four-wheel-drive models were fitted with longer front springs and a standard front stabilizer bar. All of the Pickups now used a Salisbury rear end. Only the C10 had this feature before. On C20 and C30 Pickups an Eaton locking differential was optional. It locked in upon a 100 rpm difference in the rear axles and had a governor to keep it from locking-in at above 15 mph. Gas tanks were moved from inside the cabs to under them at the rear. Full-time four-wheel-drive was introduced. It was available with only the V-8/Turbo-Hydramatic power train. All 1972 models except the Longhorn Pickup were continued. The C10 with 6-1/2-ft. bed was nicknamed the "Fleetwood." This truck name is rarely heard today. Available trim levels included Custom, Custom Deluxe, Cheyenne, and Cheyenne Super. The features of each level were as follows: [Base Custom] Plain black rubber window gaskets and white-painted bumpers. The grille shell had bright metal finish. The vent window pillars and frames were flat black. The standard hubcaps were painted. Rear moldings around the taillamps and tailgate were not available on Customs. [Custom Deluxe] Included full-width bench seat with comfortably padded seat cushions and back rest, vinyl seat upholstery and door panels, steel roof panel

painted in main exterior color, black rubber floor mat extending to firewall, padded arm rests, padded sun shades, courtesy lamp, prismatic rear view mirror, foam-padded instrument panel, bright upper and lower grille outline moldings, bright headlamp bezels, bright outside rear view mirrors, bright door handles, white-painted front bumper, hubcaps and wheels, and bright Custom Deluxe nameplates. [Cheyenne] Included bench seat with full-depth foam cushions and back rests, custom-grained vinyl upholstery or nylon-and-vinyl upholstery, special door trim panels, cab headliner, deep-twist nylon carpeting extending to firewall, color-keyed garnish moldings, ash tray-mounted cigar lighter, Custom steering wheel, Cheyenne dashboard nameplates, door- or manually-operated courtesy lights, extra acoustical insulation, and all Custom Deluxe exterior items, plus cab-mounted cargo lamp, bright metal cab trim and moldings, bright upper body side and tailgate moldings, and central taillight appliqués for Fleetside and Cheyenne nameplates. [Cheyenne Super] Added upper, lower body side and wheelhouse moldings and a chrome-plated tailgate release. Cheyenne Super nameplates on front fender sides and dash. A new offering was the "Big Doolie" type C30 Pickup with dual rear wheels.

1/2-TON, 3/4-TON, 1-TON FORWARD-CONTROL — MODEL P/SERIES 10, 20, 30 — SIX/V-8: The Forward-Control chassis was designed for door-to-door delivery service. Body lengths ranged from seven to eight feet for the P10 series up to 14 ft. in the P30 series. Step-Vans looked identical to 1972 versions. The P10 models were sold in chassis and steel panel models on a 102-in. wheelbase. These were advertised as Step Van 7 models (due to their seven-foot long bodies). The P20 and P30 series offered larger chassis, plus Step-Van and Step-Van King models with steel or aluminum bodies. The basic body lengths were 10 ft. for the 125-in. wheelbase chassis, 12 ft. for the 133-in. wheelbase, and 14 ft. for the 157 in. chassis. The P30 chassis was also used for Chevrolet's new High-Cube vans and numerous custom motorhome conversions. The Step-Van grilles had single round headlights in the top of the housings, with rectangular parking lamps below. Features included independent coil spring front suspension, and three six-cylinder engines. Buyers could also get full-height doors, sliding side doors, and double rear doors.

I.D. DATA: Serial number located. Combination VIN and rating plate located on left door pillar. [El Camino] First symbol indicates manufacturer, 1=Chevrolet. Second symbol indicates car-line/series: C=El Camino, D=El Camino Custom. Third and fourth symbols indicate body type: 80=Sedan-Pickup. Fifth symbol indicates engine: 1[El Camino] H=350-cid/145-nhp two-barrel V-8, L=350-cid/160-nhp four-barrel V-8, R=400-cid/150-nhp two-barrel V-8, U=402-cid/180-nhp four-barrel V-8, Y=454-cid/235-nhp four-barrel V-8. Sixth symbol indicates model-year: 3=1973. Seventh symbol indicates assembly plant. Symbols 8-13 indicate the production sequence number starting at 100,001. Ending numbers not available. [All Light-Duty] The first symbol indicates manufacturer: 1=Chevrolet Motor Div. The second symbol indicates chassis type: C=96 in. or 106 in. Conventional Cab, G=Sportvan, H=92 in. Conventional Cab, J=92 in. Conventional Cab with tandem, K=4x4, L=Light-Utility, M=96 in. or 114 in. Conventional Cab with tandem, P=Forward-Control, Z=Motorhome. The third symbol indicates engine as follows: L=454-cid/245-nhp four-barrel V-8, N=110-cid/75-nhp two-barrel L4, Q=250-cid/100-nhp one-barrel L-6, S=292-cid L-6 with LPG conversion, T=292-cid/120-hp one-barrel L-6, X=307-cid/120-nhp two-barrel V-8, Y=350-cid/145-nhp two-barrel V-8, W=350-cid V-8 with LPG conversion, Y=350-cid/160-nhp four-barrel V-8, Z=454-cid/235-nhp four-barrel V-8. The fourth symbol indicates series and tonnage: 1=1/2-ton, 2=3/4-ton, 3=1-ton. The fifth symbol indicates body type: 2=Chassis-and-Cowl, 3=Chassis-and-Cab or Motorhome Chassis, 4=Cab with pickup box, 5=Panel or Panel Van, 6=Sportvan, 7=Motorhome, 8=Blazer. The sixth symbol indicated model-year: 3=1973. The seventh symbol indicates the assembly plant: A=Lakewood, Ga., B=Baltimore, Md., F=Flint, Mich., J=Janesville, Wis., K=Leeds, Mo., U=Lordstown, Ohio, V=Pontiac, Mich., , Z=Fremont, Calif., 1=Oshawa, Canada, 3=GMAD, Detroit, Mich., 8=Fujisawa, Japan. Symbols 8-13 are the production sequence number. Starting number: 10001 Ending numbers not available. Engine numbers located: [Six] on pad at right-hand side of cylinder block at rear of distributor, [V-8] on pad at front, right-hand side of cylinder block.

1973 Chevrolet Cheyenne Fleetside Pickup (DFW/TSC)

Model	Body Type	Price	Weight	Prod. Total
1/2-Ton LUV — Model L/Series 82 — 102.4 in. w.b.				
82	Mini-Pickup	2406	2450	18,771
1/2-Ton Vega — Model HV/Series 14000 — 97 in. w.b. -Four				
1HV05	Panel Express	2106	2303	-
El Camino — Model C/Series 13000 — 116 in. w.b. — Six				
1AC80	Sedan-Pickup	2976	3725	Note 1
El Camino Custom — Model D/Series 13000 — 116 in. w.b. — V-8				
1AD80	Custom Sedan-Pickup	3038	3735	Note 1
NOTE 1: Total El Camino production was 64,987.				
1/2-Ton Van — Model G/Series 10 — 110 in. w.b.				
CG11005	Chevy Van	2818	3486	13,408
CG11006	Sportvan	3331	3790	1,111
1/2-Ton Van — Model G/Series 10 — 110 in. w.b. — V-8				
CG11036	Beauville	3785	4078	475
1/2-Ton Van — Model G/Series 10 — 125 in. w.b.				
CG11305	Panel	2954	3651	13,956
CG11306	Sportvan	3455	3960	1,936
1/2-Ton Van — Model G/Series 10 — 125 in. w.b. — V-8				
CG11336	Beauville	3910	4308	1,045
3/4-Ton Van — Model G/Series 20 — 110 in. w.b.				
CG21005	Panel	2929	3582	5,988
CG21006	Sportvan	3381	3825	552
3/4-Ton Van — Model G/Series 20 — 110 in. w.b. — V-8				
CG21036	Beauville	3861	4150	299
3/4-Ton Van — Model G/Series 20 — 125 in. w.b.				
CG21305	Panel	3064	3708	20,515
CG21306	Sportvan	3505	3994	3,966

Model	Body Type	Price	Weight	Prod. Total
3/4-Ton Van — Model G/Series 20 — 125 in. w.b. — V-8				
CG21336	Beauville	3986	4379	7,750
1-Ton Van — Model G/Series 30 — 110 in. w.b.				
CG31005	Panel	3038	3886	596
1-Ton Van — Model G/Series 30 — 125 in. w.b. — V-8				
CG31305	Chevy Van	3173	3988	13,420
CG31306	Sportvan	3622	4282	2,307
1-Ton Van — Model G/Series 30 — 125 in. w.b. — V-8				
CG31336	Beauville	4102	4667	1,999
1/2-Ton Blazer 4x2 — Model C/Series 5 — 106.5 in. w.b.				
CC10514	Open Utility	2637	3595	3,342
1/2-Ton Blazer 4x4 — Model K/Series 5 — 106.5 in. w.b.				
CK10514	Open Utility	3200	3912	44,841
1/2-Ton Conventional — Model C/Series 10 — 117.5 in. w.b.				
CC10703	Chassis & Cab	2577	3234	1,922
CC10704	Step-Side 6.5 ft.	2763	3664	19,408
CC10734	Fleetside 6.5 ft.	2763	3560	43,987
1/2-Ton Carryall Suburban — Model C/Series 10 — 129.5 in. w.b.				
CC10906	Suburban (doors)	3560	4195	6,822
CC10916	Suburban (gate)	3590	4203	17,278
1/2-Ton Conventional — Model C/Series 10 — 131.5 in. w.b.				
CC10903	Chassis & Cab	2608	3331	877
CC10904	Step-Side 8 ft.	2799	3836	7,040
CC10934	Fleetside 8 ft.	2799	3726	309,085
1/2-Ton Conventional 4x4 — Model K/Series 10 — 117.5 in. w.b.				
CK10703	Step-Side 6.5 ft.	3510	3989	2,112
CK10703	Fleetside 6.5 ft.	3510	4108	9,605
1/2-Ton Conventional 4x4 — Model K/Series 10 — 129.5 in. w.b.				
CK10906	Suburban (doors)	4338	5200	1,128
CK10916	Suburban (gate)	-	-	3,770
1/2-Ton Conventional 4x4 — Model K/Series 10 — 131.5 in. w.b.				
CK10903	Step-Side 8 ft.	3546	4085	417
CK10903	Fleetside 8 ft.	3546	4210	29,157
1/2-Ton Forward-Control — Model P/Series 10 — 102 in. w.b.				
CP10542	Chassis	2090	2318	281
CP10542	Steel Step-Van	3458	4161	2,877
3/4-Ton Conventional — Model C/Series 20 — 131.5 in. w.b.				
CC20903	Chassis & Cab	2815	3637	8,162
CC20903	Step-Side 8 ft.	3001	4142	4,654
CC20903	Fleetside 8 ft.	3001	4032	131,624
3/4-Ton Conventional — Model C/Series 20 — 129.5 in. w.b.				
CC20906	Suburban (doors)	4009	4817	2,424
CC20916	Suburban (gate)	4040	4825	7,368
NOTE 2: Stake option included with C20 Chassis-and-Cab production.				
3/4-Ton Crew-Cab — Model C/Series 20 — 164.5 in. w.b.				
CE20963	Crew-Cab Chassis	-	-	712
CE20963	Crew-Cab Pickup 8 ft.	4001	-	7,137
NOTE 3: Crew-Cab Model 963 was an option, average price $1,000.				
3/4-Ton Conventional 4x4 — Model K/Series 20 — 131.5 in. w.b.				
CK20903	Chassis & Cab	3562	4119	880
CK20904	Step-Side 8 ft.	3747	4514	525
CK20934	Fleetside 8 ft.	3747	4640	29,769
3/4-Ton Conventional 4x4 — Model K/Series 20 — 129.5 in. w.b.				
CK20906	Suburban (doors)	4668	5136	780
CK20916	Suburban (gate)	-	-	1,862
3/4-Ton Forward Control — Model P/Series 20 — 125 in. w.b.				
CP20842	Chassis	2295	2902	409
CP20835	Steel Step-Van	4115	5310	2,099
CP20855	Alum. Step-Van King	-	-	107
3/4-Ton Forward Control — Model P/Series 20 — 133 in. w.b.				
CP21042	Chassis	2326	2942	156
CP21035	Steel Step-Van	4222	5559	1,282
CP21035	Alum. Step-Van King	5015	4841	58
1-Ton Conventional — Model C/Series 30 — 131.5 in. w.b.				
CC30903	Chassis & Cab	3075	3811	17,422
CC30903	Step-Side 8 ft.	3087	4321	1,939
CC30903	Fleetside 8 ft.	3087	4246	7,281
NOTE 3: Stake option included with C30 Chassis-and-Cab production.				
1-Ton Conventional — Model C/Series 30 — 135.5 in. w.b.				
CC31063	Crew-Cab Fleetside	2915	3811	479
1-Ton Conventional — Model C/Series 30 — 159.5 in. w.b.				
CC31403	Crew-Cab & Chassis	2955	3934	12,088
1-Ton Conventional — Model C/Series 30 — 164.5 in. w.b.				
CC31963	Crew-Cab & Chassis	-	-	80
CC31963	Crew-Cab Fleetside	-	-	2,925
1-Ton Forward-Control — Model P/Series 30 — 125 in. w.b.				
CP30842	Chassis 10 ft.	2469	2992	649
CP30842	Steel Step-Van 10	4284	5379	631
CP30842	Alum. Step-Van King 10	-	-	118
CP30842	Motorhome Chassis	-	-	2,341
1-Ton Forward-Control — Model P/Series 30 — 133 in. w.b.				
CP31042	Chassis	2500	3015	-
CP31042	Steel Step-Van King 12	4392	5611	2,522
CP31042	Alum. Step-Van King 12	-	-	244
CP31042	Motorhome Chassis	3285	3254	1,093
1-Ton Forward-Control — Model P/Series 30 — 157 in. w.b.				
CP31442	Chassis	-	-	-
CP31442	Steel Step-Van King 14	-	6677	2,395
CP31442	Alum. Step-Van King 14	-	5714	526
CP31142	Motorhome Chassis	3821	3383	4,160

NOTE 4: Model codes, prices and weights on charts are for sixes, except where model is a V-8 only truck.

NOTE 5: Detailed Chevrolet records show above production totals with separate breakouts for country of origin and type of engine. To put these in a convenient format, the totals above show combined U.S. output, plus imports from Canada. They include both six-cylinder and V-8 trucks. The model codes no longer indicate type of engine.

NOTE 6: Platform/stake options, big-block V-8s, diesel engines, and LPG conversions were options. See the options section below for partial data on options usage.

NOTE 7: Additional C30 1-ton production included 1,093 motorhomes on a 127-in. wheelbase, 7,194 motorhomes on a 158.5-in. wheelbase, and 115 motorhomes on a 178-in. wheelbase.

1973 Chevrolet 1/2-Ton C10 Cheyenne Fleetside short box Pickup (CP)

ENGINE: [Standard: LUV] Inline. OHV. Four-cylinder. Cast iron block. Bore & stroke: 3.31 in. x 3.23 in. Displacement: 110.8 cid. Compression ratio: 8.5:1. Net horsepower: 75 at 5000 rpm. Maximum torque: 88 lb.-ft. at 3000 rpm. Five main bearings. Hydraulic valve lifters. Carburetor: two-barrel.
ENGINE: [Standard: Vega] Inline. OHV. Four-cylinder. Aluminum block. Bore & stroke: 3.501 in. x 3.625 in. Displacement: 140 cid. Compression ratio: 8.0:1. Net horsepower: 72 at 4200 rpm. Maximum torque: 115 lb.-ft. at 2400 rpm. Five main bearings. Hydraulic valve lifters. Carburetor: one-barrel.
ENGINE: [Optional: Vega] Inline. OHV. Four-cylinder. Aluminum block. Bore & stroke: 3.501 in. x 3.625 in. Displacement: 140 cid. Compression ratio: 8.0:1. Net horsepower: 85 at 4400 rpm. Maximum torque: 122 lb.-ft. at 2400 rpm. Five main bearings. Hydraulic valve lifters. Carburetor: Staged two-barrel.

1973 Chevrolet Vega Panel Express (CP)

ENGINE: [Standard: all, except El Camino/LUV/Vega/K20-30/ C20] Inline. OHV. Six-cylinder. Cast iron block. Bore & stroke: 3-7/8 in. x 3-1/2 in. Displacement: 250 cid. Compression ratio: 8.25:1. Net horsepower: 100 at 3600 rpm. Maximum torque: 175 lb.-ft. at 2000 rpm. Seven main bearings. Hydraulic valve lifters. Carburetor: Rochester one-barrel.
ENGINE: [Optional: C/K Series/P20-30] Inline. OHV. Six-cylinder. Cast iron block. Bore & stroke: 3-7/8 in. x 4-1/8 in. Displacement: 292 cid. Compression ratio: 8.0:1. Net horsepower: 120 at 3600 rpm. Maximum torque: 225 lb.-ft. at 2000 rpm. Seven main bearings. Hydraulic valve lifters. Carburetor: one-barrel.
ENGINE: [Optional: C10/Blazer/G10/P Series, Standard El Camino] V-block. OHV. Eight-cylinder. Cast iron block. Bore & stroke: 3-7/8 in. x 3-1/4 in. Displacement: 307 cid. Compression ratio: 8.5:1. Net horsepower: 115 at 3600 rpm. Maximum torque: 205 lb.-ft. at 2000 rpm. Five main bearings. Hydraulic valve lifters. Carburetor: two-barrel.

1973 Chevrolet 3/4-Ton C20 Cheyenne Carryall Suburban (IMSC/JM)

ENGINE: [Standard: C20/K20/K30, Optional: G10/G20/G30/P Series/ El Camino] V-block. OHV. Eight-cylinder. Cast iron block. Bore & stroke: 4 in. x 3.48 in. Displacement: 350 cid. Compression ratio: 8.5:1. Net horsepower: 155 at 4000 rpm. Maximum torque: 225 lb.-ft. at 2400 rpm. Five main bearings. Hydraulic valve lifters. Carburetor: two-barrel.
ENGINE: [Optional: El Camino] V-block. OHV. Eight-cylinder. Cast iron block. Bore & stroke: 4 in. x 3.48 in. Displacement: 350 cid. Compression ratio: 8.5:1. Net horsepower: 175 at 4000 rpm. Maximum torque: 260 lb.-ft. at 2800 rpm. Five main bearings. Hydraulic valve lifters. Carburetor: Rochester model Quadra-Jet, four-barrel.

ENGINE: [Optional: El Camino/C20/C30/Carryall Suburban 4x2/ P30] V-block. OHV. Eight-cylinder. Cast iron block. Bore & stroke: 4.251 in. x 4.0 in. Displacement: 454 cid. Compression ratio: 8.25:1. Net horsepower: 240 at 4000 rpm. Maximum torque: 355 lb.-ft. at 2800 rpm. Five main bearings. Hydraulic valve lifters. Carburetor: Rochester model Quadra-Jet, four-barrel.
CHASSIS: [LUV] Wheelbase: 102.4 in. Overall length: 173.8 in. Height: 59.3 in. Front tread: 54 in. Rear tread: 52.2 in. Tires: A78-13B.
CHASSIS: [Vega] Wheelbase: 97 in. Overall length: 176 in. Height: 51.8 in. Front tread: 54.8 in. Rear tread: 53.6 in. Tires: A78-13B.
CHASSIS: [El Camino] Wheelbase: 116 in. Overall length: 201.6 in. Height: 53.8 in. Front tread: 58.5 in. Rear tread: 57.8 in. Tires: G78-14B.
CHASSIS: [All Carryall Suburbans] Wheelbase: 129.5 in. Tires: H78-15B.
CHASSIS: [G10] Wheelbase: 110/125 in. Overall length: 178/202.2 in. Tires: E78-14A.
CHASSIS: [G20] Wheelbase: 110/125 in. Overall length: 178/202.2 in. Tires: G78-15B.
CHASSIS: [G30] Wheelbase: 110/125 in. Overall length: 178/202.2 in. Tires: 8.00 x 16.5C.

1973 Chevrolet 1/2-Ton K5 Blazer 4x4 Sport Utility Vehicle (JAG)

CHASSIS: [Blazer] Wheelbase: 106.5 in. Overall length: 184.5 in. Height: [4x2 without top] 67.5 in., [4x2 with top] 69.5, [4x4 without top] 69.5, [4x4 with top] 71.5. Front tread: [4x2] 64.5 in. Rear tread: [4x2] 63.0 in. Front tread: [4x4] 65.75 in. Rear tread: [4x4] 62.75 in. Tires: E78-15B.
CHASSIS: [C10] Wheelbase: 117.5 in./131.5 in. Overall length: 191.2/212 in. Height: 69.8 in. Front tread: 65.8 in. Rear tread: 62.7 in. Tires: G78-15B.
CHASSIS: [K10] Wheelbase: 117.5 in./131.5 in. Overall length: 191.3/212 in. Height: 72 in. Front tread: 65.8 in. Rear tread: 62.7 in. Tires: G78-15B.
CHASSIS: [P10] Wheelbase: 102 in. Height: 75 in. Tires: G78-15B.
CHASSIS: [C20] Wheelbase: 117.5 in./131.5/164.5 in. Overall length: 191.5 in./212 in./244.43 in. Height: 69.8 in. Front tread: 65.8 in. Rear tread: 62.7 in.
CHASSIS: [K20] Wheelbase: 117.5 in./131.5 in. Overall length: 191.3 in./212 in. Height: 73.9 in. Front tread: 65.8 in. Rear tread: 62.7 in. Tires: 8.75 x 16.5C.
CHASSIS: [P20] Wheelbase: 125 in./133 in. Overall length: 220.75 in./244.75 in. Tires: 8.75 x 16.5C.
CHASSIS: [C30] Wheelbase: 131.5 in./164.5 in. Overall length: 212 in./244.43 in. Height: 71.8 in. Front tread: 65.8 in. Rear tread: 62.7 in. Tires: [Regular cab] 8.75 x 16.5C, [Crew-Cab] 9.50 x 16.5E.
CHASSIS: [P30] Wheelbase: 125/157 in. Overall length: 220.75 in./265.75 in. Tires: 8.75 x 16.5C.
TECHNICAL: Transmission: Three-speed synchromesh. Gears: [1-ton] 4F/1R, [Others] 3F/1R. Column-mounted gear shift lever. Single-plate, dry-disc clutch [250-cid engine], coil-spring single-dry-plate (292/307/350/402-cid engines). Rear axle: [1/2-ton] semi-floating, [3/4-ton and 1-ton] full-floating. Hydraulic four-wheel brakes. Kelsey-Hayes pressed steel wheels.
TRUCK OPTIONS: Front chrome bumper. Radio AM, AM/FM. Clock. Power steering. Custom deluxe interior. Cheyenne interior. Cheyenne super interior. Below-Eye-Line mirrors. Drip moldings. Sliding rear window. Cargo lamp. Gauge package. Air conditioning. Tachometer. Comfortilt steering wheel. Chrome bumper. Exterior tool and storage compartment. wheelcovers. White wall tires. Special trim molding. Wood-grain exterior trim. Rear-step bumper. Glide-out spare tire carrier. [Vega] Special ride and handling package. Rear window air deflector.
COLOR OPTIONS: See 1970 options section for complete chart of 1970-1974 Chevrolet Commercial Truck colors.
HISTORICAL: Calendar-year sales: 923,189. First year for 454-cid V-8 option for standard trucks. Salisbury rear axle optional. Six-passenger model introduced. Fuel tank relocated outside cab to a position on the right frame rail. New energy-absorbing steering column.

1974 CHEVROLET

1/2-TON LUV — MODEL L/SERIES 82 — FOUR: The LUV for 1974 adopted vertical taillights with a square back-up light lens at the bottom. A Mikado trim package with striped upholstery and a sporty three-spoke steering wheel was available.
1/2-TON VEGA — MODEL V/SERIES 14000 — FOUR: The Vega Panel Express had a new front end with a divided four-louver grille and recessed headlamps. Parking lamps moved from under the bumper to between the headlamps and grille. They changed from round to a tall rectangular shape. The front and rear side marker lamps were raised above bumper level and the rear license plate was now housed in the tailgate center, instead of below the bumper (the bumper was a thicker five mile per hour crash-test type). The Vega Panel Express had the same large swing-up tailgate arrangement as the Kammback Station Wagon. The Chevrolet brochure described it as an economy truck. It still came with just one bucket seat, rubber floor coverings and no side windows. Maximum cargo capacity was 50.2 cu.-ft. All 14 Vega color combinations were available. The Panel Express used the standard interior (without dash grab handle) in choices of black, neutral, green, saddle, red, and chamois colors. Technical improvements included front brake lining wear sensors, electric windshield washer, and a new 16-gallon gas tank. It held five more gallons of fuel than 1973. Interestingly, Chevrolet used the same artwork in the catalog illustration both years, airbrushing in the minor changes and adding "T. Tonies Bakery" lettering in the panel sides.

1974 Chevrolet Vega Panel Express (DFW)

1/2-TON CAMINO — MODEL C, D/SERIES 13000 — SIX/V-8: EL The El Camino continued to be a model of the Malibu series and carried a grille with obvious Mercedes-Benz overtones. The grille was split into six horizontal segments, three on each side of a vertical center molding. A new Classic model was added to the El Camino line. It featured a bright lower body sill molding, a full-width custom seat with a fold-down center arm rest, door panel trim, deluxe vinyl-coated headliner, and a black-finished rear view mirror.

1974 Chevrolet 1/2-Ton El Camino SS Sedan-Pickup (DFW)

1/2-TON, 3/4-TON, 1-TON VAN — MODEL G/SERIES 10, 20, 30 — SIX/V-8: Chevy Vans and Sportvans were offered with a new two-tone paint treatment. Also new were improved optional below-eye-line mirrors, and new optional bright roof drip moldings. Both models also had a restyled instrument cluster and panel, as well as a new optional air conditioning system with air outlets designed into the instrument panel. An AM/FM radio, not previously available, was new for 1974. All vans now had a coolant recovery system, too.

1974 Chevrolet 1/2-Ton K5 Blazer 4x4 Sport Utility Vehicle (CP)

1/2-TON BLAZER UTILITY — MODEL C, K/SERIES 5 — SIX/V-8: The Blazer continued with the 106.5-in. wheelbase introduced in 1973. New was a factory-padded roll bar. The limited-slip differential could be ordered with the full-time four-wheel-drive system. Steel-belted radial tires were added to the option list.

1974 Chevrolet 1/2-Ton K10 Fleetside 4x4 Pickup (RCA)

1974 Chevrolet 1/2-Ton C10 Custom Deluxe Fleetside Pickup (IMSC/JM)

1/2-TON, 3/4-TON, 1-TON CONVENTIONAL — MODEL C, K/SERIES 10, 20, 30 — SIX/V-8: After being totally restyled in 1973, the latest Chevrolet Pickups and Carryall Suburbans were visually virtually unchanged. Exterior changes were highlighted by four new colors, improved below-eye-line mirrors and new optional bright roof drip moldings. The C10/K10 Pickups with a 6-1/2-ft. box came on the standard 117-1/2-in. wheelbase, which was used only for these models and small chassis models. The C10/K10 Pickups with an 8-ft. box featured a 131-1/2-in. wheelbase. This wheelbase was also used for 1/2-ton chassis models and all basic C30 models. The C20/K20 trucks, except Carryall Suburbans, were on a 127-in. wheelbase. All Carryall Suburbans, both 1/2-ton and 3/4-ton, were on a 129.5-in. wheelbase. Longer wheelbases were provided for Chassis-and-Cab and Crew-Cab trucks. Crew-Cab bodies that seated six, could be had as an option on all 3/4-ton and 1-ton Pickups. The Crew-Cab was actually an option costing about $1,000. The box used for factory-made Crew-Cab Pickups was the 8-ft. Fleetside box. Technical developments included use of a full-time unit on all V-8-engined 4x4 drive models and the computer-matching of all brake systems to the GVW rating of each truck. The new braking system included a lining sensor on the front disc brakes. It sounded an audible signal when the pads needed replacement. In addition, all Pickups had larger front disc and rear drum brakes, as well as a new hydraulic booster power assist called Hydro-boost. Interior refinements included foam instrument panel padding with all trim levels. All models had an energy-absorbing steering column and, on all models with automatic transmission, an anti-theft ignition system was used.

1974 Chevrolet 1-Ton G30 Hi-Cube Van (CMD)

1/2-TON, 3/4-TON, 1-TON FORWARD-CONTROL — MODEL P/SERIES 10, 20, 30 — SIX/V-8: The Forward-Control chassis was designed for door-to-door delivery service. Body lengths ranged from seven to eight feet for the P10 series up to 14 ft. in the P30 series. Step-Vans looked identical to 1973 versions. The P20 and P30 series offered larger chassis, plus Step-Van and Step-Van King models with steel or aluminum bodies. The basic body lengths were 10 ft. for the 125-in. wheelbase chassis, 12 ft. for the 133-in. wheelbase, and 14 ft. for the 157-in. chassis. The P30 chassis was also used for Chevrolet's new High-Cube vans and numerous custom motorhome conversions.

1974 Chevrolet 1/2-Ton K5 Blazer 4x4 Sport Utility Vehicle (RCA)

I.D. DATA: Serial number located. Combination VIN and rating plate located on left door pillar. [El Camino] First symbol indicates manufacturer, 1=Chevrolet. Second symbol indicates car-line/series: C=El Camino, D=El Camino Custom. Third and fourth symbols indicate body type: 80=Sedan-Pickup. Fifth symbol indicates engine: 1[El Camino] H=350-cid/145-nhp two-barrel V-8, L=350-cid/160-nhp four-barrel V-8, R=400-cid/150-hp two-barrel V-8, U=402-cid/180-nhp four-barrel V-8, Y=454-cid/235-nhp four-barrel V-8. Sixth symbol indicates model-year: 4=1974. Seventh symbol indicates assembly plant. Symbols 8-13 indicate the production sequence number starting at 100,001. Ending numbers not available. [All Light-Duty] The first symbol indicates manufacturer: 1=Chevrolet Motor Div. The second symbol indicates chassis type: C=96 in. or 106 in. Conventional Cab, G=Sportvan, H=92 in. Conventional Cab, J=92 in. Conventional Cab with tandem, K=4x4, L=Light-Utility, M=96 in. or 114 in. Conventional Cab with tandem, P=Forward-Control, Z=Motorhome. The third symbol indicates engine as follows: L=454-cid/245-nhp four-barrel V-8, N=110-cid/75-nhp two-barrel L4, Q=250-cid/100-nhp one-barrel L-6, S=292-cid L-6 with LPG conversion, T=292-cid/120-hp one-barrel L-6, X=307-cid/120-nhp two-barrel V-8, Y=350-cid/145-nhp two-barrel V-8, W=350-cid V-8 with LPG conversion, Y=350-cid/160-nhp four-barrel V-8, Z=454-cid/235-nhp four-barrel V-8. The fourth symbol indicates series and tonnage: 1-1/2-ton, 2=3/4-ton, 3=1-ton. The fifth symbol indicates body type: 2=Chassis & Cowl, 3=Chassis-and-Cab or Motorhome Chassis, 4=Cab with pickup box, 5=Panel or Panel Van, 6=Sportvan, 7=Motorhome, 8=Blazer. The sixth symbol indicated model-year: 4=1974. The seventh symbol indicates the assembly plant: A=Lakewood, Ga., B=Baltimore, Md., F=Flint, Mich., J=Janesville, Wis., K=Leeds, Mo., U=Lordstown, Ohio, V=Pontiac, Mich., , Z=Fremont, Calif., 1=Oshawa, Canada, 3=GMAD, Detroit, Mich., 8=Fujisawa, Japan. Symbols 8-13 are the production sequence number. Starting number: 10001 Ending numbers not available. Engine numbers located: [Six] on pad at right-hand side of cylinder block at rear of distributor, [V-8] on pad at front, right-hand side of cylinder block.

1974 Chevrolet 1/2-Ton K10 Fleetside 4x4 Pickup (JAG)

Model	Body Type	Price	Weight	Prod. Total
1/2-Ton LUV — Model L/Series 82 — 102.4 in. w.b.				
82	Mini-Pickup	2406	2475	Note 1
1/2-Ton Vega — Model HV/Series 14000 — 97 in. w.b. -Four				
1HV05	Panel Express	2404	2470	-
El Camino — Model C/Series 13000 — 116 in. w.b. — Six				
1AC80	Sedan-Pickup	3139	3950	Note 2
El Camino Classic- Model D/Series 13000 — 116 in. w.b. — V-8				
1AD80	Classic Sedan-Pickup	3277	3975	Note 2
1/2-Ton Sportvan — Model G/Series 10 — 110 in. w.b.				
CG11005	Chevy Van	3092	3479	Note 3
CG11006	Sportvan	3721	3806	Note 3
1/2-Ton Chevy Van — Model G/Series 10 — 110 in. w.b. — V-8				
CG11036	Beauville	4232	4109	Note 3
1/2-Ton Chevy Van — Model G/Series 10 — 125 in. w.b.				
CG11305	Panel	3228	3638	Note 3
CG11306	Sportvan	3856	3974	Note 3
1/2-Ton Chevy Van — Model G/Series 10 — 125 in. w.b. — V-8				
CG11336	Beauville	4384	4331	Note 3
3/4-Ton Chevy Van — Model G/Series 20 — 110 in. w.b.				
CG21005	Panel	3214	3576	Note 3
CG21006	Sportvan	3802	3861	Note 3
3/4-Ton Chevy Van — Model G/Series 20 — 110 in. w.b. — V-8				
CG21036	Beauville	4330	4168	Note 3
3/4-Ton Chevy Van — Model G/Series 20 — 125 in. w.b.				
CG21305	Panel	3349	3716	Note 3
CG21306	Sportvan	3937	4021	Note 3
3/4-Ton Chevy Van — Model G/Series 20 — 125 in. w.b. — V-8				
CG21336	Beauville	4465	4378	Note 3
1-Ton Chevy Van — Model G/Series 30 — 110 in. w.b.				
CG31005	Panel	3332	3860	Note 3
1-Ton Chevy Van — Model G/Series 30 — 125 in. w.b. — V-8				
CG31305	Chevy Van	3467	4007	Note 3
CG31306	Sportvan	4037	4331	Note 3
1-Ton Chevy Van — Model G/Series 30 — 125 in. w.b. — V-8				
CG31336	Beauville	4585	4688	Note 3
1/2-Ton Blazer 4x4 — Model C/Series 5 — 106.5 in. w.b.				
CC10514	Open Utility	2936	3606	Note 3
1/2-Ton Blazer 4x4 — Model K/Series 5 — 106.5 in. w.b.				
CK10514	Open Utility	3577	3931	Note 3
1/2-Ton Conventional — Model C/Series 10 — 117.5 in. w.b.				
CC10703	Step-Side 6.5 ft.	2971	3563	Note 3
CC10703	Fleetside 6.5 ft.	2971	3664	Note 3
1/2-Ton Carryall Suburban — Model C/Series 10 — 129.5 in. w.b.				
CC10906	Suburban (doors)	3832	4177	Note 3
CC10916	Suburban (gate)	3863	4185	Note 3
1/2-Ton Conventional — Model C/Series 10 — 131.5 in. w.b.				
CC10903	Chassis & Cab	3104	3669	Note 3
CC10904	Step-Side 8 ft.	3007	3711	Note 3
CC10934	Fleetside 8 ft.	3007	3821	Note 3
1/2-Ton Conventional 4x4 — Model K/Series 10 — 117.5 in. w.b				
CK10703	Step-Side 6.5 ft.	3703	3973	Note 3
CK10703	Fleetside 6.5 ft.	3703	4077	Note 3

Model	Body Type	Price	Weight	Prod. Total
1/2-Ton Conventional 4x4 — Model K/Series 10 — 129.5 in. w.b.				
CK10906	Suburban (doors)	4902	5090	Note 3
CK10916	Suburban (gate)	4933	5098	Note 3
1/2-Ton Conventional 4x4 — Model K/Series 10 — 131.5 in. w.b.				
CK10903	Step-Side 8 ft.	3739	4175	Note 3
CK10903	Fleetside 8 ft.	3739	4271	Note 3
1/2-Ton Forward-Control — Model P/Series 10 — 102 in. w.b.				
CP10542	Chassis	-	-	Note 3
CP10542	Steel Step-Van	-	-	Note 3
3/4-Ton Conventional — Model C/Series 20 — 131.5 in. w.b.				
CC20903	Chassis & Cab	3104	3669	Note 3
CC20903	Step-Side 8 ft.	3271	4064	Note 3
CC20903	Fleetside 8 ft.	3271	4174	Note 3
3/4-Ton Conventional — Model C/Series 20 — 129.5 in. w.b.				
CC20906	Suburban (doors)	4902	5090	Note 3
CC20916	Suburban (gate)	4040	4825	Note 3
3/4-Ton Crew-Cab — Model C/Series 20 — 164.5 in. w.b.				
CE20963	Crew-Cab Chassis	4214	4395	Note 3
CE20963	Crew-Cab Pickup 8 ft.	4381	4904	Note 3
3/4-Ton Conventional 4x4 — Model K/Series 20 — 131.5 in. w.b.				
CK20903	Chassis & Cab	3974	3981	Note 3
CK20904	Step-Side 8 ft.	4141	4372	Note 3
CK20934	Fleetside 8 ft.	4141	4486	Note 3
3/4-Ton Conventional 4x4 — Model K/Series 20 — 129.5 in. w.b.				
CK20906	Suburban (doors)	5307	5220	Note 3
CK20916	Suburban (gate)	5276	5228	Note 3
3/4-Ton Forward Control — Model P/Series 20 — 125 in. w.b.				
CP20842	Chassis	2491	2885	Note 3
CP20835	Steel Step-Van	4471	5293	Note 3
CP20855	Alum. Step-Van King	-	-	Note 3
3/4-Ton Forward Control — Model P/Series 20 — 133 in. w.b.				
CP21042	Chassis	2522	2915	Note 3
CP21035	Steel Step-Van	4578	5532	Note 3
CP21035	Alum. Step-Van King	5371	4814	Note 3
1-Ton Conventional — Model C/Series 30 — 131.5 in. w.b.				
CC30903	Chassis & Cab	3201	3828	Note 3
CC30903	Step-Side 8 ft.	3368	4271	Note 3
CC30903	Fleetside 8 ft.	3368	4329	Note 3
1-Ton Conventional — Model C/Series 30 — 135.5 in. w.b.				
CC31063	Crew-Cab Fleetside	4296	4459	Note 3
1-Ton Conventional — Model C/Series 30 — 159.5 in. w.b.				
CC31403	Crew-Cab & Chassis	3251	3945	Note 3
1-Ton Conventional — Model C/Series 30 — 164.5 in. w.b.				
CC31963	Crew-Cab & Chassis	4296	5469	Note 3
1-Ton Forward-Control — Model P/Series 30 — 125 in. w.b.				
CP30842	Chassis 10	2699	3061	Note 3
CP30842	Steel Step-Van 10	4786	5708	Note 3
CP30842	Alum. Step-Van King 10	5579	4989	Note 3
CP30842	Motorhome Chassis	-	-	Note 3
1-Ton Forward-Control — Model P/Series 30 — 133 in. w.b.				
CP31042	Chassis	2730	3090	Note 3
CP31042	Steel Step-Van King 12	4786	5708	Note 3
CP31042	Alum. Step-Van King 12	5579	4989	Note 3
CP31042	Motorhome Chassis	-	-	Note 3
1-Ton Forward-Control — Model P/Series 30 — 157 in. w.b.				
CP31442	Chassis	2766	3189	Note 3
CP31442	Steel Step-Van King 14	4786	5708	Note 3
CP31442	Alum. Step-Van King 14	5579	4989	Note 3
CP31142	Motorhome Chassis	-	-	Note 3

NOTE 1: Calendar-year sales: [1973] 39,422, [1974] 30,328.
NOTE 2: Total El Camino production was 51,223.
NOTE 3: Production [C10/K10] 445,699, [C20/K20] 178,829, [C30/K30] 39,964, [P10/P20/P30 Step-Vans] 19,759, [Blazer] 56,798, [Chevy Van] 70,763; [Sportvan/Beauville] 20,779; [Carryall Suburbans] 41,882.
NOTE 4: Production includes trucks built in Canada for U.S. market.
NOTE 5: Prices/weights for V-8s, except four- or six-cylinder only trucks.

1974 Chevrolet 1/2-Ton El Camino Sedan-Pickup (OCW)

ENGINE: [Standard LUV] Inline. OHV. Four-cylinder. Cast iron block. Bore & stroke: 3.31 in. x 3.23 in. Displacement: 110.8 cid. Compression ratio: 8.5:1. Net horsepower: 75 at 5000 rpm. Maximum torque: 88 lb.-ft at 3000 rpm. Five main bearings. Hydraulic valve lifters. Carburetor: two-barrel.
ENGINE: [Standard Vega] Inline. OHV. Four-cylinder. Aluminum block. Bore & stroke: 3.501 in. x 3.625 in. Displacement: 140 cid. Compression ratio: 8.0:1. Net horsepower: 75 at 4200 rpm. Maximum torque: 115 lb.-ft. at 2400 rpm. Five main bearings. Hydraulic valve lifters. Carburetor: one-barrel.
ENGINE: [Standard all except El Camino/LUV/Vega] Inline. OHV. Six-cylinder. Cast iron block. Bore & stroke: 3-7/8 in. x 3-1/2 in. Displacement: 250 cid. Compression ratio: 8.25:1. Net horsepower: 100 at 3600 rpm. Maximum torque: 175 lb.-ft. at 1800 rpm. Seven main bearings. Hydraulic valve lifters. Carburetor: one-barrel.
ENGINE: [Optional C20/C30/K20, Standard G20/G30] Inline. OHV. Six-cylinder. Cast iron block. Bore & stroke: 3-7/8 in. x 4.12 in. Displacement: 292 cid. Compression ratio: 8.0. Net horsepower: 120 at 3600 rpm. Maximum torque: 215 lb.-ft. at 2000 rpm. Seven main bearings. Hydraulic valve lifters. Carburetor: one-barrel. (An LPG conversion was available).
ENGINE: [Optional C10/G10, Standard El Camino] Inline. OHV. Eight-cylinder. Cast iron block. Bore & stroke: 4 in. x 3.48 in. Displacement: 350 cid. Compression ratio: 8.5. Brake horsepower: 145 at 3800 rpm. Net horsepower: 145 at 3600 rpm. Maximum torque: 250 lb.-ft. at 2200 rpm. Five main bearings. Hydraulic valve lifters. Carburetor: two-barrel. (An LPG conversion was available).

1974 Chevrolet 3/4-Ton G20 Sportvan Beauville (CP)

ENGINE: [Optional C30/K10/K20/G10/G20/G30/El Camino] Inline. OHV. Eight-cylinder. Cast iron block. Bore & stroke: 4 in. x 3.48 in. Displacement: 350 cid. Compression ratio: 8.5. Brake horsepower: 245 at 3800 rpm. Net horsepower: 160 at 3800 rpm. Maximum torque: 255 lb.-ft. at 2400 rpm. Five main bearings. Hydraulic valve lifters. Carburetor: four-barrel.
ENGINE: [Optional: El Camino] V-block. OHV. Eight-cylinder. Cast iron block. Bore & stroke: 4.126 in. x 3.76 in. Displacement: 400 cid. Compression ratio: 8.5:1. Net horsepower: 150. Five main bearings. Hydraulic valve lifters. Carburetor: Rochester four-barrel.
ENGINE: [Optional: El Camino] V-block. OHV. Eight-cylinder. Cast iron block. Bore & stroke: 4.125 in. x 3.75 in. Displacement: 400 cid. Compression ratio: 8.5:1. Net horsepower: 180. Five main bearings. Hydraulic valve lifters. Carburetor: Rochester four-barrel.

1974 Chevrolet 3/4-Ton K20 Carryall Suburban 4x4 (JAG)

ENGINE: [Optional C10/C20/C30/El Camino] Inline. OHV. Eight-cylinder. Cast iron block. Bore & stroke: 1-1/4 in. x 4 in. Displacement: 454 cid. Compression ratio: 8.5. Net horsepower: 220. Five main bearings. Hydraulic valve lifters. Carburetor: Rochester four-barrel model Quadra-Jet.
ENGINE: [El Camino] Inline. OHV. Eight-cylinder. Cast iron block. Bore & stroke: 1-1/4 in. x 4 in. Displacement: 454 cid. Compression ratio: 8.5. Net horsepower: 235 at 4000 rpm. Five main bearings. Hydraulic valve lifters. Carburetor: Rochester four-barrel model Quadra-Jet.
ENGINE: [Optional C10/C20/C30] Inline. OHV. Eight-cylinder. Cast iron block. Bore & stroke: 1-1/4 in. x 4 in. Displacement: 454 cid. Compression ratio: 8.5. Brake horsepower: 5. Net horsepower: 245 at 4000 rpm. Maximum torque: 365 lb.-ft. at 2800 rpm. Five main bearings. Hydraulic valve lifters. Carburetor: Rochester four-barrel model Quadra-Jet.
CHASSIS: [El Camino] Wheelbase: 116 in. Overall length: 201.6 in. Height: 53.8 in. Front tread: 58.5 in. Rear tread: 57.8 in. Tires: GR78-14B.
CHASSIS: [LUV] Wheelbase: 102.4 in. Overall length: 173.8 in. Height: 59.3 in. Front tread: 54 in. Rear tread: 52.2 in. Tires: A78-13B.
CHASSIS: [Vega] Wheelbase: 97 in. Overall length: 176 in. Height: 51.8 in. Front tread: 54.8 in. Rear tread: 53.6 in. Tires: A78-13B.
CHASSIS: [G10] Wheelbase: 110 in./125 in. Overall length: 178 in./202.2 in. Tires: E78-14A.
CHASSIS: [G20] Wheelbase: 110 in./125 in. Overall length: 178 in./202.2 in. Tires: G78-15B.

1974 Chevrolet 3/4-Ton K20 Carryall Suburban 4x4 (RCA)

Standard Catalog of Chevrolet Trucks

1974 Chevrolet 1-Ton C30 "Big Dooley" Crew-Cab Pickup (CP)

CHASSIS: [G30] Wheelbase: 110 in./125 in. Overall length: 178 in./202.2 in. Tires: 8.00 x 16.5C.
CHASSIS: [Blazer] Wheelbase: 106.5 in. Overall length: 184.5 in. Height: [4x2] 67.5 in. [without top], 69.5 in. [with top]. [4x4] 69.5 in. [without top], 71.5 in. [with top]. Front tread: 64.5 in. Rear tread: 63.0 in. [4x2]. Front tread: 65.75 in. Rear tread: 62.75 in. [4x4]. Tires: E78-15B.
CHASSIS: [C10] Wheelbase: 117.5 in./131.5 in. Overall length: 191.2 in./211.25 in. Height: 69.8 in. Front tread: 65.8 in. Rear tread: 62.7 in. Tires: G78-15B.
CHASSIS: [K10] Wheelbase: 117.5 in./131.5 in. Overall length: 191.3 in./212 in. Height: 72 in. Front tread: 65.8 in. Rear tread: 62.7 in. Tires: G78-15B.

1974 Chevrolet 1/2-Ton K10 Carryall Suburban 4x4

EL CAMINO OPTIONS: SS package ($215). Conquista package. Estate package (Classic models only). Deluxe bumpers. Power door locks. Dual sport mirrors. Turbine I wheels. Wire wheelcovers. [Vega Panel Express] Variable-ratio power steering. Electro-clear rear window. Defroster. Radio AM, AM/FM. Power steering. Custom Deluxe interior. Cheyenne interior. Cheyenne Super interior. Below-eye-line mirrors. Drip molding. Sliding rear window. Cargo lamp. Gauge package. Air conditioning. Tachometer. Comfortilt steering wheel. Chrome bumpers. Chrome front bumper with rubber impact strips. Exterior tool and storage compartment. Wheelcovers. White wall tires. Special trim molding. Wood-grain exterior trim. Rear step bumper. Glide-out spare tire carrier.

1974 Chevrolet 1/2-Ton P10 Step-Van 7 (CP)

CHASSIS: [P10] Wheelbase: 102 in. Height: 75 in. Tires: G78-15B.
CHASSIS: [C20] Wheelbase: 117.5 in./131.5/164.5 in. Overall length: 191.5 in./212 in./244.43 in. Height: 69.8 in. Front tread: 65.8 in. Rear tread: 62.7 in. Tires: 8.75 x 16.5C. [Crew-Cab: 9.50 x 16.5D.]
CHASSIS: [K20] Wheelbase: 117.5 in./131.5 in. Overall length: 191.3 in./212 in. Height: 73.9 in. Front tread: 65.8 in. Rear tread: 62.7 in. Tires: 8.75 x 16.5C.
CHASSIS: [P20] Wheelbase: 125 in./133 in. Overall length: 220.75 in./244.75 in. Tires: 8.75 x 16.5C.
CHASSIS: [C30] Wheelbase: 131.5 in./164.5 in. Overall length: 212 in./244.43 in. Height: 71.8 in. Front tread: 65.8 in. Rear tread: 62.7 in. Tires: 8.75 x 16.5C. [Crew-Cab: 9.50 x 16.5E.]
CHASSIS: [P30] Wheelbase: 125 in./157 in. Overall length: 220.75 in./265.75 in. Tires: 8.75 x 16.5C.
TECHNICAL: Transmission: Three-speed synchromesh. Gears: [1-ton] 4F/1R, [Others] 3F/1R. Column-mounted gear shift lever. Single-plate, dry-disc clutch [250-cid engine], coil-spring single-dry-plate (292/307/350/402-cid engines). Rear axle: [1/2-ton] semi-floating, [3/4-ton and 1-ton] full-floating. Hydraulic four-wheel brakes. Kelsey-Hayes pressed steel wheels.

1974 Chevrolet 1-Ton C30 "Camper Special" Fleetside Pickup (CP)

OPTIONS FOR 1/2- TO 1-TON CHEVROLET TRUCKS WITH FACTORY INSTALLATION RATES: [El Camino] Automatic transmission (95.8 percent). Power steering (97.3 percent). AM radio (77.5 percent). AM/FM stereo radio (16.4 percent). Small V-8 (66.4 percent). Large V-8 (33.1 percent). Air conditioning (72.4 percent). Limited-slip differential (9.9 percent). Tinted glass (90.9 percent). Steel-belted radial tires (16.8 percent). Wheelcovers (70.3 percent). Interior trim package (44.5 percent). Exterior trim package (44.5 percent). [Blazer] Automatic transmission (81.5 percent). Power steering (95 percent). AM radio (77.4 percent). AM/FM stereo radio (11.8 percent). Small V-8 (96 percent). Air conditioning (47.4 percent). Limited-slip differential (8.6 percent). Tinted glass (63.7 percent). Steel-belted radial tires (3.8 percent). Wheelcovers (34.2 percent). Interior trim package (59.5 percent). Exterior trim package (59.5 percent). Four-wheel-drive (94.6 percent). [Chevy Van] Automatic transmission (73.5 percent). Manual disc brakes (23.3 percent). Power disc brakes (76.7 percent). Power steering (41.8 percent). AM radio (43.4 percent). AM/FM stereo radio (2.4 percent). Small V-8 (77 percent). Air conditioning (11.6 percent). Limited-slip (3.6 percent). Tinted glass (28.3 percent). Interior trim package (21.6 percent). Exterior trim package (21.6 percent). [Sportvan] Automatic transmission (91.5 percent). Power steering (89.1 percent). AM radio (69 percent). AM/FM stereo radio (10.3 percent). Small V-8 (94.2 percent). Air conditioning (64 percent). Limited-slip (5.1 percent). Tinted glass (73.4 percent). Steel-belted radial tires (6.3 percent). Interior trim package (17 percent). Exterior trim package (17 percent). [Carryall Suburban] Automatic transmission (89.3 percent). Power steering (71.5 percent). AM radio (67.7 percent). AM/FM stereo radio (12.5 percent). Small V-8 (62.7 percent). Large V-8 (33.7 percent). Air conditioning (76 percent). Limited-slip (13 percent). Tinted glass (68.2 percent). Steel-belted radial tires (6.4 percent). Wheelcovers (24.1 percent). Interior trim package (72.5 percent). Exterior trim package (72.5 percent). [C10] Automatic transmission (63.4 percent). Manual disc brakes (58.5 percent). Power disc brakes (41.4 percent). Power steering (63.3 percent). AM radio (71.6 percent). AM/FM stereo radio (3.6 percent). Small V-8 (74.4 percent). Large V-8 (5.9 percent). Air conditioning (33.3 percent). Limited-slip differential (3.3 percent). Tinted glass (38.9 percent). Steel-belted radial tires (1.2 percent). Wheelcovers (29.3 percent). Interior trim package (47.3 percent). Exterior trim package (47.3 percent). Four-wheel-drive (9.8 percent). [C20] Automatic transmission (66.9 percent). Power disc brakes (100 percent). Power steering (85.5 percent). AM radio (74.5 percent). AM/FM Stereo radio (3.7 percent). Small V-8 (78.6 percent). Large V-8 (15.8 percent). Air conditioning (30.7 percent). Limited-slip differential (14.3 percent). Tinted glass (40.5 percent). Interior trim package (47.3 percent). Exterior trim package (47.3 percent). Four-wheel-drive (21.6 percent). (C30): Automatic transmission (28.9 percent). Power steering (68.9 percent). AM radio (49.4 percent). AM/FM stereo radio (3.9 percent). Small V-8 engine (64.4 percent). Large V-8 engine (23.8 percent). Air conditioning (20 percent). Limited-slip differential (10.1 percent). Dual rear wheels (75.6 percent). Tinted glass (29.5 percent). Wheelcovers (1.8 percent). Interior trim package (22.6 percent). Exterior trim package (22.6 percent). [P-Series] Automatic transmission (56.2 percent). Manual disc brakes (9.2 percent). Power disc brakes (90.8 percent). Power steering (42 percent). Small V-8 (57.6 percent). Air conditioning (2.1 percent). Limited-slip differential (1 percent). Dual rear wheels (56.1 percent). Tinted glass (11.5 percent). Wheelcovers (1.7 percent).
NOTE 6: Small V-8 means 350 cid or less, large V-8 means over 350 cid.

1974 Chevrolet 1-Ton P30 Step-Van King with Telsta aerial lift conversion (CMD)

COLOR OPTIONS: See 1970 options section for complete chart of 1970-1974 Chevrolet Commercial Truck colors.

HISTORICAL: Introduced Sept. 2, 1973. Calendar-year registrations: 803,864. Calendar-year registrations by weight class: [6,000 lb. and less] 575,348, [6,000 to 10,000 lb.] 228,516. Calendar-year production: 838,959 units (not including Vega/El Camino/LUV). Chevrolet held 29.44 percent of the U.S. truck market. On a calendar-year basis, this was Chevrolet's second best year in truck sales in history with sales of 885,362 units and production of 896,130. The model-year figures were, however, even more impressive with 975,257 sales and 925,696 trucks built to 1974 specifications. This production total includes trucks built in Canada for sale here, but does not include LUVs (which are included in the sales total). An all-time production record, for the Flint, Mich. factory (339,678 trucks) was set. On a calendar-year basis, 85.5 percent of Chevrolet's output was V-8 powered, 15.1 percent had six-cylinder engines and a mere 0.4 percent were diesel engined.

1975 CHEVROLET

1975 Chevrolet Fleetside Pickup (CP)

1/2-TON LIGHT UTILITY (LUV) — MODEL 82 — FOUR: The LUV truck again offered the Mikado cloth trim package including striped upholstery, a fancier steering wheel, finer seat cloth, carpets and upgraded trim throughout.

1/2-TON VEGA — MODEL V/SERIES 14000 — FOUR: The Vega Panel Express had the same appearance as 1974. A new GVW of 3,283-3,552 lb. was listed for 1975. The Vega Panel Express had the same large swing-up tailgate arrangement as the Vega Kammback wagon. The Chevrolet brochure described it as an economy truck. It still came with just one bucket seat, rubber floor coverings and without side windows. Maximum cargo capacity was 50.2 cu.-ft. Technical features included front brake lining wear sensors, an electric windshield washer and a 16-gal. gas tank.

1/2-TON EL CAMINO — MODEL C, D/SERIES 13000 — V-8: The 1975 Chevrolet El Camino continued the basic 1974 look, but had a slightly revised grille. It was vertically segmented with nine prominent members. There was now a built-in license plate holder at the center of the bumper.

1/2-TON, 3/4-TON, 1-TON VAN — MODEL G/SERIES 10, 20, 30 — SIX/V-8: Chevy Vans and Sportvans were offered again. They had no major changes. The G10 and G20 series offered Chevy Van Panels and windowed Sportvans on 110- or 125-in. wheelbases. The fancy Beauville Sportvans came only with V-8s. The G30 line offered the Chevy Van with a six or V-8 on the small wheelbase and the other styles on the 125-in. wheelbase with V-8s. A new two-tone paint treatment was available.

1975 Chevrolet Cheyenne Blazer (CP)

1/2-TON BLAZER UTILITY — MODEL C, K/SERIES 5 — SIX/V-8: Blazers had a revamped grille with a larger grillwork, clear-lens parking lights, and new front fender model identification combining model nameplates and series identification plaques. A restyled tailgate with a quick-release control was used. Two types of 4x4 systems were optionally available in 1975. With a six-cylinder engine or manual gear box, a conventional 4x4 drive train was provided. In combination with a V-8 and Turbo-Hydramatic transmission, buyers got the full-time 4x4 system. This applied to both Pickups and Carryall Suburbans, as well as to Blazers. According to Four-Wheeler magazine's June 1975 issue, you could not order a V-8 powered Chevrolet 4x4 with manual transmission. The magazine said, "In 1974, they did build some that way and had many problems with the New Process full-time 4x4 system. The full-time transfer case just didn't want to work with the manual transmission."

1975 Chevrolet 'Big Dooley' Crew-Cab Pickup (CP)

1/2-TON, 3/4-TON, 1-TON CONVENTIONAL — MODEL CK/SERIES 10, 20, 30 — SIX/V-8: Styling changes for light-duty conventional trucks were headed by revamped grille with a larger grillwork, clear-lens parking lights, and new front fender model identification combining model nameplates and series identification plaques. A restyled tailgate with a quick-release control was used. The C10/K10 Pickups with a 6-1/2-ft. box came on the standard 117-1/2-in. wheelbase, which was used only for these models and small chassis models. The C10/K10 Pickups with an 8-ft. box featured a 131-1/2-in. wheelbase. This wheelbase was also used for 1/2-ton chassis models and all basic C30 models. The C20/K20 trucks, except Carryall Suburbans, were on a 127-in. wheelbase. All Carryall Suburbans, both 1/2-ton and 3/4-ton, were on a 129.5-in. wheelbase. Longer wheelbases were provided for the Chassis-and-Cab and the Crew-Cab trucks. Crew-Cab bodies that seated six could be had as an option on all 3/4-ton and 1-ton Pickups. The Crew-Cab was an option costing about $1,000. The box used for factory-made Crew-Cab Pickups was the 8-ft. Fleetside box. Custom Deluxe was the base interior. It included a foam-padded bench seat with blue, green, red or saddle plaid upholstery, a body color steel roof panel, black rubber floor mat, padded arm rests, courtesy lamps, prismatic rear view mirror, foam padded dash, bright upper and lower grille outline moldings, bright headlamps bezels, silver plastic grille insert, bright outside rear view mirror, bright door handles, bright Custom Deluxe nameplates and white-painted bumper, hubcaps and wheels. The next-step-up was Scottsdale trim ($137-$199 extra), full-depth foam padded seat, which included wood-grain door trim inserts, an ash tray cigarette lighter, door or manually-operated courtesy lamps, bright door sill plates, color-keyed rubber floor mats, a high-note horn, patterned nylon cloth upholstery with vinyl trim, and all Custom Deluxe exterior features, plus a chrome bumper, chrome hubcaps, chrome body side moldings on Fleetsides, bright windshield and window trim, bright-rimmed parking, side marker and taillights, and Scottsdale nameplates. Cheyenne trim ($258-$315) was the next notch on the totem pole. It added full-depth foam seat cushions, a choice of custom-grained vinyl or cloth-and-vinyl seats (bucket type optional), an ash tray-mounted cigarette lighter, wood-grain door panel inserts, door or manually-operated courtesy and dome lights, extra cab insulation, and all Scottsdale exterior items, plus bright metal cab back appliqués and moldings, bright upper body side and tailgate moldings, central appliqués for Fleetsides, and Cheyenne nameplates. At the top of the line was the Silverado option ($312-$531) featuring 7-in. thick seat foam, richer basketweave nylon cloth or buffalo hide vinyl, full gauges, wood-graining on the dash panel and door panel inserts, door storage pockets, carpeting, an insulated headliner, extra body insulation, and all Cheyenne exterior items, plus lower body side and tailgate moldings, wheel lip moldings, Scottsdale nameplates, and a tailgate appliqué on Fleetsides. All Pickups could be equipped with an optional glide-out spare tire carrier. Carryall Suburbans came with the Custom Deluxe, Scottsdale, or Silverado (but not Cheyenne) trim levels. An Estate option with wood-grain exterior paneling was offered, too. A removable rear seat was available at extra cost. Buyers still had a choice of end-gate or double panel-door rear styling. Trucks with under-6,001-lb. GVWs (except LUVs) were equipped with catalytic converters. They significantly reduced hydrocarbon and carbon monoxide emissions to meet 1975 EPA standards. Chevrolet promoted them as having "newly designed engines with increased efficiency." However, one truck enthusiast publication recommended that since the converter added to cost, it might be a good idea to specify chassis equipment sufficiently heavy-duty to exceed a 6,000-lb. GVW for C10s, K10s and Blazers. Then the converter wasn't required. Introduced on all engines, except the LUV's, was a high-energy ignition (HEI) system, which delivered a hotter and more consistent spark for better starting power. Also introduced was an outside air carburetion intake and an early fuel evaporation system which provided faster engine warm up after cold start. Chevrolet's stalwart 250-cid six-cylinder engine had a new, integrally-cast cylinder head with improved-flow intake manifold. All 1/2-ton models with this engine had a larger standard clutch. The "Big Doolie" Pickup, with dual rear wheels, was one of several equipment offerings. The year's exterior colors were Skyline Blue, Hawaiian Blue, Catalina Blue, Grecian Bronze, Buckskin, Yuba Gold, Moss Gold, Willoway Green, Spring Green, Glenwood Green, Crimson Red, Rosedale Red, Saratoga Silver, Sante Fe Tan, and Frost White. Two-tone color options came in conventional, special and deluxe combinations, each requiring specific moldings packages.

1/2-TON, 3/4-TON, 1-TON FORWARD-CONTROL — MODEL P/SERIES 10, 20, 30 — SIX/V-8: The Forward-Control chassis was designed for door-to-door delivery service. Body lengths ranged from seven to eight feet for the P10 series up to 14 ft. in the P30 series. Step-Vans looked identical to 1973 versions. The P20 and P30 series offered larger chassis, plus Step-Van and Step-Van King models with steel or aluminum bodies. The basic body lengths were 10 ft. for the 125-in. wheelbase chassis, 12 ft. for the 133-in. wheelbase, and 14 ft. for the 157-in. wheelbase chassis. The P30 chassis was also used for Chevrolet's new High-Cube vans and numerous custom motorhome conversions.

152

I.D. DATA: Serial number located. Combination VIN and rating plate located on: [El Camino] Top left side of dash, [Conventionals] left door pillar. Serial number systems: [El Camino] First symbol indicates manufacturer, 1=Chevrolet. Second symbol indicates car-line/series: C=El Camino, D=El Camino Custom. Third and fourth symbols indicate body type: 80=Sedan-Pickup. Fifth symbol indicates engine: [El Camino] H=350-cid/145-nhp two-barrel V-8, L=350-cid/160-nhp four-barrel V-8, U=402-cid/175-nhp four-barrel V-8, Y=454-cid/235-nhp four-barrel V-8. Sixth symbol indicates model-year: 5=1975. Seventh symbol indicates assembly plant. Symbols 8-13 indicate the production sequence number starting at 100,001. Ending numbers not available. [All Light-Duty] The first symbol indicates manufacturer: 1=Chevrolet Motor Div. The second symbol indicates chassis type: C=96 in. or 106 in. Conventional Cab including Blazer, G=Chevy Van or Sportvan, K=106-in. wheelbase Conventional cab 4x4, P= Forward-Control. The third symbol indicates engine as follows: L=454-cid/245-nhp four-barrel V-8 (P-Series only), M=400-cid/175-nhp four-barrel V-8, N=110-cid/75-nhp two-barrel L4, P=250-cid/105-nhp one-barrel six, Q=250-cid/100-nhp one-barrel L-6, R=292-cid/120-hp one-barrel L-6, T=292-cid/150-nhp one-barrel L-6, U=350-cid four-barrel V-8, V=350-cid/145-nhp two-barrel V-8, Y=350-cid/160-nhp four-barrel V-8, Z=454-cid/230-nhp four-barrel V-8. The fourth symbol indicates series and tonnage: 1=1/2-ton, 2=3/4-ton, 3=1-ton. The fifth symbol indicates body type: 2=Chassis & Cowl, 3=Chassis-and-Cab or Motorhome Chassis, 4=Cab with pickup box, 5=Panel or Panel Van, 6=Sportvan, Carryall Suburban (doors) 7=Motorhome chassis, 8=Blazer. The sixth symbol indicates model-year: 5=1975. The seventh symbol indicates the assembly plant: A=Lakewood, Ga., B=Baltimore, Md., D=Doraville, Ga., F=Flint, Mich., J=Janesville, Wis., K=Leeds, Mo., S=St. Louis, Mo., R=Arlington, Texas, U=Lordstown, Ohio, V=Pontiac, Mich. GMAD, Z=Fremont, Calif., 1=Oshawa, Canada, 3=GMAD, Detroit, Mich., 4=Scarborough, Ontario, Canada, 8=Fujisawa, Japan. Symbols 8-13 are the production sequence number. Starting number: 10001 Ending numbers not available. Engine numbers located: [Six] on pad at right-hand side of cylinder block at rear of distributor, [V-8] on pad at front, right-hand side of cylinder block.

Model	Body Type	Price	Weight	Prod. Total
1/2-Ton LUV — Model L/Series 82 — 102.4 in. w.b.				
CL10503	Mini-Pickup	2976	2380	Note 1
NOTE 1: Calendar-year sales: [974] 30,328.				
1/2-Ton Vega — Model HV/Series 14000 — 97 in. w.b. — Four				
1HV05	Panel Express	2822	2401	-
El Camino — Model C/Series 13000 — 116 in. w.b. — Six				
1AC80	Sedan-Pickup	3828	3706	Note 2
El Camino Classic — Model D/Series 13000 — 116 in. w.b.				
1AD80	Classic Sedan-Pickup	3966	3748	Note 2
NOTE 2: Total El Camino production was 33,620.				
1/2-Ton Van — Model G/Series 10 — 110 in./125 in. w.b.				
CG11005	Chevy Van	3443	3584	Note 13
CG11006	Sportvan	4103	3925	Note 13
CG11006	Beauville	4506	4088	Note 13
NOTE 3: Add for 125-in. wheelbase.				
3/4-Ton Van — Model G/Series 20 — 110 in./125 in. w.b.				
CG21005	Panel	3653	3625	Note 13
CG21006	Sportvan	4275	3910	Note 13
CG21006	Beauville	4880	4583	Note 13
NOTE 4: Add for 125-in. wheelbase.				
1-Ton Van — Model G/Series 30 — 110 in./125 in. w.b.				
CG31005	Panel	3743	3917	Note 13
CG31006	Sportvan	4477	4369	Note 13
CG31006	Beauville	4880	4583	Note 13
NOTE 5: Add for 125-in. wheelbase.				
1-Ton Hi-Cube Van — Model G/Series 30 — 125 in./146 in. w.b.				
CG31303	Hi-Cube 10 ft.	4970	4998	Note 13
CG31603	Hi-Cube 12 ft.	4477	4369	Note 13
1/2-Ton Blazer 4x4 — Model K/Series 5 — 106.5 in. w.b.				
CK10514	Open Utility	4569	4046	Note 13
CK10516	Hardtop Utility	4998	4313	Note 13
NOTE 6: Deduct $1,089 for two-wheel-drive Blazer.				
1/2-Ton Conventional — Model C/Series 10 — 117.5 in. w.b.				
CC10703	Chassis & Cab	3676	3318	Note 13
CC10703	Step-Side 6.5 ft.	3609	3649	Note 13
CC10703	Fleetside 6.5 ft.	3609	3713	Note 13
1/2-Ton Carryall Suburban — Model C/Series 10 — 129.5 in. w.b.				
CC10906	Suburban (gate)	4707	4336	Note 13
NOTE 7: Deduct for panel door Carryall Suburban.				
1/2-Ton Conventional — Model C/Series 10 — 131.5 in. w.b.				
CC10903	Step-Side 8 ft.	3652	3774	Note 13
CC10903	Fleetside 8 ft.	3652	3844	Note 13
NOTE 8: Add $1,089 for K10 (4x4) Pickups and Carryall Suburbans.				
1/2-Ton Forward-Control — Model P/Series 10 — 102 in. w.b.				
CP10542	Steel Step-Van	4532	4220	Note 13
3/4-Ton Conventional — Model C/Series 20 — 131.5 in. w.b.				
CC20903	Chassis & Cab	3863	3737	Note 13
CC20903	Step-Side 8 ft.	4030	4137	Note 13
CC20903	Fleetside 8 ft.	4030	4207	Note 13
3/4-Ton Conventional — Model C/Series 20 — 129.5 in. w.b.				
CC20916	Suburban (gate)	5045	4664	Note 13
NOTE 9: Deduct for panel-door Carryall Suburban.				
NOTE 10: Add $1,009 for K20 (4x4) Pickups and Carryall Suburbans.				
3/4-Ton Bonus-Cab — Model C/Series 20 — 164.5 in. w.b.				
CE20943	Step-Side 8 ft.	4613	-	Note 13
CE20943	Fleetside 8 ft.	4613	4904	Note 13
3/4-Ton Crew-Cab — Model C/Series 20 — 164.5 in. w.b.				
CE20963	Chassis	4835	4461	Note 13
CE20963	Step-Side 8 ft.	5002	4861	Note 13
CE20963	Fleetside 8 ft.	5002	4935	Note 13
3/4-Ton Forward-Control — Model P/Series 20 — 125 in./133 in. w.b.				
CP20842	Steel Step-Van 10 ft.	5242	5382	Note 13
NOTE 11: Add for Step-Van King, aluminum body, 12 ft. body etc.				
1-Ton Conventional — Model C/Series 30 — 131.5 in. w.b.				
CC30903	Chassis & Cab	3996	3913	Note 13
CC30903	Step-Side 8 ft.	4163	4344	Note 13
CC30903	Fleetside 8 ft.	4163	4379	Note 13
1-Ton Conventional — Model C/Series 30 — 164.5 in. w.b.				
CC31963	Crew-Cab & Chassis	4988	4517	Note 13
CC31963	Crew-Cab Step-Side 8 ft.	5155	4948	Note 13
CC31963	Crew-Cab Fleetside 8 ft.	5155	4987	Note 13
1-Ton Step-Van — Model P/Series 30 — 125 in./133 in./157 in. w.b.				
CP30842	Steel Step-Van 10 ft.	5499	5588	Note 13

NOTE 12: Add for Step-Van King, aluminum body, 12-ft./14-ft. body etc.
NOTE 13: Industry records show the following 1975 Chevrolet light-duty truck model-year production break-outs: [C10/K10 Pickup] 318,234, [C20/K20 Pickup] 144,632, [C30/K30 Pickup] 44,929, [All Carryall Suburban] 30,032, [All Step-Van] 16,877, [All El Camino] 33,620, [Blazer] 50,548, [Sportvan] 21,326 and [Chevy Van] 87,290, [Grand Total] 747,488.

1975 Chevrolet El Camino Sedan-Pickup (CP)

ENGINE: [LUV] Inline. OHV. Four-cylinder. Cast iron block. Bore & stroke: 3.31 in. x 3.23 in. Displacement: 110.8 cid. Compression ratio: 8.5:1. Net horsepower: 75 at 5000 rpm. Maximum torque: 88 lb.-ft. at 3000 rpm. Five main bearings. Hydraulic valve lifters. Carburetor: two-barrel.
ENGINE: [Standard Vega] Inline. OHV. Four-cylinder. Aluminum block. Bore & stroke: 3.501 in. x 3.625 in. Displacement: 140 cid. Compression ratio: 8.0:1. Net horsepower: 78 at 4200 rpm. Five main bearings. Hydraulic valve lifters. Carburetor: one-barrel.
ENGINE: [Standard C10/K10/Blazer/El Camino/G10] Inline. Gasoline. Six-cylinder. Cast iron block. Bore & stroke: 3-7/8 in. x 3-1/2 in. Displacement: 250 cid. Compression ratio: 8.25:1. Net horsepower: 105 at 3800 rpm. Maximum torque: 185 lb.-ft. at 1200 rpm. Seven main bearings. Hydraulic valve lifters. Carburetor: one-barrel.
ENGINE: [Optional C10/El Camino] V-block. Gasoline. Eight-cylinder. Cast iron block. Bore & stroke: 4 in. x 3-1/2 in. Displacement: 350 cid. Compression ratio: 8.5:1. Net horsepower: 145 at 3800 rpm. Maximum torque: 250 lb.-ft. at 2200 rpm. Five main bearings. Hydraulic valve lifters. Carburetor: two-barrel.
ENGINE: [Standard C20/C30/K20/P10/P20/P30/G20/G30] Inline. OHV. Six-cylinder. Cast iron block. Bore & stroke: 3-7/8 in. x 4-1/8 in. Displacement: 292 cid. Compression ratio: 8.0:1. Net horsepower: 120 at 3600 rpm. Maximum torque: 215 lb.-ft. at 2000 rpm. Seven main bearings. Hydraulic valve lifters. Carburetor: one-barrel.
ENGINE: [Optional C10/G10, Standard El Camino] Inline. OHV. Eight-cylinder. Cast iron block. Bore & stroke: 4 in. x 3.48 in. Displacement: 350 cid. Compression ratio: 8.5. Brake horsepower: 145 at 3800 rpm. Net horsepower: 145 at 3600 rpm. Maximum torque: 250 lb.-ft. at 2200 rpm. Five main bearings. Hydraulic valve lifters. Carburetor: two-barrel. (An LPG conversion was available).
ENGINE: [Optional all except Vega/LUV] V-block. Gasoline. Eight-cylinder. Cast iron block. Bore & stroke: 4 in. x 3-1/2 in. Displacement: 350 cid. Net horsepower: 160 at 3800 rpm. Maximum torque: 250 lb.-ft. at 2400 rpm. Five main bearings. Hydraulic valve lifters. Carburetor: four-barrel.
ENGINE: [Optional K10/K20/El Camino — $113] V-block. OHV. Eight-cylinder. Cast iron block. Bore & stroke: 4-1/8 in. x 4 in. Displacement: 400 cid. Compression ratio: 8.5:1. Net horsepower: 175 at 3600 rpm. Five main bearings. Hydraulic valve lifters. Carburetor: four-barrel.
ENGINE: [Optional C10/C20/C30] V-block. OHV. Eight-cylinder. Cast iron block. Bore & stroke: 4-1/8 in. x 4 in. Displacement: 454 cid. Compression ratio: 8.25:1. Net horsepower: 230 at 3800 rpm. Five main bearings. Hydraulic valve lifters. Carburetor: Rochester four-barrel Quadra-Jet.
ENGINE: [El Camino] V-block. OHV. Eight-cylinder. Cast iron block. Bore & stroke: 4-1/8 in. x 4 in. Displacement: 454 cid. Compression ratio: 8.25:1. Net horsepower: 235 at 3800 rpm. Five main bearings. Hydraulic valve lifters. Carburetor: Rochester four-barrel Quadra-Jet.
ENGINE: [Optional P20/P30 only] V-block. OHV. Eight-cylinder. Cast iron block. Bore & stroke: 4-1/8 in. x 4 in. Displacement: 454 cid. Compression ratio: 8.25:1. Net horsepower: 245 at 4000 rpm. Maximum torque: 355 lb.-ft. at 3000 rpm. Five main bearings. Hydraulic valve lifters. Carburetor: Rochester four-barrel Quadra-Jet.

1975 Chevrolet LUV Mini-Pickup (CP)

CHASSIS: [LUV] Wheelbase: 102.4 in. Overall length: 173.8 in. Height: 59.3 in. Front tread: 54 in. Rear tread: 52.2 in. Tires: 6.00 x 14C.
CHASSIS: [Vega] Wheelbase: 97 in. Overall length: 176 in. Height: 51.8 in. Front tread: 54.8 in. Rear tread: 53.6 in. Tires: A78-13B.
CHASSIS: [El Camino] Wheelbase: 116 in. Overall length: 201.60 in. Height: 53. 8 in. Front tread: 58.5 in. Rear tread: 57.8 in. Tires: GR78-15B.
CHASSIS: [G10] Wheelbase: 110 in. /125 in. Overall length: 178 in./202.2 in. Height: 78.8 x 81.2 in. Tires: E78-14A.
CHASSIS: [G20] Wheelbase: 110 in./125 in. Overall length: 178 in./202.2 in. Height: 78.8 x 81.2 in. Tires: G78-15B.
CHASSIS: [G30] Wheelbase: 125 in./146 in. Tires: 8.00 x 16.5C.
CHASSIS: [Blazer] Wheelbase: 106.5 in. Overall length: 184.5 in. Height: [4x2 without top] 66.75 in., [4x2 with top] 68 in. , [4x2 without top] 69 in., [4x4 with top] 71 in. Tread: [4x2] front 64.5 in., rear 63 in., [4x4] front 65.75 in., rear 62.75 in. Tires: [Six] E78-15B, [V-8] H78-15B.

CHASSIS: [C10] Wheelbase: 117.5 in./131.5 in. Overall length: [Fleetside] 191-1/4 in./211-1/4 in., [Step-Side] 190-1/4 in./210-1/4 in. Front tread: 65.8 in. Rear tread: 62.7 in. Tires: G78-15B. (Larger size tubeless and tube-type tires available for all models and series.)
CHASSIS: [K10] Wheelbase: 117.5 in./131.5 in. Overall length: [Fleetside] 191-1/4 in./211-1/4 in., [Step-Side] 190-1/4 in./210-1/4 in. Height: 72 in. Front tread: 65.8 in. Rear tread: 62.7 in. Tires: G78-15B.
CHASSIS: [P10] Wheelbase: 102 in. Height: 75 in. Tires: G78-15B.
CHASSIS: [C20] Wheelbase: 117.5 in./131.5 in./164.5 in. Overall length: [Fleetside] 191-1/4 in./211-1/4 in./244-1/4 in., [Step-Side] 210-1/4 in./244-1/4 in. Height: 69.8 in. Front tread: 65.8 in. Rear tread: 62.7 in. Tires: [Standard] 8.75 x 16.5C in. [Crew-Cab] 9.50 x 16.5D.
CHASSIS: [K20] Wheelbase: 131.5 in. Overall length: [Fleetside] 211-1/4 in., [Step-Side] 210-1/4 in. Height: 73.9 in. Front tread: 65.8 in. Rear tread: 62.7 in. Tires: 8.75 x 16.5C.
CHASSIS: [P20] Wheelbase: 125 in./133 in. Overall length: 220.75 in./244.75 in. Tires: 8.75 x 16.5C.
CHASSIS: [C30] Wheelbase: 131.5 in./164.5 in. Overall length: [Fleetside] 211-1/4 in./244-1/4 in., [Step-Side] 210-1/4 in./244-1/4 in. Height: 71.8 in. Front tread: 65.8 in. Rear tread: 62.7 in. Tires: [Standard] 8.75 x 16.5C in. [Crew-Cab] 9.50 x 16.5E.
CHASSIS: [P30] Wheelbase: 125 in./133 in./157 in. Overall length: 220.75 in./268.75 in. Tires: 8.75 x 16.5C.

1975 Chevrolet Fleetside Pickup (CP)

TECHNICAL: (Selected Specifications) [C10] Three-speed manual transmission or Turbo-Hydramatic transmission with 454-cid. V-8. [C20] Same as C10 except Turbo-Hydramatic with Crew-Cab also. [K10/K20] Three-speed manual transmission or Turbo-Hydramatic with 400-cid V-8. New Process transfer case with 4x4 trucks. Single-plate, dry-disc clutch (with base six-cylinder). Rear axle ratio (with base six-cylinder) 3.73:1 on C10s and 4.10:1 on C20s. Front disc/rear drum brakes. Standard equipment includes steel disc wheels.
OPTIONS: Radio: AM or AM/FM. Windshield embedded antenna. Gauge package (ammeter, oil pressure, temperature) available with either tachometer or clock or with exomomindor gauge only. Tachometer. Drip molding. Exterior tool and storage compartment. Air conditioning. Stainless steel Wheelcovers. White sidewall tires (Series 10 only). Below-eye-line mirrors. Comfortilt steering wheel. Rear step bumper. Special trim molding (Fleetside only). Chrome bumpers. Chrome front bumper with rubber impact strips. Wood-grain exterior trim (Fleetside only). Sliding rear window. Cargo area lamp. Box-mounted spare tire. Glide-out spare tire carrier.

1975-1978 CHEVROLET COLOR OPTIONS

Name	Ditzler Code	Model Years			
Acanthus Blue (Dark) [L]	14448				75
Adonis Yellow [L]	82025				75
Black (Exterior & Interior) [L]	9000	78	77	76	75
Black (Interior)	9248	78	77	76	75
Black (Interior-flat)	9317	78	77	76	75
Black (Interior)	9387	78	77	76	75
Black (Interior)	9396	78	77	76	75
Blue (4061-P) [L]	15174	78			
Blue Gray Poly (Interior) [L]	33041	78	77	76	75
Brown Poly	2947	78	77		
Buckskin	2829	78	77		
Cardinal Red	70704			76	
Catalina Blue Poly	2672			76	75
Clematis Blue Light {L]	14449				75
Crimson Red [L]	72096	78	77	76	75
Dark Argent [L]	33042	78	77	76	75
Dark Blue	2904	78	77		
Dark Blue (Interior)	14783				75
Dark Blue (Interior)	14796				75
Dark Blue (Interior)	15070	78	77		
Flat Dark Blue (Interior)	15072	78	77		
Dark Blue Green (Interior)	45064	78	77		
Flat Dark Blue Green (Interior)	45092	78	77		
Dark Brown (Interior)	24407	78	77		
Flat Dark Brown (Interior)	24408	78	77		
Dark Firethorn (Interior)	72145	78	77		
Flat Dark Firethorn (Interior)	72158	78	77		
Dark Gold Poly	2779			76	75
Dark Graystone (Interior)	33154				75
Dark Graystone (Interior)	33156				75
Dark Green	2951	78	77		
Dark Green (Interior)	44863				75
Dark Green (Interior)	44898				75
Dark Green Poly	2781			76	75
Dark Mandarin (Interior)	60764	78	77		
Flat Dark Mandarin (Interior)	60783	78	77		
Dark Oxblood (Interior)	72007				75
Dark Oxblood Poly (Interior)	72008				75

Name	Ditzler Code	Model Years			
Dark Saddle (Interior)	23942	78	77		
Flat Dark Saddle (Interior)	23988	78	77		
Dark Saddle (Interior)	23774				75
Dark Saddle (Interior)	23778				75
Dark Sandstone (Interior)	24106				75
Dark Sandstone (Interior)	24123				75
Desert Tan [L]	24310	78	77	76	
Glenwood Green	42850			76	75
Grecian Bronze	2671			76	75
Hawaiian Blue	2188			76	
Horizon Blue [L]	14719	78	77	76	75
Jasmine Yellow [L]	82162	78	77		
Light Blue	2892	78	77		
Light Buckskin (Interior)	24174	78	77		
Light Graystone	2780			76	75
Light Green	2775			76	75
Light Green Poly	2905	78	77		
Light Saddle	2778			76	75
Light Smoke Gray (Interior)	33187	78	77		
Madder Red [L]	71993				75
Mahogany	2948	78	77		
Mandarin Orange (Interior)	60761	78	77		
Matte Black [L]	9222	78	77	76	75
Matte Black [L]	9396	78	77	76	75
Matte Black [L]	9371	78	77	76	75
Medium Blue (Exterior/Interior)	2188	78	77		
Medium Gold Poly	2176			76	75
Medium Graystone (Interior)	33155				75
Medium Graystone Poly	2773	78	77	76	75
Medium Green (Interior)	44862				75
Medium Lime Poly	2774			76	75
Medium Red (Interior)	72054				75
Medium Saddle (Interior)	23797	78	77		
Medium Sandstone (Interior)	24107				75
Midnight Black [L]	9000	78	77	76	75
Midnight Blue (Interior)	15071	78	77		
Flat Midnight Blue (Interior)	15073	78	77		
Neutral	2777	78	77	76	75
Ochre [L]	82056	78	77	76	75
Palm Green [L]	44935				75
Polar White	2680	78	77	76	75
Red	2932	78	77		
Red-Brown Poly [L]	24188				75
Red Poly	2933	78	77		
Rosedale Red	2673			76	75
Russet Poly	2926	78	77		
Saddle Poly	2783			76	75
School Bus Yellow	2785				75
Shannon Green [L]	45199	78	77	76	
Silver [L]	8593	78	77	76	75
Silver Gray Poly	2860	78	77	76	
Silver Poly	8982	78	77		
Sky Blue [L]	14965	78	77	76	
Skyline Blue	2563			76	75
Strato White [L]	0883	78	77	76	75
Tangier Orange	60156	78	77	76	75
Walnut Beige [L]	23735				75
Weldenia White	0831	78	77	76	75
Westway Tan [L]	24003				75
Wheatland Yellow	2785	78	77	76	
White [L]	2185	78	77	76	
Yellow	2929	78	77		

Specify DQE for alkyd enamel, DDL for acrylic lacquer, DAR for acrylic enamel, DL or DIA for interior.
[L] = LUV Mini-Pickup truck color.
[V] = Vega Panel Express color
HISTORICAL: Introduced Sept. 1, 1974. Calendar-year sales: 771,518. High-energy ignition standard. Six-cylinder more efficient and powerful. Extended maintenance schedules. Catalytic converters now standard on Pickups under 6,001 lb. GVW.

1976 CHEVROLET

1/2-TON LIGHT UTILITY VEHICLE (LUV) — MODEL L/SERIES 10500 — FOUR: Model-year 1976 marked the discontinuance of the Vega Panel Express truck. The badge-engineered LUV mini-Pickup, built by Isuzu, of Japan, returned with a Chevrolet bow tie. It had fenderless-pickup styling, similar to the Fleetside, but in a much smaller scale. Changes for the LUV included an optional new three-speed automatic transmission. The standard all-vinyl interior had plaid pattern upholstery. A Mikado cloth trim package was available at extra cost. The EPA mileage rating for the mini-pickup was 33 highway/23 city versus the 1975 model's 29 highway/19 city rating.

1976 Chevrolet LUV Mini-Pickup (CP)

1976 Chevrolet El Camino Classic Sedan-Pickup (CP)

1/2-TON EL CAMINO — MODEL C, D/SERIES 14000 — SIX/V-8: This season's standard El Camino had single round headlights. Classic models used dual square headlamps stacked vertically at either side. The standard grille had a tight cross-hatched pattern. Others used a mesh insert. Returning to the center of the grille was a bow tie badge. The performance edition had its SS emblem at the lower left-hand grille corner. There was also a Conquista option package.

1/2-TON, 3/4-TON, 1-TON VAN — MODEL G/SERIES 10, 20, 30 — SIX/V-8: Chevrolet vans had the same styling as 1975. The panel-side Chevy Van, windowed Sportvan and fancy Beauville Sportvan all came on 110-in. or 125-in. wheelbases in the 1/2-ton G10 series. The 3/4-ton G20 series offered Chevy Vans and Sportvans in both sizes and a long wheelbase Beauville. In the 1-ton G30 series all three models came on the long wheelbase, and the small Chevy Van was available. All Beauvilles had a V-8 as standard equipment. New was a "Vantastic" option with wild decal graphics, side exhaust pipes, mag wheels, and fat tires.

1976 Chevrolet Blazer 4x4 Sport Utility Vehicle (RCA)

1/2-TON BLAZER — MODEL CK/SERIES 10500 — SIX/V-8: The Blazer remained more or less a short wheelbase version of C10/K10 trucks. The front end sheet metal of the 1969-1975 models had been essentially identical to a short Chassis-Cowl-and-Windshield version of the regular trucks with an open cab and a short Fleetside pickup box at the rear. The box had been designed to hold a fully removable full-length roof that gave the Blazer a station wagon appearance. A major development of 1976 was a new body design. It featured a steel half-cab with an integral roll bar built into the steel front compartment roof and lock pillar structures. Available at extra cost was a removable fiberglass-reinforced plastic roof that attached to the pickup box with 16 bolts. Soft-Ride suspension was made standard. The optional Cheyenne package ($626), included a Cheyenne nameplate, front bucket seats, console, gauges, simulated wood-grain trim, chrome front and rear bumpers, bright upper and lower body side moldings, bright hubcaps, bright accents, and Cheyenne nameplates. The hardtop version included color-keyed carpets, door pockets, special interior trim, and wood-grain accents. The body design for the 1976 model was introduced as a major change for Blazers.

1976 Chevrolet Cheyenne 4x4 Fleetside Pickup (RCA)

1/2-TON, 3/4-TON, 1-TON — MODEL CK/SERIES 10, 20, 30 — SIX/V-8: Conventional trucks included the Chassis-and-Cab, Fleetside and Step-Side Pickups, and the Carryall Suburban with its single-unit body. The four-door Carryall Suburban had its own exclusive 129.5-in. wheelbase. An end-gate was standard, but double rear panel doors were optional. Other models came on 117.5- or 131.5-in. wheelbases. Short wheelbase Pickups had a 6.5-ft. box and long wheelbase Pickups had an 8-ft. box. All these models were available in the 1/2-ton C10 series. The 3/4-ton C20 series offered the Carryall Suburban, plus long wheelbase versions of the other models. Also available were longer Bonus-Cab and Crew-Cab models on a stretched 164.5-in. wheelbase. The Bonus-Cab had two doors, but the cab was extended for added passenger space. The Crew-Cab had four doors and a full rear seat. The 1-ton C30 series offered all models in the C30 line, except the Carryall Suburban. The C10 and C20 trucks could be had as K10/K20 four-wheel-drives. In 1976, the grille texture was changed slightly, and the engine call-out badges were removed from in the grille. The 400-cid (actually 402-cid) big-block V-8 was replaced with a 400-cid small-block V-8. Custom Deluxe was the base interior. It included a foam-padded bench seat with blue, green, red or saddle plaid upholstery, a body color steel roof headliner panel, black rubber floor mat, padded arm rests, courtesy lamps, prismatic rear view mirror, foam padded dash, bright upper and lower grille outline moldings, bright headlamps bezels, silver plastic grille insert, bright outside rear view mirror, bright door handles, bright Custom Deluxe nameplates and white-painted bumper, hubcaps and wheels. The next-step-up was Scottsdale trim with a full-depth foam padded seat, wood-grain door trim inserts, an ash tray cigarette lighter, door or manually-operated courtesy lamps, bright door sill plates, color-keyed rubber floor mats, a high-note horn, patterned nylon cloth upholstery with vinyl trim, and all Custom Deluxe exterior features, plus a chrome bumper, chrome hubcaps, chrome body side moldings on Fleetsides, bright windshield and window trim, bright-rimmed parking, side marker and taillights, and Scottsdale nameplates. Cheyenne trim included full-depth foam seat cushions, new ribbed pattern velour or buffalo-hide vinyl upholstery (vinyl bucket seats optional), folding seat backs, ash tray-mounted cigarette lighter, wood-grain dash insert, door or manually-operated courtesy and dome lamps, and added cab insulation. The exterior featured all Custom Deluxe and Scottsdale features, plus bright metal cab appliqués and moldings, bright upper body side and tailgate moldings, tailgate center appliqués on Fleetsides and Cheyenne nameplates. At the top of the line was the Silverado option featuring extra-thick seat padding, basketweave nylon cloth or buffalo hide vinyl trim, full gauges, wood-grain dash panel, door storage pockets, carpeting, an insulated headliner, extra body insulation, and all Custom Deluxe and Scottsdale exterior items, plus lower body side and tailgate moldings, wheel lip moldings, Silverado nameplates, and a tailgate appliqué on Fleetsides. All Pickups could be equipped with an optional glide-out spare tire carrier. Step-Side Pickups with the 6-1/2-foot box were not ignored, they were available with a new trim package including special striping, chromed bumpers, Rally wheels and white-lettered tires. The package was offered in four body colors: Blue, Orange, Red or Black. Exterior colors for other models were Skyline Blue, Hawaiian Blue, Catalina Blue, Grecian Bronze, Buckskin, Yuba Gold, Moss Gold, Willoway Green, Spring Green, Glenwood Green, Crimson Red, Rosedale Red, Saratoga Silver, Santa Fe Tan, and Frost White. Two-tone color options came in conventional, special, and deluxe combinations, each requiring specific moldings packages.

1/2-TON, 3/4-TON, 1-TON FORWARD-CONTROL — MODEL P-SERIES 10, 20, 30 — SIX/V-8: Forward-Control trucks were P (parcel delivery) models available in the 10 (1/2-ton), 20 (3/4-ton), and 30 (1-ton) series The P10s had a 102-in. wheelbase and a 7-ft. body. P20s came with 125-in. or 133-in. wheelbases designed for 10-ft. or 12-ft. bodies. P30s came in these sizes, plus a 157-in. wheelbase designed for 14-ft. bodies. Styling was boxy and unchanged. The grille had two horizontal rectangular openings. The bar between them said Chevrolet. Outside the grille on either end were tall rectangles housing the parking lights and headlamps. An interesting thing about P models was that they were available with the most powerful engine offered in trucks, a 245 net horsepower (nhp) version of the 454-cid V-8.

1976 Chevrolet Blazer 4x4 Sport Utility Vehicle (RCA)

I.D. DATA: Serial number located. Combination VIN and rating plate located on: [El Camino] Top left side of dash, [Conventionals] left door pillar. Serial number systems: [El Camino] First symbol indicates manufacturer, 1=Chevrolet. Second symbol indicates car-line/series: C=El Camino, D=El Camino Classic. Third and fourth symbols indicate body type: 80=Sedan-Pickup. Fifth symbol indicates engine: [El Camino] D=250-cid/105-nhp one-barrel L6, Q=305-cid/140-nhp two-barrel V-8 (except Calif.), H=350-cid/145-nhp two-barrel V-8 (except Calif.), L=350-cid/165-nhp four-barrel V-8, U=400-cid/175-nhp four-barrel V-8. Sixth symbol indicates model-year: 6=1976. Seventh symbol indicates assembly plant. Symbols 8-13 indicate the production sequence number starting at 100,001. Ending numbers not available. [All Light-Duty] The first symbol indicates manufacturer: 1=Chevrolet Motor Div. The second symbol indicates chassis type: C=96 in. or 106 in. Conventional cab including Blazer, G=Chevy Van or Sportvan, K=106 in. Conventional cab 4x4, P= Forward-Control. The third symbol indicates engine as follows: D=250-cid/105-nhp one-barrel L6, L=350-cid/160-nhp four-barrel V-8, N=110-cid/75-nhp two-barrel L4 (LUV), Q=305-cid/130-nhp four-barrel V-8 (except Calif.), S=454-cid/240-nhp four-barrel V-8 (C models only), T=292-cid/120-nhp one-barrel L-6, U=400-cid/175-nhp four-barrel V-8, V=350-cid/145-nhp two-barrel V-8, Y=454-cid/245-nhp four-barrel V-8 (P models only). The fourth symbol indicates series and tonnage: 1= 1/2-ton, 2=3/4-ton, 3= 1-ton. The fifth symbol indicates body type: 2=Chassis & Cowl, 3=Chassis-and-Cab, 4=Cab with pickup box, 5=Panel or Panel Van,

6=Sportvan, Carryall Suburban (doors) 7=Motorhome chassis, 8=Blazer. The sixth symbol indicates model-year: 6=1976. The seventh symbol indicates the assembly plant: A=Lakewood, Ga., B=Baltimore, Md., F=Flint, Mich., J=Janesville, Wis., S=St. Louis, Mo., U=Lordstown, Ohio, V=Pontiac, Mich. GMAD, Z=Fremont, Calif., 1=Oshawa, Canada, 3=GMAD, Detroit, Mich., 4=Scarborough, Ontario, Canada, 8=Fujisawa, Japan. Symbols 8-13 are the production sequence number. Starting number: 10001 Ending numbers not available. Engine numbers located: [Six] on pad at right-hand side of cylinder block at rear of distributor, [V-8] on pad at front, right-hand side of cylinder block.

1976 Chevrolet Blazer Sport Utility Vehicle (CP)

Model	Body Type	Price	Weight	Prod. Total
1/2-Ton LUV — Model L/Series 10500 — 102.4 in. w.b.				
CL10503	Pickup	3285	2460	Note 1
NOTE 1: Calendar-year sales: 45,670.				
1/2-Ton El Camino — Model C, D/Series 14000 — 116 in. w.b.				
IAC80	Sedan-Pickup	4333	3791	Note 2
IAD80	Classic Sedan-Pickup	4468	3821	Note 2
NOTE 2: Model-year production: 44,890 El Camino/El Camino Classic.				
1/2-Ton Vans — Model G/Series 10 — 110 in./125 in. w.b.				
CG11005	Panel	3811	3593	Note 13
CG11006	Sportvan	4509	3917	Note 13
NOTE 3: Add for 125-in. wheelbase.				
1/2-Ton Van — Model G/Series 10 — 125 in. w.b.				
CG11006	Beauville	5102	4293	Note 13
3/4-Ton Vans — Model G/Series 20 — 110 in./125 in. w.b.				
CG21005	Panel Van	4022	3620	Note 13
CG21006	Sportvan	4682	3903	Note 13
NOTE 4: Add for 125-in. wheelbase.				
3/4-Ton Vans — Model G/Series 20 — 125 in. w.b.				
CG21306	Beauville	5220	4259	Note 13
1-Ton Vans — Model G/Series 30 — 110 in./125 in. w.b.				
CG31005	Panel Van	4143	3861	Note 13
1-Ton Vans — Model G/Series 30 — 125 in. w.b.				
CG31306	Sportvan	4915	4321	Note 13
CG31306	Beauville	5318	4508	Note 13
1-Ton High-Cube — Model G/Series 30 — 125 in. w.b.				
CG31303	Hi-Cube 10 ft.	5405	4990	Note 13
1-Ton High-Cube — Model G/Series 30 — 146 in. w.b.				
CG31603	High-Cube 12 ft.	5883	5732	Note 13
1/2-Ton Blazer 4x4 — Model K/Series 10500 — 106.5 in. w.b.				
CK10516	Utility Hardtop	5365	4017	Note 13
CK10516	Open Utility	5265	-	Note 13
1/2-Ton Conventional — Model C/Series 10 — 117.5 in. w.b.				
CC10703	Chassis & Cab	3957	3449	Note 13
CC10703	Step-Side 6.5 ft.	3863	3790	Note 13
CC10703	Fleetside 6.5 ft.	3863	3848	Note 13
1/2-Ton Carryall Suburban — Model C/Series 10 — 129.5 in. w.b.				
CC10906	Suburban 9 ft. (gate)	5087	4335	Note 13
NOTE 5: Panel doors optional.				
1/2-Ton Conventional — Model CK/Series 10 — 131.5 in. w.b.				
CC10903	Step-Side 6.5 ft.	3908	3877	Note 13
CC10903	Fleetside 6.5 ft.	3908	3953	Note 13
NOTE 6: Add for K10 (4x4) Pickup and Carryall Suburban.				
1/2-Ton Step-Van — Model P/Series 10 — 102 in. w.b.				
CP10542	Steel Step-Van 7 ft.	4855	4204	-
3/4-Ton Conventional — Model C/Series 20 — 131.5 in. w.b.				
CC20903	Chassis & Cab	4139	3730	Note 13
CC20903	Step-Side	4306	4128	Note 13
CC20903	Fleetside	4306	4204	Note 13
3/4-Ton Carryall Suburban — Model C/Series 20 — 129.5 in. w.b.				
CC10906	Suburban 9 ft. (gate)	5375	4717	Note 13
NOTE 7: Panel doors optional.				
CC20943	Chassis & Bonus-Cab	4786	4198	Note 13
CC20943	Bonus-Cab Fleetside	4953	4676	Note 13
CC20963	Chassis & Crew-Cab	5160	4441	Note 13
CC20963	Crew-Cab Fleetside	5327	4919	Note 13
NOTE 8: Add for K20 (4x4) Pickup and Carryall Suburban.				
3/4-Ton Step-Van — Model P/Series 20 — 125 in./133 in. w.b.				
CP20842	Steel Step-Van 10 ft.	5563	5300	-
NOTE 9: Add for 12-ft./133-in. wheelbase P10842 model.				
1-Ton Conventional — Model C/Series 30 — 131.5 in. w.b.				
CC30903	Chassis & Cab	4279	3887	Note 13
CC30903	Step-Side 8 ft.	4446	4316	Note 13
CC30903	Fleetside 8 ft.	4446	4357	Note 13
1-Ton Conventional — Model C/Series 30 — 164.5 in. w.b.				
CC30943	Chassis & Bonus-Cab	5210	4420	Note 13
CC30943	Bonus Cab Fleetside 8 ft.	5377	4894	Note 13
CC30963	Chassis & Crew-Cab	5320	4497	Note 13
CC30963	Crew-Cab Fleetside 8 ft.	5487	5506	Note 13
1-Ton Step-Van — Model P/Series 30 — 125/133/157 in. w.b..				
CP30842	Steel Step-Van 10 ft.	5506	5506	-
NOTE 10: Add for 12-ft./133-in. wheelbase P30842 model.				
NOTE 11: Add for 14-ft./157-in. wheelbase P31042 model.				

NOTE 12: Prices/weights for base V-8s (except six-cylinder only models).
NOTE 13: Model-year production: [Chevy Van] 125,695, [Sportvan/Beauville] 26,860, [Hi-Cube] No separate breakout, [Blazer] 74,389, [C10/K10 Cab models] 458,424, [C10/K10/C20/K20 Carryall Suburban] 44,977, [C20/K20 Cab models] 172,419, [C30] 45,299.
ENGINE: [Standard LUV] Inline. OHV. Four-cylinder. Cast iron block. Bore & stroke: 3.31 in. x 3.23 in. Displacement: 110.8 cid. Compression ratio: 8.5:1. Net horsepower: 75 at 5000 rpm. Maximum torque: 88 lb.-ft. at 3000 rpm. Five main bearings. Hydraulic valve lifters. Carburetor: Rochester Quadra-Jet four-barrel.

1976 Chevrolet Silverado Suburban (CP)

ENGINE: [Standard C10/K10/F44/El Camino/Blazer/Vans] Inline. OHV. Six-cylinder. Cast iron block. Bore & stroke: 3-7/8 in. x 3-1/2 in. Displacement: 250 cid. Compression ratio: 8.25:1. Net horsepower: 100 at 3600 rpm. Maximum torque: 175 lb.-ft. at 1800 rpm. Seven main bearings. Hydraulic valve lifters. Carburetor: one-barrel.
ENGINE: [Standard C20/C30/K20/Step-Van] Inline. OHV. Six-cylinder. Cast iron block. Bore & stroke: 3-7/8 in. x 4-1/8 in. Displacement: 292 cid. Compression ratio: 8.0:1. Net horsepower: 120 at 3600 rpm. Maximum torque: 215 lb.-ft. at 2000 rpm. Seven main bearings. Hydraulic valve lifters. Carburetor: one-barrel.

1976 Chevrolet Fleetside "Camper Special" Pickup (CP)

ENGINE: [Optional El Camino] V-block. OHV. Eight-cylinder. Cast iron block. Bore and stroke: 3.736 x 3.48 in. Displacement: 305 cid. Net horsepower: 140. Taxable horsepower: 44.66. Five main bearings. Hydraulic lifters. Carburetor: two-barrel.
ENGINE: [Optional C Series] V-block. OHV. Eight-cylinder. Cast iron block. Bore and stroke: 3.736 x 3.48 in. Displacement: 305 cid. Net horsepower: 130. Taxable horsepower: 44.66. Five main bearings. Hydraulic lifters. Carburetor: two-barrel.
ENGINE: [Optional C10/El Camino] V-block. OHV. Eight-cylinder. Cast iron block. Bore & stroke: 4 in. x 3-1/2 in. Displacement: 350 cid. Compression ratio: 8.5:1. Net horsepower: 145 at 3800 rpm. Maximum torque: 250 lb.-ft. at 2200 rpm. Five main bearings. Hydraulic valve lifters. Carburetor: two-barrel.

1976 Chevrolet Beauville Sportvan (CP)

ENGINE: [Optional: Except LUV/El Camino] V-block. OHV. Eight-cylinder. Cast iron block. Bore & stroke: 4 in. x 3-1/2 in. Displacement: 350 cid. Compression ratio: 8.5:1. Net horsepower: 160 at 3800 rpm. Maximum torque: 255 lb.-ft. at 2800 rpm. Five main bearings. Hydraulic valve lifters. Carburetor: Rochester Quadra-Jet four-barrel.

ENGINE: [Optional: El Camino] V-block. OHV. Eight-cylinder. Cast iron block. Bore & stroke: 4 in. x 3-1/2 in. Displacement: 350 cid. Compression ratio: 8.5:1. Net horsepower: 165 at 3800 rpm. Maximum torque: 255 lb.-ft. at 2800 rpm. Five main bearings. Hydraulic valve lifters. Carburetor: Rochester Quadra-Jet four-barrel.

ENGINE: [Optional K10/K20/Vans/Blazer/El Camino-$148] V-block. OHV. Eight-cylinder. Cast iron block. Bore & stroke: 4-1/8 in. x 4 in. Displacement: 400 cid. Compression ratio: 8.5:1. Net horsepower: 175 at 3600 rpm. Maximum torque: 290 lb.-ft. at 2800 rpm. Five main bearings. Hydraulic valve lifters. Carburetor: Rochester four-barrel Quadra-Jet.

ENGINE: [Optional C10/C20/C30-$423] V-block. OHV. Eight-cylinder. Cast iron block. Bore & stroke: 4-1/4 in. x 4 in. Displacement: 454 cid. Compression ratio: 8.25:1. Net horsepower: 240 at 3800 rpm. Maximum torque: 370 lb.-ft. at 2800 rpm. Five main bearings. Hydraulic valve lifters. Carburetor: Rochester Quadra-Jet four-barrel.

ENGINE: [Step-Van] V-block. OHV. Eight-cylinder. Cast iron block. Bore & stroke: 4-1/8 in. x 4 in. Displacement: 454 cid. Compression ratio: 8.25:1. Net horsepower: 245 at 3800 rpm. Five main bearings. Hydraulic valve lifters. Carburetor: Rochester four-barrel Quadra-Jet.

1976 Chevrolet Crew-Cab Pickup (CP)

CHASSIS: [LUV] Wheelbase: 102.4 in. Overall length: 173.8 in. Height: 59.3 in. Front tread: 54 in. Rear tread: 52.2 in. Tires: E78 x 14B.

CHASSIS: [El Camino] Wheelbase: 116 in. Overall length: 201.6 in. Height: 53.8. Front tread: 58.5 in. Rear tread: 57.8 in. Tires: GR78-15B.

CHASSIS: [Blazer] Wheelbase: 106.5 in. Overall length: 184.5 in. Height: [4x2] (without top) 66.75 in., (with top) 68.75 in. [4x4] (without top) 69 in., (with top) 71 in. Front/rear tread: [4x2] 64.5 in./63 in., [4x4] 65.75 in./62.75 in. Tires: [Six] E78-15B, [V-8] H78-15B.

CHASSIS: [G10] Wheelbase: 110 in./125 in. Overall length: 178 in./202.2 in. Height: 78.8 x 81.2 in. Tires: [SWB] E78 x 15B, [LWB] F78 x 15B.

CHASSIS: [G20] Wheelbase: 110 in./125 in. Overall length: 178 in./202.2 in. Height: 78.8 x 81.2 in. Tires: J78-15B.

CHASSIS: [G30] Wheelbase: 125 in./146 in. Tires: 8.00 x 16.5C.

CHASSIS: [C10/C10] Wheelbase: 117.5/131.5 in. Overall length: Fleetside: 191.5 in./211.40 in., Step-Side: 190.75 in./210.50 in. Height: 69.8 in. Front tread: 65.8 in. Rear tread: 62.7 in. Tires: G70-15B. Tires: [Six] L78-15B, [V-8] L78-15C [V-8].

CHASSIS: [K10] Wheelbase: 117.5 in./131.5 in. Overall length: Fleetside: 192.10 in./212 in., Step-Side: 191.30 in./211.20 in. Height: 72 in. Front tread: 65.8 in. Rear tread: 62.7 in. Tires: L78-15B.

CHASSIS: [P10] Wheelbase: 102 in. Tires: L78-15B.

CHASSIS: [C20] Wheelbase: 131.5 in./164.5 in. Overall length: Fleetside: 211.40 in./244.40 in., Step-Side: 210.50 in. Height: 69.8 in. Front tread: 65.8 in. Rear tread: 62.7 in. Tires: 8.75 x 16.5C. Bonus-Cab tires: [Front] 8.75 x 16.5C [Rear], 8.75 x 16.5D. Crew-Cab tires: 9.50 x 16.5D.

CHASSIS: [K20] Wheelbase: 131.5 in. Overall length: Fleetside: 212 in., Step-Side: 211.20 in. Height: 73.9 in. Front tread: 65.8 in. Rear tread: 62.7 in. Tires: 8.75 x 16.5C.

CHASSIS: [P20] Wheelbase: 125 in./133 in. Overall length: 220.75 in./244.75 in. Tires: 8.75 x 16.5C.

CHASSIS: [C30] Wheelbase: 131.5 in./164.5 in. Overall length: Fleetside: 211.40 in./244.40 in., Step-Side: 210.50 in. Height: 71.8 in. Front tread: 65.8 in. Rear tread: 62.7 in. Tires: 8.75 x 16.5C. Bonus and Crew-Cab tires: 9.50 x 16.5E.

CHASSIS: [P30] Wheelbase: 125 in./157 in. Overall length: 220.75 in./268.75 in. Tires: 8.75 x 16.5C.

1976 Chevrolet "Big 10" Fleetside Pickup (CP)

TECHNICAL: [C10] Three-speed manual transmission or Turbo-Hydramatic transmission with 454-cid. V-8. [C20] Same as C10 except Turbo-Hydramatic with Crew-Cab also. [K10/K20] Three-speed manual transmission or Turbo-Hydramatic with 400-cid. V-8. New Process transfer case with 4x4 trucks. Single-plate, dry-disc clutch (with base six-cylinder). Rear axle ratio (with base six-cylinder) 3.73:1 on C10s and 4.10:1 on C20s. Front disc/rear drum brakes. Standard equipment includes steel disc wheels.

1976 Chevrolet Suburban 4x4 Sport Utility Vehicle (RCA)

EL CAMINO OPTIONS: SS equipment package ($226). Conquista package for El Camino Classic ($128). 350-cid V-8 ($30). 400-cid V-8 ($148).

BLAZER OPTIONS: Cheyenne package ($626). 400-cid four-barrel V-8 engine ($144). [Pickups/Carryall Suburbans] 400-cid V-8 engine ($144). C20 eight-foot stake equipment ($595). C30 nine-foot stake equipment ($695). C10 4x4 option ($1,147). C20 4x4 option ($1,066).

VAN OPTIONS: 350-cid four-barrel V-8 for G10 ($17). M40 Turbo-Hydramatic transmission ($246). Optional axle ratios ($13). Limited-slip axle ($137). Polywrap air cleaner ($11). Air conditioning ($527). Front and rear air conditioning ($840). Heavy-duty battery ($16). Power brakes, G10 ($50). Chrome bumpers ($33). Heavy-duty clutch ($7). Heavy-duty radiator ($24). Push-button radio ($67). AM/FM radio ($145). Painted outside rear view mirror ($19.50). Stainless outside rear view mirror ($31). Back door glass ($45). Extra heavy-duty cooling ($48). Custom Deluxe trim package ($14). Gauge package ($13). 42-ampere generator ($25). Tinted glass ($14). Body moldings ($55). Auxiliary seat ($67). Heavy-duty shocks ($14). Comfortilt steering ($58). 50-gal. fuel tank ($50). Rally wheels ($70). Custom Appearance package ($99). **STEP-VAN OPTIONS:** 11,000-pound rear axle ($152).

C/K OPTIONS: 454-cid V-8 engine ($452). Radios: AM, AM/FM ($151.00). Tachometer. Sliding rear window. Speed and cruise control. Cargo area lamp. Below-eye-line mirrors. Bucket seats. Two-tone paint combinations. Pickup box side rails. Rear chromed step bumper. Deluxe chromed bumper. Stainless steel wheelcovers. White-stripe or white-lettered tires, Series 10 only ($187.55). Glide-out spare tire carrier. Silverado trim package ($172.00). Scottsdale trim package.

COLOR OPTIONS: See 1975 options section for complete chart of 1975-1978 Chevrolet Commercial Truck colors.

HISTORICAL: Introduced Oct. 2, 1975. Calendar-year sales: 1,048,135. Model-year sales: [Light-duty Pickups] 682,039, [Vans] 128,040, [Blazer] 66,368, [El Camino] 43,595, [LUV] 41,693, [Carryall Suburban] 40,122, [Medium- and heavy-duty] 43,312. [Total] 1,045,169. Innovations: All-new Blazer with station wagon type New trim packages and options. J.T. Riley was sales manager for Chevrolet Motor Div.'s truck group. All-time high output of Blazers, Vans, and Carryall Suburbans in calendar-year 1976. Chevrolet was America's leading truck-maker with its strong 35.02 percent market share for calendar 1976.

1977 CHEVROLET

1977 Chevrolet El Camino Classic Sedan-Pickup (CP)

1/2-TON LIGHT UTILITY VEHICLE (LUV) — MODEL L/SERIES 10500 — FOUR: The badge-engineered LUV mini-Pickup, built by Isuzu, of Japan, returned with a Chevrolet bow tie. It had fenderless-pickup styling like a Fleetside, but in a much smaller scale. The standard all-vinyl interior had plaid pattern upholstery. A Mikado cloth trim package was available at extra cost. For the first time, the LUV was merchandised as a Chassis & Cab. The main reason for this was to provide a mini-motorhome chassis. Platform, and Stake models were also seen. The "Mighty Mike" package came with a new, wide tape stripe running from doors to the rear. A "color spectrum" paint treatment was featured at the beginning of the decal, on the doors. At the rear, reversed-out lettering identified the package, which included white spoke wheels and fat white-letter tires.

1/2-TON EL CAMINO — MODEL C, D/SERIES 14000 — SIX/V-8: Standard El Camino continued to feature single headlights and a cross-hatched grille insert. Classic models had a vertical members grille and dual stacked headlights. The grille surround molding was a much thicker piece of chrome. Classics carried a model identification script below the front fender's El Camino lettering. Their rocker panels had bright metal underscores. The sporty package included SS identification letters for the lower left-hand grille corner, plus SS decals for the cowl sides. Twin tape stripes ran from behind the decal to the rear. Styled wheels and white-letter tires were other extras. There was also a Conquista option package.

1/2-TON, 3/4-TON, 1-TON VAN — MODEL G/SERIES 10, 20, 30 — SIX/V-8: Chevrolet vans had the same styling as 1976. The panel-side Chevy Van and windowed Sportvan both came on 110-in. or 125-in. wheelbases in the 1/2-ton G10 series. The 3/4-ton G20 series offered Chevy Vans and Sportvans in both sizes, plus a long wheelbase Beauville Sportvan. In the 1-ton G30 series, all three models came on the long wheelbase and the small Chevy Van was available. All Beauvilles had a V-8 as standard equipment.

1/2-TON BLAZER — MODEL CK/SERIES 10500 — SIX/V-8: The Blazer remained more or less a short wheelbase version of C10/K10 trucks. It featured a steel half-cab with an integral roll bar built into the steel front compartment roof and lock pillar structures. There was a short Fleetside-like pickup box at the rear. A new optional soft-top came in white, black, blue or buckskin. Also available, at extra cost, was a removable fiberglass-reinforced plastic roof that attached to the pickup box with 16 bolts. Soft-Ride suspension was standard. For 1977 there was a restyled eggcrate grille with 15 openings (instead of 32) and dark gray metallic finish (instead of Argent Silver). Custom Deluxe trim was standard. The optional Cheyenne package included a Cheyenne nameplate, front bucket seats, console, gauges, simulated wood-grain trim, chrome front and rear bumpers, bright upper and lower body side moldings, bright hubcaps, bright accents, and Cheyenne nameplates. Cheyenne hardtops also included color-keyed carpets, door pockets, special interior trim, and wood-grain accents.

1977 Chevrolet Blazer Sport Utility Vehicle (CP)

1/2-TON, 3/4-TON, 1-TON — MODEL CK/SERIES 10, 20, 30 — SIX/V-8: Conventional trucks included the Chassis-and-Cab, Fleetside, and Step-Side Pickups, and the Carryall Suburban with its single-unit body. The four-door Carryall Suburban had its own exclusive 129.5-in. wheelbase. An end-gate was standard, but double rear panel doors were optional. Other models came on 117.5-in. or 131.5-in. wheelbases. Short wheelbase Pickups had a 6.5-ft. box and long wheelbase Pickups had an 8-ft. box. All these models were available in the 1/2-ton C10 series. The 3/4-ton C20 series offered the Carryall Suburban, plus long wheelbase versions of the other models. Also available were longer Bonus-Cab and Crew-Cab models on a stretched 164.5-in. wheelbase. The Bonus-Cab had two doors, but the cab was extended for added passenger space. The Crew-Cab had four doors and a full rear seat. The 1-ton C30 series offered all models in the C30 line, except the Carryall Suburban. Beginning this year, the C30 models, as well as the C10 and C20 trucks, could be had with four-wheel-drive. The 4x4s were called K10s, K20s and K30s. The new K30s carried a heavier capacity 4,500-lb. front driving axle, instead of the 3,800-lb. axle on 3/4-ton models. Other equipment on the K30s included a modified 7,500-lb. rear axle, power steering, and a standard four-speed manual transmission. Also for 1977, all Chevrolet conventional trucks had a new grille arrangement with four (rather than eight) vertical dividers and two (rather than three) horizontal bars. A secondary mesh was placed behind the major grille sections. Single unit combination tail, stop, back-up lights replaced the former separate units on Step-Side models. A new Pickup option was the Sport package with special hood and body side striping, and white-spoke or Rally wheels. The Sport tape stripes followed the body feature lines and continued in tiara fashion across the roof. "Chevy Sport" lettering appeared on the upper box sides of Fleetsides and the rear spare tire cover on Step-Sides. Appearance changes to the 1977 truck interiors consisted of new seat trim colors, fabrics and wood-grain trim. Custom Deluxe was the basic trim level. It included a foam-padded bench seat with plaid upholstery, a body-color steel roof headliner panel, black rubber floor mat, padded arm rests, courtesy lamps, prismatic rear view mirror, foam padded dash, bright upper and lower grille outline moldings, bright headlamp bezels, silver plastic grille insert, bright outside rear view mirror, bright door handles, bright Custom Deluxe nameplates and white-painted bumper, hubcaps, and wheels. The next-step-up was Scottsdale trim with a full-depth foam padded seat, wood-grain door trim inserts, an ash tray cigarette lighter, door or manually-operated courtesy lamps, bright door sill plates, color-keyed rubber floor mats, a high-note horn, patterned nylon cloth upholstery with vinyl trim, and all Custom Deluxe exterior features, plus a chrome bumper, chrome hubcaps, bright chrome side moldings on Fleetsides, bright windshield and window trim, bright-rimmed parking, side marker and taillights, and Scottsdale nameplates. Cheyenne trim included full-depth foam seat cushions, ribbed pattern velour or buffalo-hide vinyl upholstery (vinyl bucket seats optional), folding seat backs, ash tray-mounted cigarette lighter, chestnut wood-grain dash and door inserts, door or manually-operated courtesy and dome lamps, and added cab insulation. The exterior featured all Custom Deluxe and Scottsdale features, plus bright metal cab appliqués and moldings, bright upper body side and tailgate moldings, tailgate center appliqués on Fleetsides, and Cheyenne nameplates. At the top of the line was the Silverado option featuring extra-thick seat padding, velour cloth-and-vinyl or buffalo hide vinyl trim, tilting seat backs, full gauges, chestnut wood-grain dash panel and door inserts, door storage pockets, carpeting, an insulated headliner, extra body insulation, and all Custom Deluxe, Scottsdale and Cheyenne exterior items, plus lower body side and tailgate moldings, wheel lip moldings, Silverado nameplates, and a tailgate appliqué on Fleetsides. Joining the optional equipment list was an Operating Convenience package with power windows and power door locks. These could also be ordered separately and represented a first in the truck industry. Another new option was an Exterior Decor package. It included a spring-loaded hood emblem, two-tone paint, and color-coordinated hood striping. Six new two-tone color schemes were offered in this package. They featured a secondary color on the hood, between body side moldings, and on the roof of cab models. Also offered were new wheelcovers for 1/2-ton models, and an inside hood release. The big 454-cid V-8 was now fitted with double-honed piston walls and modified rings for improved oil consumption. Also debuting was a new method of gasketing rocker covers and redesigned distributor cap and rotor. Exterior colors for 1977 were Mariner Blue, Cordova Brown, Saratoga Silver, Light Blue, Cardinal Red, Buckskin Tan, Holy Green, Russet Metallic, Hawaiian Blue, Santa Fe Tan, Mahogany, Red Metallic, Colonial Yellow, Frost White, and Seamist Green.

1977 Chevrolet Cheyenne Fleetside Pickup (CP)

1/2-TON, 3/4-TON, 1-TON FORWARD-CONTROL — MODEL P-SERIES 10, 20, 30 — SIX/V-8: Forward-Control trucks were P (parcel delivery) models available in the 10 (1/2-ton), 20 (3/4-ton), and 30 (1-ton) series. The P10s had a 102-in. wheelbase and 7-ft. body. P20s came with 125-in. or 133-in. wheelbases designed for 10-ft. or 12-ft. bodies. P30s came in these sizes, plus a 157-in. wheelbase designed for 14-ft. bodies. Styling was boxy and unchanged. The grille had two horizontal rectangular openings. The bar between them said Chevrolet. Outside the grille on either end were tall rectangles housing the parking lights and headlamps. A channel type front bumper was used. An interesting thing about P models was that they were available with the most powerful engine offered in trucks, a 240 net horsepower (nhp) version of the 454-cid V-8.

1977 Chevrolet Cheyenne C10 Fleetside long box Pickup (OCW)

I.D. DATA: Serial number located. Combination VIN and rating plate located on: [El Camino] Top left side of dash, [Conventionals] left door pillar. Serial number systems: [El Camino] First symbol indicates manufacturer, 1=Chevrolet. Second symbol indicates car-line/series: C=El Camino, D=El Camino Classic. Third and fourth symbols indicate body type: 80=Sedan-Pickup. Fifth symbol indicates engine: [El Camino] D=250-cid/110-nhp one-barrel L6, U=305-cid/145-nhp two-barrel V-8, L=350-cid/170-nhp four-barrel V-8. Sixth symbol indicates model-year: 7=1977. Seventh symbol indicates assembly plant. Symbols 8-13 indicate the production sequence number starting at 100,001. Ending numbers not available. [All Light-Duty] The first symbol indicates manufacturer: 1=Chevrolet Motor Div. The second symbol indicates chassis type: C=96 in. or 106 in. Conventional Cab including Blazer, G=Chevy Van or Sportvan, K=106 in. Conventional cab 4x4, P=Forward-Control, L=Light Utility. The third symbol indicates engine as follows: D=250-cid/110-nhp one-barrel L6, L=350-cid/165-nhp four-barrel V-8, N=110-cid/80-nhp two-barrel L4 (LUV), S=454-cid/245-nhp four-barrel V-8 (C models only), T=292-cid/120-nhp one-barrel L-6, U=305-cid/145-nhp two-barrel V-8, Y=454-cid/240-nhp four-barrel V-8 (P models only). The fourth symbol indicates series and tonnage: 1=1/2-ton, 2=3/4-ton, 3=1-ton. The fifth symbol indicates body type: 2=Chassis & Cowl, 3=Chassis-and-Cab, 4=Cab with pickup box or Hi-Cube van, 5=Panel or Panel Van, 6=Sportvan, Carryall Suburban (doors) 7=Motorhome chassis, 8=Utility. The sixth symbol indicates model-year: 7=1977 The seventh symbol indicates the assembly plant: A=Lakewood, Ga., B=Baltimore, Md., F=Flint, Mich., J=Janesville, Wis., S=St. Louis, Mo., U=Lordstown, Ohio, V=Pontiac, Mich. GMAD, Z=Fremont, Calif., 1=Oshawa, Canada, 3=GMAD, Detroit, Mich., 4=Scarborough, Ontario, Canada, 8=Fujisawa, Japan. Symbols 8-13 are the production sequence number. Starting number: 10001 Ending numbers not available. Engine numbers located: [Six] on pad at right-hand side of cylinder block at rear of distributor, [V-8] on pad at front, right-hand side of cylinder block.

1977 Chevrolet K10 Step-Side 4x4 Pickup (RCA)

Model	Body Type	Price	Weight	Prod. Total
1/2-Ton LUV — Model L/Series 10500 — 102.4 in. w.b.				
CL10503	Chassis & Cab	3084	2380	Note 1
CL10503	Pickup	3284	2380	Note 1
NOTE 1: Calendar-year sales: 67,539.				
1/2-Ton El Camino — Model C, D/Series 14000 — 116 in. w.b.				
IAC80	Sedan-Pickup	4268	3797	Note 2
IAD80	Classic Sedan-Pickup	4403	3763	Note 2
NOTE 2: Model-year production: 54,321 El Camino/El Camino Classic.				
NOTE 3: Add $244 for SS package.				
1/2-Ton Vans — Model G/Series 10 — 110 in./125 in. w.b.				
CG11005	Panel	4112	3586	Note 14
CG11006	Sportvan	4885	3913	Note 14
NOTE 4: Add for 125-in. wheelbase.				
1/2-Ton Van — Model G/Series 10 — 125 in. w.b.				
CG11006	Beauville	5548	4314	Note 14
3/4-Ton Vans — Model G/Series 20 — 110 in./125 in. w.b.				
CG21005	Panel Van	4375	3607	Note 14
CG21006	Sportvan	5110	3890	Note 14
NOTE 5: Add for 125-in. wheelbase.				
3/4-Ton Vans — Model G/Series 20 — 125 in. w.b.				
CG21306	Beauville	5775	4267	Note 14
1-Ton Vans — Model G/Series 30 — 110 in./125 in. w.b.				
CG31005	Panel Van	4496	3840	Note 14
1-Ton Vans — Model G/Series 30 — 125 in. w.b.				
CG31306	Sportvan	5368	4300	Note 14
CG31306	Beauville	5871	4508	Note 14
1-Ton High-Cube — Model G/Series 30 — 125 in. w.b.				
CG31303	Hi-Cube 10 ft.	6410	4961	Note 14
1-Ton High-Cube — Model G/Series 30 — 146 in. w.b.				
CG31603	High-Cube 12 ft.	6593	5727	Note 14
1/2-Ton Blazer 4x4 — Model K/Series 10500 — 106.5 in. w.b.				
CK10516	Utility Hardtop	5603	4268	Note 14
CK10516	Open Utility	5503	-	Note 14
1/2-Ton Conventional — Model C/Series 10 — 117.5 in. w.b.				
CC10703	Chassis & Cab	4116	3251	Note 14
CC10703	Step-Side 6.5 ft.	4122	3585	Note 14
CC10703	Fleetside 6.5 ft.	4122	3645	Note 14
1/2-Ton Carryall Suburban — Model C/Series 10 — 129.5 in. w.b.				
CC10906	Suburban 9 ft. (gate)	5248	4315	Note 14
NOTE 6: Panel doors optional.				
1/2-Ton Conventional — Model CK/Series 10 — 131.5 in. w.b.				
CC10903	Step-Side 6.5 ft.	3908	3877	Note 14
CC10903	Fleetside 6.5 ft.	3908	3953	Note 14
NOTE 7: Add for K10 (4x4) Pickup and Carryall Suburban.				
1/2-Ton Step-Van — Model P/Series 10 — 102 in. w.b.				
CP10542	Steel Step-Van 7 ft.	5391	4176	-
3/4-Ton Conventional — Model C/Series 20 — 131.5 in. w.b.				
CC20903	Chassis & Cab	4399	3662	Note 14
CC20903	Step-Side	4624	4051	Note 14
CC20903	Fleetside	4624	4142	Note 14
3/4-Ton Carryall Suburban — Model C/Series 20 — 129.5 in. w.b.				
CC10906	Suburban 9 ft. (gate)	5775	4671	Note 14
NOTE 8: Panel doors optional.				
CC20943	Chassis & Bonus-Cab	5046	4164	Note 14
CC20943	Bonus-Cab Fleetside	5271	4644	Note 14
CC20963	Chassis & Crew-Cab	5420	4850	Note 14
CC20963	Crew-Cab Fleetside	5645	4880	Note 14
NOTE 9: Add for K20 (4x4) Pickup and Carryall Suburban.				
3/4-Ton Step-Van — Model P/Series 20 — 125 in./133 in. w.b.				
CP20842	Steel Step-Van 10 ft.	6287	5273	-
NOTE 10: Add for 12-ft./133-in. wheelbase P10842 model.				
1-Ton Conventional — Model C/Series 30 — 131.5 in. w.b.				
CC30903	Chassis & Cab	4539	3803	Note 14
CC30903	Step-Side 8 ft.	4764	4192	Note 14
CC30903	Fleetside 8 ft.	4764	4283	Note 14
1-Ton Conventional — Model C/Series 30 — 164.5 in. w.b.				
CC30943	Chassis & Bonus-Cab	5470	4444	Note 14
CC30943	Bonus-Cab Fleetside	5695	4924	Note 14
CC30963	Chassis & Crew-Cab	5580	5475	Note 14
CC30963	Crew-Cab Fleetside	5805	5015	Note 14
1-Ton Step-Van — Model P/Series 30 — 125/133/157 in. w.b..				
CP30842	Steel Step-Van 10 ft.	6603	5493	-

NOTE 11: Add for 12-ft./133-in. wheelbase P30842 model.
NOTE 12: Add for 14-ft./157-in. wheelbase P31042 model.
NOTE 13: Prices/weights for base V-8s (except six-cylinder only models).
NOTE 14: Model-year production: [Chevy Van] 147,377 (no 4x4), [Sportvan/Beauville] 43,386 (no 4x4), [Blazer] 86,838 (87.8 percent 4x4), [C10/K10 Conventional] 525,791 (21 percent 4x4), [C10/K10/C20/K20 Carryall Suburban] 60,273 (20.9 percent 4x4), [C20/K20 Cab models] 189,150 (31 percent 4x4), [C30/K30] 60,779 (8 percent 4x4), [P10/P20/P30 Step-Van] 30,886 (no 4x4).

ENGINE: [Standard LUV] Inline. OHV. Four-cylinder. Cast iron block. Bore & stroke: 3.31 in. x 3.23 in. Displacement: 110.8 cid. Compression ratio: 8.5:1. Net horsepower: 80 at 5000 rpm. Maximum torque: 88 lb.-ft. at 3000 rpm. Five main bearings. Hydraulic valve lifters. Carburetor: Rochester Quadra-Jet four-barrel.
ENGINE: [Standard C10/K10/El Camino/Blazer/Vans] Inline. OHV. Six-cylinder. Cast iron block. Bore & stroke: 3-7/8 in. x 3-1/2 in. Displacement: 250 cid. Compression ratio: 8.25:1. Net horsepower: 110 at 4800 rpm. Maximum torque: 175 lb.-ft. at 1800 rpm. Seven main bearings. Hydraulic valve lifters. Carburetor: one-barrel.
ENGINE: [Standard C20/C30/K20/Step-Van] Inline. OHV. Six-cylinder. Cast iron block. Bore & stroke: 3-7/8 in. x 4-1/8 in. Displacement: 292 cid. Compression ratio: 8.0:1. Net horsepower: 120 at 3600 rpm. Maximum torque: 215 lb.-ft. at 2000 rpm. Seven main bearings. Hydraulic valve lifters. Carburetor: one-barrel.
ENGINE: [Optional El Camino] V-block. OHV. Eight-cylinder. Cast iron block. Bore and stroke: 3.736 x 3.48 in. Displacement: 305 cid. Net horsepower: 145. Taxable horsepower: 44.66. Five main bearings. Hydraulic lifters. Carburetor: two-barrel.
ENGINE: [Optional C Series] V-block. OHV. Eight-cylinder. Cast iron block. Bore and stroke: 3.736 x 3.48 in. Displacement: 305 cid. Net horsepower: 130. Taxable horsepower: 44.66. Five main bearings. Hydraulic lifters. Carburetor: two-barrel.
ENGINE: [Optional C Series] V-block. OHV. Eight-cylinder. Cast iron block. Bore & stroke: 4 in. x 3-1/2 in. Displacement: 350 cid. Compression ratio: 8.5:1. Net horsepower: 145 at 3800 rpm. Maximum torque: 250 lb.-ft. at 2200 rpm. Five main bearings. Hydraulic valve lifters. Carburetor: two-barrel.
ENGINE: [Optional El Camino] V-block. OHV. Eight-cylinder. Cast iron block. Bore & stroke: 4 in. x 3-1/2 in. Displacement: 350 cid. Compression ratio: 8.5:1. Net horsepower: 170 at 3800 rpm. Maximum torque: 255 lb.-ft. at 2800 rpm. Five main bearings. Hydraulic valve lifters. Carburetor: Rochester Quadra-Jet four-barrel.
ENGINE: [Optional K10/K20/Vans/Blazer] V-block. OHV. Eight-cylinder. Cast iron block. Bore & stroke: 4-1/8 in. x 4 in. Displacement: 400 cid. Compression ratio: 8.5:1. Net horsepower: 175 at 3600 rpm. Maximum torque: 290 lb.-ft. at 2800 rpm. Five main bearings. Hydraulic valve lifters. Carburetor: Rochester four-barrel Quadra-Jet.
ENGINE: [Optional P Series] V-block. OHV. Eight-cylinder. Cast iron block. Bore & stroke: 4-1/4 in. x 4 in. Displacement: 454 cid. Compression ratio: 8.25:1. Net horsepower: 240 at 3800 rpm. Maximum torque: 370 lb.-ft. at 2800 rpm. Five main bearings. Hydraulic valve lifters. Carburetor: Rochester Quadra-Jet four-barrel.
ENGINE: [Step-Van] V-block. OHV. Eight-cylinder. Cast iron block. Bore & stroke: 4-1/8 in. x 4 in. Displacement: 454 cid. Compression ratio: 8.25:1. Net horsepower: 245 at 3800 rpm. Five main bearings. Hydraulic valve lifters. Carburetor: Rochester four-barrel Quadra-Jet.

1977 Chevrolet Beauville Sportvan (CP)

CHASSIS: [LUV] Wheelbase: 102.4 in. Overall length: 173.8 in. Height: 59.3 in. Front tread: 54 in. Rear tread: 52.2 in. Tires: E78 x 14B.
CHASSIS: [El Camino] Wheelbase: 116 in. Overall length: 210.6 in. Height: 53.8. Front tread: 58.5 in. Rear tread: 57.8 in. Tires: GR78-15B.
CHASSIS: [Blazer] Wheelbase: 106.5 in. Overall length: 184.5 in. Height: [4x2] (without top) 66.75 in., (with top) 68.75 in. [4x4] (without top) 69 in., (with top) 71 in. Front/rear tread: [4x2] 64.5 in./63 in., [4x4] 65.75 in./62.75 in. Tires: [Six] E78-15B, [V-8] H78-15B.
CHASSIS: [G10] Wheelbase: 110 in./125 in. Overall length: 178 in./202.2 in. Height: 78.8 x 81.2 in. Tires: [SWB] E78 x 15B, [LWB] F78 x 15B.
CHASSIS: [G20] Wheelbase: 110 in./125 in. Overall length: 178 in./202.2 in. Height: 78.8 x 81.2 in. Tires: J78-15B.
CHASSIS: [G30] Wheelbase: 125 in./146 in. Tires: 8.00 x 16.5C.
CHASSIS: [C10/C10] Wheelbase: 117.5/131.5 in. Overall length: Fleetside: 191.5 in./211.40 in., Step-Side: 190.75 in./210.50 in. Height: 69.8 in. Front tread: 65.8 in. Rear tread: 62.7 in. Tires: G70-15B. Tires: [Six] L78-15B, [V-8] L78-15C [V-8].
CHASSIS: [K10] Wheelbase: 117.5 in./131.5 in. Overall length: Fleetside: 192.10 in./212 in., Step-Side: 191.30 in./211.20 in. Height: 72 in. Front tread: 65.8 in. Rear tread: 62.7 in. Tires: L78-15B.
CHASSIS: [P10] Wheelbase: 102 in. Tires: L78-15B.
CHASSIS: [C20] Wheelbase: 131.5 in./164.5 in. Overall length: Fleetside: 211.40 in./244.40 in., Step-Side: 210.50 in. Height: 69.8 in. Front tread: 65.8 in. Rear tread: 62.7 in. Tires: 8.75 x 16.5B. Bonus-Cab tires: [Front] 8.75 x 16.5C [Rear], 8.75 x 16.5D. Crew-Cab tires: 9.50 x 16.5D.
CHASSIS: [K20] Wheelbase: 131.5 in. Overall length: Fleetside: 212 in., Step-Side: 211.20 in. Height: 73.9 in. Front tread: 65.8 in. Rear tread: 62.7 in. Tires: 8.75 x 16.5C.
CHASSIS: [P20] Wheelbase: 125 in./133 in. Overall length: 220.75 in./244.75 in. Tires: 8.75 x 16.5C.
CHASSIS: [C30] Wheelbase: 131.5 in./164.5 in. Overall length: Fleetside: 211.40 in./244.40 in., Step-Side: 210.50 in. Height: 71.8 in. Front tread: 65.8 in. Rear tread: 62.7 in. Tires: 8.75 x 16.5C. Bonus and Crew-Cab tires: 9.50 x 16.5E.
CHASSIS: [P30] Wheelbase: 125 in./157 in. Overall length: 220.75 in./268.75 in. Tires: 8.75 x 16.5C.
TECHNICAL: [C10] Three-speed manual transmission or Turbo-Hydramatic transmission with 454-cid. V-8. [C20] Same as C10 except Turbo-Hydramatic with Crew-Cab also. [K10/K20] Three-speed manual transmission or Turbo-Hydramatic with 400-cid V-8. New Process transfer case with 4x4 trucks. Single-plate, dry-disc clutch. Rear axle ratio (with base six-cylinder) 3.73:1 on C10s and 4.10:1 on C20s. Front disc/rear drum brakes. Standard equipment includes steel disc wheels.

1977 Chevrolet Blazer 4x4 Sport Utility Vehicle (RCA)

LUV OPTIONS: Mikado trim package. Mighty Mike package.
EL CAMINO OPTIONS: 305-cid two-barrel V-8 ($120). 350-cid four-barrel V-8 ($210). Turbo-Hydramatic ($282). Power steering ($146). Power windows ($108). Front air conditioning ($499). All tinted glass ($54). AM radio ($72). AM/FM radio ($137). Stereo tape with AM radio ($209). Stereo tape with AM/FM radio ($324). Performance axle ($14). Positraction ($54). Heavy-duty battery ($17). Heavy-duty radiator ($29). Conquista package ($138). Box tonneau ($96). Box rails ($68). SS equipment ($244). Tie down cargo box ($14). Speed and cruise control ($80). Vinyl roof ($65). Econo gauges ($47). Exterior decor package, with vinyl roof ($20), without vinyl roof ($46). Swing-out vinyl bucket seats ($129). Power seat ($137).
CHEVY VAN OPTIONS: 305-cid two-barrel V-8 ($120). 350-cid four-barrel V-8, G10 ($210), G20 ($135). 400-cid four-barrel V-8 ($319). Turbo Hydramatic ($315). Power steering ($179). Power brakes ($62). Heavy-duty vacuum power brakes ($53). Front air conditioning ($601). All tinted glass, Nomad ($43), other vans ($60). AM radio ($79). AM/FM radio ($155). Rear speaker ($36). Optional axle ratio ($16). Locking differential ($160). Heavy-duty battery ($31). Heavy-duty radiator ($29). Beauville trim, with Caravan ($173), without Caravan ($295). Caravan package, G10/SWB ($938), G10/LWB ($990), G20/SWB ($830), G20/LWB ($882). Custom Appearance package ($104). Custom Comfort & Convenience package, Chevy Van ($141), Sportvan/SWB ($320), Sportvan/LWB ($363). Custom vinyl bucket seats, without Caravan ($365). Custom cloth bucket seats, without Caravan ($365). 12-passenger seating option, Sportvan ($363). Front and rear air conditioning ($964).
BLAZER OPTIONS: 305-cid two-barrel V-8 ($120). 350-cid four-barrel V-8 ($210). 400-cid four-barrel V-8 ($369). Turbo-Hydramatic ($282). Four-speed manual transmission ($142). Power steering, with 4x2 ($169), with 4x4 ($188). Front air conditioning ($509). All windows tinted ($43). Tinted sliding side window with hardtop ($156). AM radio ($79). AM/FM radio ($155). Rear speaker ($36). Optional axle ratio ($16). Locking differential ($160). Heavy-duty battery ($31). Auxiliary battery ($88). Heavy-duty radiator ($34). Wood-grain exterior trim, with Cheyenne ($126), without Cheyenne ($266). Cold climate package, with trailer special ($89), without ($120). Cheyenne package, with 16 in. tires ($713), without ($735). Custom vinyl seats, with Cheyenne one-seater (NC), with Cheyenne two-seater ($38), regular one-seater ($222), regular two-seater ($260). Three-passenger rear seat ($179). Trailering Special package, with 4x2 ($200), with 4x4 ($219).
CARRYALL SUBURBAN OPTIONS: 305-cid V-8, C10 ($120). 350-cid V-8, C10 ($210), C20 ($90). 400-cid V-8 ($249). 454-cid V-8, C10 ($465), C20 ($335). Turbo-Hydramatic with 454-cid V-8 ($330), without 454-cid V-8 ($315). Four-speed manual transmission ($142). Power steering, with 4x2 ($169), with 4x4 ($188). Front air conditioning, Scottsdale/Silverado ($500), others ($599). Front/rear air conditioning ($780). All tinted glass ($50). AM radio ($79). AM/FM radio ($155). Rear speaker ($36). Optional axle ratio ($16). Locking differential ($160). Heavy-duty battery ($31). Auxiliary battery ($88). Heavy-duty radiator ($34). Wood-grain exterior trim, Silverado ($208), Scottsdale ($210), others ($266). Scottsdale package, with 4x2 ($315), with 4x4 ($318). Silverado package, with 4x2 ($591), with 4x4 ($582). Custom vinyl seats, with Silverado ($103 or $141 depending on number of seats), with Scottsdale ($38, $88 or $216 depending on number/type of seats). Center seat ($265), center and rear seats, C10 ($466), K10/C20/K20 ($444). Trailering Special, 4x2 ($200), 4x4 ($219). Special Custom cloth seat, (same prices as Custom Vinyl seat options).

1977 Chevrolet Scottsdale Crew-Cab Fleetside Pickup (CP)

C/K CAB MODEL OPTIONS: 305-cid V-8 ($120). 350-cid V-8, 10 Series ($210), 20 Series ($90). 400-cid V-8, K10 ($369), K20 ($294). 454-cid V-8, C10 ($465), C20 ($380). Turbo-Hydramatic, without 454-cid V-8 ($315), with 454-cid V-8 ($330). Four-speed manual transmission ($142). Power steering, with 4x2 ($169), with 4x4 ($188). Power brakes ($62). Heavy-duty vacuum power brakes, C20 ($53). Power windows ($120). Power sliding rear window ($62) Front air conditioning ($509). All tinted glass, Bonus-Cab and Crew-Cab ($34), other models ($27) AM radio ($79). AM/FM radio ($155). Optional axle ratio ($16). Locking differential ($160). Heavy-duty battery ($31). Auxiliary battery ($88). Heavy-duty radiator ($34). Speed and Cruise Control ($80). 8-ft. Pickup box floor ($63). Scottsdale package (without dual rear wheels, unless otherwise noted): For C10/C20 Step-Side with bench seat ($236), for same with bucket seats ($205). For K10/K20 Step-Side with bench seat ($239), for same with bucket seats ($208). For C10/C20 Fleetside with bench seats ($286), for same with bucket seats ($255). For Fleetside C20 Bonus-Cab ($236), for C20 Crew-Cab ($255). For Fleetside K10/K20 with bench seats ($289), for same with bucket seats ($258). For C10/C20 Chassis-and-Cab with bench seat ($236), for same with bucket seats ($205). For C20 Chassis-and-Bonus-Cab ($180). For C20 Chassis-and-Crew-Cab ($210). For K10/K20 Chassis-and-Cab with bench seat ($239), for same with bucket seats ($208). For C20 Crew-Cab with dual rear wheels ($195). Silverado package (without dual rear wheels, unless otherwise noted): For C10/C20 Step-Side with bench seat ($431), for same with bucket seats ($400). For K10/K20 Step-Side with bench seat ($422), for same with bucket seats ($391). For C10/C20 Fleetside with bench seats ($585), for same with bucket seats ($554). For Fleetside C20 Bonus-Cab ($641), for C20 Crew-Cab ($720). For Fleetside K10/K20 with bench seat ($575), for same with bucket seats ($545). For C10/C20 Chassis-and-Cab with bench seat ($431). For C20 Chassis-and-Bonus-Cab ($487). For C20 Chassis-and-Crew-Cab ($566). For K10/K20 Chassis-and-Cab with bench seat ($422), for same with bucket seats ($391). For C20 Crew-Cab with dual rear wheels ($556). Operating Convenience package, including power windows ($206). Custom vinyl bucket seats ($207). Knit vinyl bench seat ($38). Special order Custom bench seat with Scottsdale Bonus-Cab Pickup ($38), with Crew-Cab ($76). Folding seat back ($23). Trailering Special package, includes power steering: [C10/C20] ($200), [K10/K20] ($219). Eight-foot stake body for C20 ($640).

COLOR OPTIONS: See 1975 options section for complete chart of 1975-1978 Chevrolet Commercial Truck colors.
HISTORICAL: Introduced: Fall 1976. Calendar-year registrations: [All Series] 1,133,201. Innovations: New grilles on most models. First year for 1-ton with 4x4 chassis. New Sport Truck Pickup option. Improvements in 454-cid V-8.

1978 CHEVROLET

1/2-TON LIGHT UTILITY VEHICLE (LUV) — MODEL L/SERIES 10500 — FOUR: The imported LUV model moved into its Series 8 mode, which provided a new grille with horizontal bars and a re-designed instrument panel. Two box lengths, 6-ft. and 7-1/2 ft., were offered. The wheelbase on the latter extended to 117.9 in.

1978 Chevrolet El Camino Sedan-Pickup (CMD)

1/2-TON EL CAMINO — MODEL W/SERIES 14000 — SIX/V-8: The El Camino underwent its most extensive redesign since 1964. The 1978 model was on a longer 117.1-in. wheelbase, but overall length was reduced to 201.6 in. or 11.7 in. less than in 1977. A V-6 engine was now the base power plant. Key styling features included a sweeping roof line with small side quarter windows, a wraparound rear window, and single rectangular headlights. Curb weight was reduced by nearly 600 lb., but load capacity, at 800 lb., was unchanged. The standard 3.3-liter V-6 was a derivative of the Chevrolet small-block V-8. It weighed almost 80 lb. less than the six-cylinder engine it replaced. A second V-6, with a 3.8-liter displacement, was mandatory for California.
1/2-TON, 3/4-TON, 1-TON VAN — MODEL G/SERIES 10, 20, 30 — SIX/V-8: Chevy Van's had a facial. A new grille resembled the eggcrate version of other models. However, the headlight housings were distinct. They were sort of D-shaped and had a square headlight at top and a rectangular parking lamp on bottom. The Beauville continued to come only on the longer wheelbase with standard V-8 power. A new model was the Sporty Nomad, available only in the G20 line. It was essentially a factory custom van.

1978 Chevrolet K10 Blazer 4x4 Sport Utility Vehicle (RCA)

1/2-TON BLAZER — MODEL CK/SERIES 10500 — SIX/V-8: The Blazer was a short wheelbase version of C10/K10 trucks. It featured a steel half-cab with an integral roll bar built into the steel front compartment roof and lock pillar structures. There was a short Fleetside pickup box at the rear. Soft-top and hardtop models were optional. For 1978 the instrument panel trim and nameplate were changed. There was a Deluxe instrument panel option with black-textured center section for Custom Deluxe models, and bright brush finish for Cheyennes. Also new was an improved wiper motor, improved front seat belt system, redesigned rear compartment entry/exit system, smoother oxen textured vinyl upholstery, a new rear folding seat, and a flatter floor panel behind the seat for extra leg room. Power door locks and windows were added to the options list. Also new was a smaller 16-in. diameter soft vinyl steering wheel/horn button. Custom Deluxe trim was standard. The optional Cheyenne package included a Cheyenne nameplate, front bucket seats, console, gauges, simulated chestnut wood-grain trim, chrome front and rear bumpers, bright upper and lower body side moldings, bright hubcaps, bright accents, and Cheyenne nameplates. Cheyenne hardtops also included color-keyed carpets, door pockets, special interior trim, and wood-grain accents. Colors were the same as those for conventional trucks.

1978 Chevrolet K10 Cheyenne Super 4x4 short box Fleetside Pickup (RCA)

1/2-TON, 3/4-TON, 1-TON — MODEL CK/SERIES 10, 20, 30 — SIX/V-8: All Chevrolet Pickup trucks available during the 1977 model-year were retained for 1978 with no additions or deletions. The C30 dual rear wheel option was called the "Big Dooley" option. Chevrolet introduced a new GM-built 5.7-liter V-8 diesel engine for use in the 1/2-ton two-wheel-drive C10 Pickup. Its design features included aluminum alloy pistons with three rings, a cast iron regrindable crankshaft, three-inch diameter main bearings, rotary fuel-injection plug, electric glow plugs, and a seven-quart oil pump. Custom Deluxe was the basic trim level. It included a foam-padded bench seat with plaid upholstery, a body color steel roof headliner panel, black rubber floor mat, padded arm rests, courtesy lamps, prismatic rear view mirror, foam padded dash, bright upper and lower grille outline moldings, bright headlamp bezels, silver plastic grille insert, bright outside rear view mirror, bright door handles, bright Custom Deluxe nameplates, and white-painted bumper, hubcaps and wheels. The next-step-up was Scottsdale trim with a full-depth foam-padded seat, wood-grain door trim inserts, an ash tray cigarette lighter, door or manually-operated courtesy lamps, bright door sill plates, color-keyed rubber floor mats, a high-note horn, patterned nylon cloth upholstery with vinyl trim, and all Custom Deluxe exterior features, plus a chrome bumper, chrome hubcaps, chrome body side moldings on Fleetsides, bright windshield and window trim, bright-rimmed parking, side marker and taillights, and Scottsdale nameplates. Cheyenne trim included full-depth foam seat cushions, ribbed pattern velour or buffalo-hide vinyl upholstery (vinyl bucket seats optional), folding seat backs, ash tray-mounted cigarette lighter, chestnut wood-grain dash and door inserts, door or manually-operated courtesy and dome lamps, and added cab insulation. The exterior featured all Custom Deluxe and Scottsdale features, plus bright metal cab appliqués and moldings, bright upper body side and tailgate moldings, tailgate center appliqués on Fleetsides, and Cheyenne nameplates. At the top of the line was the Silverado option featuring extra-thick seat padding, velour cloth-and-vinyl or buffalo hide vinyl trim, tilting seat backs, full gauges, chestnut wood-grained dash panel and door inserts, door storage pockets, carpeting, an insulated headliner, extra body insulation, and all Custom Deluxe, Scottsdale and Cheyenne exterior items, plus lower body side and tailgate moldings, wheel lip moldings, Silverado nameplates, and a tailgate appliqué on Fleetsides. Exterior colors for 1978 were again Mariner Blue, Cordova Brown, Saratoga Silver, Light Blue, Cardinal Red, Buckskin Tan, Holy Green, Russet Metallic, Hawaiian Blue, Santa Fe Tan, Mahogany, Red Metallic, Colonial Yellow, Frost White, and Seamist Green.

1/2-TON, 3/4-TON, 1-TON FORWARD-CONTROL — MODEL P-SERIES 10, 20, 30 — SIX/V-8: Forward-Control trucks were P (parcel delivery) models available in the 10 (1/2-ton), 20 (3/4-ton), and 30 (1-ton) series. The P10s had a 102-in. wheelbase and 7-ft. body. P20s came with 125 in. or 133-in. wheelbases designed for 10-ft. or 12-ft. bodies. P30s came in these sizes, plus a 157-in. wheelbase designed for 14-ft. bodies. Styling was boxy and unchanged.

1978 Chevrolet K30 "Big Dooley" 4x4 Crew-Cab Pickup (RCA)

I.D. DATA: Serial number located. Combination VIN and rating plate located on: [El Camino] Top left side of dash, [Conventionals] left door pillar. Serial number systems: [El Camino] First symbol indicates manufacturer, 1=Chevrolet. Second symbol indicates car-line/series: W=El Camino. Third and fourth symbols indicate body type: 80=Sedan-Pickup. Fifth symbol indicates engine: [El Camino] A=231-cid/105-hp two-barrel V-6, D=250-cid/105-nhp one-barrel L6, H=305-cid/140-nhp two-barrel V-8, L=350-cid/170-nhp four-barrel V-8. Sixth symbol indicates model-year: 8=1978. Seventh symbol indicates assembly plant. Symbols 8-13 indicate the production sequence number starting at 100,001. Ending numbers not available. [All Light-Duty] The first symbol indicates manufacturer: 1=Chevrolet Motor Div. The second symbol indicates chassis type: C=96 in. or 106 in. Conventional Cab including Blazer, G=Chevy Van or Sportvan, K=106 in. Conventional cab 4x4, P=Forward-Control, L=Light Utility. The third symbol indicates engine as follows: D=250-cid/one-barrel L6 (horsepower rated 115 for models with GVW under 6,000 lb., 100 for models with GVWs over 6,000 lb.), L=350-cid/165-hp four-barrel V-8, N=110-cid/80-nhp two-barrel L4 (LUV), R=400-cid/175-hp four-barrel V-8, S=454-cid-nhp four-barrel V-8 for C models only (horsepower rated 205 for models with GVW under 6,000 lb., 240 for models with GVWs over 6,000 lb.), T=292-cid/120-

nhp one-barrel L-6, U=305-cid two-barrel V-8 (horsepower rated 145 for models with GVW under 6,000 lb., 140 for models with GVWs over 6,000 lb.), Z=5.7 liter LF9 350-cid/120-hp diesel V-8. The fourth symbol indicates series and tonnage: 1=1/2-ton, 2=3/4-ton, 3=1-ton, 4=1/2-ton with heavy-duty suspension. The fifth symbol indicates body type: 2=Chassis-and-Cowl, 3=Chassis-and-Cab, 4=Cab with pickup box or van with Hi-Cube box, 5=Panel or Panel Van, 6=Sportvan, Carryall Suburban (doors) 7=Motorhome chassis, 8=Utility (Blazer). The sixth symbol indicates model-year: 8=1978. The seventh symbol indicates the assembly plant: A=Lakewood, Ga., B=Baltimore, Md., F=Flint, Mich., J=Janesville, Wis., S=St. Louis, Mo., L=Lordstown, Ohio, V=Pontiac, Mich. GMAD, Z=Fremont, Calif., O=Pontiac (GMC) Michigan, 1=Oshawa or London, Ontario, Canada, 3=GMAD, Detroit, Mich., 4=Scarborough, Ontario, Canada, 8=Fujisawa, Japan. Symbols 8-13 are the production sequence number. Starting number: 10001 Ending numbers not available. Engine numbers located: [Six] on pad at right-hand side of cylinder block at rear of distributor, [V-8] on pad at front, right-hand side of cylinder block.

1978 Chevrolet Scottsdale Suburban (CP)

Model	Body Type	Price	Weight	Prod. Total
1/2-Ton LUV — Model L — 102.4/117.9 in. w.b. — Four				
CL10503	Chassis & Cab	3721	2095	Note 1
CL10503	Pickup	3885	2315	Note 1
NOTE 1: U.S. Sales of LUV: 71,145.				
1/2-Ton El Camino — Model W — 117.1 in. w.b. — V-6				
1AW80	Pickup	3807	-	Note 8
1AW80	Super Sport Pickup	3956	-	Note 8
1/2-Ton El Camino — Model W — 117.1 in. w.b. — V-8				
1AW80	Pickup	4843	3076	Note 8
1AW80	Super Sport Pickup	5022	3076	Note 8
1/2-Ton Van — Model G10 — 110 in. w.b. — V-8				
CG11005	Panel	4609	3652	Note 8
CG11006	Sportvan	5468	5468	Note 8
1/2-Ton Van — Model G10 — 125 in. w.b. — V-8				
CG11306	Beauville	6296	4323	Note 8
1/2-Ton Van — Model G10 — 110 in. w.b. — Six				
CG11305	Panel	4584	-	Note 8
CG11306	Sportvan	5443	-	Note 8
3/4-Ton Van — Model G20 — 110 in. w.b. — V-8				
CG21005	Panel	4904	3661	Note 8
CG21006	Sportvan	5726	3944	Note 8
3/4-Ton Van — Model G20 — 125 in. w.b. — V-8				
CG21306	Beauville	6439	4282	Note 8
CG21305	Nomad	6334	3801	Note 8
CG21305	Panel	3429	-	Note 8
CG21306	Sportvan	5641	-	Note 8
1-Ton Van — Model G30 — 110 in. w.b. — V-8				
CG31005	Panel	5055	3896	Note 8
1-Ton Van — Model G30 — 125 in. w.b. — V-8				
CG31306	Sportvan	6037	4357	Note 8
CG31306	Beauville	6590	4530	Note 8
1-Ton Hi-Cube Van — Model G30 — 125 in. w.b. — V-8				
CG31303	Van 10 ft.	6857	5047	Note 8
1-Ton Hi-Cube Van — Model G30 — 146 in. w.b. — V-8				
CG31603	Van 12 ft.	7157	5153	Note 8
1/2-Ton Blazer — Model K10 — 106.5 in. w.b. — V-8				
CK10516	Hardtop 4x4	6397	3928	Note 8
CK10516	Softtop 4x4	6297	3780	Note 8
NOTE 2: Deduct for C10 Blazer (4x2).				
1/2-Ton Step-Van — Model P10 — 102 in. w.b. — Six				
CP10542	Steel Step-Van	5771	4172	Note 8
1/2-Ton Conventional 4x2 — Model C10 — 117.5 in. w.b. — V-8				
CC10703	Chassis & Cab	4428	3246	Note 8
CC10703	Step-Side	4418	3579	Note 8
CC10703	Fleetside	4418	3639	Note 8
1/2-Ton Carryall Suburban 4x2 — Model C10 — 129.5 in. w.b. — V-8				
CC10906	Suburban (gate)	5810	4257	Note 8
NOTE 3: Add for panel door Carryall Suburban.				
1/2-Ton Conventional 4x2 — Model C10 — 131.5 in. w.b. — V-8				
CC10903	Step-Side	4493	3694	Note 8
CC10903	Fleetside	4493	3775	Note 8
1/2-Ton Diesel 4x2 — Model C10 Diesel — 117.5 in. w.b. — V-8				
CC10703	Step-Side	6228	3765	Note 8
CC10703	Fleetside	6228	3824	Note 8
1/2-Ton Diesel 4x2 — Model C10 Diesel — 131.5 in. w.b. — V-8				
CC10903	Step-Side	6303	3841	Note 8
CC10903	Fleetside	6303	3962	Note 8
1/2-Ton Conventional 4x4 — Model K10 — 117.5 in. w.b. — V-8				
CK10703	Chassis & Cab	5006	4143	Note 8
CK10703	Step-Side	5006	4477	Note 8
CK10703	Fleetside	5006	4537	Note 8
1/2-Ton Carryall Suburban 4x4 — Model K10 — 129.5 in. w.b. — V-8				
CK10906	Suburban (gate)	6348	5273	Note 8
NOTE 4: Add for panel door Carryall Suburban.				

Model	Body Type	Price	Weight	Prod. Total
1/2-Ton Conventional 4x4 — Model K10 — 131.5 in. w.b. — V-8				
CK10903	Step-Side	5062	4639	Note 8
CK10903	Fleetside	5062	4720	Note 8
3/4-Ton Conventional 4x2 — Model C20 — 131.5 in. w.b. — V-8				
CC20903	Chassis & Cab	4813	3665	Note 8
CC20903	Step-Side	5038	4054	Note 8
CC20903	Fleetside	5038	4135	Note 8
3/4-Ton Carryall Suburban 4x4 — Model C20 — 129.5 in. w.b. — V-8				
CC20906	Suburban (gate)	6795	6800	Note 8
NOTE 5: Add for panel door Carryall Suburban.				
3/4-Ton Conventional 4x2 — Model C20 — 164.5 in. w.b. — V-8				
CC20943	Chassis & Bonus-Cab	5512	4176	Note 8
CC20943	Bonus-Cab Fleetside	5737	4646	Note 8
CC20963	Chassis & Crew-Cab	5886	4233	Note 8
CC20963	Crew-Cab Fleetside	6111	4703	Note 8
3/4-Ton Conventional 4x4 — Model K20 — 131.5 in. w.b. — V-8				
CK20903	Chassis & Cab	5209	4485	Note 8
CK20903	Step-Side	5434	4874	Note 8
CK20903	Fleetside	5434	4955	Note 8
3/4-Ton Carryall Suburban 4x4 — Model K20 — 129.5 in. w.b. — V-8				
CK20906	Suburban (gate)	6381	4620	Note 8
NOTE 6: Add for panel door Carryall Suburban.				
3/4-Ton Step-Van — Model P20 — 125/133 in. w.b. — V-8				
CP20842	Panel	6753	5283	Note 8
NOTE 7: Add for 133 in. w.b. 12 ft. Step-Van Model CP20842.				
CP30842	Panel (133 in. w.b.)	6978	5503	Note 8
1-Ton Conventional 4x2 — Model C30 — 131.5 in. w.b. — V-8				
CC30903	Chassis & Cab	5055	3792	Note 8
CC30903	Step-Side	5280	4181	Note 8
CC30903	Fleetside	5280	4262	Note 8
1-Ton Conventional 4x2 — Model C30 — 164.5 in. w.b. — V-8				
CC30943	Chassis & Cab	5937	4439	Note 8
CC30943	Bonus-Cab Fleetside	6162	4909	Note 8
CC30943	Chassis & Crew-Cab	6047	4772	Note 8
CC30963	Fleetwood Crew-Cab	6272	4941	Note 8
1-Ton Conventional 4x4 — Model K30 — 131.5 in. w.b. — V-8				
CK30903	Chassis & Cab	5589	4956	Note 8
CK30903	Fleetside	5814	5426	Note 8
1-Ton Conventional 4x4 — Model K30 — 164.5 in. w.b. — V-8				
CK30943	Chassis & Bonus-Cab	6250	5370	Note 8
CK30943	Bonus-Cab Fleetside	6745	5840	Note 8
CK30963	Chassis & Crew-Cab	6630	5370	Note 8
CK30963	Fleetwood Crew-Cab	6855	5840	Note 8

NOTE 8: Model-year production: [El Camino] 54,286, [All Chevy Van] 203,007, [All Sportvan] 44,058, [Blazer] 88,858, [C10/C20 Carryall Suburban] 57,788, [Other C10] 540,968, [Other C20] 176,735, [C30] 68,010, [P10/P20/P30] 28,127. (Includes trucks built in Canada for U.S. market).

1978 Chevrolet Cheyenne Fleetside Pickup (CP)

ENGINE: [Standard LUV] Inline. OHV. Four-cylinder. Cast iron block. Bore & stroke: 3.31 x 3.23 in. Displacement: 110.8 cid. Compression ratio: 8.5:1. Net horsepower: 80 at 4800 rpm. Maximum torque: 95 lb.-ft at 3000 rpm. Five main bearings. Hydraulic valve lifters. Carburetor: One-barrel.
ENGINE: [Standard El Camino] V-block. OHV. Six-cylinder. Cast iron block. Bore & stroke: 3.50 x 3.48 in. Displacement: 200 cid. Compression ratio: 8.2:1. Net horsepower: 95 at 3800 rpm. Maximum torque: 160 lb.-ft at 2000 rpm. Hydraulic valve lifters. Carburetor: Rochester two-barrel.
ENGINE: [Optional: El Camino] (Standard for California delivery) Available only automatic transmission. V-type. OHV. Six-cylinder. Cast iron block. Bore & stroke: 3.80 x 3.40 in. Displacement: 231 cid. Compression ratio: 8.0:1. Net horsepower: 105 at 3400 rpm. Net torque: 185 lb.-ft at 2000 rpm. Carburetor: Rochester two-barrel.
ENGINE: [Standard: C10/Big 10/K10] Inline. OHV. Six-cylinder. Cast iron block. Bore & stroke: 3.876 x 3.530 in. Displacement: 250 cid. Compression ratio: 8.25:1. Net horsepower: 115 at 3800 rpm. Torque: 195 lb.-ft. at 1800 rpm. Seven main bearings. Hydraulic valve lifters. Carburetor: Mono-jet model 1ME. RPO Code: LD4.

1978 Chevrolet Chevy Van Panel (CP)

1978 Chevrolet El Camino SS Sedan-Pickup (CP)

ENGINE: [Standard: C20/C30/K20/K30] Inline. OHV. Six-cylinder. Cast iron block. Bore & stroke: 3.8764 x 4.120 in. Displacement: 292 cid. Compression ratio: 8.0:1. Net horsepower: 120 at 3600 rpm. Net torque: 215 lb.-ft. at 2000 rpm. Seven main bearings. Hydraulic valve lifters. Carburetor: One-barrel. RPO Code: L25.
ENGINE: [Optional: C10/El Camino] V--block. OHV. Eight-cylinder. Cast iron block. Bore & stroke: 3.736 x 3.480 in. Displacement: 305 cid. Compression ratio: 8.5:1. Net horsepower: 145 at 3800 rpm. Net torque: 245 lb.-ft. at 2400 rpm. Five main bearings. Hydraulic valve lifters. Carburetor: Two-barrel model 2GC. RPO Code: LG9.
ENGINE: [Optional: all models] V-type. OHV. Eight-cylinder. Cast iron block. Bore & stroke: 4.0 x 3.480 in. Displacement: 350 cid. Compression ratio: 8.5:1. Net horsepower: 165 at 3800 rpm. Net torque: 260 lb.-ft. at 2400 rpm. Five main bearings. Hydraulic valve lifters. Carburetor: Four-barrel model M4MC/MV. RPO Code: LS9.

1978 Chevrolet K30 Chassis-and-Cab with wrecker body and dual rear wheels (RCA)

ENGINE: [Optional: K10/K20/K30] V-type. OHV. Eight-cylinder. Cast iron block. Bore & stroke: 4.125 x 3.750 in. Displacement: 400 cid. Compression ratio: 8.5:1. Net horsepower: 175 at 3600 rpm. Net torque: 290 lb.-ft. at 2800 rpm. Five main bearings. Hydraulic valve lifters. Carburetor: Four-barrel model M4MC/MV. RPO Code: LF4.
ENGINE: [Optional: C1500/C2500/C3500 ($235)] V-type. OHV. Eight-cylinder. Cast iron block. Bore & stroke: 4.250 x 4.0 in. Displacement: 454 cid. Compression ratio: 8.5:1 Net horsepower: 205 at 3600 rpm. Net torque: 355 lb.-ft. at 2800 rpm. Five main bearings. Hydraulic valve lifters. Carburetor: Four-barrel model M4MC/MV. RPO Code: LF8.
ENGINE: [Optional: C10/Big 10] V-type. OHV diesel. Eight-cylinder. Cast iron block. Bore & stroke: 4.057 x 3.385 in. Displacement: 350 cid. Compression ratio: 20.5:1. Net horsepower: 120 at 3600 rpm. Net torque: 222 lb.-ft. at 1900 rpm. Five main bearings. Hydraulic valve lifters. RPO Code: LF9.
CHASSIS: [LUV] Wheelbase: 102.4/117.9 in. Overall length: 173.8/190.9 in. Front tread: 54 in. Rear tread: 52.2 in. Tires: E78 x 14B.
CHASSIS: [El Camino] Wheelbase: 117.1 in. Overall length: 201.6 in. Height: 53.8 in. Front tread: 58.5 in. Rear tread: 57.8 in. Tires: P205/75R x 14 in.
CHASSIS: [G10] Wheelbase: 110/125 in. Overall length: 178.2/202.2 in. Tires G78 x 15B in.
CHASSIS: [G20] Wheelbase: 110/125 in. Overall length: 178.2/202.2 in. Tires: J78 x 15B in.
CHASSIS: [G30] Wheelbase: 110/125 in. Overall length: 178.2/202.2 in. Tires: 8.00 x 16.5 in.

CHASSIS: [K10 Blazer] Wheelbase: 106.5 in. Overall length: 184.8 in. Height: 73.4 in. Front tread: 66.1 in. Rear tread: 63 in. Tires: H78 x 15B in.
CHASSIS: [C10/C10/Big 10] Wheelbase: 117.5/131.5 in. Overall length: 191.3/212 in. Height 69.8 in. Front tread: 65.8 in. Rear tread: 62.7 in. Tires: G78 x 15B in. [C10, Big 10], L78 x 15B in.
CHASSIS: [K10] Wheelbase: 117.5/131.5 in. Overall length: 191.3/212 in. Height: 72 in. Front tread: 65.8 in. Rear tread: 62.7 in. Tires: L78 x 15B in.
CHASSIS: [P10] Wheelbase: 102 in. Tires: L78 x 15B in.
CHASSIS: [P20] Wheelbase: 125/133 in. Tires: 8.75 x 16.5C in.
CHASSIS: [C20] Wheelbase: 117.5/131.5/164.5 in. Overall length: 191.3/212/244.43 in. Height: 69.8 in. Front tread: 65.8 in. Rear tread: 62.7 in. Tires: 8.75 x 16.5C in., [Bonus-Cab] 8.75 x 16.5 in., [F-C, R-D], [Crew-Cab] 9.50 x 16.5D in.
CHASSIS: [K20] Wheelbase: 131.5 in. Overall length: 212 in. Height: 73.9 in. Front tread: 65.8 in. Rear tread: 62.7 in. Tires: 8.75 x 16.5C in.
CHASSIS: [C30] Wheelbase: 131.5/164.5 in. Overall length: 212/244.43 in. Height: 71.8 in. Front tread: 65.8 in. Rear tread: 62.7 in. Tires: 8.75 x 16.5C in., [Bonus/Crew-Cab] 9.50 x 16.5E in.
CHASSIS: [K30] Wheelbase: 131.5/164.5 in. Overall length: 212/244.43 in. Height: 74.7/75 in. Front tread: 65.8 in. Rear tread: 62.7 in. Tires: 9.50 x 16.5D in.
CHASSIS: [P30] Wheelbase: 125/157 in. Tires: 8.75 x 6.5 in.

1978 Chevrolet Cheyenne Blazer Sport Utility Vehicle (CP)

TECHNICAL: C10] Three-speed manual transmission or Turbo-Hydramatic transmission with 454-cid. V-8. [C20] Same as C10 except Turbo-Hydramatic with Crew-Cab also. [K10/K20] Three-speed manual transmission or Turbo-Hydramatic with 400-cid V-8. New Process transfer case with 4x4 trucks. Single-plate, dry-disc clutch (with base six-cylinder). Rear axle ratio (with base six-cylinder) 3.73:1 on C10s and 4.10:1 on C20s. Front disc/rear drum brakes. Standard equipment includes steel disc wheels.
LUV OPTIONS: Mikado interior. High-back bucket seats. Mighty Mike decal package. Decor package. Sliding rear window. E78 x 14B Steel-belted whitewall tires. Mud flaps. Below-eye-line mirrors. Right-hand exterior mirror. Rear bumper. Rear-mounted spare tire.

1978 Chevrolet K10 Step-Side 4x4 Sport Pickup (RCA)

FULL-SIZE TRUCK OPTIONS: Chevy Van Custom Appearance package ($92). Chevy Van Custom Comfort package ($342). Bumper guards. Radio AM, AM/FM. Heater (deletion). Electric clock. Cigar lighter. Radio antenna. Chevy Van Caravan package ($980 to $1,050). 454-cid V-8 in Step-Van ($235). F44 Big 10 package. Chevy Van Sport package ($497). Scottsdale trim package, light trucks ($251). Cheyenne trim package, light trucks ($781). Silverado trim package, light trucks. Short-box Step-Side Sport package. Short-box Fleetside sport package. Rear step bumper. Cargo area lamp. Power windows. Power door locks. Glide-out spare tire carrier. Rally wheels. Styled wheels. Exterior Decor package with Silverado package only. Comfortilt steering wheel. C20 8-ft. stake ($728). El Camino Conquista package ($146). Sliding rear window. Pickup box side rails. Speed and cruise controls. Bucket seats/center console. Gauges. Air conditioning. Tachometer. Whitewall tires. Bumper guards. Auxiliary fuel tank. Chromed front and rear bumpers. Below-eye-line mirrors. Color-keyed floor mats. Intermittent windshield wipers. Inside hood lock release. Simulated wood grain. Exterior trim, Blazer and Carryall Suburban. Special two-tone paint. Spare tire cover (Blazer and Carryall Suburban). Rear radio speaker (Blazer and Carryall Suburban). Soft-Ray tinted glass.
COLOR OPTIONS: See 1975 options section for complete chart of 1975-1978 Chevrolet Commercial Truck colors.
HISTORICAL: Introduced: Fall 1977. Calendar-year registrations: 1,275,787. Calendar-year sales: [All Series] 1,233,932. Innovations: El Camino down-sized. New V-8 engines introduced. Big Dooley name replaces Big Dualie. New 5.7-liter V-8 diesel in half-ton Pickups. Historical notes: Chevrolet reported an all-time record of 1.34 million truck sales in 1978. The number of trucks registered by Chevrolet dealers, per sales outlet, was 215 units, up from 187 in 1977.

1979 Chevrolet LUV Mini-Pickup (CP)
1/2-TON LIGHT UTILITY VEHICLE (LUV) — MODEL L/SERIES 10500 — FOUR: Chevrolet's captive import, the LUV truck, looked the same in 1979 as it did the year before. Until you started adding some new options, that is. Four-wheel-drive was now available at extra-cost. Trucks so-equipped were seen with wide striping, and 4x4 decals on the sides of their cargo boxes.

1979 Chevrolet Ell Camino Royal Knight Sedan-Pickup (OCW)

1/2-TON EL CAMINO — MODEL W/SERIES 14000 — SIX/V-8: El Caminos featured a new grille with eight distinct horizontal segments formed by the bright metal molding. The moldings ran three across, with a thin one down the center. A Royal Knight dress-up package featured two dragon decals on its hood, styled wheels, and other goodies. A new item was a 267-cid V-8 for all non-California trucks. The Super Sport was again merchandised as a model-option rather than an individual package.
1/2-TON, 3/4-TON, 1-TON VAN — MODEL G/SERIES 10, 20, 30 — SIX/V-8: Vans were available in various configurations. Appearance updates were mainly in terms of new decal and paint treatments. On most vans, the grille had more of a horizontal theme due to the method of finishing the grille bars with paint.

1979 Chevrolet Blazer Sport Utility Vehicle (CP)

1/2-TON BLAZER — MODEL CK/SERIES 10500 — SIX/V-8: The new Blazer had a smoother, more aerodynamic hood lip, new integral head/parking lamps, and a concealed fuel filter. Custom Deluxe interiors featured bucket seats in blue or camel hounds tooth. Custom vinyl trim came in blue or camel, too. Cheyennes included Custom vinyl trim in blue, camel or carmine or Custom cloth trim in carmine or camel, plus bright trim, color-keyed carpeting, a color-keyed plastic console, full instrumentation, and a new Custom steering wheel. Two-tone vinyl or cloth upholstery was optional.

1979 Chevrolet Beauville Sportvan (CP)

1/2-TON, 3/4-TON, 1-TON — MODEL CK/SERIES 10, 20, 30 — SIX/V-8: Light-duty trucks got a new front end with integral park/head lights, a bright metal lower grille outline molding, and a new paint scheme for the grille. The 1979 grille was slightly narrower top-to-bottom, but of the same basic design as last year's style. The slotted area, directly below the grille was now bright metal. An optional sport grille had only two full-width horizontal members, and a center bow tie, the background being blacked-out. There was also a new concealed fuel filler. The base 250-cid six got a new staged two-barrel carburetor, and a dual take-down exhaust system. Custom Deluxe was the basic trim level. It included a foam-padded bench seat with plaid upholstery, a body color steel roof headliner panel, black rubber floor mat, padded arm rests, courtesy lamps, prismatic rear view mirror, foam padded dash, bright upper and lower grille outline moldings, bright headlamp bezels, silver plastic grille insert, bright outside rear view mirror, bright door handles, bright Custom Deluxe nameplates, and white-painted bumper, hubcaps and wheels. The next-step-up was Scottsdale trim with a full-depth foam padded seat, wood-grain door trim inserts, an ash tray cigarette lighter, door or manually-operated courtesy lamps, bright door sill plates, color-keyed rubber floor mats, a high-note horn, patterned nylon cloth upholstery with vinyl trim, and all Custom Deluxe exterior features, plus a chrome bumper, chrome hubcaps, chrome body side moldings on Fleetsides, bright windshield and window trim, bright-rimmed parking, side marker and taillights, and Scottsdale nameplates. Cheyenne trim included full-depth foam seat cushions, ribbed pattern velour or buffalo-hide vinyl upholstery (vinyl bucket seats optional), folding seat backs, ash tray-mounted cigarette lighter, chestnut wood-grain dash and door inserts, door or manually-operated courtesy and dome lamps, and added cab insulation. The exterior featured all Custom Deluxe and Scottsdale features, plus bright metal cab appliqués and moldings, bright upper body side and tailgate moldings, tailgate center appliqués on Fleetsides, and Cheyenne nameplates. At the top of the line was the Silverado option featuring extra-thick seat padding, basketweave nylon cloth or buffalo hide vinyl trim, full gauges, wood-grain dash panel, door storage pockets, carpeting, an insulated headliner, extra body insulation, and all Custom Deluxe and Scottsdale exterior items, plus lower body side and tailgate moldings, wheel lip moldings, Silverado nameplates, and a tailgate appliqué on Fleetsides. Exterior colors for 1979 were White, Silver Metallic, Dark Bright Blue, Medium Blue, Dark Blue, Medium Green Metallic, Bright Green Metallic, Dark Green, Yellow, Neutral, Camel Metallic, Dark Carmine, Bright Red, Russet Metallic, Dark Brown Metallic, Dark Yellow, Charcoal, and Black.

1/2-TON, 3/4-TON, 1-TON FORWARD-CONTROL — MODEL P-SERIES 10, 20, 30 — SIX/V-8: Forward-Control trucks were P (parcel delivery) models available in the 10 (1/2-ton), 20 (3/4-ton) and 30 (1-ton) series. The P10s had a 102-in. wheelbase and 7-ft. body. P20s came with 125 in. or 133-in. wheelbases designed for 10-ft. or 12-ft. bodies. P30s came in these sizes, plus a 157-in. wheelbase designed for 14-ft. bodies. Styling was boxy and unchanged.

1979 Chevrolet C10 Blazer 4x2 Sport Utility Vehicle (Owner: Paul Tofte)

I.D. DATA: Serial number located. Combination VIN and rating plate located on: [El Camino] Top left side of dash, [Conventionals] left door pillar. Serial number systems: [El Camino] First symbol indicates manufacturer, 1=Chevrolet. Second symbol indicates car-line/series: W=El Camino. Third and fourth symbols indicate body type: 80=Sedan-Pickup. Fifth symbol indicates engine: [El Camino] A=231-cid (3.8 liter)/115-hp two-barrel V-6, J=267-cid (4.4 liter)/125-nhp two-barrel V-8, L=350-cid (5.7 liter)/170-nhp four-barrel V-8, M=200-cid (3.3 liter)/94-nhp two-barrel, V-6. Sixth symbol indicates model-year: 9=1979. Seventh symbol indicates assembly plant. Symbols 8-13 indicate the production sequence number starting at 100,001. Ending numbers not available. [All Light-Duty] The first symbol indicates manufacturer: 1=Chevrolet Motor Div. The second symbol indicates chassis type: C=106 in. Conventional Cab including Blazer, G=Chevy Van or Sportvan, K=106 in. Conventional cab 4x4, P=Forward-Control, L=LUV, R=LUV (4x4). The third symbol indicates engine as follows: D=250-cid (4.1 liter)/one-barrel L6 (horsepower rated 115 for models with GVW under 6,000 lb., 100 for models with GVWs over 6,000 lb.), L=350-cid (5.7 liter)/165-nhp four-barrel V-8, M=350-cid (5.7 liter)/145-nhp four-barrel V-8, N=110-cid (1.8 liter)/80-nhp two-barrel L4 (LUV), R=400-cid (6.6 liter)/175-hp four-barrel V-8, S=454-cid (7.4 liter) four-barrel V-8 for C models only (horsepower rated 205 for models with GVW under 6,000 lb., 245 for models

with GVWs over 6,000 lb.), T=292-cid (4.8 liter)/120-nhp one-barrel L-6, U=305-cid (5.0 liter) two-barrel V-8 (horsepower rated 145 for models with GVW under 6,000 lb., 140 for models with GVWs over 6,000 lb.), Z=5.7 liter LF9 350-cid/120-hp diesel V-8. The fourth symbol indicates series and tonnage: 1=1/2-ton, 2=3/4-ton, 3=1-ton, 4=1/2-ton with heavy-duty suspension. The fifth symbol indicates body type: 2=Chassis & Cowl, 3=Chassis-and-Cab, 4=Cab with pickup box or van with Hi-Cube box, 5=Panel or Panel Van, 6=Sportvan, Carryall Suburban (doors) 7=Motorhome chassis, 8=Utility (Blazer). The sixth symbol indicates model-year: 9=1979. The seventh symbol indicates the assembly plant: A=Lakewood, Ga., B=Baltimore, Md., F=Flint, Mich., J=Janesville, Wis., S=St. Louis, Mo., U=Lordstown, Ohio, V=Pontiac, Mich. GMAD, Z=Fremont, Calif., O=Pontiac (GMC) Michigan, 1=Oshawa or London, Ontario, Canada, 3=GMAD, Detroit, Mich., 4=Scarborough, Ontario, Canada, 8=Fujisawa, Japan. Symbols 8-13 are the production sequence number. Starting number: 10001 Ending numbers not available. Engine numbers located: [Six] on pad at right-hand side of cylinder block at rear of distributor, [V-8] on pad at front, right-hand side of cylinder block.

1979 Chevrolet Fleetside Pickup (CP)

Model	Body Type	Price	Weight	Prod. Total
LUV — 1/2-Ton — 102.4 in. w.b. — Four				
CL10503	Chassis & Cab	4132	2095	Note 1
CL10503	Pickup	4276	2345	Note 1
LUV — 1/2-Ton — 117.9 in. w.b. — Four				
CL10803	Pickup	4486	2405	Note 1
NOTE 1: U.S. Sales of LUV: 100,192.				
NOTE 2: Add $971 for 4x4 LUVs.				
El Camino — 1/2-Ton — 117.1 in. w.b. — V-8				
1AW80	Pickup	5377	3242	Note 8
Z15	SS Pickup	5579	3242	Note 8
1AW80	Conquista	5532	3242	Note 8
Chevy Van 10 — 1/2-Ton — 110 in. w.b. — V-8				
CG11005	Panel	5312	3693	Note 8
CG11006	Sportvan	6229	3998	Note 8
Chevy Van 10 — 1/2-Ton — 125 in. w.b. — V-8				
CG11306	Beauville	7030	4367	Note 8
Chevy Van 20 — 3/4-Ton — 110 in. w.b. — V-8				
CG21005	Panel	5606	3689	Note 8
CG21006	Sportvan	6397	3970	Note 8
Chevy Van 20 — 3/4-Ton — 125 in. w.b. — V-8				
CG21306	Beauville	7198	4318	Note 8
CG21305	Nomad	7108	3830	Note 8
Chevy Van 30 — 1-Ton — 110 in. w.b. — V-8				
CG31005	Panel	5822	3914	Note 8
Chevy Van 30 — 1-Ton — 125 in. w.b. — V-8				
CG31306	Sportvan	6474	4378	Note 8
CG31306	Beauville	7410	4556	Note 8
Hi-Cube Van — 1-Ton — 125 in. w.b. — V-8				
CG31303	Hi-Cube 10 ft.	7662	-	Note 8
Hi-Cube Van — 1-Ton — 146 in. w.b. — V-8				
CG31603	Hi-Cube 12 ft.	7828	-	Note 8
Blazer 4x4 — 1/2-Ton — 106.5 in. w.b. — V-8 — 4x4				
CK10516	Hardtop	7373	4371	Note 8
CK10516	Softtop	7273	-	Note 8
NOTE 3: Deduct for C10 Blazer (4x2).				
C10 — 1/2-Ton — 117.5 in. w.b. — V-8				
CC10703	Chassis & Cab	4943	3406	Note 8
CC10703	Step-Side Pickup	5091	3570	Note 8
CC10703	Fleetside Pickup	5091	3629	Note 8
C10 — 1/2-Ton — 131.5 in. w.b. — V-8				
CC10903	Step-Side Pickup	5171	3693	Note 8
CC10903	Fleetside Pickup	5171	3767	Note 8
C10 — 1/2-Ton — 129.5 in. w.b. — V-8				
CC10906	Suburban (gate)	6614	4285	Note 8
NOTE 4: Add for K10 4x4 models (CK prefix).				
NOTE 5: Add $1,758 and 295 lb. for C10 diesel.				
P10 Step-Van — 1/2-Ton — 102 in. w.b. — Six				
CP10542	Steel Step-Van	6189	4226	Note 8
C20 — 3/4-Ton — 131.5 in. w.b. — V-8				
CC20903	Chassis & Cab	5481	3693	Note 8
CC20903	Step-Side Pickup	5777	4077	Note 8
CC20903	Fleetside Pickup	5777	4151	Note 8
C20 — 3/4-Ton — 164.5 in. w.b. — V-8				
CC20943	Chassis & Bonus-Cab	6233	4224	Note 8
CC20943	Bonus-Cab Pickup	6516	4682	Note 8
CC20943	Chassis & Crew-Cab	6634	-	Note 8
CC20943	Crew-Cab Pickup	6918	-	Note 8
C20 — 3/4-Ton — 129.5 in. w.b. — V-8				
CC20906	Suburban (gate)	7075	-	Note 8
NOTE 6: Add for K20 4x4 models (CK prefix).				
P20 Step-Van — 3/4-Ton — 125/133 in. w.b. — V-8				
CP20842	Steel Step-Van	7287	5311	Note 8
C30 — 1-Ton — 131.5 in. w.b. — V-8				
CC30903	Chassis & Cab	5941	3899	Note 8
CC30903	Step-Side Pickup	6237	4283	Note 8
CC30903	Fleetside Pickup	6237	4358	Note 8
C30 — 1-Ton — 164.5 in. w.b. — V-8				
CC30943	Chassis-Bonus-Cab	6740	4453	Note 8
CC30943	Chassis-Crew-Cab	7023	4911	Note 8
CC30943	Bonus-Cab Pickup	6900	-	Note 8
CC30943	Crew-Cab Pickup	7183	-	Note 8
NOTE 7: Add for K30 4x4 models (CK prefix).				
P30 Step-Van — 1-Ton — 125/133/157 in. w.b. — V-8				
CP30842	Steel Step-Van	7487	5485	-

1979 Chevrolet 1/2-Ton LUV 4x4 Mini-Pickup (RCA)

1979 Chevrolet Blazer Sport Utility Vehicle (CP)

1979 Chevrolet "Old Cars Weekly" Scottsdale Suburban (OCW)

1979 Chevrolet Step-Side Pickup (CP)

NOTE 8: Model-year production: [El Camino] 54,008, [All Chevy Van] 212,513, [All Sportvan] 40,560, [Blazer] 90,987, [C10/C20 Carryall Suburban] 54,987, [Other C10] 535,056, [Other C20] 148,782, [C30] 80,500, [P10/P20/P30] 28,536. (Includes trucks built in Canada for U.S. market).
ENGINE: [Standard LUV] Inline. OHV overhead camshaft. Four-cylinder. Cast iron block. Bore & stroke: 3.31 x 3.23 in. Displacement: 110.8 cid. Compression ratio: 8.5:1. Net horsepower: 80 at 4800 rpm. Maximum torque: 95 lb.-ft at 3000 rpm. Five main bearings. Hydraulic valve lifters. Carburetor: One-barrel.
ENGINE: [Standard El Camino] V-type. OHV. Six-cylinder. Cast iron block. Bore & stroke: 3.5 x 3.48 in. Displacement: 200 cid. Compression ratio: 8.2:1. Net horsepower: 95. Four main bearings. Hydraulic valve lifters. Carburetor: Rochester two-barrel model 210.
ENGINE: [Optional: El Camino] V-type. OHV. Six-cylinder. Cast iron block. Bore & stroke: 3.8 x 3.4 in. Displacement: 231 cid. Compression ratio: 8.0:1. Net horsepower: 105. Four main bearings. Hydraulic valve lifters. Carburetor: Rochester two-barrel model 2GC.

1979 Chevrolet LUV 4x4 Mini-Pickup (OCW)

ENGINE: [Standard: C10/Big 10/K10] Inline. OHV. Six-cylinder. Cast iron block. Bore & stroke: 3.876 x 3.530 in. Displacement: 250 cid. Compression ratio: 8.3:1. Net horsepower: 130 at 3800 rpm. Torque: 210 lb.-ft. at 2400 rpm. Seven main bearings. Hydraulic valve lifters. Carburetor: Two-barrel.
NOTE 9: Base engine in California had 125 horsepower at 4000 rpm/Torque: 205 lb.-ft. at 2000 rpm.
ENGINE: [Optional El Camino] V-type. OHV. Eight-cylinder. Cast iron block. Bore & stroke: 3.5 x 3.48 in. Displacement: 267 cid. Five main bearings. Hydraulic valve lifters. Carburetor: two-barrel.
ENGINE: [Standard: C20/C30/K20/K30] Inline. OHV. Six-cylinder. Cast iron block. Bore & stroke: 3.876 x 4.120 in. Displacement: 292 cid. Compression ratio: 8.0:1. Net horsepower: 115 at 3400 rpm. Net torque: 215 lb.-ft. at 3400 rpm. Seven main bearings. Hydraulic valve lifters. Carburetor: Rochester one-barrel.
ENGINE: [Optional C10] V-type. OHV. Eight-cylinder. Cast iron block. Bore & stroke: 3.736 x 3.480 in. Displacement: 305 cid. Compression ratio: 8.4:1. Net horsepower: 140 at 4000 rpm. Net torque: 235 lb.-ft. at 2000 rpm. Five main bearings. Hydraulic valve lifters. Carburetor: Rochester two-barrel model 2GC.
NOTE 10: Base engine in California had 155 horsepower at 3600 rpm/Torque: 260 lb.-ft. at 2000 rpm. (Four-barrel California engine) 155 horsepower at 4000 rpm. Torque: 260 lb.-ft. at 2000 rpm.
ENGINE: [Optional El Camino] V-type. OHV. Eight-cylinder. Cast iron block. Bore & stroke: 3.736 x 3.480 in. Displacement: 305 cid. Compression ratio: 8.4:1. Net horsepower: 145/135*. Five main bearings. Hydraulic valve lifters. Carburetor: Rochester two-barrel model 2GC.
NOTE 10: * indicates California rating.

1979 Chevrolet Silverado Suburban (CP)

ENGINE: [Optional El Camino] V-type. OHV. Eight-cylinder. Cast iron block. Bore & stroke: 4.0 x 3.48 in. Displacement: 350 cid. Compression ratio: 8.2:1. Net horsepower: 170/160* at 3800 rpm. Maximum torque: 270 lb.-ft. at 2400 rpm. Five main bearings. Hydraulic valve lifters. Carburetor: Rochester four-barrel model M4 MC/MV.
NOTE 11: * indicates California rating.
ENGINE: [Optional: C10/Big 10] V-type. OHV diesel. Eight-cylinder. Cast iron block. Bore & stroke: 4.057 x 3.385 in. Displacement: 350 cid. Compression ratio: 20.5:1. Net horsepower: 120 at 3600 rpm. Net torque: 222 lb.-ft. at 1900 rpm. Five main bearings. Hydraulic valve lifters.
ENGINE: [Optional: all models except LUV] V-type. OHV. Eight-cylinder. Cast iron block. Bore & stroke: 4.0 x 3.48 in. Displacement: 350 cid. Compression ratio: 8.2:1. Net horsepower: 165 at 3600 rpm. Net torque: 270 lb.-ft. at 2700 rpm. Five main bearings. Hydraulic valve lifters. Carburetor: Rochester four-barrel model M4 MC/MV.

1979 Chevrolet Silverado Suburban (CP)

ENGINE: [Optional: K10/K20/K30] V-type. OHV. Eight-cylinder. Cast iron block. Bore & stroke: 4.125 x 3.750 in. Displacement: 400 cid. Compression ratio: 8.5:1. Net horsepower: 185 at 3600 rpm. Net torque: 300 lb.-ft. at 2400 rpm. Five main bearings. Hydraulic valve lifters. Carburetor: Rochester four-barrel model M4 MC/MV.
ENGINE: [Optional: All models except Blazer/El Camino/LUV] V-type. OHV. Eight-cylinder. Cast iron block. Bore & stroke: 4.250 x 4.0 in. Displacement: 454 cid. Compression ratio: 7.6:1. Net horsepower: 245 at 4000 rpm. Net torque: 380 lb.-ft. at 2500 rpm. Five main bearings. Hydraulic valve lifters. Carburetor: Rochester four-barrel model M4 MC/MV.
CHASSIS: [LUV] Wheelbase: 102.4 in./117.9 in. Overall length: 173.8 in./190.9 in. Front tread: 54 in. Rear tread: 52.2 in. Tires: E78 x 14B in.
CHASSIS: [El Camino] Wheelbase: 117.1 in. Overall length: 201.6 in. Height: 53.8 in. Front tread: 58.5 in. Rear tread: 57.8 in. Tires: P205/75R x 14 in.
CHASSIS: [G10] Wheelbase: 110 in./125 in. Overall length: 178.2 in./202.2 in. Tires G78 x 15B in.
CHASSIS: [G20] Wheelbase: 110 in./125 in. Overall length: 178.2 in./202.2 in. Tires: J78 x 15B in.
CHASSIS: [G30] Wheelbase: 110 in./125 in. Overall length: 178.2 in./202.2 in. Tires: 8.00 x 16.5 in.
CHASSIS: [K10 Blazer] Wheelbase: 106.5 in. Overall length: 184.8 in. Height: 73.4 in. Front tread: 66.1 in. Rear tread: 63 in. Tires: H78 x 15B in.
CHASSIS: [C10/Big 10] Wheelbase: 117.5 in./131.5 in. Overall length: 191.3 in./212 in. Height 69.8 in. Front tread: 65.8 in. Rear tread: 62.7 in. Tires: [C10] G78 x 15B in. [Big 10], L78 x 15B in.
CHASSIS: [K10] Wheelbase: 117.5 in./131.5 in. Overall length: 191.3 in./212 in. Height: 72 in. Front tread: 65.8 in. Rear tread: 62.7 in. Tires: L78 x 15B in.
CHASSIS: [P10] Wheelbase: 102 in. Tires: L78 x 15B in.
CHASSIS: [C20] Wheelbase: 117.5 in./131.5 in./164.5 in. Overall length: 191.3 in./212 in./244.43 in. Height: 69.8 in. Front tread: 65.8 in. Rear tread: 62.7 in. Tires: [Pickup] 8.75 x 16.5C in., [Bonus-Cab] Front, 8.75 x 16.5C in., Rear, 8.75 x 16.5D in., [Crew-Cab] 9.50 x 16.5D in.
CHASSIS: [K20] Wheelbase: 131.5 in. Overall length: 212 in. Height: 73.9 in. Front tread: 65.8 in. Rear tread: 62.7 in. Tires: 8.75 x 16.5C in.
CHASSIS: [P20] Wheelbase: 125 in./133 in. Tires: 8.75 x 16.5C in.
OPTIONS: Chrome front bumper ($33). Electric clock ($55). Chevy Van Caravan package. Custom comfort package. Chevy Sport package. F44 Big 10 package ($375). Scottsdale package. C20 Stake, 8 ft. Air conditioning ($574). Color-keyed floor mats ($11). Tinted glass ($49). Chromed grille ($29). Exterior eye-level mirror ($55). Convenience package ($231). Comfortilt steering wheel ($78). Rally wheels ($84). Intermittent wipers ($33). Sliding side window glass, Blazer ($176). Folding rear seat, Blazer ($260). Electric tailgate window, Blazer ($65).
HISTORICAL: Introduced: Fall 1978. Calendar-year registrations: 1,085,855. Calendar-year sales: [Light trucks/Pickups] 644,775, [Vans] 166,850, [Carryall Suburbans] 37,215, [Blazers] 57,734, [LUV] 100,192, [El Camino] 52,803, [Sportvan] 30,135, [Total] 1,090,204. Innovations: New El Camino Black Knight model option. 4x4 introduced for LUV Pickup. New 267-cid V-8.

1980 CHEVROLET

1980 Chevrolet LUV Mini-Pickup (DFW)

1/2-TON LIGHT UTILITY VEHICLE (LUV) — MODEL L/SERIES 10500 — FOUR: The 1980 LUV Pickup looked just like the 1979 model. New under the hood was an 80-hp engine. Exterior colors were the same as 1979, but the White, Yellow and Red paints were modified to remove lead in the formula. Standard and Mikado cloth trim came in blue, red or saddle. Sport package decals were light orange/orange/red or light blue metallic/dark blue/medium blue.

1/2-TON EL CAMINO — MODEL W/SERIES 14000 — SIX/V-8: The biggest change in the 1980 El Camino was the grille. It had 21 fine vertical members on either side of a slightly heavier vertical center molding. Base power train was a 229-cid. (3.8-liter) V-6 and three-speed manual transmission. The ribbed steel, six-foot cargo box provided 35.5 cu.-ft. of room and a gross payload of 1,250 lb. including passengers. Contrasting lower body perimeter finish with Super Sport shadow graphics along the door bottoms identified this model-option. Other SS features included Rally wheels, a large front air dam, color sport mirrors, white-letter tires, and Super Sport tailgate decals. The Royal Knight option included the double dragon hood decal, large front air dam, Rally wheels, and painted sport mirrors.

1980 Chevrolet El Camino Royal Knight Sedan-Pickup (CP)

1/2-TON, 3/4-TON, 1-TON VAN — MODEL G/SERIES 10, 20, 30 — SIX/V-8: Vans and light-duty trucks had a new ice-cube-tray grille with 10 vertical bars and two horizontal bars forming 33 square openings. There was a Chevrolet bow tie emblem in the center. The 1-ton G30 line no longer offered the 110-in. wheelbase Chevy Van panel. Other series offered Chevy Vans and Sportvans with either wheelbase and Beauvilles on the long wheelbase only. A brand new long wheelbase 3/4-ton model was the Nomad. It had a camper-style window treatment, with a door window and slider window behind the door, but panel truck styling at the rear. Model-options included Caravan and Chevy Sport packages. There was a "Van Sport" option with two-tone exterior graphics.
1/2-TON BLAZER — MODEL C/K SERIES 10500 — SIX/V-8: Blazers had a new Argent colored grille with 33 square openings and new gauges with international symbols. A Silverado package was now available and included rectangular headlamps, a chromed grille and larger parking lamps, plus Custom cloth or Brahman-grain vinyl interiors. Radial tires became standard equipment. The 305-cid and 400-cid V-8s were dropped. A popular new option was styled aluminum wheels. Colors were the same as on conventional trucks.

1980 Chevrolet Fleetside Pickup (CP)

1/2-TON, 3/4-TON, 1-TON — MODEL C/K SERIES 10, 20, 30 — SIX/V-8: The same new grille was used on the conventional trucks. Silverados got new rectangular parking lamps. The seat back angle was changed for greater comfort. There was a new thermostatic-controlled cooling fan. A single inlet dual exhaust system was new for the 292-cid six-cylinder engine. Custom Deluxe was the basic trim level. It included a foam-padded bench seat with plaid upholstery, a body color steel roof headliner panel, black rubber floor mat, padded arm rests, courtesy lamps, prismatic rear view mirror, foam padded dash, bright upper and lower grille outline moldings, bright headlamp bezels, silver plastic grille insert, bright outside rear view mirror, bright door handles, bright Custom Deluxe nameplates, and white-painted bumper, hubcaps and wheels. The next step up was Scottsdale trim with a full-depth foam padded seat, wood-grain door trim inserts, an ash tray cigarette lighter, door or manually-operated courtesy lamps, bright door sill plates, color-keyed rubber floor mats, a high-note horn, patterned nylon cloth upholstery with vinyl trim, and all Custom Deluxe exterior features, plus a chrome bumper, chrome hubcaps, chrome body side moldings on Fleetsides, bright windshield and window trim, bright-rimmed parking, side marker and taillights, and Scottsdale nameplates. Cheyenne trim included full-depth foam seat cushions, ribbed pattern velour or buffalo-hide vinyl upholstery (vinyl bucket seats optional), folding seat backs, ash tray-mounted cigarette lighter, chestnut wood-grain dash and door inserts, door-operated or manually-operated courtesy and dome lamps, and added cab insulation. The Cheyenne exterior featured all Custom Deluxe and Scottsdale features, plus bright metal cab appliqués and moldings, bright upper body side and tailgate moldings, tailgate center appliqués on Fleetsides, and Cheyenne nameplates. At the top of the line was the Silverado option featuring extra-thick seat padding, basketweave nylon cloth or buffalo hide vinyl trim, full gauges, wood-grain dash panel, door storage pockets, carpeting, an insulated headliner, extra body insulation, and all Custom Deluxe and Scottsdale exterior items, plus lower body side and tailgate moldings, wheel lip moldings, Silverado nameplates, and a tailgate appliqué on Fleetsides. The 1980 exterior colors were Frost White, Medium Blue, Light Blue Metallic, Nordic Blue Metallic, Emerald Green, Sante Fe Tan, Carmine Red, Cardinal Red, Midnight Black, and Burnt Orange Metallic. Also seen were new exterior graphics and eight new two-tones.

1/2-TON, 3/4-TON, 1-TON FORWARD-CONTROL — MODEL P-SERIES 10, 20, 30 — SIX/V-8: Forward-Control trucks were P (parcel delivery) models available in the 10 (1/2-ton), 20 (3/4-ton) and 30 (1-ton) series. The P10s had a 102-in. wheelbase and 7-ft. body. P20s came with 125-in. or 133-in. wheelbases designed for 10-ft. or 12-ft. bodies. P30s came in these sizes, plus a 157-in. wheelbase designed for 14-ft. bodies. Styling was boxy and unchanged.

1980 Chevrolet Sportvan (CP)

I.D. DATA: Serial number located. Combination VIN and rating plate located on: [El Camino] Top left side of dash, [Conventionals] left door pillar. Serial number systems: [El Camino] First symbol indicates manufacturer, 1=Chevrolet. Second symbol indicates car-line/series: W=El Camino. Third and fourth symbols indicate body type: 80=Sedan-Pickup. Fifth symbol indicates engine: [El Camino] A=229-cid (3.8-liter)/115-nhp two-barrel V-6, J=267-cid (4.4-liter)/120-nhp two-barrel V-8, M=305-cid (5.0-liter)/155-nhp four-barrel V-8. Sixth symbol indicates model-year: A=1980. Seventh symbol indicates assembly plant. Symbols 8-13 indicate the production sequence number starting at 100,001. Ending numbers not available. [All Light-Duty] The first symbol indicates manufacturer: 1=Chevrolet Motor Div. The second symbol indicates chassis type: C=106-in. Conventional Cab including Blazer, G=Chevy Van or Sportvan, K=106-in. Conventional cab 4x4, P=Forward-Control, L=LUV, R=LUV (4x4). The third symbol indicates engine as follows: D=250-cid (4.1-liter)/one-barrel L6 (horsepower rated 115 nhp for models with GVW under 6,000 lb., 100 nhp for models with GVWs over 6,000 lb.), G=305-cid (5.0-liter)/140-nhp two-barrel V-8, L=350-cid (5.7-liter)/165-nhp four-barrel V-8, M=350-cid (5.7-liter)/145-nhp two-barrel V-8, N=110-cid (1.8-liter)/80-nhp two-barrel L4 (LUV), P=350-cid (5.7-liter) 120-nhp two-barrel V-8, R=400-cid (6.6-liter)/175-nhp four-barrel V-8, S=454-cid (7.4-liter) four-barrel V-8 for C models only (horsepower rated 205 for models with GVW under 6,000 lb., 245 for models with GVWs over 6,000 lb.), T=292-cid (4.8-liter)/120-nhp one-barrel L-6, W=454-cid (7.4-liter)/245-nhp four-barrel V-8, X=400-cid (6.6-liter) 180-nhp four-barrel V-8, Z=350-cid (5.7-liter)/120-nhp diesel V-8. The fourth symbol indicates series and tonnage: 1=1/2-ton, 2=3/4-ton, 3=1-ton, 4=1/2-ton with heavy-duty suspension. The fifth symbol indicates body type: 2=Chassis-and-Cowl, 3=Chassis-and-Cab, 4=Cab with pickup box or van with Hi-Cube box, 5=Panel or Panel Van, 6=Sportvan, Suburban (doors) 7=Motorhome chassis, 8=Utility (Blazer). The sixth symbol indicates model year: A=1980. The seventh symbol indicates the assembly plant: A=Lakewood, Ga., B=Baltimore, Md., F=Flint, Mich., J=Janesville, Wis., S=St. Louis, Mo., U=Lordstown, Ohio, V=Pontiac, Mich. GMAD, Z=Fremont, Calif., 0=Pontiac (GMC) Michigan, 1=Oshawa or London, Ontario, Canada, 3=GMAD, Detroit, Mich., 4=Scarborough, Ontario, Canada, 8=Fujisawa, Japan. Symbols 8-13 are the production sequence number. Starting number: 10001 Ending numbers not available. Engine numbers located: [Six] on pad at right-hand side of cylinder block at rear of distributor, [V-8] on pad at front, right-hand side of cylinder block.

Model	Body Type	Price	Weight	Prod. Total
LUV — 1/2-Ton — 102.4 in. w.b. — Four				
CL10503	Chassis & Cab	4448	2095	Note 8
CL10503	Pickup	4612	2315	Note 8
LUV — 1/2-Ton — 117.9 in. w.b. — Four				
CL10803	Long-Box Pickup	4787	2405	Note 8
El Camino — 1/2-Ton — 117.1 in. w.b. — V-8				
1AW80	Pickup	5911	3238	Note 9
RPOZ15	Super Sport Pickup	6128	3238	Note 9
Blazer 4x4 — 1/2-Ton — 106.5 in. w.b. — V-8				
CK10516	Hardtop	8233	4429	Note 9
CK10516	Softtop	8130	-	Note 9
NOTE 1: Deduct for C10 (4x2) Blazer.				
Chevy Van 10 — 1/2-Ton — 110 in. w.b. — V-8				
CG11005	Panel	5748	3652	Note 9
CG11006	Sportvan	6747	3971	Note 9
Chevy Van 10 — 1/2-Ton — 125 in. w.b. — V-8				
CG11306	Beauville	7854	4203	Note 9
Chevy Van 20 — 3/4-Ton — 110 in. w.b. — V-8				
CG21005	Panel	6183	3756	Note 9
CG21006	Sportvan	7023	4012	Note 9
Chevy Van 20 — 3/4-Ton — 125 in. w.b. — V-8				
CG21306	Beauville	7975	4901	Note 9
CG21305	Nomad	7864	3915	Note 9

Model	Body Type	Price	Weight	Prod. Total
Chevy Van 30 — 1-Ton — 125 in. w.b. — V-8				
CG31305	Panel	7060	4154	Note 9
CG31306	Sportvan	7901	4450	Note 9
CG31306	Beauville	8680	4450	Note 9
C30 Hi-Cube Van — 1-Ton — 125 in. w.b. — V-8				
CG31303	Hi-Cube 10 ft.	7666	3524	Note 9
C30 Hi-Cube Van — 1-Ton — 146 in. w.b. — V-8				
CG31603	Hi-Cube 12 ft.	8793	8793	Note 9
P10 Step-Van — 1/2-Ton — 102 — Six				
CP10542	Steel Step-Van 7 ft.	6681	4226	Note 9
CP20842	10-ft. Steel Panel	8021	5346	Note 9
CP20842	12-ft. Steel Panel	8287	5522	Note 9
C10 — 1/2 Ton — 117.5 in. w.b. — V-8				
CC10703	Chassis & Cab	5785	3243	Note 9
CC10703	Step-Side	5505	3550	Note 9
CC10703	Fleetside	5505	3609	Note 9
C10 — 1/2-Ton — 129.5 in. w.b. — V-8				
CC10906	Suburban	7456	4242	Note 9
C10 — 1/2-Ton — 131.5 in. w.b. — V-8				
CC10903	Step-Side	5590	3692	Note 9
CC10903	Fleetside	5590	3767	Note 9
NOTE 2: Add $1,120 for K10 (4x4) models.				
C20 — 3/4-Ton — 131.5 in. w.b. — V-8				
CC20903	Chassis & Cab	6216	3585	Note 9
CC20903	Step-Side	2326	3969	Note 9
CC20903	Fleetside	6326	4044	Note 9
C20 — 3/4-Ton — 129.5 in. w.b. — V-8				
CC20906	Suburban	7923	4538	Note 9
C20 — 3/4-Ton — 164.5 in. w.b. — V-8				
CC20943	Chassis Bonus-Cab	6964	4330	Note 9
CC20943	Fleetside Bonus-Cab	7241	4789	Note 9
CC20943	Chassis & Crew-Cab	7218	-	Note 9
CC20943	Fleetside Crew-Cab	7495	-	Note 9
NOTE 3: Add for K20 (4x4) models.				
P20 — 3/4-Ton — 125 in./133 in. w.b. — V-8				
CP20842	Steel Step-Van 10 ft.	8021	5346	Note 9
NOTE 4: Add for C20 12 ft. Step-Van on 133 in. wheelbase.				
C30 — 1-Ton — 131.5 in. w.b. — V-8				
CC30903	Chassis & Cab	6399	3848	Note 9
CC30903	Step-Side	6687	4232	Note 9
CC30903	Fleetside	6687	4307	Note 9
C30 — 1-Ton — 164.5 in. w.b. — V-8				
CC30943	Chassis-Bonus-Cab	7120	4364	Note 9
CC30943	Fleetside Bonus-Cab	7397	-	Note 9
CC30943	Chassis-Crew-Cab	7374	-	Note 9
CC30943	Fleetside Crew-Cab	7651	-	Note 9
NOTE 5: Add for K30 (4x4) models.				
P30 Step-Van — 1-Ton — 125/133/157 in. w.b. — V-8				
CP30842	Steel Step-Van 12 ft.	8287	5522	Note 9

NOTE 6: Deduct for C30 10 ft. Step-Van on 125 in. wheelbase.
NOTE 7: Add for C30 14 ft. Step-Van on 157-in. wheelbase.
NOTE 8: U.S. sales of LUV were 88,447.
NOTE 9: Model-year production: [El Camino] 40,932, [All Chevy Van] 77,424 [All Sportvan] 14,148, [Blazer] 31,776, [C10/C20 Suburban] 30,859, [Other C10] 305,167, [Other C20] 85,553, [C30] 59,251, [P10/P20/P30] 13,232. (Includes trucks built in Canada for U.S. market.)

1980 Chevrolet Fleetside Pickup (Lowell E. Eisenhour photo)

ENGINE: [Standard LUV] Inline. OHV. OHC. Four-cylinder. Cast iron block. Bore & stroke: 3.31 x 3.23 in. Displacement: 110.8 cid. Compression ratio: 8.5:1. Net horsepower: 80 at 4800 rpm. Maximum torque: 95 lb.-ft at 3000 rpm. Five main bearings. Hydraulic valve lifters. Carburetor: One-barrel.
ENGINE: [Standard El Camino] V-block. OHV. Six-cylinder. Cast iron block. Bore & stroke: 3.5 x 3.48 in. Displacement: 200 cid. Compression ratio: 8.2:1. Net horsepower: 95. Four main bearings. Hydraulic valve lifters. Carburetor: Rochester two-barrel model 210.
ENGINE: V-block. OHV. Six-cylinder. Cast iron block. Bore & stroke: 3.8 x 3.4 in. Displacement: 231 cid. Compression ratio: 8.0:1. Net horsepower: 105. Four main bearings. Hydraulic valve lifters. Carburetor: Rochester two-barrel model 2GC.
ENGINE: [Standard: C10/Big 10/K10]: Inline. OHV. Six-cylinder. Cast iron block. Bore & stroke: 3.876 x 3.530 in. Displacement: 250 cid. Compression ratio: 8.3:1. Net horsepower: 130 at 3800 rpm. Torque: 210 lb.-ft. at 2400 rpm. Seven main bearings. Hydraulic valve lifters. Carburetor: Two-barrel model Rochester.

ENGINE: [Optional El Camino] V-block. Eight-cylinder. Cast iron block. Bore & stroke: 3.5 x 3.48 in. Displacement: 267 cid. Five main bearings. Hydraulic valve lifters. Carburetor: two-barrel

ENGINE: [Standard: C20/C30/K20/K30] Inline. OHV. Six-cylinder. Cast iron block. Bore & stroke: 3.876 x 4.120 in. Displacement: 292 cid. Compression ratio: 8.0:1. Net horsepower: 115 at 3400 rpm. Torque: 215 lb.-ft. at 3400 rpm. Seven main bearings. Hydraulic valve lifters. Carburetor: Rochester model one-barrel

ENGINE: [Optional C10] V-block. OHV. Eight-cylinder. Cast iron block. Bore & stroke: 3.736 x 3.480 in. Displacement: 305 cid. Compression ratio: 8.4:1. Net horsepower: 140 at 4000 rpm. Net torque: 235 lb.-ft. at 2000 rpm. Five main bearings. Hydraulic valve lifters. Carburetor: Rochester two-barrel model 2GC.

1980 Chevrolet Suburban (CP)

ENGINE: [Optional El Camino] V-block. OHV. Eight-cylinder. Cast iron block. Bore & stroke: 3.736 x 3.480 in. Displacement: 305 cid. Compression ratio: 8.4:1. Net horsepower: 145/135*. Five main bearings. Hydraulic valve lifters. Carburetor: Rochester two-barrel model 2GC.

NOTE 10: California rating.

ENGINE: [Optional: C10/Big 10] V-type. OHV Diesel. Eight-cylinder. Cast iron block. Bore & stroke: 4.057 x 3.385 in. Displacement: 350 cid. Compression ratio: 20.5:1. Net horsepower: 120 at 3600 rpm. Net torque: 222 lb.-ft. at 1900 rpm. Five main bearings. Hydraulic valve lifters.

ENGINE: [Optional: all models except LUV] V-block. OHV. Eight-cylinder. Cast iron block. Bore & stroke: 4.0 x 3.48 in. Displacement: 350 cid. Compression ratio: 8.2:1. Net horsepower: 165 at 3600 rpm. Net torque: 270 lb.-ft. at 2700 rpm. Five main bearings. Hydraulic valve lifters. Carburetor: Rochester four-barrel model M4 MC/MV.

ENGINE: V-type. OHV. Eight-cylinder. Cast iron block. Bore & stroke: 4.0 x 3.48 in. Displacement: 350 cid. Compression ratio: 8.2:1. Net horsepower: 170/160 at 3800 rpm. Maximum torque: 270 lb.-ft. at 2400 rpm. Five main bearings. Hydraulic valve lifters. Carburetor: Rochester four-barrel model M4 MC/MV.

ENGINE: [Optional: K10/K20/K30] V-block. OHV. Eight-cylinder. Cast iron block. Bore & stroke: 4.125 x 3.750 in. Displacement: 400 cid. Compression ratio: 8.5:1. Net horsepower: 185 at 3600 rpm. Net torque: 300 lb.-ft. at 2400 rpm. Five main bearings. Hydraulic valve lifters. Carburetor: Rochester four-barrel model M4 MC/MV.

ENGINE: [Optional: all models except Blazer, El Camino, LUV] V-block. OHV. Eight-cylinder. Cast iron block. Bore & stroke: 4.250 x 4.0 in. Displacement: 454 cid. Compression ratio: 7.6:1. Net horsepower: 245 at 4000 rpm. Net torque: 380 lb.-ft. at 2500 rpm. Five main bearings. Hydraulic valve lifters. Carburetor: Rochester four-barrel model M4 MC/MV.

NOTE: On all engines horsepower and torque can vary ion vehicles sold in California.

CHASSIS: [LUV] Wheelbase: 102.4 in./117.9 in. Overall length: 173.8 in./190.9 in. Front tread: 54 in. Rear tread: 52.2 in. Tires: E78 x 14B in.

CHASSIS: [El Camino] Wheelbase: 117.1 in. Overall length: 201.6 in. Height: 53.8 in. Front tread: 58.5 in. Rear tread: 51.8 in. Tires: P205/75R x 14 in.

CHASSIS: [Blazer] Wheelbase: 106.5 in. Overall length: 184.8 in. Height: 73.4 in. Front tread: 66.1 in. Rear tread: 63 in. Tires: P215/75R x 15 in.

CHASSIS: [Chevy Van 10] Wheelbase: 110 in./125. Overall length: 178 in./202.2 in. Height: 78.8 in./81.2 in. Front tread: 69.5 in. Rear tread: 69.7 in. Tires: GR78 x 15B in.

CHASSIS: [Chevy Van 20] Wheelbase: 110 in./125. Overall length: 178.2 in./202.2 in. Height: 78.8 in./81.2 in. Front tread: 69.5 in. Rear tread: 69.7 in. Tires: JR78 x 15B in.

CHASSIS: [Chevy Van 30] Wheelbase: 125 in./146. Overall length: 207.6 in./231.3 in. Tires: 8.75 x 16.5E in.

CHASSIS: [Series C10/K10] Wheelbase: 117.5 in./131.5 in. Overall length: 193.3 in./212 in. Height: 72 in. Front tread: 65.8 in. Rear tread: 62.7 in. Tires: GR78 x 15B in.

1980 Chevrolet Chevy Van with Sport Package (CP)

CHASSIS: [Step-Van 10] Wheelbase: 102 in. Tires: L78 x 15B in.

CHASSIS: [Series C20/K20] Wheelbase: 131.5 in. Overall length: 212 in. Height: 73.9 in. Front tread: 65.8 in. Rear tread: 62.7 in. Tires: 8.75 x 16.5C in.

CHASSIS: [Step-Van 20] Wheelbase: 125 in./133 in. Tires: 8.75 x 16.5 in.

CHASSIS: [C30] Wheelbase: 131.5 in./164.5 in. Overall length: 212 in./244.43 in. Height: 71.8 in. Front tread: 65.8 in. Rear tread: 62.7 in. Tires: [Pickup] 8.75 x 16.5C in., [Bonus/Crew-Cab] 9.50 x 16.5E in.

CHASSIS: [K30] Wheelbase: 131.5 in./164.5 in. Overall length: 212 in./244.43 in. Height: 74.7 in./75 in. Front tread: 65.8 in. Rear tread: 62.7 in. Tires: 9.50 x 16.5D in.

CHASSIS: [P30] Wheelbase: 125 in./133 in./157 in. Tires: 8.75 x 16.5 in.

TECHNICAL: Selective synchromesh transmission (Diesel with Turbo-Hydramatic only). Speeds: 3F/1R (LUV includes 4F/1R transmission). Column-mounted gearshift, except LUV. Single dry-disc type clutch. Salisbury rear axle. Overall ratio: (C10) 3.07:1, (K10) 4.11:1, (C20) 4.10:1. Front disc/rear drum brakes. Pressed steel wheels. Drive train options: Turbo-Hydramatic transmission ($370). Locking differential and 3.73 axle ($210). Freedom battery ($39). Engine oil cooler ($91). Heavy-duty springs and shocks ($71). Blazer towing device ($30). Dead-weight trailer hitch ($43). UniRoyal Land Trac tires, 10.00 x 15 ($362.85). Blazer rear roll bar ($105). Big 10 package ($375).

OPTIONS: Chrome front bumper ($33). Radio AM, AM/FM. Electric clock ($55). Caravan package (Van). Custom comfort package. Chevy Sport package. F44 Big 10 package ($375). Scottsdale package. C20 8 ft. stake rack body. Air conditioning ($574). Color-keyed floor mats ($11). Tinted glass ($49). Chromed grille ($29). Exterior below eye-level mirror ($55). Convenience package ($23). Comfortilt steering wheel ($78). Rally wheels ($84). Intermittent wipers ($33). Sliding side window glass, Blazer ($176). Folding rear seat, Blazer ($260). Electric tailgate window, Blazer ($65).

HISTORICAL: Introduced: Fall 1979. Calendar-year registrations: [All Chevrolet trucks] 737,788. Calendar-year sales: [Pickups] 403,487, [Vans] 86,727, [Suburbans] 19,518, [Blazer] 21,399, [LUV] 61,724, [El Camino] 33,086, [Sportvan] 13,576, [Total] 724,330. Innovations: New grilles for all series, except LUV. One-ton Chevrolet vans no longer come on a 110-in. chassis. Rising gasoline prices and a slackening economy made this a poor year for truck sales. At Chevrolet, calendar-year registrations dropped below the one-million level for the first time since 1976. In midyear, Chevrolet discontinued its heavy, over-the-road type trucks to concentrate on the light-duty and medium-duty market products.

1981 CHEVROLET

1981 Chevrolet LUV Pickup (CP)

1/2-TON LIGHT UTILITY VEHICLE (LUV) — MODEL L/SERIES 10500 — FOUR: New Aerodynamic styling was seen inside and outside this year's Series 11 LUV Mini-Pickup. This "captive import" had a smoother hood. The new cab provided more glass area. A curved rear window was used. A major functional change added some 2-1/2-in. of leg room, and about an inch of shoulder room. Wheelbase was increased to 104.3 in. with a new frame design. The grille was of eggcrate style, with a larger Chevrolet bow tie in its center. Bumper slots again numbered four, but those near the center were now the widest, while the smaller outer pair housed the parking lamps. Headlamp housings could no longer be seen in profile. The body sides were now smoothly curved with a sculptured feature line near the bottom rather than the belt. Chevrolet medallions were positioned on the side roof panel. The load tie-downs were now located on the inner side of the box. Interiors featured a restyled, color-keyed instrument panel and pad with a new instrument cluster, color-keyed steering wheel, new seat trim material, door and window regulator handles, headliner, door trim panel materials, and redesigned steering column. The Mikado package was revised with new seat trim, door trim panels, steering wheel and instrument panel trim. A new color-keyed floor console was standard with automatic transmission. Realigned cab door openings made for easier exit and entry. Other improvements included a weight reduction, heavier payload capacities, improved 4x2 front suspension, larger front brake area, and power brake booster, improved heating/ventilation system, and new electronic ignition system.

1/2-TON EL CAMINO — MODEL C, D/SERIES 14000 — SIX/V-8: The El Camino featured a new grille of horizontal design with bright upper and lower moldings. A Chevrolet name was at the lower left-hand corner of the grille. El Camino lettering decorated the lower rear quarter, above the feature line. Attractive new wheelcovers were introduced. They had a turbine-fin look around a plain center disc. Inside was a redesigned instrument panel with a new pad and glossy appliqué, convenient door-pull straps, new seat trim and, international symbols on the controls. A new 55/45 split front seat with single folding arm rests was optional. A "resume" function was added to the optional automatic speed control. Standard tires were now P205/75R tires with reduced rolling resistance for better mileage. A side-lift jack replaced the former bumper type. Power trains were carried over, but all engines were now equipped with GM's Computer Command Control (CCC) emissions system. It utilized an on-board computer for precise fuel-air ratio control. Option packages included the Conquista and Royal Knight equipment groups, while the Super Sport version was merchandised as a separate model-option, rather than individual package. New-for-1981 options also included a trip odometer.

1/2-TON, 3/4-TON, 1-TON VAN — MODEL G/SERIES 10, 20, 30 — SIX/V-8: Chevy Vans were essentially unchanged in appearance. This went for Hi-Cube Vans and Step-Vans, as well. A new Chevy Van model-option was the Bonaventure. This was a mid-level passenger van with special identification nameplates, high-back bucket seats (standard in Sportvans), Custom vinyl trim, a full-length headliner, door and sidewall trim panels, and a deluxe instrument panel. It was available in all tonnage classes, on the 125-in. w.b. Offered for the first time in a Chevrolet factory van was a travel bed package consisting of a three-passenger bench seat with folding back rest, plus a hinged extension which unfolded into a travel bed. Technical changes included improvements to the base six-cylinder engine, a new high-compression 5.0-liter V-8 with ESC (not available in California with ESC), and better corrosion protection measures. Anti-rust measures included the use of new, two-sided galvanized steel for rear door outer panels, and the use of zinc-rich paints on brake and fuel lines.

1981 Chevrolet Blazer Sport Utility Vehicle (CP)

1/2-TON BLAZER — MODEL C/K SERIES 10500 — SIX/V-8: Blazers, for 1981, had an aerodynamically restyled front end. The smoother new hood and fenders, together with a front bumper mounted air dam, were designed to improve fuel economy. A handsome new grille (also used on Pickups) continued the ice-cube-tray look with 16 openings running across the truck between the stacked square headlamps. A wide center horizontal molding — bright-finished with a bow tie in the middle — spanned the full width of the front end. Rectangular parking lamps/turn signals were placed in the new front bumper, directly beneath the headlamps. On the body sides, the belt-level feature line ran the length of the Blazer, and blended more smoothly into the fender edge at the front. Two-tone paint treatments were now separated at the lower perimeter feature line. New front inner fender skirts with attached shields helped reduce engine compartment splash. Standard engine was still the 250-cid six-cylinder. A new 305-cid V-8 with electronic spark control (ESC) was optional, except in California. Blazer 4x4 models had a new aluminum transfer case and automatic locking hubs. Other technical improvements included bumpers made of lighter-weight high-strength/low-alloy steel, and a new front quad shock package. A Custom trim package included an exterior decor package or special two-tone paint. Also available were the Deluxe and Silverado options, and new Deluxe front appearance package.

1981 Chevrolet Step-Side Pickup (CP)

1/2-TON, 3/4-TON, 1-TON — MODEL C/K SERIES 10, 20, 30 — SIX/V-8: Chevrolet's 1981 Pickups were 87 to 300 lb. lighter than their 1980 counterparts, while retaining the same cab size and bed size as before. They received the same new grille and sheet metal treatments described above for Blazers. The grille could be had with the square headlamps only in the top level or with a Halogen High-Beam option in which both grille levels held a square lamp unit at each end. A new one-piece IP. trim panel was used on the dash eliminating the vertical seam between the banks of gauges. Collectible trim options include

the Chevy Sport, Cheyenne, Scottsdale, and Silverado packages. Custom and Custom Deluxe trims were more commonly seen. Among light-duty power plants was a new high-compression 5.0-liter V-8 with ESC (not used in California) that was designed to give both economy and performance improvements. Also new for the season were improved corrosion resistance, low-drag disc brakes, new 6,000-pound semi-floating axle (specific models), resume speed cruise controls, quad-shock 4x4 front suspension, heavier-duty rear springs, and a water-in-fuel warning lamp for diesel-powered trucks. K20s and K10s adopted the new automatic locking hubs, and shot-peened rear springs. Standard on all models were high-efficiency radiators, and Delco Freedom II battery. Suburbans were restyled, along the lines of the Blazer, at the front. Like other 1981 trucks, they had reduced weights (about 200-300 lb.). A new standard 305-cid V-8 was featured outside California. Half-tons had new drag-free disc brakes and quick-makeup master cylinder, plus lighter weight rear springs. Due to the use of new automatic-locking front hubs, Suburbans with 4x4 drive could be shifted into the 4x4 mode at speeds up to 20 mph.

1/2-TON, 3/4-TON, 1-TON FORWARD-CONTROL — MODEL P-SERIES 10, 20, 30 — SIX/V-8: Forward-Control trucks were P (parcel delivery) models available in the 10 (1/2-ton), 20 (3/4-ton) and 30 (1-ton) series The P10s had a 102-in. wheelbase and 7-ft. body. P20s came with 125-in. or 133-in. wheelbases designed for 10-ft. or 12-ft. bodies. P30s came in these sizes, plus a 157-in. wheelbase designed for 14-ft. bodies. Styling was boxy and unchanged.

1981 Chevrolet Fleetside Pickup (CP)

I.D. DATA: Combination VIN and rating plate located on: [El Camino] Top left side of dash, [Conventionals] left door pillar. Serial number systems: New system for all Light-Duty and Medium-Duty models including El Camino. The first symbol indicates country of origin: 1=U.S.A., 2=Canada, J=Japan. The second symbol indicates manufacturer: 8=Isuzu, G=General Motors Chevrolet Motor Div. The third symbol indicates brand: C=Chevrolet Truck, 8=Chevrolet MPV, A=Chevy Van with fourth seat, Z=LUV. The fourth symbol indicates GVWR and brake system: B=3,001-4,000 lb. (hydraulic brakes), C=4,001-5,000 lb. (hydraulic brakes), etc. The fifth symbol indicates line and chassis type: C=106-in. Conventional Cab 4x2 including Blazer, G=Chevy Van or Sportvan, K=106-in. Conventional cab 4x4 including Blazer, P=Forward-Control 4x2, L=LUV 4x2, R=LUV 4x4, W=El Camino, Z=Special body. The sixth symbol indicates series: 1=1/2-ton, 2=3/4-ton, 3=1-ton, 8=1/2-ton El Camino, 9=Chassis-and-Short Sill Cowl. The seventh symbol indicates body type: 0=El Camino, 1=Hi-Cube and Cut-away Van, 2=Forward-Control, 3=Four-door Cab, 4=Two-door cab, 5=Van, 6=Suburban (doors), 7=Motorhome chassis, 8=Utility (Blazer), 9=Stake. The eighth symbol indicates engine as follows: D=250-cid (4.1-liter)/one-barrel L6 (horsepower rated 115 for models with GVW under 6,000 lb., 100 for models with GVWs over 6,000 lb.), F/H=305-cid (5.0-liter) four-barrel V-8, G=305-cid (5.0-liter)/140 -nhp two-barrel V-8, L=350-cid (5.7-liter)/165-nhp four-barrel V-8, M=350-cid (5.7-liter)/145-nhp two-barrel V-8, N=110-cid (1.8-liter)/80-nhp two-barrel L4 (LUV), P=350-cid (5.7-liter) 120 -nhp two-barrel V-8, T=292-cid (4.8-liter)/120-nhp one-barrel L-6, W=454-cid (7.4-liter)/245-nhp four-barrel V-8, Z=350-cid (5.7-liter)/120 -nhp diesel V-8. The ninth symbol indicates model-year: B=1981. The tenth symbol indicates the assembly plant: A=Lakewood, Ga., B=Baltimore, Md., F=Flint, Mich., J=Janesville, Wis., S=St. Louis, Mo., U=Lordstown, Ohio, V=Pontiac, Mich. GMAD, Z=Fremont, Calif., 0=Pontiac (GMC) Michigan, 1=Oshawa or London, Ontario, Canada, 3=GMAD, Detroit, Mich., 4=Scarborough, Ontario, Canada, 8=Fujisawa, Japan. Symbols 11-17 are the production sequence number. Starting number: 10001 Ending numbers not available. Engine numbers located: [Six] on pad at right-hand side of cylinder block at rear of distributor, [V-8] on pad at front, right-hand side of cylinder block.

Model	Body Type	Price	Weight	Prod. Total
LUV — 1/2-Ton — 104.3 in. w.b. — Four				
CL10503	Chassis & Cab	5913	-	Note 8
CL10503	Pickup	6586	2315	Note 8
LUV — 1/2-Ton — 117.9 in. w.b. — Four				
CL10803	Pickup	6795	2405	Note 8
El Camino — 1/2-Ton — 117.1 in. w.b. — V-6				
A1AW80	Pickup	6988	3181	Note 9
RPOZ15	Super Sport Pickup	7217	3188	Note 9
G10 Van — 1/2-Ton — 110 in. w.b. — Six				
CG11005	Panel	6434	3577	Note 9
CG11006	Sportvan	7465	3907	Note 9
G10 Van — 1/2-Ton — 125 in. w.b. — Six				
CG11306	Bonaventure	8305	4016	Note 9
CG11306	Beauville	8515	4016	Note 9
G20 Van — 3/4-Ton — 110 in. w.b. — Six				
CG21005	Panel	6756	3631	Note 9
CG21006	Sportvan	7617	3928	Note 9
G20 Van — 3/4-Ton — 125 in. w.b. — Six				
CG21306	Bonaventure	8457	-	Note 9
CG21306	Beauville	8667	-	Note 9
CG21305	Nomad	8644	-	Note 9

Model	Body Type	Price	Weight	Prod. Total
G30 Van — 1-Ton — 125 in. w.b. — V-8				
CG31305	Panel	8056	4285	Note 9
CG31306	Sportvan	8997	4602	Note 9
CS31306	Bonaventure	9653	-	Note 9
CG31306	Beauville	9863	-	Note 9
G30 Hi-Cube Van — 1-Ton — 125/146 in. w.b. — V-8				
CG31303	10-ft. Panel & Cab	8921	-	Note 9
CG31603	12-ft. Panel & Cab	10,257	-	Note 9
Blazer 4x4 — 1/2-Ton — 106.5 in. w.b. — Six				
CK10516	Hardtop	8856	4087	Note 9
CK10516	Softtop	8750	-	Note 9

NOTE 1: Deduct for C10 (4x2) Blazer.

Model	Body Type	Price	Weight	Prod. Total
C10 4x2 — 1/2-Ton — 117.5 — Six				
CC10703	Step-Side 6.5 ft.	6012	3328	Note 9
CC10703	Fleetside 6.5 ft.	6012	3391	Note 9
C10 4x2 — 1/2-Ton — 129.5 in. w.b. — V-8				
CC10906	Suburban 9 ft.	8517	4276	Note 9
C10 4x2 — 1/2-Ton — 131.5 — Six				
CC10903	Step-Side 8 ft.	6099	3457	Note 9
CC10903	Fleetside 8 ft.	6099	3518	Note 9

NOTE 2: Add $1,750 for K10 (4x4) Pickups and Suburbans.

Model	Body Type	Price	Weight	Prod. Total
C20 — 3/4-Ton — 131.5 w.b. — Six				
CC20903	Chassis & Cab	6605	3326	Note 9
CC20903	Step-Side 8 ft.	7109	3710	Note 9
CC20903	Fleetside 8 ft.	7109	3771	Note 9
C20 — 3/4-Ton — 129.5 w.b. — V-8				
CC20906	Suburban	8771	4596	Note 9
C20 Bonus-Cab — 3/4-Ton — 164.5 in. w.b. — Six				
CC20943	Chassis & Cab	7447	4246	Note 9
CC20943	Fleetside 8-ft.	7935	-	Note 9
C20 Crew-Cab — 3/4-Ton — 164.5 in. w.b. — Six				
CC20943	Chassis & Cab	7737	-	Note 9
CC20943	Fleetside 8-ft.	8225	-	Note 9

NOTE 3: Add $1,370 for K20 (4x4) Pickups and Suburbans.

Model	Body Type	Price	Weight	Prod. Total
P20 Step-Van — 3/4-Ton — 125/133 in. w.b.- Six				
CP20842	Steel Step-Van 10	9536	5472	Note 9

NOTE 4: Add for C20 12 ft. Step-Van on 133 in. wheelbase.

Model	Body Type	Price	Weight	Prod. Total
C30 — 1-Ton — 131.5 w.b. — Six				
CC30903	Chassis & Cab	6720	3893	Note 9
CC30903	Step-Side 8 ft.	7214	4251	Note 9
CC30903	Fleetside 8 ft.	7214	4310	Note 9
C30 Bonus-Cab — 1-Ton — 164.5 in. w.b. — Six				
CC30943	Chassis & Cab	7625	4327	Note 9
CC30943	Fleetside 8-ft.	8114	-	Note 9
C30 Crew-Cab — 1-Ton — 164.5 in. w.b. — Six				
CC30943	Chassis & Cab	7915	-	Note 9
CC30943	Fleetside 80ft.	8404	-	Note 9

NOTE 5: Add for K30 4x4 models, price not available.

Model	Body Type	Price	Weight	Prod. Total
P30 Step-Van — 1-Ton — 125/133/157 in. w.b. — V-8				
CP30842	Steel Step-Van 10	9784	5671	Note 9

1981 Chevrolet Beauville Sportvan (CP)

NOTE 6: Add for P30 12-ft. Step-Van on 133-in. wheelbase.
NOTE 7: Add for P30 14-ft. Step-Van on 157-in. wheelbase.
NOTE 8: U.S. Sales of LUV: 61,724.
NOTE 9: Model-year production: [El Camino] 37,533, [All Chevy Van] 85,135 [All Sportvan] 13,844, [Blazer] 23,635, [C10/C20 Suburban] 25,983, [Other C10] 318,003, [Other C20] 76,288, [C30] 50,250, [P10/P20/P30] 22,134. (Includes trucks built in Canada for U.S. market.)

ENGINE: [Standard: LUV] Inline. OHV. OHC. Four-cylinder. Cast iron block. Bore & stroke: 3.31 x 3.23 in. Displacement: 110.8 cid. Compression ratio: 8.5:1. Net horsepower: 80 at 4800 rpm. Maximum torque: 95 lb.-ft. at 3000 rpm. Five main bearings. Hydraulic valve lifters. Carburetor: Single one-barrel.

ENGINE: [Standard: El Camino (Except California)] V-block. OHV. Six-cylinder. Cast iron block. Bore & stroke: 3.7 x 3.48 in. Displacement: 229 cid. Compression ratio: 8.6:1. Net horsepower: 110 at 4200 rpm. Maximum torque: 170 lb.-ft. at 2000 rpm. Four main bearings. Hydraulic valve lifters. Order Code LC3(A).

ENGINE: [Standard: El Camino (California only)] V-block. OHV. Six-cylinder. Cast iron block. Bore & stroke: 3.8 x 3.4 in. Displacement: 231 cid. Compression ratio: 8.0:1. Net horsepower: 110 at 3800 rpm. Maximum torque: 190 lb.-ft. at 1600 rpm. Four main bearings. Hydraulic valve lifters. Order Code LD5(C).

ENGINE: [Standard: C10/C20/K10/G10/G20/G30/Blazer] Inline. OHV. Six-cylinder. Cast iron block. Bore & stroke: 3.9 x 4.5 in. Displacement: 250 cid. Compression ratio: 8.3:1. Net horsepower: 115 at 3600 rpm. Torque: 200 lb.-ft. at 2000 rpm. Seven main bearings. Hydraulic valve lifters. Carburetor: Rochester model staged two-barrel. Order Code LE3(A).

1981 Chevrolet El Camino Knight (CP)

ENGINE: [Optional El Camino, except in California)] V-block. OHV. Eight-cylinder. Cast iron block. Bore & stroke: 3.5 x 3.48 in. Displacement: 267 cid. Compression ratio: 8.3:1. Net horsepower: 115 at 4000 rpm. Maximum torque: 200 lb.-ft. at 2400 rpm. Five main bearings. Hydraulic valve lifters. Carburetor: Rochester model staged two-barrel. Order Code L39(B).

ENGINE: [Standard: C20 HD (C6P)/C20 Bonus and Crew-Cab/ C30/C30 Bonus and Crew-Cab/K20 HD (P6)] Inline. OHV. Six-cylinder. Cast iron block. Bore & stroke: 3.876 x 4.12 in. Displacement: 292 cid. Compression ratio: 7.8:1. Net horsepower: 115 at 3400 rpm. Maximum torque: 215 lb.-ft. at 1600 rpm. Five main bearings. Hydraulic valve lifters. Carburetor: Rochester model one-barrel. Order Code L25(B).

ENGINE: [Optional C10/C20/K10/Blazer] V-block. OHV. Eight-cylinder. Cast iron block. Bore & stroke: 3.736 x 3.480 in. Displacement: 305 cid. Compression ratio: 8.5:1. Net horsepower: 130 at 4000 rpm. Maximum torque: 240 lb.-ft. at 2000 rpm. Five main bearings. Hydraulic valve lifters. Carburetor: Rochester model staged two-barrel. Order Code LG9(C).

ENGINE: [Optional C10/C20/K10/Blazer] V-block. OHV. Eight-cylinder. Cast iron block. Bore & stroke: 3.736 x 3.480 in. Displacement: 305 cid. Compression ratio: 9.2:1. Net horsepower: 160 at 4400 rpm. Maximum torque: 235 lb.-ft. at 2000 rpm. Five main bearings. Hydraulic valve lifters. Carburetor: Rochester model staged four-barrel with Electronic Spark Control. Order Code LE9(C). Not available for California.

ENGINE: [Optional El Camino] V-block. OHV. Eight-cylinder. Cast iron block. Bore & stroke: 3.7 x 3.48 in. Displacement: 305 cid. Compression ratio: 8.6:1. Net horsepower: 145 at 3800 rpm. Maximum torque: 248 lb.-ft. at 2400 rpm. Five main bearings. Hydraulic valve lifters. Carburetor: Rochester model staged four-barrel. Order Code LG4(B).

ENGINE: [Optional C10/C20/K10/G10/G20] V-block. OHV. Eight-cylinder. Cast iron block. Bore & stroke: 3.736 x 3.480 in. Displacement: 305 cid. Compression ratio: 8.6:1. Net horsepower: 150 at 4200 rpm. Maximum torque: 240 lb.-ft. at 2000 rpm. Five main bearings. Hydraulic valve lifters. Carburetor: Rochester model staged four-barrel. Order Code LF3(C).

ENGINE: [Standard: G30/C20/K10/K20 Suburban, Optional: C20/K20/K20 HD (CP6)/K30/C10 Suburban] V-block. OHV. Eight-cylinder. Cast iron block. Bore & stroke: 4.3 x 3.5 in. Displacement: 350 cid. Compression ratio: 8.2:1. Five main bearings. Hydraulic valve lifters. Carburetor: Rochester model four-barrel. Order Code L59(A).

ENGINE: [Optional C10] V-block. OHV Diesel. Eight-cylinder. Cast iron block. Bore & stroke: 4.06 x 3.38 in. Displacement: 350 cid. Compression ratio: 22.5:1. Net horsepower: 125 at 3600 rpm. Maximum torque: 225 lb.-ft. at 1600 rpm. Five main bearings. Hydraulic valve lifters. Carburetor: Fuel injection. Order Code LS9(A).

ENGINE: [Optional: C20/C20 HD/CP6/C30] V-block. OHV. Eight-cylinder. Cast iron block. Bore & stroke: 4.250 x 4.0 in. Displacement: 454 cid. Compression ratio: 7.9:1. Net horsepower: 210 at 3800 rpm. Maximum torque: 340 lb.-ft at 2800 rpm. Five main bearings. Hydraulic valve lifters. Carburetor: Rochester model four-barrel. Order Code LE8(A).

NOTE 10: Versions of some engines used in trucks for California sale have different horsepower and torque ratings.

CHASSIS: [LUV] Wheelbase: 104.3 in./117.9 in. Overall length: 174.5 in./191.6 in. Height: [4x2] 59.3 in., [4x4] 61.0 in. Front tread: [4x2] 53.8 in., [4x4] 54.2 in. Rear tread: [4x2] 51.2 in., [4x4] 52.7 in. Tires: [4x2] E78 x 14B in., [4x4] F70 x 14B in. white-lettered.

CHASSIS: [El Camino] Wheelbase: 117.1 in. Overall length: 201.6 in. Height: 53.8 in. Front tread: 58.5 in. Rear tread: 57.8 in. Tires: P205/75R x 14 in.

CHASSIS: [Chevy Van 10] Wheelbase: 110 in./125 in. Overall length: 178.2 in./202.2 in. Height: 78.8 in./81.2 in. Front tread: 69.5 in. Rear tread: 69.7 in. Tires: FR78 x 15B in.

CHASSIS: [Chevy Van 20] Wheelbase: 110 in./125 in. Overall length: 178.2 in./202.2 in. Height: 78.8 in./81.2 in. Front tread: 69.5 in. Rear tread: 69.7 in. Tires: P225/75R x 15 in.

CHASSIS: [Chevy Van 30] Wheelbase: 125 in./146 in. Tires: 8.75 x 16.5E in.

CHASSIS: [Hi-Cube Van]: Wheelbase: 125 in./146 in. Overall length: 207.3 in./231.3 in. Height: 85 x 16 in., [rear] 8.00 x 16 in.

CHASSIS: [Blazer 4x4] Wheelbase: 106.5 in. Overall length: 184.8 in. Height: 73.4 in. Front tread: 66.1 in. Rear tread: 63 in. Tires: [4x2] P215/75R x 15 in., [4x4] P215/75R x 15 in.

CHASSIS: [C10 Pickups] Wheelbase: 117.5 in./131.5 in. Overall length: 192.2 in./211.4 in. Height: [Fleetside] 69.8 in., [Step-Side] 71.9 in. Tires: FR78 x 15B in.

CHASSIS: [C10/C20 Suburban] Wheelbase: 129.5 in. Overall length: 218.7 in. Height: 71.8 in. Tires: 8.75R x 16.5 in.

CHASSIS: [C20 Pickup] Wheelbase: 131.5 in./164.5 in. Overall length: [SWB Fleetside C10] 211.4 in., [SWB Fleetside K10] 212.1 in. Height: [4x2] 70.8 in., [4x4] 73.9 in. Tires: 8.75R x 16.5C in.

CHASSIS: [P20 Step-Van] Wheelbase: 125 in./133 in. Tires: 8.75 x 16.5C in.
CHASSIS: [C30 Pickup] Wheelbase: 131.5 in./164.5 in. Overall length: [SWB Fleetside] 211.4 in. Height: [SWB Fleetside 4x2] 70.9 in. Tires: 8.75 x 16.5C in.
CHASSIS: [P30 Step-Van] Wheelbase: 125 in./157 in. Tires: 8.75 x 16.5 in.
TECHNICAL: Selective, synchromesh transmission. Speeds: 3F/1R (LUV and 30 have 4F/1R speeds). Column-mounted gear shift (except LUV). Single disc type clutch. Salisbury rear axle. Overall ratio: various. Power front disc/rear drum brakes. Pressed steel wheels.

1981 Chevrolet Silverado Suburban (CP)

TECHNICAL: Selective synchromesh transmission (Diesel with Turbo-Hydramatic only). Speeds: 3F/1R (LUV includes 4F/1R transmission). Column-mounted gear shift, except LUV. Single dry-disc type clutch. Salisbury rear axle. Overall ratio: (C10) 3.07:1, (K10) 4.11:1, (C20) 4.10:1. Front disc/rear drum brakes. Pressed steel wheels.
LUV OPTIONS: Air conditioning ($603). Chrome rear step bumper ($122). Painted rear step bumper ($122). Chrome front bumper guards ($38). Sport stripe decals ($45). Decals and stripes ($111). California emissions ($111). Exterior Decor package, includes chrome center hubcaps and moldings for belt line, windshield and roof rails ($98). Mikado trim, with bench seat ($228), with bucket seat ($354). Stainless below-eye-line mirrors ($61). Solid paint, metallic ($75). AM radio ($98). AM/FM radio ($176). Passenger type whitewall tires, front ($19), rear, ($19), spare ($10). Automatic transmission ($420). Sliding rear window ($92).
BLAZER OPTIONS: Silverado ($881). Custom high-back vinyl bucket seats, without Silverado and rear seat ($170), two seats without Silverado ($212), one seat with Silverado (no charge), two seats with Silverado ($42). Custom cloth high-back bucket seats, without rear seat (no charge), with rear seat ($42). Special two-tone, without Silverado ($314), with Silverado ($130). Exterior Decor package, without Silverado ($430), with Silverado ($246). 5.0-liter two-barrel V-8 ($295). 5.0-liter four-barrel V-8 ($345). 5.0-liter four-barrel V-8 with ESC ($345). Four-speed manual transmission ($170). Automatic transmission ($384). Optional axle ($26). High-altitude 3.73:1 rear axle ($26). Air conditioning ($591). Deluxe front ($88). Locking differential ($191). Auxiliary battery ($101). Heavy-duty battery ($40). Chromed bumpers ($58). Deluxe chrome bumpers, with Silverado ($38), without Silverado ($96). Front bumper guards ($34). Quartz electric clock ($60). Power door locks ($98). Halogen high-beam headlamps ($26). Sliding side window ($184). One-way glass ($147). Below-eye-line mirror, stainless ($63), painted ($39), camper ($74). Body side moldings ($92). Operating convenience package ($243). Rally wheels ($88). Aluminum forged wheels ($360). Styled wheels ($176). Power windows ($145). Tailgate ($67). Power steering ($205). Fuel tank shield ($135). AM/FM with 8-track stereo ($320). Roll bar ($108).
VAN OPTIONS: Custom vinyl high-back bucket seats ($34). Custom cloth swivel bucket seats ($420). Special two-tone paint ($185). Deluxe two-tone paint ($195). 5.0-liter four-barrel V-8 ($345). 5.7-liter four-barrel V-8 ($345). Automatic transmission ($384). Axle options ($26). Air conditioning, front ($696), front and rear, ($1,138). Locking differential ($191). Heavy-duty battery ($40). Heavy-duty power brakes ($63). Chrome bumpers front/rear ($58). Front chrome bumper guards ($34). Electric clock ($27). Engine oil cooler ($95). Heavy-duty cooling ($42). Spare tire cover ($26). Power door locks ($147). California emissions ($80). Side rear door extender link ($29). All glass tinted ($75). Windshield tinted ($25). One-way glass ($296). Rear heater, without air conditioner ($189), with ($156). Cigar lighter ($19). Auxiliary lighting ($77). Below-eye-line mirrors, painted ($39), stainless ($63). Body side moldings ($102). Door edge guards ($13). Wheel opening moldings ($57). Operating convenience package, includes power door locks and windows ($292). Passenger seats, eight-man ($219), 12-man ($467). Swivel bucket seats ($426). Travel bed with 8-passenger ($770), regular ($561). Heavy-duty shocks ($27). Automatic speed control ($132). Power steering ($217). Comfort tilt steering wheel ($81). Custom steering wheel ($21). Rear door stop ($29). Front seat storage compartment ($29). Body striping ($56). Large 33-gallon fuel tank ($68). Theft deterrent system ($148). Dead-weight trailer hitch ($145). Roof ventilator ($62). Special wheelcovers ($51). Forged aluminum wheels ($360). Rally wheels with trim rings ($88). Styled wheels ($176). Power windows ($145). Windshield wiper system, intermittent ($34). Deluxe front appearance ($59). Beauville trim for cargo van ($516). Trailering special ($456). Gauge package ($29). Custom vinyl high-back bucket seats in cargo van, with auxiliary seat ($50), without auxiliary seat ($25). 5.0-liter two-barrel V-8 in cargo van ($295). Automatic transmission.
C/K OPTIONS: Scottsdale, with bucket seats ($290), without ($310). Cheyenne, without decor and bucket seats ($452), without decor with bucket seats ($394), with decor without bucket seats ($395), with decor and bucket seats ($338). Silverado, without decor and bucket seats ($718), without decor with bucket seats ($668), with decor without bucket seats ($693) and with bucket seats and decor ($642). Regular two-tone paint, with Cheyenne or Silverado ($37), without Cheyenne or Silverado ($61). Special two-tone paint, without Scottsdale-Silverado-Cheyenne ($256), with Scottsdale ($153), with Silverado ($130), with Cheyenne ($222). 4.1-liter two-barrel six (no charge). 5.0-liter two-barrel V-8 ($295). 5.0-

liter four-barrel V-8 with ESC ($345). 5.0-liter four-barrel V-8 ($345). 5.7-liter four-barrel V-8 ($315). 7.4-liter four-barrel V-8 ($425). Automatic transmission ($384). Four-speed manual transmission ($170). Deluxe two-tone paint ($288), with Scottsdale ($185), with Silverado ($138), with Cheyenne ($230). Air conditioning ($591). Chrome bumpers ($111), with Scottsdale/Cheyenne/Silverado ($82). Chrome rear step bumper ($151), with Chevy Sport ($98). Chrome bumper with rub strip ($149), with Scottsdale/Cheyenne/Silverado ($120). Chevy Sport, with bucket seats ($722), without bucket seats ($767). AM radio ($141). AM/FM radio ($224), with 8-track ($320), with cassette tape ($325). AM/FM/CB radio with tri-band mast antenna ($420). Auxiliary rear speaker ($19). Tachometer, ($90), in combination with Silverado package ($61). Cargo lamps in combination with Scottsdale/Silverado/Cheyenne/Chevy Sport ($28), without ($49). Pickup box side rails ($77). Heavy-duty springs, front ($112), rear ($44). One-inch front stabilizer bar ($27). Trim rings ($45). Wheelcovers ($69). Sliding gear window ($88). Basic camper group C20/C30 ($48). Deluxe camper group for C20/C30 with cab-over camper bodies ($292).
NOTE 11: Some of this equipment was slightly less expensive on Step-Sides and slightly more expensive on Suburbans and larger pickups.
OPTION PACKAGES: [Scottsdale]: includes front and rear bumpers, black body side moldings, cigarette lighter, headliner and dome lamp. [Silverado]: includes front and rear bumpers, wheel opening trim, deluxe molding package, visor mirror, bright body side moldings, deluxe front appearance headliner, carpeting, Custom steering wheel, cigarette lighter, dome lamp, voltmeter, temperature and oil pressure gauges.
HISTORICAL: Introduced: Fall 1980. Calendar-year registrations: 650,460. Calendar-year sales: [Pickups] 403,487, [S-10] 15,473, [Van] 86,727, [Suburban] 19,518, [Blazer] 21,399, [LUV] 61,724, [El Camino] 33,086, [Sportvan] 13,576, [Total] 654,990. Innovations: Low-alloy steel panels. New light-weight window glass. Aerodynamic Styling. Electronic spark control. Historical notes: The fuel crisis and high interest rates continued to have a negative effect on Chevrolet's light-duty truck sales. The Chevrolet S10 Mini-Pickup was introduced in mid-1981 as a 1982 model.

1982 CHEVROLET

1982 Chevrolet 1/2-Ton LUV Pickup 4x2 (Lowell E. Eisenhour photo)

1/2-TON LUV — MODEL L — FOUR: The Series 12 LUV Pickups were similar to 1981 models. The Mikado trim option came with cloth/vinyl seat upholstery, full carpeting, a deluxe steering wheel, and other goodies.
1/2-TON S10 MINI-PICKUP — MODEL S/SERIES 10 — FOUR/V-6: An important extension of the Chevrolet truck line was accomplished by introduction of the S10 Series. It was a new-sized compact Pickup, larger than a LUV, but smaller than a C10. Styling was in the big truck mold, but with flatter body sides. Single rectangular headlamps were featured. They had parking lamps on the outer ends that went around the body corners. The inner front edge was slanted to complement the grille design. The grille was formed with three rows of six rectangular segments, each row a little narrower than the one above. This gave an inverted trapezoid shape to the overall arrangement. A Chevrolet bow tie was in the center. Bumper-mounted turn signals and vertical taillights were other touches. Standard equipment included a 1.9-liter four-cylinder engine, four-speed manual transmission, bench seat, and dual outside rear view mirrors. Trim levels included standard, Sport and top-of-the-line Durango.
1/2-TON EL CAMINO — MODEL W — SIX/V-8: El Caminos adopted a new cross-hatched grille and quadruple rectangular headlights. Standard equipment included a 3.8-liter V-6 engine, three-speed automatic transmission, power brakes, cloth bench seat and carpeting. The Super Sport model-option added dual sport mirrors, front air dam, accent color on lower body and rally wheels.
1/2-TON BLAZER — MODEL C (4x2)/MODEL K (4x4) — SIX/V-8: New for 1982 Blazers was a 6.2-liter (379-cid) Chevrolet-built diesel V-8 and four-speed overdrive transmission, both costing extra. Appearance features were virtually identical to last season, except a chrome grille was standard. Standard equipment included the 4.1-liter six, three-speed manual transmission (four-speed on 4x4 models), power brakes, vinyl bench seats, chrome bumpers, automatic locking hubs, and, on 4x4s, power steering. Improved rust protection was promoted.

1/2-TON, 3/4-TON, 1-TON VAN/HI-CUBE VAN — MODEL G/SERIES 10, 20, 30 — SIX/V-8: Hi-Cube vans, Chevy Vans and Sportvans were pretty much devoid of any earth-shaking differences from 1981.

1/2-TON, 3/4-TON, 1-TON CONVENTIONAL — MODEL C (4x2), MODEL K (4x4)/SERIES 10, 20, 30 — SIX/V-8: Since they were, more or less, longer wheelbase versions of the Blazer, Chevrolet conventional trucks had the same type of appearance and same new options. Essentially, the 1982 models were carbon copies of 1981s, except a chrome grille was standard on all models. Standard equipment also included the trusty 250-cid six (292-cid in C30/K20/K30), column-mounted three-speed gear box (four-speed on C30/K30), power brakes (except C10/C20), chrome bumpers, and a bench seat. Four-wheel-drive models came with standard power steering and the K30s featured a two-speed transfer case. The Cheyenne trim level was eliminated. Custom Deluxe, Scottsdale, and Silverado packages were still available. Improved rust protection was advertised.

3/4-TON, 1-TON FORWARD-CONTROL — MODEL P SERIES 20, 30 — SIX/V-8: Step-Vans also had no earth-shaking differences from 1981. The P20 offered two wheelbases, 125 in. for 10-ft. bodies and 133 in. for 12-ft. bodies. The P30 offered the same, plus a 157-in. wheelbase for 14-ft. bodies.

1982 Chevrolet 1/2-Ton LUV Pickup 4x4 (RCA)

I.D. DATA: Location of serial number: The VIN is stamped on a plate attached to the left top of the instrument panel on C/K/G Series. On P Series the plate is attached to the front of the dash and the panel to the left of the steering column. The first symbol indicates country of origin: 1=U.S., 2=Canada, J=Japan. The second symbol indicates manufacturer: G=General Motors, 8=Isuzu. The third symbol indicates make: A=Chevrolet bus, B=Chevrolet (incomplete), C=Chevrolet truck, Y=LUV (incomplete), Z=LUV truck, 8=Chevy MPV. The fourth symbol indicates GVW rating (and brake system): B=3,001 lb.-4,000 lb. (hydraulic), C=4,001 lb.-5,000 lb. (hydraulic), etc. through K for hydraulic brakes. The fifth symbol indicates line and chassis type: C=Conventional cab (including Blazer and Suburban) 4x2, G=Chevy Van and Sportvan 4x2, K=Conventional cab (including Blazer and Suburban) 4x4, L=LUV 4x2, R=LUV 4x4, P=Forward-Control, S=Conventional cab 4x2, W=El Camino 4x2, Z=Special body 4x2. The sixth symbol indicates series: 1=1/2-ton, 2=3/4-ton, 3=1-ton, 8=El Camino. The seventh symbol indicates body type: 0=El Camino Pickup-Delivery, 1=Hi-Cube and Cutaway Vans, 2=Forward-Control, 3=Four-door cab, 4=Two-door cab, 5=Van, 6=Suburban, 7=Motorhome chassis, 9=Stake. The eighth symbol indicated engine: [El Camino] A=231-cid (3.8-liter)/110-nhp two-barrel V-6), K=229-cid (3.8-liter)/110-nhp two-barrel V-6 for California, J=267-cid (4.4-liter)/115-nhp two-barrel V-8, H=305-cid (5.0-liter)/145-nhp four-barrel V-8, T=262-cid (4.3-liter)/85-nhp diesel V-8. [Trucks] A=119-cid (1.9-liter)/82-nhp two-barrel Isuzu four-cylinder, B=173-cid (2.8-liter)/110-nhp two-barrel V-6, C or J=379-cid (6.2-liter)/110-nhp diesel V-8, D=250-cid (4.1-liter)/105-nhp two-barrel inline six-cylinder, F or H=305-cid (5.0-liter)/140-nhp two-barrel V-8, L or M=350-cid (5.7-liter)/160-nhp four-barrel V-8, N=110.8-cid (1.8-liter) two-barrel Isuzu four-cylinder, P=350-cid (5.7-liter)/145-nhp four-barrel V-8, S=136.6-cid (2.2-liter)/58-nhp Isuzu four-cylinder diesel, T=292-cid (4.8-liter)/120-nhp one-barrel inline six-cylinder, W=454-cid (7.5-liter)/245-nhp four-barrel V-8. The ninth symbol was a check digit. The 10th symbol indicated model-year: C=1982. The 11th symbol indicated the assembly plant: A=Lakewood, Ga., B=Baltimore, Md., C=Southgate, Calif., D=Doraville, Ga., E=Linden, N.J., F=Flint, Mich., G=Framingham, Mass., H=Flint, Mich., J=Janesville, Wis., K=Leeds, Mo., L=Van Nuys, Calif., M=Lansing, Mich., N=Norwood, Ohio, P=Pontiac, Mich., R=Arlington, Texas, S=St. Louis, Mo., T=Tarrytown, N.Y., V=GMC, Pontiac, Mich., W=Willow Run, Mich., X=Fairfax, Va., Y=Wilmington, Dela., Z=Fremont, Calif., O=GMAD, Pontiac, Mich., 1=Oshawa, Canada, 2=Moraine, Ohio, 2=Ste. Therese, Quebec, Canada, 3=Chevrolet-Detroit, Mich., 3=St. Eustache, Quebec, Canada, 4=Orion Plant, Pontiac, Mich., 4=Scarborough, Ontario, Canada, 5=Bowling Green, Ken., 5=London, Ontario, Canada, 6=Oklahoma City, Okla., 7=Lordstown, Ohio, 8=Shreveport, La., 8=Fujisawa, Japan, 9=Cadillac, Detroit, Mich. (Note: Trucks not built at all factories.) Symbols 12-17 were the production sequence number starting at 100001. Ending numbers not available. Engine number location: [Six] located on pad at right-hand side of cylinder block at rear of distributor. [V-8] located on pad at right front side of cylinder block.

Model	Body Type	Price	Weight	Prod. Total
LUV — 1/2-Ton — 104.3 in. w.b. — Four				
CL10503	Pickup	6256	2375	Note 6
LUV — 1/2-Ton — 117.9 in. w.b. — Four				
CL10803	Pickup	6465	2470	Note 6
S10 — 1/2-Ton — 108.3 in. w.b. — V-6				
CS10603	Pickup	6600	2476	Note 7

Model	Body Type	Price	Weight	Prod. Total
S10 — 1/2-Ton — 118 in. w.b. — V-6				
CS10803	Chassis & Cab	-	2878	Note 7
CS10803	Pickup	6750	2552	Note 7
CS10803	Utility	-	3276	Note 7
El Camino — 1/2-Ton — 117.1 in. w.b. — V-6				
1GW80	Sedan-Pickup	7995	3294	Note 7
1GW80	Super Sport Sedan-Pickup	8244	3300	Note 7
Chevy Van 10 — 110 in. w.b. — Six				
CG11005	Panel	6908	3708	Note 7
CG11006	Sportvan	8122	4039	Note 7
Chevy Van 10 — 125 in. w.b. — Six				
CG11306	Bonaventure	9040	-	Note 7
CG11306	Beauville	9268	-	Note 7
Chevy Van 20 — 110 in. w.b. — Six				
CG21005	Panel	7256	3782	Note 7
Chevy Van 20 — 125 in. w.b. — Six				
CG21306	Sportvan	8486	4251	Note 7
CG21306	Bonaventure	9204	-	Note 7
CG21306	Beauville	9432	-	Note 7
Chevy Van 30 — 125 in. w.b. — Six				
CG31305	Panel	8494	4251	Note 7
Chevy Van 30 — 146 in. w.b. — Six				
CG31306	Sportvan	10,228	4608	Note 7
CG31306	Bonaventure	10,946	-	Note 7
CG31306	Beauville	11,174	-	Note 7
G30 Hi-Cube Van — 125/146 in. w.b. — V-8				
CG31403	Hi-Cube Van 10 ft.	10,141	5515	Note 7
CG31603	Hi-Cube Van 12 ft.	11,607	5848	Note 7
Blazer — 1/2-Ton — 106.5 in. w.b. — Six				
CK10516	Hardtop 4x4	9874	4294	Note 7
CK10516	Hardtop 4x2	8533	-	Note 7
C10 Conventional — 1/2-Ton — 117.5 in. w.b. — Six				
CC10703	Step-Side 6.5 ft.	6689	3418	Note 7
CC10703	Fleetside 6.5 ft.	6564	3461	Note 7
C10 Suburban — 1/2-Ton — 129.5 in. w.b. — V-8				
CC10906	Suburban (gate)	9744	4295	Note 7
C10 Conventional — 1/2-Ton — 131.5 in. w.b. — Six				
CC10903	Fleetside 8 ft.	6714	3613	Note 7
NOTE 1: Add $2,185 for K10 (4x4) Pickups/Suburbans.				
C20 — 3/4-Ton — 131.5 in. w.b. — Six				
CC20903	Chassis & Cab	7865	3661	Note 7
CC20903	Step-Side 8 ft.	7857	3956	Note 7
CC20903	Fleetside 8 ft.	7732	3999	Note 7
C20 Suburban — 1/2-Ton — 129.5 in. w.b. — V-8				
CC20906	Suburban (gate)	9978	4677	Note 7
C20 — 3/4-Ton — 164.5 in. w.b. — Six				
CC20943	Bonus-Cab	9123	4748	Note 7
CC20943	Crew-Cab	9439	4809	Note 7
NOTE 2: Add $1,974 for K20 (4x4) Fleetside/Suburban, add $1,849 for K20 (4x4) Step-Side.				
P20 Step-Van — 3/4-Ton — 125/133 in. w.b. — Six				
CP20842	Step-Van 10 ft.	11,744	5777	Note 7
C30 — 1-Ton — 131.5 in. w.b. — Six				
CC30903	Chassis & Cab	7990	3973	Note 7
CC30903	Step-Side 8 ft.	8474	4323	Note 7
CC30903	Fleetside 8 ft.	8349	4394	Note 7
C30 Bonus-Cab — 1-Ton — 164.5 in. w.b. — Six				
CC30943	Chassis & Cab	8943	4400	Note 7
CC30943	Fleetside 8 ft.	9286	4817	Note 7
C30 Crew-Cab — 1-Ton — 164.5 in. w.b. — Six				
CC30943	Chassis & Cab	9259	4461	Note 7
CC30943	Fleetside 8 ft.	9602	4878	Note 7
NOTE 3: Add for K30 (4x4) Pickups, price not available.				
P30 Step-Van — 1-Ton — 125/133/157 in. w.b. — Six				
CP30842	Steel Step-Van 10.6 ft.	11,820	5939	Note 7

1982 Chevrolet El Camino Conquista Sedan-Pickup (CP)

NOTE 4: Add for 12-ft. model on 133-in. wheelbase.
NOTE 5: Add for 14-ft. model on 157-in. wheelbase.
NOTE 6: U.S. sales of LUV: 22,304.
NOTE 7: Model-year production: [El Camino] 23,104, [All Chevy Van] 99,019, [All Sportvans] 15,262, [Blazer] 24,514, [C10/C20/K10/K20 Suburbans] 28,916, [Other C10/K10, except Blazer] 243,834, [Other C20/K20] 75,714, [C30/K30] 49,230, [P10/P20/P30] 27,919. (Includes all trucks with GVWs of 10,000 lb. or less built in U.S. and built in Canada for the U.S. market).
NOTE 8: Percent of above totals with four-wheel-drive used on chassis and pickup trucks: [CK10] 17.5 percent, [CK20] 30.5 percent, [CK30] 16 percent.
NOTE 9: Percent of above totals with four-wheel-drive used on Suburbans: [CK10/CK20 combined] 28.6 percent.
ENGINE: [Standard: S10] Inline. OHV. OHC. Four-cylinder. Cast iron block. Bore & stroke: 3.42 x 3.23 in. Displacement: 119 cid. Compression ratio: 8.4:1. Net horsepower: 82 at 4600 rpm. Maximum torque: 101 lb.-ft. at 3000 rpm. Hydraulic valve lifters. Order Code LR1.

ENGINE: [Standard: 4x4 LUV] Inline. OHV. OHC. Four-cylinder. Cast iron block. Bore & stroke: 3.31 x 3.23 in. Displacement: 110.8 cid. Compression ratio: 8.5:1. Net horsepower: 80 at 4800 rpm. Maximum torque: 95 lb.-ft at 3000 rpm. Five main bearings. Hydraulic valve lifters. Carburetor: one-barrel. Order Code L10.
ENGINE: [Standard: 4x2 LUV models, Optional: LUV 4x4] Inline. OHV Diesel. Four-cylinder. Cast iron block. Displacement: 136.6 cid. Compression ratio: 21:1. Net horsepower: 58 at 4300 rpm. Maximum torque: 93 lb.-ft. at 2200 rpm. Hydraulic valve lifters. Order Code LQ7.
ENGINE: [Optional: S10] V-block. OHV. Six-cylinder. Cast iron block. Bore & stroke: 3.50 x 2.99 in. Displacement: 173 cid. Compression ratio: 8.5:1. Net horsepower: 110 at 4800 rpm. Maximum torque: 148 lb.-ft. at 2000 rpm. Hydraulic valve lifters. Order Code LR2.
ENGINE: [Standard: El Camino (except California) V-block. OHV. Six-cylinder. Cast iron block. Bore & stroke: 3.7 x 3.48 in. Displacement: 229 cid. Compression ratio: 8.6:1. Net horsepower: 110 at 4200 rpm. Maximum torque: 170 lb.-ft. at 2000 rpm. Four main bearings. Hydraulic valve lifters. Code LC3(A).
ENGINE: [Optional El Camino, California only] V-block. OHV. Six-cylinder. Cast iron block. Bore & stroke: 3.8 x 3.4 in. Displacement: 231 cid. Compression ratio: 8.0:1. Net horsepower: 110 at 3800 rpm. Maximum torque: 190 lb.-ft. at 1600 rpm. Five main bearings. Hydraulic valve lifters. Carburetor: Rochester two-barrel. Order Code LO5(C).
ENGINE: [Standard: C10/C20/K10/G10/G20/G30]: Inline. OHV. Six-cylinder. Cast iron block. Bore & stroke: 3.9 x 4.5 in. Displacement: 250 cid. Compression ratio: 8.3:1. Net horsepower: 110 at 3600 rpm. Torque: 195 lb.-ft. at 2000 rpm. Seven main bearings. Hydraulic valve lifters. Carburetor: Rochester staged two-barrel. Order Code LE3(A).
ENGINE: [Optional: El Camino (except California] V-block. OHV. Eight-cylinder. Cast iron block. Bore & stroke: 3.5 x 3.48 in. Displacement: 267 cid. Compression ratio: 8.3:1. Net horsepower: 115 at 4000 rpm. Maximum torque: 200 lb.-ft. at 2400 rpm. Five main bearings. Hydraulic valve lifters. Carburetor: Rochester staged two-barrel. Order Code L39(B).
ENGINE: [Standard: C20 HD (C6P)/C20/C30/K20 HD (C6P)/K30 P20/P30] Inline. OHV. Six-cylinder. Cast iron block. Bore & stroke: 3.876 x 4.12 in. Displacement: 292 cid. Compression ratio: 7.8:1. Net horsepower: 115 at 3400 rpm. Maximum torque: 215 lb.-ft. at 1600 rpm. Seven main bearings. Hydraulic valve lifters. Carburetor: Rochester one-barrel. Order Code L25(B).
ENGINE: [Optional El Camino] V-block. OHV. Eight-cylinder. Cast iron block. Bore & stroke: 3.7 x 3.48 in. Displacement: 305 cid. Compression ratio: 8.6:1. Net horsepower: 150 at 3800 rpm. Maximum torque: 240 lb.-ft. at 2400 rpm. Five main bearings. Hydraulic valve lifters. Carburetor: Rochester staged four-barrel. Order Code LG4(B).
ENGINE: [Optional C10/C20/K10] V-block. OHV. Eight-cylinder. Cast iron block. Bore & stroke: 3.736 x 3.480 in. Displacement: 305 cid. Compression ratio: 9.2:1. Net horsepower: 160 at 4400 rpm. Maximum torque: 235 lb.-ft. at 2000 rpm. Five main bearings. Hydraulic valve lifters. Carburetor: Rochester staged four-barrel with Electronic Spark Control. Order Code LE9(C). Not available in California.
ENGINE: [Optional C20/C20 HD (C6P)/C30/K20 HD (C6P)/K30/P20/P30/G10/G20] V-block. OHV. Eight-cylinder. Cast iron block. Bore & stroke: 4.0 x 3.5 in. Displacement: 350 cid. Compression ratio: 8.2:1. Net horsepower: 165 at 3800 rpm. Maximum torque: 275 lb.-ft. at 1600 rpm. Five main bearings. Hydraulic valve lifters. Carburetor: Rochester four-barrel. Order Code LS9(A). Not available in California.
ENGINE: [Optional: C10/C20/C30/K10/K20/K30/C20 HD (C6P)/K20 HD (C6P)/All Suburbans] V-block. OHV. Diesel. Eight-cylinder. Cast iron block. Bore & stroke: 3.98 x 3.80 in. Displacement: 379 cid. Compression ratio: 21.5:1. Net horsepower: 130 at 3600 rpm. Maximum torque: 240 lb.-ft. at 2000 rpm. Hydraulic valve lifters. Carburetor: fuel-injection. Order Code LH6(A).
ENGINE: [Optional: C20 HD (C6P)/C20/C30/K30/C20 Suburban] V-block. OHV. Eight-cylinder. Cast iron block. Bore & stroke: 4.25 x 4 in. Displacement: 454 cid. Compression ratio: 7.9:1. Net horsepower: 210 at 3800 rpm. Maximum torque: 340 lb.-ft. at 2800 rpm. Five main bearings. Hydraulic valve lifters. Carburetor: Rochester four-barrel. Order Code LE8(A).
CHASSIS: [LUV] Wheelbase: [4x2] 104.3/117.9 in., [4x4] 104.3 in. Overall length: 174.5/191.6 in. Height: [4x2] 59.3 in., [4x4] 61.0 in. Front tread: [4x2] 53.8 in., [4x4] 54.2 in. Rear tread: [4x2] 51.2 in., [4x4] 52.7 in. Tires: [4x2] E78 x 14B in., [4x4] F70 x 14B in. white-lettered.
CHASSIS: [S10] Wheelbase: 108.3/117.9 in. Overall length: 178.2/194.1 in. Height: 59 in. Front tread: 64.7 in. Rear tread: 64.7 in. Tires: P195/75R x 14 in. Fiberglass-belted.
CHASSIS: [El Camino] Wheelbase: 117.1 in. Overall length: 201.6 in. Height: 53.8 in. Front tread: 58.5 in. Rear tread: 57.8 in. Tires: P205/75R x 14 in.
CHASSIS: [C10] Wheelbase: 117.5/131.5 in. Overall length: 191.3/212 in. Height: 69.8 in. Front tread: 65.8 in. Rear tread: 62.7 in. Tires: FR78 15B in.

1982 Chevrolet 1/2-Ton S10 Indy 500 Pickup (IMSC/JLM)

CHASSIS: [G10] Wheelbase: 110/125 in. Overall length: 178.2/202.2 in. Height: 78.8/81.2 in. Front tread: 69.5 in. Rear tread: 69.7 in. Tires: FR7815B in.
CHASSIS: [G20] Wheelbase: 110/125 in. Overall length: 178.2/202.2 in. Height: 78.8/81.2 in. Front tread: 69.5 in. Rear tread: 69.7 in. Tires: P225/75R15 in.
CHASSIS: [G30] Wheelbase: 110/125 in. Overall length: 178.2/202.2 in. Height: 78.8/81.2 in. Front tread: 69.5 in. Rear tread: 69.7 in. Tires: 8.75 x 16.5E in.
CHASSIS: [G30 Hi-Cube] Wheelbase: 125/146 in. Overall length: 207.3/231.3 in. Tires: [front] 8.75 x 16 in., [rear] 8.00 x 16.5C in.
CHASSIS: [K10/ Blazer] Wheelbase: 106.5 in. Overall length: 184.8 in. Height: 73.4 in. Front tread: 66.1 in. Rear tread: 63 in. Tires: [Two-wheel drive] P215/75R15 in., [Four-wheel-drive] P215/75R15 in. Larger sizes available.
CHASSIS: [C10/C20 Suburban] Wheelbase: 129.5 in. Overall length: 218.7 in. Height: 75.4 in. Front tread: 66.7 in. Rear tread: 63.0 in. Tires: [C10] P235/75R15, [C20] 9.50 x 16.5 in., [K10] P215/75R15, [K20] 9.50 x 16.5 in.
CHASSIS: [K10] Wheelbase: 117.5/131.5 in. Overall length: 191.3 in./212 in. Height: 72 in. Front tread: 65.8 in. Rear tread: 62.7 in. Tires: P235/75R15 in.
CHASSIS: [C20] Wheelbase: 117.5/131.5/164.5 in. Overall length: 191.3 in./212 in./244.43 in. Height: 69.8 in. Front tread: 65.8 in. Rear tread: 62.7 in. Tires: 8.75R x 16.5C in., [front] 9.50 x 16.5D in., [rear] 9.50 x 16.5E in., C20 HD [C6P]
CHASSIS: [K20] Wheelbase: 131.5 in. Overall length: 212 in. Height: 73.9 in. Front tread: 65.8 in. Rear tread: 62.7 in. Tires: 8.75R x 16.5C in., 9.50 x 16.5D in. [front] E [rear] K20 Heavy-duty (CP6).
CHASSIS: [P20] Wheelbase: 125 in./133 in. Tires: 8.75 x 16.5C in.
CHASSIS: [C30] Wheelbase: 131.5 in./164.5 in. Overall length: 212 in./244.43 in. Height: 77.8 in. Front tread: 65.8 in. Rear tread: 62.7 in. Tires: 9.50 x 16.5D in., [Bonus/Crew] 9.50 x 16.5E in.
CHASSIS: [K30] Wheelbase: 131.5 in./164.5 in. Overall length: 212 in./244.43 in. Height: 74.7/75 in. Front tread: 65.8 in. Rear tread: 62.7 in. Tires: 9.50 x 16.5D in.
CHASSIS: [P30] Wheelbase: 125 in./157 in. Tires: 8.75 x 16.5 in.
TECHNICAL: Same as 1981 except for S-10. This model had a selective synchromesh transmission with four speeds forward/one reverse, floor-mounted shifter, single dry-disc clutch, 2.73:1 final drive ratio, front disc/rear drum brakes, and pressed steel wheels.
LUV OPTIONS: Air conditioning ($677). Chrome rear step bumper ($131). Painted rear step bumper ($106). Front bumper guards ($38). Sport Stripe decals: For 104.3-in. wheelbase 4x2 ($45), for 117.9-in. wheelbase 4x2 ($50), for 104.3-in. wheelbase 4x4 ($119). Exterior decor package ($105). Mikado package: With bench seats ($244), with bucket seats ($379). Dual mirrors ($61). Metallic paint ($80). AM radio ($104). AM/FM radio ($176). Power steering ($325). Sliding rear window ($100). E78-14B whitewall tires, two for front or rear ($20). E78-14B whitewall spare tire ($10).
CHEVROLET TRUCK OPTIONS: 2.8-liter (173-cid) V-6 in S-10 ($215). 4.4-liter (267-cid) V-8 in El Camino ($70). 5.0-liter (305-cid) V-8 in El Camino ($70). 5.0-liter (305 cid) V-8 with electronic spark control in Blazers/Pickups without Special Economy package ($170), same in Pickups with Special Economy package ($170). 5.0-liter (305-cid) V-8 four-barrel in Blazer/Pickups ($170). 5.7-liter (350-cid) V-8 in Blazer/Pickups ($345). 5.7-liter (350-cid) V-8 in Pickups ($315). 6.2-liter (379-cid) diesel V-8 in K20 Pickups ($1,164), same in Blazer/C10/K10/C20 Pickups ($1,134). 7.4-liter (454-cid) V-8 in Pickups ($425). Four-speed manual transmission in C10 Pickup ($198). Four-speed overdrive manual transmission in C10 Pickup without Special Economy package ($273), in C20/K10/K20 Pickups ($75). Three-speed automatic transmission in S10/C10 Pickup ($438), in C20/K20/C30/K30 Pickup ($455). Four-speed automatic transmission in C10 Blazer ($199), in K10 Blazer/C10/K10/C20/K20 Pickups ($637). Air Conditioning: In Pickups without diesel equipment package, except K30 ($677), in Pickups with diesel equipment package, except K30 ($619), in S10 and Blazer without diesel equipment package ($677), in Blazer with diesel equipment package ($619). Deluxe front appearance package, on Blazers and Pickups ($100). Limited-slip rear axle, El Camino ($76). Locking axle/differential (except El Camino) ($217). Optional axle ratio, El Camino ($21), others ($35). Auxiliary battery in Blazer and Pickup ($118) Heavy-duty battery in El Camino ($25), in others ($45). Power brakes in Pickups and S10 ($87). Heavy-duty power brakes, in C10 Pickup without diesel equipment package ($159), in C10 Pickup with diesel equipment package ($72), in C20/K20 Pickups ($82). Chrome rear bumper on Pickups ($97). Painted rear step bumper, on Pickups ($106). Chromed rear step bumper on Pickups ($177). Color-keyed front bumper on S10 ($56). Color-keyed rear step bumper on S10 ($127). Deluxe chromed front and rear bumpers on Blazer ($44). Glide-out spare carrier on Pickups ($27). Slide-mount spare carrier on Pickups ($39). Electric quartz clock: in El Camino ($32), in Blazers/Pickups without Silverado ($70), in Blazer/Pickups with Silverado ($36). Electric digital clock on S10 ($60). Conquista package on El Camino ($183). Console in S10 ($96). Engine oil cooler, except El Camino ($112). Transmission oil cooler: On S10 without air conditioning ($103), on S10 with air conditioning, on others except El Camino ($55). Heavy-duty cooling system: On El Camino without air conditioning ($70), on El Camino with air conditioning ($40), on others ($48). Cargo box cover (tonneau) on El Camino ($129). Diesel equipment package, for Blazer ($1,125), for C10 Pickup ($1,287), for C20 Pickup ($1,723), for C30 Pickup ($1,073), for K10 and K20 Pickups ($1,041), for K30 Pickup ($783). Power door locks: For El Camino ($106), for others ($115). Dual exhaust system on Pickups ($48). Exterior Decor package: For Blazer without Silverado package ($423), for Blazer with Silverado package ($279), for Pickup without Scottsdale or Silverado ($503), for Pickup with Scottsdale package ($385), for Pickup with Silverado package ($359). Optional fuel tanks: 20-gallon tank on S10 ($39), 22-gallon tank on El Camino ($25), 31-gallon tank on Blazer ($39), Auxiliary 16-gallon tank on C10/K10/C20/K20 Pickups ($208). Gauges: For S10 ($51), for El Camino ($111), for others ($34). Tinted glass: For El Camino ($88), for Pickups and S10 ($40). Deep-tinted glass with tinted rear window on Blazer ($119). Deep-tinted glass group on Blazer ($168). Chromed grille on S10 ($53). Durango equipment group on S10 ($325). Sport equipment group on S10 ($775). Camper wiring harness on Pickups ($37). Trailer wiring harness on Blazer ($42). Five-lead trailer wiring harness on S10 ($37). Halogen headlamps: high/low beam, except El Camino ($20), high-beam on El Camino ($10), on others ($15). Headlamp warning buzzer on Blazer ($11). Headliner on Blazer ($74). Instrumentation package on El Camino ($187). Cargo area light on Pickups ($56). Dome light on Pickups ($24). Roof marker lights on Pickups ($46). Auxiliary lighting: For El Camino ($30), for S10 without Durango or Sport package ($87), for S10 with Durango or Sport package ($45). Left-hand remote-control outside rear view mirror for El Camino ($22). Left-hand remote-control sport-type and right-hand manual sport-type rear view mirror on El Camino ($55). Camper-type left- and right-hand rear view mirrors on Pickups ($86). Dual rear view mirrors (6-1/2 in. x 9 in. painted) for trucks, except El Camino ($44), same in stainless, for trucks except El Camino ($72). Senior West Coast mirrors on Pickups ($59). Custom Molding package: For Pickups without Scottsdale trim and Blazers ($144), for Pickups with Scottsdale trim ($26). Deluxe Molding package, ($157). Operating convenience group: For Blazers and Pickups ($281). Two-tone paint: On Pickups without Silverado package ($69), on Pickups with Silverado package ($42). Special two-tone paint: On Pickups without Scottsdale or Silverado packages ($291), on Pickups with Scottsdale package ($173), on Pickups and Blazers with Silverado package ($147), on Blazer without Silverado package ($291), on S10 Pickup ($275). Deluxe two-tone Paint: On Pickups without Scottsdale or Silverado ($328), on Pickups with Scottsdale ($210), on Pickups

with Silverado ($157). Sport two-tone paint on S10 ($135). Payload capacity package of 1,500 lb. on S10 ($173). Radio equipment: AM in El Camino ($111), in S10 ($104), in others ($92). AM/FM in El Camino ($165), in S10 ($173), in others ($144). AM/FM Stereo in El Camino ($196), in S10 ($256), in others ($226). AM/FM stereo with 8-track tape in El Camino ($282), in others except S10 ($322). AM/FM stereo with cassette tape in El Camino ($283), in others except S10 ($327). AM/FM stereo with cassette and clock in S10 ($425). AM/FM/CB with power antenna in Pickups and Blazers ($559). AM/FM stereo/CB in Blazers and Pickups ($559). Windshield antenna (not available with S10 or El Camino) ($31). Power antenna on El Camino ($55). Cargo box rails on El Camino ($81). Roll bar on Blazer ($123). Scottsdale package: For Step-Side Pickup ($208), for Fleetside Pickup without dual rear wheels ($318), for Fleetside Pickup with dual rear wheels ($217). Folding rear seats for Blazer without custom trim ($308), for Blazer with custom trim ($334). Seats/trim: Custom vinyl high-back bucket seats: In Blazer without Silverado or rear seat ($193), in Blazer without Silverado, with rear seat ($241), in Blazer with Silverado without rear seat (no charge), in Blazer with Silverado with rear seat ($48), in S10 without Durango or Sport package ($166), in S10 with Durango or Sport package ($118). Custom cloth high-back bucket seats: In Blazer without rear seat (no charge), in Blazer with rear seat ($48). Special custom cloth bench seat in Pickups (no charge). Custom vinyl bench seat: In Pickup without Scottsdale or Silverado ($48), in S10 without High Sierra or Gypsy packages ($48). Fuel tank shield: For C10 Blazer, for C-Series Pickups with auxiliary fuel tank ($115), for K10 Blazer, for K-Series Pickups with auxiliary fuel tank ($154), for C-Series Pickups without auxiliary fuel tank ($45), for K-Series Pickups without auxiliary fuel tank ($84). Heavy-duty shock absorbers, front and rear (not El Camino) ($31). Quad front shock absorbers on Blazer and K10/K20 Pickups ($117). Pickup box side rails on Pickups ($88). Silverado package: For Blazer ($931), for Step-Side Pickups ($614), for Fleetside Pickups without exterior decor package or dual rear wheels ($780), for Fleetside Pickups with exterior decor package without dual rear wheels ($753), for Fleetside without special Big Dooley package ($640), for Fleetside Pickups without special Big Dooley package and dual rear wheels ($596). Special Big Dooley two-tone paint package: For Pickups without Scottsdale package ($429), for Pickups with Scottsdale package ($412), for Fleetside Pickup, add to above ($27). Automatic Speed Control: For El Camino ($155), for others with manual transmission ($169), for others with automatic transmission ($159). Heavy-duty front springs: For Blazer and K10/K20 Pickups without quad shocks ($84), for Blazer and K10/K20 Pickups with quad shocks ($53), for C10/C20 Pickups ($36), combined with heavy-duty rear springs on C10/C20 Pickups ($51). Extra capacity rear springs on C10 Pickup ($66). Main and auxiliary rear springs on Pickups ($91). Front stabilizer bar (not available on El Camino) ($31), Heavy-duty front stabilizer bar on C-Series Pickups ($51), Power steering on Blazer, S10, C-Series Pickups ($234), Tahoe equipment on S10 ($550), Tilt steering wheel ($95), Sport suspension on El Camino ($15). Tachometer: In S10 without Sport package ($105), in S10 with Sport package ($54). Cargo box tie downs ($23). Towing device (not S10 or El Camino) ($34). Deadweight trailer hitch on Blazer ($53). Weight distribution platform on Blazer ($145). Heavy-duty Trailering Special package: For C20/C30 Pickup without air or diesel equipment ($646), for C20/C30 Pickup with air without diesel equipment ($588), for K20 Pickup without air or diesel equipment ($412), for K20 Pickup with air without diesel equipment ($354), for K30 Pickup without diesel equipment ($354), for Blazer and Pickups with diesel equipment ($242), S10 ($187), for C10 Blazer without air conditioning ($677), for C10 Blazer with air conditioning ($619), for K10 Blazer without air or diesel equipment ($412), for K10 Blazer with air without diesel equipment ($354). Wheelcover lock package on El Camino ($39). Bright wheelcovers on Blazer C/K10 Pickups, on S10 without Durango trim ($38). Sport wheelcovers: For base El Camino ($62), for El Camino Super Sport ($6). Wire wheelcovers on El Camino ($153). Wheel trim rings on Pickups and Blazers ($52). Rally wheels: For base El Camino ($56), for S10 without Durango or Sport ($83), for S10 with Durango ($31), for others ($103). Styled wheels, not available on S10 or El Camino ($201). Forged aluminum wheels, not available for El Camino ($411). Dual rear wheels: For C30 Fleetside without air or diesel equipment ($677), for C30 Fleetside with air or diesel equipment ($619), for K30 Pickups without air or diesel equipment ($644), for K30 Pickups with air or diesel equipment ($606). Intermittent windshield wipers: For El Camino ($47), for others ($45). Sliding rear window on Pickups ($100). Power windows ($166). Power tailgate window on Blazer ($79).

1982 Chevrolet 1/2-Ton K10 Blazer Silverado Utility Hardtop (CP)

HISTORICAL: Introduced: Fall 1981. Calendar-year registrations: 758,107. Calendar-year sales: [Vans] 101,932, [Sportvan] 15,843, [S10] 177,758, [S10 Blazer] 8,161, [LUV] 22,304, [El Camino] 22,732, [Blazer] 24,103, [Suburban] 28,004, [Pickups] 393,277. Calendar-year production at U.S. factories: [Blazer] 24,238, [El Camino] 22,621, [Pickups] 268,080, [Chevy Van/Sportvan] 98,764, [Suburban] 34,846, [Compact Pickups] 209,517, [Total] 658,066. Innovations: New-sized compact S10 line introduced. LUV comes with four-cylinder diesel as standard power plant. New 6.2-liter Chevy-built diesel V-8 for larger trucks. *Consumer Guide* gave the 1982 Blazer 68 out of a possible 100 points in its road test covering performance, interior, utility and finish characteristics. The new S10 Pickups scored 69 points on the same scale, while the standard C10 Pickup racked up 70 points. The 1982 LUV Pickup earned 65 points. Chevrolet truck sales started on an upswing this season, but Ford Motor Co. was again beginning to threaten Chevrolet's ranking as the number one truck maker. Chevrolet had held the number one position steadily from 1951 to 1968. From 1969 to 1974, Ford was on top. In 1975 and 1976, Chevrolet was back in first position again. The next five years were counted in Ford's favor. The final totals for calendar-year registrations in 1982 were 758,107 for Chevy versus 733,120 for Ford.

1/2-TON LUV — MODEL L — FOUR: Even though the LUV Mini-Pickup was replaced by the new S10, Chevrolet did sell 15,530 of them in the 1983 calendar-year. However, these were leftover 1982 models.

1983 Chevrolet S10 Fleetside short box Mini-Pickup (CMD)

1/2-TON S10 MINI-PICKUP — MODEL S/SERIES 10 — FOUR/V-6: Chevrolet entered what it called "Year II of a New Era for Chevy trucks." New four-wheel-drive, Extended-Cab, and Blazer models were added to the S10 line. All S10 models, except Chassis-and-Cab and Utility Cabs, were available with four-wheel-drive. The S10 Blazer, compared to the 13-year-old full-size Blazer, was 15.3 in. shorter and 14.8 in. narrower. Its total floor space was only 4.8 sq.-ft. less. The S10 Extended-Cab Pickup, the first such configuration ever offered by Chevrolet, added 14.5 inches to Regular-Cab length. Added to the S10 engine lineup was a new 2.0-liter 83-hp L-4. Four-wheel-drive models had a new independent front suspension utilizing computer-matched torsion bars.

1983 Chevrolet El Camino Custom Sedan-Pickup (CMD)

1/2-TON EL CAMINO — MODEL W — SIX/V-8: The 1983 El Camino was luxurious. Standard equipment included an automatic transmission, power steering, air adjustable rear shocks, notch-back seat with arm rest, and color-keyed cut-pile carpeting. Both the Super Sport model-option and the Conquista package were available again. The base El Camino had dual square headlamps on either side of a cross-hatch grille with long, narrow parking lights directly below the headlamps. This was the first year the El Camino could be ordered with a 5.7-liter diesel V-8.

1/2-TON BLAZER — MODEL C (4x2)/MODEL K (4x4) — SIX/V-8: The full-size Blazer had a revised grille. It featured a blacked-out appearance. Parking lights were moved from the bumper to bottom of the grille. The horizontal center-bar was finished in body color. The Blazer was otherwise unchanged in appearance from 1982.

1/2-TON, 3/4-TON, 1-TON VAN/HI-CUBE VAN — MODEL G/SERIES 10, 20, 30 — SIX/V-8: For the first time G20 and G30 Chevy Vans and Sportvans were available with the 6.2-liter diesel engine, as well as a four-speed overdrive automatic transmission. Other changes in the 1983 vans included a steering column angle approximating that used on Pickups, floor-mounted manual transmission shift lever, and wet arms windshield washers (with nozzles located on the wiper arms). Tilt steering was available with manual transmission. There was an anti-chip coating along the lower body from front the wheel wells to the rear doors. A new rear pivot hinge, rear latch, and a floating roller mechanism improved operation of the sliding door. Also new was an inside hood release.

1/2-TON, 3/4-TON, 1-TON CONVENTIONAL — MODEL C (4x2), MODEL K (4x4)/SERIES 10, 20, 30 — SIX/V-8: Chevrolet's Conventional-Cab C/K Pickups were unchanged, except for a revised grille treatment, and parking lamp placement. The grille featured a black out look. The parking lights were moved from the bumper to the bottom of the grille. The horizontal center-bar was finished in body color. The Scottsdale trim package was upgraded slightly. Base Custom Deluxe and top-of-the-line Silverado trims were unchanged. Added corrosion protection was provided with the use of galvanized steel in the pickup box front panel and a Zincro-metal hood inner liner.

3/4-TON, 1-TON FORWARD-CONTROL — MODEL P/SERIES 20, 30 — SIX/V-8: Step-Vans also had no earth shaking differences from 1981. The P20 offered two wheelbases, 125 in. for 10-ft. bodies and 133 in. for 12-ft. bodies. The P30 offered the same, plus a 157-in. wheelbase for 14-ft. bodies.

1983 Chevrolet S10 Blazer Utility Wagon (CMD)

I.D. DATA: Location of serial number: The VIN is stamped on a plate attached to the left top of the instrument panel on C/K/G series. On P series the plate is attached to the front of the dash and the panel to the left of the steering column. The first symbol indicates country of origin: 1=U.S., 2=Canada, J=Japan. The second symbol indicates manufacturer: G=General Motors, 8=Isuzu. The third symbol indicates make: A=Chevrolet bus, B=Chevrolet (incomplete), C=Chevrolet truck, Y=LUV (incomplete), Z=LUV truck, 8=Chevy MPV. The fourth symbol indicates GVW rating (and brake system): B=3,001 lb.-4,000 lb. (hydraulic), C=4,001 lb.-5,000 lb. (hydraulic), etc. through K for models with hydraulic brakes. The fifth symbol indicates line and chassis type: C=Conventional cab (including Blazer and Suburban) 4x2, G=Chevy Van and Sportvan 4x2, K=Conventional cab (including Blazer and Suburban) 4x4, L=LUV 4x2, R=LUV 4x4, P=Forward-Control, S=Conventional Cab 4x2, W=El Camino 4x2, Z=Special body 4x2. The sixth symbol indicates series: 1=1/2-ton, 2=3/4-ton, 3=1-ton, 8=El Camino. The seventh symbol indicates body type: 0=El Camino Pickup-Delivery, 1=Hi-Cube and Cutaway Vans, 2=Forward-Control, 3=Four-door cab, 4=Two-door cab, 5=Van, 6=Suburban, 7=Motorhome chassis, 8=Blazer Utility, 9=Stake. The eighth symbol indicates engine: [El Camino] A=231-cid (3.8-liter)/110-nhp two-barrel V-6, K=229-cid (3.8-liter)/110-nhp two-barrel V-6 for California, H=305-cid (5.0-liter)/145-nhp four-barrel V-8, T=262-cid (4.3-liter)/85-nhp diesel V-8, N=350-cid (5.7-liter)/105-nhp diesel V-8. [Trucks] A=119-cid (1.9-liter)/82-nhp two-barrel Isuzu four-cylinder, B=173-cid (2.8-liter)/110-nhp two-barrel V-6, C or J=379-cid (6.2-liter)/110-nhp diesel V-8, D=250-cid (4.1-liter)/105-nhp two-barrel inline six-cylinder, F or H=305-cid (5.0-liter)/140-nhp two-barrel V-8, L or M=350-cid (5.7-liter)/160-nhp four-barrel V-8, P=350-cid (5.7-liter)/145-nhp two-barrel V-8, S=136.6-cid (2.2-liter)/58-nhp Isuzu four-cylinder diesel, T=292-cid (4.8-liter)/120-nhp one-barrel inline six-cylinder, W=454-cid (7.5-liter)/245-nhp four-barrel V-8. The ninth symbol was a check digit. The 10th symbol indicated model-year: D=1983. The 11th symbol indicated the assembly plant: A=Lakewood, Ga., B=Baltimore, Md., C=Southgate, Calif., D=Doraville, Ga., E=Linden, N.J., F=Flint, Mich., G=Framingham, Mass., H=Flint, Mich., J=Janesville, Wis., K=Leeds, Mo., L=Van Nuys, Calif., M=Lansing, Mich., N=Norwood, Ohio, P=Pontiac, Mich., R=Arlington, Texas, S=St. Louis, Mo., T=Tarrytown, N.Y., V=GMC, Pontiac, Mich., W=Willow Run, Mich., X=Fairfax, Va., Y=Wilmington, Dela., Z=Fremont, Calif., 0=GMAD, Pontiac, Mich., 1=Oshawa, Canada, 2=Moraine, Ohio, 2=Ste. Therese, Quebec, Canada, 3=Chevrolet-Detroit, Mich., 3=St. Eustache, Quebec, Canada, 4=Orion Plant, Pontiac, Mich., 4=Scarborough, Ontario, Canada, 5=Bowling Green, Ken., 5=London, Ontario, Canada, 6=Oklahoma City, Okla., 7=Lordstown, Ohio, 8=Shreveport, La., 8=Fujisawa, Japan, 9=Cadillac, Detroit, Mich. (Note: Trucks were not built at all factories.) Symbols 12-17 were the production sequence number starting at 100001. Ending numbers not available. Engine number location: [Six] located on pad at right-hand side of cylinder block at rear of distributor. [V-8] located on pad at right front side of cylinder block.

Model	Body Type	Price	Weight	Prod. Total
El Camino — 1/2-Ton — 117.1 in. w.b. — V-6				
1GW80	Sedan Pickup	8191	3332	Note 10
1GW80	Super Sport Pickup	8445	3337	Note 10
1/2-Ton Mini-Truck — Model S/ Series 10 — 108.3 in. w.b. — Six				
CS10603	Pickup	6343	2537	Note 10
1/2-Ton Mini-Truck — Model S/Series 10 — 122.0 in. w.b. — Six				
CS10803	Pickup	6496	2618	Note 10
CS10653	Extended Pickup	6725	2647	Note 10
NOTE 1: Add for S10 four-wheel-drive models.				
1/2-Ton Blazer 4x4 — Model S/Series 10 — 100.5 in. w.b. — V-6				
CT10516	Hardtop (gate)	9433	3106	Note 10
NOTE 2: Deduct for two-wheel drive S10 Blazer.				
1/2-Ton Van — Model G/Series 10 — 110 in. w.b. — Six				
CG11005	Panel	7101	3711	Note 10
CG11006	Sportvan	8596	4039	Note 10
1/2-Ton Van — Model G/Series 10 — 125 in. w.b. — Six				
CG11306	Bonaventure	9533	-	Note 10
CG11306	Beauville	9789	-	Note 10
3/4-Ton Van — Model G/Series 20 — 110 in. w.b. — Six				
CG21005	Panel	7714	3812	Note 10
3/4-Ton Van — Model G/Series 20 — 125 in. w.b. — Six				
CG21306	Sportvan	8968	4278	Note 10
CG21306	Bonaventure	9701	-	Note 10
CG21306	Beauville	9957	-	Note 10
1-Ton Van — Model G/Series 30 — 125 in. w.b. — Six				
CG31305	Panel	8718	4399	Note 10
CG31306	Sportvan	11,371	4719	Note 10
CG31306	Bonaventure	12,104	-	Note 10
CG31306	Beauville	12,360	-	Note 10
1-Ton Hi-Cube Van — Model G/Series 30 — 125 in. w.b. — V-8				
CG31305	Hi-CubeVan 10 ft.	11,151	5052	Note 10

Model	Body Type	Price	Weight	Prod. Total
1-Ton Hi-Cube Van — Model G/Series 30 — 146 in. w.b. — V-8				
CG31603	Hi-Cube Van 12 ft.	12,388	5881	Note 10
1/2-Ton Blazer 4x4 — Model K/Series 10 — 106.5 in. w.b. — V-8				
CK10516	Hardtop	10,287	4426	Note 10
1/2-Ton Conventional — Model C/Series 10 — 117.5 in. w.b. — Six				
CC10703	Step-Side	6835	3408	Note 10
CC10703	Fleetside	6707	3471	Note 10
1/2-Ton Suburban — Model C/Series 10 — 129.5 in. w.b. — V-8				
CC10906	Suburban V-8	9951	4293	Note 10
1/2-Ton Conventional — Model C/Series 10 — 131.5 in. w.b. — Six				
CC10903	Fleetside	6860	3633	Note 10
NOTE 3: Add for 1/2-ton K10 four-wheel-drive Pickups/Suburbans.				
3/4-Ton Conventional — Model C/Series 20 — 131.5 in. w.b. — Six				
CC20903	Chassis & Cab	8032	3614	Note 10
CC20903	Step-Side	8525	3964	Note 10
CC20903	Fleetside	8397	4025	Note 10
3/4-Ton Suburban — Model C/Series 20 — 129.5 in. w.b. — V-8				
CC20906	Suburban V-8	10,187	4697	Note 10
3/4-Ton Conventional — Model C/Series 20 — 164.5 in. w.b. — V-8				
CC20943	Bonus-Cab Fleetside	9315	4745	Note 10
CC20943	Crew-Cab Fleetside	9637	4806	Note 10
NOTE 4: Add for 3/4-ton K20 four-wheel-drive Pickups and Suburbans.				
3/4-Ton Step-Van — Model P/Series 20 — 125/133 in. w.b. — Six				
CP20842	Steel Step-Van 10.5 ft.	12,031	5801	Note 10
NOTE 5: Add for 133 in. wheelbase 12.5 ft. Step-Van.				
1-Ton Conventional — Model C/Series 30 — 131.5 in. w.b. — Six.				
CC30903	Chassis & Cab	8160	3965	Note 10
CC30903	Step-Side	8654	4319	Note 10
CC30903	Fleetside	8526	4380	Note 10
1-Ton Conventional — Model C/Series 30 — 164.5 in. w.b. — V-8.				
CC30943	Chassis Bonus-Cab	9131	4406	Note 10
CC30943	Bonus-Cab Fleetside	9481	4817	Note 10
CC30943	Chassis Crew-Cab	453	4467	Note 10
CC30943	Crew-Cab Fleetside	9803	4878	Note 10
NOTE 6: Add for 1-ton K30 four-wheel-drive Pickups.				
1-Ton Step-Van — Model P/Series 30 — 125/133/157 in. w.b. — Six				
CP30842	Steel Step-Van 10.5 ft.	12,071	5946	Note 10

NOTE 7: Add for 133-in. wheelbase 12.5 ft. Step-Van.
NOTE 8: Add for 157-in. wheelbase 14.5 ft. Step-Van.
NOTE 9: U.S. sales of LUV: 15,530.
NOTE 10: Model-year production: [S10] 179,157, [S10 Blazer] 84,672, [El Camino] 22,429, [All Chevy Van] 126,420, [All Sportvans] 17,960, [Full-sized Blazer] 26,245, [C10/C20/K10/K20 Suburbans] 37,928, [Other C10/K10, except Blazer] 219,961, [Other C20/K20] 66,548, [C30/K30] 35,625, [P10/P20/P30] 34,369. (Includes all trucks with GVWs of 10,000 lb. or less built in U.S. and in Canada for the U.S. Market).
NOTE 11: Percent of above totals with four-wheel-drive used on chassis models and pickup trucks: [S10] 24.6 percent, [S10 Blazer] 78.8 percent, [CK10] 22.6 percent, [CK20] 38.4 percent, [CK30] 20 percent.
NOTE 12: Percent of above totals with four-wheel-drive used on Suburbans: [CK10/CK20 combined] 29.6 percent.

1983 Chevrolet K20 Scottsdale Fleetside Pickup (RCA)

ENGINE: [Standard: S10 Ordering] Inline. OHV. OHC. Four-cylinder. Cast iron block. Bore & stroke: 3.42 x 3.23 in. Displacement: 119 cid. Compression ratio: 8.4:1. Net horsepower: 82 at 4600 rpm. Maximum torque: 101 lb.-ft. at 3000 rpm. Hydraulic valve lifters. Order Code LR1.
ENGINE: [Standard: S10 Blazer/optional Extended-Cab S10 models]. Inline. OHV. Four-cylinder. Cast iron block. Bore & stroke: 3.50 x 3.15 in. Displacement: 121 cid. Compression ratio: 9.3:1. Net horsepower: 83 at 4000 rpm. Maximum torque: 108 lb.-ft. at 2400 rpm. Hydraulic valve lifters. Carburetor: Rochester two-barrel. Order Code LQ2.
ENGINE: [Optional S10/S10 Blazer] Inline. OHV. Diesel. Four-cylinder. Cast iron block. Bore & stroke: 3.46 x 3.62 in. Displacement: 136.6 cid. Net horsepower: 62 at 4300 rpm. Maximum torque: 96 lb.-ft. at 2200 rpm. Hydraulic valve lifters. Order Code LQ7.
ENGINE: [Optional S10/S10 Blazer] V-block. OHV. Six-cylinder. Cast iron block. Bore & stroke: 3.50 x 2.99 in. Displacement: 173 cid. Compression ratio: 8.5:1. Net horsepower: 110 at 4800 rpm. Maximum torque: 145 lb.-ft. at 2100 rpm. Hydraulic valve lifters.
ENGINE: [Standard: El Camino]: V-block. OHV. Six-cylinder. Cast iron block. Bore & stroke: 3.7 x 3.48 in. Displacement: 229 cid. Compression ratio: 8.6:1. Net horsepower: 110 at 4200 rpm. Torque: 170 lb.-ft. at 2000 rpm. Four main bearings. Hydraulic valve lifters. Carburetor: Rochester two-barrel.
ENGINE: [Standard C10/C20/K10]. Inline. OHV. Six-cylinder. Cast iron block. Bore & stroke: 3.9 x 3.5 in. Displacement: 4.1-liter (250 cid). Compression ratio: 8.3:1. Net horsepower: [C10] 120 at 4000 rpm. Torque 205 lb.-ft. at 2000 rpm. Seven main bearings. Hydraulic valve lifters. Carburetor: Rochester two-barrel. Order Code LE3(A).
ENGINE: [Optional: C20 HD/C20/C30/K20 HD/K301] Inline. OHV. Six-cylinder. Cast iron block. Bore & stroke: 3.9 x 4.1 in. Displacement: 4.8-liters (292 cid). Compression ratio: 7.8:1. Net horsepower: 115 at 3600 rpm. Net torque: 215 lb.-ft. at 1600 rpm. Five main bearings. Hydraulic valve lifters. Carburetor: Rochester one-barrel. Order Code L25(B).

1983 Chevrolet C20 Suburban With Panel Doors (OCW)

ENGINE: [Optional C10/C20 K10/El Camino]. V-block. OHV. Eight-cylinder. Cast iron block. Bore & stroke: 3.74 x 3.48 in. Displacement: 5-liters (305 cid). Compression ratio: 9.2:1. Net horsepower: [C10] 165 at 4400 rpm. Torque: 240 lb.-ft. at 2000 rpm. Five main bearings. Hydraulic valve lifters. Carburetor: Rochester four-barrel. Order Code LE9(C).
ENGINE: [Optional: El Camino]: V-block. OHV. Diesel. Eight-cylinder. Cast iron block. Bore & stroke: 4.0 x 3.5 in. Displacement: 350 cid. Net horsepower: 105 rpm. Five main bearings. Fuel-injected.
ENGINE: [Optional: C20/C20 HD/C30/K10/K20/K20 HD/K30] V-block. OHV. Eight-cylinder. Cast iron block. Bore & stroke: 4.0 x 3.5 in. Displacement: 5.7-liters (350 cid). Compression ratio: 8.2:1. Net horsepower: 165 at 3800 rpm. Torque: 275 lb.-ft. at 1600 rpm. Five main bearings. Hydraulic valve lifters. Carburetor: Rochester four-barrel. Order Code LS9(A).
ENGINE: [Optional: C10/C20/C20 HD/C30/K10/K20/K20 HD/K30] V-block. OHV. Diesel. Eight-cylinder. Cast iron block. Bore & stroke: 3.98 x 3.80 in. Displacement: 6.2-liters (379 cid). Compression ratio: 21.3:1. Net horsepower: 130 at 3600 rpm. Torque: 240 lb.-ft. at 2000 rpm. Order Code LH6(D).
ENGINE: [Optional: C20 HD/C20/C30/K30] V-block. OHV. Eight-cylinder. Cast iron block. Bore & stroke: 4.3 x 4.0 in. Displacement: 7.4-liters (454 cid). Compression ratio: 7.9:1. Net horsepower: 230 at 3800 rpm. Net. Torque: 360 lb.-ft. at 2800 rpm. Five main bearings. Hydraulic valve lifters. Carburetor: four-barrel. Order Code LE8(A).
CHASSIS: [S10] Wheelbase: 108.3/117.9 in. Overall length: 178.2/194.1 in. Height: 59 in. Front tread: 64.7 in. Rear tread: 64.7 in. Tires: P195/75R x 14 in. Fiberglass-belted.
CHASSIS: [S10 Extended-Cab Pickup] Wheelbase: 122.9 in., Height: 59.4 in. Front tread: 64.7 in. Rear tread: 64.7 in., Tires: D195/75R x 14 in.
CHASSIS: [S10 Blazer] Wheelbase: 100.5 in. Overall length: 170.3 in. Height: 65 in. Front tread: 55.6 in. Rear tread: 55.1 in. Tires: D195/75R15 in.
CHASSIS: [El Camino] Wheelbase: 117.1 in. Overall length: 201.6 in. Height: 53.8 in. Front tread: 58.5 in. Rear tread: 57.8 in. Tires: P205/75R x 14 in.
CHASSIS: [C10] Wheelbase: 117.5/131.5 in. Overall length: 191.3/212 in. Height: 69.8 in. Front tread: 65.8 in. Rear tread: 62.7 in. Tires: FR7815B in.
CHASSIS: [G10] Wheelbase: 110 in./125 in. Overall length: 178.2 in./202.2 in. Height: 78.8 in./81.2 in. Front tread: 69.5 in. Rear tread: 69.7 in. Tires: FR7815B in.
CHASSIS: [G20] Wheelbase: 110 in./125 in. Overall length: 178.2 in./202.2 in. Height: 78.8 in./81.2 in. Front tread: 69.5 in. Rear tread: 69.7 in. Tires: P225/75R15 in.
CHASSIS: [G30] Wheelbase: 110 in./125 in. Overall length: 178.2 in./202.2 in. Height: 78.8 in./81.2 in. Front tread: 69.5 in. Rear tread: 69.7 in. Tires: 8.75 x 16.5E in.
CHASSIS: [G30 Hi-Cube] Wheelbase: 125 in./146 in. Overall length: 207.3 in./231.3 in. Tires: [front] 8.75 x 16 in., [rear] 8.00 x 16.5C in.
CHASSIS: [K10/ Blazer] Wheelbase: 106.5 in. Overall length: 184.8 in. Height: 73.4 in. Front tread: 66.1 in. Rear tread: 63 in. Tires: [Two-wheel-drive] P215/75R15 in., [Four-wheel-drive] P215/75R15 in. Larger sizes available.
CHASSIS: [C10/C20 Suburban] Wheelbase: 129.5 in. Overall length: 218.7 in. Height: 75.4 in. Front tread: 66.7 in. Rear tread: 63.0 in. Tires: [C10] P235/75R15, [C20] 9.50 x 16.5 in. [K10] P215/75R15, [K20] 9.50 x 16.5 in.
CHASSIS: [K10] Wheelbase: 117.5 in./131.5 in. Overall length: 191.3 in./212 in. Height: 72 in. Front tread: 65.8 in. Rear tread: 62.7 in. Tires: P235/75R15 in.
CHASSIS: [C20] Wheelbase: 117.5 in./131.5 in./164.5 in. Overall length: 191.3 in./212 in./244.43 in. Height: 69.8 in. Front tread: 65.8 in. Rear tread: 62.7 in. Tires: 8.75R x 16.5C in., [front] 9.50 x 16.5D in., [rear] 9.50 x 16.5E in., C20 HD [C6P]

1983 Chevrolet S10 Blazer Utility Hardtop (CMD)

CHASSIS: [K20] Wheelbase: 131.5 in. Overall length: 212 in. Height: 73.9 in. Front tread: 65.8 in. Rear tread: 62.7 in. Tires: 8.75R x 16.5C in., 9.50 x 16.5D in. [front] E [rear] K20HD (CP6)
CHASSIS: [P20] Wheelbase: 125 in./133 in. Tires: 8.75 x 16.5C in.
CHASSIS: [C30] Wheelbase: 131.5 in./164.5 in. Overall length: 212 in./244.43 in. Height: 77.8 in. Front tread: 65.8 in. Rear tread: 62.7 in. Tires: 9.50 x 16.5D in., [Bonus/Crew] 9.50 x 16.5E in.
CHASSIS: [K30] Wheelbase: 131.5 in./164.5 in. Overall length: 212 in./244.43 in. Height: 74.7 in./75 in. Front tread: 65.8 in. Rear tread: 62.7 in. Tires: 9.50 x 16.5D in.

CHASSIS: [P30] Wheelbase: 125 in./157 in. Tires: 8.75 x 16.5 in.
TECHNICAL: Manual, synchromesh. 3F/1R (most models). Controls located: Column (most). Single dry-disc type clutch. Shaft drive. Salisbury rear axle. Front disc/rear drum (power on most). Pressed steel disc wheels.
OPTIONS: Engine oil cooler. Heavy-duty automatic transmission. Heavy-duty battery. Heavy-duty radiator. Camper chassis equipment. Fuel tank shield. 66-ampere generator (standard on K30). Heavy-duty automatic transmission cooler. Four-speed manual transmission. Four-speed overdrive transmission. Four-speed automatic with overdrive. Three-speed automatic. Locking differential. Cruise control. Chromed front bumper. Rear bumper (chromed or painted). Radio, AM, AM/FM, AM/FM with cassette. Cigar lighter. Chromed rear step bumper. Side-mounted spare tire carrier. Glide-out spare tire carrier (Fleetside only). Cargo area lamp. Color keyed floor mats. Comfortilt steering wheel. Deluxe front appearance package. Dome lamp. Quartz electric clock. Air conditioning. Gauge package (volt meter, temperature, oil pressure). Halogen headlamps. Intermittent windshield wipers. Tinted glass. Outside rear view mirrors: Painted or stainless steel below-eye-line type, stainless steel camper type, painted West Coast type. Sliding rear window. Durango equipment (S10). Tahoe equipment (S10). Sport equipment (S10). Body moldings, black, bright, custom package, black or bright (Fleetside only). Paint options: Conventional two-tone. (Fleetside only). Deluxe two-tone. Exterior decor. Special two-tone paint. Pickup side rails. Power door locks. Power windows. Roof marker lamps. Rally wheels. Styled wheels. Bright metal wheelcovers. Special bright metal wheelcovers. Conquista package, El Camino ($189).

1983 Chevrolet 1/2-Ton S10 Bonus-Cab Fleetside Pickup (CMD)

HISTORICAL: Introduced: Sept. 14, 1982. Calendar-year registrations: [All Chevrolet trucks] 904,672. Calendar-year sales. [Vans] 141,575, [Sportvan] 18,178, [S10] 198,222, [S10 Blazer] 106,214, [El Camino] 24,010, [C/K Blazer] 31,282, [C/K Suburban] 37,222, [C/K Pickups] 412,533. Calendar-year production: [C10/K10 Blazer] 35,179, [El Camino] 28,322, [C/K Pickups] 280,209, [Chevy Van/Sportvan] 142,555, [Suburban] 41,261, [S10] 321,054, [Total] 848,580. Innovations: New S10 Blazer introduced. Extend cab Pickups added to S10 Pickup series. Full-size 4x4s now use 15-in. wheels and tires. Chevrolet dealers recorded 176 registrations per outlet in 1983, compared to 156 the previous season. Chevrolet slipped behind Ford in calendar-year registrations for all types of trucks. In van and light truck production (calendar-year) in U.S. factories, Chevrolet was also behind Ford's output of 848,580 units. The big news, however, was the auto and truck industry's general recovery from the bleak period of the early 1980s. Chevrolet's overall market penetration in the light truck and van field was up 1.58 percent to a 39.72 percent share of industry.

1984 CHEVROLET

1/2-TON S10 MINI-PICKUP — MODEL S/SERIES 10 — FOUR/V-6: Disappearance of the LUV Pickup made the S10 Chevrolet's small truck. While styling was unaltered, new features included a Sport suspension for regular-cab 4x2 models, new quiet-set trip odometer, new ignition warning buzzer, and a hydraulic (rather than cable-type) clutch. Gasoline-powered 4x2 and 4x4 models, plus the diesel 4x2, came on the short 108.3-in. wheelbase with either the 73.1-in. short box or 89-in. long box. Gas and diesel 4x2s and gas 4x4s with the extended Maxi-Cab used the 122.9-in. wheelbase with short box only. The gas 4x2 Chassis-and-Cab was on the 117.9-in. stance. Standard equipment varied by trim level. Durango added such things as color-keyed floor mats, courtesy lights, and Custom cloth/vinyl or special Custom cloth bench seats. The Tahoe package added carpeting, gauges, and a right-hand visor mirror. Including all Tahoe features, plus a Sport steering wheel, and Sport cloth bucket-seats with console, was the high-priced Sport package. The standard interior was vertically pleated vinyl. Durango's interior featured rectangular pleats in three rows on each end of the seat with a plain center section. Sport upholstery used vinyl backs and bolsters with a textured woven cloth on the seat cushions and backs. Side-mounted vertically pleated jump seats were optional for Maxi-Cab models. After being selected "Four wheeler of the Year" in 1983, the S10 Blazer was back with new features. One was an optional off-road package with gas-pressure shock absorbers and an hydraulic clutch. Both the 4x2 and 4x4 versions used a 2.0-liter four and four-speed gear box as standard equipment. The only options featured on standard S10 Blazers included a cigar lighter, chrome grille, and dome lamp. The Tahoe package added a right-hand visor mirror, body side and wheelhouse moldings, spare tire cover, and wheel trim rings. On top of this, the Sport model came with a color-keyed front bumper, center console, and black wheel opening moldings. Interior options included the standard type with high-back vinyl "memory" bucket seats and other niceties, the Tahoe type with Custom vinyl or special Custom cloth upholstery and side window defoggers and gauges, or the Sport type with reclining seats in charcoal or saddle Sport cloth. The latter was available with optional "High-Country" sheepskin front bucket seats.

1/2-TON EL CAMINO — MODEL W — SIX/V-8: The El Camino for 1984 was a very luxurious vehicle. Standard equipment included an automatic transmission, power steering, air adjustable rear shocks, notch-back seat with arm rest, and color-keyed cut-pile carpeting. Both the Super Sport model-option and Conquista package were available again. The base El Camino had dual square headlamps on either side of a cross-hatch grille with long, narrow parking lights directly below the headlamps.

1984 Chevrolet S10 Blazer Sport Utility Vehicle 4x4 (CP)

1/2-TON BLAZER — MODEL C (4x2)/MODEL K (4x4) — SIX/V-8: Chevrolet included the full-size Blazer 4x4 in its 1984 Station Wagon sales catalog. The big Blazer also had its own separate catalog. It noted that the Army Tank Automotive Command had recently placed an order for 23,000 diesel-powered Blazers. A bold new grille had a bi-level design with three black-finished horizontal bars, square headlamps in both sections (optional), parking lamps behind the bars on the bottom, and a yellow bow tie on the body color strip in the middle. Only 4x4 models were available. The Custom Deluxe standard interior offered foam-padded seats (front buckets) in vinyl, with color-keyed door trim panels. Also included were integrated arm rests and instrument panel pads. A rear seat was optional. With the upscale Silverado package, Custom vinyl or cloth upholstery was added. Fender badges now identified these trucks as K5 models. Scottsdale versions carried an identification badge on the rear fender sides near the taillights.

1/2-TON, 3/4-TON, 1-TON VAN/HI-CUBE VAN — MODEL G/SERIES 10, 20, 30 — SIX/V-8: The Chevy Van grille also had the bi-level arrangement with quad Halogen headlamps optional. Upper and lower sections of the grille each contained three horizontal blades, and seven vertical members. A body-color horizontal center piece held a yellow bow tie in the middle. With standard equipment, rectangular parking lamps were used in the lower grille section under the regular rectangular headlamps. If the halogen headlamp option was ordered, the parking lamps were mounted behind the lower grille. The G10 and G20 models offered a choice of 110- or 125-in. wheelbases. G30s came only on the larger chassis. A 146-in. wheelbase was also available for G30 RV, commercial and Hi-Cube Van applications. Power steering and heavy-duty power brakes were standard on the G20/G30 vans. RV versions of the Chevy Van 30 also came with chromed front bumpers, cigar lighters, and ash trays as standard equipment. The Hi-Cube versions included an extended-arm outside rear view mirror. In November 1983, a new 60/40 swing-out side door option was introduced. Standard interiors featured striped vinyl low-back bucket seats. Custom trim included high-back bucket seats in vinyl or Custom vinyl.

1/2-TON, 3/4-TON, 1-TON CONVENTIONAL — MODEL C (4x2), MODEL K (4x4)/SERIES 10, 20, 30 — SIX/V-8: Chevrolet's full-sized Pickup also had the bi-level grille, as used on the big Blazer. There were three horizontal bars showing prominently in each section with seven less prominent vertical members behind them. When bright-plated, the grille had a cross-hatch look, when black-finished, it appeared more horizontal. Halogen quad headlamps were an option. New for the season were two galvanized steel interior door panels for better rust protection. Also new were semi-metallic front brake linings on C/K10 and C/K20 series trucks, new non-asbestos rear brake linings on most models, and plastic fuel tank stone shields for all Pickups and Chassis-and-Cabs. This was the first year for optional power windows and door locks on Bonus-Cab and Crew-Cab models, both of which came on a 164.5-in. wheelbase with Fleetside boxes. Trucks with Deluxe two-tone paint had the cab and lower perimeter finished in the secondary color. Special two-toning meant only the lower perimeter was in the secondary color, and there was bright trim on the body side and wheel openings. The Exterior Decor package included dual-tone body side finish, and a rear tape stripe keyed to body colors, plus a hood ornament. The secondary color was used between the decal stripes and moldings. Interior options included standard Custom Deluxe trim, plus Scottsdale and Silverado options. There were 39 models all total. C10 and K10 Pickups came in short box Step-Side and long box Step-Side and Fleetside models. C20 and K20 models came in Step-Side or Fleetside form, only with the 8-ft. long box. The heavy-duty C20 added Chassis-and-Cab, Bonus-Cab, and Crew-Cab models. Heavy-duty K10s came as Fleetsides and Step-Sides with the long box. The C30 heavies offered three 4x2 and four 4x4 configurations in Chassis-and-Cab form for commercial and RV applications.

3/4-TON, 1-TON FORWARD-CONTROL — MODEL P/SERIES 20,30 — SIX/V-8: Chevy issued separate 1984 sales catalogs for steel-bodied and aluminum-bodied Step-Vans. The steel models came as CP208/CP308 models on a 125-in. wheelbase, as CP210/CP310 models on the 133-in. wheelbase, and as CP314 models on the 157-in. wheelbase. Aluminum body models could be had in the same configurations, plus a model CP318 version with a 178-in. wheelbase. Load lengths were: [CP208/CP308] 129.6 in., [CP210/CP310] 153.6 in., [CP314] 177.6 in., and [CP318] 178 in. Series 30 Hi-Cube models came in 10-ft. models on the 125-in. wheelbase or 12-ft. models on the 146-in. wheelbase.

1984 Chevrolet C10 Fleetside Pickup (CP)

I.D. DATA: Location of serial number: The VIN is stamped on a plate attached to the left top of the instrument panel on C/K/G series. On P series the plate is attached to the front of the dash and the panel to the left of the steering column. The first symbol indicates country of origin: 1=U.S., 2=Canada, J=Japan. The second symbol indicates manufacturer: G=General Motors, 8=Isuzu. The third symbol indicates make: A=Chevrolet bus, B=Chevrolet (incomplete), C=Chevrolet truck, Y=LUV (incomplete), Z=LUV truck, 8=Chevy MPV. The fourth symbol indicates GVW rating (and brake system), B=3,001 lb.-4,000 lb. (hydraulic), C=4,001 lb.-5,000 lb. (hydraulic), etc. through K for hydraulic brakes. The fifth symbol indicates line and chassis type: C=Conventional cab (including Blazer and Suburban) 4x2, G=Chevy Van and Sportvan 4x2, K=Conventional cab (including Blazer and Suburban) 4x4, L=LUV 4x2, R=LUV 4x4, P=Forward-Control, S=Conventional Cab 4x2, W=El Camino 4x2, Z=Special body 4x2. The sixth symbol indicates series: 1=1/2-ton, 2=3/4-ton, 3=1-ton, 8=El Camino. The seventh symbol indicates body type: 0=El Camino Pickup-Delivery, 1=Hi-Cube and Cutaway Vans, 2-Forward-Control, 3=Four-door cab, 4=Two-door cab, 5=Van, 6=Suburban, 7=Motorhome chassis, 8=Blazer Utility, 9=Stake. The eighth symbol indicated engine. Engine codes were generally the same as 1983. The ninth symbol was a check digit. The 10th symbol indicated model-year: E=1984. The 11th symbol indicated the assembly plant: A=Lakewood, Ga., B=Baltimore, Md.,C=Southgate, Calif., D=Doraville, Ga., E=Linden, N.J., F=Flint, Mich., G=Framingham, Mass., H=Flint, Mich., J=Janesville, Wis., K=Leeds, Mo., L=Van Nuys, Calif., M=Lansing, Mich., N=Norwood, Ohio, P=Pontiac, Mich., R=Arlington, Texas, S=St. Louis, Mo., T=Tarrytown, N.Y., V=GMC, Pontiac, Mich., W=Willow Run, Mich., X=Fairfax, Va., Y=Wilmington, Dela., Z=Fremont, Calif., O=GMAD, Pontiac, Mich., 1=Oshawa, Canada, 2=Moraine, Ohio, 2=Ste. Therese, Quebec, Canada, 3=Chevrolet-Detroit, Mich., 3=St. Eustache, Quebec, Canada, 4=Orion Plant, Pontiac, Mich., 4=Scarborough, Ontario, Canada, 5=Bowling Green, Ken., 5=London, Ontario, Canada, 6=Oklahoma City, Okla., 7=Lordstown, Ohio, 8=Shreveport, La., 8=Fujisawa, Japan, 9=Cadillac, Detroit, Mich. (Note: Trucks were not built at all factories). Symbols 12-17 were the production sequence number starting at 100001. Ending numbers not available. Engine number location: [Six] located on pad at right-hand side of cylinder block at rear of distributor. [V-8] located on pad at right front side of cylinder block.

Model	Body Type	Price	Weight	Prod. Total
S10 Pickup — 1/2-Ton — 108.3 in. w.b. — V-6				
S10	Pickup	6398	2574	Note 8
S10 Pickup — 1/2-Ton — 122.9 in. w.b. — V-6				
S10	Pickup	6551	2649	Note 8
S10	Maxi-Cab Pickup	6924	2705	Note 8
S10 Blazer 4x4 — 1/2-Ton — 100.5 in. w.b. — V-6				
T10	4x4 Hardtop	9685	3146	Note 8
NOTE 1: Deduct for two-wheel drive S10 Blazer.				
El Camino — 1/2-Ton — 117.1 in. w.b. — V-6				
W80	Pickup	8522	3298	Note 8
W80	Super Sport Pickup	8781	3305	Note 8
Chevy Van 10 — 1/2-Ton — 110 in. w.b. — Six				
G11	Panel	7541	3732	Note 8
G11	Sportvan	9089	4085	Note 8
Chevy Van 10 — 1/2-Ton — 125 in. w.b. — Six				
G11	Bonaventure	10,062	-	Note 8
G11	Beauville	10,327	-	Note 8
Chevy Van 20 — 3/4-Ton — 110 in. w.b. — Six				
G21	Panel	8176	3813	Note 8
Chevy Van 20 — 3/4-Ton — 125 in. w.b. — Six				
G21	Sportvan	9477	4276	Note 8
G21	Bonaventure	10,238	-	Note 8
G21	Beauville	10,503	-	Note 8
Chevy Van 30 — 1-Ton — 125 in. w.b. — Six				
G31	Panel	9212	4305	Note 8
G31	Sportvan	11,964	4984	Note 8
Chevy Van 30 — 1-Ton — 125 in. w.b. — V-8				
G31	Bonaventure	12,724	-	Note 8
G31	Beauville	12,990	-	Note 8
Hi-Cube Van 30 — 1-Ton — 125 in. w.b. — V-8				
G31/303	Hi-Cube 10 ft.	11,624	5860	Note 8
Hi-Cube Van 30 — 1-Ton — 125 in. w.b. — V-8				
G31/603	Hi-Cube 12 ft	12,894	5891	Note 8
Full-Size Blazer 4x4 — 1/2-Ton — 106.5 in. w.b. — V-8				
K10	Hardtop	10,819	4409	Note 8
Series C10 — 1/2-Ton — 117.5 in. w.b. — Six				
C10	Step-Side	7101	3434	Note 8
C10	Fleetside	6970	3481	Note 8
Series C10 — 1/2-Ton — 131.5 in. w.b. — Six				
C10	Fleetside	7127	3644	Note 8
Series C10 — 1/2-Ton — 129.5 in. w.b. — V-8				
C10	Suburban (V-8)	10,368	4310	Note 8
NOTE 2: Add for four-wheel-drive K10 Pickup/Suburban.				
Series C20 — 3/4-Ton — 131.5 in. w.b. — Six				
C20	Chassis & Cab	8342	3617	Note 8
C20	Step-Side	8319	3977	Note 8
C20	Fleetside	8188	4039	Note 8
Series C20 — 3/4-Ton — 164.5 in. w.b. — Six				
C20	Bonus-Cab	9645	4742	Note 8
C20	Crew-Cab	9975	4803	Note 8
Series C20 — 3/4-Ton — 129.5 in. w.b. — Six				
C20	Suburban	10,579	4698	Note 8
NOTE 3: Add for four-wheel-drive K20 Pickup/Suburban.				
Step-Van 20 — 3/4-Ton — 125 in. w.b. — Six				
P20	Steel Step-Van 10.5 ft.	12,588	5860	Note 8
NOTE 4: Add for 12.5 ft. Step-Van 20 body.				
Series C30 — 1-Ton — 131.5 in. w.b. — Six				
C30903	Chassis & Cab	8474	3990	Note 8
C30903	Step-Side	8966	4342	Note 8
C30903	Fleetside	8834	4404	Note 8
Series C30 Bonus-Cab- 1-Ton — 164.5 in. w.b. — Six				
C30943	Chassis & Cab	9471	4412	Note 8
C30943	Fleetside	4822	-	Note 8
Series C30 Crew-Cab- 1-Ton — 164.5 in. w.b. — Six				
C30943	Chassis & Cab	9802	4473	Note 8
C30943	Fleetside	10,146	4883	Note 8
Step-Van 30 — 3/4-Ton — 146 in. w.b. — V-8				
P30	Steel Panel 12.5 ft.	12,666	5998	Note 8

NOTE 5: Deduct for 10.5-ft. Step-Van 30 body.
NOTE 6: Add for 14.5-ft. Step-Van 30 body.
NOTE 7: Add for four-wheel-drive K30 Pickup.
NOTE 8: Model-year production: [S10] 209,377, [S10 Blazer] 149,937, [El Camino] 24,244, [All Chevy Van] 172,806, [All Sportvans] 24,005, [K5 Blazer] 39,329, [C10/C20/K10/K20 Suburbans] 54,250, [Other C10/K10] 275,428, [Other C20/K20] 89,811, [C30/K30] 45,095, [P10/P20/P30] Not available (Includes all trucks with GVWs of 10,000 lb. or less built in U.S. and built in Canada for the U.S. Market).

NOTE 9: Percent of above totals with four-wheel-drive used on chassis and Pickup trucks: [S10] 20.1 percent, [S10 Blazer] 72.8 percent, [CK10] 26.0 percent, [CK20] 38.5 percent, [CK30] 20.8 percent, [K5 Blazer] 100 percent.
NOTE 10: Percent of above totals with four-wheel-drive used on Suburbans: [CK10/CK20 combined] 31.6 percent.

1984 Chevrolet C10 Silverado Suburban (CP)

ENGINE: [Standard: 108.3-in. w.b. Regular-Cab S10 models and all models with California emissions] Inline. OHV. OHC. Four-cylinder. Cast iron block. Bore & stroke: 3.42 x 3.23 in. Displacement: 119 cid. Compression ratio: 8.4:1. Net horsepower: 82 at 4000 rpm. Maximum torque: 101 lb.-ft. at 3000 rpm. Order Code LR1(A).
ENGINE: [Standard: All S10 models except short wheelbase Regular-Cab models. Not available: California] Inline. OHV. Four-cylinder. Cast iron block. Bore & stroke: 3.50 x 3.15 in. Displacement: 121 cid. Compression ratio: 9.3:1. Net horsepower: 83 at 4600 rpm. Maximum torque: 108 lb.-ft. at 2400 rpm. Order Code LQ2(B).
ENGINE: [Optional S10 4x2 regular and Maxi-Cab models] Inline. OHV. Diesel. Four-cylinder. Cast iron block. Bore & stroke: 3.46 x 3.62 in. Displacement: 137 cid. Compression ratio: 21:1. Net horsepower: 62 at 4300 rpm. Maximum torque: 96 lb.-ft. at 2200 rpm. Order Code LQ7(A).
ENGINE: [Optional All S10 models] V-block. OHV. Six-cylinder. Cast iron block. Bore & stroke: 3.50 x 2.99 in. Displacement: 173 cid. Compression ratio: 8.5:1. Net horsepower: 110 at 4800 rpm. Maximum torque: 145 lb.-ft. at 2100 rpm. Order Code LR2(B).
ENGINE: [Standard: El Camino] V-block. OHV. Six-cylinder. Cast iron block. Bore & stroke: 3.7 x 3.48 in. Displacement: 229 cid. Net horsepower: 110 at 4000 rpm. Torque: 190 lb.-ft. at 1600 rpm. Four main bearings. Hydraulic valve lifters. Carburetor: Two-barrel.
ENGINE: [Standard C10/C20/K10/G10/G20/G30] Inline. OHV. Six-cylinder. Cast iron block. Bore & stroke: 3.9 x 3.5 in. Displacement: 250 cid. Compression ratio: 8.3:1. Net horsepower: 115 at 3600 rpm. Maximum torque: 200 lb.-ft. at 2000 rpm. Seven main bearings. Hydraulic valve lifters. Carburetor: Rochester staged two-barrel. Order Code LE3(A).
ENGINE: [Standard: C20 HD (C6P)/C20 Bonus/Crew/C30/K20 HD (C6P)/K30] Inline. OHV. Six-cylinder. Cast iron block. Bore & stroke: 3.876 x 4.12 in. Displacement: 292 cid. Compression ratio: 7.8:1. Net horsepower: 115 at 3600 rpm. Maximum torque: 215 lb.-ft. at 1600 rpm. Five main bearings. Hydraulic valve lifters. Carburetor: Rochester one-barrel. Order Code L25(B).
ENGINE: [Optional C10/G10/G10/G20, Standard: K10 Blazer/C10 Suburban] V-block. OHV. Eight-cylinder. Cast iron block. Bore & stroke: 3.736 x 3.480 in. Displacement: 305 cid. Compression ratio: 9.2:1. Net horsepower: 160 at 4400 rpm. Maximum torque: 235 lb.-ft. at 2000 rpm. Five main bearings. Hydraulic valve lifters. Carburetor: Rochester staged four-barrel (Electronic spark control). Order Code LE9(C).

1984 Chevrolet C10 Fleetside Silverado Pickup (CP)

ENGINE: [Optional: El Camino] V-block. OHV. Eight-cylinder. Cast iron block. Bore & stroke: 3.7 x 3.48 in. Displacement: 305 cid. Compression ratio: 9.2:1. Net horsepower: 160 at 4400 rpm., 235 lb.-ft. at 2000 rpm. Five main bearings. Hydraulic valve lifters. Carburetor: Rochester model four-barrel.
ENGINE: [Optional El Camino] V-block. OHV. Eight-cylinder. Cast iron block. Bore & stroke: 4.0 x 3.5 in. Displacement: 350 cid. Net horsepower: 105. Five main bearings. Hydraulic valve lifters. Fuel-injection.
ENGINE: [Standard Hi-Cube Vans and Suburbans/Optional in specific other Series 10/20/30 models] V-8. OHV. Eight-cylinder. Cast iron block. Bore & stroke: 4.0 x 3.5 in. Displacement: 350 cid. Compression ratio: 8.2:1. Net horsepower: 165 at 3800 rpm. Maximum torque: 275 lb.-ft. at 1600 rpm. Five main bearings. Hydraulic valve lifters. Carburetor: Rochester four-barrel. Order Code LS9(A).
ENGINE: [Optional: All 4x2/4x4/Full Size Pickups/Suburbans/K10 Blazer/G20/G30/C6P] V-block. OHV. Diesel. Eight-cylinder. Cast iron block. Bore & stroke: 3.98 x 3.80 in. Displacement: 379 cid. Compression ratio: 21.3:1. Net horsepower: 130 at 3600 rpm. Maximum torque: 240 lb.-ft. at 2000 rpm. Hydraulic valve lifters. Order Code LH6(D).

ENGINE: [Optional: C20 HD (C6P)/C20/C30/K30] V-block. OHV. Eight-cylinder. Cast iron block. Bore & stroke: 4.250 x 4 in. Displacement: 454 cid. Compression ratio: 7.9:1. Net horsepower: 230 at 3800 rpm. Maximum torque: 360 lb.-ft. at 2800 rpm. Five main bearings. Hydraulic valve lifters. Carburetor: Rochester four-barrel. Order Code LE8(A).
CHASSIS: [El Camino] Wheelbase: 117.1 in. Overall length: 201.6 in. Height: 53.8 in. Front tread: 58.5 in. Rear tread: 57.8 in. Tires: P205/75R x 14 in.
CHASSIS: [S10] Wheelbase: 108.3 in./117.9 in./122.9 in. Overall length: 178.2 in./194.1 in. Height: 59.4 in. Front tread: 64.7 in. Rear tread: 64.7 in. Tires: P195/75R x 14 in.
CHASSIS: [S10 Blazer] Wheelbase: 100.5 Overall length: 170.3 in. Height: 65 Front tread: 55.6 in. Rear tread: 55.1 in. Tires: P195/75R15
CHASSIS: [G10] Wheelbase: 110 in./125 Overall length: 178.2 in./202.2 in. Height: 78.8 in./81.2 in. Front tread: 69.5 Rear tread: 69.7 in. Tires: P205/75R15
CHASSIS: [G20] Wheelbase: 110 in./125 Overall length: 178.2 in./202.2 in. Height: 78.8 in./81.2 in. Front tread: 69.5 Rear tread: 69.7 in. Tires: P225/75R15
CHASSIS: [G30] Wheelbase: 125 Overall length: 202.2 in. Height: 81.2 in. Front tread: 69.5 Rear tread: 69.7 in. Tires: 8.75R x 16.5D in.
CHASSIS: [G30 Hi-Cube] Wheelbase: 125 in./146 in. Overall length: 207.3 in./231.3 in. Tires: 8.75 x 16.5
CHASSIS: [K10 Blazer] Wheelbase: 106.5 Overall length: 184.8 in. Height: 73.4 in. Front tread: 66.1 in. Rear tread: 63 in. Tires: P215/75R15
CHASSIS: [C10] Wheelbase: 117.5 in./131.5 (129.5 Suburban). Overall length: 191.3 in./212 in. Height: 69.8 in. Front tread: 65.8 in. Rear tread: 62.7 in. Tires: P195/75R15, Suburban P235/75R15
CHASSIS: [Series C20] Wheelbase: 131.5 in./164.5 (129.5 Suburban). Overall length: 212 in./244.43 in. Height: 69.8 in. Tires: LT215/85R x 16C in., Bonus in./Crew: LT235/85R x 16D in. (rear E).
CHASSIS: [P20] Wheelbase: 125 in./133 in. Tires: LT215/85R x 16C in.
CHASSIS: [Series C30] Wheelbase: 131.5 in./164.5 Overall length: 212 in./244.43 in. Height: 77.8 in. Front tread: 65.8 in. Rear tread: 62.7 in. Tires: LT235/85R x 16D in.
CHASSIS: [P30] Wheelbase: 125 in./178 in. Tires: LT215/85R x 16C in.

1984 Chevrolet S10 Blazer Sport Utility Vehicle 4x2 (CP)

TECHNICAL: Selective synchromesh transmission (Automatic on Suburban and some vans). Speeds: 3F/1R (four-speed manual in 20 and 30 series and S10s). Steering column-mounted gear shift (or four-speed on floor). Single dry-disc type clutch. Semi-floating rear axle (C30/K30/Crew and Bonus-Cabs have full-floating) rear axle. Overall ratio: various. Power front disc/rear drum brakes. Pressed steel wheels.
OPTIONS: [S10 Pickup] Color-keyed bumper. Air conditioning. Rear step bumper, chrome or black. Chrome bumpers with rub strip. Black front bumper guards. Console. Chrome grille. Cigarette lighter. Color-keyed floor mats. Comfortilt steering wheel. Tinted glass. Deep tinted glass. Intermittent wipers. Auxiliary lighting. Cargo area lamp. Dome lamp. Halogen headlamps. Dual below-eye-line mirrors/painted or chrome. Right-hand visor mirror. Black body side/bright wheel opening moldings. Bright door edge moldings. Black or bright wheel opening moldings. Power windows. Power door locks. Special two-tone. Sport two-tone. AM radio. AM/FM radio. AM/FM stereo radio. AM/FM stereo radio with cassette and clock, same with Seek-and-Scan. Premium rear speakers. High-back bucket seats/with custom vinyl, with "High-Country" sheepskin, with special custom cloth, with adjustable seat backs. Rear jump seats in Maxi-Cab. Tinted sliding rear window. Swing-out rear quarter windows. Cast aluminum wheels. Styled wheels. Wheel trim rings. Bright wheelcovers. Resume cruise control. Sport suspension. 2.2-liter diesel engine. Insta-Trac 4x4 system. Off-road package. P235/75R15 steel-belted radial tires. Heavy-duty "Trailerite" package (with V-6). Heavy-duty battery. Vacuum power brakes. Cold climate package. Engine and oil cooler (V-6 only). Radiator and transmission oil cooler (V-6 only). 20-gallon fuel tank. Gauge package. Tachometer. 66-ampere generator. Fuel tank shield. Transfer case and differential shield. Locking rear axle differential. Heavy-duty shocks. Heavy-duty springs. Front stabilizer bar. Power steering. Two front tow hooks. "Trailerite" wiring harness. Three-speed automatic transmission (California only). 1.9-liter four-cylinder engine (California only, standard in California). Four-speed automatic overdrive transmission. Fully-synchronized five-speed manual transmission with overdrive. Snowplow (special order). 2.8-liter V-6 engine. Stake body (For Chassis-and-Cab). Durango interior trim. Tahoe interior trim. Sport interior trim. Exterior colors: Silver Metallic, Frost White, Light Blue Metallic, Galaxy Blue Metallic, Doeskin Tan, Indian Bronze Metallic/Desert Sand Metallic, Apple Red, Cinnamon Red and Satin Black (secondary). S10 Blazer: Air conditioning. Color-keyed front bumper (requires two-tone). Black front bumper guards. Console. Chromed grille. Cigarette lighter. Color-keyed floor mats. Comfortilt steering wheel. Rear window defogger. Digital clock (requires radio). Deep-tint glass. Deep-tint with light tint rear window. Sliding rear quarter windows. Intermittent wipers. Engine compartment lamp. Dome lamp. Halogen headlamps. Luggage carrier and rear air deflector. Dual painted below-eye-line mirrors. Chrome below-eye-line mirrors. Right-hand visor mirror. Body side and wheel opening moldings. Door edge guards. Separate wheel opening moldings/black or bright. Operating convenience package. Special two-tone. Sport two-tone. Striping (requires solid paint). AM radio. AM/FM radio. AM/FM stereo with cassette and clock. Same with Seek-and-Scan. Premium rear speakers. Folding rear bench seat. Sliding rear tinted quarter window. Spare tire cover. 4x2 styled wheels. 4x4 cast aluminum wheels. Bright wheel trim rings. Insta-Trac 4x4 system. Cold climate package. Heavy-duty cooling with transmission oil cooler. Cruise control. 20-gallon fuel tank. Gauges. 66-ampere generator. Heavy-duty battery. Heavy-duty front/rear shocks. Locking rear axle differential. Off-road chassis equipment. Power steering. Tachometer. Tailgate window release. Trailerite Special equipment. Transfer case shield (4x4). 1.9-liter four-cylinder engine (California only). 2.8-liter V-6. Five-speed manual transmission. Four-speed automatic

178

overdrive transmission. Larger size tubeless tires. Dealer-installed black-finish brush guard. Tahoe interior trim (custom vinyl, special custom cloth, "High-Country" sheepskin). Sport cloth interior. Paint colors: Same as S10 Pickups. Snowplow (special order). Full-size Blazer: Air cleaner. Air conditioning. Bright wheelcovers. Chrome front bumper guards. Deluxe bumpers. Cigarette lighter. Color-keyed floor mats. Comfortilt steering wheel. Deluxe front appearance. Electric quartz clock. Deep-tint glass. Sliding side window. Halogen headlamps. Headlight warning buzzer. Full-length headliner. Intermittent wipers. Painted below-eye-line mirrors. Stainless below-eye-line mirrors. Black body side moldings. Bright body side moldings. Black molding package. Bright molding package. Door edge guards. Operating convenience package. Power door locks. Power windows. Special two-tone paint. Exterior decor package. AM radio. AM/FM radio. AM/FM stereo radio. AM/FM stereo with cassette. Windshield antenna. Folding rear seat. Electric tailgate window. Rally wheels. Styled wheels. Cold climate package. Engine oil cooler. Transmission oil cooler. Cruise control. Deadweight trailer hitch. Front quad shocks. Front stabilizer bar. Front tow hooks. 31-gallon fuel tank. Fuel tank stone shield. Gauges package. 66-ampere generator. Heavy-duty battery. Heavy-duty shocks. Heavy-duty radiator. Locking differential. Trailerite Special equipment. Weight distributing hitch. Four-speed overdrive automatic. 5.0-liter V-8 engine (with electronic spark control, not in California). 5.7-liter V-8 engine. 6.2-liter diesel V-8. Dealer installed brush guard. Silverado interior trim. Silverado Custom cloth trim. Full-length black top. 3/4-length black top. Paint colors: Frost White, Silver Metallic, Midnight Black, Light Blue Metallic, Midnight Blue, Colonial Yellow, Doeskin Tan, Desert Sand Metallic, Indian Bronze Metallic, and Apple Red. Chevy Vans: Front air conditioning. Front and rear air conditioning. "Resume" speed control, Auxiliary lighting package. Auxiliary rear heater. Chrome bumpers. Front bumper guards. Cigar lighter and ash tray light. Comfortilt steering wheel. Custom steering wheel. Deluxe front appearance. Quartz electric clock. Floor carpeting. All windows tinted. Tinted windshield. Halogen headlights. Intermittent windshield wipers. Fixed extended arm mirrors, painted or stainless. Below-eye-line mirrors, painted or stainless. Black body side moldings. Wheel opening moldings. Operating convenience package. Power door locks. Power windows. Special two-tone paint. Power brakes. Deluxe two-tone paint. Rear door stop. AM radio. AM/FM radio. AM/FM stereo. AM/FM stereo with cassette. Roof ventilator. Front auxiliary seat. High-back front bucket seat. Sliding door extender link. Special exterior trim. Special interior trim. Right-hand sunshade. Rally wheels. Bright wheelcovers. Inside spare carrier. Spare tire cover. Side and rear windows. Auxiliary battery. Engine oil cooler. Transmission oil cooler. Dual rear wheels (Cutaway Vans). Voltmeter. Temperature gauge. Oil pressure gauge. 66-ampere generator. Heavy-duty battery. Heavy-duty power brakes. Heavy-duty cooling. Heavy-duty front springs. Heavy-duty front/rear shocks. Heavy-duty rear springs. Locking differential. Power steering (G10). School bus equipment (G30). Deadweight trailer hitch. Weight distributing hitch. Heavy-duty "Trailerite" special equipment. Light-duty "Trailerite" Special equipment. 250-cid six-cylinder engine. 5.0-liter V-8 engine (with Electronic spark control, not available in California). 5.0-liter V-8 (California only). 5.7-liter V-8 engine. 6.2-liter Diesel V-8 engine. Four-speed automatic overdrive transmission. Four-speed manual overdrive transmission. Oversize tires. Paint colors: Galaxy Blue, Metallic, Colonial Yellow, Doeskin Tan, Desert Sand Metallic, Indian Bronze Metallic, Apple Red Metallic, Autumn Red Metallic, Frost White, Silver Metallic, Light Blue Metallic and (Cutaway vans only) Polar White. [Step-Van]: 4.8-liter one-barrel LPG engine. (standard) 5.7-liter four-barrel V-8, engine. 6.2,-liter diesel V-8 engine. Four-speed manual transmission (standard). Three-speed automatic transmission (optional, except P20 with standard six-cylinder). 125,-in. wheelbase (standard). 133-in. and 157-in. wheelbases (optional). Steel panel bodies: 10.5 ft., 12.5 ft. and 14.5 ft. Wide (74-in.) rear doors. Aluminum panel bodies (same sizes as above, plus 14 ft. 10-in.). X-950 aluminum bodies. Merchandise shelf interior. Snack food interior. Bakery pallet rack interior. Industrial laundry interior. Fiberglass skylight. Step-type bumper with recessed lights. Deluxe high-back bucket seat. Auxiliary seats with arm rests. Expanded metal partition. Plywood interior lining. Right-hand sliding panel with key-locking handle. Special Custom cloth interior. All-weather air conditioning. Right-hand inside spare tire carrier. 66-in. wide rear door. 60-in. wide rear door opening. Dual rear wheels. Larger size tubeless tires. P30 Step-Van 18-ft. aluminum body. Hi-Cube Vans: 5.7-liter V-8 engine (standard). 6.2-liter Diesel V-8 engine. Overhead rear door. Hi-back bucket seats. Three-speed automatic (with column shift) transmission (standard). Dual rear wheels on 125-in. wheelbase (standard with extra-cost6,200-lb. rear axle). 7,500-lb. rear axle also available. Loadspace skylight. Step type rear bumper. Plywood interior lining. Expanded metal partition. Right-hand sliding panel with key-locking handle, custom cloth interior trim. Inside spare tire carrier. Plywood partition with center sliding panel. C/K10/20/30: (Suburban-only): Electric tailgate window. Tailgate window defogger. Front and rear air conditioning. Bucket seats. Deluxe front and rear bumpers. Rear right-hand heater. Three-speed automatic. Three-passenger folding center seat. Three-passenger center and rear seats. 60-in. wide double panel doors. Wagon-type rear tailgate. Standard transmissions for Suburbans were as follows: C10 (gas) four-speed automatic with overdrive, C20 (gas) three-speed automatic, K10 (gas) same as C10, K20 (gas) same as C20. With diesel engines the C10 came with four-speed automatic with overdrive and all other models came with four-speed manual as standard equipment. 14-gallon or 31-gallon fuel tanks. Headlamp warning buzzer. Full-length headliner. (Pickups only): Chromed rear bumper. Chromed rear step bumper (Fleetside). Painted rear step bumper. Cargo area lamp. Dome lamp. Gauges. Conventional two-tone. Deluxe two-tone paint (Fleetside only). Sliding rear window. Side-mounted spare tire carrier (Fleetside only). Auxiliary fuel tank. Engine oil cooler. Heavy-duty automatic transmission cooler. Vacuum power brakes. Extra-capacity rear springs. G50 heavy-duty rear springs. G60 main and auxiliary rear springs. Special camper chassis equipment. Special commercial chassis equipment. Heavy-duty 4.8-liter six-cylinder engine (heavy-duty emissions trucks). Heavy-duty 4.1-liter six-cylinder engine. Special bright metal wheelcovers. Pickup box side rails. Painted West Coast mirrors. Glide-out spare tire carrier. (Suburbans and Pickups): Front air conditioning. Chromed front bumper guards. Cigarette lighter. Color-keyed floor mats. Comfortilt steering wheel. Deluxe front appearance. Quartz electric clock. Deep tinted glass. Deluxe molding package, bright (Fleetside only pickups). Door edge guards. Power door locks. Power windows. Operating convenience package. Special two-tone (Fleetside only on Pickups). Exterior decor package (Fleetside only on pickups). AM radio. AM/FM radio. AM/FM stereo with cassette. Windshield antenna. High-beam Halogen headlamps. Intermittent windshield wipers. Painted below-eye-line mirrors. Stainless below-eye-line mirrors. Stainless camper mirrors. Black body side moldings (Fleetside only pickups). Bright body side moldings (Fleetside only on Pickups). Roof marker lamps. Rally wheels. Styled wheels. Bright wheelcovers. Pre-cleaner air cleaner. Locking differential. Cold climate package. Electronic speed control. Front quad shocks. Front stabilizer bar. Heavy-duty front stabilizer. Front tow hooks. Stone shield. Gauges. 66-ampere generator. Heavy-duty battery. Heavy-duty shocks. Heavy-duty front springs. Heavy-duty radiator. Power steering. Trailer wiring. Trailer right-hand hitches. 5.0-liter V-8 with electronic speed control (not in California). 5.7-liter V-8. 6.2-liter diesel V-8. 7.4-liter V-8 (Suburban and heavy-duty emissions pickups). Scottsdale interior trim. Silverado interior trim. Paint colors: Frost White, Silver Metallic, Midnight Black, Light Blue Metallic, Midnight Blue, Colonial Yellow, Doeskin Tan, Desert Sand Metallic, Indian Bronze Metallic, and Apple Red.

1984 Chevrolet K20 Silverado Suburban (CP)

HISTORICAL: Introduced: Fall, 1983. Calendar-year sales: [All models] 1,111,839. [El Camino] 22,997. [K10 Blazer] 46,919. [S10 Blazer] 150,599. [Chevy Van] 155,421. [Sportvan] 21,902. [S10 Pickup] 199,631. [C20 Pickups] 50,823. Calendar-year production: [Chevy Van/Sportvan] 120,878, [Suburban] 57,286, [Pickups] 332,404 and [Step-Van/Hi-Cube/Cutaway] 53,097. [Total] 563,665. Innovations: Newly designed grilles. S10 trucks feature hydraulic clutch in place of cable type. Improved rust protection on Pickups. Improved brake linings for Blazers, Suburbans and Pickups. Step-Vans feature new exterior Velvac outside rear view mirrors, new rotary side door latches and new key-locking push-button side door handles. Chevrolet products were named as the official cars and trucks of the XIV Olympic winter games in Sarajevo. Chevrolet advertised the U.S. Army's purchase of nearly 30,000 full-size Chevrolet 4x4 Pickups and over 23,000 full-size Blazers with 6.2-liter diesel V-8 engines. These trucks were said to be "regular production trucks like the ones you can get, except for a few specialized military adaptions like a special electrical system."

1985 CHEVROLET

1985 Chevrolet S10 Fleetside Pickup (CP)

1/2-TON S10 — MODEL S/SERIES 10 — FOUR/V-6: The easiest way to spot a 1985 Chevrolet S10 was by its larger and more stylized fender badges with the S done in red (the dash between the letter and the numbers was gone). At the rear, the taillights were framed in chrome and the large Chevrolet name (formerly running across the tailgate center) was changed to a smaller name at the right-hand side of a tailgate trim panel. A new 2.5-liter engine with EFI (electronic fuel-injection) was standard in 4x4 models. Standard, Durango, Tahoe, and Sport trim treatments were available again. Trim options included Custom two-tone (second color below belt), Sport two-tone (second color on bottom below four-stripe decals or moldings), and Special two-tone (second color between belt line and lower feature line). Also standard in S10 Blazers was the 2.5-liter four-cylinder EFI engine. A new Custom vinyl interior amounted to little more than wider door panel pleats, and brushed aluminum door panel trim plates. Much of the artwork used in the 1984, and 1985 sales catalogs is close to identical. Even the 10 paint colors available (not counting Satin Black) were the same. As in 1984, Satin Black could only be ordered as a secondary color. Custom two-toning (with belt line decal and second color below it) was new for 1985, however.

1985 Chevrolet El Camino Custom Sedan-Pickup (CP)

1/2-TON EL CAMINO — MODEL W — V-6/V-8: In addition to last year's standard features, the 1985 El Camino had a new 4.3-liter V-6 base engine. Standard grille was the same as last year. Also back was the El Camino SS, and the Conquista. The SS had an aero-style nose cap like the Monte Carlo SS. A non-functional power blister hood, dummy side pipes, and Pickup bed rails were optional. Model identification decals were used on the doors, and above the lower feature line. Conquista and SS Sport decors each included five distinctive two-tones.

1985 Chevrolet Astro Van (CP)

1/2-TON ASTRO VAN — Model M/Series 10 — V-6: Chevrolet's all-new Astro was a compact van featuring a standard V-6 engine, five-speed manual transmission, and rear drive axle. The mini-van body featured a sloping hood, and aerodynamically rounded front end with wraparound parking lamps, single rectangular headlights, and a grille with seven horizontal bars. Each bar decreased slightly in width, from top to bottom. A yellow bow tie badge was in the center. Additional standard equipment included an engine cover storage box, front arm rests, swing-out side windows, black rubber floor covering, high-back bucket seats, five-passenger seating, and P195/75R15 all-season steel-belted radial tires. CS trim added color-keyed floor coverings, side window defoggers, inside fuel door release, lighted vanity mirrors, and an under-the-floor spare tire carrier. The optional CL package included added features such as bumper rub strips, a trip odometer, gauges, custom steering wheel, wheel trim rings, auxiliary lighting, cigar lighter, and carpets. Cargo van versions had a standard low-back driver's seat in saddle color, black rubber floor covering, solid panel body sides, and the same arrangement of a sliding right-hand side cargo door with double panel type rear doors. Custom cloth upholstery was optional. Paint treatments included 10 solid colors, special two-tones (with decal strips at belt line, and secondary color below the belt), and Sport two-tones (with secondary color on lower body perimeter). The Astro name appeared on both entry doors, just behind the front wheel openings. Taillamps were vertical units positioned on the rear body corners just below the belt line. The rear doors of all models had large windows.

1/2-TON, 3/4-TON, 1-TON VAN/HI-CUBE VAN — MODEL G/SERIES 10, 20, 30 — SIX/V-8: Chevy Vans had new grilles of the same design described below for Blazers. Model identification nameplates featured somewhat smaller, and thinner lettering. Chrome trim around the taillights was no longer used. Chevrolet's new 4.3-liter Vortec V-6 was base equipment in G10/G20/G30 models, while the 6.2-liter diesel V-8 was available in G20/G30-CP6 series vans. The 5.7-liter V-8 could also be had in G30/CP6 Cutaway vans. Custom vinyl seats now used a four-pleat pattern. 60/40 style side doors were now regularly available, at no extra cost, in place of the sliding right-hand side load door. G30 Hi-Cube vans again come in 10 ft. (125-in. wheelbase), and 12-ft. (146-in. wheelbase) models, with RV, and Commercial Cutaway vans available on both of these chassis as well. All manual transmissions (three-speed type standard in G10/G20) came with floor-mounted gear shifts.

1/2-TON BLAZER — MODEL K (4x4) — SIX/V-8: Full-size 1985 Blazers were easier to spot. They had a much wider body color panel between upper, and lower grilles, and the grilles had only a single horizontal bar intersected by seven vertical bars. The headlight housing had more of a vertical look than last year's, although the rectangular lamps were stacked atop each other again. An amber-colored parking lamp was standard on the bottom, but when halogen high-beams were ordered, the parking lamps moved behind the lower grille. New features included fluidic wiper arms with built-in washers, and standard color-keyed tops in a choice of four new colors, plus the old black, and white. Custom Deluxe interiors were standard, with Silverado trim available at extra cost. Special two-tones, and Exterior Decor packages were optional. Colonial Yellow, and Desert Sand Metallic finishes were no longer offered. Engine and transmission selections were unchanged.

1/2-TON, 3/4-TON, 1-TON CONVENTIONAL — MODEL C (4x2), MODEL K (4x4)/SERIES 10, 20, 30 — SIX/V-8: Full-sized pickups shared the new 1985 grille with Blazers, and Suburbans. A new custom two-tone treatment used the secondary color above the belt line on the Fleetside box, on the rear of the cab, on the doors, and on the fender sides above the belt. It was not used on the hood or window frames. This gave a sportier look (something like a tapering racing stripe) to the cab, and fender sides. Under the hood, as standard equipment, was the Vortec six. The trucks continued to come in a wide range of choices including 1/2-, 3/4-, and 1-ton series with long or short cargo boxes, Fleetside or Step-Side styling, Crew-Cabs or Bonus-Cabs, and 4x2 or 4x4 drive. A real "Country Cadillac" was the Crew-Cab "Big Dooley" with its flared rear fenders, and dual rear wheels. Custom Deluxe, Scottsdale, and Silverado trims were again available. Suburbans also had the new-for-1985 wide center panel grille styling. Also standard were fluidic arm window washer/wipers. Custom Deluxe trim was standard. Scottsdales had color-keyed floor mats, plus added cowl and headliner insulation. Door-to-door carpeting, and velour or grained vinyl upholstery, were featured with Silverado interiors. Special two-tones, and Exterior Decor finish options were available. The latter included a hood ornament. End-gate, and panel door options were still cataloged for Suburbans. Standard engines were all V-8s.

3/4-TON, 1-TON FORWARD-CONTROL — MODEL P/SERIES 20, 30 — SIX/V-8: Chevy issued separate 1984 sales catalogs for steel-bodied, and aluminum-bodied Step-Vans. The steel models came as CP208/CP308 models on a 125-in. wheelbase, as CP210/CP310 models on the 133-in. wheelbase, and as CP314 models on the 157-in. wheelbase. Aluminum body models could be had in the same configurations, plus a model CP318 version with a 178-in. wheelbase. Load lengths were: [CP208/CP308] 129.6 in., [CP210/CP310] 153.6 in., [CP314] 177.6 in., and [CP318] 178 in. Series 30 Hi-Cube models came in 10-ft. models on the 125-in. wheelbase or 12-ft. models on the 146-in. wheelbase.

I.D. DATA: Location of serial number: The VIN is stamped on a plate attached to the left top of the instrument panel on C/K/G series. On P series the plate is attached to the front of the dash, and the panel to the left of the steering column. The first symbol indicates country of origin: 1=U.S., 2=Canada, J=Japan. The second symbol indicates manufacturer: G=General Motors, 8=Isuzu. The third symbol indicates make: A=Chevrolet bus, B=Chevrolet (incomplete), C=Chevrolet truck, Y=LUV (incomplete), Z=LUV truck, 8=Chevy MPV. The fourth symbol indicates GVW rating (and brake system), B=3,001 lb.-4,000 lb. (hydraulic), C=4,001 lb.-5,000 lb. (hydraulic), etc. through K for models with hydraulic brakes. The fifth symbol indicates line, and chassis type: C=Conventional cab (including Blazer, and Suburban) 4x2, G=Chevy Van, and Sportvan 4x2, K=Conventional cab (including Blazer, and Suburban) 4x4, L=LUV 4x2, R=LUV 4x4, P=Forward-Control, S=Conventional Cab 4x2, W=El Camino 4x2, Z=Special body 4x2. The sixth symbol indicates series: 1=1/2-ton, 2=3/4-ton, 3=1-ton, 8=El Camino. The seventh symbol indicates body type: 0=El Camino Pickup-Delivery, 1=Hi-Cube, and Cutaway Vans, 2-Forward-Control, 3=Four-door cab, 4=Two-door cab, 5=Van, 6=Suburban, 7=Motorhome chassis, 8=Blazer Utility, 9=Stake. The eighth symbol indicated engine. Engine codes were generally the same as 1983. The ninth symbol was a check digit. The 10th symbol indicated model-year: F=1985. The 11th symbol indicated the assembly plant: A=Lakewood, Ga., B=Baltimore, Md.,C=Southgate, Calif., D=Doraville, Ga., E=Linden, N.J., F=Flint, Mich., G=Framingham, Mass., H=Flint, Mich., J=Janesville, Wis., K=Leeds, Mo., L=Van Nuys, Calif., M=Lansing, Mich., N=Norwood, Ohio, P=Pontiac, Mich., R=Arlington, Texas, S=St. Louis, Mo., T=Tarrytown, N.Y., V=GMC, Pontiac, Mich., W=Willow Run, Mich., X=Fairfax, Va., Y=Wilmington, Dela., Z=Fremont, Calif., 0=GMAD, Pontiac, Mich., 1=Oshawa, Canada, 2=Moraine, Ohio, 2=Ste. Therese, Quebec, Canada, 3=Chevrolet-Detroit, Mich., 3=St. Eustache, Quebec, Canada, 4=Orion Plant, Pontiac, Mich., 4=Scarborough, Ontario, Canada, 5=Bowling Green, Ken., 5=London, Ontario, Canada, 6=Oklahoma City, Okla., 7=Lordstown, Ohio, 8=Shreveport, La., 8=Fujisawa, Japan, 9=Cadillac, Detroit, Mich. (Note: Trucks were not built at all factories). Symbols 12-17 were the production sequence number starting at 100001. Ending numbers not available. Engine number location: [Six] located on pad at right-hand side of cylinder block at rear of distributor. [V-8] located on pad at right front side of cylinder block.

1985 Chevrolet Silverado Fleetside Pickup (CP)

Model	Body Type	Price	Weight	Prod. Total
El Camino — 1/2-Ton — 117.1 in. w.b. — V-6				
1GW80	Sedan Pickup	9058	3252	Note 16
1GW80	Super Sport Pickup	9327	3263	Note 16
S10 Pickup 4x2 — 1/2-Ton — 108.3 in. w.b. — V-6				
CS10603	Pickup	5999	2561	Note 16
S10 Pickup 4x2 — 1/2-Ton — 122.9 in. w.b. — V-6				
CS10803	Chassis Cab	6500	2954	Note 16
CS10803	Pickup	6702	2623	Note 16
CS10653	Maxi-Cab Pickup	7167	3030	Note 16
S10 Pickup 4x4 — 1/2-Ton — 108.3 in. w.b. — V-6				
CT10603	Pickup	8258	2898	Note 16
S10 Pickup 4x4 — 1/2-Ton — 122.9 in. w.b. — V-6				
CT10803	Pickup	8412	2623	Note 16
CT10653	Maxi-Cab Pickup	8756	3030	Note 16
S10 Blazer 4x2 — 1/2-Ton — 100.5 in. w.b. — V-6				
CS10516	Hardtop Utility	8881	2894	Note 16
S10 Blazer 4x4 — 1/2-Ton — 100.5 in. w.b. — V-6				
CT10516	Hardtop Utility	10,134	3151	Note 16
Astro Van — 1/2-Ton — 111 in. w.b. — V-6				
CM10905	Cargo Van	7821	3048	Note 16
CM10906	Passenger Van	8195	3277	Note 16
CM10906	CS Passenger Van	8623	3277	Note 16
CM10906	CL Passenger Van	9359	3277	Note 16
Chevy Van 10 — 1/2-Ton — 110 in. w.b. — V-6				
CG11006	Panel Van	9650	4802	Note 16
Chevy Van 10 — 1/2-Ton — 125 in. w.b. — V-6				
CG11306	Sportvan	9870	4966	Note 16
CG11306	Bonaventure	10,661	5067	Note 16
CG11306	Beauville	10,979	5110	Note 16
Chevy Van — 3/4-Ton — 110 in. w.b. — V-6				
CG21006	Panel Van	8581	3811	Note 16
Chevy Van — 3/4-Ton — 125 in. w.b. — V-6				
CG21306	Sportvan	10,054	4994	Note 16
CG21306	Bonaventure	10,845	5095	Note 16
CG21306	Beauville	11,161	5138	Note 16
Chevy Van 30 — 1-Ton — 125 in. w.b. — V-8				
CG31306	Panel	10,342	4402	Note 16
CG31306	Sportvan	12,463	6915	Note 16
CG31306	Bonaventure	13,254	7016	Note 16
CG31306	Beauville	13,569	7059	Note 16
Chevy Van 30 — 1-Ton — 125 in. w.b. — Diesel V-8				
CG31306	Sportvan	13,545	5971	Note 16
CG31306	Bonaventure	14,350	6070	Note 16
CG31306	Beauville	14,587	6113	Note 16
Hi-Cube Vans 30 — 1-Ton — 125 in. w.b. — V-8				
CG31	Steel Hi-Cube 10-ft.	12,097	5054	Note 16
Hi-Cube Vans 30 — 1-Ton — 146 in. w.b. — V-8				
CG31	Steel Hi-Cube 12 ft.	13,351	5891	Note 16

NOTE 1: Add for 10-ft./12-ft. aluminum Hi-Cube or RV/Commercial Cutaway on 125/146-in. wheelbase.

Model	Body Type	Price	Weight	Prod. Total
K5 Blazer 4x4 — 1/2-Ton — 106.5 w.b. — V-8				
K10516	Hardtop Utility	11,223	4462	Note 16

NOTE 2: Add $2,730 and 375 lb. for diesel.

C10 — 1/2-Ton Conventional — 117.5 in. w.b. — V-6				
CC10703	Step-Side	7532	3844	Note 16
CC10703	Fleetside	7397	3891	Note 16
C10 — 1/2-Ton Conventional — 131.5 in. w.b. — V-6				
CC10903	Fleetside	7565	4060	Note 16

NOTE 3: Add $2,322 for CK10 (4x4) Pickup with Vortec six engine.
NOTE 4: Add $2,913 for 6.2-liter diesel V-8 option.

C10 — 1/2-Ton Suburban — 129.5 in. w.b. — V-8				
CC10906	Suburban (doors)	10,812	4755	Note 16
CC10916	Suburban (tailgate)	10,850	4790	Note 16

NOTE 5: Add $2,322 for 4x4 Suburban with larger 350-cid V-8.
NOTE 6: Add $2,557 for 6.2-liter diesel V-8 option.

C20 — 3/4-Ton Conventional — 131.5 in. w.b. — V-6				
CC20903	Step-Side	8798	4417	Note 16
CC20903	Fleetside	8663	4479	Note 16
C20 — 3/4-Ton Heavy-Duty Conventional — 131.5 in. w.b. — V-6				
CC20903	Chassis & Cab	9198	4057	Note 16
CC20903	Step-Side	9756	4417	Note 16
CC20903	Fleetside	9622	4479	Note 16
C20 — 3/4-Ton Conventional — 164.5 in. w.b. — V-6				
CC20943	Bonus-Cab Fleetside	10,584	5258	Note 16
CC20943	Crew-Cab Fleetside	10,920	5258	Note 16

NOTE 7: Add $1,525 for CK20 (4x4) Pickups with 350-cid V-8.
NOTE 8: Add $2,276 for 6.2-liter diesel V-8 option on C20 Pickups.

C10 — 3/4-Ton Suburban — 129.5 in. w.b. — V-8				
CC20906	Panel Door (V-8)	10,953	4705	Note 16
CC20916	End-gate (V-8)	10,991	4740	Note 16

NOTE 9: Add $1,479 for CK20 (4x4) Suburban with larger 350-cid V-8.
NOTE 10: Add $2,196 for 6.2-liter diesel V-8 option on C20 Suburbans.

Step-Van — P20 — 125 in./133 in./178 in. w.b. — Six				
CP20842	Steel Panel 10.5 ft.	13,119	5998	Note 16

NOTE 11: Add for P20 with 12.5-ft. Step-Van body.

C30 — 1-Ton Conventional — 131.5 in. w.b. — Six				
CC30903	Chassis & Cab	9332	4485	Note 16
CC30903	Step-Side	9849	4838	Note 16
CC30903	Fleetside	9715	4900	Note 16
C30 Bonus-Cab — 1-Ton Conventional — 164.5 in. w.b. — V-8				
CC30943	Chassis & Cab	10,349	4912	Note 16
CC30943	Fleetside	10,715	5323	Note 16
C30 Crew-Cab — 1-Ton Conventional — 164.5 in. w.b. — V-8				
CC30943	Chassis & Cab	9446	4520	Note 16
CC30943	Fleetside	11,053	5323	Note 16

NOTE 12: Add $2,344 average for CK30 (4x4) models with six-cylinder engine.
NOTE 13: Add $1,800 average for 6.2-liter diesel V-8 option on C30 models.

P30 Step-Van — 1-Ton — 125 in./133 in./178 in. w.b. — Six				
CP30842	Steel Panel 10.5 ft.	13,119	5998	-

NOTE 14: Add for P30 with 12.5-ft. Step-Van body.
NOTE 15: Add for P30 with 14.5-ft. Step-Van body.
NOTE 16: Mode-year production: [El Camino] 24,582 (Built in Mexico for U.S. sale), [S10] 250,194, [S-Blazer] 231,605, [Chevy Van] 149,881, [Sportvan] 21,448, [Astro Van] 59,019, [Astro Wagon] 31,085, [K5 Blazer] 40,011, [Suburban] 64,670, [C/K10] 292,681, [C/K20] 91,002, [C/K30] 46,917.

ENGINE: Inline. OHV. Four-cylinder. Cast iron block. Bore & stroke: 3.42 x 3.23 in. Displacement: 119 cid. Compression ratio: 8.4:1. Net horsepower: 82 at 4600 rpm. Net torque: 101 lb.-ft. at 3000 rpm. Ordering code LR1.
ENGINE: Inline. OHV. Diesel Four-cylinder. Cast iron block. Bore & stroke: 3.46 x 3.62 in. Displacement: 137 cid. Compression ratio: 21:1. Net horsepower: 62 at 4300 rpm. Net torque: 96 lb.-ft. at 2200 rpm. Ordering code LQ7.
ENGINE: Inline. OHV. Four-cylinder. Cast iron block. Bore & stroke: 4 x 3.00 in. Displacement: 151 cid. Compression ratio: 9.0:1. Net horsepower: 92 at 4400 rpm. Net torque: 132 lb.-ft. at 2800 rpm. Electronic fuel injection. Ordering code LN8.

1985 Chevrolet 1/2-Ton K10 Step-Side Pickup (CP)

ENGINE: V-block. OHV. Six-cylinder. Cast iron block. Bore & stroke: 3.50 x 2.99 in. Displacement: 173 cid. Compression ratio: 8.5:1. Net horsepower: 110 at 4800 rpm. Net torque: 145 lb.-ft. at 2100 rpm. Electronic fuel injection. Ordering code LB1.
ENGINE: V-block. OHV. Six-cylinder. Cast iron block. Bore & stroke: 4.0 x 3.48 in. Displacement: 262 cid. Compression ratio: 9.3:1. Net horsepower: 155 at 4000 rpm. Torque: 230 lb.-ft. at 2400 rpm. Hydraulic valve lifters. Carburetor: Single four-barrel. Ordering code LB1.
ENGINE: V-block. OHV. Six-cylinder. Cast iron block. Bore & stroke: 4.0 x 3.48 in. Displacement: 202 cid. Compression ratio: 9.3:1. Net horsepower: 130 at 3600 rpm. Net torque: 210 lb.-ft. at 2000 rpm. Hydraulic valve lifters. Electronic fuel injection. Ordering code LB4.
ENGINE: Inline. OHV. Six-cylinder. Cast iron block. Bore & stroke: 3.9 x 4.1 in. Displacement: 292 cid. Compression ratio: 7.8:1. Net horsepower: 115 at 3600 rpm. Net torque: 215 lb.-ft. at 1600 rpm. Seven main bearings. Hydraulic valve lifters. Carburetor: Rochester single one-barrel. Ordering code L25.
ENGINE: V-block. OHV. Eight-cylinder. Cast iron block. Bore & stroke: 3.74 x 3.48 in. Displacement: 305 cid. Compression ratio: 9.5:1. Net horsepower: 150 at 4000 rpm. Net torque: 240 lb.-ft. at 2000 rpm. Five main bearings. Hydraulic valve lifters. Carburetor: Single four-barrel. Ordering code LG4.

ENGINE: V-block. OHV. Eight-cylinder. Cast iron block. Bore & stroke: 3.74 x 3.48 in. Displacement: 305 cid. Compression ratio: 9.2:1. Net horsepower: 160 at 4400 rpm. Net torque: 235 lb.-ft. at 2000 rpm. Four main bearings. Hydraulic valve lifters. Carburetor: Rochester single four-barrel. Ordering code LE9.
ENGINE: V-block. OHV. Eight-cylinder. Cast iron block. Bore & stroke: 4.0 x 3.5 Displacement: 350 cid. Compression ratio: 8.3:1. Net horsepower: 160 at 3800 rpm. Net torque: 250 lb.-ft. at 2800 rpm. Five main bearings. Hydraulic valve lifters. Carburetor: Rochester four-barrel. Ordering code LT9.
ENGINE: V-block. OHV. Eight-cylinder. Cast iron block. Bore & stroke: 4.0 x 3.48 in. Displacement: 350 cid. Compression ratio: 8.2:1. Net horsepower: 165 at 3800 rpm. Net torque: 275 lb.-ft. at 1600 rpm. Carburetor: Rochester single four-barrel. Ordering code LS9.
ENGINE: V-block. OHV. Diesel eight-cylinder. Cast iron block. Bore & stroke: 3.98 x 3.82 in. Displacement: 379 cid. Compression ratio: 21.3:1. Net horsepower: 130 at 3600 rpm. Net torque: 240 lb.-ft. at 2000 rpm. Hydraulic valve lifters. Fuel-injection. Ordering code LH6.
ENGINE: Inline. Diesel. OHV. Eight-cylinder. Cast iron block. Bore & stroke: 3.98 x 3.80 in. Displacement: 379 cid. Compression ratio: 21.3:1. Net horsepower: 151 at 3600 rpm. Net torque: 248 lb.-ft at 2000 rpm. Hydraulic valve lifters. Fuel-injection. Ordering code LL4.
ENGINE: V-block. OHV. Eight-cylinder. Cast iron block. Bore & stroke: 4.3 x 4.0 in. Displacement: 454 cid. Compression ratio: 7.9:1. Net horsepower: 230 at 3800 rpm. Net torque: 360 lb.-ft. at 2800 rpm. Five main bearings. Carburetor: Rochester single four-barrel. Ordering code LE8

1985 Chevrolet El Camino SS "Designer Series" Sedan-Pickup (JAG)

CHASSIS: [S10 Pickup] Wheelbase: 108.3 in./122.9 in. Tires: P195/75R14.
CHASSIS: [S10 Blazer] Wheelbase: 100.5, Tires P195/75R15.
CHASSIS: [El Camino] Wheelbase: 117.1 in. Tires: P205/75R14.
CHASSIS: [Astro Van] Wheelbase: 111 in. Tires P195/75R15.
CHASSIS: [Chevy Van 10] Wheelbase: 110 in. Tires: P195/75R15.
CHASSIS: [Sportvan 10] Wheelbase: 125 Tires: P205/75R15.
CHASSIS: [Chevy Van 20] Wheelbase: 110 in. Tires: P225/75R15.
CHASSIS: [Sportvan 20] Wheelbase: 125 Tires: P225/75R15.
CHASSIS: [Chevy Van 30] Wheelbase: 125 Tires: 8.75-R-16.5C.
CHASSIS: [Sportvan 30] Wheelbase: 125 Tires: 8.75-R-16.5D.
CHASSIS: [Hi-Cube Van 10 ft.] Wheelbase: 125 Tires: 8.00-16.5D.
CHASSIS: [Hi-Cube Van 12 ft.] Wheelbase: 146 in. Tires: 8.75-16.5D.
CHASSIS: [K10 Blazer] Wheelbase: 106.5 Tires: P215/75R15.
CHASSIS: [C10 Pickup] Wheelbase: 117.5 in./131.5 Tires: 195/75R15.
CHASSIS: [C10 Suburban] Wheelbase: 129.5 Tires: P233/75R15.
CHASSIS: [C20 Pickup] Wheelbase: 131.5 Tires: LT215/85R16C.
CHASSIS: [C20 Pickup] Wheelbase: 164.5 Tires: [Front] LT235/85R16D, [Rear] LT235/85R16E.
CHASSIS: [C20 Suburban] Wheelbase: 129.5. Tires: [Front] LT235/85R16D, [Rear] LT235/85R16E.
CHASSIS: [P20 Step-Van] Wheelbase: 125 in./133 in. Tires: LT215/85R16C.
CHASSIS: [C30 Pickup] Wheelbase: 131.5 in./164.5. Tires: [Front] [Rear] LT235/85R16E.
CHASSIS: [P30 Step-Van] Wheelbase: 125 in./178 in. Tires: LT215/85R16C.
TECHNICAL: [El Camino] Automatic transmission. Speeds: 3 F/1 R. Floor-mounted gear shift. Semi-floating rear axle. Overall ratio: 2.41, 2.56, 2.73, 3.08:1. Hydraulic power front disc/rear drum brakes. Pressed steel wheels.
TECHNICAL: [S10] Manual, synchromesh transmission. Speeds: 4 F/1 R. Floor-mounted gear shift. Semi-floating rear axle. Overall ratio: 3.08, 3.42, 3.73, 4.11:1. Hydraulic, front disc/rear drum brakes. Pressed steel wheels.
TECHNICAL: [S10 Blazer] Manual, synchromesh transmission. Speeds: 4 F/1 R. Floor-mounted gear shift. Semi-floating rear axle. Overall ratio: 2.73, 3.08, 3.42, 3.73. Hydraulic power front disc/rear drum brakes. Pressed steel 6-in. wheels.
TECHNICAL: [Astro] Manual, synchromesh transmission. Speeds: 4 F/1 R. Floor-mounted gear shift. Semi-floating rear axle. Overall ratio: 2.56, 2.73, 3.08, 3.42, 3.73, 4.11:1. Hydraulic disc front/rear drum brakes. Pressed steel wheels.
TECHNICAL: [G10/G20] Synchromesh/manual transmission. Speeds: 3 F/1 R. Column-mounted gear shift. Semi-floating rear axle. Hydraulic front disc/rear drum brakes. Pressed steel wheels.
TECHNICAL: [G30] Automatic, overdrive transmission. Speeds: 4 F/1R. Column-mounted gear shift. Full-floating rear axle. Overall ratio: 3.73, 4.10:1. Power front disc/rear drum brakes. Pressed steel wheels.
TECHNICAL: [C10 Suburban] Automatic with overdrive transmission. Speeds: 4 F/1 R. Column-mounted gear shift. Semi-floating rear axle. Overall ratio: 3.21, 3.42, 3.73, 4.10, 3.56:1. Power hydraulic front disc/rear drum brakes. Pressed steel wheels.
TECHNICAL: [C10] Manual, synchromesh transmission. Speeds: 3 F/1 R. Column-mounted gear shift. Semi-floating rear axle. Overall ratio: 2.73, 3.08, 3.42, 3.73:1. Hydraulic front disc/rear drum brakes. Pressed steel, 6.00-in. wide wheels.
TECHNICAL: [All C20/C30] Manual, synchromesh transmission. Speeds: 4 F/1 R. Floor-mounted gear shift. Rear axle: [C30/K30] full-floating, [others] semi-floating. Overall ratio: 3.23, 3.42, 3.73, 4.10, 4.56:1 (LE 8 engine, and locking differential: 3.21:1).
TECHNICAL: [C20 Suburban] Manual, synchromesh (standard on C20/K10/K20) transmission. Speeds: 4 F/1 R. Floor-mounted gear shift. Semi-floating (full-floating with 454 V-8) rear axle. Overall ratio: 3.21, 3.42, 3.73, 4.10, 4.56:1. Power hydraulic front disc/rear drum brakes. Pressed steel wheels.

OPTIONS: [S10 Models] Gauge package, S10 ($55-$113). Tinted glass, S10 ($135-$190). Exterior mirrors, S10 ($50-$83). Speed control, S10 ($195). [ASTRO] Four-speed automatic transmission ($520). Four-passenger seating CL ($552), others ($634). Seven-passenger seating, CL ($1195), others ($1277). Eight-passenger seating, CL ($643), others ($593). Seat back recliner, and dual arm rests ($230). Custom high-back buckets, 8-passenger ($150), 5-passenger ($100). Front air conditioning, base ($740), CL/CS ($697). Front, and rear air conditioning, CL/CS ($1249). Deluxe front/rear bumpers, base, and CS ($122), CL ($72). Color-keyed bumpers, base, and CS ($50). Increased cargo capacity, regular 4/5 passenger seats ($314). Heavy-duty radiator ($53), with transmission cooler ($112), with transmission cooler, and air conditioning ($171). Remote fuel filler release ($25). Rubber floor covering, base ($43). Gauge package, base, and CS ($58). 100 ampere alternator ($30). Tinted glass, complete ($98), standard ($71). Deluxe grille, base, and CS ($25). Halogen headlamps ($22). Engine block heater ($31). Rear heater, base ($256). Deluxe heater ($43). Special two-tone ($237). Sport two-tone ($162). California emissions ($99). Optional axle ratio ($36). Locking differential ($238). Heavy-duty battery ($53). Spare tire carrier, base ($21). Engine oil cooler ($120). Roof console ($79). Power door locks ($198). Carpeting in CS ($111). Rear heater ($256). Complete body glass ($121). Tinted windshield ($38). Swing-out door glass ($55). Trailer wiring harness ($39). Dome, and reading lamps ($31). Auxiliary lighting, base ($142), CS ($121). Dual deluxe mirrors ($50). Black body side moldings, base, and CS ($55). Power windows, and door locks ($388). Door edge guards ($17). Right-hand visor mirror, base ($48), CL/CS ($33). Protective interior panels ($25). AM radio ($112). AM/FM stereo, base ($243), CL/CS ($283). AM/FM stereo with electronic tuning, base ($424), CL/CS ($464). Above with quadraphonic, base ($574), CL/CS ($614). Cruise control ($195). Front stabilizer bar ($38). Power steering ($276). Tilt steering column ($115). Custom steering wheel, base, and CS ($26). Power windows ($190). Positive stop rear door, base ($35). Left-hand front seat storage compartment ($35). Left-, and right-hand front seat storage compartments ($70). Body striping ($75). 27-gallon fuel tank ($66). Cargo tie-downs ($30). Dead weight trailer hitch ($64). Heavy-duty "Trailerite" package, with front, and rear air conditioning ($471), without front, and rear air conditioning ($524). Light-duty "Tailerite" package ($103). Wheel trim rings, base, and CS ($56). Rally wheels, base, and CS ($88), CL ($48). Cast aluminum wheels, base, and CS ($299), CL ($259). Intermittent wipers ($55). Tahoe/Sierra classic equipment, S10 ($595). Sport Gypsy equipment, S10 ($972). Seat trim, S10 ($24). "High-Country" bucket seats, S10 ($295). Custom two-tone paint, S10 ($200). Special two-tone paint, S10 ($311). Sport two-tone paint, S10 ($227). Air conditioning, S10 ($705). Console, S10 ($108). [Full-size C/K trucks] Rear step bumper, Fleetside ($189). Chromed front bumper guards ($41). Exterior mirrors ($50-$94). Body side molding package ($115-$173). Rally wheels for C10/K10/K5 Blazer ($115). Styled wheels for C10/K10/K5 Blazer ($174). Cast aluminum wheels for C10/K10/K5 Blazer ($299). Radio: AM/AM/FM/AM/FM, clock, AM/FM stereo, and stereo cassette, AM stereo/FM stereo, Seek-and-Scan ($112-$594). Scottsdale/High-Sierra C/K series ($250). Silverado/Sierra Classic C/K series ($671). Conventional two-tone C/K series ($72). Special two-tone C/K series ($327). Deluxe two-tone C/K series/Fleetside ($184-$370). Custom two-tone C/K series/Fleetside ($531). Special Big Dooley two-tone Fleetside, dual wheels ($426-$444). Deluxe front appearance package C/K series ($109). All-weather air-conditioning C/K series ($678-740). Chromed rear bumper C/K series ($103). Silverado/Sierra classic package K Blazer ($1015). Special two-tone paint K Blazer ($170-$327). Custom two-tone paint K Blazer ($314-$471). Deluxe front appearance package K Blazer ($109). Deluxe chromed bumpers K5 Blazer ($49). Body side moldings K5 Blazer ($115-$173). Scottsdale/High-Sierra package for Suburban ($311-$459). Silverado/Sierra Classic ($1,111-$1,259). [El Camino] Conquista package ($195). Air conditioning ($750). Gauge package ($115). Sport mirrors ($61). Rally wheel rims ($56). Wire wheelcovers ($199).

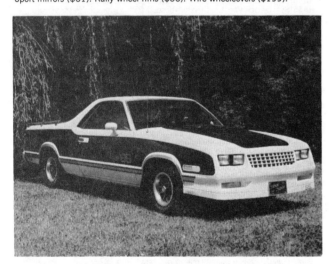

1985 Chevrolet El Camino "Choo-Choo Customs" Sedan-Pickup (Owner/photo: Jean A. Allen)

HISTORICAL: Introduced Sept. 21, 1984. Calendar-year production: [Pickups] 430,600, [Step-Vans] 46,978, [Vans/Sportvans] 171,329. [Total all models] 1,325,491. Innovations: New Astro Van truck line introduced. El Camino has new 4.3-liter base V-6. New 2.5-liter base engine for S10 trucks with 4x4 drive. Custom two-toning extended to S10 Pickups. New 4.3-liter Vortec Six also used in Chevy Vans as standard engine. Full-size trucks adopt new grille styling. Every new 1985 light-duty Chevy truck delivered by a Chevrolet dealer in the U.S. came with a one-year, $10,000 seat belt insurance certificate from MIC General Insurance Corp. at no additional charge. Under the policy, $10,000 would be paid to the estate of any occupant suffering fatal injuries as a result of an accident involving that vehicle while wearing a GM seat belt. The 1985 sales catalog also stated, "For three, and a half decades there have been more Chevy trucks in use than any other make."

1/2-TON S10 — MODEL S/SERIES 10 — FOUR/V-6: For 1986, Chevrolet's light-duty trucks were little changed in terms of styling and trim packages. However, a number of technical refinements were made in practically all of the product lines. Getting a new high-tech instrument cluster was the compact S10 pickup. Both the standard 2.5 liter EFI (electronic fuel-injection) engine or the optional 2.8-liter V-6 were changed for improved performance, fuel economy and durability. An optional TBI (throttle body injection) system for the V-6 was another technical update. It boosted the horsepower rating by nine percent. New for the S10 Blazer was a redesigned instrument cluster, the TBI V-6, low-pressure Delco/Bilstein gas shocks and new paint and trim options. Chevrolet advised that the 4x2 compact Blazer was rising in popularity. The 4x4 Blazer Mini-trucks came with an Insta-Trac system. It let the driver shift from 4x2 mode to 4x4 high, and back again, without stopping. The stylized fender badges had an S done in red. At the rear, the taillights were framed in chrome and the large Chevrolet name was changed to a smaller name at the right-hand side of a tailgate trim panel. Standard, Durango, Tahoe and Sport trim treatments were available again. Trim options included Custom two-tone (second color below belt), Sport two-tone (second color on bottom below four-stripe decals or moldings), and Special two-tone (second color between belt line and lower feature line). The S10 Blazer's Custom vinyl interior had wider door panel pleats and brushed aluminum door panel trim plates.

1/2-TON EL CAMINO — MODEL W — Six/V-8: The El Camino featured a new instrument panel and revised gauge cluster graphics to modernize it. It continued to offer 35.5 cu. ft. of cargo capacity and a 1,250-lbs. payload. A four-speed automatic transmission with overdrive was made available with the standard 4.3-liter V-6. Both it and the three-speed manual gear box were offered with this engine or the optional 5.0-liter V-8. El Caminos again had a 4.3-liter V-6 base engine. Standard grille was the same as last year. Also back was the El Camino Super Sport and the Conquista. The SS had an aero nose treatment. A non-functional power blister hood, dummy side pipes and pickup bed rails were optional. Model identification decals were used on the doors, above the lower feature line. Conquista and SS Sport decors each included distinctive two-tones.

1986 Chevrolet 1/2-Ton Astro CS Passenger Minivan (CMD)

1/2-TON ASTRO VAN — Model M/Series 10 — V-6: The Astro Van was back with virtually no changes. It was a compact van featuring a standard V-6 engine, five-speed manual transmission, and rear drive axle. The minivan body featured a sloping hood and aerodynamically rounded front end with wraparound parking lamps, single rectangular headlights, and a grille with seven horizontal bars. Each bar decreased slightly in width, from top to bottom. A yellow Chevrolet bow tie badge was in the center. Additional standard equipment included an engine cover storage box, front arm rests, swing-out side windows, black rubber floor covering, high-back bucket seats, five-passenger seating, and P195/75R15 all-season steel-belted radial tires. CS trim added color-keyed floor coverings, side window defoggers, inside fuel door release, lighted vanity mirrors, and an under-the-floor spare tire carrier. The optional CL package included added such features as bumper rub strips, a trip odometer, gauges, custom steering wheel, wheel trim rings, auxiliary lighting, cigar lighter, and carpets. Cargo van versions had a standard low-back driver's seat in saddle color, black rubber floor covering, solid panel body sides, and the same arrangement of a sliding right-hand side cargo door with double panel type rear doors. Custom cloth upholstery was optional. Paint treatments included 10 solid colors, special two-tones (with decal strips at belt line and secondary color below the belt) and Sport two-tones (with secondary color on lower body perimeter). The Astro name appeared on both entry doors, just behind the front wheel openings. Taillamps were vertical units positioned on the rear body corners just below the belt line. The rear doors of all models had large windows. Standard power for the commercial versions was Chevrolet's 2.5-liter Tech IV power plant with electronic fuel-injection. The Vortec Six, with TBI (throttle body injection) and a five-speed manual transmission, was the standard power team for Astro passenger vans in 1986. This made them the most powerful of any small vans available in America. The Vortec six developed 155 hp, a five percent increase over 1985. With all auxiliary seats removed, the Astro passenger van had a 151.8 cu.-ft. cargo capacity, while the commercial version offered up to 183 cu.-ft. Many industry observers felt that this model's rear-drive configuration made it better suited to commercial use than other minivans available from competing manufacturers.

1/2-TON, 3/4-TON, 1-TON VAN/HI-CUBE VAN — MODEL G/SERIES 10, 20, 30 — SIX/V-8: Sportvans and Chevy Vans were again offered in G10/G20/G30 Series with engines including the Vortec Six, a choice of two gas V-8s, and Chevrolet's 6.2-liter diesel V-8 available in G20/G30 models. One change for the season was that the conventional sliding door could be replaced, at no extra cost, by the 60/40 swing-out type incorporating a new sliding 90-degree door-check system. This change prevented fouling between the right front side door and the forward side swing-out door. G30 Hi-Cube vans again come in 10 ft. (125-in. wheelbase) and 12 ft. (146-in. wheelbase) models, with RV and Commercial Cutaway vans available on both of these chassis as well. All manual transmissions (three-speed type standard in G10/G20) came with floor-mounted gear shifts.

1986 Chevrolet 1/2-Ton S10 Blazer 4x4 Utility Hardtop (CMD)

1/2-TON BLAZER — MODEL K (4x4) — SIX/V-8: Full-size Blazers, for 1986, had new molded front bucket seats with folding seat backs. The cloth trim option included a reclining seat back feature, and the passenger seat had the same slide-forward, easy-entry system previously used on the S10 Blazer. Three new paint colors, Canyon Copper Metallic, Nevada Gold Metallic, and Steel Gray Metallic were released. A new steel-gray top was designed expressly to go with the third added paint scheme. A body color panel ran between upper and lower grilles, and the grilles had only a single horizontal bar intersected by seven vertical bars. The headlight housings had a vertical look with rectangular parking lamps stacked atop each other again. An amber-colored parking lamp was standard on the bottom, but when halogen high-beam headlamps were ordered, the parking lamps moved behind the lower grille. Features included fluidic wiper arms with built-in washers, and standard color-keyed hardtops in a choice of colors or black and white. Custom Deluxe interiors were standard, with Silverado trim available at extra cost. Special two-tone and Exterior Decor packages were optional.

1986 Chevrolet 3/4-Ton K20 Fleetside Custom Deluxe Pickup 4x4

1/2-TON, 3/4-TON, 1-TON CONVENTIONAL — MODEL C (4x2), MODEL K (4x4)/SERIES 10, 20, 30 — SIX/V-8: Continuing as standard equipment on full-size Chevy pickups was the Vortec Six. Swirl-port cylinder heads helped it pump out 155 hp and 230 lb.-ft. of torque. "It is the most powerful standard engine ever offered in a Chevrolet pickup," advised a Chevrolet press release. An electric booster fan, mounted ahead of the radiator, was a new feature used with the optional 7.4-liter diesel V-8. The 5.0-liter and 5.7-liter gas V-8s, as well as the 6.2-liter diesel V-8, were used again. The diesel trucks came with a 50,000 mile warranty and had up to 148 hp (on trucks with over 8,500 lb. GVW ratings). The Suburban began its second half-century in 1986. The same three new colors available for the big Blazer were offered for the Suburban as well. New outboard arm rests were made a part of the year's reclining bucket seat option. According to Chevy, the Suburban could hold nine passengers and 40.8 cu.-ft. of luggage behind the third seat when outfitted for use as a station wagon. With the second seat folded and the optional rear seat removed, it became a truck with a 167 cu.-ft. cargo area and payload capacity up to 3,911 lb. The trucks continued to come in a wide range of choices including 1/2-, 3/4- and 1-ton series with long or short cargo boxes, Fleetside or Step-Side styling, Crew-Cab and Bonus-Cab configurations, and 4x2 or 4x4 drive. A real "Country Cadillac" was the "Big Dooley." Custom Deluxe, Scottsdale and Silverado trims were again available. Custom Deluxe trim was standard. Scottsdales had color-keyed floor mats and added cowl and headliner insulation. Door-to-door carpeting and velour or grained vinyl upholstery were featured with Silverado interiors. Special two-tone and Exterior Decor finish options were available. The latter included a hood ornament. End-gate and panel door options were still cataloged for Suburbans, in which a V-8 was standard engine.

3/4-TON, 1-TON FORWARD-CONTROL — MODEL P/SERIES 20, 30 — SIX/V-8: Steel-bodied and aluminum-bodied Step-Vans again came in two lines. The steel models came as CP208/CP308 models on a 125-in. wheelbase, as CP210/CP310 models on the 133-in. wheelbase and as CP314 models on the 157-in. wheelbase. Aluminum body models could be had in the same configurations, plus a model CP318 version with a 178-in. wheelbase. Load lengths were: [CP208/CP308] 129.6 in., [CP210/CP310] 153.6 in., [CP314] 177.6 in. and [CP318] 178 in. Series 30 Hi-Cube models came in 10 ft. models on the 125-in. wheelbase and 12 ft. models on the 146-in. wheelbase.

I.D. DATA: Location of serial number: The VIN is stamped on a plate attached to the left top of the instrument panel on C/K/G Series. On P Series the plate is attached to the front of the dash and the panel to the left of the steering column. The first symbol indicates country of origin: 1=U.S., 2=Canada, J=Japan. The second symbol indicates manufacturer: G=General Motors, 8=Isuzu. The third symbol indicates make: A=Chevrolet bus, B=Chevrolet (incomplete),

C=Chevrolet truck, Y=LUV (incomplete), Z=LUV truck, 8=Chevy MPV. The fourth symbol indicates GVW rating (and brake system), B=3,001 lb.-4,000 lb. (hydraulic), C=4,001 lb.-5,000 lb. (hydraulic), etc. through K for hydraulic brakes. The fifth symbol indicates line and chassis type: C=Conventional cab (including Blazer and Suburban) 4x2, G=Chevy Van and Sportvan 4x2, K=Conventional cab (including Blazer and Suburban) 4x4, L=LUV 4x2, R=LUV 4x4, P=Forward-Control, S=Conventional cab 4x2, W=El Camino 4x2, Z=Special body 4x2. The sixth symbol indicates series: 1=1/2-ton, 2=3/4-ton, 3=1-ton, 8=El Camino. The seventh symbol indicates body type: 0=El Camino Pickup-Delivery, 1=Hi-Cube and Cutaway Vans, 2=Forward-Control, 3=Four-door cab, 4=Two-door cab, 5=Van, 6=Suburban, 7=Motorhome chassis, 8=Blazer Utility, 9=Stake. The eighth symbol indicated engine. Engine codes were generally the same as 1983. The ninth symbol was a check digit. The 10th symbol indicated model year: G=1986. The 11th symbol indicated the assembly plant: A=Lakewood, Ga., B=Baltimore, Md. C=Southgate, Calif., D=Doraville, Ga., E=Linden, N.J., F=Flint, Mich., G=Framingham, Mass., H=Flint, Mich., J=Janesville, Wis., K=Leeds, Mo., L=Van Nuys, Calif., M=Lansing, Mich., N=Norwood, Ohio, P=Pontiac, Mich., R=Arlington, Texas, S=St. Louis, Mo., T=Tarrytown, N.Y., V=GMC, Pontiac, Mich., W=Willow Run, Mich., X=Fairfax, Va., Y=Wilmington, Dela., Z=Fremont, Calif., O=GMAD, Pontiac, Mich., 1=Oshawa, Canada, 2=Moraine, Ohio, 2=Ste. Therese, Quebec, Canada, 3=Chevrolet-Detroit, Mich., 3=St. Eustache, Quebec, Canada, 4=Orion Plant, Pontiac, Mich., 4=Scarborough, Ontario, Canada, 5=Bowling Green, Ken., 5=London, Ontario, Canada, 6=Oklahoma City, Okla., 6=Lordstown, Ohio, 8=Shreveport, La., 8=Fujisawa, Japan, 9=Cadillac, Detroit, Mich. (Note: Trucks were not built at all factories). Symbols 12-17 were the production sequence number starting at 100001. Ending numbers not available. Engine number location: [Six] located on pad at right-hand side of cylinder block at rear of distributor. [V-8] located on pad at right front side of cylinder block.

1986 Chevrolet 1-Ton C30 Custom Deluxe "Big Dooley" Fleetside

Model	Body Type	Price	Weight	Prod. Total
El Camino — 1/2-Ton — 117.1 in. w.b. — V-6				
W80	Sedan Pickup	9572	3234	Note 6
W80	Super Sport Pickup	9885	3239	Note 6
S10 Pickup — 1/2-Ton — 108.3 in. w.b. — V-6				
S10	Fleetside EL	5990	-	Note 6
S14	Fleetside	6999	2574	Note 6
S10 Pickup — 1/2-Ton — 122.9 in. w.b. — V-6				
S14	Fleetside	7234	2645	Note 6
S14	Maxi-Cab	7686	2713	Note 6
S10 Blazer 4x4 — 1/2-Ton — 100.5 in. w.b. — V-6				
T18	Utility Hardtop	10,698	3152	Note 6
NOTE 1: Deduct for 4x2 Model S10 Blazer.				
Astro — 1/2-Ton — 111 in. w.b. — V-6				
M15	Cargo Van	8431	3258	Note 6
M15	Passenger Van	9037	3434	Note 6
M15	CS Passenger Van	9492	3509	Note 6
M15	CL Passenger Van	10,216	3569	Note 6
Chevy Van 10 — 1/2-Ton — 110 in. w.b. — V-6				
G15	Chevy Van	8626	3700	Note 6
G15	Sportvan	10,232	4052	Note 6
Chevy Van 10 — 1/2-Ton — 125 in. w.b. — V-6				
G15	Bonaventure	11,290	4153	Note 6
G15	Beauville	11,622	4196	Note 6
Chevy Van 20 — 3/4-Ton — 110 in. w.b. — V-8				
G25	Chevy Van	9257	3786	Note 6
Chevy Van 20 — 3/4-Ton — 125 in. w.b. — V-8				
G25	Sportvan	10,655	4244	Note 6
G25	Bonaventure	11,482	4345	Note 6
G25	Beauville	11,813	4388	Note 6
Chevy Van 30 — 1-Ton — 125 in. w.b. — V-8				
G35	Chevy Van (V-6)	11,128	4526	Note 6
G35	Sportvan	13,173	5117	Note 6
G35	Bonaventure	14,001	5218	Note 6
G35	Beauville	14,331	5261	Note 6
G35	Cutaway Van	10,204	3906	Note 6
Hi-Cube Van — 1-Ton — 125 in. w.b. — V-8				
G31	Hi-Cube 10 ft.	13,492	5209	Note 6
Hi-Cube Van — 1-Ton — 146 in. w.b. — V-8				
G31	Hi-Cube 12 ft.	14,803	5886	Note 6
K10 Blazer 4x4 — 1/2-Ton — 106.5 in. w.b. — V-8				
K18	Utility Hardtop	12,034	4444	Note 6
C10 Pickup — 1/2-Ton — 117.5 in. w.b. — V-6				
C14	Step-Side 6.5 ft.	7904	3385	Note 6
C14	Fleetside 6.5 ft.	7764	3432	Note 6
C10 Pickup — 1/2-Ton — 131.5 in. w.b. — V-6				
C14	Fleetside 8 ft.	7938	3595	Note 6
C10 Suburban — 1/2-Ton — 129.5 in. w.b. — V-8				
C16	Suburban	11,476	4279	Note 6
NOTE 2: Add for CK10 Pickups/Suburbans with 4x4.				
C20 Pickup — 3/4-Ton — 131.5 in. w.b. — V-8				
C24	Chassis & Cab	9667	3570	Note 6
C24	Step-Side	9253	3930	Note 6
C24	Fleetside	9113	3992	Note 6
C20 Pickup — 3/4-Ton — 164.5 in. w.b. — I-6				
C24	Bonus Cab Pickup	11,103	4773	Note 6
C24	Crew Cab Pickup	11,451	4834	Note 6
C20 Suburban — 3/4-Ton — 129.5 in. w.b. — V-8				
C24	Suburban	12,297	4771	Note 6
NOTE 3: Add for CK20 Pickups/Suburbans with 4x4.				

Model	Body Type	Price	Weight	Prod. Total
P20 Step-Van — 3/4-Ton — 125/133 in. w.b. — I-6				
P22	Steel Panel	14,338	5869	Note 6
C30 Pickup — 1-Ton — 131.5 in. w.b. I-6				
C34	Chassis & Cab	9843	4011	Note 6
C34	Step-Side	10,381	4426	Note 6
C34	Fleetside	10,242	4426	Note 6
C30 Pickup — 1-Ton — 164.5 in. w.b. I-6				
C33	Chassis-Bonus-Cab	10,901	4451	Note 6
C33	Bonus Cab Fleetside	11,282	4862	Note 6
C33	Chassis-Crew-Cab	11,253	4512	Note 6
C33	Crew Cab Fleetside	11,633	4923	Note 6

NOTE 4: Add for CK30 Pickups/Suburbans with 4x4.

P30 Step-Vans — 1-Ton — 133/178 in. w.b. — I-6

P32	Steel Panel	14,422	6022	Note 6

NOTE 5: All C20 and C30 Pickups have 8-ft. pickup boxes.

NOTE 6: Model-year production: [S10 Maxi-Cabs] 34,865, [Other S10 cab models] 138,090, [S10 Blazer] 132,977, [Astro] 140,729, [C10/K10 cab models] 282,192, [C20/K20 regular-cab models] 75,487, [C30/K30 regular-cab models] 39,823, [C20/C30/K20/K30 Crew-Cab] 17,405, [K10 Blazer] 37,310, [C10/K10/C20/K20 Suburban] 61,242, [El Camino] 16,229, [Chevy Van] 125,077, [Sportvan] 16,883. Figures include trucks built in U.S. and Canada for the U.S. market.

NOTE 7: The percentage of above trucks with four-wheel-drive, by model, was: [S10 Maxi-Cabs] 26 percent, [Other S10 cab models] 24 percent, [S10 Blazer] 75 percent, [Astro] 0, [K10 cab models] 31 percent, [K20 regular-cab models] 43 percent, [K30 regular-cab models] 20 percent, [K20/K30 Crew-Cabs] 0 percent, [K10 Blazer] 100 percent, [K10/K20 Suburbans] 37 percent, [El Camino] 0 percent, [Chevy Van] 0 percent, [Sportvan] 0 percent.

ENGINE: (Diesel). Inline. OHV. Four-cylinder. Cast iron block. Bore & stroke: 3.46 x 3.62 in. Displacement: 137 cid (2.2 liter). Brake horsepower: 62 at 3200 rpm. Taxable horsepower: 19.50. Torque: 96 lb.-ft. at 2200 rpm. Hydraulic valve lifters. VIN code S. Manufactured by Isuzu of Japan. Diesel optional in S10 Pickups and Blazers.

1986 Chevrolet Silverado Fleetside Pickup (CMD)

ENGINE: (Gas). Inline. OHV. Four-cylinder. Cast iron block. Bore & stroke: 4.0 x 3.0 in. Displacement: 151 cid (2.5 liter). Compression ratio: 9.0:1. Brake horsepower: 92 at 4400 rpm. Taxable horsepower: 25.6. Torque: 134 lb.-ft. at 2800 rpm. Carburetor: Two-barrel. VIN code E. This engine manufactured by Pontiac. Standard in S10 Blazers and Pickups. Also standard in Astro commercial vans.

ENGINE: (Gas). V-block. OHV. Six-cylinder. Cast iron block. Bore & stroke: 3.5 x 2.99 in. Displacement: 173 cid (2.8 liter). Compression ratio: 8.5:1. Brake horsepower: 125 at 4800 rpm. Taxable horsepower: 29.4. Torque: 150 lb.-ft. at 2200 rpm. Hydraulic valve lifters. Induction system: TBI. VIN code B. Manufactured by Chevrolet. Optional in S10 Blazer and Pickups.

ENGINE: (Gas). V-block. OHV. Six-cylinder. Cast iron block. Bore & stroke: 4.0 x 3.48 in. Displacement: 262 cid (4.3 liter). Compression ratio: 9.3:1. Brake horsepower: 140 at 4000 rpm. Taxable horsepower: 38.4. Torque: 225 lb.-ft. at 2000 rpm. Hydraulic valve lifters. Carburetor: Two-barrel. VIN code Z. Manufactured by Chevrolet. Standard in El Camino.

ENGINE: (Gas). V-block. OHV. Six-cylinder. Cast iron block. Bore & stroke: 4.0 x 3.48 in. Displacement: 262 cid (4.3 liter). Compression ratio: 9.5:1. Brake horsepower: 155 at 4000 rpm. Taxable horsepower: 38.4. Torque: 230 lb.-ft at 2400 rpm. Hydraulic valve lifters. Induction system: TBI. VIN code N. Manufactured by Chevrolet. Standard in full-size pickups and Blazer and Suburbans and Vans.

ENGINE: (Gas). Inline. OHV. Six-cylinder. Cast iron block. Bore & stroke: 3.88 x 4.12 in. Displacement: 292 cid (4.8 liter). Brake horsepower: 115 at 4000 rpm. Taxable horsepower: 36.13. Torque: 210 lb.-ft. at 2800 rpm. Hydraulic valve lifters. Carburetor: Two-barrel. VIN code T. Manufactured by Chevrolet. Standard in Step-Vans and Crew Cab/Bonus Cab Pickups.

ENGINE: (Gas). V-block. OHV. Eight-cylinder. Cast iron block. Bore & stroke: 3.74 x 3.48 in. Displacement: 305 cid (5.0 liter). Compression ratio: 8.6:1. Brake horsepower: 155 at 4000 rpm. Taxable horsepower: 44.76. Torque: 245 lb.-ft. at 1600 rpm. Hydraulic valve lifters. Carburetor: Four-barrel. VIN code F. Manufactured by Chevrolet. Optional in full-size Pickups, Blazers, Suburban and El Camino. Also optional in light-duty vans with under 8500 lb. GVWs and El Camino.

ENGINE: (Gas). V-block. OHV. Eight-cylinder. Cast iron block. Bore & stroke: 3.74 x 3.48 in. Displacement: 305 cid (5.0 liter). Brake horsepower: 160 at 4400 rpm. Taxable horsepower: 44.76. Torque: 235 lb.-ft. at 2000 rpm. Hydraulic valve lifters. Carburetor: Four-barrel. VIN code H. Manufactured by Chevrolet. Optional in full-sized pickups, Blazer, Suburban and El Camino. Also optional in light-duty vans with under 8,500 lb. GVW.

ENGINE: (Gas). V-block. OHV. Eight-cylinder. Cast iron block. Bore & stroke: 4.0 x 3.48 in. Displacement: 350 cid (5.7 liter). Compression ratio: 8.3:1. Brake horsepower: 160 at 3800 rpm. Taxable horsepower: 51.2. Torque: 275 lb.-ft. at 2400 rpm. Hydraulic valve lifters. Carburetor: Four-barrel. VIN code A. This engine manufactured by various GM divisions. Optional in Pickups, full-size Blazer and Suburbans with heavy-duty emissions.

ENGINE: (Gas). V-block. OHV. Eight-cylinder. Cast iron block. Bore & stroke: 4.0 x 3.48 in. Displacement: 350 cid (5.7 liter). Compression ratio: 8.2:1. Brake horsepower: 165 at 3800 rpm. Taxable horsepower: 51.2. Torque: 275 lb.-ft. at 1600 rpm. Hydraulic valve lifters. Carburetor: Four-barrel. VIN code L. Manufactured by Chevrolet. Optional in full-size pickups and Blazers and Suburbans. Also optional in light-duty vans under 8,500 lb. GVW.

1986 Chevrolet 1/2-Ton K10 Custom Deluxe Step-Side Pickup (RCA)

ENGINE: (Gas). V-block. OHV. Eight-cylinder. Cast iron block. Bore & stroke: 4.0 x 3.48 in. Displacement: 350 cid (5.7 liter). Brake horsepower: 185 at 4000 rpm. Taxable horsepower: 51.2. Torque: 285 lb.-ft. at 2400 rpm. Hydraulic valve lifters. Carburetor: Four-barrel. VIN code M. Manufactured by Chevrolet. Optional in full-size pickups, Blazers and Suburbans.

ENGINE: (Diesel). V-block. OHV. Eight-cylinder. Cast iron block. Bore & stroke: 3.98 x 3.82 in. Displacement: 379 cid (6.2 liter). Brake horsepower: 130 at 3600 rpm. Taxable horsepower: 50.69. Torque: 240 lb.-ft. at 2000 rpm. Hydraulic valve lifters. Carburetor: Four-barrel. VIN code C. Manufactured by Chevrolet. Diesel option.

ENGINE: (Diesel). V-block. OHV. Eight-cylinder. Cast iron block. Bore & stroke: 3.98 x 3.82 in. Displacement: 379 cid (6.2 liter). Brake horsepower: 148 at 3600 rpm. Taxable horsepower: 50.69. Torque: 246 lb.-ft. at 2000 rpm. Hydraulic valve lifters. Carburetor: Four-barrel. VIN code J. Manufactured by Chevrolet. Diesel option.

ENGINE: (Gas). V-block. OHV. Eight-cylinder. Cast iron block. Bore & stroke: 4.25 x 4.0 in. Displacement: 454 cid (7.4 liter). Brake horsepower: 240 at 3800 rpm. Taxable horsepower: 57.8. Torque: 375 lb.-ft. at 3200 rpm. Hydraulic valve lifters. Carburetor: Four-barrel. VIN code W. Manufactured by Chevrolet. Available for motorhome chassis.

CHASSIS: [El Camino] Wheelbase: 117.1 in. Overall length: 201.6 in. Height: 53.8 in. Tires: P205/75R14.

CHASSIS: [S10 Pickup] Wheelbase: 108.3 in. 122.9 in. Overall length: 178.2 in./194.2 in. Height: 61.3 in. Tires: P195/75R14.

CHASSIS: [S10 Blazer] Wheelbase: 100.5 in. Overall length: 170.3 in. Height: 64.7 in. P195/75R15.

CHASSIS: [Astro Van] Wheelbase: 111 in. Overall length: 176.8 in. Height: 74.5 in. Tires: P195/75R15.

CHASSIS: [G10 Vans] Wheelbase: 110 in./125 in. Overall length: 178.2 in./202.2 in. Height: 79.4 in. Tires: [Chevy Van] P195/75R15, [Others] P205/75R15.

CHASSIS: [G20 Vans] Wheelbase: 110 in./125 in. Overall length: 178.2 in./202.2 in. Height: 79.4 in. Tires: [Chevy Van] P225/75R15, [Others] P235/75R15.

CHASSIS: [G30 Vans] Wheelbase: 125 in. Overall length: 202.2 in. Height: 79.4 in. Tires: [Chevy Van] 8.75R16.5C, [Others] 8.75R16.5D.

CHASSIS: [Hi-Cube Van] Wheelbase: 125 in./146 in. Tires: 8.75 x 16.5D.

CHASSIS: [K10 Blazer] Wheelbase: 106.5 in. Overall length: 184.8 in. Height: 73.8 in. Tires: P215/75R15.

CHASSIS: [C10] Wheelbase: 117.5 in./131.5 in. Overall length: 193.5 in./212.2 in. Height: 69.2 in. Tires: [Pickups] P195/74R15, [Suburban] P235/75R15.

CHASSIS: [C20/C30] Wheelbase: 131.5 in./164.5 in. Overall length: 212.2 in./246.4 in. Height: 72.2 in. Tires: [C20 Pickups] LT235/85R16C, [C20 Suburbans/Bonus/Crew] (Front) LT235/85R16D (Rear) LT235/85R16E. The C30 pickups also used the latter sizes.

CHASSIS: [Step-Vans] Wheelbase: 125/133/178 in. Tires: LT215/85R16C.

1986 Chevrolet Fleetside Indy 500 Pace Truck (IMSC/JLM)

TECHNICAL: Same as 1985, except the El Camino now offers both the three-speed and four-speed (with overdrive) automatic transmissions with both the 4.3-liter V-6 and optional 5.0-liter V-8. The 4.3-liter engine and four-speed automatic with overdrive was standard. Also, the five-speed manual transmission (made available in May 1985) was now standard in Astro passenger vans.

S10 OPTIONS: Gauge package, S10 ($55-$113). Tinted glass, S10 ($135-$190). Exterior mirrors, S10 ($50-$83). Speed control, S10 ($195).

ASTRO OPTIONS: Four-speed automatic transmission ($520). Four-passenger seating CL ($552), Others ($634). Seven-passenger seating, CL ($1195), Others ($1277). Eight-passenger seating, CL ($643), Others ($593). Seat back recliner and dual arm rests ($230). Custom high-back buckets, 8-passenger ($150), 5-passenger ($100). Front air conditioning, base ($740), CL/CS ($697). Front and rear air conditioning, CL/CS ($1249). Deluxe front/rear bumpers, base and CS ($122), CL ($72). Color-keyed bumpers, base and CS ($50). Increased cargo capacity, regular 4/5 passenger seats ($314). Heavy-duty radiator ($53), with transmission cooler ($112), with transmission cooler and air conditioning ($171). Remote fuel filler release ($25). Rubber floor covering, base ($43). Gauge package, base and CS ($58). 100 amp. alternator ($30). Tinted glass, complete ($98), standard ($71). Deluxe grille, base and CS ($25). Halogen headlamps ($22). Engine block heater ($31). Rear heater, ($256). Deluxe heater ($43). Special two-tone ($237). Sport two-tone ($162). California emissions ($99).

Optional axle ratio ($36). Locking differential ($238). Heavy-duty battery ($53). Spare tire carrier, base ($21). Engine oil cooler ($120). Roof console ($79). Power door locks ($198). Carpeting in CS ($111). Rear heater ($256). Complete body glass ($121). Tinted windshield ($38). Swing-out door glass ($55). Trailer wiring harness ($39). Dome and reading lamps ($31). Auxiliary lighting, base ($142), CS ($121). Dual deluxe mirrors ($50). Black body side moldings, base and CS ($55). Power windows and door locks ($388). Door edge guards ($17). Right-hand visor mirror, base ($48), CL/SC ($41). Protective interior panels ($25). AM radio ($112). AM/FM stereo, base ($243), CL/CS ($283). AM/FM stereo with electronic tuning, base ($424), CL/CS ($464). Above with quadraphonic, base ($574), CL/CS ($614). Heavy-duty front/rear shocks ($34). Cruise control ($195). Front stabilizer bar ($38). Power steering ($276). Tilt steering column ($115). Custom steering wheel, base and CS ($26). Power windows ($190). Positive stop rear door, base ($35). Left-hand front seat storage compartment ($35). Left- and right-hand front seat storage compartments ($70). Body striping ($75). 27-gal. fuel tank ($66). Cargo tie-downs ($30). Dead weight trailer hitch ($64). Heavy-duty trailering package, with front and rear air conditioning ($471), without front and rear air conditioning ($524). Light-duty trailering package ($103). Wheel trim rings, base and CS ($56). Rally wheels, base and CS ($88), CL ($48). Cast aluminum wheels, base and CS ($299), CL ($259). Intermittent wipers ($55). Tahoe/Sierra classic equipment, S10 ($595). Sport Gypsy equipment, S10 ($972). Seat trim, S10 ($24). High-Country bucket seats, S10 ($295). Custom two-tone paint, S10 ($200). Special two-tone paint, S10 ($311). Sport two-tone paint, S10 ($227). Air conditioning, S10 ($705). Console, S10 ($108).

1986 Chevrolet 1/2-Ton C10 Fleetside Pickup (OCW)

C/K OPTIONS: Rear step bumper, Fleetside ($189). Chromed front bumper guards ($41). Exterior mirrors ($50-$94). Body side molding package ($115-$173). Rally wheels for C10/K10/K5 Blazer ($115). Styled wheels for C10/K10/K5 Blazer ($174). Cast aluminum wheels for C10/K10/K5 Blazer ($299). Radio: AM/AM/FM/AM/FM, clock, AM/FM stereo and stereo cassette, AM stereo/FM stereo, seek-and-scan ($112-$594). Scottsdale/High-Sierra C-K Series ($250). Silverado/Sierra Classic C-K Series ($671). Conventional two-tone C-K Series ($72). Special two-tone C-K Series ($327). Deluxe two-tone C-K Series/Fleetside ($184-$370). Custom two-tone C-K Series/Fleetside ($531). Special Big Dooley two-tone Fleetside, dual wheels ($426-$444). Deluxe front appearance package C-K Series ($109). All-weather air conditioning C-K Series ($678-740). Chromed rear bumper C-K Series ($103)

BLAZER OPTIONS: Silverado/Sierra classic package K Blazer ($1015). Special two-tone paint K Blazer ($170-$327). Exterior decor package K Blazer ($314-$471). Deluxe front appearance K Blazer ($109). Deluxe chromed bumpers K5 Blazer ($49). Body side moldings K5 Blazer ($115-$173). Scottsdale/High-Sierra package for Suburban ($311-$459). Silverado/Sierra Classic ($1,111-$1,259).

EL CAMINO OPTIONS: Conquista package ($195). Air conditioning ($750). Gauge package ($115). Sport mirrors ($61). Rally wheel rims ($56). Wire wheelcovers ($199).

HISTORICAL: Introduced fall 1985. Sales: [November, 1985-November, 1986). [Chevy Van] 139,338, [Sportvan] 19,455, [Astro] 95,701, [S10] 195,620, [S10 Blazer] 170,742, [El Camino] 19,231, [Blazer] 41,866, [Suburban] 53,842, [Pickups] 438,422, [Total Chevrolet] 1,174,217. Innovations: Electronic fuel-injection used for 2.8-liter gas V-6 for nine percent horsepower boost. New high-tech instrument cluster for many models. Vortec Six has increased horsepower. Diesel V-8 gets durable steel crankshaft, modular iron crankshaft, cast-aluminum pistons and glow-plug system for fast cold-engine starts. Five-speed manual transmission standardized for Astro. New sliding 90-degree door check system made no-cost option on vans. The Chevrolet Astro Van was included in a special "Century of the Automobile" display at the 1986 Iola Old Car Show. Chevrolet kicked off a year long celebration of its 75th year as an automaker in 1986. Of course, the 75th anniversary of Chevrolet trucks is 1993.

1987 CHEVROLET

1/2-TON — S (4x2)/T (4x4) SERIES PICKUP — L/4/V-6: The 1987 S/T10's standard 2.5-liter Tech IV four-cylinder engine featured new high flow ports in the cylinder head and a redesigned intake manifold. Chevrolet's 2.8-liter EFI V-6 was optional. A single-belted accessory "serpentine" drive replaced the conventional multiple V-belts on both the 2.5- and 2.8-liter engines. The automatic belt tensioning feature in this system eliminated the need for belt adjustment and provided an expected belt life of 100,000 miles. A new 85-ampere Delcotron generator was standard, replacing the 78-ampere unit used in 1986. The new unit was lighter and provided improved performance and durability. A new Delco battery increased cold cranking amps from 405 to 525. An optional heavy-duty Delco battery featured cold cranking amps from 540 to 630. The tailgate appliqué for the Tahoe and Sport models was restyled. The Cinnamon Red color of 1986 was not offered for 1987. A new color added to the remaining exterior colors carried over from 1986 was Emerald Metallic. The interior color selection was unchanged from 1986. Standard equipment included padded arm rests on both doors, an instrument panel ash tray, a passenger side coat hook, color-keyed molded plastic door trim panels, a black rubber floor mat, a grab handle over the passenger door on T10s, a color-keyed headliner, an outside air type heater and defogger, an inside-operated hood release, gauges including a speedometer/odometer and fuel level indicator, warning lights for generator, oil pressure and engine temperature, warning lights for parking brake, direction-hazard signal and high beam headlights, insulation and sound deadening material, instrument cluster and cab interior dome light except EL models, a 10-inch prismatic rear view mirror, AM radio except EL models, full-width foam vinyl bench seat with folding back rest, 15-1/4-inch soft black plastic two-spoke steering wheel with energy-absorbing steering column, locking glove box, dual padded and color-keyed sun shades, a jack and wheel lug wrench, a black front bumper with parking lights, an Argent Silver molded plastic grille, tinted glass in all Maxi-Cab windows, single high-note electric horn, bright metal hubcaps with black trim, taillamps with integral back-up lamps, rectangular halogen headlamps except EL, dual black aero mirrors, double-wall welded pickup box with steel floor, winch-type under-frame spare tire carrier, Argent-painted wheels, and two-speed electric windshield wiper/washers. S/T10s were available in solid colors or three two-tone schemes. Custom two-tones included belt line striping with a second color below the stripe. Sport two-tones included a four-stripe wide decal or optional body side moldings at the lower crease line with the second color below around the lower body perimeter. Special two-tones featured one color above the belt line and on the lower body perimeter, with the second color between the belt line and lower crease line. Available colors were Steel Gray Metallic, Frost White, Midnight Black, Light Blue Metallic, Galaxy Blue Metallic, Doeskin Tan, Indian Bronze Metallic, Nevada Gold Metallic, Apple Red, Emerald Metallic, and Silver Metallic secondary color only. The EL (economy level) model was Chevrolet's "price leader" and came with the standard vinyl seats in blue, carmine, charcoal or saddle tan. Also available for standard models were a custom cloth bench seat interior or custom vinyl high-back bucket seats. The Durango trim level offered custom cloth bench seats and custom vinyl high-back bucket seats in regular-cab models or special custom cloth high-back bucket seats in Maxi-Cabs only. All Durango trims came in the same four colors. The Tahoe trim level was offered on the custom vinyl bench, custom cloth bench, custom vinyl high-back bucket and special custom cloth high-back bucket seats in the same four colors. A rarer Tahoe option for Maxi-Cabs was high-back reclining bucket seats in charcoal or saddle tan cloth or leather. A Sport interior was also offered in two versions in the charcoal or saddle tan colors. The first was Sport cloth on high-back bucket seats and the second (for Maxi-Cabs only) was cloth or leather trim on reclining high-back bucket seats.

1987 Chevrolet 1/2-Ton El Camino Conquista Coupe-Pickup (CMD)

1/2-TON — EL CAMINO — V-6/V-8: The El Camino combined the utility of a pickup truck with the beauty of a Sport Coupe passenger car. Apparently, this was a combination that was no longer in great demand, as this was the last full year for El Camino production. A few hundred were built in the first four months of 1988, before the model was dropped. Chevrolet's separate sales catalog for the 1987 El Camino said, "The end product makes a uniquely bold, personal statement." The El Camino's trim lines and sleek good looks were available in three ways. The standard El Camino was elegantly understated with solid color paint, a bright grille, and bright appearance items throughout. The optional El Camino Conquista model featured two-tone paint marked by bright moldings. The no-holds-barred SS Sport Decor model incorporated a front air dam, dual aerodynamic mirrors, a lower body accent color emphasized by a pin striping decal, Rally wheel rims, and blacked-out trim. Standard interior features included a full-width cloth bench seat with pull-down center arm rest, cut-pile carpeting, a cleanly designed instrument panel and gauges, a storage space hidden behind the driver's seat, door pull straps, a color-keyed cloth-over-foam headliner, a lighted ash tray, a lighted glove box, and vinyl door trim panels. Options included bucket seats or a 55/45 split bench seat in cloth or custom cloth fabric, a front console, air conditioning, power windows, tinted glass, and a full complement of audio equipment Also standard were left- and right-hand air vents and padded arm rests, a lighted instrument panel ash tray, color-keyed carpeting, an outside air type heater and defroster, gauges (speedometer/odometer/fuel) and switches (lights/directionals/ignition) and warning lights (generator, oil pressure, temperature/seat belts/parking brake/directionals/hazard lamps/high-beams), sound deadening insulation (on firewall and under floor, lights for instrument panel and dome and glove box), 10-inch prismatic rear view mirror, safety belts, behind-passenger-seat spare tire, color-keyed plastic steering wheel with energy-absorbing column, glove box with light and key, left- and right-hand sun shades, air-adjustable rear shocks, chromed front and rear bumpers, plastic grille with bright trim, dual-note electric horn, back lights, tail/stop lights, front and rear parking lights, side marker lights, dual rectangular headlights, left-hand black rear view mirror with styled head, mechanical jack and wheel wrench, painted wheels with bright full wheelcovers, and two-speed electric windshield wipers and washers. Interiors were offered in blue, gray, light green, maroon, and saddle. Options included cloth bench, cloth bucket, cloth 55/45 bench, vinyl bench, and custom cloth 55/45 bench seats. Exterior colors available were Black, Medium Gray Metallic, Light Blue Metallic, Dark Blue Metallic, Light Brown Metallic, Medium Brown Metallic, Light Green Metallic, Maroon Metallic, Dark Maroon Metallic, Silver Metallic, White, and Yellow Beige. The Conquista and SS Sport Decor models offered a limited number of two-tone exterior color choices. The standard engine was the 4.3-liter V-6. A 5.0-liter V-8 was optional. Shown on the back of the 1987 El Camino sales catalog was the optional El Camino SS in white with a decorative hood treatment, aero style front fascia, non-functional side pipes, and box side rails that were provided by an independent supplier that marketed this package through authorized Chevrolet dealers. (Choo-Choo Customs of Tennessee supplied such packages.)

1987 Chevrolet 1/2-Ton S10 Blazer 4x4 Sport Utility Vehicle (CMD)

1/2-TON — S (4x2)/T (4x4) SERIES BLAZER — L4/V-6: The 1987 S-Series Blazer was the most popular vehicle of its kind in the United States. It was officially called a Blazer SUV (Sport Utility Vehicle). It took the form of a two-door station wagon. It was built on a rugged ladder type frame with double-wall construction in the windshield pillars, cowl, hood, front fenders, tailgate, and rear side panels. Two-wheel-drive, and four-wheel-drive models were offered. At the heart of the S-Series Blazer 4x4 was an Insta-Trac four-wheel-drive system that allowed shifting from 2WD to 4WD high and back again on the run, with no hubs to lock or multiple levers to shift. The 4x4 model featured independent front suspension, a 4x4 front axle immersed in oil to reduce friction and wear, generous 7.1-inch ground clearance, self-adjusting front disc/rear drum power brakes, and P195/75R-15 all-season steel-belted radial tires. The standard 2.5-liter EFI Tech IV four-cylinder engine had a redesigned intake manifold, and high flow ports in the cylinder head. A single belt accessory "serpentine" drive replaced the conventional multiple V belts on both the 2.5-liter four and the optional 2.8-liter EFI V-6. This system featured automatic belt tensioning that eliminated the need for adjustments throughout the life of the truck. The expected belt life was 100,000 miles. Both the standard Delcotron generator and all batteries had higher capacities for 1987. Standard equipment included front and rear chromed bumpers with black rub strips, a rear hinged tailgate with cable stops on the tailgate (the tailgate trim on Tahoe and Sport models was redesigned), a rear lift glass with gas cylinders and a key-operated latch handle, all tinted windows, a single electric high-note horn, bright metal hubcaps (with black trim black plastic hubcaps on 4x4 model), taillamps with integral back-up lamps, rectangular headlamps, front and rear parking lamps and side marker lamps, directional signals, hazard lamps, black-painted left-hand and right-hand rear view mirrors, Argent-paint wheels, two-speed electric windshield washers/wipers, left- and right-hand padded arm rests, an instrument panel ash tray, right-hand coat hooks, door-operated front and rear dome lamps, color-keyed molded plastic door trim panels, a grab handle over right-hand door on passenger side, full-coverage color-keyed headliner, outside-air type heater and defogger, inside-operated hood lock release, speedometer with odometer and fuel gauge, gauges (speedometer/odometer/fuel) and switches (lights/directionals/ignition), and warning lights (generator, oil pressure, temperature/seat belts/parking brake/directionals/hazard lamps/high-beams), instrument cluster light, dome lamps, glove box lamp, 10-inch prismatic rear view mirror, foam-padded driver and passenger seats high-back buckets (with custom vinyl trim), spare tire carrier on left-hand side behind wheel housing, 15-1/4-inch soft black plastic two-spoke steering wheel on energy-absorbing column, stowage glove box on right-hand side of instrument panel, padded and color-keyed dual sun shades, a mechanical jack, a wheel lug wrench, and a four-speed manual transmission. A road-smoothing fully-independent front suspension was standard.. Standard S-Series Blazers came with high-back front bucket seats with custom vinyl trim, a color-keyed rubber floor mat for the entire floor area, a headlamp-on warning buzzer, extensive insulation and sound deadening, courtesy dome lamp and glove box light, deluxe steering wheel, side window defoggers, and color-eyed door panels with map pockets. Tahoe trim added a choice of custom vinyl or custom cloth seat trim, optional leather or sheepskin seat trim, color-keyed full carpeting with or without color-keyed rubber floor mats, a gauge package, zippered rear storage pockets with optional rear seat, a color-keyed spare tire cover, special custom cloth door trim panels with a carpeted lower panel and coin holder in driver's door, color-keyed kick panels and rear compartment trim panels, a right-hand visor mirror, body side moldings, bright wheel opening moldings, wheel trim rings, a hood insulator pad, and specific Tahoe tailgate trim. The top-of-the-line Sport option added a color-keyed center console with locking compartment, reclining deluxe custom cloth bucket seats (leather or High-Country sheepskin seats optional), a color-keyed sport steering wheel, black plastic wheel opening moldings, styled steel wheels on 4x2 only, and two-tone paint with color-keyed bumpers. A new option for the 4x4 S-Series Blazer was the High-Country package featuring the Midnight Black over Nevada Gold custom two-toning, graduated-color gold body side decals, special gold-tone aluminum wheels, gold color key bumpers with rub strips, gold fender nameplates, a black grille, black exterior mirrors, black body side moldings, black wheel opening moldings, deep-tinted glass, black low-profile side mirrors, and a center storage console. The High-Country package also required the buyer to purchase Tahoe interior trim in saddle tan, custom two-tone paint, and white-lettered tires. The Tahoe trim was available in custom cloth or with optional genuine leather in the seating surfaces. S-Series Blazers were available in solid colors or three two-tone schemes. Custom two-tones included decal striping with a second color below the belt line. Sport two-tones included a four-stripe wide decal below the lower crease line with the second color below around the lower body perimeter. Special two-tones featured one color above the belt line and on the lower body perimeter, with the second color between the belt line and lower crease line. Available colors were Steel Gray Metallic, Frost White, Midnight Black, Light Blue Metallic, Galaxy Blue Metallic, Doeskin Tan, Indian Bronze Metallic, Nevada Gold Metallic, Apple Red, Emerald Metallic, and Silver Metallic secondary color only. The interior color selections were unchanged from 1986.

S-10 BLAZER PAINT OPTIONS

CUSTOM TWO-TONE includes decal striping with Color Code 2 applied below the beltline.

SPORT TWO-TONE includes a four-stripe decal below the crease line, with Color Code 2 applied below the decal.

SPECIAL TWO-TONE includes Color Code 2 on areas between the molding and the crease line.

1987 Chevrolet 1/2-Ton S10 Blazer 4x4 SUV Two-Tone (CMD)

1987 Chevrolet 1/2-Ton Astro Wagon Passenger Van (CMD)

1/2-TON — ASTRO VAN SERIES M (RWD) SERIES — L4/V-6: The Astro was Chevrolet's rear-wheel-drive minivan. All 1987 Astros featured compact dimensions, seven-step base coat/clear coat paint, flush windows and door handles, hidden drip gutters, front doors that tilted out at the tops (when open) for ease of access, low step-up heights (16.74 in. for Cargo Van models and 16.33 in. for Passenger Van models), a smooth sliding side door, rear panel doors that opened wide while allowing long loads to be carried on the roof, a rear bumper for easy step-in loading, a variety of optional window configurations, and a 6,000-pound towing capacity. The Cargo Van featured a standard Tech IV 2.5-liter EFI four-cylinder engine, four-speed manual transmission, a standard 1,000-pound payload, and 189.9 cubic feet of cargo space with a single driver's seat. The Astro Passenger Van featured a standard Tech IV 4.3-liter EFI Vortec V-6, a five-speed manual overdrive transmission, and five-passenger seating. A vinyl-covered low-back driver's bucket seat was standard in Astro Cargo Vans. Options included twin vinyl high-back buckets, twin custom vinyl high-back buckets, and twin custom cloth high-back buckets. Also standard were black rubber floor mats, a high-tech instrument panel, a glove box, a fold-down beverage tray, molded storage pockets in both front doors, and a choice of four interior colors: teal blue, saddle tan, burgundy or slate gray. The standard Astro Passenger Van model featured two vinyl high-back buckets and one matching middle bench seat, a black rubber floor mat, molded door panels, and front and middle dome lamps. The CS interior added color-keyed floor mats, color-keyed moldings, color-keyed trim panels and side pockets, a color-keyed headliner, a molded storage compartment in the left rear, a remote fuel filler door release, a molded jack and tool area in the right rear, and an under-body spare tire carrier. The CL interior also had color-keyed sill-to-sill carpeting, carpeted kick panels, an upgraded instrument panel with gauge package, a custom steering wheel, and a choice of custom vinyl or custom cloth upholstery. The CS and CL interiors came in the same in blue or saddle regular vinyl or all four colors with custom cloth or custom vinyl upholstery. Also available was a special Astro Luxury Touring (LT) model with standard five-passenger seating covered in lush velour fabric, reclining high-back bucket front seats with full-width headrests, a contoured split-back middle seat with convenience tray and cup pockets, an optional matching split-back rear seat, swing-out rear window glass, a luxury Sport steering wheel, and blue or saddle tan interior color options. The LT's middle seat had a right-side portion that folded forward for access to the rear of the vehicle and both rearward seats snapped out for extra room. This model came in special Sapphire Blue Metallic or Dark Saddle Metallic colors. Optional two-tone color schemes matched California Gold Metallic with Dark Saddle Metallic or Iced Blue Metallic with Sapphire Blue Metallic. The LT also had a unique color stripe at its belt line, color-coordinated Rally wheels (similarly finished aluminum wheels optional), and specific LT nameplates. Additional standard equipment included a left-hand arm rest in all models (dual arm rest in Passenger Vans), an ash tray on the engine cover console, left-hand side coat hooks, a fuel gauge, a speedometer with odometer, switches (main, directionals, headlamps, wiper/washers, hazard lights, heater fan, and ignition), warning lights (generator, oil pressure, temperature, service brake, directionals, hazard lamps, and high beams), insulation and sound deadening materials, instrument cluster and dome lights, safety belts, a 15-1/4-inch black vinyl steering wheel mounted on energy-absorbing column, left-hand sun shade (dual sun shades in Passenger Van), front and rear bumpers painted lower body color, driver and passenger front side doors, right-hand side sliding cargo door, double rear panel doors, a single high-note electric horn, bright metal hubcaps with black trim, taillamps with integral back-up lamps, rectangular headlamps, front and rear side marker lamps, black-painted right- and left-hand adjustable mirrors, a scissors type jack, a wheel wrench, two wheel blocks, two-speed electric windshield wipers and washers, four P195/75R-15 all-season radial tires and one T145/80D-15 compact spare tire. All Astros came standard in solid colors. Also available was special two-toning with the upper half of the minivan in one color and the lower half in a second color. Sport two-toning featured a second color on the lower body perimeter and around the wheel flares only. The standard Cargo Van had only side door windows. The standard Passenger Van had one additional window on each side (just behind the door window), plus windows in both rear panel doors. This configuration was optional on Cargo Vans. A full window treatment, with three windows on each side, was optional for both models. Colors offered in 1987 were Sterling Silver Metallic, Gray Metallic, Burnt Red Metallic, Deep Red Metallic, California Gold Metallic, Dark Brown Metallic, Tan, Summit White, Midnight Blue Metallic, and Iced Blue Metallic.

1987 Chevrolet 1-Ton G30 Beauville Sportvan Passenger Van (CMD)

1/2-TON, 3/4-TON, 1-TON VAN — G SERIES 10:20:30 (RWD) — V-6/V-8: Chevrolet continued to offer full-size vans in two versions. The Chevy Van was designed for those needing a hardworking business partner. The Sportvan was a passenger model with seating for up to 12 fun-loving people. Every van came standard with rear-wheel-drive, a 4.3-liter EFI Vortec V-6 (or a wide selection of optional V-8s), rugged unitized construction, independent girder beam front suspension, a choice of sliding right-hand rear side door or 60/40 swing-out doors, extensive anti-corrosion treatments including two-sided galvanized steel panels and aluminized wax coatings, and two-stage rear leaf springs. Chevy Van buyers could pick from 110-inch or 125-inch wheelbase models in G10, G20 and G30 classes with GVWRs from 4,900 to 8,600 pounds. Without rear seats, the 125-inch wheelbase model had a load floor long enough to fit a 14-foot-long ladder. A low-back driver's bucket seat with vinyl trim was base equipment in the entry-level cargo van. Optional high-back bucket seats and passenger seats were available for Chevy Vans. Sportvans also came in G10, G20 and G30 lines. Five-passenger seating was standard. The G20 and G30 offered an eight-passenger seating option. The G30 offered the 12-passenger option. Windows all around were standard in Sportvans, as were power steering, power brakes, and all-season steel-belted radial tires. A complete selection of luxury and convenience options could convert a Sportvan into an upscale family wagon. All Sportvan seats had quick release mechanisms to convert the truck to a cargo hauler. The standard interior came with all-vinyl trim in blue or saddle tan, rear seat arm rests with ash trays, side and rear windows, a swing-down instrument panel stowage box, black rubber floor mats, bright instrument panel trim, a padded steering wheel, and a convenient column-mounted multi-function switch for fingertip operation of turn signals, headlamp beams, and windshield wipers. The Bonaventure interior added custom vinyl seat trim in blue, burgundy, saddle tan or slate gray and specific Bonaventure trim. The top-of-the-line Beauville model represented the Sportvan at its finest. It offered a choice of custom vinyl or custom cloth seat trim, a choice of five interior colors (blue, burgundy, mahogany, saddle tan or slate gray), door-to-door carpeting, custom instrument panel trim items, optional reclining front bucket seats with arm rests, and specific Beauville exterior identification. Standard equipment for Chevy Vans and Sportvans included silver-painted front and rear bumpers, right- and left-hand front side doors, rear load doors, right-hand sliding side load door (or 60/40 hinged side load doors),

windshield and front side glass all, side load door glass and rear door glass, plus left-hand front quarter flip-out glass and left and right fixed quarter glass in Sportvans, molded plastic grille with Argent paint finish, single high-note electric horn in Chevy Vans (dual high/low-note in Sportvan), bright metal hubcaps with black trim, taillamps with integral back-up lamps, two rectangular headlamps, front and rear directional lamps, front and rear side marker lamps, chrome right- and left-hand outside mirrors, two rectangular headlamps, electric two-speed wiper/washers, left-hand padded arm rest (also right-hand in Sportvan), instrument panel ash tray in all models, center seat arm rest ash tray in Sportvans, left-hand coat hooks, painted metal door trim panels with decorative embossments (front and rear side doors), embossed black rubber floor (covering front area only in Chevy Vans), outside air type heater and defroster, inside hood release, speedometer with odometer, fuel gauge, switches and warning lights (as on other trucks), insulation and sound deadening materials, instrument panel lighting, front and rear dome lamps, 10-inch prismatic rear view mirror, safety belts, black plastic two-spoke steering wheel, energy-absorbing steering column, glove box with latched door, and color-keyed right- and left-hand sun visors. A three-speed manual transmission was standard. A three-speed automatic transmission was standard in G30s and optional in other models. A four-speed automatic overdrive transmission was standard in G20 diesels and optional in other vans. Three two-tone paint options were available. The exterior decor package version included moldings and decal striping at the belt line with a second color applied below the moldings and around all windows. Special two-toning included body side and rear moldings with the second color applied below them. Deluxe two-toning included moldings with the second color applied between the belt line and the moldings. Colors were Galaxy Blue Metallic, Light Blue Metallic, Indian Bronze Metallic, Steel Gray Metallic, Burgundy Metallic, Champagne Metallic, Nevada Gold Metallic, Doeskin Tan, Apple Red and Frost White. Besides interior colors already mentioned, standard vans could be had with custom high-back bucket seats done in black vinyl.

CHEVY VAN/SPORTVAN PAINT TREATMENTS
Solid color is standard on all models.

EXTERIOR DECOR PACKAGE (Optional, NA Chevy Van) includes moldings and decal striping at the beltline with Color Code 2 below the moldings and around windows.

SPECIAL TWO-TONE (Optional) includes body side and rear moldings with Color Code 2 applied below.

DELUXE TWO-TONE (Optional) includes moldings with Color Code 2 applied between the beltline and moldings.

1987 Chevrolet 3/4-Ton G20 Sportvan with Two-Tone and Exterior Decor package (CMD)

3/4-TON/1-TON — P20/P30 STEP-VAN — V-8: Also available in 1988 were two series of Step-Vans. They had boxy bodies well-suited for stop-and-go delivery service. The base body offered, in both the P20 3/4-ton and P30 1-ton lines had a 10-1/2-foot length. Step-Vans offered wheelbases ranging from 125 to 178 in.. A 350-cubic-inch V-8 was the standard engine. A 6.2-liter diesel V-8 was optional. Standard size tires were LT215/85R16Cs.

1987 Chevrolet 1/2-Ton S10 Blazer 4x4 SUV High-Country (CMD)

1/2-TON — V10 BLAZER (4x4) — V-8: The full-size Blazer combined the front end sheet metal of full-size Chevrolet pickups with a two-door station wagon body on a short wheelbase chassis. Four-wheel-drive running gear, a 5.0-liter EFI V-8, a four-speed manual transmission, and P215/75R-15 all-season steel-belted radial tires were standard. Also standard were chrome front and rear bumpers, tinted glass, an Argent-painted molded plastic grille, a single low-note electric horn, bright metal hubcaps with black trim, taillamps with integral back-up lamps, two rectangular headlamps, front and rear direction and parking lamps, chromed right- and left hand outside rear view mirrors, a removable molded plastic top reinforced with fiberglass, a double-wall tailgate with reel-type cables (including a drop glass and lock), a jack and wheel wrench, two-speed electric windshield washers and wipers, right- and left-hand padded arm rests, an instrument panel ash tray, two left-hand coat hooks, two door-operated dome lamps, black rubber floor covering mats, outside air type heater and defogger, inside-operated hood release, speedometer with odometer, fuel gauge, switches and warning lights, insulation and sound-deadening materials, instrument cluster and cab interior and dome lights, a 10-inch prismatic rear view mirror, foam-padded high-back driver and passenger seats with vinyl trim, seat belts, a 16-inch soft black plastic two-spoke steering wheel, an energy-absorbing steering column, a lockable instrument panel stowage box and dual padded sun shades. Custom Deluxe trim was standard and included all-vinyl upholstery (blue or saddle tan), an embossed black rubber floor mat, and all-tinted glass. The top-level Silverado package added custom vinyl or cloth upholstery in the same colors plus burgundy or slate gray, color-keyed carpeting throughout vehicle (when extra rear seat is added), a custom steering wheel, brushed pewter-toned door and instrument panel trim, a center console with storage and beverage pockets, full instrumentation with pewter-toned brushed finish on instrument panel, a right-hand visor mirror, a spare tire cover, and specific Silverado exterior trim with deluxe body side moldings, bright marker lamp bezels, a bright grille trim, bright headlamps, and nameplates. Colors for 1987 full-size Blazers were Frost White, Steel Gray Metallic, Midnight Black, Light Blue Metallic, Midnight Blue, Doeskin Tan, Indian Bronze Metallic, and Apple Red. Paint treatments included a solid body (with color-keyed matching) removable top in six colors. Black or white tops were standard with body colors of Apple Red or Light Blue Metallic. The black and white tops could also be ordered with all other body colors, in place of a color-keyed top. Optional special two-toning featured black vinyl body side and rear moldings with a second color around the lower body perimeter below the moldings. Also available was an exterior decor package with moldings, rear decal striping, and a second paint color around the center of the body, between the moldings and the decal striping.

1/2-TON, 3/4-TON — R (4x2)/ V (4x4) SUBURBAN — V-8: Chevrolet said that the 1987 Suburban was "America's Superwagon." Four variations were offered. The 10 Series 1/2-ton came with or without four-wheel-drive. The 20 Series 3/4-ton also came with or without four-wheel-drive. Standard equipment included front and rear chromed bumpers, two right- and left-hand side doors, two panel type rear doors, tinted glass in all windows, an Argent-painted molded plastic grille, a single low-note electric horn, bright metal hubcaps with black trim, taillamps with integral back-up lamps, two rectangular headlamps, directionals, side markers, right- and left-hand chromed outside rear view mirrors, a jack and wheel wrench, white-painted wheels, two-speed electric windshield washers and wipers, right- and left-hand padded arm rests, an instrument panel ash tray, rear door trim panel ash trays, right-and left-hand coat hooks, black rubber floor covering, outside air type heater and defogger, inside-operated hood release, speedometer with odometer, fuel gauge, switches and warning lights, insulation and sound-deadening materials, instrument cluster and cab interior lights, a 10-inch prismatic rear view mirror, full-depth foam front bench seat with vinyl trim, safety belts, a 16-inch soft black plastic two-spoke steering wheel, an energy-absorbing steering column, a lockable instrument panel stowage box, dual padded sun shades, color-keyed molded plastic trim panels on side doors, V-8 engine 5.0-liter in R10/5.7-liter in V10, R20 and V20, four-speed automatic overdrive transmission (R10/V10) or four-speed manual transmission (R20/V20), and P235/75R-15 tires LT235/85R-126 on 4x4 "V" models. Custom Deluxe trim was standard and included embossed all-vinyl upholstery (blue or saddle tan), an embossed black rubber floor mat, all-tinted glass, and Quiet-Ride insulation. The mid-level Scottsdale package added a color-keyed rubber floor mat, color-keyed insulated headliner, front and rear dome lamps, added sound insulation, exterior body side and rear moldings, and special Scottsdale identification. The top-level Silverado package added custom vinyl or cloth upholstery in the same colors plus burgundy or slate gray, door-to-door carpeting, luxury door panels with cloth inserts and pull straps, full instrumentation, a right-hand visor mirror, and specific Silverado exterior trim with body side moldings, a bright grille with color-keyed center bar, and quad headlamps. The latest versions of the Suburbans were fitted with a new seat belt system providing reduced belt effort on both front seat positions. This arrangement also incorporated a dual-mode operation to secure a child safety seat. Under full extension, the belt had an automatic lock feature that overrode the inertia locking mechanism and provided positive child seat retention. Suburban models with either the RPO C69 rear air conditioning or the combination of RPO C36 auxiliary heater and RPO C49 rear defogger had a 78-ampere alternator with the diesel engine or a 105-ampere unit with gasoline engines. Also new for 1987 was the use of a 94-ampere alternator on Suburbans equipped with the combination of RPO C60 air conditioner, RPO C36 auxiliary heater, or RPO C40 rear defogger. The exterior and interior color selections were Frost White, Steel Gray Metallic, Midnight Black, Light Blue Metallic, Midnight Blue, Canyon Copper Metallic, Doeskin Tan, Nevada Gold Metallic, Indian Bronze Metallic, and Apple Red.

1/2-TON, 3/4-TON, 1-TON — R (4x2)/V (4x4) PICKUP — V-6/V-8: Chevrolet's *1987 Full-Size Pickup* sales catalog redesignated the "C/K" style pickups (the ones with stacked, square headlamps) R/V10, R/V20 and R/V30 models. Then, in the spring of 1987, a Chevrolet full-size pickup based on the GMT400 platform was introduced as an all-new "1988" model. The new-design trucks had small headlamps with a horizontal-rectangular shape placed side-by-side above larger horizontal-rectangular parking lamps. These trucks also used the new R/V designations. They were offered in smaller weight classes. Trucks in larger weight classes (as well as Suburbans and full-size Blazers) retained the "C/K" look. To confuse matters, some of both types of trucks were included in Chevrolet's 1987 model-year production totals. The trucks described in this section are the ones depicted in *Chevrolet's 1987 Full Size Pickup* sales catalog. (However, separate production total break-outs are given for both types of trucks.) Even though the "1987" trucks looked like 1986 models, some improvements were made. All V-6 and V-8 engines had engines equipped with throttle body electronic fuel injection. This system replaced the carburetor and allowed for higher compression ratios and greater horsepower. As the engine section indicates both the 305- and 350-cid V-8 engines were significantly more powerful for 1987. Computer controls were incorporated into the spark advance fuel to air ratio, idle speed and fuel cut-off, enhancing driveability and performance. For 1987, the engine-mounted mechanical fuel pump was replaced by an electric unit mounted in the fuel tank. This pump, along with a fuel pressure regulator, provided instant and constant fuel pressure for more precise fuel control during engine starting and driving. No longer offered was the 292-cid six-cylinder engine. The 262-cid Vortex V-6 was now the standard base engine. For 1987 it was equipped with lower friction roller hydraulic valve lifters. These increased engine efficiency while proving a three percent fuel economy increase. Chevrolet offered new lower-weight Delco batteries with higher cold cranking current for all gasoline engine applications. Cold cranking amperes were increased from 500 to 525 on the 4.3-liter V-6, and from 405 to 525 on 5.0-liter V-8s with automatic transmission and all 5.7-liter applications. They also climbed from 540 to 630 amperes on the 7.4-liter gasoline engine. The 6.2-liter diesel for 1987 continued to use two batteries, each with 540 cold cranking amperes. The RPO UA1 heavy-duty battery option for the 5.0- and 5.7-liter V-8 engines was revised to include an increased performance cranking motor for 1987. Alternator changes for 1987 involved replacement of the standard 37-ampere output alternator with a 66-ampere alternator as standard equipment. The 66-ampere alternator had been an option in 1986. Custom Deluxe trim was standard and included color-keyed all-vinyl upholstery (blue, burgundy, charcoal, mahogany or saddle tan), a black rubber floor mat, a padded instrument panel, and color-keyed molded door trim panels with arm rests. The mid-level Scottsdale package added a color-keyed rubber floor mat, a full headliner, added insulation, a choice of deluxe cloth or custom vinyl upholstery, and special Scottsdale identification. The top-level Silverado package added a color-keyed headliner, color-keyed carpeting, a custom steering wheel, full gauge instrumentation, and specific Silverado exterior trim. The exterior and interior color selections were Frost White, Steel Gray Metallic, Midnight Black, Light Blue Metallic, Midnight Blue, Canyon Copper Metallic, Doeskin Tan, Nevada Gold Metallic, Indian Bronze Metallic, and Apple Red. Two-tone paint options included conventional with the cab roof and back panel in one color and the rest of the truck in another, special two-tone with a second color below the lower body side moldings, deluxe two-tone a combination of conventional and special, and the exterior decor package with the second color around the center of the body, between the upper and lower body side moldings. Standard pickup equipment included a front chromed bumpers, two right- and left-hand side doors (with rear side doors on both sides of Bonus-Cab and Crew-Cab models) , a removable tailgate with Chevrolet lettering, an Argent-painted molded plastic grille, a single low-note electric horn, bright metal hubcaps with black trim, taillamps with integral back-up lamps, two rectangular headlamps, directionals, parking lamps, front side markers, right- and left-hand chromed outside rear view mirrors, a jack and wheel wrench, white-painted wheels, two-speed electric windshield washers and wipers, right- and left-hand padded arm rests, an instrument panel ash tray, rear door trim panel ash trays on Bonus-Cab and Crew-Cab, color-keyed molded plastic door trim panels, black rubber floor covering, outside air type heater and defogger, inside-operated hood release, speedometer with odometer, fuel gauge, switches and warning lights, insulation and sound-deadening materials, instrument cluster and cab interior lights, a 10-inch prismatic rear view mirror, full-depth foam front bench seat with vinyl trim, full-width rear bench seat in Bonus-Cab and Crew-Cab, safety belts, a 16-inch soft black plastic two-spoke steering wheel, an energy-absorbing steering column, a lockable instrument panel stowage box, dual padded sun shades, color-keyed molded plastic trim panels on side doors, 4.3-liter V-6 engine (in R10/R20/V10 models) or 5.7-liter V-8 (in R20HD/R20 Bonus-Cab or Crew-Cab/R30/V20/V20HD/V30 Bonus-Cab and Crew-Cab models), three-speed manual (R10) or four-speed manual (all other models) transmission, and P195/75R-15 tires (LT215/85R-16C on base 4x4 models and LT235/85R-16 on larger 4x2 and 4x4 models).

1987 Chevrolet 1/2-Ton S10 Pickup (CMD)

1987 Chevrolet 1/2-Ton S10 Maxicab Pickup (CMD)

I.D. DATA: Location of serial number: The VIN is stamped on a plate attached to the left top of the instrument panel on C/K and R/V and G Series. On P Series the plate is attached to the front of the dash and the panel to the left of the steering column. The first symbol indicates country of origin: 1=U.S., 2=Canada, J=Japan. The second symbol indicates manufacturer: G=General Motors, 8=Isuzu. The third symbol indicates make: C=Chevrolet truck, 8=Chevy MPV. The fourth symbol indicates GVW rating and brake system: B=3,001 lb.-4,000 lb. hydraulic, C=4,001 lb.-5,000 lb. hydraulic, etc. through K for hydraulic brakes. The fifth symbol indicates line and chassis type: C/R=Conventional cab (including Blazer and Suburban) 4x2, G=Chevy Van and Sportvan 4x2, K/V=Conventional cab (including Blazer and Suburban) 4x4, P=Forward-Control, S=Conventional Cab 4x2, W=El Camino 4x2, Z=Special body 4x2. The sixth symbol indicates series: 1=1/2-ton, 2=3/4-ton, 3=1-ton. 3=El Camino. The seventh symbol indicates body type: 0=El Camino Pickup-Delivery, 1=Hi-Cube and Cutaway Vans, 2=Forward-Control, 3=Four-door cab, 4=Two-door cab, 5=Van, 6=Suburban, 7=Motorhome chassis, 8=Blazer Utility, 9=Stake. The eighth symbol identifies the engine [Chevrolet engines] C=6.2-liter/130 hp diesel V-8, H=5.0-liter V-8, J=6.2-liter/148 hp diesel V-8, K=5.7-liter V-8, M=5.7-liter V-8,N=7.4-liter V-8, R=2.8-liter V-6, T=4.8-liter L6, W=7.4-liter V-8, Z=4.3-liter V-6. [GM engines] A=5.7-liter V-8, [Pontiac engine] E=2.5-liter L4. The ninth symbol was a check digit. The 10th symbol indicated model year: G=1986. The 11th symbol indicated the assembly plant: A=Lakewood, Ga., B=Baltimore, Md., C=Southgate, Calif., D=Doraville, Ga., E=Linden, N.J., F=Flint, Mich., G=Framingham, Mass., H=Flint, Mich., J=Janesville, Wis., K=Leeds, Mo., L=Van Nuys, Calif., M=Lansing, Mich., N=Norwood, Ohio, P=Pontiac, Mich., R=Arlington, Texas, S=St. Louis, Mo., T=Tarrytown, N.Y., V=GMC, Pontiac, Mich., W=Willow Run, Mich., X=Fairfax, Va., Y=Wilmington, Dela., Z=Fremont, Calif., 1=Oshawa, Canada, 2=Moraine, Ohio, 2=Ste. Therese, Quebec, Canada, 3=Chevrolet-Detroit, Mich., 3=St. Eustache, Quebec, Canada, 4=Orion Plant, Pontiac, Mich., 4=Scarborough, Ontario, Canada, 5=Bowling Green, Ken., 5=London, Ontario, Canada, 6=Oklahoma City, Okla., 7=Lordstown, Ohio, 8=Shreveport, La., 8=Fujisawa, Japan, 9=Cadillac, Detroit, Mich. Note: Trucks were not built at all factories. Symbols 12-17 were the production sequence number starting at 100001. Ending numbers not available. Engine number location: [Six] located on pad at right-hand side of cylinder block at rear of distributor. [V-8] located on pad at right front side of cylinder block.

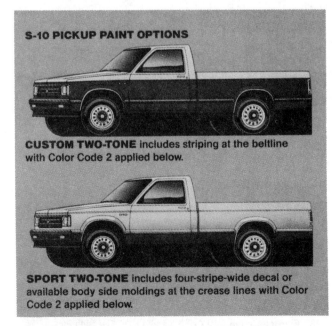

S-10 PICKUP PAINT OPTIONS

CUSTOM TWO-TONE includes striping at the beltline with Color Code 2 applied below.

SPORT TWO-TONE includes four-stripe-wide decal or available body side moldings at the crease lines with Color Code 2 applied below.

1987 Chevrolet 1/2-Ton S10 Pickup with Two-Tone (CMD)

Model	Body Type	Price	Weight	Prod. Total
S10 Fleetside Pickup — 1/2-Ton — 108.3/117.9/122.9 in. w.b. — 2.5-liter EFI L4				
S10603	Reg. Cab Short Box EL	6595	2567	Note 12
S10603	Reg. Cab Short Box	7435	2579	Note 12
S10803	Reg. Cab Long Box	7702	2657	Note 12
S10653	Ext. Cab Short Box	8167	2721	Note 12
T10 Fleetside Pickup — 1/2-Ton — 108.3/117.9/122.9 in. w.b. — 2.5-liter EFI L4				
T10603	Reg. Cab Short Box	9,845	2913	Note 12
T10803	Reg. Cab Long Box	10,013	2965	Note 12
T10653	Ext. Cab Short Box	10,359	3042	Note 12
NOTE: 1: $400 dealer destination charge applied to S-Series pickups				
W80 El Camino Coupe-Pickup — 1/2-Ton — 117.1-in. w.b. — 4.3-liter EFI V-6				
W80	Coupe Pickup	10,453	3234	Note 12
W80	Conquista Cpe P.U.	10,869	3239	Note 12
W80	SS Coupe Pickup	10,784	3244	Note 12
NOTE: 2: A $400 dealer destination charge applied to El Camino coupe-pickups				
S10 Blazer 4x2 Sport Utility Wagon — 1/2-Ton — 100.5/107 in. w.b. — 2.5-liter EFI L4				
CS10516	2-dr Tailgate	10,124	2804	Note 12
T10 Blazer 4x4 Sport Utility Wagon — 1/2-Ton — 100.5/107 in. w.b. — 2.5-liter EFI L4				
CT10516	2-dr Tailgate	11,588	3104	Note 12
NOTE: 3: A $435 dealer destination charge applied to S-Series Blazers				
M10 Astro Minivan (RWD) — 1/2-Ton — 111 in. w.b. — 2.5-liter EFI L4/4.3-liter EFI V-6				
CM10906	Standard Cargo Van	8797	3100	Note 12
CM10906	Standard Wagon	9833	3461	Note 12
CM10906/ZW9	Standard CS Wagon	10,314	3544	Note 12
CM10906	Standard CL Wagon	11,079	3594	Note 12
CM10906	Standard LT Wagon	12,370	3636	Note 12
NOTE: 4: A $500 dealer destination charge applied to Astros				
G10 Van — 1/2-Ton — 110/125 in. w.b. — 4.3-liter EFI V-6				
CG11005	SWB Chevy Van	9464	3666	Note 12
CG11006/ZW9	SWB Sportvan	11,162	4006	Note 12
CG11306/ZW9	LWB Bonaventure	12,279	4105	Note 12
CG11306/ZW9	LWB Beauville	12,649	4151	Note 12
G20 Van — 3/4-Ton — 110/125 in. w.b. — 4.3-liter EFI V-6				
CG21005	SWB Chevy Van	10,131	3754	Note 12
CG21005	SWB Chevy Van diesel	13,278	4363	Note 12
CG21305/ZW9	LWB Sportvan	11,609	4216	Note 12
CG21306/ZW9	LWB Bonaventure	12,483	4315	Note 12
CG21306/ZW9	LWB Beauville	12,833	4361	Note 12
G30 Van — 1-Ton — 125/146 in. w.b. — 5.7-liter EFI V-8				
CG31305	LWB Chevy Van	12,110	4436	Note 12
CG31305	LWB Chevy Van HD	12,742	4860	Note 12
CG31306/ZW9	LWB Sportvan 12P	14,004	5031	Note 12
CG31306/ZW9	LWB Bonaventure	14,879	5130	Note 12
CG31306/ZW9	LWB Beauville	15,228	5176	Note 12
CG31306	LWB Cutaway	n.a.	3802	Note 12
G30 Hi-Cube Van — 1-Ton — 125/146 in. w.b. — 5.7-liter EFI V-8				
CG31	10-ft. Van	11,934	5500	Note 12
CG31	12-ft. Van	13,183	5971	Note 12
NOTE: 5: A $550 dealer destination charge applied to full-size vans				
P20 — 3/4-Ton Step-Van — 125/133 in. w.b. — 5.7-liter EFI V-8				
P22	10.5-ft. Step-Van	15,185	5847	Note 12
P30 — 1-Ton Step-Van — 125/178 in. w.b. — 5.7-liter EFI V-8				
P32	10.5-ft. Step-Van	15,273	6207	Note 12
V10 Blazer — 1/2-Ton — 111.5 in. w.b. — 5.7-liter EFI V-8				
V18	Utility Hardtop	13,066	4379	Note 12
NOTE: 6: A $550 dealer destination charge applied to full-size Blazers				
R/V 10 Suburban — 1/2-Ton — 131.5 in. w.b. — 5.7-liter EFI V-8				
R16	Panel Door (4x2)	12,983	4758	Note 12
R16	Panel Door diesel (4x2)	15,741	5227	Note 12
V16	Panel Door (4x4)	14,060	5544	Note 12
R/V 20 Suburban — 3/4-Ton — 131.5 in. w.b. — 5.7-liter EFI V-8				
R26	Panel Door (4x2)	13,584	5196	Note 12
V26	Panel Door (4x4)	15,490	5958	Note 12
NOTE: 7: A $610 dealer destination charge applied to Suburbans				
NOTE: 8: Add $40 for tailgate models				
R10 Pickup — 1/2-Ton Short Box — 117.5 in. w.b. — 4.3-liter EFI V-6				
R14	Regular-Cab Step-Side	8,651	3363	Note 12
R14	Regular-Cab Fleetside	8,503	3410	Note 12
R10 Pickup — 1/2-Ton Long Box — 131.5 in. w.b. — 4.3-liter EFI V-6				
R14	Regular-Cab Fleetside	8,687	3565	Note 12
NOTE: 9: Add approximately $2,800 for V10 Pickups with 4x4				
R20 Pickup — 3/4-Ton Long Box — 131.5 in. w.b. — 4.3-liter EFI V-6 (HDE 5.7-liter V-8)				
R24	Chassis & Regular-Cab	n.a.	4454	Note 12
R24	Regular-Cab Step-Side	10,007	3905	Note 12
R24	Regular-Cab Fleetside	9,924	3967	Note 12
R24	Reg.-cab Step-Side HDE	11,498	4027	Note 12
R24	Reg.-cab Fleetside HDE	11,351	4089	Note 12
R2500 Pickup — 3/4-Ton EEWB Long Box — 164.5 in. w.b. — 5.7-liter EFI V-8				
R23	Bonus-Cab Fleetside HDE	11,775	4773	Note 12
R23	Crew-cab Fleetside HDE	13,142	4834	Note 12
NOTE: 10: Add approximately $2,890 for V20 Pickups with 4x4 5.7-liter V-8 standard in V20s				
R30 HDE Pickup — 1-Ton Long Box — 131.5 in. w.b. — 5.7-liter EFI V-8				
R34	Chassis-and-cab Fleetside	n.a.	4026	Note 12
R34	Regular-Cab Step-Side	11,712	4364	Note 12
R34	Regular-Cab Fleetside	11,565	4443	Note 12
R3500 HDE Pickup — 1-Ton EEWB Long Box — 164.5 in. w.b. — 5.7-liter EFI V-8.				
R33	Chassis & Bonus-Cab	n.a.	4450	Note 12
R33	Bonus-Cab Fleetside HDE	12,664	4861	Note 12
R33	Chassis & Crew-cab	n.a.	4512	Note 12
R23	Crew-cab Fleetside HDE	13,034	4923	Note 12

NOTE 11: A $550 dealer destination charge applied to R/V Pickups
NOTE 12: Model year production [S10 regular-cab pickup] 178,842, [S10 extended-cab pickup] 45,184, [R/V10] 183,857, [R/V20] 53,522, [R/V30] 32,384, [C/K10] 78,130, [C/K20] 16,281, [C/K30] 2,708, [S-Series Blazer] 174,797, [V10 Blazer] 32,437, [Suburban] 58,674, [Astro Wagon] 110,910 [Astro Cargo Van] 57,266, [Sportvan] 10,983, [Chevy Van] 178,085, [El Camino] 15,589..

GASOLINE ENGINE:S DISPLACEMENT ORDER
ENGINE: Inline. Tech IV four-cylinder. Bore & stroke: 4.00 x 3.00 in. Displacement: 2.5-liter 151 cid. BHP: 92 at 4400 rpm. Torque: 130 lb.-ft. at 2300 rpm. Compression ratio: 8.3:1. EFI/Throttle-body-injection. VIN Code E. GM-built. [Standard in S10/T10, S-Series Blazer (all)]
ENGINE: V-block. Six-cylinder. Bore & stroke: 3.52 x 2.99 in. Displacement: 2.8-liter 173 cid. BHP: 125 at 4800 rpm. Torque: 150 lb.-ft. at 2400 rpm. Compression ratio: 8.9:1. EFI/Throttle-body-injection. VIN Code R. Chevrolet-built. [Optional in S10, optional in S-Series Blazers]
ENGINE: V-block. Six-cylinder. Bore & stroke: 4.0 x 3.48 in. Displacement: 4.3-liter 262 cid. BHP: 145 at 4200 rpm. Torque: 230 lb.-ft. at 2000 rpm. Compression ratio: 9.3:1. EFI/Throttle-body-injection. VIN Code n.a. GM-built. [Standard in El Camino]

ENGINE: V-block. Six-cylinder. Bore & stroke: 4.0 x 3.48 in. Displacement: 4.3-liter 262 cid. BHP: 150 at 4000 rpm. Torque: 230 lb.-ft. at 2400 rpm. Compression ratio: 9.3:1. EFI/Throttle-body-injection. VIN Code n.a. GM-built. [Standard in G10, G20, Astro]

ENGINE: V-block. Six-cylinder. Bore & stroke: 4.0 x 3.48 in. Displacement: 4.3-liter 262 cid. BHP: 160 at 4000 rpm. Torque: 235 lb.-ft. at 2400 rpm. Compression ratio: 9.1:1. EFI/Throttle-body-injection. VIN Code Z. Chevrolet-built. [Standard in R/V10 and R20 pickups, standard in C/K 1500/2500, optional in S10/T10 pickups, optional in all S-Blazers]

ENGINE: V-block. Eight-cylinder. Bore & stroke: 3.74 x 3.48 in. Displacement: 5.0-liter 305 cid. BHP: 150 at 4000 rpm. Torque: 240 lb.-ft. at 2400 rpm. EFI/Throttle-body-injection. VIN Code n.a. Chevrolet-built. [Standard in El Camino]

ENGINE: V-block. Eight-cylinder. Bore & stroke: 3.74 x 3.48 in. Displacement: 5.0-liter 305 cid. BHP: 170 at 4000 rpm. Torque: 255 lb.-ft. at 2400 rpm. EFI/Throttle-body-injection. VIN Code H. Chevrolet-built. [Standard in R10 Suburban, optional in G10, G20, optional in R/V10, R/V20,]

ENGINE: V-block. Eight-cylinder. Bore & stroke: 4.0 x 3.48 in. Displacement: 5.7-liter 350 cid. BHP: 190 at 4000 rpm. Torque: 300 lb.-ft. at 2400 rpm. Compression ratio: 8.6:1. EFI/Throttle-body-injection. VIN Code A. GM-built. [Standard in heavy-duty R/V30, standard in Suburbans, and heavy-duty G30 vans, optional in R/V and C/K pickups, optional in G20 Sportvan]

ENGINE: V-block. Eight-cylinder. Bore & stroke: 4.0 x 3.48 in. Displacement: 5.7-liter 350 cid. BHP: 210 at 4000 rpm. Compression ratio: 9.3:1. Torque: 300 lb.-ft. at 2800 rpm. EFI/Throttle-body-injection. VIN Code K. Chevrolet-built. [Standard in R/V Blazer, optional in G10 Sportvan]

ENGINE: V-block. Eight-cylinder. Bore & stroke: 4.25 x 4.00 in. Displacement: 7.4-liter 454 cid. BHP: 230 at 3600 rpm. Torque: 385 lb.-ft. at 1600 rpm. Throttle-body-fuel-injection. VIN Code N. Chevrolet-built. [Optional in Suburban]

DIESEL ENGINE:S (DISPLACEMENT ORDER)

ENGINE: V-block. Light-duty. Eight-cylinder. Bore & stroke: 3.98 x 3.82 in. Displacement: 6.2-liter 379 cid. BHP: 148 at 3600 rpm. Torque: 248 lb.-ft. at 2000 rpm. VIN Code J. GM-built. [Optional in R/V30 pickup, optional in G30 Chevy Van and 12-passenger Sportvan]

ENGINE: V-block. Heavy-duty. Eight-cylinder. Bore & stroke: 3.98 x 3.82 in. Displacement: 6.2-liter 379 cid. BHP: 130 at 3600 rpm. Torque: 240 lb.-ft. at 2000 rpm. VIN Code C. GM-built. [Optional in R/V30 pickup, optional in G30 Chevy Van and 12-passenger Sportvan, optional in R10 Suburban]

1987 Chevrolet 1-Ton G30 Chevy Van Cargo Van (CMD)

CHASSIS: [S10] Regular-Cab. Short Box. Wheelbase: 108.3 in. Length: 178.2 in. Width: 64.7 in. Height: 61.3 in. Standard GVW: 3,570 lb. Maximum GVW: 45959 lb. Tires: P195/75R14 black sidewall.

CHASSIS: [T10] Regular-Cab. Short Box. Wheelbase: 108.3 in. Length: 178.2 in. Width: 64.7 in. Height: 61.3 in. Standard GVW: 3,899 lb. Maximum GVW: 5,284 lb. Tires: P205/75R15 black sidewall.

CHASSIS: [S10] Regular-Cab. Long box. Wheelbase: 117.9 in. Length: 194.2 in. Width: 64.7 in. Height: 61.3 in. Standard GVW: 3,570 lb. Maximum GVW: 4,959 lb. Tires: P195/75R14 black sidewall.

CHASSIS: [T10] Regular-Cab. Long box. Wheelbase: 117.9 in. Length: 194.2 in. Width: 64.7 in. Height: 61.3 in. Standard GVW: 3,899 lb. Maximum GVW: 5,284 lb. Tires: P205/75R15 black sidewall

CHASSIS: [S10] Extended-Cab. Short box. Wheelbase: 122.9 in. Length: 192.8 in. Width: 64.7 in. Height: 61.3 in. Standard GVW: 3,570 lb. Maximum GVW: 4,959 lb. Tires: P195/75R14 black sidewall.

CHASSIS: [T10] Extended-Cab. Short box. Wheelbase: 122.9 in. Length: 192.8 in. Width: 64.7 in. Height: 61.3 in. Standard GVW: 3,899 lb. Maximum GVW: 5,284 lb. Tires: P205/75R15 black sidewall.

CHASSIS: [El Camino] Wheelbase: 117.1 in. Length: 201.6 in. Width: 71.9 in. Height: 53.8 in. Standard GVW: 3,234 lb. Maximum GVW: 4,560 lb. Tires: P205/75R-14 all-season steel-belted radial.

CHASSIS: [El Camino SS] Wheelbase: 117.1 in. Length: 201.6 in. Width: 71.9 in. Height: 53.8 in. Standard GVW: 3,239 lb. Maximum GVW: 4,560 lb. Tires: P205/75R-14 all-season steel-belted radial with raised white letters.

CHASSIS: [S-Blazer 4x2] Two-door. Wheelbase: 100.5 in. Length: 170.3 in. Width: 65.4 in. Height: 64.7 in. Standard GVW: 3,894 lb. Maximum GVW: 4,549 lb. Tires: P195/75R15 black sidewall.

CHASSIS: [S-Blazer 4x4] Two-door. Wheelbase: 100.5 in. Length: 170.3 in. Width: 65.4 in. Height: 64.7 in. Standard GVW: 4,149 lb. Maximum GVW: 4,872 lb. Tires: P195/75R15 black sidewall.

CHASSIS: [Astro Cargo regular-body] Wheelbase: 111 in. Length: 176.8 in. Width: 77.0 in. Height: 73.7 in. Standard GVW: 4,088 lb. Maximum GVW: 5,681 lb. Tires: P195/75R15 black sidewall.

CHASSIS: [Astro Passenger regular-body] Wheelbase: 111 in. Length: 176.8 in. Width: 77.0 in. Height: 73.7 in. Standard GVW: 4,404 lb. Maximum GVW: 5,439 lb. Tires: P195/75R15 black sidewall.

CHASSIS: [G10/Short Body] Chevy Van. Wheelbase: 110 in.. Length: 178.2 in. Width: 79.5 in. Height: 79.2 in. Standard GVW: 4,900 lb. Maximum GVW: 6,000 lb. Tires: P205/75R15 black sidewall.

CHASSIS: [G10/Short Body] Chevy Van. Wheelbase: 110 in. Length:178.2 in. Width: 79.5 in. Height: 79.4 in. Standard GVW: 5,600 lb. Maximum GVW: 6,000 lb. Tires: P205/75R15 black sidewall.

CHASSIS: [G10/Long Body] Sportvan/Bonaventure/Beauville. Wheelbase: 125 in.. Length: 202.2 in. Width: 79.5 in. Height: 79.2 in. Standard GVW: 5,600 lb. Maximum GVW: 6,000 lb. Tires: P200/75R15 black sidewall.

CHASSIS: [G20/Short Body] Chevy Van. Wheelbase: 110 in. Length: 178.2 in. Width: 79.5 in. Height: 79.5 in. Standard GVW: 6,600 lb. Maximum GVW: 6,600 lb. Tires: P225/75R15 black sidewall.

CHASSIS: [G20/Long Body] Chevy Van. Wheelbase: 125 in. Length: 202.2 in. Width: 79.5 in. Height: 79.2 in. Standard GVW: 6,600 lb. Maximum GVW: 6,600 lb. Tires: P225/75R15 black sidewall.

CHASSIS: [G20/Long Body] Sportvan/Bonaventure/Beauville. Wheelbase: 125 in.. Length: 202.2 in. Width: 79.5 in. Height: 79.5 in. Standard GVW: 6,600 lb. Maximum GVW: 6,850 lb. Tires: P225/75R15 black sidewall.

CHASSIS: [G30/Long Body Chevy Van] Wheelbase: 125 in.. Length: 202.2 in. Width: 79.5 in. Height: 81.9 in. Standard GVW: 7,100 lb. Maximum GVW: 8,600 lb. Tires: 8.75-16.5D black sidewall.

CHASSIS: [G30/Long Body Heavy-duty Chevy Van] Wheelbase: 125 in.. Length: 202.2 in. Width: 79.5 in. Height: 81.9 in. Standard GVW: 7,400 lb. Maximum GVW: 8,600 lb. Tires: 8.75-16.5D black sidewall.

CHASSIS: [G30/Long Body Sportvan/Bonaventure/Beauville] Wheelbase: 125 in.. Length: 202.2 in. Width: 79.5 in. Height: 81.9 in. Standard GVW: 7,400 lb. Maximum GVW: 8,600 lb. Tires: 8.75-16D black sidewall.

CHASSIS: [G30/Long Body Heavy-duty Sportvan] Wheelbase: 125 in.. Length: 202.2 in. Width: 79.5 in. Height: 81.9 in. Standard GVW: 7,400 lb. Maximum GVW: 8,600 lb. Tires: 8.75-16D black sidewall.

CHASSIS: [G30/Extended Body Heavy-duty Sportvan/Bonaventure/Beauville] Wheelbase: 146 in. Length: 223.2 in. Width: 79.5 in. Height: 81.9 in. Standard GVW: 8,600 lb. Maximum GVW: 3,957 lb. Tires: 8.75-16D black sidewall

CHASSIS: [G30/Extended Body 12-Passenger Sportvan] Wheelbase: 146 in. Length: 223.2 in. Width: 79.5 in. Height: 81.9 in. Standard GVW: 10,000 lb. Maximum GVW: 10,000 lb. Tires: 8.75-16.5D black sidewall

CHASSIS: [K10 Blazer 4x4] Wheelbase: 106.5 in. Length: 184.8 in. Width: 79.6 in. Height: 73.8 in. Standard GVW: 6,100 lb. Maximum GVW: 6,100 lb. Tires: LT245/75R16C black sidewall.

CHASSIS: [Suburban R10/and diesel] Wheelbase: 129.5 in. Length: 219.1 in. Width: 79.6 in. Height: 72.0 in. Standard GVW: 6,100 lb. Maximum GVW: 7,000 lb. Tires: P235/75R-15XLS black sidewall.

CHASSIS: [Suburban R20] Wheelbase: 129.5 in. Length: 219.1 in. Width: 79.6 in. Height: 74.3 in. Standard GVW: 8,600 lb. Maximum GVW: 8,600 lb. Tires: P235/75R-15XLS black sidewall.

CHASSIS: [Suburban V10] Wheelbase: 129.5 in. Length: 219.1 in. Width: 79.6 in. Height: 73.8 in. Standard GVW: 6,100 lb. Maximum GVW: 7,300 lb. Tires: LT235/75R-15XLS black sidewall.

CHASSIS: [Suburban V20] Wheelbase: 129.5 in. Length: 219.1 in. Width: 79.6 in. Height: 76.1 in. Standard GVW: 8,600 lb. Maximum GVW: 8,600 lb. Tires: LT235/75R-15XLS black sidewall.

CHASSIS: [R10 Sportside Regular-Cab Short Box Pickup] Regular-Cab. Short Box. Wheelbase: 117.5 in. Length: 194.0 in. Width: 76.8 in. Height: 70.4 in. Standard GVW: 5,200 lb. Maximum GVW: 5,600 lb. Tires: P225/75R15 black sidewall AS SBR Tires.

CHASSIS: [R10 Fleetside Regular-Cab Short Box Pickup] Wheelbase: 117.5 in. Length: 194.0 in. Width: 76.8 in. Height: 70.4 in. Standard GVW: 5,200 lb. Maximum GVW: 5,600 lb. Tires: P225/75R15 black sidewall AS SBR Tires.

CHASSIS: [R10 Extended-Cab] Wheelbase: 155.5 in. Length: 236.9 in. Width: 107.3 in. Height: 70.6 in. Standard GVW: 6,000 lb. Maximum GVW: 6,000 lb. Tires: P225/75R15 black sidewall AS SBR Tires.

CHASSIS: [V10 Sportside Regular-Cab Short Box Pickup] Wheelbase: 117.5 in. Length: 194.0 in. Width: 76.8 in. Height: 73.8 in. Standard GVW: 5,600 lb. Maximum GVW: 5,600 lb. Tires: P225/75R15 black sidewall AS SBR Tires.

CHASSIS: [V10 Fleetside Regular-Cab Short Box Pickup] Wheelbase: 117.5 in. Length: 194.0 in. Width: 76.8 in. Height: 73.8 in. Standard GVW: 5,600 lb. Maximum GVW: 5,6000 lb. Tires: P225/75R15 black sidewall AS SBR Tires.

CHASSIS: [V10 Fleetside Extended-Cab Short Box Pickup] Wheelbase: 155.5 in. Length: 236.9 in. Width: 107.3 in. Height: 73.9 in. Standard GVW: 6,200 lb. Maximum GVW: 6,200 Lb. Tires: P225/75R15 black sidewall AS SBR Tires.

CHASSIS: [R20 Fleetside Regular-Cab Long Box Pickup] Wheelbase: 131.5 in. Length: 208.9 in. Width: 76.8 in. Height: 73.0 in. Standard GVW: 7,200 lb. Maximum GVW: 7,200 lb. Tires: P225/75R15 black sidewall AS SBR tires.

CHASSIS: [R20 Fleetside Extended-Cab Short Box Pickup] Wheelbase: 155.5 in. Length: 236.9 in. Width: 107.3 in. Height: 73.2 in. Standard GVW: 7,200 lb. Maximum GVW: 7,200 lb. Tires: P225/75R15 black sidewall AS SBR tires.

CHASSIS: [V20 Fleetside Regular-Cab Long Box Pickup] Wheelbase: 131.5 in. Length: 208.2 in. Width: 76.4 in. Height: 74.3 in. Standard GVW: 7,200 lb. Maximum GVW: 7,200 lb. Tires: P225/75R15 black sidewall AS SBR tires.

CHASSIS: [V20 Fleetside Extended-Cab Short Box Pickup] Wheelbase: 155.5 in. Length: 236.9 in. Width: 107.3 in. Height: 74.5 in. Standard GVW: 7,200 lb. Maximum GVW: 7,200 lb. Tires: P225/75R15 black sidewall AS SBR tires.

CHASSIS: [R30 Fleetside Regular-Cab Long Box Pickup] Wheelbase: 131.5 in. Length: 208.2 in. Width: 76.8 in. Height: 75.4 in. Standard GVW: 8,600 lb. Maximum GVW: 10,000 lb. Tires: P225/75R15 black sidewall AS SBR tires.

CHASSIS: [R30 Fleetside Extended-Cab Long Box Pickup] Wheelbase: 155.5 in. Length: 236.9 in. Width: 107.3 in. Height: 75.6 in. Standard GVW: 8,600 lb. Maximum GVW: 10,000 lb. Tires: P225/75R15 black sidewall AS SBR tires.

CHASSIS: [V30 Fleetside Long Box Pickup] Wheelbase: 131.5 in. Length: 208.2 in. Width: 76.8 in. Height: 5.8 in. Standard GVW: 8,600 lb. Maximum GVW: 8,600 lb. Tires: P225/75R15 black sidewall AS SBR tires.

CHASSIS: [V30 Fleetside Extended-Cab Long Box Pickup] Wheelbase: 155.5 in. Length: 236.9 in. Width: 107.3 in. Height: 76.0 in. Standard GVW: 8,600 lb. Maximum GVW: 8,600 lb. Tires: P225/75R15 black sidewall AS SBR tires.

CHASSIS: [R/V30 Pickup] Motor home chassis. Wheelbase: 183.5 in. Tires: P225/75R15 black sidewall AS SBR tires.

1987 Chevrolet 1-Ton R30 4x2 Silverado HDE Fleetside Pickup (CMD)

TWO-TONE PAINT OPTIONS.

CONVENTIONAL TWO-TONE. (Combination A). Includes Color Code 1 on cab roof and back panel down to the beltline moldings with Color Code 2 applied on the rest of the truck.

SPECIAL TWO-TONE.* (Combination B). Includes body side/wheel-opening moldings, bright trim for standard marker lights and taillights. Color Code 1 is applied to cab roof, hood and upper body above the body side moldings, Color Code 2 is below.

DELUXE TWO-TONE.* (Combination C). Includes Special Two-Tone trim items with Color Code 1 on cab roof and back panel and below the side moldings. Color Code 2 is applied between belt and side moldings.

EXTERIOR DECOR PACKAGE. Includes body side moldings, dual-tone body side and rear decal striping keyed to exterior color, with Color Code 1 above the striping and below the moldings and Color Code 2 in between.

1987 Chevrolet 1/2-Ton Fleetside Pickup with Two-Tone (CMD)

S/T SERIES PICKUP OPTIONS: Durango package ($339). Tahoe package ($442). Sport package ($940). Custom vinyl bench seat ($50). Custom vinyl high-back bucket seats ($128-$178 depending upon trim package). Custom two-tone paint ($200). Special two-tone paint ($167-$311 depending upon trim package). Sport two-tone paint ($162-$227 depending upon trim package). California emissions system ($99). 2.6-liter V-6 engine ($225). Four-speed overdrive automatic transmission ($670). Optional axle ratio ($36). Locking rear differential ($238). Pre-cleaner air cleaner ($49). Five-speed manual overdrive transmission ($175). All-weather air conditioning ($705). Heavy-duty battery ($53). Front black bumper guards ($30). Off-road package ($602-$658 depending upon trim package). Cold-climate package ($107-$179 depending upon trim package). Front compartment console ($108). Engine oil cooling system ($120). Heavy-duty radiator ($53). Heavy-duty radiator and transmission oil cooler ($59 with air conditioning, $112 without air conditioning). Spare tire cover ($32). Air deflector ($41). Rear window defogger ($114 with air conditioning, $145 without air conditioning). Power door locks ($135). Color-keyed floor mats ($15). Gauge package includes voltmeter, engine coolant temperature, and oil pressure gauges ($58). Gauge package plus tachometer ($55-$113 depending upon trim package). 66-ampere Delcotron generator ($31). Tinted-glass back window glass with light-tinted windshield and side door glass ($55). Tinted glass, all windows ($46). Halogen headlights ($22). Engine block heater ($31). Engine compartment light ($15). Exterior left and right side painted mirrors ($50). Exterior left and right side bright mirrors ($83). Body side and wheel opening moldings ($17-$144 depending upon trim package). Door edge guards ($17). Bright wheel opening moldings ($28). Black wheel opening moldings ($12-$41 depending upon trim package). Operating convenience

package ($325). AM radio ($112). AM/FM radio ($171). AM/FM radio with clock ($210). AM/FM stereo radio with electronic tuning ($238). AM/FM stereo radio and clock with electronic tuning ($277). AM/FM stereo radio with Seek-and-Scan, stereo cassette tape, clock and graphic equalizer and electronic tuning and premium rear speakers ($594). Premium rear speakers ($25). Transfer case shield ($67). Heavy-duty front and rear shock absorbers ($34). Full size spare tire ($46-$90 depending upon size). Electronic speed control ($260). Comfortilt steering wheel ($115). Striping ($65). Heavy-duty suspension equipment ($59). 20 gallon fuel tank ($49). Two front towing hooks ($36). Deadweight trailer hitch ($64). Heavy-duty Trailering Special ($199). Light-duty Trailering Special ($103). Wheel trim rings ($56). Rally wheels ($32-$88 depending upon trim package). Styled wheels ($32-$88 depending upon trim package). Cast aluminum wheels ($238-$294 depending upon trim package). Power side door windows ($190). Intermittent windshield wiper system ($55).

1987 Chevrolet 3/4-Ton V20 4x4 Scottsdale Fleetside Pickup (CMD)

EL CAMINO OPTIONS: Air conditioning. Electronic speed control. Limited-slip rear axle differential. Heavy-duty battery (V-8 only). Front and rear bumper guards. Front and rear bumper rub strips (available alone or teamed with bumper guards). Color-keyed floor mats. Front console (requires bucket seats). Heavy-duty cooling. Power door lock system. Gauge package with trip odometer. Tinted glass. Halogen high- and low-beam headlights. Auxiliary lighting package. Sport rear view mirrors with right-hand manual and left-hand remote-controlled (standard on SS Sport Decor model). Conquista package moldings (not available on SS Sport Decor). Deluxe black body side moldings (not available on SS Sport Decor). Black door edge guards. GM Delco Am radio. GM Delco AM radio with digital clock. GM Delco AM/FM ETR radio with Seek-and-Scan. GM Delco AM/FM ETR radio with Seek-and-Scan. and digital clock GM Delco AM/FM ETR radio with Seek-and-Scan and cassette tape and clock. GM Delco AM/FM ETR radio with Seek-and-Scan, cassette, clock, and Search-and-Repeat. Fixed mast radio antenna. Cargo box side rails. Comfortilt steering wheel. Sport suspension. Tachometer (requires gauge package). 22-gallon fuel tank. Cargo box tie-downs. Wire wheelcovers with locks (not available with SS Sport Decor). Rally wheels (standard with SS Sport Decor). Power windows. Intermittent windshield wipers.

S-SERIES BLAZER OPTIONS: Tahoe package. Sport package. High-Country package. Sport cloth vinyl high-back bucket seat trim. High-Country sheepskin high-back bucket seats. Custom two-tone paint. Special two-tone paint. Sport two-tone paint. California emissions system. 2.8-liter V-6 engine. Four-speed overdrive automatic transmission. Optional axle ratio. Locking rear differential. Pre-cleaner air cleaner. Five-speed manual overdrive transmission. All-weather air conditioning. Heavy-duty battery. Front black bumper guards. Luggage carrier with black or bright finish. Spare wheel and tire carrier. Off-road package. Cold-climate package. Front compartment console. Engine oil cooling system. Heavy-duty radiator. Heavy-duty radiator and transmission oil cooler. Spare tire cover. Air deflector. Rear window defogger. Power door locks $135. Color-keyed floor mats. Gauge package (includes voltmeter, engine coolant temperature, oil pressure). Gauge package plus tachometer. 66-ampere Delcotron generator. Deep-tinted glass. Deep-tinted glass with light tinted rear window. Halogen headlights. Engine block heater. Engine compartment light. Exterior left and right side painted mirrors. Exterior left and right side bright mirrors. Body side and wheel opening moldings. Door edge guards. Bright wheel opening moldings. Black wheel opening moldings. Operating convenience package. AM radio. AM/FM radio. AM/FM radio with clock. AM/FM stereo radio with electronic-tuning. AM/FM stereo radio and clock with electronic-tuning. AM/FM stereo radio with Seek-and-Scan, stereo cassette tape, clock and graphic equalizer and electronic-tuning and premium rear speakers. Premium rear speakers. Folding rear bench seat. Reclining front seat backs. Transfer case shield. Heavy-duty front and rear shock absorbers. Full size spare tire. Electronic speed control. Comfortilt steering wheel. Striping. Heavy-duty suspension equipment. Power release tailgate window. 20 gallon fuel tank. Two front towing hooks. Deadweight trailer hitch $64. Heavy-duty Trailering Special $199. Light-duty Trailering Special. Wheel trim rings. Rally wheels. Styled wheels. Cast aluminum wheels. Power side door windows. Intermittent windshield wiper system.

ASTRO/ASTRO VAN OPTIONS: Auxiliary lighting (standard on CL). Color-keyed bumper rub strips and end caps (standard on CL). Under floor spare tire carrier (standard on CL and CS). Cigarette lighter (standard on CL). Right-hand coat hook (standard on CS/CL, not available on others). Jack and tool cover (standard on CS/CL, not available on others). Black rubber floor covering (not on CS or CL). Color-keyed rubber floor covering (standard CS, optional base, not available CL). Gauges (standard CL). Deluxe grille (standard CL). Full-length headliner (standard CS and CL, not available on others). Deluxe heater with side window defoggers (standard CS and CL, optional others). Inside fuel door release (standard on CS and CL). Lighted vanity mirror (not available on Cargo Van). Black body side and wheel opening moldings (standard on CL). Sill plates and step well mats (standard on CS and CL, not available on others). Custom steering wheel (standard on CL). Positive rear door stops (standard on CS and CL). Rear storage compartment (standard on CS and CL, not available on others). Bright metal wheelcovers (standard on CL). Wheel trim rings (not available on CL). Front air conditioning. Front and rear air conditioning (Passenger Van only). Rear compartment heater. High-back bucket seats (Cargo Van only). Intermittent wiper system. Special two-tone paint. Sport two-tone paint. Power door lock system. Power windows. Reading lamps. Roof console. Two-passenger seating in Cargo Van. Four-passenger seating. Seven- or eight-passenger seating (both in Passenger Van only). Seat back recliners and arm rests. Comfortilt steering wheel. Custom steering wheel. Luxury steering wheel. Sport steering wheel. Right-hand sun shade (Cargo Van only). Chrome bumpers with end caps and rub strips. Tinted glass.

Deep-tinted glass. Rear door glass (Cargo Van). Rear quarter glass. Swing-out rear door glass. Swing-out side door glass (Cargo Van). Halogen headlamps. Deluxe black-painted mirrors. Rally wheels. Black -painted roof luggage rack (available after January 1987). Cast aluminum wheels. Full wheelcovers. Wheel trim rings. Engine block heater. Engine oil cooler. Front stabilizer bar. Heavy-duty battery. Heavy-duty radiator. Heavy-duty radiator and transmission oil cooler. Performance rear axle ratio. Locking rear axle differential. 4.3-liter Vortec V-6 (in Cargo Van). Five-speed manual overdrive transmission (standard on Passenger Van). Four-speed automatic overdrive transmission. Deadweight trailer hitch. Electronic speed control. 27-gallon fuel tank. Heavy-duty shock absorbers. Power brakes (Cargo Van only). Power steering. Trailering Special equipment. Under floor spare tire carrier. Delco AM radio. AM/FM radio. AM/FM radio with clock. AM/FM stereo radio with electronic-tuning. AM/FM stereo radio and clock with electronic-tuning. AM/FM stereo radio with Seek-and-Scan, stereo cassette tape, clock and graphic equalizer and electronic-tuning and premium rear speakers. Premium rear speakers.

G-SERIES VAN OPTIONS: Front air conditioning. Front and rear air conditioning. Automatic speed control with resume. Auxiliary lighting package. Auxiliary rear heater. Chromed front and rear bumpers. Chromed front bumper guards. Cigarette lighter and ash tray ampere Comfortilt steering wheel. Custom steering wheel. Deluxe front end package with quad headlamps. Electric clock with quartz movement. Floor carpeting. Front seat storage compartment. Deep-tinted glass. All windows tinted glass. Tinted windshield only. Halogen headlamps. Intermittent windshield wipers. Painted below-eye-line mirrors. Stainless steel below-eye-line mirrors. Black body side moldings. Black wheel opening moldings. Operating convenience package with power door locks. Operating convenience package with power windows. Special two-tone paint. Deluxe two-tone paint. Exterior decor package paint. Positive-stop rear door. AM radio. AM/FM radio. AM/FM radio with cassette. AM/FM stereo with cassette, Seek-and-Scan and digital clock. Auxiliary front seat standard in Sportvan. Center front seat standard in Sportvan. Center front Travel Bed seat (Sportvans only). Center rear Travel Bed seat (G20 and G30 Sportvan only). High-back front bucket seat (standard in Sportvans). One additional rear bench seat (G20/G30 Sportvans only). Two additional rear bench seats (G30 Sportvans only). Two reclining front bucket seats (Sportvans only). Sliding front door extender link. Sun shades standard in Sportvans. Rally wheels. Cast aluminum wheels. Bright metal wheelcovers (Sportvans only, except G30 Sportvan). Side and rear windows (standard in Sportvans). Engine oil cooler. Transmission oil cooler. Front stabilizer bar. Larger 33-gallon fuel tank. Voltage, temperature and oil gauges. Heavy-duty battery. Heavy-duty cooling system. Heavy-duty front springs. Heavy-duty front and rear shock absorbers. Heavy-duty power brakes. Heavy-duty rear springs. Limited-slip differential. Power brakes. Power steering. Trailering equipment. Light-duty Trailering Special package. Heavy-duty Trailering Special package. 5.0-liter/170-hp V-8, 5.7-liter 195-hp V-8, 6.2-liter 130-hp light-duty emissions equipped diesel V-8, 5.7-liter 185-hp V-8, 6.2-liter 145-hp heavy-duty emissions equipped diesel V-8. Three-speed automatic transmission G30. Four-speed automatic overdrive transmission (standard in G20 diesel and optional in other models). Four-speed manual overdrive transmission.

V10 BLAZER OPTIONS: Front air conditioning. Bright metal wheelcovers. Folding rear seat. Chromed front bumper guards. Deluxe front and rear bumpers. Cigarette lighter. Color-keyed floor mats. Comfortilt steering wheel. Deluxe front appearance package. Electric clock with quartz movement. Deep-tinted glass. Glass sliding side windows in removable top. Halogen headlamps. Headlight warning buzzer. Full-length interior headliner. Door edge guards. Operating convenience package with power door locks/power windows. GM Delco AM radio. GM Delco AM radio with digital clock. GM Delco AM/FM ETR radio with Seek-and-Scan. GM Delco AM/FM ETR radio with Seek-and-Scan. and digital clock GM Delco AM/FM ETR radio with Seek-and-Scan and cassette tape and clock. GM Delco AM/FM ETR radio with Seek-and-Scan, cassette, clock, and Search-and-Repeat. Windshield radio antenna. Intermittent windshield wipers. Painted below-eye-line mirrors. Stainless steel below-eye-line mirrors. Stainless steel camper mirrors. Black body side moldings. Bright body side moldings. Black custom molding package. Bright deluxe molding package. Windshield antenna. Power door locks. Power windows. Special two-tone paint. Exterior decor package. Folding rear seat. Electric tailgate window. Bright metal wheelcovers. Rally wheels. Styled wheels. Forged aluminum wheels. Cold climate package. Engine oil cooler. Transmission oil cooler. Deadweight trailer hitch. Cruise control. Front quad shocks. Front tow hooks. 31-gallon gas tank. Fuel tank stone shield plate. Heavy-duty battery. Heavy-duty front springs. Heavy-duty radiator. Automatic locking front hubs. Limited-slip differential. Trailering Special equipment. Trailer wiring harness. Weight distributing hitch platform. 5.7-liter EFI V-8. 6.2-liter diesel (standard with diesel equipment package). Four-speed automatic overdrive transmission.

SUBURBAN OPTIONS: Front air conditioning. Front and rear air conditioning. Bright metal wheelcovers (1/2-tons). Bucket seats. Chromed front bumper guards. Deluxe front and rear bumpers. Cigarette lighter. Color-keyed floor mats. Comfortilt steering wheel. Deluxe front appearance package. Electric clock with quartz movement. Deep-tinted glass. Door edge guards. Operating convenience package with power door locks/power windows. GM Delco AM radio. GM Delco AM radio with digital clock. GM Delco AM/FM ETR radio with Seek-and-Scan. GM Delco AM/FM ETR radio with Seek-and-Scan and digital clock. GM Delco AM/FM ETR radio with Seek-and-Scan and cassette tape and clock. GM Delco AM/FM ETR radio with Seek-and-Scan, cassette, clock, and Search-and-Repeat. Hi-beam halogen headlamps. Headlamp warning buzzer. Full-length interior headliner. Rear heater. Intermittent windshield wipers. Painted below-eye-line mirrors. Stainless steel below-eye-line mirrors. Stainless steel camper mirrors. Black body side moldings. Bright body side moldings. Black custom molding package. Bright deluxe molding package. Windshield antenna. Roof marker lamps. Three-passenger folding center seat. Three-passenger rear seat. Electric tailgate window. Electric tailgate window and defogger. Wagon-type tailgate. Aluminum wheels. Rally wheels (1/2-tons only). Styled wheels (1/2-ton 4x4 only). Pre-cleaner air cleaner. Auxiliary battery. Cold climate package. Engine oil cooler. Transmission oil cooler. Deadweight trailer hitch. Electronic speed control with resume and accelerate. Front quad shocks. Front stabilizer bar. Heavy-duty front stabilizer bar. Front tow hooks. 31-gallon gas or 32-gallon diesel fuel tank. 40-gallon gas or 41-gallon diesel fuel tank. Fuel tank stone shield plate. Temperature, voltage and oil pressure gauges. Heavy-duty battery. Heavy-duty front and rear shocks. Heavy-duty front springs. Heavy-duty radiator. Limited-slip differential. Power steering. Seven-wire trailering harness. Trailering Special equipment. Weight-distributing hitch platform. Three-speed automatic transmission in R20/V20. 5.7-liter V-8 in R10. 7.4-liter V-8 in R20. 6.2-liter diesel part of diesel package (available for all models, but not available in 1/2-tons in California.)

R/V AND C/K PICKUP OPTIONS: Silverado package RPO YE9. Deluxe bench seat. Bonus-Cab custom bench seat Crew-Cab bonus seats. Regular-Cab and Bonus-Cab custom vinyl bench seat. Crew-Cab custom vinyl bench seat. Conventional two-tone paint. Exterior decor package RPO ZY5. Special Big Dooley two-tone paint. California emissions equipment. 5.0-liter V-8 RPO LE9 or RPO LF3. 5.7-liter V-8 RPO L05. 7.4-liter V-8 RPO LE8. 6.2-liter diesel V-8. Three-speed automatic transmission RPO MX1. Four-speed manual overdrive transmission. Four-speed automatic transmission with overdrive RPO MXO. Optional axle ratios. Locking rear differential RPO G80. Heavy-duty power brakes for V10 and V20 RPO J55. Chromed rear bumper RPO VF1. Chromed rear step bumper RPO V42 (for Fleetside only). Painted rear step bumper RPO V43. Chromed front bumper guards RPO V31. Camper Special chassis equipment RPO Z81. Glide-out spare tire carrier RPO P11. Side-mounted spare tire carrier RPO P13 (for Fleetside only). Quartz electric clock RPO U35 including RPO Z53 voltmeter, temperature and oil pressure gauges (not available when UM6 radio is specified). Cold climate package including special insulation, RPO K81 66-ampere generator, special heater and defroster, RPO KO5 engine block heater, anti-freeze protection to -32 degrees and RPO UA1 heavy-duty battery RPO V10 (not available when RPO C60 air conditioning or RPO B3J diesel equipment is specified). Engine oil cooling system RPO KC4 (not available with RPO L250 engine or RPO B3J). Heavy-duty radiator RPO VO1. Heavy-duty radiator and transmission oil cooler RPO VO2 with RPO MX1 or RPO MXO transmissions (not available with RPO L25 engine or RPO VO1). Decor value package RPO YJ6 including black-painted radiator grille, headlight bezels, and special body stripe between body feature lines on front fenders, pickup box and the tailgate (not available on Bonus-Cab, Crew-Cab and Step-Side models or with options RPO YE9, RO5, V22, PA6, N90, B84 or B85). The RPO YJ6 decor value package also required RPO ZY1 solid paint and blackwall or white-lettered tires. Power door lock system RPO AU3. Color-keyed front floor mats RPO B32 (requires RPO YE9). Gauge package including voltmeter, engine coolant temperature and oil pressure RPO Z53. 66-ampere Delcotron generator RPO Z53 (standard on V30 except when RPO LE8 engine is ordered). 94-ampere Delcotron generator RPO K22 (included with LE8 engine on V30 models). Tinted glass-all windows RPO AO1. Halogen hi-beam headlamps RPO TT5 (available only when RPO V22 or RPO YE9 is specified). 600-watt engine block heater RPO KO5 (not available when RPO BK3 or RPO LF3 engine is specified). Heavy-duty front heater RPO C42 (available only when RPO B3J is specified and not available with RPO C60 air conditioning). Automatic front locking hubs RPO X6Z (available only for V10). Cargo lamp RPO UF2. Dome Lamp RPO C91. Roof marker lamps RPO UO1 (available for V20 only and standard on V30). Cigarette lighter RPO U37 (included when RPO Z62 or RPO YE9 were specified). Exterior left- and right-hand painted below-eye-line mirrors RPO D44 or stainless steel RPO D45. Camper-type stainless steel left and right side exterior mirrors RPO DF2. Senior West Coast type painted exterior left and right side mirrors RPO DG5. Black body side molding RPO B84 (available for Fleetsides only). Bright body side moldings RPO B85 (available for Fleetside only). Custom package RPO YG1 (available for Fleetside only including wheel opening moldings, RPO B84 , RPO B96 and bright trim for front side marker lamps and taillights.) Deluxe package RPO YG3 including bright trim for front side marker lamps and taillights (available for Fleetside only and not available with RPO YG1 or RPO RO5). Wheel opening molding RPO B96 (available only with RPO ZY6). Door edge guards RPO B93. Operating convenience package RPO ZQ2 including RPO AU3 power door locks and RPO A31 power windows. AM radio RPO U63. AM/FM radio RPO U69. AM./FM stereo radio RPO U58. AM/FM stereo radio with stereo cassette tape player RPO UN3. Electronically-tuned AM/FM stereo radio with Seek-and-Scan, stereo cassette player and clock RPO UM6. Windshield antenna RPO U76. Pickup box side rails RPO D73. Transfer case shield RPO NY7. Front quad shock absorbers RPO Z75. Electronic speed control RPO K34 (not available for V10 with MM7 transmission or V20 and V30 with LS9, LT9, LE8 or MM4 transmissions). Heavy-duty front springs RPO F60 for V10/V20, includes heavy-duty front and rear shock absorbers and recommended with snow plow use on V10 (not available for V30). Comfortilt steering wheel RPO N33 (not available when RPO MM3 was specified). Auxiliary fuel tank RPO NL2. Two front towing hooks RPO V76. Bright metal wheelcovers for V10 only RPO PO1. Special wheelcovers for V20 only RPO PA1. Rally wheels for V10 only RPO N67. Styled wheels RPO PA6. Aluminum cast wheels RPO N90. Dual rear wheels for V30 only RPO RO5. Power windows RPO A31. Sliding rear window RPO A28. Intermittent windshield wiper system RPO CD4.

NOTE 13: Options shown are representative. Some "options" may be standard equipment on certain models, such as V-8s in R/V30 pickups. Descriptions of options are edited. Full option contents can be determined by consulting sales-literature.

1987 Chevrolet 1/2-Ton El Camino SS "Choo-choo Customs" Pickup (CMD)

HISTORICAL: Chevrolet ran second in the 1987 truck sales race, behind rival Ford. American truck-makers saw their sales volume reach a record 4.9 million units in 1987, but Chevrolet dealers retailed just 1,191,848 units. This was a six percent drop from 1986. Chevrolet general manager Robert D. Burger was way off in his prediction of 1.3 million sales. Confusion among Chevrolet truck buyers may have been one reason for the sluggish sales. Chevrolet renamed its *old design* full-size trucks with R/V coding. The C1500 became the R10 and the K1500 became the V10. Chevrolet used these codes in the 1987 sales catalog. Later, in the spring of 1987, new full-size Chevrolet pickup trucks bowed as 1988 models. These all-new 1/2-ton pickups were based on the GMT400 corporate truck platform. They were also called R10/V10 models, adding to the confusion. After the new-design trucks were on the market, Chevrolet began referring to the old-design trucks as C/Ks and the new-design trucks as R/Vs, which was technically incorrect. Also, this was done despite the fact that larger pickups (R30/V30s for example) retained the old-design (C/K?) look, as did the big Blazer and both Suburbans. All this made it very hard to follow the model nomenclature that the factory used. Even though the new-design trucks were 1988 models, their early production totals are included with Chevrolet's 1987 model-year totals. This is another confusing policy. In addition to general manager Robert D. Burger, the Chevrolet Motor Division truck team included John M. Kelley as marketing manager for trucks, Thomas P. Cutler as manager of truck advertising, and Kenneth P. Wechselberger as truck merchandising manager. Ralph J. Kramer was overall director of public relations, including Chevrolet truck publicity. Chevrolet calendar-year new-truck sales were 417,670 Light-Duty Conventionals, 224,807 S10/T10 Pickups, 153,064 S-Series Blazers, 114,835 Chevy Vans, 57,292 Astro Vans, 57,962 Suburbans, 30,859 K10 Blazers, 90,913 Astro Wagons, 11,979 Sportvans, 13,743 El Caminos, 588 W4 Tiltmaster imports, and 18,136 Medium-Duty R/V models. This gave the company sales of 1,191,848 light-duty trucks in the calendar-year. The 1987 Chevrolet light-duty truck models were introduced on September 7, 1986. The all-new Chevrolet full-size Pickup bowed in April 1987.

1988

1988 Chevrolet 1/2-Ton S10 "Back Country" Extended-cab Pickup

1/2-TON — S (4x2)/T (4x4) SERIES PICKUP — L4/V-6: Initially, the 1988 S10 was offered with either the 2.5-liter or 2.8-liter engines. Beginning in April 1988, Chevrolet's new 4.3-literVortex V-6 became an option. Redeveloped all-season tires were available for the 1988 Chevrolet S10. Front brakes had new noise reducing "SAS II" brake lining insulators. The S10 instrument panel now had gray trim plate accents. The knobs and switches remained black. LED displays on stereo radios were replaced by vacuum fluorescent lights. During 1988, the optional air conditioning system was fitted with illuminated blue heating, ventilation, and air conditioning control lighting for improved indication of knob locations. Map lights were added to the inside rear view mirror. For 1988, the S10 was available with an optional factory-installed-tinted sunroof. This non-removable roof had manual operation for its five different opening positions. Four new exterior colors were added for 1988: Light Mesa Brown, Bright Blue Metallic, Light Mesa Brown Metallic, and Dark Mesa Brown Metallic. Replacing saddle tan as an interior color was cognac. The base model's standard equipment included a three-passenger vinyl bench seat with folding back rest, sound insulation and sound-deadening material installed in dash and doors and roof, color-keyed door trim panels with padded arm rests, embossed color-keyed headliner, and AM radio. The Durango stepped up the base interior equipment to include bright Durango nameplate on storage box door, choice of custom vinyl or special custom cloth seat trim, color-keyed rubber matting for floor area, a deluxe steering wheel, side window defoggers, bright dome lamp trim, a cigarette lighter, a headlamps-on warning buzzer, and a deluxe heater and defogger. The Durango exterior included bright Durango nameplates with series designation on front fenders, bright front bumper with black rub strips, bright trim on a black grille, bright taillight trim, bright wheel trim rings, and reflectorized Chevrolet tailgate lettering. The Tahoe package included all interior Durango items, plus bright Tahoe nameplate on the stowage box, color-keyed carpeting for floor area and cab back panel, color-keyed cowl kick panels, a visor mirror on right side sun visor, special custom cloth inserts in the door trim panels, a carpeted lower door panel insert with storage pocket, a coin holder in the left side door, a full-coverage molded styrene headliner of full foam with color-keyed cloth (in regular-cab) and an instrument panel cluster including voltmeter, oil pressure gauge, engine coolant and temperature gauges, and a trip odometer. The Tahoe exterior had bright Tahoe nameplates with the series designations on the front fenders, black body side moldings with bright trim, bright wheel opening lip moldings, black hub covers, body-color door handle inserts, black appliqué tailgate trim with Chevrolet lettering, and Argent colored wheels. The Sport package included all interior Tahoe items, plus a bright Sport nameplate on the stowage box door, "Sport Cloth" high-back front bucket seats, a Sport steering wheel, door trim panels with Sport Cloth inserts that matched the seat trim, and a color-keyed console with lockable storage compartment operated by door key. The Sport exterior featured Sport nameplates with series designations on the front fenders, Sport two-tone paint, a color-keyed front bumper with black rib strips (keyed to the lower accent stripe of two-tone paint schemes), base Argent wheels with black ornamental hubs and bright trim rings, black chrome door handles, grille and headlamp bezels, and black wheel opening lip moldings. Introduced during the 1987 model-year and continued for 1988 was the Back Country option for Tahoe-equipped S10 trucks. It featured a front grille guard with driving lamps and headlight brush hoops, a light "bridge" with off-road lamps, a tubular rear bumper, switches in the instrument panel for driving and off-road lights, black chrome accents on the wheels and headlight and taillight bezels and grille, and striping around the wheel openings and around the front of the grille. Required options for the Back Country package included power steering, a 1,500 pound. load package, off-road chassis equipment, and the 2.8-literV-6.

1/2-TON — S-SERIES BLAZER — L4/V-6: The 1988 S-Series Blazer's standard engine was the 2.8-literV-6. Additional changes for 1988 models were very limited. Models with rear seats were fitted with rear seat shoulder belts midway into the model-year. Redeveloped all-season tires were available, too. Installed on all front brakes were new "SAS II" brake lining insulators that reduced brake noise. For 1988, the S-Series Blazer was available with a new optional factory-installed-tinted sun roof. It was manually-operated with five different opening positions and was non-removable. The S-Series Blazer's instrument panel was revised with gray accents on the trim plates. The knobs and switches remained black. LED displays on stereo radios were replaced by vacuum florescent lights. During the model-year S-Series Blazers with air conditioning were equipped with illuminated blue heating, ventilation, and air-conditioning control lighting for improved indication of knob locations. Map lights were added to the inside rear view mirror. Four new exterior colors were added for 1988: Light Mesa Brown, Bright Blue Metallic, Light Mesa Brown Metallic and Dark Mesa Brown Metallic. Replacing saddle tan as an interior color was cognac. Beginning in April 1988, the new 4.3-literVortex V-6 became an option for the S-Series Blazer.

1/2-TON — ASTRO M (RWD) SERIES — V-6: The Astro was Chevrolet's rear-wheel-drive minivan. The base model was the Astro Cargo Van. Its standard equipment included a 2.5-liter EFI four-cylinder engine, front disc brakes, five-speed manual transmission with overdrive, and P205/75R15 all-season black sidewall steel-belted-radial tires. The Cargo Van model had a sliding tight-hand load door as standard equipment. It featured a vinyl interior with choice of low- or high-back bucket seats. The Astro also came in three Passenger Van version featuring CS (Custom Sport), CL (Custom Luxury) or LT (Luxury Touring) trim levels. The passenger model had standard double swing-out door on the right-hand side. The CS model had a standard vinyl interior with high-back bucket seats. The CL model added custom vinyl upholstery. The LT model added custom cloth upholstery. Standard equipment included a 4.3-liter EFI V-6, front disc brakes, five-speed manual transmission with overdrive, and P205/75R15 all-season black sidewall steel-belted-radial tires.

1/2-TON, 3/4-TON, 1-TON VAN — G-SERIES 10, 20, 30 — V-6/V-8: The basic models were the Chevy Van and the Sportvan. Both came as G10/G20/G30 class models. The Chevy Vans were primarily designed as cargo vans. The Sportvan series consisted of windowed passenger vans. The fancy version of the Sportvan was called the Beauville. The Chevy Van cargo vans and Sportvan/Beauville passenger vans came with a 110-in. short wheelbase (SWB) or 125-in. long wheelbase (LWB). Hi-Cube trucks made from full-size vans came with the 125-in. LWB stance or a 146-in. extended wheelbase (EWB). Respective body lengths were 178, 202, and 223 in.. One G10 Chevy Van and one G10 Sportvan came as SWB models. There was an SWB G20 cargo van, too. The G20 Chevy Van, Sportvan and Beauville models also came as LWB models. G30 Chevy Van, Sportvan and Beauville models were offered only as LWB models. The High-Cube vans were on the G30 chassis. Standard equipment in Chevy Vans included a 4.3-liter V-6, heavy-duty power brakes with rear antilock feature, three-speed automatic transmission, and P205/75R14 all-season steel-belted-radial tires. The 5.0-liter, 5.7-liter, and 7.4-liter gas V-8s were optional in these models, as was a 6.2-liter diesel V-8. Sportvan models had about the same standard features, except for a four-speed automatic overdrive transmission being standard in all lines. The 5.7-liter V-8 was standard in heavy-duty G30 Chevy Van, Sportvan and Beauville models.

3/4-TON/1-TON — P20/P30 STEP-VAN — V-8: Also available in 1988 were two series of Step-Vans. They had boxy bodies well-suited for stop-and-go delivery service. The base body offered, in both the P20 (3/4-ton)and P30 (1-ton) lines had a 10-1/2-foot length. Step-Vans offered wheelbases ranging from 125 to 178 in.. A 350-cid V-8 was the standard engine. A 6.2-liter diesel V-8 was optional. Standard size tires were LT215/85R16Cs.

1/2-TON — V1500 BLAZER (4x4) — V-8: The 1988 full-size K1500 Blazer was offered with either a standard 5.7-liter electronic fuel injected (EFI) V-8 or a 6.2-liter diesel, also with EFI. Four new colors were introduced for 1988: Bright Blue Metallic, Forest Green Metallic, Light Mesa Brown Metallic, and Dark Mesa Brown Metallic. New features for 1988 include a fixed mast antenna in place of the old windshield antenna, a trip odometer as part of the gauge package cluster, and an improved pulse windshield wiper control. Helping to reduce air leaks in the K1500 Blazer's doors was a new door handle seal. Brake noise was lowered due to new front lining noise insulators. The "big" Blazer's fuel tank corrosion-protection was upgraded to be more tolerant of methanol fuel.

1/2-TON, 3/4-TON — R (4x2)/V (4x4) SUBURBAN — V-8: The famous Chevy Suburban resembled a giant four-door station wagon. It was built on a light-duty truck chassis. They were manufactured in the General Motors assembly plant at Flint, Michigan. The Suburban's standard engine was the 5.7-liter EFI V-8. Optional was a 7.4-liter V-8 that was the most powerful engine available in any Chevrolet light-duty trucks. The standard and heavy-duty 6.2-liter diesel V-8s carried different horsepower and torque ratings. Both 1/.2- and 3/4-ton Suburbans comfortably sat nine adults. They shared 165 cubic feet of cargo space. The 4x2 and 4x4 models were each available as 1/2- and 3/4-ton models. They continued to be offered in Scottsdale or Silverado trim. Suburbans came standard with double panel doors at the rear. Suburbans equipped with tailgates offered manual- and power-operated rear window options.

1988 Chevrolet 1/2-Ton C1500 Sportside Short Box Pickup 4x2

1/2-TON, 3/4-TON, 1-TON — C (4x2)/K (4x4) PICKUP, R (4x2), V (4x4) H-D PICKUP — V-6/V-8: Chevrolet introduced an all-new range of full-size R/V pickups on April 23, 1987 as 1988 models. The new trucks were produced at three assembly plants in Fort Wayne, Indiana, Pontiac, Michigan and Oshawa, Ontario, Canada. Adding sales appeal, as well as representing a new avenue of versatility, were the extended-cab models with optional six-passenger seating. The wheelbases of the new models were (SWB) 117.5 in., (LWB and chassis-and-cab) 131.5 in., and (EWB/extended-cab) 155.5 in.. These dimensions were unchanged from the earlier C/K trucks, although the new models were longer than the older models. The exterior was 3.5-in. narrower, but the interior had more leg and shoulder room, as well as more seat travel. The new model's doors were larger. They extended upward into the roof line and downward nearly to the bottom of the rocker. The new doors, along with a low step-up height and high headroom, made for ease of entry and exit. The Fleetside pickup box measured 49.15-in. between the wheel wells and 63.8-in. between the side panels. Numerous features, such as flush side glass, a modular-assembled bonded-flush windshield, single-piece door frames, and robotic welding marked the latest R/V Chevrolet trucks as very advanced vehicles. Chevrolet went to great lengths to improve the fit and finish of its 1988 models. The use of hidden roof pillars and built-in drip rails eliminated matching problems on door cuts. The back of the cab and the front of the pickup box were both mounted on a single, one-piece fixture. This bracket eliminated mismatch of the two sections, especially when the box was loaded. The new model's front end was fitted with a single-piece grille which eliminated potential molding mismatch with single headlamps at each corner. The Silverado was equipped with dual halogen headlamps. Structural rigidity was improved with double-panel construction for the roof, hood, fenders, doors, and pickup box. One of the most apparent features of the new generation Chevrolet truck was its greatly increased glass area which, at 4,256 square in., was one-third larger than the older model's. The use of a bonded, angled and curved backlight was credited with reducing glare. To improve visibility in poor weather, the wiper pattern was enlarged. Improved anti-corrosion protection was a high priority for designers of the Chevrolet. The all-welded pickup box had a seamless floor without bolts for enhanced corrosion resistance. Two-sided galvanized steel was used for all major exterior panels, except the roof. All exterior sheet metal was primer dipped. Anti-stone protection was applied to the lower fenders, door, and pickup box. Both the windshield and backlight were constructed without mitered corners. The front bumper was devoid of attaching bolts. This had the dual result of improving appearance while also removing another source of potential corrosion. Prior to painting, all sheet metal panels were immersion-washed to remove contaminants for better paint adhesion. A uniprime ELPO dip treatment drew the protective primer into recessed areas. The color coat/clear coat paint provided a hard, high-luster finish. The color selection for 1988 consisted of Brandywine Metallic, Sandstone Metallic, Pacific Blue Metallic, Adobe Gold Metallic, Sable Black Metallic, Quicksilver Metallic, Spice Brown Metallic, Summit White, Flame Red, and Iced Blue Metallic. Three optional exterior two-tone schemes were offered. Conventional two-toning placed the accent color below the lower styling line. Special two-toning included a multi-stripe decal at the upper styling line and the accent color below. Deluxe two-toning featured a multi-stripe decal at the upper styling line and the accent color between the decal and the lower feature line. In place of the former C/K10, C/K20 and C/K30 designations (and the short-lived V prefix), the 1988 designations for Chevrolet's 1/2 ton, 3/4 ton and 1 ton models were R/V1500, R/V2500, and R/V3500. No Step-Side models were offered. Chevrolet used three well-known names for the trim packages available for 1988. The base package was the Cheyenne, which was depicted as "a new value standard in full-size work trucks." The mid-range Scottsdale was described as "a big step up in a sensible blend of function and form." The Silverado, regarded as "the finest expression of the new '88 Chevy full-size Pickup," remained the top-of-the line trim package. Standard interior features on all models were the following items: Right- and left-hand arm rests, an instrument panel-mounted ash tray, a right side coat hook (also a left-hand hook in extended-cabs), painted areas in the same color as the exterior primary color, interior trim identical to seat trim, color-keyed molded plastic door trim panels, a left-door jam switch-operated dome light,-tinted glass (in all windows on extended-cab models), a heater and defroster with side window defoggers, an inside-operated hood lock release, a speedometer, an odometer, and a fuel gauge, warning lights for generator and oil pressure and engine coolant temperature, safety belts, a service/parking brake, direction/hazard signals and high beams, insulation and sound-deadening material installed on the firewall, under floor mats and on extended-cab-rear quarter and cab back panels, a storage box located on right side of instrument panel with beverage holder on inside of door, instrument cluster and cab interior lights, a shift point indicator light with manual transmissions and gasoline engines, a 4x4 lighted display, a 10-in. inside day/night rear view mirror, a foam-padded and full-width bench seat with folding back rest and vinyl trim, safety belts for all seating positions, a 15.25-in. soft black plastic four-spoke steering wheel, an energy-absorbing steering column, left and right side padded vinyl sun shades, a front chrome bumper, a molded plastic Argent Silver-painted grille, a single electric low-tone horn, black plastic hubcaps with 4x4 identification, backup lights integral with taillamps, two rectangular headlights, front and rear directional and parking lamps, front side marker lamps, a removable tailgate with embossed Chevrolet lettering, a mechanical jack, a wheel wrench, silver-painted wheels, and electric two-speed windshield wipers and washers. All models were fitted with new anti-theft door locks with sliding levers integrated into the door trim panels. Cheyenne features included a Cheyenne designation on the rear cab side pillars and a choice of five interior colors: gray, blue, saddle, beige or garnet. The Scottsdale package Z62) had the following equipment in addition to or replacing that of the Cheyenne level: Dual electric high-note and low-note horns, Scottsdale nameplates on the rear cab side pillars, a chrome front bumper with black rub strip, a Chevrolet block lettering decal on the tailgate, a standard bench seat with cloth upholstery and folding back rest in the same color selection as Scottsdales offered, grained plastic interior door panels with soft-vinyl upper trim and integral arm rests, map pockets and Scottsdale identification on doors, color-keyed door-sill plates, color-keyed rubber floor mats (front compartment only on Bonus-Cab), a full-length mystic-colored insulated cloth headliner with matching retainer moldings, left and right-side coat hooks, and Scottsdale identification on door trim panels. The Silverado Package YE9), included all Scottsdale features plus the following: Hood and cab-to-fender insulators, a deluxe front end appearance with Dark Argent Silver grille and quad rectangular halogen headlamps, a deluxe bright-accented front bumper rub strip, bright accent body side moldings, bright accent wheel-opening molding (single rear wheel Fleetside models only), deluxe tailgate trim with Chevrolet lettering over bright aluminum appliqué, Silverado identification on cab back pillars, custom vinyl seat trim in gray, blue, beige, garnet or saddle (custom cloth seat trim at no extra cost), soft-vinyl two-tone door trim panels with integral arm rests and door map pockets and door-closing assist straps and Silverado identification, color-keyed full-length carpeting, carpeted cowl/kick panels with insulators, carpeted cab back panels, a color-keyed headliner, cloth-covered sun shades with left-hand storage provisions and a strap, a right-hand vanity mirror, a custom four-spoke steering wheel, and a cigarette lighter in the ash tray. The 4x2 Chevrolets featured an independent coil spring front suspension in all weight classes. The C1500/C2500 models used a semi-floating rear axle, while the C3500s had a full-floating rear axle. The 4x4 trucks were fitted with a new independent front suspension with a hypoid driving axle and torsion bar springs. It utilized a new wire-form design for the upper control arms with lighter and stronger parts than the components previously used. The torsion bar springs and jounce bumpers were connected to the lower control arms. The torsion bars were computer selected to correspond with the truck's GVW rating and balance with the rear springs. The frame used on 4x4 trucks had an additional front cross member located under the transmission case. The 4x4 trucks also had a new "Shift-On-The-Fly Instra-Trac" transfer case system allowing for shifting from 4x2 to 4x4 high, and back, without stopping at any speed. The front axle disconnect system locked the front hubs automatically when the single lever operating the 4x4 system was pulled backward. This shifter was located in the center of the cab floor and was connected directly to the transfer case, rather than using cables. In the 4x2 mode, the front-axle disconnect allowed the front wheels to turn freely . In the 4x4 mode, the transfer case split the power and directed it equally to the front and rear wheels. Rear axles used on 4x4 models were of the same type and capacity as the ones used on 4x2 trucks. The K1500 was available with an optional off-road chassis package consisting of a front differential carrier, engine and transfer case shields, front stabilizer bar, Delco/Bilstein high-pressure gas shock absorbers, and heavier front and rear jounce bumpers. The standard V-6 engine for the K1500 and K2500 series had a new one-piece rubber oil pan gasket to help prevent oil leakage. As a midyear treat, Chevrolet introduced a new K1500 Sportside model on the 117.5-in. wheelbase chassis. It had a 6.5 foot long pickup box. The fiberglass rear fenders or side panels were flanked by functional steps to aid in loading and unloading. The Sportside was available with any trim level and with most appearance, convenience, and performance options offered for other 4x4 models. This new truck's body style designator was E62. Also introduced during the latter part of the 1988 model-year was a new instrument cluster featuring enhanced cluster graphics that increased clarity of instrument readings at all light levels.

I. D. DATA: The VIN plate was mounted on the lower left side windshield corner. The VIN consisted of 17 symbols. The first three symbols identify the country, the manufacturer and the type of vehicle. The fourth symbol designate the GVWR. The fifth, sixth and seventh symbols identify the line and chassis type, series and body type. The eighth symbol identifies the engine [Chevrolet engines] C=6.2-liter/130 hp diesel V-8, H=5.0-liter V-8, J=6.2-liter/148 hp diesel V-8, K=5.7-liter V-8, M=5.7-liter V-8,N=7.4-liter V-8, R=2.8-liter V-6, T=4.8-liter L6, W=7.4-liter V-8, Z=4.3-liter V-6. [GM engines] A=5.7-liter V-8, [Pontiac engine] E=2.5-liter L4. The ninth symbol is the check digit. The tenth symbol indicates model-year. The eleventh symbol identifies the assembly plant. The last six symbols are the sequential production number.

1988 Chevrolet 1/2-Ton C1500 Fleetside Long Box Pickup 4x2 (CMD)

Model	Body Type	Price	Weight	Prod. Total
S10 Fleetside Pickup — 1/2-Ton — 108.3/117.9/122.9 in. w.b. — 2.5-liter EFI L4				
S10603	Reg. Cab Short Box EL	6595	2568	Note 12
S10603	Reg. Cab Short Box	8238	2625	Note 12
S10803	Reg. Cab Long Box	8412	2703	Note 12
S10653	Ext. Cab Short Box	9257	2767	Note 12
T10 Fleetside Pickup — 1/2-Ton — 108.3/117.9/122.9 in. w.b. — 2.5-liter EFI L4				
T10603	Reg. Cab Short Box	10,414	2919	Note 12
T10803	Reg. Cab Long Box	10,579	2997	Note 12
T10653	Ext. Cab Short Box	11,197	3061	Note 12
NOTE 1: A $400 dealer destination charge applied to S-Series pickups				
S10 Blazer 4x2 Sport Utility Wagon — 1/2-Ton — 100.5/107 in. w.b. — 2.5-liter L4				
CS10516	2-dr Tailgate	10,505	2804	Note 12
T10 Blazer 4x4 Sport Utility Wagon — 1/2-Ton — 100.5/107 in. w.b. — 2.8-liter EFI V-6				
CT10516	2-dr Tailgate	12,737	3217	Note 12
NOTE 2: A $435 dealer destination charge applied to S-Series Blazers				
M10 Astro Minivan (rear-wheel-drive) — 1/2-Ton — 111 in. w.b. — 4.3-liter EFI V-6				
CM10906	Standard Cargo Van	9585	3268	Note 12
CM10906/ZW9	Standard CS Van	10,696	3544	Note 12
CM10906	Standard CL Van	11,489	3594	Note 12
CM10906	Standard LT Van	12,828	3636	Note 12
NOTE 3: A $500 dealer destination charge applied to Astros				
G10 Van — 1/2-Ton — 110/125 in. w.b. — 4.3-liter EFI V-6				
CG11005	SWB Chevy Van	10,735	4003	Note 12
CG11006/ZW9	SWB Sportvan	12,417	4954	Note 12
CG11306/ZW9	LWB Bonaventure	13,825	5265	Note 12
CG11306/ZW9	LWB Beauville	13,984	5252	Note 12
G20 Van — 3/4-Ton — 110/125 in. w.b. — 4.3-liter EFI V-6				
CG21005	SWB Chevy Van	11,360	4086	Note 12
CG21005	SWB Chevy Van diesel	13,787	4872	Note 12
CG21305/ZW9	LWB Sportvan	12,918	5138	Note 12
CG21306/ZW9	LWB Bonaventure	13,825	5265	Note 12
CG21306/ZW9	LWB Beauville	14,231	5273	Note 12
G30 Van — 1-Ton — 125/146 in. w.b. — 5.7-liter EFI V-8				
CG31305	LWB Chevy Van	12,594	4573	Note 12
CG31305	LWB Chevy Van HD	13,230	4528	Note 12
CG31306/ZW9	LWB Sportvan 12P	14,663	5486	Note 12
CG31306/ZW9	LWB Bonaventure	15,571	6867	Note 12
CG31306/ZW9	LWB Beauville	15,976	6912	Note 12
CG31306	LWB Cutaway	11,305	3925	Note 12
G30 Hi-Cube Van — 1-Ton — 125/146 in. w.b. — 5.7-liter EFI V-8				
CG31	10-ft. Van	16,042	5580	Note 12
CG31	12-ft. Van	16,239	6058	Note 12
NOTE 4: A $550 dealer destination charge applied to full-size vans				
P20 — 3/4-Ton Step-Van — 125/133 in. w.b. — 5.7-liter EFI V-8				
P22	10.5-ft. Step-Van	15,747	6028	Note 12
P30 — 1-Ton Step-Van — 125/178 in. w.b. — 5.7-liter EFI V-8				
P32	10.5-ft. Step-Van	15,896	6154	Note 12
K1500 Blazer — 1/2-Ton — 111.5 in. w.b. — 5.7-liter EFI V-8				
CK10516	Utility Hardtop	14,509	4676	Note 12
NOTE 5: A $550 dealer destination charge applied to full-size Blazers				
R/V 1500 Suburban — 1/2-Ton — 131.5 in. w.b. — 5.7-liter EFI V-8				
R16	Panel Door (4x2)	13,945	4917	Note 12
R16	Panel Door diesel (4x2)	16,808	4815	Note 12
R16	Panel Door (4x4)	15,418	4800	Note 12
R/V 2500 Suburban — 3/4-Ton — 131.5 in. w.b. — 5.7-liter EFI V-8				
R26	Panel Door (4x2)	14,559	5266	Note 12
R26	Panel Door (4x4)	16,799	5496	Note 12
NOTE 6: A $610 dealer destination charge applied to Suburbans				
NOTE 7: Add $40 for tailgate models				
R1500 — 1/2-Ton Short Box — 117.5 in. w.b. — 4.3-liter EFI V-6				
RC10703	Regular-cab Sportside	10,472	4093	Note 12
RC10703	Regular-cab Fleetside	10,264	4181	Note 12
R1500 Pickup — 1/2-Ton Long Box — 131.5 in. w.b. — 4.3-liter EFI V-6				
RC10903	Regular-cab Fleetside	10,454	4250	Note 12
R1500 Pickup — 1/2-Ton Short Box — 141.5 in. w.b. — 4.3-liter EFI V-6				
RC10753	Extended-cab Fleetside	11,661	4608	Note 12
NOTE 8: Add approximately $2,077 for RK1500 Pickups with 4x4.				
R2500 Pickup — 3/4-Ton Long Box — 131.5 in. w.b. — 4.3-liter EFI V-6				
RC20903	Regular-cab Fleetside	11,291	4454	Note 12

Model	Body Type	Price	Weight	Prod. Total
R2500 Pickup — 3/4-Ton Long Box — 141.5 in. w.b. — 4.3-liter EFI V-6				
RC20953	Extended-cab Fleetside	12,611	4758	Note 12
R2500 Pickup — 3/4-Ton EEWB Long Box — 164.5 in. w.b. — 4.8-liter EFI L6				
TR20953	Bonus-Cab Fleetside	13,632	5197	Note 12
TR20953	Crew-cab Fleetside	14,608	5528	Note 12

NOTE 9: Ad approximately $1,552 for RK2500 Pickups with 4x4.

Model	Body Type	Price	Weight	Prod. Total
R3500 Pickup — 1-Ton Long Box — 131.5 in. w.b. — 5.7-liter EFI V-8				
RC30934	Chassis-and-cab Fleetside	11,451	4032	Note 12
RC30934	Regular-cab Fleetside	11,291	4454	Note 12
R3500 Pickup — 1-Ton Long Box — 141.5 in. w.b. — 5.7-liter EFI V-8				
RC30939	Chassis-&-Extended Fleetside	12,454	4657	Note 12
RC30939	Extended-cab Fleetside	13,033	5012	Note 12
R3500 Pickup — 1-Ton EEWB Long Box — 155.5 in. w.b. — 4.8-liter EFI L6				
TR30943	Chassis & Cab	11,545	4348	Note 12
TR30943	Bonus-Cab Fleetside	13,828	5233	Note 12
TR30943	Crew-cab Fleetside	14,268	5564	Note 12
R3500 Pickup—1-Ton EEWB Long Box—164.5 in. w.b.—4.8-liter EFI L6/5.7-liter EFI V-8.				
TR30953	Chassis & Bonus-Cab	12,700	4859	Note 12
TR30953	Chassis & Crew-cab	13,142	5371	Note

NOTE 10: Add approximately $2,020 for CK3500 Pickups with 4x4.

NOTE 11: A $550 dealer destination charge applied to R/V Pickups.

NOTE 12: Model year production [S10 regular-cab pickup] 216,301, [S10 extended-cab pickup] 42,416, [R/V1500] 375,330, [R/V2500] 97,200, [R/V3500] 41,988, [R/V 25/35] 47,406, [S-Series Blazer] 157,264, [K1500 Blazer] 28,446, [Suburban] 70,660, [Astro Wagon] 106,247, [Astro Cargo Van] 63,286, [Sportvan] 12,407, [Chevy Van] 121,560.

GASOLINE ENGINES (DISPLACEMENT ORDER)

ENGINE: Inline. Four-cylinder. Bore & stroke: 4.00 x 3.00 in. Displacement: 2.5-liter (151 cid). BHP: 92 at 4400 rpm. Torque: 130 lb.-ft. at 2300 rpm. Compression ratio: 8.3:1. EFI/Throttle-body-injection. VIN Code E. GM-built. [Standard in S10/T10, S-Series Blazer 4x2]

ENGINE: V-block. Six-cylinder. Bore & stroke: 3.52 x 2.99 in. Displacement: 2.8-liter (173 cid). BHP: 125 at 4800 rpm. Torque: 150 lb.-ft. at 2400 rpm. Compression ratio: 8.9:1. EFI/Throttle-body-injection. VIN Code R. Chevrolet-built. [Standard in S-Series Blazer 4x4s, optional in S10]

ENGINE: V-block. Six-cylinder. Bore & stroke: 4.0 x 3.48 in. Displacement: 4.3-liter (262 cid). BHP: 150 at 4000 rpm. Torque: 230 lb.-ft. at 2400 rpm. Compression ratio: 9.3:1. EFI/Throttle-body-injection. VIN Code n.a. GM-built. [Standard in G10, G20, Astro]

ENGINE: V-block. Six-cylinder. Bore & stroke: 4.0 x 3.48 in. Displacement: 4.3-liter (262 cid). BHP: 160 at 4000 rpm. Torque: 235 lb.-ft. at 2400 rpm. Compression ratio: 9.1:1. EFI/Throttle-body-injection. VIN Code Z. Chevrolet-built. [Standard in R/V 1500/2500, optional in S10/T10 pickups, optional in all S-Blazers]

ENGINE: Inline. Six-cylinder. Bore & stroke: 3.88 x 4.12 in. Displacement: 4.8-liter (292 cid). BHP: 115 at 4000 rpm. Torque: 210 lb.-ft. at 800 rpm. Compression ratio: 7.8:1, Carburetor: 1V. VIN Code T. Chevrolet-built. [Standard in R/V C3500]

ENGINE: V-block. Eight-cylinder. Bore & stroke: 3.74 x 3.48 in. Displacement: 5.0-liter (305 cid). BHP: 170 at 4000 rpm. Torque: 255 lb.-ft. at 2400 rpm. EFI/Throttle-body-injection. VIN Code H. Chevrolet-built. [Optional in R/V1500, R/V2500, G10, G20]

ENGINE: V-block. Eight-cylinder. Bore & stroke: 4.0 x 3.48 in. Displacement: 5.7-liter (350 cid). BHP: 190 at 4000 rpm. Torque: 300 lb.-ft. at 2400 rpm. Compression ratio: 8.6:1. EFI/Throttle-body-injection. VIN Code A. GM-built. [Standard in heavy-duty R/V3500, Suburbans, and heavy-duty G30 vans, optional in R/V pickups]

ENGINE: V-block. Eight-cylinder. Bore & stroke: 4.0 x 3.48 in. Displacement: 5.7-liter (350 cid). BHP: 210 at 4000 rpm. Compression ratio: 9.3:1. Torque: 300 lb.-ft. at 2800 rpm. EFI/Throttle-body-injection. VIN Code K. Chevrolet-built. [Standard in R/V Blazer, optional, optional in Suburban, optional in Chevy Van, optional in Sportvan]

ENGINE: V-block. Eight-cylinder. Bore & stroke: 4.25 x 4.00 in. Displacement: 7.4-liter (454 cid). BHP: 230 at 3600 rpm. Torque: 385 lb.-ft. at 1600 rpm. Throttle-body- fuel-injection. VIN Code N. Chevrolet-built. [Optional in Suburban, and heavy-duty G30 vans]

1988 Chevrolet 3/4-Ton C2500 Fleetside Long Box Pickup 4x2 (CMD)

DIESEL ENGINES (DISPLACEMENT ORDER)

ENGINE: V-block. Light-duty. Eight-cylinder. Bore & stroke: 3.98 x 3.82 in. Displacement: 6.2-liter (379 cid). BHP: 148 at 3600 rpm. Torque: 248 lb.-ft. at 2000 rpm. VIN Code J. GM-built. [Optional in R/V3500 pickup, optional in G30 Chevy Van and 12-passenger Sportvan]

ENGINE: V-block. Heavy-duty. Eight-cylinder. Bore & stroke: 3.98 x 3.82 in. Displacement: 6.2-liter (379 cid). BHP: 130 at 3600 rpm. Torque: 240 lb.-ft. at 2000 rpm. VIN Code C. GM-built. [Optional in R/V3500 pickup, optional in G30 Chevy Van and 12-passenger Sportvan]

CHASSIS: [S10] Regular-cab. Short Box. Wheelbase: 108.3 in. Length: 178.2 in. Width: 64.7 in. Height: 61.3 in. Standard GVW: 3,570 lb. Maximum GVW: 5,054 lb. Tires: P195/75R14 black sidewall.

CHASSIS: [T10] Regular-cab. Short Box. Wheelbase: 108.3 in. Length: 178.2 in. Width: 64.7 in. Height: 61.3 in. Standard GVW: 3,919 lb. Maximum GVW: 5,380 lb. Tires: P205/75R15 black sidewall.

CHASSIS: [S10] Regular-cab. Long box. Wheelbase: 117.9 in. Length: 194.2 in. Width: 64.7 in. Height: 61.3 in. Standard GVW: 3,570 lb. Maximum GVW: 5,429 lb. Tires: P195/75R14 black sidewall.

CHASSIS: [S10] Regular-cab. Long box. Wheelbase: 117.9 in. Length: 194.2 in. Width: 64.7 in. Height: 61.3 in. Standard GVW: 3,919 lb. Maximum GVW: 5,380 lb. Tires: P205/75R15 black sidewall.

CHASSIS: [S10] Extended-cab. Short box. Wheelbase: 122.9 in. Length: 192.8 in. Width: 64.7 in. Height: 61.3 in. Standard GVW: 3,570 lb. Maximum GVW: 5,034 lb. Tires: P195/75R14 black sidewall.

1988 Chevrolet 1/2-Ton K1500 Pickups and NASCAR Support Vehicles 4x4 (CMD)

CHASSIS: [T10] Extended-cab. Short box. Wheelbase: 122.9 in. Length: 192.8 in. Width: 64.7 in. Height: 61.3 in. Standard GVW: 3,919 lb. Maximum GVW: 5,380 lb. Tires: P205/75R15 black sidewall.

CHASSIS: [S-Blazer 4x2] Two-door. Wheelbase: 100.5 in. Length: 170.3 in. Width: 65.4 in. Height: 64.7 in. Standard GVW: 3,870 lb. Maximum GVW: 4,638 lb. Tires: P205/75R15 black sidewall.

CHASSIS: [S-Blazer 4x4] Two-door. Wheelbase: 100.5 in. Length: 170.3 in. Width: 65.4 in. Height: 64.7 in. Standard GVW: 4,150 lb. Maximum GVW: 5,013 lb. Tires: P205/75R15 black sidewall.

CHASSIS: [Astro Cargo regular-body] Wheelbase: 111 in. Length: 176.8 in. Width: 77.0 in. Height: 73.7 in. Standard GVW: 4,088 lb. Maximum GVW: 5,600 lb. Tires: P205/75R15 black sidewall.

CHASSIS: [Astro Passenger regular-body] Wheelbase: 111 in. Length: 176.8 in. Width: 77.0 in. Height: 73.7 in. Standard GVW: 4,404 lb. Maximum GVW: 5,439 lb. Tires: P205/75R15 black sidewall.

CHASSIS: [G10/Short Body] Chevy Van. Wheelbase: 110 in.. Length: 178.2 in. Width: 79.5 in. Height: 79.2 in. Standard GVW: 4,900 lb. Maximum GVW: 6,000 lb. Tires: P215/75R15 black sidewall.

CHASSIS: [G10/Short Body] Sportvan. Wheelbase: 110 in.. Length:178.2 in. Width: 79.5 in. Height: 79.4 in. Standard GVW: 5,600 lb. Maximum GVW: 6,000 lb. Tires: P215/75R15 black sidewall.

CHASSIS: [G10/Long Body] Sportvan/Bonaventure/Beauville. Wheelbase: 125 in.. Length: 202.2 in. Width: 79.5 in. Height: 79.2 in. Standard GVW: 5,600 lb. Maximum GVW: 6,000 lb. Tires: P215/75R15 black sidewall.

CHASSIS: [G20/Short Body] Chevy Van. Wheelbase: 110 in.. Length: 178.2 in. Width: 79.5 in. Height: 79.5 in. Standard GVW: 6,600 lb. Maximum GVW: 6,600 lb. Tires: P215/75R15 black sidewall.

CHASSIS: [G20/Long Body] Chevy van. Wheelbase: 125 in. Length: 202.2 in. Width: 79.5 in. Height: 79.2 in. Standard GVW: 6,600 lb. Maximum GVW: 6,600 lb. Tires: P215/75R15 black sidewall.

CHASSIS: [G20/Long Body] Sportvan/Bonaventure/Beauville. Wheelbase: 125 in.. Length: 202.2 in. Width: 79.5 in. Height: 79.5 in. Standard GVW: 6,600 lb. Maximum GVW: 6,850 lb. Tires: P215/75R15 black sidewall.

CHASSIS: [G30/Long Body Chevy van] Wheelbase: 125 in.. Length: 202.2 in. Width: 79.5 in. Height: 81.9 in. Standard GVW: 7,100 lb. Maximum GVW: 876,100 lb. Tires: P215/75R15 black sidewall.

CHASSIS: [G30/Long Body Heavy-duty Chevy van] Wheelbase: 125 in.. Length: 202.2 in. Width: 79.5 in. Height: 81.9 in. Standard GVW: 7,400 lb. Maximum GVW: 8,600 lb. Tires: P215/75R15 black sidewall.

CHASSIS: [G30/Long Body Sportvan/Bonaventure/Beauville] Wheelbase: 125 in.. Length: 202.2 in. Width: 79.5 in. Height: 81.9 in. Standard GVW: 7,400 lb. Maximum GVW: 8,600 lb. Tires: P215/75R15 black sidewall.

CHASSIS: [G30/Long Body Heavy-duty Sportvan] Wheelbase: 125 in.. Length: 202.2 in. Width: 79.5 in. Height: 81.9 in. Standard GVW: 7,400 lb. Maximum GVW: 8,600 lb. Tires: P215/75R15 black sidewall.

CHASSIS: [G30/Extended Body Heavy-duty Sportvan/Bonaventure/Beauville] Wheelbase: 146 in. Length: 223.2 in. Width: 79.5 in. Height: 81.9 in. Standard GVW: 8,600 lb. Maximum GVW: 3,957 lb. Tires: P215/75R15 black sidewall

CHASSIS: [G30/Extended Body 12-Passenger Sportvan] Wheelbase: 146 in. Length: 223.2 in. Width: 79.5 in. Height: 81.9 in. Standard GVW: 10,000 lb. Maximum GVW: 10,000 lb. Tires: P215/75R15 black sidewall.

CHASSIS: [R10 Blazer 4x4] Wheelbase: 106.5 in. Length: 184.8 in. Width: 79.6 in. Height: 73.8 in. Standard GVW: 6,100 lb. Maximum GVW: 6,100 lb. Tires: LT245/75R16C black sidewall.

CHASSIS: [Suburban R16/and diesel] Wheelbase: 129.5 in. Length: 219.1 in. Width: 79.6 in. Height: 72.2 in. Standard GVW: 6,100 lb. Maximum GVW: 7,000 lb. Tires: P235/75R-15XLS black sidewall.

CHASSIS: [Suburban R26] Wheelbase: 129.5 in. Length: 219.1 in. Width: 79.6 in. Height: 74.3 in. Standard GVW: 8,600 lb. Maximum GVW: 8,600 lb. Tires: P235/75R-15XLS black sidewall.

CHASSIS: [Suburban V16] Wheelbase: 129.5 in. Length: 219.1 in. Width: 79.6 in. Height: 73.8 in. Standard GVW: 6,100 lb. Maximum GVW: 7,300 lb. Tires: P235/75R-15XLS black sidewall.

CHASSIS: [Suburban V26] Wheelbase: 129.5 in. Length: 219.1 in. Width: 79.6 in. Height: 76.1 in. Standard GVW: 8,600 lb. Maximum GVW: 8,600 lb. Tires: P235/75R-15XLS black sidewall.

CHASSIS: [C1500 Sportside Regular-cab Short Box Pickup] Regular-cab. Short Box. Wheelbase: 117.5 in. Length: 194.0 in. Width: 76.8 in. Height: 70.4 in. Standard GVW: 5,200 lb. Maximum GVW: 5,600 lb. Tires: P225/75R15 black sidewall AS SBR Tires.

1988 Chevrolet 1/2-Ton S10 "Cameo" Pickup 4x2 (CMD)

CHASSIS: [R1500 Fleetside Regular-cab Short Box Pickup] Wheelbase: 117.5 in. Length: 194.0 in. Width: 76.8 in. Height: 70.4 in. Standard GVW: 5,200 lb. Maximum GVW: 5,600 lb. Tires: P225/75R15 black sidewall AS SBR Tires.
CHASSIS: [R1500 Extended-cab] Wheelbase: 155.5 in. Length: 236.9 in. Width: 107.3 in. Height: 70.6 in. Standard GVW: 6,000 lb. Maximum GVW: 6,000 lb. Tires: P225/75R15 black sidewall AS SBR Tires.
CHASSIS: [V1500 Sportside Regular-cab Short Box Pickup] Wheelbase: 117.5 in. Length: 194.0 in. Width: 76.8 in. Height: 73.8 in. Standard GVW: 5,600 lb. Maximum GVW: 5,600 lb. Tires: P225/75R15 black sidewall AS SBR Tires.
CHASSIS: [V1500 Fleetside Regular-cab Short Box Pickup] Wheelbase: 117.5 in. Length: 194.0 in. Width: 76.8 in. Height: 73.8 in. Standard GVW: 5,600 lb. Maximum GVW: 5,6000 lb. Tires: P225/75R15 black sidewall AS SBR Tires.
CHASSIS: [V1500 Fleetside Extended-cab Short Box Pickup] Wheelbase: 155.5 in. Length: 236.9 in. Width: 107.3 in. Height: 73.9 in. Standard GVW: 6,200 lb. Maximum GVW: 6,200 Lb. Tires: P225/75R15 black sidewall AS SBR Tires.
CHASSIS: [R2500 Fleetside Regular-cab Long Box Pickup] Wheelbase: 131.5 in. Length: 208.9 in. Width: 76.8 in. Height: 73.0 in. Standard GVW: 7,200 lb. Maximum GVW: 7,200 lb. Tires: P225/75R15 black sidewall AS SBR tires.
CHASSIS: [R2500 Fleetside Extended-cab Short Box Pickup] Wheelbase: 155.5 in. Length: 236.9 in. Width: 107.3 in. Height: 73.2 in. Standard GVW: 7,200 lb. Maximum GVW: 7,200 lb. Tires: P225/75R15 black sidewall AS SBR tires.
CHASSIS: [V2500 Fleetside Regular-cab Long Box Pickup] Wheelbase: 131.5 in. Length: 208.2 in. Width: 76.4 in. Height: 74.3 in. Standard GVW: 7,200 lb. Maximum GVW: 7,200 lb. Tires: P225/75R15 black sidewall AS SBR tires.
CHASSIS: [V2500 Fleetside Extended-cab Short Box Pickup] Wheelbase: 155.5 in. Length: 236.9 in. Width: 107.3 in. Height: 74.5 in. Standard GVW: 7,200 lb. Maximum GVW: 7,200 lb. Tires: P225/75R15 black sidewall AS SBR tires.
CHASSIS: [R3500 Fleetside Regular-cab Long Box Pickup] Wheelbase: 131.5 in. Length: 208.2 in. Width: 76.8 in. Height: 75.4 in. Standard GVW: 8,600 lb. Maximum GVW: 10,000 lb. Tires: P225/75R15 black sidewall AS SBR tires.
CHASSIS: [R3500 Fleetside Extended-cab Long Box Pickup] Wheelbase: 155.5 in. Length: 236.9 in. Width: 107.3 in. Height: 75.6 in. Standard GVW: 8,600 lb. Maximum GVW: 10,000 lb. Tires: P225/75R15 black sidewall AS SBR tires.
CHASSIS: [V3500 Fleetside Long Box Pickup] Wheelbase: 131.5 in. Length: 208.2 in. Width: 76.8 in. Height: 5.8 in. Standard GVW: 8,600 lb. Maximum GVW: 8,600 lb. Tires: P225/75R15 black sidewall AS SBR tires.
CHASSIS: [V3500 Fleetside Extended-cab Long Box Pickup] Wheelbase: 155.5 in. Length: 236.9 in. Width: 107.3 in. Height: 76.0 in. Standard GVW: 8,600 lb. Maximum GVW: 8,600 lb. Tires: P225/75R15 black sidewall AS SBR tires.
CHASSIS: [R/V 3500 Pickup] Motor home chassis. Wheelbase: 183.5 in. Tires: P225/75R15 black sidewall AS SBR tires.

1988 Chevrolet 1/2-Ton K1500 Fleetside Short Box Pickup 4x4 (CMD)

SELECTED OPTIONS
S/T SERIES PICKUP OPTIONS: Durango package. Tahoe package. Sport package. Custom two-tone paint. Special two-tone paint. Sport two-tone paint. California emissions System. 2.6-literV-6 engine. Four-speed overdrive automatic transmission. Optional axle ratio. Locking rear differential. Pre-cleaner air cleaner. Five-speed manual overdrive transmission. All-Weather air conditioning. Heavy-duty battery. Front black bumper guards. Luggage carrier with black or bright finish. Off-road package. Cold-climate package. Front console. Engine oil cooling system. Heavy-duty radiator. Heavy-duty radiator and transmission oil cooler. Air deflector. Power door locks. Color-keyed floor mats. Gauge package (includes voltmeter, engine coolant temperature, oil pressure). Gauge Package plus tachometer. 66-ampere Delcotron generator. Deep--tinted glass. Deep--tinted glass with light--tinted rear window. Halogen headlights. Engine block heater. Engine compartment light. Exterior left and right side painted mirrors. Exterior left and right side bright mirrors. Body side and wheel opening moldings. Door edge guards. Bright wheel opening moldings. Black wheel opening moldings. Operating Convenience package. AM radio. AM/FM radio. AM/FM radio with clock. AM/FM stereo radio with electronic tuning. AM/FM stereo radio and clock with electronic tuning. AM/FM stereo radio with Seek-and-Scan, stereo cassette tape, clock and graphic equalizer and electronic tuning and premium rear speakers. Premium rear speakers. Transfer case shield. Heavy-duty front and rear shock absorbers. Full size spare tire. Electronic speed control. Comfortilt steering wheel. Striping. Heavy-duty suspension equipment. 20-gallon fuel tank. Two front towing hooks. Deadweight trailer hitch ($64). Heavy-duty Trailering Special equipment ($199). Light-duty Trailering Special equipment. Wheel trim rings. Rally wheels. Styled wheels. Cast aluminum wheels. Power side door windows. Intermittent windshield wiper system.
S-SERIES BLAZER OPTIONS: Tahoe package. Sport package. High Country package. Sport cloth vinyl high-back bucket seat trim. High Country sheepskin high-back bucket seats. Custom two-tone paint. Special two-tone paint. Sport two-tone paint. California emissions system. 4.3-literV-6 engine. Four-speed overdrive automatic transmission. Optional axle ratio. Locking rear differential. Pre-cleaner air cleaner. Five-speed manual overdrive transmission. All-Weather air conditioning. Heavy-duty battery. Front black bumper guards. Luggage carrier, black or bright finish. Spare wheel and tire carrier. Off-road package. Cold-climate package. Front compartment console. Engine oil cooling system. Heavy-duty radiator. Heavy-duty radiator and transmission oil cooler. Spare tire cover. Air deflector. Rear window defogger. Power door locks. Color-keyed floor mats. Gauge package (includes voltmeter, engine coolant temperature, oil pressure). Gauge package plus tachometer. 66 ampere Delcotron generator. Deep-tinted glass. Deep-tinted glass with light-tinted rear window. Halogen headlights. Engine block heater. Engine compartment light. Exterior left and right side painted mirrors. Exterior left and right side bright mirrors. Body side and wheel opening moldings. Door edge guards. Bright wheel opening moldings. Black wheel opening moldings. Operating Convenience package. AM radio. AM/FM radio. AM/FM radio with clock. AM/FM stereo radio with electronic tuning. AM/FM stereo radio and clock with electronic tuning. AM/FM stereo radio with Seek-and-Scan, stereo cassette tape, clock and graphic equalizer and electronic tuning and premium rear speakers. Premium rear speakers. Folding rear bench seat. Reclining front seat backs. Transfer case shield. Heavy-duty front and rear shock absorbers. Full size spare tire. Electronic speed control. Comfortilt steering wheel. Striping. Heavy-duty suspension equipment. Power release tailgate window. 20 gallon fuel tank. Two front towing hooks. Deadweight trailer hitch. Heavy-duty Trailering Special. Light-duty Trailering Special. Wheel trim rings. Rally wheels. Styled wheels. Cast aluminum wheels. Power side door windows. Intermittent windshield wiper system.
ASTRO OPTIONS: Front air conditioning: Front and rear air conditioning. Optional axle ratio. Locking rear differential. Deluxe front and rear chromed bumpers. Black luggage carrier. Engine oil cooler. Heavy-duty radiator. Heavy-duty radiator and engine oil cooler. Power door locks. Driver Convenience package including Comfortilt steering wheel and intermittent wiper system. Power windows. Deep-tinted glass. Rear heater. Electronic instrumentation. Auxiliary lighting. Black below-eye-line exterior mirrors. Exterior remote electric mirrors. Special two-tone paint. Sport two-tone paint. Electronically tuned AM/FM stereo radio with Seek-and-Scan, digital clock, stereo cassette player and premium speakers. Electronically tuned AM/FM stereo radio with Seek-and-Scan, stereo cassette tape player with Search-and-Repeat, graphic equalizer, digital clock and premium speakers. Seven-passenger seating. Eight-passenger seating. Seat back recliner and dual arm rests. Six-way power seat. Front and rear heavy-duty shock absorbers. Heavy-duty Trailering Equipment. Light-duty Trailering Equipment. Aluminum wheels. Rally wheels.
G-SERIES VANS OPTIONS: Custom cloth seat trim. Special two-tone paint. Deluxe two-tone paint. Exterior decor package. California emission system. 5.7-liter V-8, except standard in G30. 5.0-liter V-8 in G1-0/G20. Four-speed automatic transmission with overdrive. Optional rear axle. Locking differential. Air conditioning. Dual air conditioning. Heavy-duty battery. Front and rear chromed bumpers (standard on Beauville model). Chrome bumper guards. Electric quartz clock. ZQ3 convenience group. AU3 door lock system. B30 carpeting on floor, wheelhousings, stepwells for 125-in. wheelbase only. Tinted glass, all windows. Deep-tinted glass. Deep-tinted glass with light-tinted rear window. Rear heater. TR9 auxiliary lighting package. B84 black body side moldings. B96 wheel opening moldings. ZQ2 operating convenience package. U63 AM radio. UM7 AM/FM stereo sound system. UM6 stereo sound system. UX1 stereo sound system. Rear seats equipment package. AQ4 seating package with two additional rear seats. Custom steering wheel. Sport steering wheel. Positive rear door stop. BA8 front seat storage compartment. D85 body striping. Heavy-duty Trailering Special equipment. Diesel equipment package, includes heavy-duty battery, heavy-duty radiator and transmission cooler. Light-duty trailering package. Rally wheels with trim rings.
V10 BLAZER OPTIONS: Silverado Package RPO YE9 includes either custom cloth or custom vinyl seats, custom steering wheel, deluxe molding package, taillight and rear door or tailgate moldings, bright front turn signal and front side marker lamp bezels, fender nameplates, bright windshield and side rear window moldings, color-keyed carpeting with bright sill plates, plastic door trim panels with storage pockets, and bright brushed finish accents, visor vanity mirror, deluxe front appearance package, dual horns, nameplate on instrument panel, cigarette lighter, headliner, wheel opening moldings, special insulation, bright body side moldings, pillar trim panels, storage console between front seats, floor and wheelwell carpeting, spare tire cover and voltmeter, engine coolant temperature and oil pressure gauges. Custom vinyl bucket seats. Custom vinyl bench seats. Special two-tone paint with custom molding package and wheel opening moldings. Exterior decor package with hood ornament. California emission systems RPO YF5. 5.7-liter V-8 . Four-speed with overdrive automatic transmission (standard on B3J diesel). Optional axle ratio. Locking rear differential RPO G80. P215/75R15 all-season steel-belted radial blackwall tires. P215/75R15 highway steel-belted radial blackwall tires. P235/75R15 highway steel-belted radial whitewall. P235/75R15 highway steel-belted radial white-lettered tires. P235/75R15 all seasons steel-belted radial blackwall tires. P235/75R 15 on/off road steel-belted radial blackwall tires. P235/75R15 all season steel-belted radial whitewall tires. P235/75R15 all-seasons steel-belted radial white-lettered tires. 31 x 10.50R/15LTB on/off road steel-belted radial blackwall tires. 31 x 10.50R/15LTB tires (available only if N67, N90 or PA6 wheels are specified). Pre-cleaner air cleaner RPO K46. Air conditioning (not available with cold-climate package). Deluxe front appearance RPO V22 includes dark Argent grille with bright trim and dual rectangular headlights. Heavy-duty battery RPO UA1. Deluxe chromed front and rear bumpers RPO VE5. Chromed front bumper guards RPO V31. Quartz electric clock RPO U35. Not available with UM6 radio (includes Z53 gauge package). Cold-climate package RPO V10 includes special insulation, special heater and defroster, engine block heater, anti-freeze protection to -31 degrees, and heavy-duty battery. Engine oil cooling system RPO KC4. Heavy-duty radiator RPO VO1. Heavy-duty radiator and transmission oil cooler RPO VO2. Power door locks RPO AU3. Color-keyed front floor mats RPO B32. Gauge package RPO Z54 includes voltmeter, engine coolant temperature and oil pressure gauges. 66-ampere generator RPO K81. Deep-tinted glass RPO AJ1 includes dark-laminated glass on side windows and rear tailgate glass. Deep-tinted glass with light-tinted rear window RPO AA3 includes-tinted glass on rear tailgate glass,

passenger and driver's side door and dark-laminated glass on side windows. Heavy-duty seven-lead wiring harness RPO UY7. Halogen high-beam headlights RPO TT5. Available only with RPO V22 or when RPO YE9 was ordered. Headlight warning buzzer RPO T63. Interior headliner RPO BB5. 600-watt engine block heater RPO KO5 (not available for diesel engine). Heavy-duty front heater RPO C42 (available only with diesel engine). Automatic locking hubs RPO X6Z. Cigarette lighter RPO U37. Painted exterior below eye-line mirrors RPO D44. Stainless steel exterior below eye-line mirrors RPO D45. Black body side molding RPO B84 (includes lower side and rear moldings of black plastic with bright trim). Bright body side molding RPO B85 (includes bright plastic body side and rear lower moldings with black paint trim, plus bright trim for front side marker lamps and taillights, fender, door, rear side panel and tailgate moldings). Custom molding package RPO YG1 includes B84 black body side moldings, wheel opening moldings and bright trim for front side marker lights and taillight trim (included with ZY3 or ZY5 packages). Deluxe molding package RPO YG3 includes bright trim for front side marker lamps and taillight trim wheel opening molding and B85 bright body side moldings. Door edge guards RPO B93. Operating Convenience package RPO ZQ2 includes power door locks and power windows. AM radio RPO U63. AM/FM radio RPO U69. AM/FM stereo radio RPO U58, available only with YE9. AM/FM electronically-tuned stereo radio with Seek-and-Scan stereo cassette tape player and clock. Windshield antenna RPO U76, included with radio. Rear seat RPO AM7. Fuel tank shield RPO NY1. Front quad shock absorbers RPO Z75 includes dual left and right hand shock absorbers on front axle, heavy-duty shock absorbers on rear axle and a front axle nose bumper to limit axle windup. Electronic speed control RPO K34.. Front heavy-duty 2,250 lb. capacity springs with heavy-duty front and rear shock absorbers. Recommended for snow plow type usage only. Comfortilt steering wheel RPO N33. 31-gallon replacement fuel tank RPO NK7. Two front towing hooks RPO V76. Deadweight type trailer hitch RPO VR2 (not available with Z82). Weight distributing platform trailer hitch RPO VR4 included with Z82. Trailering Special equipment RPO Z82 (available only with a 3.24:1 or 3.73:1 rear axle ratio and MXO automatic transmission and not available with 5.7-liter LS9 engine) includes VR4, UY7 and VO2 options. Bright metal wheelcovers RPO PO1 ($40). Rally 15 x 8 wheels RPON67 (not available with P215 tires). Styled 15 x 8 wheels RPOPA6 (not available with P215 tires). Cast aluminum 15 x 7 wheels with special hubcaps RPON90 (not available with P215 tires). Power side door electric windows RPO A31. Power tailgate electric window RPO A33. Sliding side quarter windows RPO AD5. Intermittent windshield wipers RPO CD4.

GM's one-millionth full-size pickup was a 1988 Chevrolet C1500

R/V PICKUP AND R/V H-D PICKUP AND SUBURBAN OPTIONS: RPO K46 precleaner air cleaner. RPO C60 air conditioning. RPO V22 deluxe front appearance. Optional axle ratio. RPO G80 locking rear differential. RPO TP2 heavy-duty Delco Freedom auxiliary battery with 540 cold cranking amps (not available with B3J diesel equipment). RPO UA1 heavy-duty Delco Freedom battery with 630 cold cranking amps. RPO V43 painted rear step bumper. RPO VB3 Chromed front deluxe bumper with rub strip (included with RPO Z62 and RPO YE9). RPO VB3 rear step bumper with rub strip. RPO V27 black front bumper guards (requires RPO VG3). RPO P13 spare tire and wheel carrier (not available with K10753 pickup). RPO F44 heavy-duty chassis (included with B3J diesel equip). RPO V10 cold climate package, includes UA1 battery, KO5 block heater and C42 heater (not available with RPO C60). RPO D55 console (requires bucket seats). RPO KC4 engine oil cooling system (not available with B3J diesel equipment, with RPO MXO transmission requires VO2 cooling, also included with Z82 trailering option). RPO V02 heavy-duty radiator (not available with RPO V02 or RPO VO1 heavy-duty radiator and transmission oil cooler, requires RPO MXO transmission, also included with RPO Z823). RPO Z62 Scottsdale trim package RPO YEZ Silverado trim package. RPO C49 rear window defogger (requires RPO YE9 or RPO Z62 and not available with RPO A28 window or RPO AJ1 glass. RPO LO3 5.0-liter V-8. RPO LO5 5.7-liter V-8. RPO NO5 locking fuel filler cap. RPO B32 front color-keyed floor mats (requires RPO YE9). RPO B33 rear color-keyed floor mats (requires RPO AM7 seat and RPO B32). RPO Z53 gauge package with voltmeter, engine coolant temperature and oil pressure gauges (included with RPO YE9). RPO AA3 deep-tinted glass with light-tinted rear window including RPO A20 window (not available with RPO AJ1). RPO AJ1 deep-tinted glass including RPO A20 window (not available with RPO C49 defogger). RPO UY7 heavy-duty trailering wiring harness (included with RPO Z82). RPO TT4 halogen headlights (not available with RPO V22 or RPO YE9). RPO KO5 engine block heater (included with RPO V10). RPO C42 front heavy-duty heater included with V10 (not available with RPO C60). RPO UF2 cargo area lamp. RPO UO1 roof marker lamps (not available with California emissions). RPO C95 dome and reading lamps (included with RPO TR9). RPO U37 cigarette lighter. RPO TR9 auxiliary lighting . RPO D44 below-eye-line black painted exterior mirrors. RPO D45 below-eye-line stainless steel exterior mirrors. RPO DF2 camper-type exterior mirrors. RPO B84 black body side moldings. RPO B85 bright body side moldings. RPO B74 black wheel opening moldings. RPO B96 bright wheel opening moldings (no charge). RPO ZQ2 operating convenience package including power door locks and power windows. RPO YZ2 conventional two-tone paint. RPO YZ3 special two-tone paint. RPO 243 deluxe two-tone paint. RPO U63 AM radio. RPO UM7 electronically-tuned AM/FM stereo radio with Seek-and-Scan. RPO UM7 electronically-tuned AM/FM stereo radio with Seek-and-Scan and digital clock. RPO UK5 electronically-tuned AM/FM stereo radio with Seek-and-Scan and stereo cassette tape player. RPO UM6 electronically-tuned AM/FM stereo radio with Seek-and-Scan, stereo cassette tape player and digital clock. RPO UX1

electronically-tuned AM/FM stereo radio with Seek-and-Scan, stereo cassette tape player with Search-and-Repeat, graphic equalizer and digital clock. RPO U73 fixed mast antenna (included with RPO U63, UK4, UK5, UM6, or UX1 radios). RPO AM7 rear folding seat (requires bucket or split front seat). RPO F51 heavy-duty front and rear shock absorbers. RPO NZZ off-road skid plate for K1500 only. RPO K34 electronic speed control. RPO BQ4 Chevrolet 4x4 Sport graphics package. RPO F60 heavy-duty front springs (not available with B3J diesel equipment). RPO F59 front stabilizer bar. RPO N33 Comfortilt steering wheel. RPO N31 custom steering wheel. RPO NKJ3 Sport steering wheel. RPO D85 striping package. RPO NJ8 fuel tank with approximately 34 gallon total vehicle capacity (not available with K10753 pickup). RPO B76 two front towing hooks. RPO VR4 weight distributing platform trailer hitch. RPO PZ82 heavy-duty Trailering Special equipment. RPO MM4 four-speed manual transmission. RPO MXO four-speed automatic transmission with overdrive. RPO PO1 wheelcovers. RPO N67 rally wheel rims. RPO A20 swing-out quarter windows. RPO A28 sliding rear window. RPO CD4 intermittent windshield wipers.

1988 Chevrolet 1/2-Ton K1500 Sportside Short Box Pickup 4x4

NOTE 13: Options shown are representative. Some "options" may be standard equipment on certain models, such as V-8s in R/V3500 pickups. Descriptions of options are edited. Full option contents can be determined by consulting sales literature.

HISTORICAL: At the start of 1988, Chevrolet had 4,910 dealers who sold Chevrolet trucks. They helped the company take a large chunk out of Ford's lead in light-duty truck sales in 1988, retailing 1,336,407 units compared to 1,173,675 in 1987. Ford's lead in the market segment shrank to 106,000 units. The thrust of Chevrolet's increase came from full-year availability of the restyled GMT400 R/V pickups. These were built at the Ft. Wayne, Indiana, Pontiac (Michigan) East, and Oshawa, Ontario, Canada plants. Establishing and industry record of 71 R/V trucks per year per employee, sales of just under 500,000 units were anticipated for 1988.). Chevrolet also added Sportside and Etended-Cab Pickup models, plus a heavy-duty R/V pickup with a 8,500-pounds-plus GVWR. Also gaining were sales of S10 compact pickups (which got an optional 4.3-liter V-6 at midyear) and S-Series Blazer compact sport utility vehicles (SUVs). In fact, the only 1988 Chevrolet light-duty truck-line to slump in sales was the big Blazer, which fell by about 3,500 units. During 1988, Chevrolet sold the Tracker captive import under the Geo banner with all Trackers being imported from Suzuki of Japan. (Canadian production of Trackers was schedule for mid-1989. The older style R/V full-size pickup design continued to be seen on Crew-Cab models, which were built off the previous platform. Robert D. Burger was general manager of Chevrolet Motor Division and a General Motors vice president. John M. Kelley was marketing manager for trucks. Thomas P. Cutler was manager of truck advertising. Kenneth P. Wechselberger was truck merchandising manager. Ralph J. Kramer was overall director of public relations, including Chevrolet truck publicity. Seen at the 1988 new-car shows was an exciting chrome-yellow-and-black Chevrolet S-Blazer concept vehicle with four-wheel steering. Chevrolet Calendar-year new-truck sales were: 514,870 R/V Pickups, 248,768 S10/T10 Pickups, 184,500 S-Series Blazers, 121,691 Chevy Vans, 62,079 Astro Vans, 66,897 Suburbans, 27,180 K10 Blazers, 94,754 Astro Wagons, 12,336 Sportvans, 2,145 Geo Trackers (Japanese-built), 420 El Caminos (built from January 1988 to April 1988 only). 767 W4 Tiltmaster imports, 18,084 medium-duty (R/V models). This gave the company sales of 1,354,491 light-duty trucks in the calendar-year.

1989

1989 Chevrolet 1/2-Ton S10 "Cameo" Pickup 4x2 (CMD)

1/2-TON — S (4x2)/T (4x4) SERIES PICKUP — L4/V-6: The S/T Series pickups (both said S10 on the outside) had a new standard rear-wheel antilock (RWAL) system on all models. Also standard was a new electric speedometer. Added to the options list was an electronic instrument panel cluster with speedometer, tachometer, and voltmeter, fuel, oil pressure, and engine coolant temperature gauges. The gauges utilized high-brightness vacuum fluorescent tubes for sharper visibility. S10 models had a standard 2.5-liter four-cylinder engine. A 2.8-liter V-6 was standard in T10s. It was attached to a new transfer case with redesigned gear sets for reduced noise and smoother operation. The new transfer case also had new controls, a longer shift lever, a new vacuum switch, and a relocated vent tube. For 1989 the standard models had an upgraded vinyl interior and a heavy-duty heater. A new exterior color was Woodlands Brown. Dark blue replaced medium blue as an interior color. The 4.3-liter V-6 was in greater supply for 1989. It was available only with the overdrive automatic transmission. Models with the 4.3-liter engine were changed in a number of ways to accommodate this larger V-6. The steering column was moved to the left to provide additional clearance for the left exhaust manifold, and the frame was changed to gain clearance in several locations on the right side. When the Maxi-Cab was ordered with the optional jump seats, rear shoulder safety belts were installed.

1989 Chevrolet 1/2-Ton T10 Blazer 2-door Sport Utility 4x4 (CMD)

1/2-TON — S (4x2)/T (4x4) S-SERIES BLAZER — V-6: The S-Series Blazer was fitted with standard rear-wheel antilock (RWAL) brakes for 1989. This system controlled the rear brake line pressure through a control valve located between the master cylinder, and the rear brakes. By modulating rear brake pressure, RWAL improved directional stability by preventing rear-wheel skid under varying road and rear loading factors. A new standard electric speedometer generated the speed signal necessary for RWAL. In addition to RWAL, al1 1989 S-Series Blazers had standard power steering. An optional electronic instrument panel cluster was also new for 1989. It included speedometer, tachometer, voltmeter, fuel, oil pressure, and engine coolant temperature gauges. The gauges utilized high-brightness vacuum fluorescent display tubes. All models had standard rear seat shoulder belts. Models with the standard 2.8-liter engine had a new transfer case with redesigned gear sets for reduced noise and smoother operation. This development also included new controls, a longer shift lever, a new vacuum switch, and a relocated vent tube. A new option for 1989 was a rear window wiper/washer system attached to the rear window in the upper right corner. This system used a glass-mounted motor, and wet arm nozzle. Incorporated into this system was a single-bottle reservoir, and two high-pressure pumps. One was for the front and one for the rear. One new exterior color called Woodlands Brown Metallic was offered. Dark blue replaced medium blue in the choice of interior colors. Premium rear speakers were now included with all optional stereo radios. The base model included these exterior features: A single electric horn, power brakes, power steering, front and rear chromed bumpers with black rub strips, a chrome and black molded plastic grille and headlamp/side marker lamp bezels, black hubcaps, bright finish door handles and lock cylinders, bright taillight trim, all-season steel-belted radial tires, and right and left side fixed arm black-finished mirrors. Interior features consisted of right- and left-hand padded arm rests integral with door panels, color-keyed plastic door panels with map pockets and a gray housing for the door latch release area, high-back bucket seats with folding seat backs and leather-grained custom vinyl, right and left side coat hooks, black plastic door sill plates, a color-keyed plastic endgate scuff plate, door-operated courtesy and front and rear dome lights with bright trim, color-keyed rubber mat floor-coverings, tinted glass for all windows, a convenience tray, front and rear passenger grab handles, a deluxe heater with side window defoggers, a cigarette lighter with ash tray illumination, padded and color-keyed left and right side sunshades, gauges for speedometer, odometer and fuel level, a deluxe color-keyed two-spoke steering wheel, a headlamp warning buzzer, a 10-inch rear view mirror and a full-foam headliner with a color-keyed cloth cover. The Tahoe trim level (RPO YC2) had the following items in addition to or replacing the base trim level: Bright wheel opening moldings, black body side moldings with bright inserts, rear quarter window moldings, hood insulators and cowl to fender seals, wheel trim rings, body color door handle inserts, and a black tailgate appliqué. Tahoe interior features consisted of door panels with custom cloth upper inserts, carpeted lower inserts with a map pocket and a coin holder in left hand door, color-keyed floor carpeting, a right side sun shade with mirror, a trip odometer, gauges for voltmeter, oil pressure and engine coolant temperature (replacing warning lamps), dual reading lamps, a spare tire cover, color-keyed cowl kick panels, and carpeted lower rear quarter and endgate panels. The Sport trim level had the following items in addition to or replacing the Tahoe trim level: Bumpers color-keyed to lower accent color with black rub strips, a black chrome grille with matching headlamp bezels, black finish for door handles and lock cylinders, two-tone paint (conventional or special), and black chrome taillamp trims. Interior features consisted of reclining bucket seats with folding seat backs and deluxe cloth, a floor console, a sport steering wheel with simulated leather look, and deluxe cloth trim panel inserts.

1/2-TON — ASTRO M (RWD) SERIES — V-6: The Astro was Chevrolet's rear-wheel-drive minivan. The base model was the Astro Cargo Van. Its standard equipment included a 2.5-liter EFI four-cylinder engine, front disc brakes, five-speed manual transmission with overdrive, and P205/75R15 all-season black sidewall steel-belted-radial tires. There was just one size Astro this year. The Cargo Van model had a sliding right-hand load door as standard equipment. It featured a vinyl interior with choice of low- or high-back bucket seats. The Astro also came in three passenger van versions featuring CS (Custom Sport), CL (Custom Luxury) or LT (Luxury Touring) trim levels. The passenger model had standard double swing-out door on the right-hand side. The CS model had a standard vinyl interior with high-back bucket seats. The CL model added custom vinyl upholstery. The LT model added custom cloth upholstery. Standard equipment included a 4.3-liter EFI V-6, front disc brakes, five-speed manual transmission with overdrive, and P205/75R15 all-season black sidewall steel-belted-radial tires.

1/2-TON, 3/4-TON, 1-TON VAN — G-SERIES 10, 20, 30 — V-6/V-8: The basic models were the Chevy Van and the Sportvan. Both came as G10/G20/G30 class models. The Chevy Vans were primarily designed as cargo vans. The Sportvan series consisted of windowed passenger vans. The fancy version of the Sportvan was called the Beauville. The conventional vans came as 110-inch short wheelbase (SWB), and 125-inch long wheelbase (LWB) models. Hi-Cube trucks using the van "cab" were offered on the LWB and a 146-inch extended wheelbase (EWB). Respective body lengths were 178, 202, and 223 inches. One G10 Chevy Van and one G10 Sportvan came as SWB models. There was an SWB G20 cargo van, too. The G20 Chevy Van, Sportvan and Beauville models also came as LWB models. G30 Chevy Van, Sportvan and Beauville models were offered only as LWB models. The G30 platform was also the basis for the extended wheelbase Hi-Cube trucks. Standard equipment in Chevy Vans included a 4.3-liter V-6, heavy-duty power brakes with rear antilock feature, three-speed automatic transmission, and P205/75R14 all-season steel-belted-radial tires. The 5.0-liter, 5.7-liter, and 7.4-liter gas V-8s were optional in these models, as was a 6.2-liter diesel V-8. Sportvan models had about the same standard features, except for a four-speed automatic overdrive transmission being standard in all lines. The 5.7-liter V-8 was standard in heavy-duty G30 Chevy Van, Sportvan and Beauville models.

3/4-TON/1-TON — P20/P30 STEP-VAN — V-8: Also available in 1989 were two series of Step-Vans. They had boxy bodies well-suited for stop-and-go delivery service. The base body offered, in both the P20 (3/4-ton)and P30 (1-ton) lines had a 10-1/2-foot length. Step-Vans offered wheelbases ranging from 125 to 178 inches. A 350-cubic-inch V-8 was the standard engine. A 6.2-liter diesel V-8 was optional. Standard size tires were LT215/85R16Cs.

1989 Chevrolet 1/2-Ton K1500 Blazer 2-door Sport Utility 4x4 (CMD)

1/2-TON — K1500 BLAZER (4x4) — V-8: The full-size 1989 Blazer had new base and up-level grilles, as well as new headlight bezels. The K1500 Blazer's body nameplate and emblems were identical to those used on the K-series 4x4 pickups. Also shared with these-models were the Blazer's new body side moldings, and bumper rub strips. The big Blazer's exterior had a new "wet-look" shine that was credited to the replacement of the older, high-solid enamel paint with an all-new base coat/clear coat paint. Ten solid colors were offered: Onyx Black, Smoke Blue Metallic, Mojave Beige, Sunset Gold Metallic, Wintergreen Metallic, Summit White, Fire Red, Gray Metallic, Quicksilver Metallic, and Midnight Blue Metallic. In addition, the Blazer could be ordered in 114 different two-tone combinations with new colors breaks for 1989. The K1500 Blazer's new styling was enhanced by its new body-color side door drip moldings, and newly styled full wheelcovers. Other changes for 1989 included new black below-eye-line mirrors, and standard sun visors on the Silverado. The visors were color-keyed and fitted with plastic extenders. The driver's side visor had a map strap, and the passenger side had a lighted vanity mirror. Vehicle corrosion protection was upgraded by extending the use of additional body, and front end sheet metal components with two-sided galvanized coatings. Ride characteristics of the big Blazer were improved by adding five new spring assemblies, and 16 new front and rear shock absorber assemblies. The LO5 5.7-liter V-8 now had serpentine accessory drive belts in place of the older multi-belt accessory drive. New combination lap/shoulder belts were standard for the K1500 Blazer. The auxiliary lighting package included a glove box light and an underhood reel lamp. The new series of Delco 2000 electronic tuned radios were offered. Standard on K1500 Blazers was Scottsdale trim. Silverado trim was optional. Standard equipment included the following chassis items: Dual electric high-note and low-tone horns, a front stabilizer bar, a two-speed transfer case, manual-locking front hubs, power steering, and power brakes. Standard exterior features included front and rear chromed bumpers, a molded plastic grille and front lamp bezels painted light and Dark Argent Silver, bright metal hubcaps with black trim, Argent Silver wheels, all-season steel-belted radial tires, a full-size spare and wheel, a tool kit (including mechanical jack and wheel wrench), Scottsdale nameplates, black below-eye-line exterior mirrors and a roll-down rear tailgate glass window. The standard Scottsdale interior consisted of right and left side padded arm rests, high-back front bucket seats with custom vinyl pigskin-grained trim in any of four colors (dark blue, burgundy, saddle or slate gray), easy rear entry passenger seat front sliding mechanism, two coat hooks on left side, full-length bright sill plates at front doors and rear of rear compartment floor, a map light, two dome lamps with door-operated switches, a floor covering of embossed black rubber mats in front and rear, insulation on the dash panel, floor panel and between double-wall cab roof, tinted glass on all windows, padded color-keyed left and right side sunshades, gauges for fuel level, voltmeter, oil pressure and engine pressure, a trip odometer, a heavy-duty heater and defogger, an AM radio with fixed mast antenna, a two-spoke steering wheel with anti-theft locking feature on steering column, a 10-inch rear view mirror, color-keyed, molded plastic door trim panels, a cigarette lighter with ash tray illumination, and a spare tire carrier on right-hand rear panel. Chevrolet described the RPO YE9 Silverado trim level as "designed to offer buyers an increased level of comfort and convenience features compared to the standard Scottsdale level."

1989 Chevrolet 1/2-Ton K1500 Suburban 4-door wagon 4x4 (CMD)

1/2-TON, 3/4-TON — R (4x2)/V (4x4) SUBURBAN — V-8: Chevrolet Suburbans were like large four-door station wagons built on a light-duty truck chassis. They were manufactured in the General Motors assembly plant at Flint, Michigan. The Suburban's standard engine was the 5.7-liter EFI V-8. Optional was a 7.4-liter V-8 that was the most powerful engine available in any Chevrolet light-duty truck. The standard and heavy-duty 6.2-liter diesel V-8s carried different horsepower and torque ratings. Both 1/.2- and 3/4-ton Suburbans comfortably sat nine adults. They shared 165 cu.-ft. of cargo space. The 4x2 and 4x4 models were each available as 1/2- and 3/4-ton models. They continued to be offered in Scottsdale or Silverado trim. Suburbans equipped with tailgates offered manual and power-operated rear glass options.

1/2-TON, 3/4-TON, 1-TON — C (4x2)/K (4x4) & R (4x2)/V (4x4) H-D PICKUPS — V-6/V-8: The "New Generation" full-size Chevrolet C/K trucks entered the 1989 model-year as the best-selling vehicles in General Motors' lineup. To meet consumer demand second shifts, and overtime, were added to production schedules. Also a good sign of the times for Chevrolet was the news from GM surveys that the C/K trucks had the highest customer satisfaction of any full-size pickup. Numerous changes were found in the1989 C/K models, in terms of their engineering as well as option availability and content. The regular-cab and Extended-Cab models had a new optional 4x4 sport graphic package. Chevrolet said it made "A bold statement for performance enthusiasts." Complementing the Sportside 4x4 was a new Fleetside Sport with a 6.5-foot pickup box that was available as an interim 1989 model. The 4x4 Sport models featured black-out wheel opening flares, bumpers, mirrors and a front air dam with tow hooks. A new Borg-Warner Model 1370 transfer case with an electrically actuated synchronizer was offered for K3500 models with dual rear wheels. This allowed RPO RO5 dual rear wheels to be ordered on 1-ton R/V Pickups and Chassis-and-Cab models. This development also increased the available GVWR on the K3500 1-ton four-wheel-drive trucks to 10,000 lb. Extensive changes took place in the brake system used on the C/K series trucks. The parking brake cable was given increased protection from rocks and road debris by revised routing and the addition of a shield. To reduce brake noise a new molded, semi-metallic brake lining material was used. A new 28MT starter motor and revised engine dipstick lettering were used on 6.2-liter diesel engine-equipped models. The following exterior colors were carried over from 1988: Brandywine Metallic, Sandstone Metallic, Adobe Gold Metallic, Sable Black Metallic, Quicksilver Metallic, Summit White, and Flame Red. They were joined by three new colors: Smoke Blue Metallic, Caramel Brown Metallic, and Midnight Blue Metallic. Initially, a new dark cognac replaced saddle in the interior color offerings. In January 1989, saddle rejoined beige, blue, garnet, and gray as available interior colors. Beige and gray were not available for the Extended-Cab models. Three optional exterior two-tone schemes were again offered. The conventional two-tone (RPO ZY2) was available only on single rear wheel Fleetside models. The primary color was applied to the areas above the lower side body styling crease line (including the roof) with the secondary color below the crease line. Outlined block "Chevrolet" decal lettering was applied to the tailgate. A bright trim panel with lettering was applied when the Silverado option was ordered. The Special two-tone (RPO ZY3) also available only on single rear wheel Fleetside models. It included a multi-stripe decal applied over the paint break at the belt line. One color of paint was applied to the areas above the decal (including the roof) with the second color applied to the areas below. The Deluxe two-tone (RPO ZY4) also featured a multi-stripe decal at the upper styling line and the accent color between the decal and the lower feature line. Outlined block "Chevrolet" decal lettering was applied to the tailgate. A bright trim panel with lettering was applied when the Silverado option was ordered. The base Cheyenne, mid-range Scottsdale and top-ranked Silverado trim levels were carried into 1989 with minor changes. Features of the Cheyenne were as follows: Single electric low-note horn, power steering, rear brake drums with anti-lock brake system (operated in two-wheel-drive mode only), a front chromed bumper, a molded plastic grille painted Light Argent with Dark Argent air intake areas, single rectangular headlights, silver-painted wheels with black hub ornaments, all-season steel-belted radial tires (steel-belted radials on RPO RO5), a winch-type spare tire carrier mounted under frame (K1500 models only), right and left side fixed arm mirrors with adjustable heads and black finish, right- and left-hand padded arm rests integral with door panels (with grained molded plastic finish), three-passenger all-vinyl trim bench seat with folding back rest, right-hand coat hook, left-hand coat hook on Extended-Cab models, dark gray door sill plates, a dome light with switch in left-hand door jamb, embossed black rubber floor mats, tinted glass in all windows on Extended-Cab models, padded color-keyed left and right side sun shades, a four-spoke steering wheel, a 10-inch rear view mirror, a vinyl headliner in same color as retainer moldings (Extended-Cab models had cab upper, lower and side trim panels and a molded cloth color-keyed headliner with matching retainer moldings), insulation on dash panel, cowl top and sides and doors of regular-cab models, insulation on rear quarter and back panels and floor covering of Extended-Cab models, and extra insulation for models with diesel engines. The Scottsdale trim (RPO Z62) contained the following added equipment: A front chromed bumper with bumper rub stripes, black plastic body side moldings, black wheel opening lip moldings (except on K2500 C6P, dual rear wheel models, and Sportside trucks), color-keyed door panels with grained molded plastic finish and soft vinyl trim, map pockets and Scottsdale emblems, left- and right-hand coat hooks, color-keyed door sill plates, dome light with switches in left and right side door jambs, color-keyed embossed rubber floor mats, a full width storage tray behind seat on floor, and a color-keyed cloth headliner, Regular-Cab and Extended-Cab models had matching retainer moldings, color-keyed door pillar and roof side panels, and additional insulation on their headliner. The Silverado trim package (RPO YE9), had all this equipment, plus an additional electric high-note horn, Silverado exterior nameplates, dual rectangular halogen headlights, black plastic body side moldings with bright trim, hood and cab-to-fender insulators, door panels with two-toned soft vinyl over plastic trim, door panel map pockets, door closing assist straps, door panel Silverado emblems, color-keyed floor carpeting, padded, color-keyed left- and right-hand sun shades with cloth covering, a storage strap on the left side unit and a visor mirror on right side unit, gauges for voltmeter, engine coolant temperature and oil pressure (replacing warning lights), a cigarette lighter in ash tray, color-keyed carpeting on the cab back panel, and insulation on regular-cab back panels. The content of the V3500 Crew-Cab and Bonus-Cab models differed slightly from the other 4x4 Chevrolets. The Cheyenne package had white painted wheels, bright metal hubcaps with black trim (on single rear wheel models), exterior below-eye-line mirrors, an AM radio, a two-spoke steering wheel, and a heavy-duty heater/defogger. The primary differences in the Scottsdale package for the V3500 models included a full-width front bench seat in a choice of dual-woven cloth vinyl trim or all-vinyl pigskin trim, a door-operated dome lamp with bright trim, color-keyed rubber floor mats (for front compartment only of Bonus-Cab), full-length mystic-colored insulation for headliner (with matching retainer moldings), and insulation under the cowl panel or headliner, plus on the cab back panel. The V3500 Silverado package differed from the content for other 4x4 Chevrolets in having bright body side and rear moldings with black trim, plus bright wheel opening trim (Fleetside single rear wheel models only), an under hood reel-type lamp, a bright tailgate appliqué, bright trim for the front marker lights and taillights, special color-keyed plastic door panels with cloth inserts and vinyl stowage pockets (plus carpeting and bright trim strips on lower portions), a right-hand visor mirror, a headlamp warning buzzer, a two-spoke steering wheel with bright trim on horn buttons, a mystic-colored full-length cloth headliner, and extra-thick insulation on floor panels.

I. D. DATA: The VIN plate was mounted on the lower left side windshield corner. The VIN consisted of 17 symbols. The first three symbols identify the country, the manufacturer and the type of vehicle. The fourth symbol designated the GVWR. The fifth, sixth and seventh symbols identify the line and chassis type, series and body type. The eighth symbol identifies the engine [Chevrolet engines] C=6.2-liter/130 hp diesel V-8, H=5.0-liter V-8, J=6.2-liter/148 hp diesel V-8, K=5.7-liter V-8, M=5.7-liter V-8,N=7.4-liter V-8, R=2.8-liter V-6, T=4.8-liter L6, W=7.4-liter V-8, Z=4.3-liter V-6. [GM engines] A=5.7-liter V-8, P=6.0-liter diesel V-8. [Pontiac engine] E=2.5-liter L4. The ninth symbol is the check digit. The tenth symbol indicates model-year. The eleventh symbol identifies the assembly plant. The last six symbols are the sequential production number.

1989 Chevrolet 1/2-Ton M10 Astro "CS" Passenger Minivan 4x2

Model	Body Type	Price	Weight	Prod. Total
S10 Fleetside Pickup — 1/2-Ton — 108.3/117.9/122.9 in. w.b. — 2.5-liter EFI L4				
S10603	Reg. Cab Short Box EL	7927	2624	Note 12
S10603	Reg. Cab Short Box	9041	2648	Note 12
S10803	Reg. Cab Long Box	9206	2711	Note 12
S10653	Ext. Cab Short Box	9891	2774	Note 12
T10 Fleetside Pickup — 1/2-Ton — 108.3/117.9/122.9 in. w.b. — 2.8-liter EFI V-6				
T10603	Reg. Cab Short Box	11,731	3103	Note 12
T10803	Reg. Cab Long Box	11,911	3142	Note 12
T10653	Ext. Cab Short Box	12,541	3231	Note 12
NOTE 1: A $400 dealer destination charge applied to S-Series pickups				
S10 Blazer 4x2 Sport Utility Wagon — 1/2-Ton — 100.5/107 in. w.b. — 2.8-liter EFI V-6				
CS10516	2-dr Tailgate	12,173	3030	Note 12
T10 Blazer 4x4 Sport Utility Wagon — 1/2-Ton — 100.5/107 in. w.b. — 2.8-liter EFI V-6				
CT10516	2-dr Tailgate	13,748	3319	Note 12
NOTE 2: A $435 dealer destination charge applied to S-Series Blazers				
M10 Astro Minivan (rear-wheel-drive) — 1/2-Ton — 111 in. w.b. — 4.3-liter EFI V-6				
CM10906	Standard Cargo Van	10,957	3108	Note 12
CM10906/ZW9	Standard CS Van	12,457	3586	Note 12
CM10906	Standard CL Van	13,190	3637	Note 12
CM10906	Standard LT Van	14,701	3683	Note 12
NOTE 3: A $500 dealer destination charge applied to Astros				
G10 Van — 1/2-Ton — 110/125 in. w.b. — 4.3-liter EFI V-6				
CG11005	SWB Chevy Van	11,755	3743	Note 12
CG11305	LWB Chevy Van	12,015	3882	Note 12
CG11006/ZW9	SWB Sportvan	13,248	4076	Note 12
CG11306/ZW9	LWB Sportvan	13,509	4230	Note 12
CG11306/ZW9	LWB Beauville	14,8310	4230	Note 12
G20 Van — 3/4-Ton — 110/125 in. w.b. — 4.3-liter EFI V-6				
CG21005	SWB Chevy Van	11,515	3796	Note 12
CG21305	LWB Chevy Van	12,335	3940	Note 12
CG21305/ZW9	LWB Sportvan	13,731	4259	Note 12
CG21306/ZW9	LWB Beauville	15050	4259	Note 12
G30 Van — 1-Ton — 125/146 in. w.b. — 4.3-liter EFI V-6, [Heavy-duty] 5.7-liter EFI V-8				
CG31305	LWB Chevy Van	12,852	4453	Note 12
CG31305	LWB Chevy Van HD	13,920	4453	Note 12
CG31306/ZW9	LWB Sportvan 12P	16,044	4773	Note 12
CG31306/ZW9	LWB Sportvan 12P/HD	17,363	4773	Note 12
CG31306/ZW9	LWB Beauville HD	16,705	4773	Note 12
CG31306	LWB Cutaway	11,934	3823	Note 12
G30 Hi-Cube Van — 1-Ton — 125/146 in. w.b. — 5.7-liter EFI V-8				
CG31	10-ft. Van	15,675	5403	Note 12
CG31	12-ft. Van	17,227	6112	Note 12
NOTE 4: A $550 dealer destination charge applied to full-size vans				

Model	Body Type	Price	Weight	Prod. Total
P20 — 3/4-Ton Step-Van — 125/133 in. w.b. — 5.7-liter EFI V-8				
P22	10.5-ft. Step-Van	15,590	6002	Note 12
P30 — 1-Ton Step-Van — 125/178 in. w.b. — 5.7-liter EFI V-8				
P32	10.5-ft. Step-Van	15,689	6149	Note 12
K1500 Blazer — 1/2-Ton — 111.5 in. w.b. — 5.7-liter EFI V-8				
CK10516	Utility Hardtop	15,965	4878	Note 12

NOTE 5: A $550 dealer destination charge applied to full-size Blazers

Model	Body Type	Price	Weight	Prod. Total
R/V 1500 Suburban — 1/2-Ton — 131.5 in. w.b. — 5.7-liter EFI V-8				
CR10906	Panel Door (4x2)	15,215	4433	Note 12
CV10906	Panel Door (4x4)	16,175	4675	Note 12
R/V 2500 Suburban — 3/4-Ton — 131.5 in. w.b. — 5.7-liter EFI V-8				
CR20906	Panel Door (4x2)	15,853	4816	Note 12
CV20906	Panel Door (4x4)	17,608	5128	Note 12

NOTE 6: A $610 dealer destination charge applied to Suburbans
NOTE 7: Add $40 for tailgate models

Model	Body Type	Price	Weight	Prod. Total
C1500 Pickup — 1/2-Ton Short Box — 117.5 in. w.b. — 4.3-liter EFI V-6				
CC10703	Regular-Cab Sportside	11,163	3751	Note 12
CC10703	Regular-Cab Fleetside	109450	3692	Note 12
C1500 Pickup — 1/2-Ton Long Box — 131.5 in. w.b. — 4.3-liter EFI V-6				
CC10903	Regular-Cab Fleetside	11,145	3763	Note 12
CC10903	Regular-Cab Diesel	13,931	4105	Note 12
C1500 Pickup — 1/2-Ton Short Box — 141.5 in. w.b. — 4.3-liter EFI V-6				
CC10753	Extended-cab Fleetside	12,077	4091	Note 12
C2500 Pickup — 3/4-Ton Long Box — 131.5 in. w.b. — 4.3-liter EFI V-6				
CC20903	Regular-Cab Fleetside	11,753	3909	Note 12
CC20903	Regular-Cab Fleetside HD	12,987	4780	Note 12
CC20903	Reg.-cab FS H-D diesel	14,440	4582	Note 12
C2500 Pickup — 3/4-Ton Short Box — 141.5 in. w.b. — 4.3-liter EFI V-6				
CC20954	Chassis & Extended-cab	12,995	4705	Note 12
CC20953	Extended-cab Fleetside	13,108	4185	Note 12
CC20953	Extended cab Fleet H-D	14,022	4994	Note 12

NOTE 9: Add approximately $1,700 for CK2500 Pickups with 4x4.

Model	Body Type	Price	Weight	Prod. Total
C3500 Pickup — 1-Ton Long Box — 131.5 in. w.b. — 5.7-liter EFI V-8				
CC30924	Regular Cab H-D	13,327	4349	Note 12
CC30903	Big Dooley	14,365	5071	Note 12
C3500 Pickup — 1-Ton Short Box — 155.5 in. w.b. — 5.7-liter V-8				
CC30903	Extended-cab H-D	14,362	4625	Note 12
CC30903	Big Dooley H-D	15,400	5330	Note 12
C3500 Pickup — 1-Ton Long Box — 168.5 in. w.b. — 5.7-liter V-8				
CC30933	Bonus-cab Fleetside	14,362	5275	Note 12
CC30933	Crew-cab Fleetside	14,713	5782	Note 12
CC30933	Chassis & Bonus-cab	13,928	4859	Note 12
CC30933	Crew-cab Fleetside	14,439	5371	Note 12

NOTE 10: Add approximately $2,200 for CK3500 Pickups with 4x4.
NOTE 11: A $550 dealer destination charge applied to C/K Pickups.
NOTE 12: Model year production [S10 Pickup] 249,758, [C/K1500] 369,236, [C/K2500] 106,731, [C/K3500] 24,784, [S-Series Blazer] 184,656, [K1500 Blazer] 26,663, [Suburban] 73,438, [Astro Wagon] 109,676, [Astro Cargo Van] 62,731, [RV20/30] 34,908, [Sportvan] 10,422, [Chevy Van] 126,948.

1989 Chevrolet 1/2-Ton K1500 Fleetside Short Box Pickup 4x4

GASOLINE ENGINES (DISPLACEMENT ORDER)
ENGINE: Inline. Four-cylinder. Bore & stroke: 4.00 x 3.00 in. Displacement: 2.5-liter (151 cid). BHP: 92 at 4400 rpm. Torque: 130 lb.-ft. at 2300 rpm. Compression ratio: 8.3:1. EFI/Throttle-body-injection. VIN Code E. GM-built. [Standard in S10/T10]
ENGINE: V-block. Six-cylinder. Bore & stroke: 3.52 x 2.99 in. Displacement: 2.8-liter (173 cid). BHP: 125 at 4800 rpm. Torque: 150 lb.-ft. at 2400 rpm. Compression ratio: 8.9:1. EFI/Throttle-body-injection. VIN Code R. Chevrolet-built. [Standard in S-Series Blazer, optional in S10]
ENGINE: V-block. Six-cylinder. Bore & stroke: 4.0 x 3.48 in. Displacement: 4.3-liter (262 cid). BHP: 150 at 4000 rpm. Torque: 230 lb.-ft. at 2400 rpm. Compression ratio: 9.3:1. EFI/Throttle-body-injection. VIN Code Not available. GM-built. [Standard in G10, G20, Astro]
ENGINE: V-block. Six-cylinder. Bore & stroke: 4.0 x 3.48 in. Displacement: 4.3-liter (262 cid). BHP: 160 at 4000 rpm. Torque: 235 lb.-ft. at 2400 rpm. Compression ratio: 9.1:1. EFI/Throttle-body-injection. VIN Code Z. Chevrolet-built. [Standard in C/K 1500/2500, optional in S10/T10 pickups]
ENGINE: V-block. Eight-cylinder. Bore & stroke: 3.74 x 3.48 in. Displacement: 5.0-liter (305 cid). BHP: 170 at 4400 rpm. Torque: 255 lb.-ft. at 2400 rpm. EFI/Throttle-body-injection. VIN Code H. Chevrolet-built. [Optional in C/K1500, C/K2500, G10, G20]
ENGINE: V-block. Eight-cylinder. Bore & stroke: 4.0 x 3.48 in. Displacement: 5.7-liter (350 cid). BHP: 190 at 4000 rpm. Torque: 300 lb.-ft. at 2400 rpm. Compression ratio: 8.6:1. EFI/Throttle-body-injection. VIN Code K. Chevrolet-built. [Standard in heavy-duty C/K3500, Suburbans, and heavy-duty G30 vans, optional in C/K pickups]
ENGINE: V-block. Eight-cylinder. Bore & stroke: 4.0 x 3.48 in. Displacement: 5.7-liter (350 cid). BHP: 210 at 4000 rpm. Compression ratio: 9.3:1. Torque: 300 lb.-ft. at 2800 rpm. EFI/Throttle-body-injection. VIN Code K. Chevrolet-built [Standard in C/K Blazer, optional in Suburban, optional in Chevy Van, optional in Sportvan]

ENGINE: V-block. Eight-cylinder. Bore & stroke: 4.25 x 4.00 in. Displacement: 7.4-liter (454 cid). BHP: 230 at 3600 rpm. Torque: 385 lb.-ft. at 1600 rpm. Throttle-body- fuel-injection. VIN Code N. Chevrolet-built. [Optional in Suburban, and heavy-duty G30 vans]
DIESEL ENGINES (DISPLACEMENT ORDER)
ENGINE: V-block. Light-duty. Eight-cylinder. Bore & stroke: 3.98 x 3.82 in. Displacement: 6.2-liter (379 cid). BHP: 148 at 3600 rpm. Torque: 248 lb.-ft. at 2000 rpm. VIN Code J. GM-built. [Optional in C/K3500 pickup, optional in G30 Chevy Van and 12-passenger Sportvan]
ENGINE: V-block. Heavy-duty. Eight-cylinder. Bore & stroke: 3.98 x 3.82 in. Displacement: 6.2-liter (379 cid). BHP: 130 at 3600 rpm. Torque: 240 lb.-ft. at 2000 rpm. VIN Code C. GM-built. [Optional in C/K3500 pickup, optional in G30 Chevy Van and 12-passenger Sportvan]

1989 Chevrolet 1/2-Ton K1500 Sportside Short Box Pickup 4x4 (CMD)

CHASSIS: [S10] Regular-Cab. Short Box. Wheelbase: 108.3 in. Length: 178.2 in. Width: 64.8 in. Height: 61.3 in. Standard GVW: 3,662 lb. Maximum GVW: 4,472 lb. Tires: P195/75R14 black sidewall.
CHASSIS: [T10] Regular-Cab. Short Box. Wheelbase: 108.5 in. Length: 178.2 in. Width: 64.8 in. Height: 63.4 in. Standard GVW: 4,004 lb. Maximum GVW: 5,368 lb. Tires: P205/75R15 black sidewall.
CHASSIS: [S10] Regular-Cab. Long box. Wheelbase: 117.9 in. Length: 194.2 in. Width: 64.8 in. Height: 61.3 in. Standard GVW: 3,662 lb. Maximum GVW: 4,930 lb. Tires: P195/75R14 black sidewall.
CHASSIS: [T10] Regular-Cab. Long box. Wheelbase: 117.9 in. Length: 194.2 in. Width: 64.7 in. Height: 63.4 in. Standard GVW: 4,004 lb. Maximum GVW: 5,368 lb. Tires: P205/75R15 black sidewall.
CHASSIS: [S10] Extended-cab. Short box. Wheelbase: 122.9 in. Length: 192.8 in. Width: 64.8 in. Height: 61.3 in. Standard GVW: 3,662 lb. Maximum GVW: 5,022 lb. Tires: P195/75R14 black sidewall.
CHASSIS: [T10] Extended-cab. Short box. Wheelbase: 122.9 in. Length: 192.8 in. Width: 64.8 in. Height: 63.4 in. Standard GVW: 4,004 lb. Maximum GVW: 5,368 lb. Tires: P205/75R15 black sidewall.
CHASSIS: [S-Blazer 4x2] Two-door. Wheelbase: 100.5 in. Length: 170.3 in. Width: 65.4 in. Height: 64.1 in. Standard GVW: 3,961 lb. Maximum GVW: 4,632 lb. Tires: P205/75R15 black sidewall.
CHASSIS: [S-Blazer 4x4] Two-door. Wheelbase: 100.5 in. Length: 170.3 in. Width: 65.4 in. Height: 64.3 in. Standard GVW: 4,310 lb. Maximum GVW: 5013 lb. Tires: P205/75R15 black sidewall.
CHASSIS: [Astro Cargo regular-body] Wheelbase: 111 in. Length: 176.8 in. Width: 77.0 in. Height: 74.9 in. Standard GVW: 5,000 lb. Maximum GVW: 5,400 lb. Tires: P205/75R15 black sidewall.
CHASSIS: [Astro Passenger regular-body] Wheelbase: 111 in. Length: 176.8 in. Width: 77.0 in. Height: 74.1 in. Standard GVW: 5,600 lb. Maximum GVW: 5,600 lb. Tires: P205/75R15 black sidewall.
CHASSIS: [G10/Short Body] Chevy Van. Wheelbase: 110 inches. Length: 178.2 in. Width: 79.5 in. Height: 79.4 in. Standard GVW: 4,900 lb. Maximum GVW: 6,000 lb. Tires: P215/75R15 black sidewall.
CHASSIS: [G10/Short Body] Sportvan. Wheelbase: 110 inches. Length:178.2 in. Width: 79.5 in. Height: 79.4 in. Standard GVW: 5,600 lb. Maximum GVW: 6,000 lb. Tires: P215/75R15 black sidewall.
CHASSIS: [G10/Long Body] Chevy Van. Wheelbase: 125 inches. Length: 202.2 in. Width: 79.5 in. Height: 79.4 in. Standard GVW: 4,900 lb. Maximum GVW: 6,000 lb. Tires: P215/75R15 black sidewall.
CHASSIS: [G10/Long Body] Sportvan. Wheelbase: 125 inches. Length: 202.2 in. Width: 79.5 in. Height: 79.4 in. Standard GVW: 5,600 lb. Maximum GVW: 6,000 lb. Tires: P215/75R15 black sidewall.
CHASSIS: [G20/Short Body] Chevy Van. Wheelbase: 110 in. Length: 178.2 in. Width: 79.5 in. Height: 79.8in. Standard GVW: 6,600 lb. Maximum GVW: 6,600 lb. Tires: P215/75R15 black sidewall.
CHASSIS: [G20/Long Body] Chevy Van. Wheelbase: 125 inches. Length: 202.2 in. Width: 79.5 in. Height: 79.2 in. Standard GVW: 6,600 lb. Maximum GVW: 6,600 lb. Tires: P215/75R15 black sidewall.
CHASSIS: [G20/Long Body] Sportvan/Beauville. Wheelbase: 125 inches. Length: 202.2 in. Width: 79.5 in. Height: 79.2 in. Standard GVW: 6,600 lb. Maximum GVW: 6,850 lb. Tires: P215/75R15 black sidewall.
CHASSIS: [G30/Long Body Chevy Van] Wheelbase: 125 inches. Length: 202.2 in. Width: 79.5 in. Height: 81.9 in. Standard GVW: 7,100 lb. Maximum GVW: 7,100 lb. Tires: P215/75R15 black sidewall.
CHASSIS: [G30/Long Body Heavy-duty Chevy Van] Wheelbase: 125 inches. Length: 202.2 in. Width: 79.5 in. Height: 81.9 in. Standard GVW: 8,600 lb. Maximum GVW: 8,600 lb. Tires: P215/75R15 black sidewall.
CHASSIS: [G30/Long Body Sportvan] Wheelbase: 125 inches. Length: 202.2 in. Width: 79.5 in. Height: 81.9 in. Standard GVW: 7,400 lb. Maximum GVW: 7,400 lb. Tires: P215/75R15 black sidewall.
CHASSIS: [G30/Long Body Heavy-duty Sportvan] Wheelbase: 125 inches. Length: 202.2 in. Width: 79.5 in. Height: 81.9 in. Standard GVW: 8,600 lb. Maximum GVW: 8,600 lb. Tires: P215/75R15 black sidewall.
CHASSIS: [G30/Extended Body Heavy-duty Sportvan/Beauville] Wheelbase: 146 in. Length: 223.2 in. Width: 79.5 in. Height: 81.9 in. Standard GVW: 8,600 lb. Maximum GVW: 3,957 lb. Tires: P215/75R15 black sidewall.
CHASSIS: [G30/Extended Body 12-Passenger Sportvan] Wheelbase: 146 in. Length: 223.2 in. Width: 79.5 in. Height: 81.9 in. Standard GVW: 10,000 lb. Maximum GVW: 10,000 lb. Tires: P215/75R15 black sidewall.

CHASSIS: [K10 Blazer 4x4] Wheelbase: 106.5 in. Length: 184.8 in. Width: 79.6 in. Height: 73.8 in. Standard GVW: 6,100 lb. Maximum GVW: 6,250 lb. Tires: LT245/75R16C black sidewall.
CHASSIS: [Suburban C1500] Wheelbase: 129.5 in. Length: 219.1 in. Width: 79.6 in. Height: 72.0 in. Standard GVW: 6,100 lb. Maximum GVW: 6,800 lb. Tires: P235/75R-15XLS black sidewall.
CHASSIS: [Suburban C2500] Wheelbase: 129.5 in. Length: 219.1 in. Width: 79.6 in. Height: 74.3 in. Standard GVW: 8,600 lb. Maximum GVW: 8,600 lb. Tires: P235/75R-15XLS black sidewall.
CHASSIS: [Suburban K1500] Wheelbase: 129.5 in. Length: 219.1 in. Width: 79.6 in. Height: 72.0 in. Standard GVW: 6,250 lb. Maximum GVW: 7,000 lb. Tires: P235/75R-15XLS black sidewall.
CHASSIS: [Suburban K2500] Wheelbase: 129.5 in. Length: 219.1 in. Width: 79.6 in. Height: 74.3 in. Standard GVW: 8,600 lb. Maximum GVW: 8,600 lb. Tires: P235/75R-15XLS black sidewall.
CHASSIS: [C1500 Sportside Regular-Cab Short Box Pickup] Regular-Cab. Short Box. Wheelbase: 117.5 in. Length: 194.0 in. Width: 77.1 in. Height: 70.4 in. Standard GVW: 5,600 lb. Maximum GVW: 5,600 lb. Tires: P225/75R15 black sidewall AS SBA Tires.
CHASSIS: [C1500 Fleetside Regular-Cab Short Box Pickup] Wheelbase: 117.5 in. Length: 194.1 in. Width: 76.4 in. Height: 70.4 in. Standard GVW: 5,600 lb. Maximum GVW: 5,600 lb. Tires: P225/75R15 black sidewall AS SBR Tires.
CHASSIS: [C1500 Sportside Regular-Cab Short Box] Wheelbase: 117.5 in. Length: 194.0 in. Width: 77.1 in. Height: 70.4 in. Standard GVW: 5,600 lb. Maximum GVW: 5,600 lb. Tires: P225/75R15 black sidewall AS SBR Tires.
CHASSIS: [C1500 Fleetside Regular-Cab Long Box Pickup] Wheelbase: 131.5 in. Length: 212.9 in. Width: 76.4 in. Height: 70.4 in. Standard GVW: 5,200 lb. Maximum GVW: 6,100 lb. Tires: P225/75R15 black sidewall AS SBR Tires.
CHASSIS: [C1500 Fleetside Regular-Cab Long Box Diesel Pickup] Wheelbase: 131.5 in. Length: 212.9 in. Width: 76.4 in. Height: 70.4 in. Standard GVW: 6,100 lb. Maximum GVW: 6,100 lb. Tires: P225/75R15 black sidewall AS SBR Tires.
CHASSIS: [C1500 Sportside Extended-cab Short Box Pickup] Wheelbase: 155.5 in. Length: 236.9 in. Width: 76.4 in. Height: 70.5 in. Standard GVW: 6,200 lb. Maximum GVW: 6,200 lb. Tires: P225/75R15 black sidewall AS SBR Tires.
CHASSIS: [K1500 Sportside Regular-Cab Short Box Pickup] Wheelbase: 117.5 in. Length: 194.0 in. Width: 77.1 in. Height: 73.8 in. Standard GVW: 5,600 lb. Maximum GVW: 5,600 lb. Tires: P225/75R15 black sidewall AS SBR Tires.
CHASSIS: [K1500 Fleetside Regular-Cab Short Box Pickup] Wheelbase: 117.5 in. Length: 194.1 in. Width: 76.4 in. Height: 73.8 in. Standard GVW: 5,600 lb. Maximum GVW: 5,600 lb. Tires: P225/75R15 black sidewall AS SBR Tires.
CHASSIS: [K1500 Fleetside Regular-Cab Long Box Pickup] Wheelbase: 131.5 in. Length: 212.9 in. Width: 76.4 in. Height: 73.8 in. Standard GVW: 5,600 lb. Maximum GVW: 6,100 lb. Tires: P225/75R15 black sidewall AS SBR Tires.
CHASSIS: [K1500 Fleetside Regular-Cab Long Box Diesel Pickup] Wheelbase: 131.5 in. Length: 212.9 in. Width: 76.4 in. Height: 73.8 in. Standard GVW: 5,600 lb. Maximum GVW: 6,100 lb. Tires: P225/75R15 black sidewall AS SBR Tires.
CHASSIS: [K1500 Fleetside Extended-cab Short Box Pickup] Wheelbase: 155.5 in. Length: 236.9 in. Width: 76.4 in. Height: 73.9 in. Standard GVW: 6,200 lb. Maximum GVW: 6,600 lb. Tires: P225/75R15 black sidewall AS SBR Tires.
CHASSIS: [K1500 Fleetside Regular-Cab Long Box Heavy-duty Diesel Pickup] Wheelbase: 131.5 in. Length: 212.9 in. Width: 76.4 in. Height: 74.3. Standard GVW: 8,600 lb. Maximum GVW: 8,600 lb. Tires: P225/75R15 black sidewall AS SBR Tires.
CHASSIS: [K1500 Extended-Cab Long Box Big Dooley Heavy-duty Pickup] Wheelbase: 155..5 in. Length: 236.9. Width: 76.4 in. Height: 76.0. Standard GVW: 8600 lb. Maximum GVW: 10,000 lb. Tires: P225/75R15 black sidewall AS SBR Tires.
CHASSIS: [C2500 Fleetside Regular-Cab Long Box Pickup] Wheelbase: 131.5 in. Length: 212.9 in. Width: 76.4 in. Height: 73 in. Standard GVW: 7,200 lb. Maximum GVW: 7,200 lb. Tires: P225/75R15 black sidewall AS SBR tires.
CHASSIS: [C2500 Heavy-duty Fleetside Regular-Cab Long Box Pickup] Wheelbase: 131.5 in. Length: 212.9 in. Width: 76.4 in. Height: 73 in. Standard GVW: 8,600 lb. Maximum GVW: 8,600 lb. Tires: P225/75R15 black sidewall AS SBR tires.
CHASSIS: [C2500 Fleetside Extended-cab Short Box Pickup] Wheelbase: 155.5 in. Length: 236.9 in. Width: 76.4 in. Height: 73 in. Standard GVW: 8,600 lb. Maximum GVW: 8,600 lb. Tires: P225/75R15 black sidewall AS SBR tires.
CHASSIS: [K2500 Fleetside Regular-Cab Long Box Pickup] Wheelbase: 131.5 in. Length: 212.9 in. Width: 76.4 in. Height: 74.3 in. Standard GVW: 7,200 lb. Maximum GVW: 7,200 lb. Tires: P225/75R15 black sidewall AS SBR tires.
CHASSIS: [K2500 Heavy-duty Fleetside Regular-Cab Long Box Pickup] Wheelbase: 131.5 in. Length: 212.9 in. Width: 76.4 in. Height: 74.3 in. Standard GVW: 8,600 lb. Maximum GVW: 8,600 lb. Tires: P225/75R15 black sidewall AS SBR tires.
CHASSIS: [K2500 Fleetside Extended-cab Short Box Pickup] Wheelbase: 155.5 in. Length: 236.9 in. Width: 76.4 in. Height: 74.5 in. Standard GVW: 7,200 lb. Maximum GVW: 7,200 lb. Tires: P225/75R15 black sidewall AS SBR tires.
CHASSIS: [K3500 Fleetside Extended-cab Heavy-duty Long Box Pickup] Wheelbase: 155.5 in. Length: 255.7 in. Width: 76.4 in. Height: 76 in. Standard GVW: 8,600 lb. Maximum GVW: 8,600 lb. Tires: P225/75R15 black sidewall AS SBR tires.
CHASSIS: [C/K 3500 Pickup] Motor home chassis. Wheelbase: 183.5 in. Tires: P225/75R15 black sidewall AS SBR tires.

1989 Chevrolet 1/2-Ton S10 "Baja" Pickup 4x4 (CMD)

S/T SERIES PICKUP OPTIONS: Durango package ($242). Tahoe package ($683). Sport package ($1,038). Air conditioning ($736 without LL2 engine or $680 with LL2 engine). Optional axle ratio ($38). Locking rear differential ($252). Heavy-duty battery ($56). Cold climate package ($113-$156 depending upon trim option). Center console ($114). Engine oil cooler ($126). Heavy-duty radiator ($56). Heavy-duty radiator and engine oil cooler ($63, with air conditioning, $118 without air conditioning). Spare tire cover ($33). Air deflector ($43). Driver convenience package including Comfortilt steering wheel and intermittent wiper system ($180). Rear window convenience package including electric tailgate release and rear window defogger ($197). 4.3-liter V-6 ($255). Color-keyed front floor mats ($16). Color-keyed rear floor mats ($12). Gauge package ($62). Deep-tinted glass with light tinted rear window ($56-$200 depending on trim package.) Halogen headlights ($24). Engine block heater ($33). Electronic instrumentation ($296-$358 depending on trim package). Engine compartment light ($16). Interior visor mirror ($7). Exterior below-eye-line black mirrors ($52). Exterior below-eye-line bright mirrors ($87). Interior rear view tilting mirror with dual reading lamps ($26). Body side and wheel opening moldings ($152). Black wheel opening molding ($13-$43 depending upon trim package). Bright wheel opening molding ($31). Operating convenience package includes power door locks and power windows ($344). Custom two-tone paint ($172-$344 depending upon trim package). Special two-tone paint ($163-$212 depending upon trim package). Deluxe two-tone paint ($177-$329 depending upon trim package). Electronically tuned AM/FM stereo radio ($275). Electronically-tuned AM/FM stereo radio with Seek-and-Scan, stereo cassette tape player and digital clock ($454). Electronically-tuned AM/FM stereo radio with Seek-and-Scan, stereo cassette tape player with Search-and-Repeat, graphic equalizer and digital clock ($604). Reclining seat backs ($74). Transfer case and front differential skid plates and steering linkage shield ($75). Front and rear heavy-duty shock absorbers ($36). Electronic speed control ($205). Heavy-duty front springs ($63). Body striping ($49). Sunshine striping ($116). Manual sun roof ($250). Suspension package ($160-$220 depending upon trim package). Two front tow hooks ($38). Deadweight trailer hitch ($68). Light-duty trailering package ($109). Heavy-duty Trailering Special package ($211). Four-speed automatic transmission ($795). Wheel trim rings ($60). Cast aluminum wheels ($252-$308 depending upon trim package). Sliding rear window ($257). Rear window wiper/washer ($125).

1989 Chevrolet 1/2-Ton S10 Blazer "Sport" 2-door Sport Utility 4x4

S-SERIES BLAZER OPTIONS: Air conditioning ($736 without LL2 engine, $680 with LL2 engine). Optional axle ratio ($38). Locking rear differential ($252). Heavy-duty battery 56). Luggage carrier ($126). Spare tire and wheel carrier ($159-$192 depending upon trim option). Cold climate package ($113-$156 depending upon trim option). Center console ($114). Engine oil cooler ($126). Heavy-duty radiator ($56). Heavy-duty radiator and engine oil cooler ($63 with air conditioning, $118 without air conditioning). Spare tire cover ($33). Sport package ($1,038 without High Country option, $671 with High Country option). Tahoe package ($683 without High Country option, $473 with High Country option). Air deflector ($43). Driver convenience package including Comfortilt steering wheel and intermittent wiper system ($180). Rear window convenience package including electric tailgate release and rear window defogger ($197). 4.3-liter V-6 ($255). Color-keyed front floor mats ($16). Color-keyed rear floor mats ($12). Gauge package ($62). Deep-tinted glass with light tinted rear window ($56-$200 depending on trim package). Halogen headlights ($24). Engine block heater ($33). Electronic instrumentation ($296-$358 depending on trim package). Engine compartment light ($16). Interior visor mirror ($7). Exterior below-eye-line black mirrors ($52). Exterior below-eye-line bright mirrors ($87). Interior rear view tilting mirror with dual reading lamps ($26). Body side and wheel opening moldings ($152). Black wheel opening molding ($13-$43 depending upon trim package). Bright wheel opening molding ($31). Operating convenience package including power door locks and power windows ($344). Custom two-tone paint ($172-$344 depending upon trim package). Special two-tone paint ($163-$212 depending upon trim package). Deluxe two-tone paint ($177-$329 depending upon trim package). Electronically-tuned AM/FM stereo radio ($275). Electronically-tuned AM/FM stereo radio with Seek-and-Scan, stereo cassette tape player and digital clock ($454). Electronically-tuned AM/FM stereo radio with Seek-and-Scan, stereo cassette tape player with Search-and-Repeat, graphic equalizer and digital clock ($604). Rear folding seat ($409). Reclining seat backs ($74). Transfer case and front differential skid plates and steering linkage shield ($75). Front and rear heavy-duty shock absorbers ($36). Electronic speed control ($205). Heavy-duty front springs ($63). Body striping ($49). Sunshine striping ($116). Manual sun roof ($250). Suspension package ($160-$220 depending upon trim package). High Country package ($925 with Sport package, $1,026 with Tahoe package). Two front tow hooks ($38). Deadweight trailer hitch ($68). Light-duty trailering package ($109). Heavy-duty Trailering Special package ($211). Four-speed automatic transmission ($795). Wheel trim rings ($60). Cast aluminum wheels ($252-$308 depending upon trim package). Sliding rear window ($257). Rear window wiper/washer ($125).
ASTRO OPTIONS: Air conditioning: Front ($735)/front and rear ($1,320). Optional axle ratio ($38). Locking rear differential ($252). Deluxe front and rear chromed bumpers ($76-$128 depending upon option packages). Black luggage carrier ($126). Engine oil cooler ($126). Heavy-duty radiator ($56). Heavy-duty radiator and engine oil cooler ($63 with air conditioning or $118 without air conditioning). Power door locks ($211). Driver convenience package including Comfortilt steering wheel and intermittent wiper system ($326). Power windows ($211). Deep-tinted glass ($75-$365 depending on body glass selected). Rear heater ($267). Electronic instrumentation ($88). Auxiliary lighting ($128). Black

below-eye-line exterior mirrors ($52). Exterior remote electric mirrors ($150). Special two-tone paint ($251). Sport two-tone paint ($172). Electronically tuned AM/FM stereo radio with Seek-and-Scan, digital clock, stereo cassette player and premium speakers ($122). Electronically tuned AM/FM stereo radio with Seek-and-Scan, stereo cassette tape player with Search-and-Repeat, graphic equalizer, digital clock and premium speakers ($624). Seven-passenger seating ($878-$1,069 depending upon other options). Eight-passenger seating ($344-$878 depending upon other options). Seat back recliner and dual arm rests ($241). Six-way power seat ($240). Front and rear heavy-duty shock absorbers ($36). Heavy-duty trailering equipment ($498-$555 depending upon other equipment ordered). Light-duty trailering equipment ($109). Aluminum wheels ($224-$316, depending upon other options ordered). Rally wheels ($50-$92 depending on model-option).

1989 Chevrolet 3/4-Ton G20 Chevy Van Travel Van Conversion 4x2

G-SERIES VANS OPTIONS: Custom cloth seat trim ($402). Special two-tone paint ($121-$255). Deluxe two-tone paint ($177-$269). Exterior decor package ($321-$529). California emission system ($100). 5.7-liter V-8, except standard in G30 ($755). 5.0-liter V-8 in G1-0/G20 ($555). Four-speed automatic transmission with overdrive ($485). Optional rear axle ($38). Locking differential ($252). Air conditioning ($904) Dual air conditioning ($1,499). Heavy-duty battery ($56). Front and rear chromed bumpers (standard on Beauville and $76 on other models). Chrome bumper guards ($43). Electric quartz clock ($41). ZQ3 convenience group ($326). AU3 door lock system ($211). B30 carpeting on floor, wheelhousings, stepwells for 125-inch wheelbase only ($188). Tinted glass, all windows ($104). Deep-tinted glass ($401). Deep-tinted glass with light-tinted rear window ($339). Rear heater ($267). TR9 auxiliary lighting package ($103). B84 black body side moldings ($134). B96 wheel opening moldings ($74). ZQ2 operating convenience package ($411). U63 AM radio ($122-$248). UM7 AM/FM stereo sound system ($288-$308). UM6 stereo sound system ($419-$464). UX1 stereo sound system ($569-$614). Rear seats equipment package ($371). AQ4 seating package with two additional rear seats ($729-$1,047). Custom steering wheel ($28). Sport steering wheel ($35). Positive rear door stop ($37). BA8 front seat storage compartment ($37) D85 body striping ($73). Heavy-duty Trailering Special equipment ($349-$546). Diesel equipment package, includes heavy-duty battery, heavy-duty radiator and transmission cooler ($555). Light-duty trailering package ($132). Rally wheels with trim rings and caps ($121). Cast aluminum wheels ($316). Intermittent windshield wiper system ($59).

K10 BLAZER OPTIONS: Silverado package RPO YE9 includes the following extra exterior features in addition to, or in place of Scottsdale items: Front and rear chromed bumpers with black rub stripes (front rub strip has bright trim), Silverado nameplates, a molded plastic grille and front lamp bezels painted Dark Argent with chrome trim, rectangular dual halogen headlamps, body side and rear black moldings with bright trim, bright wheel opening moldings, bright metal wheelcovers, cab-to-fender and hood insulators, underhood reel-type lamp, and electric power rear tailgate window and bright appliqué. The Silverado interior also added high-back reclining front bucket seats. Customers got a choice of custom vinyl pigskin-grained trim in dark blue or saddle or textured velour custom cloth trim in a choice of dark blue, burgundy, saddle or slate gray. The Silverado interior also included right side front and left and right side rear assist straps, a glove box light, color-keyed front compartment carpeting with matching rear compartment floor covering (including wheelhouse carpet mats with optional rear seat), insulation on dash panel and between double-wall cab roof and on floor panel (extra-thick at front, extra-thick at rear when rear seat was ordered), added insulation under the cowl panel and on the headliner, body side trim panels, extra insulation on diesel engine models, sun shades with flexible outboard ends and sliding extenders at inboard ends, a storage strap on the left side sun shade, an illuminated mirror on the right sun shade, brushed pewter-toned instrument panel trim, a four-spoke sport steering wheel with simulated stitched leather appearance, a front compartment foam-backed cloth headliner with matching retainer moldings, special door trim panels (including door closing assist strips, decorative inserts, map pockets and carpet trim), rear sidewall trim panels with ash trays and carpet trim, a cigarette lighter with ash tray illumination, a black vinyl spare tire cover, a headlight warning buzzer, and a color-keyed molded plastic console with storage and beverage pockets ($1,340). Air cleaner pre-cleaner RPO K46 ($44). Air conditioning RPO C60 ($781 without B3J or ($719 with B3J). Deluxe front end appearance RPO V22 including Dark Argent grille with chrome trim and quad halogen headlamps (included with Silverado or otherwise $145). Optional rear axle ratios ($38). Locking rear differential RPO G80 ($252). Heavy-duty Delco Freedom battery with 630 cold cranking amps RPO UA1 (included with V10 cold climate package or otherwise $56). Chromed front bumper guards RPO V31 ($43). Cold climate package RPO V10, including UA1 battery and KO5 engine block heater ($104). Engine oil cooler RPO KC4 ($126). Heavy-duty radiator RPO VO1 ($56). Heavy-duty radiator and transmission oil cooler RPO VO2 ($63). Front floor mats RPO B32 ($16). Rear floor mats RPO B33 ($22). Deep-tinted glass with light-tinted rear glass RPO AA3 ($149). Deep-tinted glass RPO AJ1 ($205). Wiring harness RPO UY7 ($46). Headlamp warning buzzer RPO T63 ($12). Engine block heater RPO KO5 ($33). Locking front hubs RPO X6Z ($60). Auxiliary lighting RPO TR9 includes glove box and underhood lights ($26). Below-eye-line stainless steel exterior mirrors RPO D45 ($35). Deluxe molding package RPO YG3 including deluxe front and rear chrome bumpers with rub strips, bright trim for front side marker lights and taillights, bright wheel opening moldings and black body side and rear moldings with bright trim ($234). Operating convenience package RPO ZQ2, including power door locks and front door power windows ($344). Conventional two-tone exterior paint RPO ZY2 ($413 without YE9 or $180 with YE9). Special two-tone exterior paint RPO ZY3 ($464 without YE9 or $450 with YE9). Deluxe two-tone exterior paint RPO ZY4 ($566 without YE9 or $332 with YE9). Puncture sealant tires RPO P42 ($230). Electronically tuned AM/FM stereo radio RPO UU9 ($148). Electronically-tuned AM/FM stereo radio with Seek-and-Scan and digital clock RPO UM7 ($208). Electronically-tuned AM/FM stereo radio with Seek-and-Scan, stereo cassette tape player and digital clock RPO UM6 ($329). Electronically-tuned AM/FM stereo radio with Seek-and-Scan, stereo cassette tape player with Search-and-Repeat, graphic equalizer and digital clock RPO UX1 ($504). Radio delete RPO UL5 ($77). Fuel tank shield RPO NY1 including protective shield on transfer case ($175). Rear folding three-passenger seat AM7 ($411). Rear seat not desired RPO YG4 (no charge). Electronic speed control RPO K34 ($205). Heavy-duty 2,250-pound front springs F60, including heavy-duty front and rear shock absorbers, recommended for front-mounted accessory applications only ($62). Comfortilt steering wheel RPO N33 ($121). Two front towing hooks RPO V76 ($38). Deadweight type trailer hitch RPO VR2 ($62). Weight distributing platform type trailer hitch RPO VR4 ($164). Trailering Special Equipment RPO Z82 including VR4 hitch, UY7 wiring and VO2 transmission oil cooler, without BJ3 includes KC4 engine oil cooler ($398). Four-speed automatic with overdrive RPO MXO ($795, but no charge with B3J equipment). Wheelcovers RPO PO1 ($42). Rally wheels RPO N67 ($121 without YE90 or $79 with YE9). Aluminum cast wheels RPO N90 ($318 without YE9 or $278 with YE9). Power electric tailgate window RPO A33 ($103). Sliding rear quarter windows AD5 ($257). Intermittent windshield wipers RPO CD4 ($59).

C/K PICKUPS AND SUBURBAN OPTIONS: Cleaner air cleaner RPO K46 ($44). Air conditioning RPO C60 ($781). Deluxe front appearance RPO V22 ($145). Optional axle ratio ($38). Locking rear differential RPO G80 ($252). Heavy-duty Delco Freedom auxiliary battery with 540 cold cranking amps (not available with B3J diesel equipment RPO TP2, otherwise $134. Heavy-duty Delco Freedom battery with 630 cold cranking amps RPO UA1 ($56). Painted rear step bumper RPO V43 ($130). RPO VB3. Chromed front deluxe bumper with rub strip (included with RPO Z62 and RPO YE9, otherwise $229). Rear step bumper with rub strip RPO VB3 ($229). RPO V27 black front bumper guards, requires RPO VG3 ($32). Spare tire and wheel carrier, not available with K10753 or RPO P13 (no charge). Heavy-duty chassis included with B3J diesel equipment RPO F44 ($230). RPO V10 Cold-Climate package (not available with RPO C60 including UA1 battery, KO5 block heater and C42 heater, otherwise $134). RPO D55 console, requires bucket seats ($114). RPO KC4 engine oil cooling system. The last option was not available with B3J diesel equipment and, when teamed with the RPO MXO transmission, VO2 cooling was required. It was also included with the Z82 trailering option (otherwise $126). RPO VO1 heavy-duty radiator, not available with RPO VO2 ($56). RPO VO2 heavy-duty radiator and transmission oil cooler, requires RPO MXO transmission and included with RPO Z823 (otherwise $63). Scottsdale trim package RPO Z62 ($223). Silverado trim package RPO YE ($665). RPO C49 rear window defogger, requires RPO YE9 or RPO Z62 and not available with RPO A28 window or RPO AJ1 glass ($1,564). 5.0-liter V-8 RPO LO3 ($555). 5.7-liter V-8 RPO LO5 ($755). Locking fuel filler cap RPO NO5 ($18). RPO B32 front color-keyed floor mats, requires RPO YE9 ($16). RPO B33 rear color-keyed floor mats, requires RPO AM7 seat and RPO B32. ($12). RPO Z53 gauge package including voltmeter, engine coolant temperature and oil pressure gauges, included with RPO YE9 (otherwise $42). RPO AA3 deep-tinted glass with light-tinted rear window, not available with RPO AJ1and including RPO A20 window ($98). RPO AJ1 deep-tinted glass, not available with RPO C49 defogger and including A20 window ($144). RPO UY7 heavy-duty trailering wiring harness (included with RPO Z82, otherwise $46). RPO TT4 halogen headlights (not available with RPO V22 or RPO YE9, otherwise $ 24). RPO C42 engine block heater (included with RPO V10 and RPO KO5, otherwise $33). Front heavy-duty heater, included with V10, not available with RPO C60 ($45). Cargo area lamp RPO UF2 ($36). RPO UO1 roof marker lamps, not available with California emissions ($52). RPO C95 dome and reading lamps (included with RPO TR9, otherwise. $33). Cigarette lighter RPO 37 ($25). Auxiliary lighting RPO TR9 ($90). Below-eye-line black painted exterior mirrors RPO D44 ($52). Below-eye-line stainless steel exterior mirrors RPO D45 ($87). Camper-type exterior mirrors RPO DF2 ($100). Black body side moldings RPO B84 ($59). Bright body side moldings RPO B85 ($17). Black wheel opening moldings RPO B74 ($31). Bright wheel opening moldings RPO B96 (no charge). Operating convenience package including power door locks and power windows RPO ZQ2 ($344). Conventional two-tone paint RPO YZ2 ($132). Special two-tone paint RPO YZ3 ($215). Deluxe two-tone paint RPO ($243). AM radio RPO U63 ($122). Electronically-tuned AM/FM stereo radio with Seek-and-Scan RPO K4 ($268). Electronically-tuned AM/FM stereo radio with Seek-and-Scan and digital clock RPO UM7 ($333). Electronically-tuned AM/FM stereo radio with Seek-and-Scan and stereo cassette tape player RPO UK5 ($390). Electronically tuned AM/FM stereo radio with Seek-and-Scan, stereo cassette tape player and digital clock RPO UM6 ($454). Electronically-tuned AM/FM stereo radio with Seek-and-Scan, stereo cassette tape player with Search-and-Repeat, Graphic equalizer and digital clock RPO UX1 ($604). RPO U73 fixed mast antenna (included with RPO U63, UK4, UK5, UM6, or UX1 radio, otherwise $41). Rear folding seat., requires bucket or split front seat RPO AM7 ($385). Heavy-duty front and rear shock absorbers RPO F51 ($36). RPO NZZ off-road skid plate, available for K1500 only. ($95). Electronic speed control RPO K34 ($205). 4x4 Sport graphics package RPO BQ4 ($110). Heavy-duty front springs, not available with B3J diesel equipment RPO F60 ($63). Front stabilizer bar RPO F59 ($40). Comfortilt steering wheel RPO N33 ($121). Custom steering wheel RPO N31 ($28). Sport steering wheel RPO NKJ3 ($7 with RPO YE9, $35 with RPO Z62). Striping RPO D85 ($69). RPO NJ8 fuel tank with approximately 34-gallons capacity (not available with K10753, otherwise $56). Two front towing hooks RPO B76 ($38). Weight distributing platform trailer hitch RPO VR4 ($164). Heavy-duty Trailering Special equipment RPO Z82 ($435 without B3J diesel equipment or $273 with B3J). Four-speed manual transmission RPO MM4 ($98 without B3J). Four-speed automatic transmission with overdrive RPO MXO ($795). Wheelcovers RPO PO1 ($42). Rally wheels RPO N67 ($75). Swing-out quarter windows RPO A20 ($43). Sliding rear window RPO A28 ($113). Intermittent windshield wipers RPO CD4 ($59).

NOTE 13: Options and prices shown are representative. The actual cost of an option or option package often varies according to other packages that the options are combined with on specific vehicles. Preferred Equipment Group (PEG) options offer specific optional equipment at discount prices. Some "options" may be standard equipment on certain models, such as V-8s in C/K3500 pickups. Descriptions of options are edited. Full option contents can be determined by consulting sales literature.

HISTORICAL: Chevrolet trucks were built in 12 factories in 1989. Geo Trackers entered production at the CAMI plant in Ingersoll, Ontario, Canada, as 1990 models. S-Series pickups were assembled in Pontiac, Michigan and Shreveport, Louisiana. S-Series Blazers were built at Pontiac, Michigan and Moraine, Ohio. Astros were made in Baltimore, Maryland. Chevy Van models were sourced from factories in Scarborough, Ontario, Canada, and Flint, Michigan. Full-size Blazers and Suburbans were made in the Chevrolet factory at Janesville, Wisconsin. C/K pickups were built in Fort Wayne, Indiana; Oshawa, Canada; Pontiac, Michigan; and Janesville, Wisconsin. Lumina APVs (1990 models) were assembled at Tarrytown, N.Y. Jim C. Perkins was general manager of Chevrolet Motor Division.

F.F. Raine, Jr. was national manager of truck merchandising. Candace M. Robbins was manager of truck advertising. W.L. Ames was truck merchandising manager. Ralph J. Kramer was overall director of public relations, including Chevrolet truck publicity. Chevrolet calendar-year new-truck sales were: 521,358 C/K Pickups, 228,691 S10/T10 Pickups, 178,691 S-Series Blazers, 116,282 Chevy Vans, 54,723 Astro Vans, 65,428 Suburbans, 22,816 K10 Blazers, 89,218 Astro Wagons, 9,776 Lumina APVs (1990 models), 10,342 Sportvans, 6,720 Geo Trackers (Japanese-built 1990 models), 4,741 Geo Trackers (Canadian-built 1990 models), 743 W4 Tiltmaster imports, 15,930 medium-duty trucks in the calendar-year. This gave the company sales of 1,325,459 light-duty trucks in the calendar-year. Chevrolet MODEL-YEAR new-truck sales were: 551,223 C/K Pickups, 241,866 S10/T10 Pickups, 193,092 S-Series Blazers, 120,240 Chevy Vans, 55,604 Astro Vans, 68,414 Suburbans, 24,597 K10 Blazers, 94,532 Astro Wagons, 68 Lumina APVs (1990 models), 10,402 Sportvans, 8,341 Geo Trackers (Japanese-built 1990 models), 1,107 Geo Trackers (Canadian-built 1990 models), 763 W4 Tiltmaster imports, and 16,616 medium-duty (possibly Step-Vans.)

1990

1990 GEO Tracker Convertible 4x4 (CMD)

1/4-TON — GEO TRACKER — L4: Geo Tracker, Chevrolet's Suzuki-designed four-wheel-drive sport utility vehicle entered North American production at CAMI Automotive, Inc. in Canada for the 1990 model-year. Tracker added a new convertible model to its lineup. All models came standard with a 1.6-liter four-cylinder engine and five-speed manual transmission. A three-speed automatic was optional.

1/2-TON — S (4x2)/T (4x4) SERIES PICKUP --L4/V-6: The S10 was Chevrolet's 4x2 compact pickup, while the 4x4 version was factory-coded as a T10. Both models carried S10 exterior badging. The T10 offered Chevrolet's "Insta-Trac" system for shifting into four-wheel-drive on the fly. Base power plant in S10s was a 2.5-liter inline four-cylinder engine. A 2.8 liter V-6 and five-speed manual transmission were available for the S10, but not the T10. A new Getrag-designed, Hydramatic-built five-speed manual transmisson with fifth gear overdrive was available with a 4.3 liter V-6. This power train was standard in T10s and optional in S10s. A new fixed gross vehicle weight rating (GVWR) replaced the net payload system. All S10 models had a redesigned instrument cluster with improved legibility. The panel now included voltmeter, engine coolant temperature, and oil pressure gauges. Added to the standard S10 equipment list were front tow hooks, P205/75R15 all-season steel-belted-radial tires, reclining seat backs on Maxi-Cab models, and an electronically-tuned AM radio. New 1990 features of the Durango included swing-out quarter windows, a right-hand visor mirror, a deluxe chrome front bumper, and a chromed grille. New for the Tahoe were right- and left-hand black exterior mirrors, color-keyed floor mats, and an engine compartment lamp. New exterior colors were Royal Blue Metallic and Garnet. The interior was now offered in garnet.

1990 Chevrolet 1/2-Ton S10 Extended-Cab Pickup 4x4 (CMD)

1990 Chevrolet 1/2-Ton S10 Blazer 2-door Sport Utility 4x4 (CMD)

1/2-TON — S (4x2)/T (4x4) SERIES BLAZER — V-6: The S-Series Blazer had a more powerful standard engine, increased standard equipment content, and a new gross vehicle weight rating system for 1990. In midyear, an all-new four-door model was added to the line. It came only with four-wheel-drive this year. Now standard in all S-Series Blazer models was the 4.3 liter Vortex EFI V-6. Its power rating was unchanged from 1989. Three trim levels were again offered: Standard, Tahoe and Sport. However, their standard equipment content was significantly increased. All three trim levels had the following new-for-1990 items: Full-size spare tire, inside spare tire cover, P205/75R15 all-season steel-belted radial tires, deluxe front appearance package, right- and left-hand exterior black-finish mirrors, halogen headlights, a redesigned instrument cluster, a voltmeter, engine coolant temperature and oil pressure gauges, an electronically-tuned AM radio, and front tow hooks. The Sport package included cast aluminum wheels. A new light-dimming control was used for the four-wheel-drive indicator. The Trailering Special equipment package was available for models equipped with manual transmission. Previously, it had been limited to S-Series Blazers with automatic transmission. The new gross vehicle weight rating (GVWR) system for 1990 replaced the older net payload system in which trucks were assigned a net payload rating and were rated to carry that payload regardless of the factory option content or aftermarket accessories. With the new fixed system, ratings were done on an individual, truck-by-truck basis. The net cargo rating was more accurately calculated by subtracting the curb weight and the weight of the options, passengers and any aftermarket equipment. Two new exterior colors were offered for 1990. The total selection of exterior colors were Frost White, Silver Metallic, Midnight Black, Aspen Blue Metallic, Wheat, Woodlands Brown Metallic, Royal Blue Metallic (which replaced Galaxy Blue Metallic), Garnet, Nevada Gold Metallic, Apple Red, and Steel Gray Metallic. The Emerald exterior color was dropped for 1990. One new interior color was offered for 1990. The custom vinyl and custom cloth interiors were offered in blue, garnet (which replaced carmine), charcoal or saddle. The deluxe cloth and leather upholstery choices were offered in either charcoal or saddle. The "High Country" option was not offered for 1990.

1/2-TON — ASTRO M (RWD)/L (AWD) SERIES — V-6: The 1990 Chevrolet Astro became the first U.S.-built minivan to offer full-time all-wheel-drive. Chevrolet reported that the Astro L10 AWD (all-wheel-drive) model required no special driving skill or experience, since it handled as easily as the M10 RWD (rear-wheel-drive) model. The AWD Astro had a higher 3.34:1 higher axle ratio (versus 3.23:1 for the RWD model) to compensate for the additional weight of the all-wheel-drive system. Chevrolet noted that drivers would feel added responsiveness to the steering as the front wheels pulled the AWD around curves and corners. Also noticeable was the firm, low pedal travel of the hydro-boost brakes. Power in the AWD system was transmitted to the rear through a planetary gear set in the transfer case to either the standard open rear axle or the optional limited-slip rear axle. At the front, the power moved via a random-toothed chain to an open differential front axle. Inside the transfer case was a viscous clutch connecting the front and rear through many closely spaced and heavily lubricated plates. When all the plates alternately splined to the front or rear drive rotated at the same rate, the viscous clutch was not active. When the front and rear wheel speed varied, the clutch transferred torque in proportion to the speed differential. The torque transfer was immediate, substantial, and in direct proportion to need. The AWD Astro used the front suspension, steering and brake system of the Chevrolet K20 full-size pickup. The body, rear drive train and wheels were from the RWD Astro M10 van. The K20's front axle and drive shafts were also used. Four-wheel antilock brakes were standard on the AWD Astro. New components for the AWD Astro included a new stub frame, a single-speed transfer case, a front stabilizer shaft, a front prop shaft with constant velocity joints, and specific exhaust manifolds for frame clearance. The AWD Astro exterior was distinguished by its black bumper guards, acrylic emblems with "All-Wheel-Drive" lettering on the rear, and side doors that ran the length of both lower sides. Chevrolet's 4.3-liter Vortex V-6 was standard, as was a four-speed automatic overdrive transmission. Initially, the AWD system was offered for the regular length Astro in either cargo or passenger configurations. Available as a mid-1990 model was an extended-body van that increased cargo capacity by nearly 19 cu.-ft. It added 10 in. of length behind the rear wheels. The extended-body model was available with an optional platform trailer hitch that fitted flush with the rear bumper. A new-for-1990 high-output (HO) version of the 4.3-liter V-6 was available at midyear. Its horsepower and torque ratings were 170 hp at 4800 rpm and 235 lb.-ft. at 3200 rpm. The added power of the HO engine came from a low-restriction intake and exhaust system and a high-lift camshaft. The HO engine also featured a high-stall torque converter, performance calibrations for the automatic transmission, and a dual spark exhaust system. As compared to the 1989 V-6, the latest Vortex engine had improved durability and reliability due to the use of a closed-bottom charcoal canister, revised exhaust manifold heat stove, and improved piston pins. The Astro was offered in three trim levels called CS, CL and LT. Standard exterior features of the CS trim level were: Front and rear bumpers painted lower body color, bright Astro nameplates, a black-painted molded plastic grille, halogen headlights, bright metal hubcaps with black trim, 15 x 6.00-inch steel wheels painted Argent Silver, all-season steel-belted radial tires, compact spare tire and wheel, intermittent windshield wiper system, right and left side black-painted mirrors with pivoting arm and adjustable 4.75 x 7.0-inch heads, hot melt wax on underbody, and front license plate bracket. Interior appointments consisted of right- and left-hand arm rests, color-keyed vinyl door trim panels with front door map pockets, front high-back adjustable bucket seats with all-vinyl trim, plus center removable three-passenger bench seat, two left and one right side coat hooks, latex foam rubber door seals, black plastic door sill plates, two dome lamps with front door-activated switches, headlight warning chimes, color-keyed carpeting on wheelhousings and floor, left and right side color-keyed sunshades with right side visor mirror, tinted glass in all windows, gauges for speedometer, odometer, fuel level, voltmeter, oil pressure, engine coolant temperature, and trip odometer, remote release for fuel filler door, black vinyl four-spoke steering wheel with anti-theft device locking feature, cigarette lighter and ash tray light, molded color-keyed plastic storage compartment in left side rear quarter area, full-length color-keyed, foam-backed cloth headliner, stowage box including beverage holder in front face of engine cover extension, swing-out glass on sliding side door, electronically-tuned AM radio with fixed mast antenna, and deluxe heater and defogger with side window defogger. The CL trim level had the following interior and exterior equipment in addition to or replacing that of the CS trim: Exterior: Front and rear bumpers with matching color-keyed end caps, rub strips and rear black combination top step surface, grille with Argent Silver paint on feature surfaces, black body side moldings and wheel opening moldings, 15 x 6.5-inch steel rally wheels, and air dam with fog lamps. Interior features were as follows: Expanded vinyl door trim panels with carpet inserts and insulation, choice of custom vinyl trim or custom cloth for seats, rear door and sliding door-actuated dome light switches as well as a door jamb defeat switch, color-keyed floor mats, lighted right-hand visor mirror, custom steering wheel, stowage box lamp, swing-out glass for rear door, convenience tray lamp, stepwell lamp, and storage compartment lamp. The LT trim had, in addition to or replacing equipment of the CL trim, these items: Exterior special nameplates on front side door B-pillars, wide color-keyed graduated-tone striping at belt line, and 15 x 6.5-inch rally wheels color-keyed to body. LT interior features were: Special front bucket seats with reclining backs, folding integral arm rests and full-width adjustable headrests, split-back center seat including fold-down center console with convenience tray and cup pockets, right side seat folded forward for access to rear, special velour fabric upholstery, deep-tinted glass, special luxury sport-type leather-wrapped steering wheel, and storage pouch with zipper on left side trim panel of storage compartment in rear quarter area. Exterior colors for 1990 were Ivory White, Sterling Silver Metallic, Onyx Black, Smoke Blue Metallic, Catalina Blue Metallic (available only for Astro LT), Mojave Beige, Sunset Gold Metallic, Caramel Brown Metallic (available only for Astro LT), Deep Red Metallic, Burnt Red Metallic, Gray Metallic and Midnight Blue Metallic. Four colors were offered for the vinyl, custom vinyl and custom cloth interiors. They were blue, garnet, saddle, and slate gray. The velour interior option was offered in blue or saddle.

1990 Chevrolet 1/2-Ton M10 Astro Passenger Minivan 4x2 (CMD)

1/2-TON — LUMINA APV SERIES U05 (FWD) — V-6: General Motors merchandised the Lumina minivan as an All Purpose Vehicle (APV), rather than as a "real" truck. However, the government considered it to be a light truck with a 4,800-pound GVW and a 1,305-pound payload rating. Along with a six-passenger coupe, the minivan joined the Lumina series (that was launched with a four-door sedan in the spring of 1989) as a 1990 model. A 3.1-liter V-6 was standard on sporty Euro versions of the Lumina car, as well as the minivan. A four-speed automatic transmission was available with the V-6. The base model did not use the Lumina name. It was called the Chevrolet APV Cargo Van. Standard equipment, in addition to the V-6 engine, included power front disc brakes, a three-speed automatic transmission, and P205/70R14 all-season black sidewall tires. Only one Cargo APV model was offered. The only options were cloth high-back bucket seats, air conditioning, an electric rear window defroster, deep-tinted glass, and a power door and tailgate locking system. The Lumina APV passenger model was merchandised in base and CL trims. Standard equipment was the same as for the APV Cargo model, but many additional options were offered including Preferred Equipment Group packages, a variety of seating arrangements for five-, six- or seven-passenger layouts, and a high-tech sound package. Interiors could be had in solid or two-tone color schemes, while cloth and custom cloth bucket seating was available.

1990 Chevrolet 1/2-Ton U05 Lumina APV Passenger Minivan 4x2 (CMD)

1990 Chevrolet 1-Ton G30 Beauville Sportvan passenger wagon 4x2 (CMD)

1/2-TON, 3/4-TON, 1-TON VAN — G-SERIES 10, 20, 30 — V-6/V-8: Although the van craze of the 1970s was long since gone, Chevrolet continued to offer a complete line of full-size vans in many classes, sizes and body configurations. The basic models were the Chevy Van and the Sportvan. Both came as G10/G20/G30 class models. The Chevy Vans were primarily designed as cargo vans. The Sportvan series consisted of windowed passenger vans. The fancy version of the Sportvan was called the Beauville. The vans came on a 110-inch short wheelbase (SWB), 125-inch long wheelbase (LWB), and 146-inch extended wheelbase (EWB). Respective body lengths were 178, 202, and 223 in. One G10 Chevy Van and one G10 Sportvan came as SWB models. There was an SWB G20 cargo van, too. The G20 Chevy Van, Sportvan and Beauville models also came as LWB or EWB models. G30 Chevy Van, Sportvan and Beauville models were offered only as LWB or EWB models. Standard equipment in Chevy Vans included a 4.3-liter V-6 (except G30), heavy-duty power brakes with rear antilock feature, three-speed automatic transmission, and P205/75R14 all-season steel-belted-radial tires. The 5.0-liter, 5.7-liter, and 7.4-liter gas V-8s were optional in these models, as was a 6.2-liter diesel V-8. Sportvan models had about the same standard features, except for a four-speed automatic overdrive transmission being standard in all lines. The 5.7-liter V-8 was standard in all G30 Chevy Van, Sportvan and Beauville models.

1-TON — P30 STEP-VAN — V-8: Also available in 1990 was the Step-Van. It had a boxy body well-suited for stop-and-go delivery service. The base model offered was a 1-ton version with a 10-1/2-foot long body. Step-Vans offered wheelbases ranging from 125 to 178 in. A 350-cubic-inch V-8 was the standard engine. A 6.2-liter diesel V-8 was optional. Standard size tires were LT215/85R16Cs.

1/2-TON — K1500 BLAZER 4x4 — V-8: There were no major changes in the Blazer's external appearance for 1990. All Blazers now had a standard rear wheel antilock braking system. A new electronic speedometer was also introduced for 1990, along with non-asbestos brake linings. The Blazer body also used double-sided, galvanized exterior sheet metal. The 5.7-liter V-8 (LO5) engine was improved for 1990 with the addition of improved oil control rings, a redesigned rear crankshaft seal, a new camshaft sprocket design, non-asbestos intake manifold gaskets, and heavy-duty intake valves. The 6.2-liter diesel had new horsepower and torque ratings for 1990, but these were due to changes in the horsepower and torque rating methodology and did not affect actual engine performance. The Blazer benefited from General Motors' efforts to simplify the production ordering and sales of its light-duty trucks. One example of this program was the de-proliferation of optional equipment for the Blazer. Many options of 1989 became standard for 1990. Many other items that had proven to be low-volume options were eliminated. These consisted of deep-tinted glass with light-tinted rear window (RPO AA3), the pre-cleaner air cleaner (RPO K46), an electronically-tuned AM/FM stereo radio with clock (RPO UU9), front bumper guards (RPO V31), puncture proof tires (RPO P42), and an auxiliary battery (RPO TP2). Options that were previously available separately were combined into packages with other options. Added to the standard Scottsdale package was a power-operated tailgate window, pulse windshield wiper system, headlight warning buzzer, and front tow hooks. A heavy-duty battery with 630 cold cranking amps was also standard on the Scottsdale model. An AM radio (RPO UT5) replaced the RPO U63 radio. The full range of Scottsdale exterior features consisted of the following: Front and rear chromed bumpers, Scottsdale nameplates, molded plastic grille and front lamp bezels (painted light and dark Argent Silver), bright metal hubcaps with black trim, Argent Silver 15 x 6.0 wheels, four all-season steel-belted radial-ply tires, tools (including a mechanical jack and wheel wrench), intermittent windshield wipers, left and right side below-eye-line 6.5 x 9.0-inch mirrors, black-painted exterior bumpers, a power-operated tailgate, and front tow hooks. The Scottsdale's interior featured left and right side padded arm rests integral with door panels, high-back front bucket seats with custom vinyl pigskin-grained trim in four colors (dark blue, garnet, saddle or slate gray), easy-rear-entry passenger seat front sliding mechanism, two coat hooks on left side, full-length bright sill plates at front doors and rear of rear compartment floor, a map light, two dome lamps with door-operated switches, embossed black rubber floor mats in front and rear, insulation on dash panel and floor panel and between double-wall cab roof, tinted glass on all windows, padded and color-keyed left-hand and right-hand sun shades, gauges for fuel level, voltmeter, oil pressure and engine pressure, trip odometer, heavy-duty heater and defogger, AM radio with fixed mast antenna, two-spoke steering wheel with anti-theft locking feature on steering column, 10-inch rear view mirror, color-keyed molded plastic door trim panels, cigarette lighter with ash tray illumination, and spare tire carrier on right-hand rear panel. Included in the Silverado option was auxiliary lighting (RPO TR9), a deluxe front appearance package (RPO V22), and a deluxe molding package (RPO YG3). The electronic speed control was now included in the convenience package (RPO ZQ3). New options for 1990 were an outside electric mirror (RPO D48), rear seat shoulder belts (RPO AK9), and the convenience package (RPO ZQ3). The K1500 Blazer's exterior colors were carried over from 1989. Garnet replaced burgundy in the Blazer's interior trim color selections.

1/2-TON, 3/4-TON — CR (4x2)/CV (4x4) SUBURBAN — V-8: Chevrolet Suburbans were like large four-door station wagons built on a light-duty truck chassis. They were manufactured in the General Motors assembly plant at Flint, Michigan. Rear-wheel antilock brakes, an electronic speedometer, greater use of two-sided galvanized steel body panels, and more standard equipment than ever topped the list of changes in the 1990 Chevrolet Suburbans. Like their K1500

Blazer sibling, the Suburbans' rear-wheel-antilock (RWAL) braking system improved directional stability by preventing rear wheel lockup for varying road and rear load conditions. Using a control valve located between the master cylinder and the rear brakes, the system modulated the rear brake line pressure. It enabled the driver to maintain critical steering control and, if necessary, bring the vehicle to a smoothly controlled stop. Integral to the Suburban's RWAL system (and standard equipment for 1990) was an electric speedometer that generated the speed signal necessary for RWAL operation. Greater use of two-side galvanized steel in the body sheet metal further protected the 1990 Suburbans against corrosion and rust. The new galvanized areas included the windshield panel, end gate outer panel, front side door frame, outer quarter panel, hood outer panel, and front inner and outer fender panels. The Suburban's standard 5.7-liter EFI V-8 engine was a carryover from 1989. An optional 7.4-liter V-8 was the most powerful engine available in any Chevrolet light-duty trucks. It received a new electronic spark control system to regulate spark advance and control knock throughout its entire performance band. The standard and heavy-duty 6.2-liter diesel V-8s carried new horsepower and torque ratings, although actual performance of the two engines was unchanged from 1989. Both 1/.2- and 3/4-ton Suburbans comfortably sat nine adults. They shared 165 cu.-ft. of cargo space. The 4x2 and 4x4 models were each available as 1/2- and 3/4-ton models. They continued to be offered in Scottsdale or Silverado trim, but the standard equipment content was considerably expanded. For 1990, Scottsdale trim added heavy-duty 32 mm shock absorbers (1/2-tons only), pulse windshield wipers, a heavy-duty battery, front tow hooks (4x4s only), an electronically-tuned AM radio, a 37-gallon fuel tank, and a headlamp warning buzzer. The Silverado trim package added to or replaced specific contents of the Scottsdale package. It included the following new-for-1990 items: Deluxe front appearance package (with special grille, dual-note horn, halogen headlamps, and bumper guards), deluxe body moldings, an auxiliary lighting package, and color-keyed front and rear floor mats. All 1990 Suburbans were also sold with non-asbestos brake linings. A rear panel door defogger and electric outside rear view mirror were new Silverado options. Suburbans equipped with tailgates received power-operated rear glass and the manual-operated rear window option was canceled. Garnet was an added interior color option.

1990 Chevrolet 1/2-Ton C1500 Work Truck Fleetside Pickup 4x2

1/2-TON, 3/4-TON, 1-TON — C (4x2)/K (4x4) PICKUP — V-6/V-8: Two new models, a new heavy-duty engine and more standard equipment than ever highlighted the 1990 Chevrolet full-size pickup lineup. Work Truck and 454SS were the names for two distinctly different new trucks. They were designed for different segments of the growing full-size pickup market. The 454SS was a high-performance, limited-edition, up-level C1500 Regular-Cab 4x2 pickup. Its special option package contents were targeted to meet increasing demand for high-style personal-use pickup trucks. Equipped with a potent 7.4-liter EFI V-8 engine, three-speed automatic transmission, performance handling package, and 3.73:1 ratio rear axle as standard equipment, the 454SS delivered 230 hp at 3600 rpm. It carried a powerful torque rating of 385 lb.-ft. at 1600 rpm. Other power train standards included a heavy-duty radiator, engine oil and transmission oil coolers, and a locking rear differential. The standard 454SS performance handling package (which was optional on other C1500 models) included 32 mm Bilstein gas-filled shock absorbers, a 32 mm front stabilizer bar, a .7:1 fast-ratio steering gear assembly, and heavy-duty jounce bumpers. The package also included five P275/60R15 steel-belted radial tires mated to five 15 x 7-inch styled chrome wheels. The upscale content of the 454SS was as impressive as its performance and handling. The package also included high-back bucket seats with a console, a Sport appearance package, air conditioning, an AM/FM stereo with cassette and clock and graphic equalizer, a sliding rear window, a tilt steering wheel, power door locks and windows, electronic speed control, and auxiliary lighting. The 454SS was a slow selling vehicle when it first came out, and Chevrolet dealers were giving buyers healthy discounts on purchases of trucks with this model-option. Also, an interesting pieces of Chevrolet truck sales literature was a full-line brochure that folded out and had a full-size picture of the 454SS on the obverse side. The C/K1500 Work Truck "WT" was similar in concept to the S10 "EL" pickup. It represented a high-value, low-option Regular-Cab pickup aimed at truck buyers looking for a no-frills workhorse pickup. The WT was available exclusively in standard Cheyenne trim, but with a new grille added. It also included a body-color filler panel, charcoal-painted bumper, and WT identification. Available in either 4x2 or 4x4 configurations, the WT carried a GVWR of 5,600 pounds. The maximum payload for the 4x2 and 4x4 versions was 1,711 pounds and 1,331 pounds, respectively. Chevrolet full-size pickup engine availability for 1990 included two V-6s, three gas V-8s, and two diesel V-8s, depending on the model. A new heavy-duty version of the 4.3-liter EFI V-6 was available as the standard engine in C/K2500 models carrying the minimum GVWR of 8,600 pounds, and as a credit option on C/K3500s. The features that distinguished the heavy-duty 4.3-liter engine from its standard counterpart included a lower 8.6:1 compression ratio (versus 9.3:1) and a larger 3.0-inch low-restriction exhaust system for improved performance in heavy-duty applications. Horsepower and torque ratings for the heavy-duty V-6 were slightly lower at 155 hp at 4000 rpm and 230 lb.-ft. of torque at 2400 rpm. The standard 4.3-liter V-6 delivered five more horsepower and five more pounds-feet of torque at the same engine speeds. The 5.0-liter and 5.7-liter EFI V-8s were carried over from 1989. The 7.4-liter V-8 featured new electronic spark control to fight spark knocks. The standard and heavy-duty 6.2-liter diesel V-8s were both back. They had revised power ratings because of a new rating system, though output was unchanged. Full-size pickups continued to be offered in three trim levels called Cheyenne, Scottsdale, and Silverado. All three had expanded contents. Added to the 1990 Cheyenne package were all tinted windows, a deluxe heater, intermittent windshield wipers, a one-inch diameter front stabilizer bar, a 34-gallon fuel tank (on most models), halogen headlamps, a heavy-duty battery (with gas engines), a cigarette lighter, an AM radio with a fixed mast antenna, front towing hooks (on 4x4s), and voltmeter, temperature and oil pressure gauges. The Scottsdale package included items adding to or replacing Cheyenne equipment. It had several new features including a custom steering wheel, Rally wheels (on most models), and a deluxe front end appearance that included halogen headlamps, a dual-note horn and a specific grille. Silverado was the top trim level that started where Scottsdale left off and added or substituted numerous extras. New-for-1990 Silverado goodies were an optional bench seat with a center arm rest, special door trim panels, cloth fabric seats, swing-out rear quarter windows with Extended-Cab designs, floor mats, a Sport steering wheel, and an electronically-tuned AM/FM stereo radio with seek-and-scan and a digital clock. Other changes for the year included the availability of 60/40 seats in both regular- and Extended-Cab models. Black Onyx, Catalina Blue Metallic, and Crimson Red Metallic were added pickup colors, while a new interior trim color was garnet. Chevrolet C/K pickups were produced at plants in Ft. Wayne, Indiana; Pontiac, Michigan; and Oshawa, Ontario, Canada.

I. D. DATA The VIN plate was mounted on the lower left side windshield corner. The VIN consisted of 17 symbols. The first three symbols identify the country, the manufacturer and the type of vehicle. The fourth symbol designated the GVWR. The fifth, sixth and seventh symbols identify the line and chassis type, series and body type. The eighth symbol identifies the engine [Chevrolet engines] C=6.2-liter/130 hp diesel V-8, H=5.0-liter V-8, J=6.2-liter/148 hp diesel V-8, K=5.7-liter V-8, N=7.4-liter V-8, R=2.8-liter V-6, Z=4.3-liter V-6. [GM engines] A=2.5-liter L4, B=4.3-liter V-6, D=3.1-liter V-6, M=7.0-liter V-8. [Pontiac engine] E=2.5-liter L4. The ninth symbol is the check digit. The tenth symbol indicates model-year. The eleventh symbol identifies the assembly plant. The last six symbols are the sequential production number.

Model	Body Type	Price	Weight	Prod. Total
CE/CJ Geo Tracker — 1/2-Ton — 86.6 in. w.b. — 1.6-liter EFI L4				
CJ10316	4x4 Hardtop	11,035	2,271	Note 14
CJ10367	4x4 Convertible	10,725	2,238	Note 14
NOTE 1: A $280 dealer destination charge applied to Geo Trackers				
S10 Fleetside Pickup — 1/2-Ton — 108.3/122.9 in. w.b. — 2.5-liter EFI L4				
S10603	Reg. Cab EL X81	7,975	2650	Note 14
S10603	Reg. Cab Short Box	9,215	2668	Note 14
S10803	Reg. Cab Long Box	9,380	2774	Note 14
S10653	Ext. Cab Short Box	10,165	2732	Note 14
T10 4x4 Fleetside Pickup — 1/2-Ton — 108.3/118/122.9 in. w.b. — 4.3-liter EFI V-6				
T10603	Reg. Cab SWB	12,430	3,103	Note 14
T10803	Reg. Cab LWB	12,615	3,142	Note 14
T10653	Ext. Cab Short Box	13,215	3,231	Note 14
NOTE 2: A $420 dealer destination charge applied to S-Series pickups				
S10 Blazer 4x2 Sport Utility Wagon — 1/2-Ton — 100.5/107 in. w.b. — 4.3-liter EFI V-6				
CS10516	2-dr Tailgate	12,930	2996	Note 14
T10 Blazer 4x4 Sport Utility Wagon — 1/2-Ton — 100.5/107 in. w.b. — 4.3-liter EFI V-6				
CT10516	2-dr Tailgate	14,595	3279	Note 14
CT10506	4-dr Tailgate	16,905	3459	Note 14
NOTE 3: A $420 dealer destination charge applied to S-Series Blazers				
NOTE 4: The four-door model was a midyear addition to the S-Series Blazer line.				
M10 Astro Minivan (rear-wheel-drive) — 1/2-Ton — 111 in. w.b. — 4.3-liter EFI V-6				
CM10906	Standard Cargo Van	12,095	3108	Note 14
CM11006	Extended Cargo Van	13,397	3554	Note 14
CM10906/ZW9	Standard CS Van	13,790	3519	Note 14
CM11006/ZW9	Extended CS Van	14,942	3713	Note 14
CM10906	Standard LT Van	16,325	3635	Note 14
CM11006	Extended LT Van	17,027	-	Note 14
L10 Astro Minivan (all-wheel-drive) — 1/2-Ton — 111 in. w.b. — 4.3-liter EFI V-6				
CL111005	Extended Cargo Van	15,612	3798	Note 14
CL10905	Standard Astro Van	14,950	3842	Note 14
CL10906	Standard CS Van	15,978	3586	Note 14
CL11006	Extended CS Van	16,427	3803	Note 14
CL10906	Standard CL Van	17,018	3519	Note 14
CL11006	Extended CL Van	17,467	3713	Note 14
CL10906	Standard LT Van	18,513	3635	Note 14
CL11006	Extended LT Van	18,962	4221	Note 14
NOTE 5: A $500 dealer destination charge applied to Astros				
U05 Lumina Minivan — 1/2-Ton — 109.8 in. w.b. — 3.1-liter MFI V-6				
1UM05	Cargo Van	12,895	3450	Note 14
1UM06	Wagon	13,995	3505	Note 14
1UM06	Wagon CL	15,745	3505	Note 14
NOTE 6: A $500 dealer destination charge applied to Lumina Minivans effective Aug. 10, 1990.				
G10 Van — 1/2-Ton — 110/125 in. w.b. — 4.3-liter EFI V-6				
CG11005/ZW9	SWB Chevy Van	12,650	3799	Note 14
CG11006/ZW9	SWB Sportvan	14,565	4126	Note 14
CG11306/ZW9	LWB Beauville	16,320	4126	Note 14
G20 Van — 3/4-Ton — 110/125 in. w.b. — 4.3-liter EFI V-6				
CG21005/ZW9	SWB Chevy Van	12,820	3850	Note 14
CG21305/ZW9	LWB Sportvan	15,615	4102	Note 14
CG21306/ZW9	LWB Beauville	16,460	4162	Note 14
G30 Van — 1-Ton — 125/146 in. w.b. — 4.3-liter EFI V-6, [Sportvan 30] 5.7-liter EFI V-8				
CG31305/ZW9	LWB Chevy Van	13,367	4576	Note 14
CG31306/ZW9	LWB Sportvan 12P	17,592	4741	Note 14
CG31306/ZW9	LWB Beauville	18,437	4641	Note 14
CG31605/ZW9	EWB Chevy Van	15,439	4883	Note 14
CG31606/ZW9	EWB Sportvan 12P	19,226	5627	Note 14
CG31606/ZW9	EWB Beauville	19,226	5652	Note 14
CG31305/ZW9	LWB Cutaway Van	13,185	4112	Note 14
G30 Hi-Cube Van — 1-Ton — 125/146 in. w.b. — 5.7-liter EFI V-8				
CG31	10-ft. Van	17,040	6154	Note 14
CG31	12-ft. Van	18,820	6213	Note 14
NOTE 7: A $550 dealer destination charge applied to full-size vans				
P30 — 1-Ton Step-Van — 125/178 in. w.b. — 5.7-liter EFI V-8				
P32	10.5-ft. Step-Van	16,380	6154	Note 14
K1500 Blazer — 1/2-Ton — 111.5 in. w.b. — 5.7-liter EFI V-8				
CK10516	Utility Hardtop	16,485	4839	Note 14
NOTE 8: A $550 dealer destination charge applied to full-size Blazers				
R/V 1500 Suburban — 1/2-Ton — 131.5 in. w.b. — 5.7-liter EFI V-8				
CR10906	Panel Door (4x2)	15,165	4526	Note 14
CV10906	Panel Door (4x4)	16,645	4675	Note 14

1990 Chevrolet/Geo 1/2-Ton Tracker Sport Utility (CMD)

1990 Chevrolet 1-Ton K-3500 "Dooley" Pickup with "chuck wagon" concept truck package (CMD)

1990 Chevrolet 1/2-Ton K-1500 4x4 Suburban (CMD)

1990 Chevrolet 1/2-Ton C1500 Fleetside 454 SS Regular-Cab Pickup (CMD)

1990 Chevrolet 1/2-ton K-1500 Sportside Pickup (CMD)

1990 Chevrolet 1/2-Ton K-1500 4x4 Blazer Sport Utility and K-1500 4x4 Suburban (CMD)

1990 Chevrolet 1/2-Ton S10 Pickup (CMD)

1990 Chevrolet 1/2-Ton T10 Blazer 4x4 Sport Utility Vehicle (CMD)

1990 Chevrolet 3/4-Ton K-2500 4x4 Extended-Cab Fleeetside Short Bed Pickup (CMD)

Model	Body Type	Price	Weight	Prod. Total
R/V 2500 Suburban — 3/4-Ton — 131.5 in. w.b. — 5.7-liter EFI V-8				
CR20906	Panel Door (4x2)	16,238	4909	Note 14
CV20906	Panel Door (4x4)	18,083	5128	Note 14

NOTE 9: A $610 dealer destination charge applied to Suburbans
NOTE 140: Add $150 for tailgate models

Model	Body Type	Price	Weight	Prod. Total
C1500 Pickup — 1/2-Ton Short Box — 117.5 in. w.b. — 4.3-liter EFI V-6				
CC10703	Regular-Cab Sportside	11,625	4167	Note 14
CC10703	Regular-Cab Fleetside	11,300	4159	Note 14
C1500 Pickup — 1/2-Ton Long Box — 131.5 in. w.b. — 4.3-liter EFI V-6				
CC10903	Regular-Cab Fleetside	11,580	4293	Note 14
CC10903	Regular-Cab Work Truck	10,445	4159	Note 14
C1500 Pickup — 1/2-Ton Short Box — 141.5 in. w.b. — 4.3-liter EFI V-6				
CC10753	Extended-Cab Fleetside	12,210	4251	Note 14
C1500 Pickup — 1/2-Ton Long Box — 155.5 in. w.b. — 4.3-liter EFI V-6				
CC10903	Extended-Cab Fleetside	12,490	4492	Note 14
C1500 Pickup — 1/2-Ton 454SS — 117.5 in. w.b. — 7.4-liter EFI V-6				
CC10703/PSS1	Regular-Cab Sportside	18,295	4662	Note 14

NOTE 141: Add approximately $1,990 for CK1500 Pickups with 4x4.

Model	Body Type	Price	Weight	Prod. Total
C2500 Pickup — 3/4-Ton Long Box — 131.5 in. w.b. — 4.3-liter EFI V-6				
CC20924	Chassis & Cab	13,038	3836	Note 14
CC20903	Regular-Cab Fleetside	12,205	4450	Note 14
C2500 Pickup — 3/4-Ton Short Box — 141.5 in. w.b. — 4.3-liter EFI V-6				
CC20954	Chassis & Extended-Cab	14,063	4301	Note 14
CC20953	Extended-Cab Fleetside	13,275	4723	Note 14
C2500 Pickup — 3/4-Ton Long Box — 155.5 in. w.b. — 4.3-liter EFI V-6				
CC20903	Extended-Cab Fleetside	13,555	4723	Note 14

NOTE 142: Add approximately $2,200 for CK2500 Pickups with 4x4.

Model	Body Type	Price	Weight	Prod. Total
C3500 Pickup — 1-Ton Long Box — 131.5 in. w.b. — 5.7-liter EFI V-8				
CC30924	Chassis & Cab	13,393	5006	Note 14
CC30903	Regular-Cab Fleetside	13,828	5281	Note 14
C3500 Pickup — 1-Ton Long Box — 155.5 in. w.b. — 5.7-liter V-8				
CC30903	Chassis & Extended-Cab	14,418	5145	Note 14
CC30903	Extended-Cab Fleetside	14,484	5552	Note 14
C3500 Pickup — 1-Ton Long Box — 168.5 in. w.b. — 5.7-liter V-8				
CC30933	Bonus-Cab Fleetside	15,383	5640	Note 14
CC30933	Crew-Cab Fleetside	15,913	5538	Note 14
CC30933	Chassis & Bonus-Cab	14,938	5125	Note 14
CC30933	Crew-Cab Fleetside	15,463	5223	Note 14

NOTE 143: Add approximately $2,200 for CK3500 Pickups with 4x4.
NOTE: A $550 dealer destination charge applied to C/K Pickups.
NOTE 144: Model-year production [S10 Pickup] 202,240, [C/K1500] 372,223, [C/K2500] 80,909, [C/K3500] 29,619, [Geo Tracker (Canadian-made)] 34,979, [S-Series Blazer] 175,450, [K1500 Blazer] 18,921, [Suburban] 62,755, [Lumina APV Wagon] 75,563, [Lumina APV Cargo] 3,529, [Astro Wagon] 125,774, [Astro Cargo Van] 45,892, [Step-Van] 6,450, [Sportvan] 9,507, [Chevy Van] 106,995.

1990 Chevrolet 1/2-Ton K1500 "Z71" Sportside Pickup 4x4 (CMD)

GASOLINE ENGINES (DISPLACEMENT ORDER)

ENGINE: Inline. Four-cylinder. Bore & stroke: 2.95 x 3.54 in. Displacement: 1.6-liter (97 cid). BHP: 80 at 5400 rpm. Torque: Unknown. Compression ratio: 8.91. EFI/Throttle-body-injection. Suzuki-built. [Standard in Geo Tracker.]
ENGINE: Inline. Four-cylinder. Bore & stroke: 4.00 x 3.00 in. Displacement: 2.5-liter (151 cid). BHP: 105 at 4800 rpm. Torque: 135 lb.-ft. at 3200 rpm. Compression ratio: 8.3:1. EFI/Throttle-body-injection. VIN Code A. GM-built. [Standard in S10]
ENGINE: V-block. Six-cylinder. Bore & stroke: 3.52 x 2.99 in. Displacement: 2.8-liter (173 cid). BHP: 125 at 4800 rpm. Torque: 150 lb.-ft. at 2400 rpm. Compression ratio: 8.9:1. EFI/Throttle-body-injection. VIN Code R. Chevrolet-built. [Optional in S10]
ENGINE: V-block. Six-cylinder. Bore & stroke: 3.5 x 3.331 in. Displacement: 3.1-liter (191 cid). BHP: 120 at 4400 rpm. Torque: 175 lb.-ft. at 2200 rpm. Compression ratio: 8.5:1. Multiport-fuel-injection. VIN Code D. GM-built. [Standard in Lumina]
ENGINE: V-block. Six-cylinder. Bore & stroke: 4.0 x 3.48 in. Displacement: 4.3-liter (262 cid). BHP: 150 at 4400 rpm. Torque: 230 lb.-ft. at 2400 rpm. Compression ratio: 9.3:1. EFI/Throttle-body-injection. VIN Code not available. GM-built. [Standard in G10, G20, Astro]
ENGINE: V-block. Heavy-duty. Six-cylinder. Bore & stroke: 4.0 x 3.48 in. Displacement: 4.3-liter (262 cid). BHP: 155 at 4000 rpm. Torque: 230 lb.-ft. at 2400 rpm. Compression ratio: 8.6:1. EFI/Throttle-body-injection. VIN Code B. GM-built. [Standard in C/K2500 Extended-Cab long-box pickups]
ENGINE: V-block. Six-cylinder. Bore & stroke: 4.0 x 3.48 in. Displacement: 4.3-liter (262 cid). BHP: 160 at 4000 rpm. Torque: 235 lb.-ft. at 2400 rpm. Compression ratio: 9.1:1. EFI/Throttle-body-injection. VIN Code Z. Chevrolet-built. [Standard in S/T-series Blazer, standard in C/K 1500/2500, standard in T10 pickups, optional in S10 pickups]
ENGINE: V-block. Eight-cylinder. Bore & stroke: 3.74 x 3.48 in. Displacement: 5.0-liter (305 cid). BHP: 170 at 4000 rpm. Torque: 255 lb.-ft. at 2400 rpm. EFI/Throttle-body-injection. VIN Code H. Chevrolet-built. [Optional in C/K1500, C/K2500, G10, G20]

ENGINE: V-block. Eight-cylinder. Bore & stroke: 4.0 x 3.48 in. Displacement: 5.7-liter (350 cid). BHP: 190 at 4000 rpm. Torque: 300 lb.-ft. at 2400 rpm. Compression ratio: 8.6:1. EFI/Throttle-body-injection. VIN Code A. GM-built. [Standard in C/K3500, Suburbans, and G30 vans, optional in C/K pickups]
ENGINE: V-block. Eight-cylinder. Bore & stroke: 4.0 x 3.48 in. Displacement: 5.7-liter (350 cid). BHP: 210 at 4000 rpm. Compression ratio: 9.3:1. Torque: 300 lb.-ft. at 2800 rpm. EFI/Throttle-body-injection. VIN Code K. Chevrolet-built [Standard in C/K Blazer, optional, optional in Suburban, optional in Chevy Van, optional in Sportvan]
ENGINE: V-block. Eight-cylinder. Bore & stroke: 4.25 x 4.00 in. Displacement: 7.4-liter (454 cid). BHP: 230 at 3600 rpm. Torque: 385 lb.-ft. at 1600 rpm. Throttle-body- fuel-injection. VIN Code N. Chevrolet-built. [Standard in 454SS, Optional in C/K1500, C/K2500, C/K3500, Suburban, and G30 vans]
DIESEL ENGINES (DISPLACEMENT ORDER)
ENGINE: V-block. Light-duty. Eight-cylinder. Bore & stroke: 3.98 x 3.82 in. Displacement: 6.2-liter (379 cid). BHP: 148 at 3600 rpm. Torque: 248 lb.-ft. at 2000 rpm. VIN Code J. GM-built. [Optional in C/K3500 pickup, optional in G30 Chevy Van and 12-passenger Sportvan]
ENGINE: V-block. Heavy-duty. Eight-cylinder. Bore & stroke: 3.98 x 3.82 in. Displacement: 6.2-liter (379 cid). BHP: 130 at 3600 rpm. Torque: 240 lb.-ft. at 2000 rpm. VIN Code C. GM-built. [Optional in C/K3500 pickup, optional in G30 Chevy Van and 12-passenger Sportvan]
CHASSIS: [Geo Tracker (All)] Wheelbase: 86.6 in. Length: 142.5 in. Width: 64.2 in. Height: 65.6 in. GVW: 3,197 lb. Payload: 900 lb. Tires (4x2) P195/75R-15, (4x4) P205/75R15 black sidewall.
CHASSIS: [S10] Regular-Cab. Short Box. Wheelbase: 108.3 in. Length: 178.2 in. Width: 64.8 in. Height: 61.3 in. GVW: 3,662 lb. Payload: 1,000 lb. Tires: P195/75R14 black sidewall.
CHASSIS: [T10] Regular-Cab. Short Box. Wheelbase: 108.5 in. Length: 178.2 in. Width: 64.8 in. Height: 63.4 in. GVW: 4,004 lb. Payload: 1,000 lb. Tires: P205/75R15 black sidewall.
CHASSIS: [S10] Regular-Cab. Long Box. Wheelbase: 117.9 in. Length: 194.2 in. Width: 64.8 in. Height: 61.3 in. GVW: 3,662 lb. Payload: 1,000 lb. Tires: P195/75R14 black sidewall.
CHASSIS: [T10] Regular-Cab. Long Box. Wheelbase: 117.9 in. Length: 194.2 in. Width: 64.7 in. Height: 63.4 in. GVW: 4,004 lb. Payload: 1,000 lb. Tires: P205/75R15 black sidewall.
CHASSIS: [S10] Extended-Cab. Short Box. Wheelbase: 122.9 in. Length: 192.8 in. Width: 64.8 in. Height: 61.3 in. GVW: 3,662 lb. Payload: 1,000 lb. Tires: P195/75R14 black sidewall.
CHASSIS: [T10] Extended-Cab. Short Box. Wheelbase: 122.9 in. Length: 192.8 in. Width: 64.8 in. Height: 63.4 in. GVW: 4,004 lb. Payload: 1,000 lb. Tires: P205/75R15 black sidewall.
CHASSIS: [S-Blazer 4x2] Two-door. Wheelbase: 100.5 in. Length: 170.3 in. Width: 65.4 in. Height: 64.1 in. GVW: 4,350 lb. Payload: 766 lb. Tires: P205/75R15 black sidewall.
CHASSIS: [S-Blazer 4x4] Two-door. Wheelbase: 100.5 in. Length: 170.3 in. Width: 65.4 in. Height: 64.3 in. GVW: 4,700 lb. Payload: 726 lb. Tires: P205/75R15 black sidewall.
CHASSIS: [S-Blazer 4x4] Four-door. Wheelbase: 107.0 in. Length: 176.8 in. Width: 65.4 in. Height: 64.1 in. GVW: 5,100 lb. Payload: 1,379 lb. Tires: P205/75R15 black sidewall.
CHASSIS: [Astro Cargo regular-body] Wheelbase: 111 in. Length: 176.8 in. Width: 77.0 in. Height: 74.9 in. GVW: 4,800 lb. Payload: 1,692 lb. Tires: P205/75R15 black sidewall.
CHASSIS: [Astro Cargo regular-body AWD] Wheelbase: 111 in. Length: 176.8 in. Width: 77.0 in. Height: 74.9 in. GVW: 5,600 lb. Payload: 1,758 lb. Tires: P205/75R15 black sidewall.
CHASSIS: [Astro Cargo extended-body] Wheelbase: 111 in. Length: 186.8 in. Width: 77.0 in. Height: 74.9 in. GVW: 5,600 lb. Payload: 2,046 lb. Tires: P205/75R15 black sidewall.
CHASSIS: [Astro Cargo extended-body AWD] Wheelbase: 111 in. Length: 186.8 in. Width: 77.0 in. Height: 74.9 in. GVW: 5,850 lb. Payload: 2,052 lb. Tires: P205/75R15 black sidewall.
CHASSIS: [Astro Passenger regular-body] Wheelbase: 111 in. Length: 176.8 in. Width: 77.0 in. Height: 74.1 in. GVW: 5,600 lb. Payload: 2,014 lb. Tires: P205/75R15 black sidewall.
CHASSIS: [Astro Passenger regular-body AWD] Wheelbase: 111 in. Length: 176.8 in. Width: 77.0 in. Height: 74.1 in. GVW: 5,800 lb. Payload: 1,640 lb. Tires: P205/75R15 black sidewall.
CHASSIS: [Astro Passenger extended-body] Wheelbase: 111 in. Length: 186.8 in. Width: 77.0 in. Height: 74.1 in. GVW: 5,850 lb. Payload: 2,047 lb. Tires: P205/75R15 black sidewall.
CHASSIS: [Astro Passenger extended-body AWD] Wheelbase: 111 in. Length: 186.8 in. Width: 77.0 in. Height: 74.1 in. GVW: 6,100 lb. Payload: 1,879 lb. Tires: P205/75R15 black sidewall.
CHASSIS: [Lumina] Wheelbase: 109.8 in. Length: 194.2 in. Width: 73.9 in. Height: 65.2 in. GVW: 4,800 lb. Payload: 1,305 lb. Tires: P205/70R15 black sidewall.
CHASSIS: [G10/Short Body] Chevy van. Wheelbase: 110 in. Length: 178.2 in. Width: 79.5 in. Height: 79.4 in. GVW: 4,900 lb. Payload: 1,157 lb. Tires: P215/75R15 black sidewall.

1990 Chevrolet 1-Ton C3500 with 12-ft. Platform Dump Body 4 x 2 (Jonathan Meyers)

CHASSIS: [G10/Long Body] Chevy van/Sportvan. Wheelbase: 125 in. Length: 202.2 in. Width: 79.5 in. Height: 79.4 in. GVW: 4,900 lb. Payload: 1,018 lb. Tires: P215/75R15 black sidewall.

CHASSIS: [G20/Long Body] Chevy van/Sportvan. Wheelbase: 125 in. Length: 202.2 in. Width: 79.5 in. Height: 79.2 in. GVW: 6,600 lb. Payload: 2,660 lb. Tires: P215/75R15 black sidewall.

CHASSIS: [G30/Long Body Chevy van] Wheelbase: 125 in. Length: 202.2 in. Width: 79.5 in. Height: 81.9 in. GVW: 7,100 lb. Payload: 2,647 lb. Tires: P215/75R15 black sidewall.

CHASSIS: [G30/Long Body Sportvan] Wheelbase: 125 in. Length: 202.2 in. Width: 79.5 in. Height: 81.9 in. GVW: 7,400 lb. Payload: 2,627 lb. Tires: P215/75R15 black sidewall.

CHASSIS: [G30/Extended Body Chevy van] Wheelbase: 146 in. Length: 223.2 in. Width: 79.5 in. Height: 81.9 in. GVW: 8,600 lb. Payload: 3,957 lb. Tires: P215/75R15 black sidewall

CHASSIS: [G30/Extended Body 12-Passenger Sportvan] Wheelbase: 146 in. Length: 223.2 in. Width: 79.5 in. Height: 81.9 in. GVW: 8,600 lb. Payload: 3,157 lb. Tires: P215/75R15 black sidewall

CHASSIS: [K10 Blazer 4x4] Wheelbase: 106.5 in. Length: 184.8 in. Width: 79.6 in. Height: 73.8 in. GVW: 6,100 lb. Payload: 1,560 lb. Tires: LT245/75R16C black sidewall.

CHASSIS: [Suburban C1500] Wheelbase: 129.5 in. Length: 219.1 in. Width: 79.6 in. Height: 72.0 in. GVW: 6,100 lb. Payload: 1,667 lb. Tires: P235/75R-15XLS black sidewall.

CHASSIS: [Suburban C2500] Wheelbase: 129.5 in. Length: 219.1 in. Width: 79.6 in. Height: 74.3 in. GVW: 8,600 lb. Payload: 3,784 lb. Tires: P235/75R-15XLS black sidewall.

CHASSIS: [Suburban K1500] Wheelbase: 129.5 in. Length: 219.1 in. Width: 79.6 in. Height: 72.0 in. GVW: 6,450 lb. Payload: 1,775 lb. Tires: P235/75R-15XLS black sidewall.

CHASSIS: [Suburban K2500] Wheelbase: 129.5 in. Length: 219.1 in. Width: 79.6 in. Height: 74.3 in. GVW: 8,600 lb. Payload: 3,472 lb. Tires: P235/75R-15XLS black sidewall.

CHASSIS: [C1500 Sportside Regular-Cab Short Box Pickup] Regular-Cab. Short Box. Wheelbase: 117.5 in. Length: 194.0 in. Width: 77.1 in. Height: 70.4 in. GVW: 5,600 lb. Payload: 1,849 lb. Tires: P225/75R15 black sidewall AS SBR Tires.

CHASSIS: [C1500 Fleetside Regular-Cab Short Box Pickup] Wheelbase: 117.5 in. Length: 194.1 in. Width: 76.4 in. Height: 70.4 in. GVW: 5,600 lb. Payload: 1,908 lb. Tires: P225/75R15 black sidewall AS SBR Tires.

CHASSIS: [C1500 Sportside Regular-Cab Short Box] Wheelbase: 117.5 in. Length: 194.0 in. Width: 77.1 in. Height: 70.4 in. GVW: 5,600 lb. Payload: 1,849 lb. Tires: P225/75R15 black sidewall AS SBR Tires.

CHASSIS: [C1500 Fleetside Regular-Cab Long Box Pickup] Wheelbase: 131.5 in. Length: 212.9 in. Width: 76.4 in. Height: 70.4 in. GVW: 5,600 lb. Payload: 1,711 lb. Tires: P225/75R15 black sidewall AS SBR Tires.

CHASSIS: [C1500 454SS Short Box] Wheelbase: 117.5 in. Length: 194.1 in. Width: 76.4 in. Height: 70.4 in. GVW: 5,600 lb. Payload: 1,795 lb. Tires: P235/75R15 white-outline-letter AS SBR Tires.

CHASSIS: [C1500 Fleetside Regular-Cab Long Box "Work Truck" Pickup] Wheelbase: 131.5 in. Length: 212.9 in. Width: 76.4 in. Height: 70.4 in. GVW: 5,600 lb. Payload: 1,711 lb. Tires: P225/75R15 black sidewall AS SBR Tires.

CHASSIS: [C1500 Sportside Extended-Cab Short Box Pickup] Wheelbase: 155.5 in. Length: 236.9 in. Width: 76.4 in. Height: 70.5 in. GVW: 6,200 lb. Payload: 2,038 lb. Tires: P225/75R15 black sidewall AS SBR Tires.

CHASSIS: [C1500 Fleetside Extended-Cab Short Box Pickup] Wheelbase: 155.5 in. Length: 236.9 in. Width: 76.4 in. Height: 70.5 in. GVW: 6,200 lb. Payload: 2,109 lb. Tires: P225/75R15 black sidewall AS SBR Tires.

CHASSIS: [C1500 Fleetside Extended-Cab Long Box Pickup] Wheelbase: 155.5 in. Length: 255.7 in. Width: 76.4 in. Height: 70.5 in. GVW: 6,200 lb. Payload: 2,038 lb. Tires: P225/75R15 black sidewall AS SBR Tires.

CHASSIS: [K1500 Sportside Regular-Cab Short Box Pickup] Wheelbase: 117.5 in. Length: 194.0 in. Width: 77.1 in. Height: 73.8 GVW: 5,600 lb. Payload: 1,525 lb. Tires: P225/75R15 black sidewall AS SBR Tires.

CHASSIS: [K1500 Fleetside Regular-Cab Short Box Pickup] Wheelbase: 117.5 in. Length: 194.1 in. Width: 76.4 in. Height: 73.8 in. GVW: 5,600 lb. Payload: 1,533 lb. Tires: P225/75R15 black sidewall AS SBR Tires.

CHASSIS: [K1500 Fleetside Regular-Cab Long Box Pickup] Wheelbase: 131.5 in. Length: 212.9 in. Width: 76.4 in. Height: 73.8 in. GVW: 5,600 lb. Payload: 1,477 lb. Tires: P225/75R15 black sidewall AS SBR Tires.

CHASSIS: [K1500 Fleetside Regular-Cab Long Box "Work Truck" Pickup] Wheelbase: 131.5 in. Length: 212.9 in. Width: 76.4 in. Height: 73.8 in. GVW: 5,600 lb. Payload: 1,331 lb. Tires: P225/75R15 black sidewall as SBR Tires.

CHASSIS: [K1500 Fleetside Extended-Cab Short Box Pickup] Wheelbase: 155.5 in. Length: 236.9 in. Width: 76.4 in. Height: 73.9 in. GVW: 6,200 lb. Payload: 1,678 lb. Tires: P225/75R15 black sidewall AS SBR Tires.

CHASSIS: [K1500 Fleetside Extended-Cab Long Box Pickup] Wheelbase: 155.5 in. Length: 255.7 in. Width: 76.4 in. Height: 73.9 in. GVW: 6,200 lb. Payload: 1,589 lb. Tires: P225/75R15 black sidewall AS SBR Tires.

CHASSIS: [C2500 Fleetside Regular-Cab Long Box Pickup] Wheelbase: 131.5 in. Length: 212.9 in. Width: 76.4 in. Height: 73 in. GVW: 7,200 lb. Payload: 3,291 lb. Tires: P225/75R15 black sidewall AS SBR tires.

CHASSIS: [C2500 Heavy-duty Fleetside Regular-Cab Long Box Pickup] Wheelbase: 131.5 in. Length: 212.9 in. Width: 76.4 in. Height: 73 in. GVW: 8,600 lb. Payload: 3,820 lb. Tires: P225/75R15 black sidewall AS SBR tires.

CHASSIS: [C2500 Fleetside Extended-Cab Short Box Pickup] Wheelbase: 155.5 in. Length: 236.9 in. Width: 76.4 in. Height: 73 in. GVW: 7,200 lb. Payload: 3,015 lb. Tires: P225/75R15 black sidewall AS SBR tires.

CHASSIS: [C2500 Fleetside Extended-Cab Long Box Pickup] Wheelbase: 155.5 in. Length: 255.7 in. Width: 76.4 in. Height: 73 in. GVW: 7,200 lb. Payload: 2,944 lb. Tires: P225/75R15 black sidewall AS SBR tires.

CHASSIS: [K2500 Fleetside Regular-Cab Long Box Pickup] Wheelbase: 131.5 in. Length: 212.9 in. Width: 76.4 in. Height: 74.3 in. GVW: 7,200 lb. Payload: 2,962 lb. Tires: P225/75R15 black sidewall AS SBR tires.

CHASSIS: [K2500 Heavy-duty Fleetside Regular-Cab Long Box Pickup] Wheelbase: 131.5 in. Length: 212.9 in. Width: 76.4 in. Height: 74.3 in. GVW: 8,600 lb. Payload: 3,867 lb. Tires: P225/75R15 black sidewall AS SBR tires.

CHASSIS: [K2500 Fleetside Extended-Cab Short Box Pickup] Wheelbase: 155.5 in. Length: 236.9 in. Width: 76.4 in. Height: 74.5 in. GVW: 7,200 lb. Payload: 2,648 lb. Tires: P225/75R15 black sidewall AS SBR tires.

CHASSIS: [K2500 Fleetside Extended-Cab Long Box Pickup] Wheelbase: 155.5 in. Length: 255.7 in. Width: 76.4 in. Height: 74.5 in. GVW: 7,200 lb. Payload: 2,559 lb. Tires: P225/75R15 black sidewall AS SBR tires.

CHASSIS: [C3500 Fleetside Regular-Cab Long Box Pickup] Wheelbase: 131.5 in. Length: 212.9 in. Width: 76.4 in. Height: 75.5 in. GVW: 8,600 lb. Payload: 4,251 lb. Tires: P225/75R15 black sidewall AS SBR tires.

CHASSIS: [K3500 Fleetside Extended-Cab Heavy-duty Long Box Pickup] Wheelbase: 155.5 in. Length: 255.7 in. Width: 76.4 in. Height: 76 in. GVW: 8,600 lb. Payload: 3,578 lb. Tires: P225/75R15 black sidewall AS SBR tires.

CHASSIS: [C/K 3500 Pickup] Motor home chassis. Wheelbase: 183.5 in. Tires: P225/75R15 black sidewall AS SBR tires.

[GEO TRACKER] PEG 2 package ($302).PEG2 Package with UM6 radio (add $441).PEG 3 package ($997). PEG 3 Package with UM6 radio ($1,136). Tuned AM/FM stereo with seek -and-scan ($302). Air conditioning ($695). Convertible rear seat ($445).Spare tire cover ($33). Power steering ($275). Trailering Special equipment ($109). Alloy wheels ($325). Three-speed automatic transmission ($565).

1990 Chevrolet 1/2-Ton C1500 Fleetside "454 SS" Pickup 4x2 (CMD)

S/T SERIES PICKUP OPTIONS: Durango Package ($73 to $108 depending on body style and other options ordered). Tahoe Package ($184-$722 depending on body style and other options ordered). Air conditioning ($755.) Air dam with fog lamps ($115.) Optional axle ratio ($38). Locking rear differential ($252). Heavy-duty battery ($56). Spare tire carrier ($100). Cold Climate package ($140-$243 depending upon trim option). Center console ($135). Heavy-duty radiator ($56). Heavy-duty radiator and engine oil cooler ($63 with air conditioning/ $118 without air conditioning). Engine oil cooler ($135). Driver Convenience package including Comfortilt steering wheel and intermittent wiper system ($180). Color-keyed front floor mats ($20). Full floor carpeting ($40). Deep-tinted glass: $101-$140 for Extended-Cabs depending upon option package, $11 for Regular-Cab). Electronic instrumentation ($296). Lighted interior visor mirror ($68-$75 depending upon trim package). Body side and wheel opening moldings ($152). Black wheel opening molding ($13-$43 depending upon trim package). Bright wheel opening molding ($31). Endgate net ($110). Operating Convenience package including power door locks and power windows ($344). Custom two-tone paint ($172-$344 depending upon trim package). Special two-tone paint including pin striping ($296). Deluxe two-tone paint ($177). Electronically-tuned AM/FM stereo radio with Seek-and-Scan, stereo cassette tape player and digital clock ($122). Electronically tuned AM/FM stereo radio with Seek-and-Scan, stereo cassette tape player with Search and Repeat, Graphic equalizer and digital clock ($272). Delete radio ($226 credit). Rear jump seats with vinyl trim ($240). Shield Package including transfer case and front differential skid plates and steering linkage shield ($126). Front and rear heavy-duty shock absorbers ($40). Electronic speed control ($225). Heavy-duty rear springs ($64). Heavy duty front suspension with heavy-duty front and rear shock absorbers ($63). Sport Suspension ($415). Body striping ($55). Manual sun roof ($250). Heavy-duty Trailering Special Package ($211). Four-speed automatic transmission ($860). Wheel trim rings ($60). Cast aluminum wheels ($269-$325 depending upon trim package). Aluminum Special wheels ($395 without spare tire carrier, ($495 with spare tire carrier). Sliding rear window ($113).

1990 Chevrolet 1/2-Ton K1500 Blazer 2-door Sport Utility 4x4 (CMD)

S/T-SERIES BLAZER OPTIONS: Air conditioning ($755). Optional axle ratio ($38). Locking rear differential ($252). Heavy-duty battery ($56). Luggage carrier ($169). Spare tire and wheel carrier ($159). Cold Climate package ($146-$189 depending upon trim option). Center console ($135). Heavy-duty radiator ($56). Heavy-duty radiator and engine oil cooler ($63 with air conditioning/ $118 without air conditioning). Sport Package ($1,239). Tahoe package ($809). Driver Convenience package including Comfortilt steering wheel and intermittent wiper system ($197). Color-keyed front floor mats ($20). Color-keyed rear floor mats ($16). Deep-tinted glass with light tinted rear window ($225). Electronic instrumentation ($296). Lighted interior visor mirror ($68-$75 depending upon trim package). Body side and wheel opening moldings ($152). Black wheel opening molding ($13-$43 depending upon trim package). Bright wheel opening molding ($31). Operating Convenience package including power door locks and power windows ($344). Custom two-tone paint ($172-$344 depending upon trim package). Special two-tone paint ($163-$218 depending upon trim package). Deluxe two-tone paint ($177-$329 depending upon trim package). Electronically tuned AM/FM stereo radio with Seek-and-Scan, stereo cassette tape player and digital clock ($122). Electronically tuned AM/FM stereo radio with Seek-and-Scan, stereo cassette tape player with Search-and-Repeat, graphic equalizer and digital clock ($272). Delete radio ($226 credit).Rear folding rear seat ($409). Transfer case and front differential skid plates and steering linkage shield ($75). Front and rear heavy-duty shock absorbers ($40). Electronic speed control ($225). Heavy-duty front springs including heavy-duty shock absorbers ($63). Body striping ($49). Sunshine striping ($70 to $125 depending upon trim package). Manual sun roof ($250). Off-road suspension equipment: ($122-$182 depending upon trim package). Light-duty trailering package ($165). Heavy-duty Trailering Special package ($211). Four-speed automatic transmission ($860). Wheel trim rings ($60). Cast aluminum wheels ($269-$325 depending upon trim package). Gray aluminum wheels ($233-$325 depending upon trim option). Sliding rear window ($257). Rear window wiper/washer ($125).

ASTRO OPTIONS: Air conditioning: Front ($820)/front and rear ($1,343). Optional axle ratio ($38). Locking rear differential ($252). Deluxe front and rear chromed bumpers ($76-$128 depending upon option packages). Black luggage carrier ($126). Engine oil cooler ($135). Heavy-duty radiator ($56). Heavy-duty radiator and engine oil cooler ($63 with air conditioning/$118 without air conditioning). Power door locks ($211). Driver Convenience package including Comfortilt steering wheel and intermittent wiper system ($346). Operating Convenience package including power door locks and power windows ($411). Deep-tinted glass ($161-$211 depending on body glass selected). Rear heater ($267). Electronic instrumentation ($88). Auxiliary lighting ($96 with roof console/$129 without roof console). Black below-eye-line exterior mirrors ($52). Exterior remote electric mirrors ($150). Special two-tone paint ($172). Deluxe two-tone paint ($172-$334 depending upon other options). Custom two-tone ($187 with SLE/$329 without SLE). Electronically tuned AM/FM stereo radio with Seek-and-Scan, digital clock, stereo cassette player and premium speakers ($122). Electronically tuned AM/FM stereo radio with Seek-and-Scan, stereo cassette tape player with Search-and-Repeat, graphic equalizer, digital clock and premium speakers ($272). Delete radio ($226 credit). Seven-passenger seating ($878-$1,069 depending upon other options). Eight-passenger seating ($344-$878 depending upon other options). Seat back recliner and dual arm rests ($241). Six-way power seat ($240). Front and rear heavy-duty shock absorbers ($40). Heavy-duty Trailering Equipment ($507-$564 depending upon other equipment ordered). Light-duty Trailering Equipment ($109). Aluminum wheels ($233-$325, depending upon other options ordered). Rally wheels ($92).

1990 Chevrolet 1/2-Ton U05 Lumina APV Commercial Minivan 4x2

LUMINA OPTIONS: PEG 1 ($1,000-$1,396). PEG 2 ($1,895-$2,135). UM6 radio ($140 extra in PEGs). U1C radio ($396 extra in PEGs). Rear window defogger ($160). Air conditioning ($805). California emissions ($100). Deep-tinted glass ($245). Power door locks and tailgate ($255). AG9 power seat ($270). AB3 six-passenger seating with twin front bucket seats ($510). ZP7 seven-passenger seating with twin front bucket seats ($425-$660). Load leveling suspension ($170). P195/70R15 black sidewall touring radial tires ($62 extra). Cast aluminum 15-inch wheels with locks ($265).

G-SERIES VAN OPTIONS: Preferred Equipment Group V1A2 ($941). Air conditioning ($950). ZQ2 convenience group ($411). Heavy-duty cooling system ($56). 5.0-liter EFI V-8 ($575). 5.7-liter EFI V-8 ($820). 7.4-liter EFI V-8 ($470). Deep-tinted glass ($306). Heater ($205). TR9 auxiliary lighting package ($135). Deluxe two-tone paint ($269). UM6 stereo equipment ($122-$263). UX1 stereo equipment ($150-$413). Rally wheels ($121). Cast aluminum wheels ($195-$316).

K1500 BLAZER OPTIONS: Silverado package RPO YE9 includes many exterior features in addition to, or in place of Scottsdale items, such as front and rear chromed bumpers with black rub stripes (front rub strip has bright trim), Silverado nameplates, molded plastic grille and front lamp bezels painted Dark Argent with chrome trim, rectangular dual halogen headlamps, body side and rear black moldings with bright trim, bright wheel opening moldings, bright metal wheelcovers, cab-to-fender and hood insulators, underhood reel-type lamp and electric power rear tailgate window and bright appliqué. ($1,281). The Silverado interior had high-back reclining front bucket seats with choice of custom vinyl pigskin-grained trim. This trim came in either dark blue, garnet, slate gray or saddle. Also offered was textured velour custom cloth trim in a choice of dark blue, garnet, saddle or slate gray. Silverado interiors also had right side front and left and right side rear assist straps, a glove box light, auxiliary lighting, and color-keyed front compartment carpeting. Matching rear compartment floor coverings, including wheelhousing covers, was also provided in trucks with the with optional rear seat. There was also insulation on the dash panel, between the double-wall cab roof, on the floor panel (extra-thick at front, extra-thick at rear when rear seat was ordered), under the cowl panel, on the headliner and on the body side trim panels. Even more insulation was used on diesel engine models. These fancy full-size Blazers also had sunshades with flexible outboard ends and sliding extenders at inboard ends, a storage strap on left side sunshade, an illuminated mirror on right sunshade, brushed pewter-toned instrument panel trim, a four-spoke sport steering wheel with simulated stitched leather appearance, a front compartment foam-backed cloth headliner with matching retainer moldings, special door trim panels (including door closing assist strips, decorative inserts, map pockets and carpet trim), rear sidewall trim panels with ash trays and carpet trim, a cigarette lighter with ash tray illumination, a black vinyl spare tire cover, and a color-keyed molded plastic console with storage and beverage pockets. Air conditioning RPO C60 ($820 without B3J or $758 with B3J). Optional rear axle ratios ($38). Locking rear differential RPO G80 ($252). Cold Climate package RPO V10 including special insulation, special heater and defroster, engine block heater, anti-freeze protection to -32 degrees, and heavy-duty battery ($48). Engine oil cooler RPO KC4 ($135). Heavy-duty radiator RPO VO1 ($56). Heavy-duty radiator and transmission oil cooler RPO VO2 ($63). Deep-tinted glass RPO AJ1 ($215). Locking front hubs RPO X6Z ($60). Below-eye-line stainless steel exterior mirrors RPO D45 ($40).

1990 Chevrolet 1/2-Ton C1500 Suburban 4-door wagon 4x2 (CMD)

C/K PICKUP/SUBURBAN OPTIONS: Air Conditioning RPO C60 ($780 or $820 for V350 without B3J or $758 for V3500 with B3J). Optional axle ratios ($38). Locking differential RPO G80 ($252). Auxiliary heavy-duty battery, not available with B3J RPO TP2 ($134). Painted rear step bumper, requires E63 body RPO V43 ($130). Front deluxe chromed Bumper with rub strip, K10703 only RPO VG3 ($26). Chromed rear step bumper with rub strip RPO VB3 ($229).Front black bumper guards RPO V27 ($32). Heavy-duty chassis equipment, K1500 only RPO F44 ($38). Off-road package, available for K1500 only including skid plate and Bilstein shock absorbers RPO Z71 ($270). Cold Climate package, not available with B3J including engine block heater RPO V10 ($33). Convenience group including power door locks and windows RPO ZQ2 ($344). Convenience group including tilt wheel and speed control RPO ZQ3 ($346). Engine oil cooling system RPO KC4 ($135). Heavy-duty radiator RPO VO1 ($56). Heavy-duty radiator and transmission oil cooler RPO VO2 ($63). Rear window defogger RPO C49 ($154). 5.0-liter V-8 RPO LO3 ($555). 5.7-liter V-8 RPO LO5 ($800). 6.2-liter diesel V-8 RPO LH6 (priced as part of diesel model). Locking fuel filler cap RPO NO5 ($18). Cargo area lamp RPO UF2 ($36). Dome and reading lamp RPO C95 ($33). Roof marker lamps, not available with California emissions RPO UO1 ($52). Auxiliary lighting includes dome and reading lamps and ash tray, glove box and underhood lamps RPO TR9 ($125). Below eye-line type painted mirrors RPO D44 ($52). Below eye-line type stainless steel mirrors RPO D45 ($92). Camper-type stainless steel mirrors RPO DF2 ($100). Black exterior moldings RPO B84 ($90). Exterior bright moldings RPO B85 ($17). Conventional two-tone exterior paint RPO ZY2 ($132). Special two-tone exterior paint RPO ZY3 ($215). Deluxe two-tone exterior paint RPO ZY4 ($243). Electronically-tuned AM/FM Stereo Radio with Seek-and-Scan and Digital Clock RPO UM7 ($210). Electronically tuned AM/FM Stereo radio with Seek-and-Scan, stereo cassette tape and digital clock RPO UM6 ($332). Electronically-tuned AM/FM stereo radio with Seek-and-Scan, stereo cassette player with Search-and-Repeat, graphic equalizer and digital clock RPO UX1 ($482). Radio delete option RPO UL5 (-$77). Scottsdale trim package RPO Z62 ($601 without RPO ZQB or $526 with RPO ZQB. Scottsdale trim package RPO E63 ($632 without RPO ZQB or $557 with RPO ZQB). Scottsdale trim for K1500 Sport pickup ($235 for chassis-and-cab or $452 for Regular-Cab with RPO RO5 or $527 for Regular-Cab without RO5. Scottsdale trim ($337 for Extended-Cab with RO5 or $412 without RO5). Heavy-duty front and rear shock absorbers RPO F51 ($40). Silverado trim package RPO YE9: Regular-Cab Pickup E62 ($1,009). Silverado trim package RPO YE9 with E63 ($1,040 without RPO ZQB or $934 with RPO ZQB). Silverado trim package for C/K1500 and C/K2500 Extended-Cab pickup ($1,056 without RPO ZQB or $950 with ZQB). Silverado trim package ($1,056 for C/K2500 Extended-Cab without C6P or $1,025 for C/K2500 Extended-Cab with C6P. Silverado trim package ($883 for C/K2500 Regular-Cab chassis-and-cab or $1,025 for C/K2500 Extended-Cab pickup. Silverado trim package ($899 for C/K2500 Extended-Cab chassis-and-cab or $942 for V3500 Bonus-Cab pickup. Silverado trim package ($976 for V3500 Crew-Cab pickup or $734 for V3500 Bonus-Cab pickup with RPO RO5). Silverado trim package ($768 for V3500 Crew-Cab with RPO RO5. Off-road skid plate, K1500 only, RPO NZZ ($95). Heavy-duty front springs for K1500 only, requires F44 heavy-duty chassis and not available with B3J or RPO Z71 Off-Road chassis RPO F60 ($63). Body striping RPO D85 ($69). Tow hooks, standard on K1500, RPO V76 ($38). Heavy-duty Trailering Special equipment RPO Z82 ($408 with RPO Z71 or XQ8 or $448 without RPO Z71 or ZQ8). Four-speed manual transmission RPO MM4 ($98). Four-speed automatic transmission with overdrive RPO MXO ($860). Three-speed automatic transmission RPO MX1 ($625). Wheelcovers RPO PO1 ($42). Aluminum wheels, C/K1500 only RPO PF4 ($295). Sliding rear window RPO A28 ($113). Camper Special chassis equipment, C/K2500 and C/K3500 only, RPO Z81 ($280 without B2J or $148 with B3J). Deep-tinted glass RPO AJ1 ($150). Sport Truck sport equipment package, C/K10703 only including V43 black bumpers, black wheel flares, deluxe front appearance , black mirrors, GL/LT265/75R16 blackwall tires, PF4 aluminum wheels with special hub caps and 4x4 Sport decal RPO BPY ($1,140). Sport steering wheel RPO NK3 ($7). Rear-mounted fuel tank, available for C/K2500 and C/K3500 chassis-and-cab models with approximate capacity of 31-gallons RPO NK7 ($63). Camper Special chassis equipment including TP2 auxiliary battery without B3J equipment, camper wiring harness and DF2 mirrors RPO Z81 ($280). Camper Special for K-series pickups ($1,436 for B3J and $81 for V3500). Dual rear wheels for C/K3500 models only, including plastic rear fender extensions with side marker lamps on front and rear sides and dual rear chassis provisions RPO RO5 ($1,038). Dual rear wheels for C/K3500 models only, including plastic rear fender extensions with side marker lamps on front and rear sides and dual rear chassis provisions RPO RO5 ($1,101 with MX1 transmission, including VO2 heavy-duty radiator and transmission oil cooler. Dual rear wheels for C/K3500 models only, including plastic rear fender extensions with side marker lamps on front and rear sides and dual rear chassis provisions RPO RO5 ($785 for V3500) Operating Convenience package RPO ZQ2 including power door locks and front door power windows ($344). The following options and prices applied to V3500 models only: Glide-out spare tire carrier RPO P11 ($43). Side-mounted spare tire carrier RPO P13 ($31). Door edge guards RPO B93 ($24).

NOTE 15: Options and prices shown are representative. The actual cost of an option or option package often varies according to other packages that the options are combined with on specific vehicles. Preferred Equipment Group (PEG) options offer specific optional equipment at discount prices. Some "options" may be standard equipment on certain models, such as V-8s in C/K3500 pickups. Descriptions of options are edited. Full option contents can be determined by consulting sales literature.

HISTORICAL: Chevrolet trucks were built in 12 factories in 1990. Geo Trackers were made at the CAMI plant in Ingersoll, Ontario, Canada. S-Series pickups were assembled in Pontiac, Michigan and Shreveport, Louisiana. S-Series Blazers were built at Pontiac, Michigan and Moraine, Ohio. Astros were made in Baltimore, Maryland. Chevy Van models were sourced from factories in Scarborough, Ontario, Canada and Flint, Michigan. Full-size Blazers and Suburbans were made in the Chevrolet factory at Janesville, Wisconsin. C/K pickups were built in Fort Wayne, Indiana, Oshawa, Canada, Pontiac, Michigan and Janesville, Wisconsin. Lumina APVs were assembled at Tarrytown, N.Y. Jim C. Perkins was general manager of Chevrolet Motor Division. W.L. Ames was national manager of truck merchandising and Candace M. Robbins was manager of truck advertising. Chevrolet Calendar-year new-truck sales were: 44,525 Astro Vans, 76,643 Astro Wagons, 60,041 Lumina APV Passenger, 3,100 Lumina APV cargo, 16,072 K-Series Blazers, 146,989 S-Series Blazers, 464,730 C/K pickups, 210,318 S/T-Series pickups, 8,334 Sportvans, 55,050 Suburbans, 33,586 Canadian-built Geo Trackers, 100,067 Chevy Vans, 678 Chevrolet W4 Tiltmaster, and 22,060 Step-Van multistop trucks. This gave the company total light-duty truck sales of 1,325,459 units in the calendar-year. Chevrolet Model-year new-truck sales were: 45,845 Astro Vans, 76,267 Astro Wagons, 61,986 Lumina APVs, 18,909 Blazers, 155,122 S-Series Blazers, 486,056 C/K pickups, 210,773 S10/T10 pickups, 9,217 Sportvans, 45,845 Suburbans, 29,273 Canadian-built Geo Trackers, 101,156 Chevy Vans, and 740 W4 Tiltmaster imports. This gave the company total light-duty truck sales of 1,255,855 units in the model-year (not counting Step-Vans). A 1990 Chevrolet pickup shattered a 37-year-old production car record at the Indianapolis Motor Speedway on October 26-27, 1989 by averaging 103.463 mph for 24 hours to win the Hulman Indy Challenge Trophy. The full-size Chevrolet C1500 Sport, assembled at the General Motors plant in Fort Wayne, Indiana, with sheet metal produced at the GM stamping facility in Indianapolis, covered 993.234 laps or 2,483.085 miles around the 2.5-mile track, including pit stops for fuel, tires and driver changes. The record, certified by the U.S. Auto Club (USAC), was announced when Chevrolet introduced the 1990 Indy 500 Official Pace Car, a Beretta convertible. The Hulman Indy Challenge Trophy — formerly called the Stevens Trophy — had belonged to a Chrysler, which averaged 89.93 mph in 1953. Driven by Indiana race drivers Steve Butler of Kokomo, Johnny Parsons of Brownsburg, and Rich Volger of Indianapolis, the Fleetside short-box pickup truck was stock except for USAC-required safety modifications such as a five-point safety harness, roll cage, fire extinguisher, full instrumentation, and a tonneau cover. Also, speed nuts were used on the wheels to facilitate use of air wrenches and a production bucket seat from a Chevrolet 454SS pickup was installed to clear the safety harness. In addition, the catalytic converter was removed to prevent excessive heat buildup. The Chevy Sport was equipped with a production 350-cubic-inch V-8 engine with electronic fuel injection, a standard five-speed manual transmission, and original equipment P275/60R15 B.F. Goodrich Comp T/A radial tires. The record and trophy added to Chevrolet's long tradition of victories at the Indianapolis Motor Speedway and complemented the then-current Chevrolet Indy V-8 used in the 1988 and 1989 race winning cars.

1991

1991 Geo Tracker Convertible 4x2 (CMD)

1/4-TON — GEO TRACKER — L4: The Geo Tracker came in a new rear-drive convertible version for 1991. Base and LSi 4x4 hardtop and convertible models remained available. Standard power train was a 1.6-liter L4 linked to a five-speed manual transaxle. A three-speed automatic was optional in four-wheel-drive models. All 1991 models also featured a standard antilock braking system.

1/2-TON — S/T-SERIES PICKUP — L4/V-6: The 1991 S10/T10 models were introduced early in 1990. The exterior appearance was revised with a new grille, nameplates, emblems, bumper rub strips and body-side moldings. The body striping, decals, wheels and wheel trim were also new, as were the optional aluminum wheels. Two new exterior colors — Sky Blue and Mint Green — were offered. Woodlands Brown Metallic and Nevada Gold Metallic were canceled. A new Baja off-road appearance package was introduced. It was based on the Tahoe trim except for a charcoal interior with red and charcoal high-back bucket seats and charcoal door inserts, the Baja name stitched just below the headrest, wider red body side stripes, a redesigned Baja graphic on the pickup box, and a black decal surrounding the front grille. The 4.3-liter V-6 had an improved 220 series

throttle-body-injection system with longer throttle shaft bearings, new throttle return springs, and improved fuel mixture distribution. These changes were designed to improve engine starts, idle and overall engine reliability and durability. A new Thermac III modified air cleaner system and Quantum spark plugs were adopted to improve cold starts and overall engine reliability. A lighter, more durable starting motor was also new for 1991. A "hardened" 72 mm distributor replaced the 89 mm Hall-Effect distributor to make the ignition more impervious to electromagnetic induction interference from other electrical components. Suspension changes included revisions to the front stabilizer bar bushings and shock absorber valving. Single-stage rear spring rates were revised and the rear shock absorbers were also re-valved. The optional front compartment floor console for models equipped with bucket seats had a revised thumb-operated catch for easier, keyless entry. Replacing the rocker type switch previously used to control the power door locks in the operating convenience package was a more convenient, redesigned lever type switch. Reception for both the AM and FM radios was also improved. Other changes that were incorporated as interim 1991 changes included an improved front axle half-shaft, improved heating/ventilation, and adoption of a heavy-duty battery as standard equipment. Replacing the Moraine interior cloth was Breton cloth.

1991 Chevrolet 1/2-Ton S10 Blazer 2-door Sport Utility 4x4 (CMD)

1/2-TON — S-SERIES BLAZER — V-6: Chevrolet added a four-door model to the S-Series Blazer lineup early in 1990. It was a 1991 model. The rear doors provided easier access and exit from a standard three-passenger rear seat. It also had as standard, the Tahoe level of interior trim, an all-wheel antilock brake system (AWAL) and a 2,900-pound. capacity rear axle. The two-door model had a standard rear-wheel antilock brake system that operated in two-wheel-drive only. Both the two-door and four-door models for 1991 had a new grille design suggestive of that found on the Chevrolet pickups of 1967-1969. Also new for 1991 were the S-Series Blazer's exterior nameplates, emblems, bumper rub stripes, body side moldings, and body stripes and decals. New wheels and wheel trim designs were also introduced. High-back front bucket seats were standard. During the 1991 model-year numerous changes were introduced. These included a 220 TBI (throttle-body-injection) system, use of Hydramatic 5LM60 five-speed manual transmission in place of the 290 unit, revised Thermac III air cleaner, use of a revised accessory drive, a new Geolast PCV connector, and new Quantum spark plugs. Additional interim 1991 improvements involved front and rear suspension changes, accelerator pedal effort reduction, revised floor console latch, revised Rally wheel center insert, use of a lever-type power door lock switch, improved AM/FM radio reception, availability of aluminum wheel colors, inclusion of a heavy-duty battery as standard equipment, improved front axle half-shaft, improved heating/ventilation and the introduction of a front bench seat for maximum six-passenger capacity. All models were available with new RPO D48 electric OSRV mirrors with control on the instrument cluster. The two-door model had single-rate rear springs with revised rates for an improved ride. The Tahoe trim had new seat fabric, door panels and rear quarter panels. The front floor console had a revised catch for easy keyless entry. Exterior colors for 1991 were Midnight Black, Aspen Blue Metallic, Sky Blue, Royal Blue Metallic, Garnet Red, Steel Gray Metallic, Mint Green, Apple Red, Wheat Frost White and Silver Metallic. The two-door models were available in four interior colors: blue, charcoal, garnet or saddle. Blue and charcoal were initially offered for four-door model interiors. By the fall of 1991 the standard Tahoe interior for the four-door was also available in blue, charcoal, garnet or saddle. A new Tahoe LT package was available for both S-Series Blazer models. It included a new interior with Ultrasoft leather surfaces, in three colors, available on the front bucket seats and folding rear bench seat, color-keyed leather and carpeted door trim panels, full carpeting, front color-keyed floor mats, a color-keyed cloth headliner, full instrumentation, an all-new two-tone exterior finish with multi-shaded stripe, a chrome grille with new silver accents, new 15 x 7-inch cast-aluminum wheels, P205/75R16 all-season white-lettered tires, front and rear bumpers color-keyed to lower body color, black taillamp bezels, an optional electronically-tuned AM/FM stereo radio with CD player, special exterior LT badges, and a Tahoe LT badge on the glove box door.

1991 Chevrolet 1/2-Ton L10 Astro Extended-Body Minivan 4x4

1/2-TON — ASTRO VAN SERIES M/L — V-6: The Chevrolet Astro continued to be offered in three trim levels for 1991: Standard CS, midrange CL and up-level LT. An improved version of the 4.3-liter Vortex V-6 was standard, as was a four-speed overdrive automatic transmission. Changes to the engine's 220 throttle-body-injection system included longer throttle shaft bearings, new throttle return springs and improved fuel mixture distribution for better start and idle qualities, reliability and performance. A Vortex III air cleaner system and "Quantum" spark plugs were added for improved cold sparks. An SD 260 starter motor replaced the SD300 to reduce overall weight and to increase starter motor reliability and life span. New options available on both the extended and standard Astro models included a storage tray located beneath the front passenger seat. Changes for 1991 found on all Astro models included swing-out glass with positive locking detents, and lap/shoulder belts for the center right-hand passenger seat. The grilles of the CS and CL models had red Chevrolet bow ties with black outlines. During the 1991 model-year the extended-body Astro vans received a unique sport graphic package, as well as a complete body window package. Twelve exterior colors were available with the addition of Field Stone Metallic for the CS and CL models. Slate Metallic Red and a two-tone Light Gray Metallic were new for the Astro LT. The Carmel Brown and Gray Metallic colors were discontinued. Four interior colors were offered including a new light gray combination. AM and FM radio reception was improved for 1990. Suspension components were carried over from 1990.

1991 Chevrolet 1/2-Ton U05 Lumina APV Passenger Minivan 4x2

1/2-TON — LUMINA WAGON SERIES U05 — V-6: The 1991 Lumina APV (all purpose vehicle) had a refined interior and minor engineering improvements. All models were equipped with an auxiliary power socket located in the left lower wheelhouse storage compartment. This convenient power outlet provided 12-volt power access for portable telephones or other auxiliary devices. Additional interior changes for the model-year included a larger, more easily read fuel level gauge and non-reflective carpeting for the area forward of the instrument panel for improved driver visibility. Rear seat passengers appreciated the new optional rear air conditioner and heater. The 1991 power door locks had a lock delay system. It allowed the sliding door to be locked, upon closing, if the power lock switch was activated while the door was open. Other 1991 improvements included better radio reception (due to an expanded AM band), improved Seek-and-Scan buttons, and an optional compact disc player. Engineering improvements included a more durable starting motor and revised strut and shock absorber valving to accommodate Lumina APV's optional P205/65R15 tires. The brakes of 1991 models were improved with a larger tandem booster and an increased reaction ratio and a single-piece caliper support bushing. The brake refinements lessened noise and reduced brake pedal effort and the tendency toward brake pulsation. The Lumina APV model lineup was offered in standard or up-level CL trim with seating for as many as seven passengers. The seats were easily removable to accommodate cargo. Standard Lumina APV features included a solar windshield for reduced sun load, composite body panels, cup holders in the center console and elsewhere, an electronically-tuned AM/FM stereo radio, a rear window wiper and washer, and a 20-gallon fuel tank. The standard Lumina power train was a 3.1-liter MPI V-6 with a three-speed automatic transmission. A cargo delivery version of the vehicle was available in basic trim. The CL upgrade featured a tilt steering wheel, air conditioning, three-passenger seating in the middle seats, and auxiliary interior lighting. McPherson struts and coil springs were found up front, and a trailing twist design rear axle with coil springs gave the Lumina APV its car-like ride. A long-life stainless steel exhaust system was also new for 1991. An optional sun roof and luggage carrier were midyear additions. Two new colors, Light Camel and Black, were added for 1991. Three new two-tone color schemes for CL models were Black with Medium Gray Metallic, White over Light Camel Metallic, and Light Camel with Black.

1991 Chevrolet 1-Ton RV30 Cut-Away Van Chassis with Camper Body (CMD)

1/2-TON, 3/4-TON, 1-TON VAN — G-SERIES 10, 20, 30 — V-6/V-8: For 1991, all full-sized Chevrolet vans with both regular and extended-body configurations offered standard steel-belted radial tires. A 4.3-liter V-6 engine with four-speed automatic transmission came standard on all but G3500 1-ton models, which featured a 5.7-liter V-8 with improved throttle-body-injection system. A new 7.4-liter V-8 with four-speed automatic transmission was optional. Available in 110-, 125- and 146-inch wheelbases, in regular and extended-body styles, the 1991 vans could carry up to 15 passengers. When properly optioned, they could tow up to 10,000 pounds. Commercial users appreciated the ample interior cargo room, which ran as high as 306 cubic-feet with the extended-body G30 van on the 146-inch wheelbase. A cutaway version of the G Series van chassis was also available for builders of motor homes, airport buses and other special-bodied trucks. Standard equipment for small Chevy Vans included the 4.3-liter throttle-body-injected V-6, heavy-duty front disc/rear drum four-wheel antilock brakes, four-speed manual transmission with overdrive, and P205/75R15 black sidewall tires. The G20 Sportvan had the same standard features as the G10 model, but a 5.7-liter TBI V-8 was standard in G30 models. The 1-ton G30 model was also available in Hi-Cube Van form with 10-foot and 12-foot body options.

1-TON — P30 STEP-VAN — V-8: Also available in 1991 was the Step-Van. It had a boxy body well-suited for stop-and-go delivery service. The base model offered was a 1-ton version with a 10-1/2-foot long body. Step-Vans offered wheelbases ranging from 125 to 178 in. A 350-cubic-inch V-8 was the standard engine. A 6.2-liter diesel V-8 was optional. Standard size tires were LT215/85R16Cs.

1/2-TON — K1500 BLAZER 4x4 — V-8: Power train refinements characterized the 1991 Blazer. The 200 Series throttle-body- injection system used on the Blazer's standard 5.7-liter V-8 had longer throttle shaft bearings, new throttle return springs, and improved fuel mixture distribution. The 5.7-liter V-8 also had new heavy-duty intake valves and powdered metal camshaft sprockets. Standard on all engines was a lighter and more powerful 100-amp CS130 alternator. Two new exterior colors, Brilliant Blue and Slate Metallic were offered. A new light gray joined the four interior colors for 1991. The AM/FM radios had improved reception.

1/2-TON, 3/4-TON — CR (4x2)/CV (4x4) SUBURBAN — V-8: Chevrolet's popular Suburban received engine refinements and a new four-speed overdrive transmission. A series of refinements to the 220 Series throttle-body-injection system on the 5.7- and 7.4-liter V-8 engines were designed to improve engine starts, idle quality, and overall engine reliability and performance. The improvements included the longer throttle shaft bearings, new throttle return springs, and improved fuel mixture distribution. The 5.7-liter V-8 also got new heavy-duty intake valves and powered metal camshaft sprockets. In addition to these changes, the heavy-duty 5.7-liter V-8 had improved oil pan baffling. Chevrolet's new 7.4-liter V-8 gasoline engine had a one-piece intake manifold with a relocated throttle-body injector eliminating previous TBI mounting adapters. Other new features included improved piston-to-cylinder tolerances, improved oil pan gaskets (to help eliminate oil leaks), rigid cast iron rocker covers, and new engine oil cooler lines with improved bracketing. A new manufacturing process and updated tooling was used to produce an engine with better overall reliability. A lighter and more powerful 100-amp CS130 alternator was added to all gas engines, and the optional 6.2-liter diesel V-8 as standard equipment. GM's all-new 4L80-E heavy-duty electronic four-speed automatic overdrive transmission was manufactured by the company's Hydramatic division. It was available in light-duty trucks rated at or above 8,600 pound GVWs, including Suburbans. It was one of the most technically-advanced transmissions ever offered in a Chevrolet truck up to the time. The electronic controls provided enhanced shifting precision and smoothness. A new dual-stator 310 mm torque converter increased low-speed torque. The "smart" transmission featured a unique power train control module that compensated for variations in temperature, altitude, and engine performance. It added to performance, driving economy and durability. All Suburbans were equipped with rear-wheel antilock brakes. Both AM and FM radios had improved reception. The Suburban was offered in Scottsdale or Silverado trim. Both had seating for up to nine adults. With the rear seats removed, cargo capacity was 165 cubic feet. Two new metallic colors, Brilliant Blue and Slate, brought the total color selections to 10. A new red interior color joined the available blue, garnet, and saddle options.

1991 Chevrolet 3/4-Ton K2500 Extended-Cab Fleetside Short Box Pickup 4x4 (CMD)

1/2-TON, 3/4-TON, 1-TON — C (4x2)/K (4x4) PICKUP — V-6/V-8: There were no major changes in Chevrolet's full-size pickups for 1991. There were, however, significant technical advances to ensure their continued competitiveness in the light-duty truck sales battles with Ford and Dodge. The big 7.4-liter "Mark V" V-8 engine had a new one-piece intake manifold with a relocated throttle-body injector, thus eliminating the previous TBI mounting adapters. Other new features included improved piston-to-cylinder tolerances, improved oil pan gaskets to help eliminate oil leaks, rigid cast iron rocker covers, and new engine oil cooler lines with improved bracketing. This engine also benefited from a new manufacturing process and updated tooling that Chevrolet noted was intended to improve the engine's overall reliability. General Motors' all-new 4L80-E heavy-duty electronic control (for enhanced shifting precision and smoothness) four-speed automatic overdrive transmission (RPO MXO) was available for all models rated at or above 8,600-pound GVWRs. The 4L80-E nomenclature had the following significance 4-= forward speeds, L=Longitudinal type, 80=transmission gears based on relative torque capacity (this transmission could handle 885 lb.-ft. of gearbox torque, which represented 440 lb.-ft. of input torque), E=electronic controls. Aside from its four-speed overdrive configuration, this transmission also featured an aluminum case and a Power train Control Module (PCM) which combined engine and transmission functions on all gasoline engines and compensated for variations in temperature, altitude, and engine performance. A Transmission

Control Module (TCM) was used with the diesel V-8. A new dual-stator 310 mm torque converter was also included for increased low-speed torque. The 4L80-E was touted by Chevrolet as "one of the most technologically advanced transmissions ever offered in a Chevrolet truck." Power train improvements on all C/K trucks included a new 220 Series throttle-body-injection system. A new SD 260 starter motor was used for the 4.3-liter V-6 and the 5.0-liter V-8. It was lighter in weight and more durable and reliable than the SD300 motor it replaced. The new TBI system was used on the 4.3-liter V-6, 5.0-liter V-8, 5.7-liter V-8 and 7.4-liter V-8 engines. It incorporated longer throttle shaft bearings, new throttle return springs, and improved fuel mixture distribution. The 4.3-liter V-6 was also improved by the use of a revised air cleaner system and processing changes in manufacturing spark plugs. Both the 5.0-liter V-8 and 5.7-liter V-8 were upgraded with heavy-duty intake valves, powdered metal camshaft sprockets, and improved oil pan baffling on the heavy-duty 5.7-liter engine. Replacing the 12-SI-100 alternator was a lighter weight, more reliable CS130 alternator. A 100-ampere alternator was now standard on the C/K3500 pickup and chassis-and-cab models. The Work Truck continued as Chevrolet's no-frills, basic pickup. Changes for 1991 included a new four-spoke steering wheel and larger outside rear view mirrors. A Custom urethane four-spoke steering wheel was standard. Below-eye-line type exterior mirrors were now standard on the C/K pickups and chassis-and-cab models. These mirrors had adjustable heads in a black finish and measured 9.0 x 6.5-in. The standard AM/FM stereo radios were improved by increasing signal sensitivity and reducing signal interference and signal tracking. The RPO C60 air conditioning option for the C/K models included an HVAC climate control system incorporating new controls allowing for manual selection of the recirculation air inlet mode. In addition, revised display graphics provided clear readings in a dark cab. A computer software change provided an indication that the system required refrigerant servicing. New options for 1991 included a bed liner for Fleetside and Extended-Cab models, high-back reclining front bucket seats, and a gauge cluster with tachometer. The Cheyenne trim package had a new impact-resistant metal grille for 1991. Two new metallic colors, Brilliant Blue and Slate, brought the total number of exterior colors to 10. A light gray was added to the list of available interior colors. An exciting option package was the 454SS high-performance truck. It included YE9 Silverado trim, a sliding rear window, Sport package equipment, air conditioning, a locking differential, an engine oil cooler, auxiliary lighting, cargo area lamp, an upgraded AM/FM ETR stereo with all the goodies, heavy-duty cooling, a Sport steering wheel, black body side moldings, power locks and windows, tilt steering, speed control, a Sport Handling chassis package, analog gauges with a tachometer, and a 7.4-liter RPO L19 EFI V-8 linked to a four-speed overdrive automatic transmission.

1991 Chevrolet 1-Ton K3500 with 10-ft. Fontaine 2/3-yard Contractor Body (Jonathan Meyers)

I. D. DATA: The VIN plate was mounted on the lower left side windshield corner. The VIN consisted of 17 symbols. The first three symbols identify the country, the manufacturer and the type of vehicle. The fourth symbol designated the GVWR. The fifth, sixth and seventh symbols identify the line and chassis type, series and body type. The eighth symbol identifies the engine [Chevrolet engines] C=6.2-liter/130 hp diesel V-8, H=5.0-liter V-8, J=6.2-liter/148 hp diesel V-8, K=5.7-liter V-8, N=7.4-liter V-8, R=2.8-liter V-6, Z=4.3-liter V-6. [GM engines] A=2.5-liter L4, B=4.3-liter V-6, D=3.1-liter V-6. [Pontiac engine] E=2.5-liter L4. The ninth symbol is the check digit. The tenth symbol indicates model-year. The eleventh symbol identifies the assembly plant. The last six symbols are the sequential production number.

1991 Chevrolet 1-Ton K3500 Chassis-and-Cab with dump body 4x4 (CMD)

Model	Body Type	Price	Weight	Prod. Total
CE/CJ Geo Tracker — 1/2-Ton — 86.6 in. w.b. — 1.6-liter EFI L4				
CE10367	4x2 Convertible	8,459	2092	Note 133
CJ10316	4x4 Hardtop	11,285	2271	Note 133
CJ10367	4x4 Convertible	10,885	2238	Note 133
CJ10316/B2Z	4x4 LSi Hardtop	12,585	2271	Note 133
CJ10367/B2Z	4x4 LSi Convertible	11,995	2238	Note 133
NOTE 1: A $280 dealer destination charge applied to Geo Trackers effective Aug. 10, 1990.				
S10 Fleetside Pickup — 1/2-Ton — 108.3/122.9 in. w.b. — 2.5-liter EFI L4				
S10603	Reg. Cab EL X81	8,382	2671	Note 13
S10603	Reg. Cab Short Box	9,700	2684	Note 13
S10803	Reg. Cab Long Box	9,870	2756	Note 13
S10653	Ext. Cab Short Box	10,970	2793	Note 13
T10 4x4 Fleetside Pickup — 1/2-Ton — 108.3/118/122.9 in. w.b. — 4.3-liter EFI V-6				
T10603	Reg. Cab SWB	12,430	3241	Note 13
T10803	Reg. Cab LWB	12,615	3288	Note 13
T10653	Ext. Cab Short Box	13,215	3366	Note 13
T10603	Reg. Cab SWB Baja	12,430	3254	Note 13
T10803	Reg. Cab LWB Baja	12,615	3301	Note 13
T10653	Ext. Cab Short Box Baja	13,215	3379	Note 13
NOTE 2: A $420 dealer destination charge applied to S-Series pickups effective Aug. 10, 1990.				
S10 Blazer 4x2 Sport Utility Wagon — 1/2-Ton — 100.5/107 in. w.b. — 4.3-liter EFI V-6				
CS10516	2-dr Tailgate	13,845	3189	Note 13
CS10506	4-dr Tailgate	15,085	3433	Note 13
T10 Blazer 4x4 Sport Utility Wagon — 1/2-Ton — 100.5/107 in. w.b. — 4.3-liter EFI V-6				
CT10516	2-dr Tailgate	15,575	3481	Note 13
CT10506	4-dr Tailgate	17,215	3727	Note 13
NOTE 3: A $455 dealer destination charge applied to S-Series Blazers effective Aug. 10, 1990.				
M10 Astro Minivan (rear-wheel-drive) — 1/2-Ton — 111 in. w.b. — 4.3-liter EFI V-6				
CM10906	Standard Cargo Van	13,460	3507	Note 13
CM11006	Extended Cargo Van	14,130	3918	Note 13
CM10906/ZW9	Standard CS Van	14,580	3826	Note 13
CM11006/ZW9	Extended CS Van	15,270	3913	Note 13
CM10906	Standard LT Van	17,210	3826	Note 13
CM11006	Extended LT Van	17,900	3913	Note 13
L10 Astro Minivan (all-wheel-drive) — 1/2-Ton — 111 in. w.b. — 4.3-liter EFI V-6				
CL10905	Standard Cargo Van	15,740	3854	Note 13
CL11006/ZW9	Extended LT Van	16,430	4237	Note 13
NOTE 4: A $525 dealer destination charge applied to Astros effective Aug. 10, 1990.				
U05 Lumina Minivan — 1/2-Ton — 109.8 in. w.b. — 3.1-liter MFI V-6				
1UM05	Cargo Van	13,592	3260	Note 13
1UM06	Wagon	14,730	3462	Note 13
1UM06	Wagon LS	16,450	3885	Note 13
NOTE 5: A $510 dealer destination charge applied to Lumina Minivans effective Aug. 10, 1990.				
G10 Van — 1/2-Ton — 110/125 in. w.b. — 4.3-liter EFI V-6				
CG11005/ZW9	SWB Chevy Van	13,610	3792	Note 13
CG11006/ZW9	SWB Sportvan	15,340	4150	Note 13
CG11306/ZW9	LWB Beauville	17,180	4536	Note 13
G20 Van — 3/4-Ton — 110/125 in. w.b. — 4.3-liter EFI V-6				
CG21005/ZW9	SWB Chevy Van	13,790	3836	Note 13
CG21305/ZW9	LWB Sportvan	16,440	4481	Note 13
CG21306/ZW9	LWB Beauville	17,320	4547	Note 13
G30 Van — 1-Ton — 125/146 in. w.b. — 4.3-liter EFI V-6, [Sportvan 30] 5.7-liter EFI V-8				
CG31005/ZW9	LWB Chevy Van	13,850	4196	Note 13
CG31306/ZW9	LWB Sportvan 12P	18,230	5077	Note 13
CG31306/ZW9	LWB Beauville	19,110	5143	Note 13
CG31605/ZW9	EWB Chevy Van	16,640	4783	Note 13
CG31606/ZW9	EWB Sportvan 12P	19,760	5527	Note 13
CG31606/ZW9	EWB Beauville	20,570	5552	Note 13
CG31305/ZW9	LWB Cutaway Van	14,330	4012	Note 13
G30 Hi-Cube Van — 1-Ton — 125/146 in. w.b. — 5.7-liter EFI V-8				
CG31	10-ft. Van	18,320	5295	Note 13
CG31	12-ft. Van	20,020	6113	Note 13
NOTE 6: A $560 dealer destination charge applied to full-size vans effective Aug. 10, 1990.				
P30 — 1-Ton Step-Van — 125/178 in. w.b. — 5.7-liter EFI V-8				
P32	10.5-ft. Step-Van	17,181	6045	Note 13
K1500 Blazer — 1/2-Ton — 111.5 in. w.b. — 5.7-liter EFI V-8				
CK10516	Utility Hardtop	17,590	4507	Note 13
NOTE 7: A $575 dealer destination charge applied to full-size Blazers effective Aug. 10, 1990.				
R/V 1500 Suburban — 1/2-Ton — 131.5 in. w.b. — 5.7-liter EFI V-8				
CR10906	Panel Door (4x2)	16,720	4558	Note 13
CV10906	Panel Door (4x4)	18,540	4897	Note 13
R/V 2500 Suburban — 3/4-Ton — 131.5 in. w.b. — 5.7-liter EFI V-8				
CR20906	Panel Door (4x2)	18,118	4974	Note 13
CV20906	Panel Door (4x4)	20,033	5262	Note 13
NOTE 8: A $620 dealer destination charge applied to Suburbans effective Aug. 10, 1990.				
C1500 Pickup — 1/2-Ton Short Box — 117.5 in. w.b. — 4.3-liter EFI V-6				
CC10703	Regular-Cab Sportside	12,445	3722	Note 13
CC10703	Regular-Cab Fleetside	12,115	3692	Note 13
C1500 Pickup — 1/2-Ton Long Box — 131.5 in. w.b. — 4.3-liter EFI V-6				
CC10903	Regular-Cab Fleetside	12,415	3838	Note 13
CC10903	Regular-Cab Work Truck	10,625	3838	Note 13
C1500 Pickup — 1/2-Ton Short Box — 141.5 in. w.b. — 4.3-liter EFI V-6				
CC10753	Extended-Cab Fleetside	13,065	4051	Note 13
C1500 Pickup — 1/2-Ton Long Box — 155.5 in. w.b. — 4.3-liter EFI V-6				
CC10903	Extended-Cab Fleetside	13,365	4153	Note 13
C1500 Pickup — 1/2-Ton 454SS — 117.5 in. w.b. — 7.4-liter EFI V-8				
CC10703/PSS1	Regular-Cab Sportside	19,610	4562	Note 13
NOTE 9: Add approximately $2,290 for CK1500 Pickups with 4x4.				
C2500 Pickup — 3/4-Ton Long Box — 131.5 in. w.b. — 4.3-liter EFI V-6				
CC20924	Chassis & Cab	13,918	3636	Note 13
CC20903	Regular-Cab Fleetside	13,055	4003	Note 13
C2500 Pickup — 3/4-Ton Short Box — 141.5 in. w.b. — 4.3-liter EFI V-6				
CC20954	Chassis & Extended Cab	14,988	3901	Note 13
CC20953	Extended-Cab Fleetside	14,175	4161	Note 13
C2500 Pickup — 3/4-Ton Long Box — 155.5 in. w.b. — 4.3-liter EFI V-6				
CC20903	Extended-Cab Fleetside	14,455	4268	Note 13
NOTE 10: Add approximately $1,770 for CK2500 Pickups with 4x4.				
C3500 Pickup — 1-Ton Long Box — 131.5 in. w.b. — 5.7-liter EFI V-8				
CC30924	Chassis & Cab	15,060	4506	Note 13
CC30903	Regular-Cab Fleetside	15,785	4812	Note 13

1991 Geo 1/2-Ton Tracker 4x4 LSi Convertible Sport Utility (CMD)

1991 Geo 1/2-Ton Tracker 4x2 Convertible and Hardtop Sport Utilities (CMD)

1991 Chevrolet 1/2-Ton S-10 Pickup with Enhanced Tahoe Value Package (CMD)

1991 Chevrolet 1/2-Ton Astro Extended-Body Minivan (CMD)

1991 Chevrolet 1/2-Ton T10 Blazer 4x4 four-door Sport Utility Vehicle (CMD)

1991 Chevrolet 1/2-ton C1500 4x2 Sportside Regular-Cab Pickup (CMD

1991 Chevrolet 1/2-Ton T10 Blazer 4x4 two- and four-door Sport Utility Vehicles (CMD)

1991 Chevrolet 1/2-Ton S-10 Blazer Tahoe LT interior (CMD)

1991 Chevrolet 1/2-Ton T10 Blazer Tahoe LT 4x4 four-door Sport Utility Vehicle (CMD)

Model	Body Type	Price	Weight	Prod. Total
C3500 Pickup — 1-Ton Long Box — 155.5 in. w.b. — 5.7-liter V-8				
CC30903	Chassis & Extended-Cab	16,130	4645	Note 13
CC30903	Extended-Cab Fleetside	16,855	5124	Note 13
C3500 Pickup — 1-Ton Long Box — 168.5 in. w.b. — 5.7-liter V-8				
CC30933	Bonus-cab Fleetside	16,258	5140	Note 13
CC30933	Crew-Cab Fleetside	16,798	5169	Note 13
CC30933	Chassis & Bonus-cab	15,788	4729	Note 13
CC30933	Crew-Cab Fleetside	16,338	4915	Note 13
CC30934	H-D Crew-Cab & Chassis	18,577	4716	Note 13

NOTE 11: Add approximately $2,340 for CK3500 Pickups with 4x4.
NOTE 12: A $575 dealer destination charge applied to C/K Pickups effective Aug. 10, 1990.
NOTE 13: Model year production [S10 pickup] 253,953, [C/K] 246,593, [Geo Tracker (Canadian-made)] 23,634, [S-Series Blazer] 81,267, [K1500 Blazer] 7,332, [Suburban] 28,603, [Lumina APV Wagon] 44,961, [Astro Wagon] 100,370, [Step-Van] 18,941, [G-Vans] 39,656.

1991 Chevrolet 1-Ton C3500 Crew-Cab "Big Dooley" Pickup 4x2 (CMD)

GASOLINE ENGINES (DISPLACEMENT ORDER)
ENGINE: Inline. Four-cylinder. Bore & stroke: 2.95 x 3.54 in. Displacement: 1.6-liter (97 cid). BHP: 80 at 5400 rpm. Torque: Unknown. Compression ratio: 8.9:1. Throttle-body-injection. Suzuki-built. [Standard in Geo Tracker]
ENGINE: Inline. Four-cylinder. Bore & stroke: 4.00 x 3.00 in. Displacement: 2.5-liter (151 cid). BHP: 105 at 4800 rpm. Torque: 135 lb.-ft. at 3200 rpm. Compression ratio: 8.3:1. Throttle-body-injection. VIN Code A. GM-built. [Standard in S10]
ENGINE: V-block. Six-cylinder. Bore & stroke: 3.52 x 2.99 in. Displacement: 2.8-liter (173 cid). BHP: 125 at 4800 rpm. Torque: 150 lb.-ft. at 2400 rpm. Compression ratio: 8.9:1. Throttle-body-injection. VIN Code R. Chevrolet-built. [Optional in S10]
ENGINE: V-block. Six-cylinder. Bore & stroke: 3.5 x 3.331 in. Displacement: 3.1-liter (191 cid). BHP: 120 at 4400 rpm. Torque: 175 lb.-ft. at 2200 rpm. Compression ratio: 8.5:1. Multiport-fuel-injection. VIN Code D. GM-built. [Standard in Lumina]
ENGINE: V-block. Six-cylinder. Bore & stroke: 4.0 x 3.48 in. Displacement: 4.3-liter (262 cid). BHP: 150 at 4000 rpm. Torque: 230 lb.-ft. at 2400 rpm. Compression ratio: 9.3:1. Throttle-body-injection. VIN Code not available. GM-built. [Standard in G10, G20, Astro]
ENGINE: V-block. Six-cylinder. Bore & stroke: 4.0 x 3.48 in. Displacement: 4.3-liter (262 cid). BHP: 155 at 4000 rpm. Torque: 230 lb.-ft. at 2400 rpm. Compression ratio: 8.6:1. Throttle-body-injection. VIN Code B. GM-built. [Standard in C/K1500/2500 pickups]
ENGINE: V-block. Six-cylinder. Bore & stroke: 4.0 x 3.48 in. Displacement: 4.3-liter (262 cid). BHP: 160 at 4000 rpm. Torque: 235 lb.-ft. at 2400 rpm. Compression ratio: 9:11. Throttle-body-injection. VIN Code Z. Chevrolet-built. [Standard in S-Series Blazer, optional in S-Series pickups, optional in C/K 1500/2500]
ENGINE: V-block. Eight-cylinder. Bore & stroke: 3.74 x 3.48 in. Displacement: 5.0-liter (305 cid). BHP: 170-175 at 4000 rpm. Torque: 255-270 lb.-ft. at 2400 rpm. Throttle-body-injection. VIN Code H. Chevrolet-built. [Optional in C/K1500, C/K2500, G10, G20]
ENGINE: V-block. Eight-cylinder. Bore & stroke: 4.0 x 3.48 in. Displacement: 5.7-liter (350 cid). BHP: 190 at 4000 rpm. Torque: 300 lb.-ft. at 2400 rpm. Compression ratio: 8.6:1. Throttle-body-injection. VIN Code A. GM-built. [Standard in C/K3500, Suburbans, and G30 vans, optional in C/K pickups]
ENGINE: V-block. Eight-cylinder. Bore & stroke: 4.0 x 3.48 in. Displacement: 5.7-liter (350 cid). BHP: 210 at 4000 rpm. Compression ratio: 9.3:1. Torque: 300 lb.-ft. at 2800 rpm. Throttle-body-injection. VIN Code K. Chevrolet-built [Standard in C/K Blazer, optional in C/K1500/2500/3500, optional in Suburban, optional in Chevy Van and Sportvan]
ENGINE: V-block. Eight-cylinder. Bore & stroke: 4.25 x 4.00 in. Displacement: 7.4-liter (454 cid). BHP: 230 at 3600 rpm. Torque: 385 lb.-ft. at 1600 rpm. Throttle-body- fuel-injection. VIN Code N. Chevrolet-built. [Optional in C/K1500, C/K2500, C/K3500, Suburban, and G30 vans]
DIESEL ENGINES (DISPLACEMENT ORDER)
ENGINE: V-block. Eight-cylinder. Bore & stroke: 3.98 x 3.82 in. Displacement: 6.2-liter (379 cid). BHP: 130 at 3600 rpm. Torque: 240 lb.-ft. at 2000 rpm. VIN Code C. GM-built. [Optional in C/K3500 pickup, optional in G30 Chevy Van and 12-passenger Sportvan]
CHASSIS: [Geo Tracker (All)] Wheelbase: 86.6 in. Length: 142.5 in. Width: 64.2 in. Height: 65.6 in. GVW: 3,197 lb. Payload: 900 lb. Tires: (4x2) P195/75R-15, (4x4) P205/75R15 black sidewall.
CHASSIS: [S10] Regular-Cab. Short Box. Wheelbase: 108.3 in. Length: 178.2 in. Width: 64.8 in. Height: 61.3 in. GVW: 4,200 lb. Payload: 1,529 lb. Tires: P195/75R14 black sidewall.
CHASSIS: [S10] Regular-Cab. Short Box. Wheelbase: 108.5 in. Length: 178.2 in. Width: 64.8 in. Height: 63.63 in. GVW: 4,650 lb. Payload: 1,409 lb. Tires: P205/75R15 black sidewall.

CHASSIS: [S10] Regular-Cab. Long Box. Wheelbase: 117.9 in. Length: 194.2 in. Width: 61.3 in. Height: 61.3 in. GVW: 4,200 lb. Payload: 1,444 lb. Tires: P195/75R14 black sidewall.
CHASSIS: [T10] Regular-Cab. Long Box. Wheelbase: 117.9 in. Length: 194.2 in. Width: 64.8 in. Height: 63.4 in. GVW: 4,650 lb. Payload: 1,362 lb. Tires: P205/75R15 black sidewall.
CHASSIS: [S10] Extended-Cab. Short Box. Wheelbase: 122.9 in. Length: 192.8 in. Width: 64.8 in. Height: 61.3 in. GVW: 4,200 lb. Payload: 1,407 lb. Tires: P195/75R14 black sidewall.
CHASSIS: [T10] Extended-Cab. Short Box. Wheelbase: 122.9 in. Length: 192.8 in. Width: 64.8 in. Height: 63.4 in. GVW: 4,650 lb. Payload: 1,284 lb. Tires: P205/75R15 black sidewall.
CHASSIS: [S-Blazer 4x2] Two-door. Wheelbase: 100.5 in. Length: 170.3 in. Width: 65.4 in. Height: 64.1 in. GVW: 4,350 lb. Payload: 1,161 lb. Tires: P205/75R15 black sidewall.
CHASSIS: [S-Blazer 4x4] Two-door. Wheelbase: 100.5 in. Length: 170.3 in. Width: 65.4 in. Height: 64.3 in. GVW: 4,700 lb. Payload: 1,219 lb. Tires: P205/75R15 black sidewall.
CHASSIS: [S-Blazer 4x2] Four-door. Wheelbase: 107 in. Length: 176.8 in. Width: 65.4 in. Height: 64.1 in. GVW: 4,850 lb. Payload: 1,417 lb. Tires: P205/75R15 black sidewall.
CHASSIS: [S-Blazer 4x4] Four-door. Wheelbase: 107 in. Length: 176.8 in. Width: 65.4 in. Height: 64.3 in. GVW: 5,100 lb. Payload: 1,379 lb. Tires: P205/75R15 black sidewall.
CHASSIS: [Astro Cargo regular-body] Wheelbase: 111 in. Length: 176.8 in. Width: 77.0 in. Height: 74.5 in. GVW: 5,000 lb. Payload: 1,493 lb. Tires: P205/75R15 black sidewall.
CHASSIS: [Astro Cargo regular-body AWD] Wheelbase: 111 in. Length: 176.8 in. Width: 77.0 in. Height: 74.5 in. GVW: 5,600 lb. Payload: 1,746 lb. Tires: P205/75R15 black sidewall.
CHASSIS: [Astro Cargo extended-body] Wheelbase: 111 in. Length: 186.8 in. Width: 77.0 in. Height: 74.5 in. GVW: 5,600 lb. Payload: 1,493 lb. Tires: P205/75R15 black sidewall.
CHASSIS: [Astro Cargo extended-body AWD] Wheelbase: 111 in. Length: 186.8 in. Width: 77.0 in. Height: 74.5 in. GVW: 5,850 lb. Payload: 1,932 lb. Tires: P205/75R15 black sidewall.
CHASSIS: [Astro Passenger regular-body] Wheelbase: 111 in. Length: 176.8 in. Width: 77.0 in. Height: 73.7 in. GVW: 5,600 lb. Payload: 1,774 lb. Tires: P205/75R15 black sidewall.
CHASSIS: [Astro Passenger regular-body AWD] Wheelbase: 111 in. Length: 176.8 in. Width: 77.0 in. Height: 73.7 in. GVW: 5,800 lb. Payload: 1,644 lb. Tires: P205/75R15 black sidewall.
CHASSIS: [Astro Passenger extended-body] Wheelbase: 111 in. Length: 186.8 in. Width: 77.0 in. Height: 73.7 in. GVW: 5,850 lb. Payload: 1,937 lb. Tires: P205/75R15 black sidewall.
CHASSIS: [Astro Passenger extended-body AWD] Wheelbase: 111 in. Length: 186.8 in. Width: 77.0 in. Height: 73.7 in. GVW: 6,100 lb. Payload: 1,863 lb. Tires: P205/75R15 black sidewall.
CHASSIS: [Lumina] Wheelbase: 109.8 in. Length: 194.2 in. Width: 73.9 in. Height: 65.2 in. GVW: 4,935 lb. Payload: 1,640 lb. Tires: P205/70R15 black sidewall.
CHASSIS: [G10/Short Body] Chevy Van. Wheelbase: 110 in. Length: 178.2 in. Width: 79.5 in. Height: 79.5. GVW: 4,900 lb. Payload: 1,108 lb. Tires: P215/75R15 black sidewall.
CHASSIS: [G10/Long Body] Chevy Van/Sportvan. Wheelbase: 125 in. Length: 202.2 in. Width: 79.5 in. Height: 79.1 in. GVW: 5,600 lb. Payload: 1,130 lb. Tires: P215/75R15 black sidewall.
CHASSIS: [G20/Long Body] Chevy Van/Sportvan. Wheelbase: 125 in. Length: 202.2 in. Width: 79.5 in. Height: 79.5 in. GVW: 6,600 lb. Payload: 2,119 lb. Tires: P215/75R15 black sidewall.
CHASSIS: [G30/Long Body Chevy Van] Wheelbase: 125 in. Length: 202.2 in. Width: 79.5 in. Height: 82.3 in. GVW: 7,100 lb. Payload: 2,904 lb. Tires: P215/75R15 black sidewall.
CHASSIS: [G30/Long Body Sportvan] Wheelbase: 125 in. Length: 202.2 in. Width: 79.5 in. Height: 81.8 in. GVW: 7,400 lb. Payload: 2,323 lb. Tires: P215/75R15 black sidewall.
CHASSIS: [G30/Extended Body Chevy Van] Wheelbase: 146 in. Length: 223.2 in. Width: 79.5 in. Height: 82.3 in. GVW: 8,600 lb. Payload: 3,817 lb. Tires: P215/75R15 black sidewall
CHASSIS: [G30/Extended Body 12-Passenger Sportvan] Wheelbase: 146 in. Length: 223.2 in. Width: 79.5 in. Height: 82.3 in. GVW: 8,600 lb. Payload: 3,073 lb. Tires: P215/75R15 black sidewall

1991 Chevrolet 1/2-Ton K1500 Blazer 2-door Sport Utility 4x4 (CMD)

CHASSIS: [K10 Blazer 4x4] Wheelbase: 106.5 in. Length: 184.8 in. Width: 79.6 in. Height: 73.8 in. GVW: 6,100 lb. Payload: 1,593 lb. Tires: LT245/75R16C black sidewall.
CHASSIS: [Suburban C1500] Wheelbase: 129.5 in. Length: 219.1 in. Width: 79.6 in. Height: 72.0 in. GVW: 6,100 lb. Payload: 1,542 lb. Tires: P235/75R-15XLS black sidewall.
CHASSIS: [Suburban C2500] Wheelbase: 129.5 in. Length: 219.5 in. Width: 79.6 in. Height: 74.3 in. GVW: 8,600 lb. Payload: 3,626 lb. Tires: P235/75R-15XLS black sidewall.
CHASSIS: [C1500 Sportside Regular-Cab Short Box Pickup] Regular-Cab. Short Box. Wheelbase: 117.5 in. Length: 194.0 in. Width: 77.1 in. Height: 70.4 in. GVW: 5,600 lb. Payload: 1,878 lb. Tires: P225/75R15 black sidewall AS SBR Tires.

1991 Chevrolet 1/2-ton C1500 4x2 Fleetside Regular-Cab "Work Truck" Pickup (CMD)

1991 Chevrolet 1/2-ton K1500 4x4 Fleetside Regular-Cab Pickup with Sport package (CMD)

1991 Chevrolet 1/2-Ton Lumina APV Cargo Van (CMD)

1991 Chevrolet 3/4-Ton G2500 Beauville Extended-Body Sportvan (CMD)

1991 Chevrolet 1/2-Ton K-1500 4x4 Extended-Cab Sportside Short Bed Pickup (CMD)

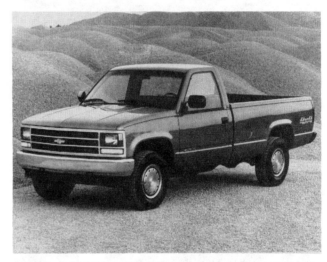

1991 Chevrolet 3/4-Ton K1500 Fleetside 4x4 Regular-Cab Pickup (CMD)

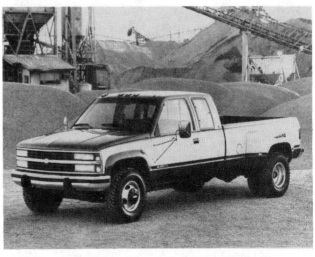

1991 Chevrolet 1-Ton K-3500 4x4 Extended-Cab Sportside "Dooley" Pickup (CMD)

1991 Chevrolet 1-Ton R3500 4x2 Crew-Cab Cabinet Body
Utility Truck (CMD)

1991 Chevrolet Light-Duty Commercial Vehicles (CMD)

1991 Chevrolet 1-Ton C3500 Chassis-and-Cab with Tilt-Back
Towing Body (CMD)

1991 Chevrolet 1/2-Ton Astro Extended-Body Cargo Van (CMD)

1991 Chevrolet 1/2-Ton S-10 Long Box Pickup (CMD)

1991 Chevrolet 3/4-Ton G2500 Extended-Body Chevy Van (CMD)

1991 Chevrolet 1/2-Ton K1500 Blazer (front) and C1500 Suburban (rear)
Sport Utilities (CMD)

1991 Chevrolet 3/4-Ton C2500 4x2 Suburban Sport Utility (CMD)

Standard Catalog of Chevrolet Trucks

CHASSIS: [C1500 Fleetside Regular-Cab Short Box Pickup] Wheelbase: 117.5 in. Length: 194.1 in. Width: 76.8 in. Height: 70.4 in. GVW: 5,600 lb. Payload: 1,908 lb. Tires: P225/75R15 black sidewall AS SBR Tires.
CHASSIS: [C1500 Fleetside Regular-Cab Long Box Pickup] Wheelbase: 131.5 in. Length: 212.6 in. Width: 76.8 in. Height: 70.4 in. GVW: 5,600 lb. Payload: 1,762 lb. Tires: P225/75R15 black sidewall AS SBR Tires.
CHASSIS: [C1500 454SS Short Box] Wheelbase: 117.5 in. Length: 194.1 in. Width: 76.8 in. Height: 70.4 in. GVW: 5,600 lb. Payload: 1,038 lb. Tires: P235/75R15 white-outline-letter AS SBR Tires.
CHASSIS: [C1500 Fleetside Regular-Cab Long Box "Work Truck" Pickup] Wheelbase: 131.5 in. Length: 212.6 in. Width: 76.8 in. Height: 70.4 in. GVW: 5,600 lb. Payload: 1,762 lb. Tires: P225/75R15 black sidewall AS SBR Tires.
CHASSIS: [C1500 Sportside Extended-Cab Short Box Pickup] Wheelbase: 141.5 in. Length: 218.0 in. Width: 76.4 in. Height: 70.6 in. GVW: 6,200 lb. Payload: 2,149 lb. Tires: P225/75R15 black sidewall AS SBR Tires.
CHASSIS: [C1500 Fleetside Extended-Cab Short Box Pickup] Wheelbase: 141.5 in. Length: 218.0 in. Width: 76.4 in. Height: 70.6 in. GVW: 6,200 lb. Payload: 2,149 lb. Tires: P225/75R15 black sidewall AS SBR Tires.
CHASSIS: [C1500 Fleetside Extended-Cab Long Box Pickup] Wheelbase: 155.5 in. Length: 255.7 in. Width: 76.8 in. Height: 70.6 in. GVW: 6,200 lb. Payload: 2,047 lb. Tires: P225/75R15 black sidewall AS SBR Tires.
CHASSIS: [K1500 Sportside Regular-Cab Short Box Pickup] Wheelbase: 117.5 in. Length: 194.0 in. Width: 77.1 in. Height: 73.8 GVW: 5,600 lb. Payload: 1,459 lb. Tires: P225/75R15 black sidewall AS SBR Tires.
CHASSIS: [K1500 Fleetside Regular-Cab Short Box Pickup] Wheelbase: 117.5 in. Length: 194.1 in. Width: 76.8 in. Height: 73.8 in. GVW: 5,600 lb. Payload: 1,489 lb. Tires: P225/75R15 black sidewall AS SBR Tires.
CHASSIS: [K1500 Fleetside Regular-Cab Long Box Pickup] Wheelbase: 131.5 in. Length: 212.9 in. Width: 76.8 in. Height: 73.8 in. GVW: 5,600 lb. Payload: 1,335 lb. Tires: P225/75R15 black sidewall AS SBR Tires.
CHASSIS: [K1500 Fleetside Regular-Cab Long Box "Work Truck" Pickup] Wheelbase: 131.5 in. Length: 212.6 in. Width: 76.8 in. Height: 73.8 in. GVW: 5,600 lb. Payload: 1,335 lb. Tires: P225/75R15 black sidewall AS SBR Tires.
CHASSIS: [K1500 Fleetside Extended-Cab Short Box Pickup] Wheelbase: 141.5 in. Length: 218.0 in. Width: 76.8 in. Height: 73.8 in. GVW: 6,200 lb. Payload: 1,750 lb. Tires: P225/75R15 black sidewall AS SBR Tires.
CHASSIS: [K1500 Fleetside Extended-Cab Long Box Pickup] Wheelbase: 155.5 in. Length: 237.0 in. Width: 76.8 in. Height: 73.8 in. GVW: 6,200 lb. Payload: 1,615 lb. Tires: P225/75R15 black sidewall AS SBR Tires.

1991 Chevrolet 1/2-Ton C1500 "454 SS" Fleetside Short Box Pickup 4x2 (CMD)

CHASSIS: [C2500 Fleetside Regular-Cab Long Box Pickup] Wheelbase: 131.5 in. Length: 212.6 in. Width: 76.8 in. Height: 73 in. GVW: 7,200 lb. Payload: 3,197 lb. Tires: P225/75R15 black sidewall AS SBR tires.
CHASSIS: [C2500 Heavy-duty Fleetside Regular-Cab Long Box Pickup] Wheelbase: 131.5 in. Length: 212.6 in. Width: 76.8 in. Height: 75.6 in. GVW: 8,600 lb. Payload: 4,126 lb. Tires: P225/75R15 black sidewall AS SBR tires.
CHASSIS: [C2500 Fleetside Extended-Cab Short Box Pickup] Wheelbase: 141.5 in. Length: 218.0 in. Width: 76.8 in. Height: 74 in. GVW: 8,600 lb. Payload: 2,366 lb. Tires: P225/75R15 black sidewall AS SBR tires.
CHASSIS: [C2500 Fleetside Extended-Cab Long Box Pickup] Wheelbase: 155.5 in. Length: 237.0 in. Width: 76.8 in. Height: 74 in. GVW: 7,200 lb. Payload: 2,932 lb. Tires: P225/75R15 black sidewall AS SBR tires.
CHASSIS: [K2500 Fleetside Regular-Cab Long Box Pickup] Wheelbase: 131.5 in. Length: 212.6 in. Width: 76.8 in. Height: 74.3 in. GVW: 7,200 lb. Payload: 2,848 lb. Tires: P225/75R15 black sidewall AS SBR tires.
CHASSIS: [K2500 Heavy-duty Fleetside Regular-Cab Long Box Pickup] Wheelbase: 131.5 in. Length: 212.6 in. Width: 76.8 in. Height: 74.3 in. GVW: 8,600 lb. Payload: 3,774 lb. Tires: P225/75R15 black sidewall AS SBR tires.
CHASSIS: [K2500 Fleetside Extended-Cab Short Box Pickup] Wheelbase: 141.5 in. Length: 218.0 in. Width: 76.8 in. Height: 74.4 in. GVW: 7,200 lb. Payload: 2,718 lb. Tires: P225/75R15 black sidewall AS SBR tires.
CHASSIS: [K2500 Fleetside Extended-Cab Long Box Pickup] Wheelbase: 155.5 in. Length: 237.0 in. Width: 76.8 in. Height: 74.4 in. GVW: 7,200 lb. Payload: 2,580 lb. Tires: P225/75R15 black sidewall AS SBR tires.
CHASSIS: [C3500 Fleetside Regular-Cab Long Box Pickup] Wheelbase: 131.5 in. Length: 212.6 in. Width: 76.4 in. Height: 75.5 in. GVW: 10,000 lb. Payload: 4,938 lb. Tires: P225/75R15 black sidewall AS SBR tires.
CHASSIS: [K3500 Fleetside Extended-Cab Heavy-duty Long Box Pickup] Wheelbase: 131.5 in. Length: 212.6 in. Width: 94.2 in. Height: 75.8 in. GVW: 10,000 lb. Payload: 4,644 lb. Tires: P225/75R15 black sidewall AS SBR tires.
CHASSIS: [C/K 3500 Pickup] Motor home chassis. Wheelbase: 183.5 in. Tires: P225/75R15 black sidewall AS SBR tires.

SELECTED OPTIONS

GEO TRACKER]OPTIONS: PEG 2 package ($302). PEG2 package with UM6 radio (add $441). PEG 3 package ($997). PEG 3 package with UM6 radio ($1,136). Tuned AM/FM stereo with Seek -and-SOcan ($302). Air conditioning ($695). Convertible rear seat ($445). Spare tire cover ($33). Power steering ($275). Trailering Special equipment ($109). Alloy wheels ($325). Three-speed automatic transmission ($565).

1991 Chevrolet 1/2-Ton T10 "Baja" Pickup 4x4 (CMD)

S/T SERIES PICKUP OPTIONS: Tahoe package ($532-$587 depending upon other options ordered). Air conditioning ($780). Air dam with fog lamps ($115). Optional axle ratio ($44). Locking rear differential ($252). Heavy-duty battery ($56). Rear step bumper ($130-$229 depending upon paint option). Spare tire carrier ($110). Cold Climate package ($140-$243 depending upon trim option.) Center console ($135). Heavy-duty radiator ($56). Heavy-duty radiator and transmission oil cooler ($63 with air conditioning/$118 without air conditioning). Engine oil cooler ($135). Driver convenience package includes Comfortilt steering wheel and intermittent wiper system ($204). Full floor carpeting ($40). Deep tinted glass in Extended-Cab ($101-$140 depending upon option package), in Regular-Cab ($110). Electronic instrumentation ($195). Auxiliary lighting ($44-$66 depending upon other options ordered). Exterior below-eye-line painted mirrors ($52). Lighted interior visor mirror ($68-$75 depending upon trim package). Body side and wheel opening moldings ($152). Black wheel opening molding ($13-$43 depending upon trim package). Bright wheel opening molding ($31). Endgate net ($110). Operating convenience package includes power door locks and power windows ($367). Special two-tone paint includes pin striping ($296). Electronically tuned AM/FM stereo radio with digital clock ($201). Electronically tuned AM/FM stereo radio with Seek-and-Scan, stereo cassette tape player and digital clock ($131). Electronically tuned AM/FM stereo radio with Seek-and-Scan, stereo cassette tape player with Search-and-Repeat, and digital clock ($253). Electronically tuned AM/FM stereo radio with Seek-and-Scan, stereo cassette tape player with Search-and-Repeat, graphic equalizer and digital clock ($150-$403 depending upon other options ordered). Delete radio ($95 credit). Rear jump seats with vinyl trim ($240). Shield package includes transfer case and front differential skid plates and steering linkage shield ($126). Heavy-duty front springs ($63). Sport suspension ($252). Off-Road suspension ($122 with Tahoe equipment, $182 without Tahoe equipment). Front and rear heavy-duty shock absorbers ($40). Electronic speed control ($238). Heavy-duty rear springs ($64). Heavy-duty front suspension with heavy-duty front and rear shock absorbers ($63). Body striping ($55). Manual sun roof ($250). Heavy-duty Trailering Special package ($211). Four-speed automatic transmission ($890). Wheel trim rings ($60). Cast aluminum wheels ($284-$340 depending upon trim package). Sliding rear window ($113).

1991 Chevrolet 1/2-Ton S10 Blazer Tahoe LT 4-door Sport Utility 4x2 (CMD)

S/T-SERIES BLAZER OPTIONS: Air conditioning ($724 with engine oil cooler/$780 without engine oil cooler). Air dam with fog lamps ($115). Optional axle ratio ($44). Locking rear differential ($252). Heavy-duty battery ($56). Spare tire and wheel carrier ($159). Cold Climate package ($146). Heavy-duty radiator ($56). Heavy-duty radiator and engine oil cooler ($63 with air conditioning, $118 without air conditioning). Driver convenience package (RPO ZM7) includes Comfortilt steering wheel and intermittent wiper system ($204). Driver convenience package RPO ZM8 includes rear window defroster and tailgate release ($197). California emissions package ($100). Color-keyed front floor mats in two-door only ($20). Rear color-keyed floor mats ($16). Deep-tinted glass RPO AJ1 ($225). Deep-tinted glass with light-tinted rear window RPO AA3 ($144). Electronic instrumentation ($195). Black luggage carrier ($169). Exterior electric remote mirrors ($83). Visor mirrors for left and right side ($68). Black wheel opening molding ($13-$43 depending on trim package). Operating convenience package includes power door locks and power windows ($542 for four-door/$367 for two-door. Special two-tone paint ($218). Deluxe two-tone paint ($177). Electronically-tuned AM/FM stereo radio with Seek-and-Scan and digital clock ($131). Electronically-tuned AM/FM stereo radio with Seek-and-Scan and stereo cassette tape player ($122-$253 depending upon other options selected). Electronically tuned AM/FM stereo radio with Seek-and-Scan, stereo cassette tape player with Search-and-Repeat, graphic equalizer, and digital clock ($403).

Delete radio ($95 credit). Special custom cloth reclining high-back bucket seats ($345). Deluxe cloth reclining high-back bucket seats ($26 with rear seat). Folding rear bench seat ($409). Leather reclining high-back bucket seats in two-door only ($312 with folding rear bench seat/$412 without folding rear seat). Transfer case and front differential skid plates and steering linkage shield ($75). Front and rear heavy-duty shock absorbers ($40). Electronic speed control ($238). Sport equipment ($714 in four-door/$1,082 in two-door.) Body striping ($55). Sunroof, manual, non-removable, two-door only ($250). Heavy-duty front springs ($63). Off-Road suspension, two-door only ($122-$182 depending on other options selected). Light-duty trailering package ($165 with oil cooler/$109 without oil cooler). Heavy-duty trailering Special package ($211). Tahoe package for four-door ($600-$3,020 depending upon Preferred Equipment Group selected. Tahoe package for two-door ($809). Sport package ($3,06-$4,260 depending upon Preferred Equipment Group selected. Four-speed automatic transmission ($890). Rally wheels ($92). Cast aluminum wheels ($284-$340 depending upon trim package). Gray aluminum wheels ($248-$340 depending upon trim option). Sliding rear side window, two-door only ($257). Rear window wiper/washer ($125).

ASTRO OPTIONS: Air conditioning (front-only $845/front and rear $1,368). Optional axle ratio ($44). Locking rear differential ($252). Deluxe front and rear chromed bumpers ($76-$128 depending upon option packages). Black luggage carrier ($126). Cold Climate package ($46). Roof console ($50-$83 depending upon other options). Engine oil cooler ($135). Heavy-duty radiator ($56). Heavy-duty radiator and engine oil cooler ($63 with air conditioning/$118 without air conditioning). Power door locks ($223). Driver convenience package includes Comfortilt steering wheel and speed control ($383). Operating convenience package includes power door locks and power windows ($434). Tinted glass for complete body ($157). Deep-tinted glass ($161-$290 depending on body glass selected). Rear heater ($205). Electronic instrumentation ($195). Auxiliary lighting ($100 with roof console/ $133 without roof console). Black below-eye-line exterior mirrors ($52). Exterior remote electric mirrors ($150). Special two-tone paint ($172). Deluxe two-tone paint ($251-$476 depending upon other options). Custom two-tone ($104 -$329 depending upon other options). Electronically tuned AM/FM stereo radio with Seek-and-Scan, digital clock, stereo cassette player, and premium speakers ($151). Electronically tuned AM/FM stereo radio with Seek-and-Scan, stereo cassette tape player with Search-and-Repeat, graphic equalizer, digital clock, and premium speakers ($273). Electronically tuned AM/FM stereo radio with Seek-and-Scan, stereo cassette tape player with Search-and-Repeat, graphic equalizer, digital clock and premium speakers ($150-$423 depending upon other options ordered). Delete radio ($95 credit). Seven-passenger seating ($878-$1,069 depending upon other options). Eight-passenger seating ($344-$878 depending upon other options). Seat back recliner and dual arm rests ($241). Front and rear heavy-duty shock absorbers ($40). Heavy-duty trailering equipment ($507-$564 depending upon other equipment ordered). Light-duty trailering equipment ($109). Aluminum wheels ($248-$340, depending upon other options ordered). Rally wheels ($92).

LUMINA OPTIONS: PEG 1 ($1,000-$1,400). PEG 2 ($1,940-$2,196). UM6 radio ($140). U1C radio ($396) Custom two-tone exterior paint ($148).Roof carrier 9$145). Rear window defogger ($160). Air conditioning ($805). California emissions ($100). Deep-tinted glass ($245). Power door locks and tailgate ($270). Twin remote Sport mirrors ($30). AG9 power seat ($2970). AB3 six-passenger seating with twin front bucket seats ($510). ZP7 seven-passenger seating with twin front bucket seats ($425-$660). Load leveling suspension ($170). Electric speed control with resume feature ($210). Comfortilt steering wheel ($135). P205/70R15 black sidewall touring radial tires ($73 extra). Cast aluminum 15-inch wheels with locks ($265). Power windows with "express down" on driver's window ($255).

1991 Chevrolet 3/4-Ton G20 Beauville Sportvan Passenger Wagon 4x2 (CMD)

G-SERIES VAN OPTIONS: Preferred Equipment Group V1A2 ($941). Air conditioning ($950). ZQ2 convenience group ($411). Heavy-duty cooling system ($56). 5.0-liter EFI V-8 ($575). 5.7-liter EFI V-8 ($820). 7.4-liter EFI V-8 ($470). Deep-tinted glass ($306). Heater ($205). TR9 auxiliary lighting package ($135). Deluxe two-tone paint ($269). UM6 stereo equipment ($122-$263). UX1 stereo equipment ($150-$413). Rally wheels ($121). Cast aluminum wheels ($195-$316).

K5 BLAZER OPTIONS: Silverado package RPO YE9 ($1,298). Air conditioning RPO C60 ($845 without B3J/ $783 with B3J). Optional rear axle ratios ($38). Locking rear differential RPO G80 ($252). Cold Climate package RPO V10 includes special insulation, special heater and defroster, engine block heater, antifreeze protection to -32 degrees and heavy-duty battery ($48). Engine oil cooler RPO KC4 ($135). Heavy-duty radiator RPO VO1 ($56). Heavy-duty radiator and transmission oil cooler RPO VO2 ($63). Deep-tinted glass RPO AJ1 ($215). Locking front hubs RPO X6Z ($60). Below-eye-line stainless steel exterior mirrors RPO D45 ($45). Below-eye-line electric remote painted mirrors ($58-$98 depending upon options selected).

1991 Chevrolet 1/2-Ton K1500 Suburban 4-door wagon 4x4 (CMD)

C/K PICKUP/SUBURBAN OPTIONS: Operating convenience package RPO ZQ2 includes power door locks and front door power windows ($367). Operating convenience package RPO ZQ3 includes tilt wheel and speed control ($383). Conventional two-tone exterior paint RPO ZY2 ($413 without YE9/$180 with YE9). Special two-tone exterior paint RPO ZY3 ($464 without YE9/ $450 with YE9). Deluxe two-tone exterior paint RPO ZY4 ($566 without YE9/ $332 with YE9. Electronically-tuned AM/FM stereo radio with Seek-and-Scan and digital clock RPO UM7 ($131). Electronically-tuned AM/FM stereo radio with Seek-and-Scan, stereo cassette tape player and digital clock RPO UM6 ($253). Electronically-tuned AM/FM stereo radio with Seek-and-Scan, stereo cassette tape player with Search-and-Repeat, graphic equalizer and digital clock RPO UX1 ($403). Radio delete RPO UL5 ($95). Fuel tank shield RPO NY1 includes protective shield on transfer case ($175). Rear folding three-passenger seat AM7 ($411 without shoulder harness/ $461 with shoulder harness). Rear seat not desired RPO YG4 (No charge). Heavy-duty 2,250 lb. front springs F60 includes heavy-duty front and rear shock absorbers and recommended for front-mounted accessory applications only ($62). Front quad shock absorbers ($100). Trailering Special equipment RPO Z82 includes trailer hitch platform and hitch, wiring harness and transmission oil cooler and requires either 3.42 or 3.73 rear axle and without B3J includes engine oil cooler ($407 without B3J diesel equipment/ $272 with B3J diesel equipment). Four-speed automatic with overdrive RPO MXO ($890, but standard with B3J equipment). Wheelcovers RPO PO1 ($42). Rally wheels RPO N67 ($121 without YE9/ $79 with YE9). Aluminum cast wheels RPO N90 ($212-$333 without YE9 and depending upon other options selected $291 with YE9). Sliding rear quarter windows AD5 ($257). P235/75R15 steel-belted radial tires on-off-road blackwall tires ($55 extra). P235/75R15 steel belted all seasons radial whitewall tires ($90 extra). P235/75R15 steel belted radial all-season white lettered tires ($125 extra). 31 x 10.50R15B white letter steel belted radial on-off-road tires ($631.10). Air conditioning RPO C60 ($705). Optional axle ratios RPO G80 ($252). Locking Differential RPO G80 ($252). RPO TP2 auxiliary heavy-duty battery, not available with B3J ($134). Painted rear step bumper, requires E63 body RPO V43 ($130). Front deluxe chromed bumper with rub strip for K10703 pickup only RPO VG3 ($26). Chromed rear step bumper with rub strip RPO VB3 ($229). Front black bumper guards RPO V27 ($32). Heavy-duty chassis equipment, K1500 only RPO F44 ($38). Off-road package, available for K1500 only, includes skid plate and Bilstein shock absorbers RPO Z71 ($270). Cold Climate package, not available with B3J, includes engine block heater RPO V10 ($33). Convenience group includes power door locks and windows RPO ZQ2 ($367). Convenience group includes tilt wheel and speed control RPO ZQ3 ($383). Engine oil cooling system RPO KC4 ($135). Heavy-duty radiator RPO VO1 ($56). Heavy-duty radiator and transmission oil cooler RPO VO2 ($63). Rear window defogger RPO C49 ($154). 5.0-liter V-8 RPO LO3 ($575). 5.7-liter V-8 RPO LO5 ($840). 6.2-liter diesel V-8 RPO LH6 (No separate extra charge, part of package). Locking fuel filler cap RPO NO5 ($18). Cargo area Lamp RPO UF2 ($36). Dome and reading Lamp RPO C95 ($33). RPO UO1 roof marker lamps, not available with California emissions package, ($52). Auxiliary lighting includes dome and reading lamps and ash tray, glove box and under hood lamps RPO TR9 ($94). Below-eye-line type stainless steel mirrors RPO D45 ($45). Camper-type stainless steel mirrors RPO DF2 ($53). Black exterior moldings RPO B84 ($90). Exterior bright moldings RPO B85 ($17). Conventional two-tone exterior paint RPO ZY2 ($132). Special two-tone exterior paint RPO ZY3 ($215). Deluxe two-tone exterior paint RPO ZY4 ($243). Electronically-tuned AM/FM stereo radio with Seek-and-Scan and digital clock RPO UM7 ($210). Electronically-tuned AM/FM stereo radio with Seek-and-Scan, stereo cassette tape and digital clock RPO UM6 ($332). Electronically-tuned AM/FM stereo radio with Seek-and-Scan, stereo cassette player with search-and -repeat, graphic equalizer and digital clock RPO UX1 ($482). Radio delete option RPO UL5 ($77). Scottsdale trim package RPO Z62 on K-Series Pickups ($573 to $604). Heavy-duty front and rear shock absorbers RPO F51 ($40). Silverado trim package RPO YE9 for K1500 Regular-Cab pickup ($981 to $1,012). Off-road skid plate, K1500 only, RPO NZZ ($95). Heavy-duty front springs, K1500 only, requires F44 heavy-duty chassis [not available with B3J or RPO Z71 Off-Road chassis] RPO F60 ($63). Body striping RPO D85 ($69). Tow hooks, standard on K1500, RPO V76 ($38). Heavy-duty trailering Special equipment RPO Z82 ($408 with RPO Z71 or XQ8/ $448 without RPO Z71 or ZQ8). Four-speed manual transmission RPO MM4 ($98). Four-speed automatic transmission with overdrive RPO MXO ($860). Three-speed automatic transmission RPO MX1 ($625). Wheelcovers RPO PO1 ($42). Aluminum wheels, K1500 only, RPO PF4 ($295). Sliding rear window RPO A28 ($113). Camper Special chassis equipment, for K2500 and K3500 only, RPO Z81 ($280 without B2J/$148 with B3J). Deep-tinted glass RPO AJ1 ($150). Sport Equipment package for Sport Truck K10703 only, includes V43 black bumpers, black wheel flares, deluxe front appearance, black mirrors, GL, LT265/75R16 blackwall tires, PF4 aluminum wheels with special hub caps, and 4x4 Sport decal, RPO BPY ($1,140).20). Sport steering wheel RPO NK3 ($7). Rear-mounted fuel tank, available for K2500 and K3500 Chassis-and-Cab models, approximate capacity of 31-gallons RPO NK7 ($63). RPO Z81 Camper Special chassis equipment includes TP2 auxiliary battery without B3J equipment, camper wiring harness and DF2 mirrors ($280 for K-series pickups/ $1,436 with B3J/ $81 for V3500). Dual rear wheels, available for C/K3500 models only, includes plastic rear fender extensions with side marker lamps on front and rear sides and dual rear chassis provisions RPO RO5 ($1,038 or $1,101 with MX1 transmission) The dual rear wheels package includes VO2 heavy-duty radiator and transmission oil cooler for V3500, ($785 extra).

NOTE 14: Options and prices shown are representative. The actual cost of an option or option package often varies according to other packages that the options are combined with on specific vehicles. Preferred Equipment Group (PEG) options offer specific optional equipment at discount prices. Some "options" may be standard equipment on certain models, such as V-8s in C/K3500 pickups. Descriptions of options are edited. Full option contents can be determined by consulting sales literature.

HISTORICAL: Chevrolet trucks were built in 12 factories in 1991. Geo Trackers were made at the CAMI plant in Ingersoll, Ontario, Canada. S-Series pickups were assembled in Pontiac, Michigan and Shreveport, Louisiana. S-Series Blazers built at Pontiac, Michigan and Moraine, Ohio. Astros were made in Baltimore, Maryland. Chevy Van models were sourced from factories in Scarborough, Ontario, Canada and Flint, Michigan. Full-size Blazers and Suburbans were made in the Chevrolet factory at Janesville, Wisconsin. C/K pickups were built in Fort Wayne, Indiana; Oshawa, Canada; Pontiac, Michigan; and Janesville, Wisconsin. Lumina APVs were assembled at Tarrytown, N.Y. Jim Perkins was general manager of Chevrolet Motor Division. J.N. Janowiak was national manager of truck merchandising and Mac Wisner was manager of truck advertising. Chevrolet calendar-year new-truck sales were: 34,565 Astro Vans, 71,242 Astro Wagons, 48,117 Lumina APVs, 9,258 Blazers, 123,346 S-Series Blazers, 404,763 C/K pickups, 200,247 S10/T10 pickups, 8,475 Sportvans, 36,106 Suburbans, 30,702 Canadian-built Geo Trackers, 79,781 Chevy Vans, and 19,191 Step-Van multi-stop trucks. This gave the company total light-duty truck sales of 1,065,794 units in the calendar-year. Chevrolet model-year new-truck sales were: 36,674 Astro Vans, 69,319 Astro Wagons, 48,913 Lumina APVs, 11,027 Blazers, 125,543 S-Series Blazers, 402,539 C/K pickups, 206,893 S10/T10 pickups, 7,933 Sportvans, 41,790 Suburbans, 33,143 Canadian-built Geo Trackers, 82,391 Chevy Vans, and 18,682 Step-Van multi-stop trucks. This gave the company total light-duty truck sales of 1,084,847 units in the model-year.

1992

1992 Geo Tracker Convertible 4x2 (CMD)

1/4-TON — GEO TRACKER — L4: Chevrolet dealers sold the Suzuki-designed Geo Tracker as a small Sport Utility Vehicle. It was actually built at the CAMI Automotive factory in Ingersoll, Ontario, Canada. Trackers had a small pickup box and were considered trucks. They were offered as a two-door Convertible with front-wheel-drive only. The convertible also came in 4x4 format, with or without optional LSi trim. The hardtop model came only as a 4x4, in the base or LSi trim levels. Standard equipment included a 1.6-liter SOHC inline four-cylinder engine, power front disc/rear drum brakes, five-speed manual transmission, and (4x2 model) P195/75R-15 tires or (4x4 models) P205/75R-15 tires.

1992 Chevrolet 1/2-Ton S10 Long Box Pickup 4x2 (CMD)

1/2-TON — S (4x2)/T (4x4) SERIES PICKUP — L4/V-6: New for 1992 was the availability of four-wheel-drive EL model. Previously, the EL, which was defined by Chevrolet as a "de-contented standard trim level designed to be a price leader for the value-conscious truck buyer" had been available only in two-wheel-drive form. It was equipped with a 160-hp Vortex V-6 engine, five-speed manual transmission, power steering, compact spare and wheel, and a solid exterior color. A convenient new two-speed electronic-shift transfer case was optional for all models except the EL. New appointments for 1992 included seats with integral head restraints for front bench seat positions, and high-back bucket seats with optional leather (Extended-Cab) seating, a standard self-aligning steering wheel, and an optional premium sound system with compact disc player. New exterior colors consisted of Midnight Black, Aspen Blue Metallic, Royal Blue Metallic, Sky Blue, Garnet Red, Steel Gray Metallic, Aquamarine Green, Forest Green Metallic, Apple Red, Frost White and, as a secondary color only, Silver Metallic. Standard equipment included a 2.5-liter EFI L4, power front disc/rear-wheel-antilock brakes, five-speed manual transmission with overdrive, and P195/75R14 all-season steel-belted radial black sidewall tires.

1992 Chevrolet 1/2-Ton S10 Sport Blazer 4-door Sport Utility 4x4 (CMD)

1/2-TON — S (4x2)/T (4x4) SERIES BLAZER — V-6: Changes for 1992 were limited primarily to minor mechanical and trim revisions. The Tahoe LT was offered for two-door models beginning in February 1992. The latest S-Series Blazers had a new grille insert with a bold eggcrate format. A new two-speed electronic shift transfer case was optional for S-Series Blazers equipped with four-wheel-drive. The new transfer case added an extra level of driver convenience by making the selection of 2WD, 4WD-HI and 4WD-LO positions push-button easy. A self-aligning steering wheel and a new 85-mph speedometer were standard equipment for 1992. Other changes included new seats with integral head restraints for front bench seats in four-door models, and high-back bucket seats with optional leather. A new compact disc player was also optional. Also, for the first time this year, four-wheel antilock brakes were featured as standard equipment on both two- and four-door models. The S/T-series Blazer line offered the convenience of two- and four-door configurations in both two-wheel-drive, and four-wheel-drive. The two-door models were available in standard, Tahoe and Sport trim levels. Four-door models came only in Tahoe or Sport styles. Standard equipment included a 4.3-liter EFI V-6, power front disc AWAL brakes, five-speed manual overdrive transmission, and P205/75R15 all-season steel-belted radial black sidewall tires.

1/2-TON — ASTRO VAN SERIES M(RWD)/L (AWD) — V-6: Chevrolet's 1992 Astro was an American-built, rear-wheel-drive, midsize family and cargo van. It came with either a high-output or high-performance V-6 engine. The all-wheel-drive Astro started model-year 1992 with a 170-hp high-output 4.3-liter V-6. However, at midyear, a high-performance 4.3-liter Vortec V-6 was substituted. It was rated at 200 hp. The increased output was due to the use of central-port-injection, a new balance shaft, a new camshaft, Vortec II cylinder heads, a dual plenum intake manifold, a remote-mounted air cleaner silencer, an external oil cooler, and a low-restriction exhaust system. Compared to midsize competitors, the Astro had more people-carrying, cargo-hauling ,and trailer-towing power. It could accommodate as many as eight passengers or pull a heavy-duty 6,000-lb. trailer. Cargo loading and unloading was a snap with the Astro's wide-opening rear, and side doors. Another new midyear 1992 option was a rear "Dutch Door." It included a one-piece lift-gate with split panel doors below, and an electronic release. New interior features included adjustable bench seats, an optional premium sound system with a compact disc player, and a new beige interior color. Astro's other strengths included outstanding corrosion protection, several safety features including four-wheel antilock braking (except in base cargo vans), optional all-wheel-drive system, shoulder belts for all outboard seating positions, and a new self-aligning steering wheel. Inside the Astro van had new adjustable bench seats, and interior assist handles on the A-pillar and B-pillar of the passenger van model. Cargo vans were equipped with an A-pillar handle for easy passenger entry and exit. Available in both Regular- and Extended-Body models, the Chevrolet Astro was widely popular throughout the country, particularly in the Central and Southern states. Standard equipment also included a four-speed automatic overdrive transmission, and P205/75R15 all-season steel-belted radial black sidewall tires.

1/2-TON — LUMINA WAGON SERIES U05 (FWD) — V-6: Chevrolet's Lumina APV boasted several mechanical changes for 1992. They were designed to significantly impact its performance both on the road, and in the marketplace. Added first was an optional new 3.8-liter/165-hp "3800" EFI V-6 engine linked to a four-speed automatic overdrive transmission. This extra-cost power team delivered 45 more horsepower and 55 lb.-ft. of extra torque over the standard 3.1-liter EFI V-6. It also raised the Lumina APV's towing capacity to 3,000 lb. That was 1,000 lb. more than the standard engine/transmission combo could handle. Features of the new 3.8-liter engine included tuned-port-fuel-injection, a computer-controlled coil ignition system, electronic spark control, hydraulic roller valve lifters, reduced-friction oil control rings, a gerotor oil pump, and a serpentine accessory drive. Specific air, fuel, and ignition calibrations in the 3800 V-6 provided ultra-smooth combustion, while precision cylinder bores, lightweight pistons, and roller valve lifters resulted in friction levels lower than smaller engines. Chevrolet also added four-wheel antilock brakes as standard equipment. General Motor's new ABS VI braking system made it possible to offer the premium performance of ABS without the premium price. Other Lumina safety equipment included locking latch seat belts for child seats, and folding outside rear view mirrors. Also new for 1992 were larger 11-in. front brakes, new variable-rate springs, improved shock/strut valve tuning, larger 15-in. wheels and tires, new bolt-on wheelcovers, new interior and exterior colors, and an optional four-way driver's seat adjuster. Although classified as a minivan, the Lumina APV competed in the expanding mid-size van segment. The functional improvements for 1992 were specifically designed to increase it competitive posture, and add to its value and appeal as affordable family transportation. Standard features included the 3.1-liter V-6, power front disc/rear drum AWAL brakes, three-speed automatic transmission, and P205/75R14 steel-belted radial tires.

1/2-TON, 3/4-TON, 1-TON VAN — G SERIES 10, 20, 30 (RWD) — V-6/V-8: The full-size Chevrolet van and Sportvan were well-equipped for big people-mover jobs, and for heavy-duty cargo hauling. Added for 1992 were more car-like comfort and convenience features. Ride and handling improvements included new 32 mm shock absorbers on the Sportvan's standard independent front suspension with upper and lower control arms and a stabilizer bar. In the rear suspension, new 32 mm rear shock absorbers (35 mm on the G30 series) and new leaf spring assemblies were added to the variable-rate multi-leaf spring setup. The beefier suspension components were designed to provide a smooth ride and responsive handling. The Sportvan exhaust system was modified from a dual "Y" tailpipe to a single tailpipe configuration. The new design provided better noise suppression, and operation. Comfort and convenience features added to the 1992 Sportvan's list of standard equipment included a modified instrument cluster with improved legibility, a high-efficiency air conditioning system, and an improved windshield wiper/washer system. Luxury and convenience options available for the first time on the Sportvan included a leather-wrapped steering wheel, remote keyless entry system, rear window defogger, electric outside mirrors, a lighted visor/vanity mirror, a power radio antenna, and an enhanced interior lighting package. Sportvans also took on a fresh appearance with new front grilles, new headlamp and parking lamp components, and restyled exterior body side moldings. A new Dark Green Blue Metallic paint added to the 1992 exterior color palette. Sportvans could be outfitted with either gasoline or diesel power. Four gas engines were offered: 4.3-liter V-6, 5.0-liter V-8, 5.7-liter V-8, and 7.4-liter V-8. The 6.2-liter diesel V-8 was available in light-duty (under 8,500-lb. GVWR), and heavy-duty versions. All Sportvans were equipped with a four-speed automatic transmission as standard equipment. Available in 110-, 125- and 146-in. wheelbases, in Regular- and Extended-Body styles, the 1992 vans could carry up to 15 passengers. When properly optioned, they could tow up to 10,000 lb. Commercial users could appreciate the ample interior cargo room, which ran as high as 306 cu.-ft. with the Extended-Body G30 van on the 146-in. wheelbase. A cutaway version of the G Series van chassis was also available for builders of motor homes, airport buses, and other special-bodied trucks. Standard equipment for small Chevy Vans included the 4.3-liter throttle-body-injected V-6, heavy-duty front disc/rear drum four-wheel anti-lock brakes, four-speed automatic transmission with overdrive, and P205/75R15 black sidewall tires. The G20 Sportvan had the same standard features as the G10 model, but a 5.7-liter EFI V-8 was standard in G30 models. The 1-ton G30 model was also available in Hi-Cube Van form with 10-foot and 12-foot body options.

1-TON — P30 STEP-VAN (RWD) — V-8: Also available in 1992 was the traditional Chevrolet Step-Van. It looked like a big box, and represented the perfect cargo carrier for stop-and-go delivery service. The only model offered was a 1-ton version with a 10-1/2-foot long body. The Step-Van offered wheelbases ranging from 125 to 178 in. A 350-cid V-8 was the standard engine. A 6.2-liter diesel V-8 was optional, along with an 11,000-lb. rear axle. Standard size tires were LT215/85R16s.

1/2-TON — K1500 BLAZER (4x4) — V-8: The 1992 K-Series Blazer was completely restyled, and was based upon Chevrolet's new C/K1500 Pickups. It offered six-passenger seating, and could tow 7,000 lb., 1,000 lb. more than its predecessor. Compared to the 1991 Blazer, the 1992 model had a four-inch longer wheelbase, a higher GVWR rating, and increased front and rear leg room and rear hip room. A good deal of the K-Series Blazer's exterior sheet metal was shared with the Chevrolet pickup. New standard features included antilock brakes, and Chevrolet's patented Insta-Trac 4wd shift-on-the-fly system. The 5.7-liter EFI V-8 was standard, as was a five-speed manual transmission with overdrive. The diesel engine was not offered. A four-speed automatic transmission with locking torque converter and overdrive was optional. New exterior and interior appointments for the Blazer included improved seats with head restraints for the front outboard positions, a standard full-gauge instrument cluster, and an extended-range AM radio. An optional new Sport Appearance package provided an up-level sport look with two-tone paint, a special grille, special bumpers, and wheel flares. New safety enhancements included a self-aligning steering wheel that aligned parallel to the driver's body to distribute force more equally in the event of a crash. Added to the interior color selection was beige. Bright Red and Beige Metallic were new exterior colors. Major standard features of the base Cheyenne model included LT225 all-season steel-belted radial tires, power steering, power brakes, tinted glass, black below-eye-line dual outside rear view mirrors, base-coat/clear coat paint, chrome front and black rear bumpers, high-back front bucket seats with custom vinyl trim and matching rear vinyl seat, inside spare tire carrier on left rear panel, full-coverage, intermittent wet-arm windshield wiper/washer system, electronically tuned AM radio, dual horns, glove box with beverage wells on door back, heavy-duty battery, dual dome lights, headlights-on reminder, voltmeter, oil pressure and engine coolant temperature gauges, trip odometer, and lift glass/drop tailgate system with electric tailgate release. The Silverado package added these items: Custom cloth 40/60 split front bench seat and matching rear cloth seat with arm rests, chrome front and rear bumpers with rub strips, body side and wheel opening moldings, Dark Argent grille with quad halogen headlights, deluxe bumper guards, Rally wheel trim, bright, below-eye-line dual outside rear view mirrors, electronically-tuned AM/FM stereo radio with seek-and-scan, spare wheel carpet cover, full-length color-keyed cloth headliner, color-keyed carpeting, front and rear color-keyed floor mats, interior assist straps, front and rear map lights, illuminated mirror on passenger's side sun visor, vinyl storage pockets and assist straps on doors.

1992 Chevrolet 1/2-Ton C1500 Suburban 4-door wagon 4x2 (CMD)

1/2-TON/3/4-TON — C (4x2) /K (4x4) SUBURBAN — V-8: The Suburban got a major updating in its 57th year, with a fresh, contemporary styling facelift. It adopted the styling and full frame construction of the full-size Chevrolet Pickup. It also used a modified version of the C/K pickup suspension. The front was independent with upper and lower control arms and a stabilizer bar. The rear featured semi-elliptic, two-stage, multi-leaf springs. The new suspension delivered a smooth, car-like ride with truck-tough construction, and heavy-duty towing capability. Improved seats with integral head restraints for the front outboard positions, all-season steel-belted radial tires, new steel wheels, and an AM radio were also standard. A convenient lift-glass/drop-gate was optional, in place of the standard panel doors. The Suburban also had decreased step-in height and load floor height. There was more towing capacity, more load space, and more front and rear leg, shoulder and hip room. Anti-lock brakes were standard for all Suburbans. They came with rear-wheel-drive or four-wheel-drive. Chevrolet's patented Insta-Trac system for "shift-on-the-fly" convenience was standard on all four-wheel-drive models. The Suburbans came in 1/2-ton-rated C1500/K1500 models or 3/4-ton-rated C2500/K2500 models. All shared a giant 149.5 cu.-ft. cargo capacity. The Suburbans could handle payloads between 1,688 lb. and 3,430 lb. The GVW range was 6,800 lb. to 8,600 lb. Three-passenger seating was standard. Five-, six-, eight- and nine-passenger options were available. Standard equipment included a 5.7-liter EFI V-8, front disc/rear drum four-wheel anti-lock brakes, a four-speed automatic transmission with overdrive, and P235/75R-15XLS all-season black sidewall steel-belted radial tires. Suburbans with a GVW over 8500 lb. used a heavy-duty version of the 5.7 liter V-8. The 7.4 liter V-8 was optional for Suburbans with GVW over 8600 lb.

1992 Chevrolet 3/4-Ton K2500 Extended-Cab Fleetside Long Box Pickup 4x4 (CMD)

1/2-TON, 3/4-TON, 1-TON — C (4x2)/K (4x4) PICKUP — V-6/V-8: Changes for 1992 in the Chevrolet trucks were lead by major developments in the four-door Crew-Cab models. Along with the Blazer and Suburban, the C/K3500 Crew-Cab pickup was the last Chevrolet truck to adopt the styling adopted in 1988. It had a four-in. longer wheelbase, nearly seven in. more rear-seat leg room, and increased front leg and shoulder room. The Crew-Cab also had antilock brakes. The standard Crew-Cab engine-transmission was a 5.7 liter V-8 and five-speed heavy-duty manual transmission with "deep low" and overdrive. Available for all trucks with a GVW rating of 8,600 lb. and up was a new 6.5-liter Turbo Diesel. This engine, built at the General Motors Moraine Engine Plant in Dayton, Ohio, had a special warranty of five years or 100,000 miles. Among its features were an all-new cylinder case design, and an optimized combustion chamber for totally smokeless performance. Added to the interior color availability for 1992 was beige. New exterior colors were Bright Red, and Beige Metallic.

1992 Chevrolet 1-Ton K3500 Crew-Cab "Big Dooley" Pickup 4x4 (CMD)

I. D. DATA: The VIN plate was mounted on the lower left side windshield corner. The VIN consisted of 17 symbols. The first three symbols identify the country, the manufacturer and the type of vehicle. The fourth symbol designates the GVW range. The fifth, sixth and seventh symbols identify the line and chassis type, series and body type. The eighth symbol identifies the engine: [Chevrolet engines] C=6.2-liter/130 hp diesel V-8, H=5.0-liter V-8, J=6.2-liter/148 hp diesel V-8, K=5.7-liter V-8, N=7.4-liter V-8, R=2.8-liter V-6, Z=4.3-liter V-6. [GM engines] A= 5.7-liter V-8 or 2.5-liter L4, D=3.1-liter V-6, F=6.5-liter diesel V-8, L=3.8-liter V-6, S=6.5-liter diesel V-8, W=4.3-liter V-6. The ninth symbol is the check digit. The tenth symbol indicates model year. The eleventh symbol identifies the assembly plant. The last six symbols are the sequential production number.

Model	Body Type	Price	Weight	Prod. Total
CE/CJ Geo Tracker — 1/2-Ton — 86.6 in. w.b. — 1.6-liter EFI L4				
CE10367	4x2 Convertible	9,162	2,189	Note 13
CJ10316	4x4 Hardtop	11,900	2,387	Note 13
CJ10367	4x4 Convertible	11,500	2,365	Note 13
CJ10316/B2Z	4x4 LSi Hardtop	13,200	2,397	Note 13
CJ10367/B2Z	4x4 LSi Convertible	12,600	2,375	Note 13

NOTE 1: A $300 dealer destination charge applied to Geo Trackers effective Aug. 16, 1991

1992 Geo 1/2-Ton Tracker 4x4 Convertible LSi Sport Utility (CMD)

1992 Geo 1/2-Ton Tracker 4x4 Convertible Sport Utility (CMD)

1992 Geo 1/2-Ton Tracker 4x4 Convertible Hardtop Sport Utility (CMD)

1992 Chevrolet 1/2-Ton S10 Blazer 4x2 two-door Sport Utility Vehicle (CMD)

1992 Chevrolet 1/2-Ton C1500 4x2 Extended-Cab Fleetside Short Bed Pickup (CMD)

1992 Chevrolet 1/2-Ton K-1500 4x4 Extended-Cab Sportside Short Bed Pickup (CMD)

1992 Chevrolet 3/4-Ton C2500 Fleetside 4x2 Regular-Cab Long Box Pickup (CMD)

Model	Body Type	Price	Weight	Prod. Total
S10 Fleetside Pickup — 1/2-Ton — 108.3/117.9/122.9 in. w.b. — 2.5-liter EFI L4				
S10603	Reg.-Cab EL	8722	2645	Note 13
S10603	Reg.-Cab Short Box	9858	2665	Note 13
S10803	Reg.-Cab Long Box	10,158	2747	Note 13
S10653	Ext.-Cab Short Box	11,358	2826	Note 13
T10 4x4 Fleetside Pickup — 1/2-Ton — 108.3/117.9/122.9 in. w.b. — 4.3L-liter EFI L4				
T10603	Reg.-Cab EL	11,512	-	Note 13
T10603	Reg.-Cab SWB	12,055	-	Note 13
T10803	Reg.-Cab LS LWB	12,324	-	Note 13
T10653	Ext.-Cab LS Short Box	13,402	-	Note 13

NOTE 2: A $470 dealer destination charge applied to S-Series pickups effective Aug. 16, 1991.

S10 Blazer 4x2 Sport Utility Wagon — 1/2-Ton — 100.5/107 in. w.b. — 4.3-liter EFI V-6				
CS10516	2-dr Tailgate	14,823	3181	Note 13
CS10506	4-dr Tailgate	15,783	3369	Note 13
T10 Blazer 4x4 Sport Utility Wagon — 1/2-Ton — 100.5/107 in. w.b. — 4.3-liter EFI V-6				
CT10516	2-dr Tailgate	16,583	3485	Note 13
CT10506	4-dr Tailgate	17,953	3712	Note 13

NOTE 3: A $475 dealer destination charge applied to S-Series Blazers effective Aug. 16, 1991.

M10 Astro Minivan (rear-wheel-drive) — 1/2-Ton — 111 in. w.b. — 4.3-liter EFI V-6				
CM10906	Standard Cargo Van	13,995	3554	Note 13
CM11006	Extended Cargo Van	14,665	3618	Note 13
CM10906/ZW9	Standard CS Van	15,185	3909	Note 13
CM11006/ZW9	Extended CS Van	15,875	3993	Note 13
L10 Astro Minivan (all-wheel-drive) — 1/2-Ton — 111 in. w.b. — 4.3-liter CPI V-6				
CL10906/ZW9	Standard CS Van	17,245	-	Note 13
CL11006/ZW9	Extended CS Van	17,885	-	Note 13

NOTE 4: A $545 dealer destination charge applied to Astros effective Aug. 16, 1991.

U05 Lumina Minivan — 1/2-Ton — 109.8 in. w.b. — 3.1-liter EFI V-6				
1UM05	Cargo Van	14,375	3370	Note 13
1UM06	Wagon	15,570	3558	Note 13
1UM06	Wagon LS	17,355	3993	Note 13

NOTE 5: A $530 dealer destination charge applied to Lumina Minivans effective Aug. 16, 1991.

G10 Van — 1/2-Ton — 110/125 in. w.b. — 4.3-liter EFI V-6				
CG11005/ZW9	SWB Chevy Van	14,315	3816	Note 13
CG11006/ZW9	SWB Sportvan	16,045	4208	Note 13
G20 Van — 3/4-Ton — 110/125 in. w.b. — 4.3-liter EFI V-6				
CG21005/ZW9	SWB Chevy Van	14,535	3887	Note 13
CG21305/ZW9	LWB Sportvan	17,185	4540	Note 13
G30 Van — 1-Ton — 125/146 in. w.b. — 5.7-liter EFI V-8				
CG31305/ZW9	LWB Chevy Van	14,555	4572	Note 13
CG31306/ZW9	LWB Sportvan 12P	18,935	5097	Note 13
CG31605/ZW9	EWB Chevy Van	17,345	4852	Note 13
CG31606/ZW9	EWB Sportvan 12P	20,465	5635	Note 13
CG31305/ZW9	LWB Cutaway Van	15,025	4076	Note 13
G30 Hi-Cube Van — 1-Ton — 125/146 in. w.b. — 5.7-liter I V-8				
CG31	10-ft. Van	19,025	5371	N/A.
CG31	12-ft. Van	20,725	6290	N/A.

NOTE 6: A $580 dealer destination charge applied to full-size vans effective Aug. 16, 1991.

P30 — 1-Ton Step-Van — 125/178 in. w.b. — 5.7-liter Heavy-duty EFI V-8				
P32	10.5-ft. Step-Van	18,095	6063	N/A.
K1500 Blazer — 1/2-Ton — 111.5 in. w.b. — 5.7-liter EFI V-8				
CK10516	Utility Hardtop	19,280	4676	Note 13

NOTE 7: A $595 dealer destination charge applied to full-size Blazers effective Aug. 16, 1991.

C/K 1500 Suburban — 1/2-Ton — 131.5 in. w.b. — 5.7-liter EFI V-8				
CC10906/ZW9	Panel Door (4x2)	18,155	4657	Note 13
CK10906/ZW9	Panel Door (4x4)	20,355	-	Note 13
C/K 2500 Suburban — 3/4-Ton — 131.5 in. w.b. — 5.7-liter EFI V-8				
CC20906/ZW9	Panel Door (4x2)	19,359	5002	Note 13
CK20906/ZW9	Panel Door (4x4)	21,559	-	Note 13

NOTE 8: A $640 dealer destination charge applied to Suburbans effective Oct. 1, 1991.

C1500 Pickup — 1/2-Ton Short Box — 117.5 in. w.b. — 4.3-liter EFI V-6				
CC10703	Regular-Cab Sportside	13,495	3735	Note 13
CC10703	Regular-Cab Fleetside	13,095	3718	Note 13
C1500 Pickup — 1/2-Ton Long Box — 131.5 in. w.b. — 4.3-liter EFI V-6				
CC10903	Regular-Cab Fleetside	13,395	3869	Note 13
CC10903	Regular-Cab Work Truck	10,600	3819	Note 13
C1500 Pickup — 1/2-Ton Short Box — 141.5 in. w.b. — 4.3-liter EFI V-6				
CC10753	Extended-Cab Sportside	14,445	4015	Note 13
CC10753	Extended-Cab Fleetside	14,045	3998	Note 13
C1500 Pickup — 1/2-Ton Long Box — 155.5 in. w.b. — 4.3-liter EFI V-6				
CC10903	Extended-Cab Fleetside	14,335	4129	Note 13

NOTE 9: Add approximately $2,150 for CK1500 Pickups with 4x4.

C2500 Pickup — 3/4-Ton Long Box — 131.5 in. w.b. — 4.3-liter EFI V-6				
CC20924	Chassis & Cab	15,078	3653	Note 13
CC20903	Regular-Cab Fleetside	14,035	4023	Note 13
C2500 Pickup — 3/4-Ton Short Box — 141.5 in. w.b. — 4.3-liter EFI V-6				
CC20954	Chassis & Extended-Cab	16,158	3899	Note 13
CC20953	Extended-Cab Fleetside	15,155	4131	Note 13
C2500 Pickup — 3/4-Ton Long Box — 155.5 in. w.b. — 5.7-liter EFI V-6				
CC20903	Extended-Cab Fleetside	15,435	4266	Note 13

NOTE 10: Add approximately $1,750 for CK2500 Pickups with 4x4.

C3500 Pickup — 1-Ton Long Box — 131.5 in. w.b. — 5.7-liter EFI V-8				
CC30924	Chassis & Cab	15,138	4269	Note 13
CC30903	Regular-Cab Fleetside	15,588	4636	Note 13
C3500 Pickup — 1-Ton Long Box — 155.5 in. w.b. — 5.7-liter V-8				
CC30903	Extended-Cab Fleetside	16,658	4981	Note 13
C3500 Pickup — 1-Ton Long Box — 168.5 in. w.b. — 5.7-liter V-8				
CC30933	Crew-Cab Fleetside	17,047	5279	Note 13
CC30934	H-D Crew-Cab & Chassis	18,498	5264	Note 13

NOTE 11: Add approximately $2,150 for CK3500 Pickups with 4x4.

NOTE 12: A $595 dealer destination charge applied to C/K Pickups effective Aug. 16, 1991.

NOTE 13: Model year production: [S10 pickup] 191,960, [C/K1500] 346,477, [C/K2500] 63,563, [C/K3500] 28,577, [Geo Tracker (Canadian-made)] 36,230, [S-Series Blazer] 124,965, [K1500 Blazer] 17,444, [Suburban] 38,885, [Lumina APV Wagon] 54,666, [Lumina APV Cargo Van] 668, [Astro Wagon] 92,415, [Astro Cargo Van] 41,600, [Sportvan] 7,808, [Chevy Van] 88,848.

NOTE 14: The percentages of the above trucks with four-wheel-drive was [S10 Pickup] 13.7 percent, [C/K1500] 32.7 percent, [C/K2500] 54.5 percent, [C/K3500] 7.3 percent, [Geo Tracker/Canadian made] 57.2 percent, [S-Blazer] 77 percent, [K-Blazer] 100 percent, [Suburban] 47.1 percent, [Astro Wagon] 13.4 percent, [Astro Cargo Van] 4.4 percent.

GASOLINE ENGINES (DISPLACEMENT ORDER)

ENGINE: Inline. Four-cylinder. Bore & stroke: 2.95 x 3.54 in. Displacement: 1.6-liter (97 cid). BHP: 80 at 5400 rpm. Torque: unknown. Compression ratio: 8.9:1. Multi-port fuel-injection. Suzuki-built. [Standard in Geo Tracker]

ENGINE: Inline. Four-cylinder. Bore & stroke: 4.00 x 3.00 in. Displacement: 2.5-liter (151 cid). BHP: 105 at 4800 rpm. Torque: 135 lb.-ft. at 3200 rpm. Compression ratio: 8.3:1. EFI/Throttle-body-injection. VIN Code A. GM-built. [Standard in S10]

ENGINE: V-block. Six-cylinder. Bore & stroke: 3.52 x 2.99 in. Displacement: 2.8-liter (173 cid). BHP: 125 at 4800 rpm. Torque: 150 lb.-ft. at 2400 rpm. Compression ratio: 8.9:1. EFI/Throttle-body-injection. VIN Code R. Chevrolet-built. [Optional in S10 (4x2) only]

ENGINE: V-block. Six-cylinder. Bore & stroke: 3.5 x 3.331 in. Displacement: 3.1-liter (191 cid). BHP: 120 at 4400 rpm. Torque: 175 lb.-ft. at 2200 rpm. Compression ratio: 8.5:1. Multiport-fuel-injection. VIN Code D. GM-built. [Standard in Lumina]

ENGINE: V-block. Six-cylinder. Bore & stroke: 3.8 x 3.4 in. Displacement: 3.8-liter (231 cid). BHP: 165-170 hp at 4800 rpm. Torque: 220-225 lb.-ft. at 3200 rpm. Sequential-port-fuel-injection (SFI). VIN Code L. GM-built. [Optional in Lumina APV]

1992 Chevrolet 1/2-Ton T10 Blazer four-door Sport Utility 4x4 (CMD)

ENGINE: V-block. Six-cylinder. Bore & stroke: 4.0 x 3.48 in. Displacement: 4.3-liter (262 cid). BHP: 150 at 4000 rpm. Torque: 230 lb.-ft. at 2400 rpm. Compression ratio: 9.3:1. EFI/Throttle-body-injection. VIN Code not available. GM-built. [Standard in G10, G20, and Astro]

ENGINE: V-block. Vortec six-cylinder. Bore & stroke: 4.0 x 3.48 in. Displacement: 4.3-liter (262 cid). BHP: 155 at 4000 rpm. Torque: 230 lb.-ft. at 2400 rpm. Compression ratio: 9.1:1. EFI/Throttle-body-injection. VIN Code B. Chevrolet-built. [Standard early-1992 S-Series Blazer]

ENGINE: V-block. Vortec six-cylinder. Bore & stroke: 4.0 x 3.48 in. Displacement: 4.3-liter (262 cid). BHP: 160 at 4000 rpm. Torque: 235 lb.-ft. at 2400 rpm. Compression ratio: 9.1:1. EFI/Throttle-body-injection. VIN Code Z. Chevrolet-built. [Standard in T10, standard in late-1992 S-Series Blazer, optional in S10, standard in C/K 1500/2500, standard in G10/G20]

ENGINE: V-block. Enhanced Vortec six-cylinder. Bore & stroke: 4.0 x 3.48 in. Displacement: 4.3-liter (262 cid). BHP: 200 at 4400 rpm. Torque: 260 lb.-ft. at 3600 rpm. Compression ratio 9.3:1. Central-point-injected. VIN Code W. GM-built. [Optional in S-Series Blazer, optional in Astro regular and Extended-Body passenger vans]

ENGINE: V-block. Eight-cylinder. Bore & stroke: 3.74 x 3.48 in. Displacement: 5.0-liter (305 cid). BHP: 170-175 at 4000 rpm. Torque: 255-270 lb.-ft. at 2400 rpm. EFI/Throttle-body-injection. VIN Code H. Chevrolet-built. [Optional in C/K1500, C/K2500, G10/G20]

ENGINE: V-block. Eight-cylinder. Bore & stroke: 4.0 x 3.48 in. Displacement: 5.7-liter (350 cid). BHP: 190 at 4000 rpm. Torque: 300 lb.-ft. at 2400 rpm. Compression ratio: 8.6:1. EFI/Throttle-body-injection. VIN Code A. GM-built. [Standard in Suburbans and G30 vans, optional in C/K1500/2500 pickups]

ENGINE: V-block. Eight-cylinder. Bore & stroke: 4.0 x 3.48 in. Displacement: 5.7-liter (350 cid). BHP: 210 at 4000 rpm. Compression ratio: 9.3:1. Torque: 300 lb.-ft. at 2800 rpm. EFI/Throttle-body-injection. VIN Code K. Chevrolet-built. [Standard in C/K Blazer, standard in C/K3500, optional in C/K1500/2500, optional in Suburban, optional in Chevy Van and Sportvan]

ENGINE: V-block. Eight-cylinder. Bore & stroke: 4.25 x 4.00 in. Displacement: 7.4-liter (454 cid). BHP: 230 at 3600 rpm. Torque: 385 lb.-ft. at 1600 rpm. Throttle-body-fuel-injection. VIN Code N. Chevrolet-built. [Optional in C/K1500, C/K2500, C/K3500, Suburban, and G30 vans]

1992 Chevrolet 1/2-Ton C1500 4x2 Extended-Cab Silverado Sportside Pickup (R. David Spangler)

1992 Chevrolet 1/2-ton K1500 4x4 Fleetside Regular-Cab Pickup with Sport package (CMD)

1992 Chevrolet 1/2-Ton T10 Blazer 4x4 four-door Sport Utility Vehicle (CMD)

1992 Chevrolet 1/2-Ton C1500 4x2 Regular-Cab Fleetside Pickup (CMD)

1992 Chevrolet 1/2-Ton T10 Extended-Cab 4x4 Pickup (CMD)

1992 Chevrolet 3/4-Ton C2500 4x2 Suburban Sport Utility Wagon (CMD)

1992 Chevrolet 1/2-Ton S10 Blazer 4x2 four-door Sport Utility Vehicle (CMD)

1992 Chevrolet 3/4-Ton C2500 4x2 Suburban Sport Utility Wagon (CMD)

DIESEL ENGINES (DISPLACEMENT ORDER)

ENGINE: V-block. Eight-cylinder. Bore & stroke: 3.98 x 3.82 in. Displacement: 6.2-liter (379 cid). BHP: 130 at 3600 rpm. Torque: 240 lb.-ft. at 2000 rpm. VIN Code C. GM-built. [Optional in C/K3500 pickup, optional in G30 Chevy Van and 12-passenger Sportvan]

ENGINE: V-block. Eight-cylinder. Turbo Diesel. Bore & stroke: 4.06 x 3.82 in. Displacement: 6.5-liter (400 cid). BHP: 190 at 3400 rpm. Torque: 380 lb.-ft. at 1700 rpm. VIN Code F. GM-built. [Optional in C/K3500 pickup, optional in G30 Chevy Van and 12-passenger Sportvan]

ENGINE: V-block. Eight-cylinder. Turbocharged. Bore & stroke: 4.06 x 3.82 in. Displacement: 6.5-liter (400 cid). BHP: 190 at 3400 rpm. Torque: 240 lb.-ft. at 2000 rpm. VIN Code F. GM-built. [Optional in all C/K2500 pickups and C/K3500 Crew-Cabs]

CHASSIS: [Geo Tracker (All)] Wheelbase: 86.6 in. Length: 142.5 in. Width: 64.2 in. Height: 65.6 in. Tires: (4x2) P195/75R-15, (4x4) P205/75R15 black sidewall.

CHASSIS: [S10] Regular-Cab. Short Box. Wheelbase: 108.3 in. Length: 178.2 in. Width: 64.7 in. Height: 61.3 in. GVW: 4,200 lb. Payload: 1,565 lb. Tires: P195/75R14 black sidewall.

CHASSIS: [T10] Regular-Cab. Short Box. Wheelbase: 108.5 in. Length: 178.2 in. Width: 64.7 in. Height: 63.4 in. GVW: 4,650 lb. Payload: 1,415 lb. Tires: P205/75R15 black sidewall.

CHASSIS: [S10] Regular-Cab. Long Box. Wheelbase: 117.9 in. Length: 194.2 in. Width: 64.7 in. Height: 61.3 in. GVW: 4,200 lb. Payload: 1,565 lb. Tires: P195/75R14 black sidewall.

CHASSIS: [T10] Regular-Cab. Long Box. Wheelbase: 117.9 in. Length: 194.2 in. Width: 64.7 in. Height: 63.4 in. GVW: 4,650 lb. Payload: 1,415 lb. Tires: P205/75R15 black sidewall

CHASSIS: [S10] Extended-Cab. Short Box. Wheelbase: 122.9 in. Length: 192.8 in. Width: 64.7 in. Height: 61.3 in. GVW: 4,200 lb. Payload: 1,366 lb. Tires: P195/75R15 black sidewall.

CHASSIS: [T10] Extended-Cab. Short Box. Wheelbase: 122.9 in. Length: 192.8 in. Width: 64.7 in. Height: 63.4 in. GVW: 4,650 lb. Payload: 1,283 lb. Tires: P205/75R15 black sidewall.

CHASSIS: [S-Blazer 4x2] Two-door. Wheelbase: 100.5 in. Length: 170.3 in. Width: 65.4 in. Height: 64.1 in. GVW: 4,350 lb. Payload: 1,152 lb. Tires: P205/75R15 black sidewall.

CHASSIS: [S-Blazer 4x4] Two-door. Wheelbase: 100.5 in. Length: 170.3 in. Width: 65.4 in. Height: 64.3 in. GVW: 4,700 lb. Payload: 1,188 lb. Tires: P205/75R15 black sidewall.

CHASSIS: [S-Blazer 4x2] Four-door. Wheelbase: 107 in. Length: 176.8 in. Width: 65.4 in. Height: 64.1 in. GVW: 4,850 lb. Payload: 1,485 lb. Tires: P205/75R15 black sidewall.

CHASSIS: [S-Blazer 4x4] Four-door. Wheelbase: 107 in. Length: 176.8 in. Width: 65.4 in. Height: 64.3 in. GVW: 5,100 lb. Payload: 1,352 lb. Tires: P205/75R15 black sidewall.

CHASSIS: [Astro Cargo regular-body] Wheelbase: 111 in. Length: 176.8 in. Width: 77.0 in. Height: 73.7 in. GVW: 5,950 lb. Payload: 1,757 lb. Tires: P205/75R15 black sidewall.

CHASSIS: [Astro Cargo regular-body AWD] Wheelbase: 111 in. Length: 176.8 in. Width: 77.0 in. Height: 73.7 in. GVW: 5,950 lb. Payload: 1,748 lb. Tires: P205/75R15 black sidewall.

CHASSIS: [Astro Cargo Extended-Body] Wheelbase: 111 in. Length: 186.8 in. Width: 77.0 in. Height: 74.5 in. GVW: 6,100 lb. Payload: 1,891 lb. Tires: P205/75R15 black sidewall.

CHASSIS: [Astro Cargo Extended-Body AWD] Wheelbase: 111 in. Length: 186.8 in. Width: 77.0 in. Height: 74.5 in. GVW: 6,100 lb. Payload: 1,841 lb. Tires: P205/75R15 black sidewall.

CHASSIS: [Astro Passenger regular-body] Wheelbase: 111 in. Length: 176.8 in. Width: 77.0 in. Height: 73.7 in. GVW: 5,950 lb. Payload: 1,757 lb. Tires: P205/75R15 black sidewall.

CHASSIS: [Astro Passenger regular-body AWD] Wheelbase: 111 in. Length: 176.8 in. Width: 77.0 in. Height: 74.5 in. GVW: 5,950 lb. Payload: 1,748 lb. Tires: P205/75R15 black sidewall.

CHASSIS: [Astro Passenger Extended-Body] Wheelbase: 111 in. Length: 186.8 in. Width: 77.0 in. Height: 73.7 in. GVW: 6,100 lb. Payload: 1,891 lb. Tires: P205/75R15 black sidewall.

CHASSIS: [Astro Passenger Extended-Body AWD] Wheelbase: 111 in. Length: 186.8 in. Width: 77.0 in. Height: 74.5 in. GVW: 6,100 lb. Payload: 1,841 lb. Tires: P205/75R15 black sidewall.

CHASSIS: [Lumina] Wheelbase: 109.8 in. Length: 194.2 in. Width: 73.9 in. Height: 65.7 in. GVW: 4,935 lb. Payload: 1.357 lb. Tires: P205/70R15 black sidewall.

1992 Chevrolet 1/2-Ton C1500 "454 SS" Fleetside Short Box Pickup 4x2 (CMD)

CHASSIS: [G10/Short Body] Chevy van. Wheelbase: 110 in. Length: 178.2 in. Width: 79.5 in. Height: 80.9 in. GVW: 6,000 lb. Payload: 1,754 lb. Tires: P215/75R15 black sidewall.

CHASSIS: [G10/Long Body] Chevy van/Sportvan. Wheelbase: 125 in. Length: 202.2 in. Width: 79.5 in. Height: 79.1 in. GVW: 6,000 lb. Payload: 1,428 lb. Tires: P215/75R15 black sidewall.

CHASSIS: [G20/Short Body] Chevy van. Wheelbase: 110 in. Length: 178.2 in. Width: 79.5 in. Height: 80.9 in. GVW: 6,000 lb. Payload: 1,754 lb. Tires: P215/75R15 black sidewall.

CHASSIS: [G20/Long Body] Chevy van/Sportvan. Wheelbase: 125 in. Length: 202.2 in. Width: 79.5 in. Height: 79.1 in. GVW: 6,875 lb. Payload: 2,142 lb. Tires: P215/75R15 black sidewall.

CHASSIS: [G30/Long Body Chevy van] Wheelbase: 125 in. Length: 202.2 in. Width: 79.5 in. Height: 82.3 in. GVW: 9,200 lb. Payload: 3,951 lb. Tires: P215/75R15 black sidewall.

CHASSIS: [G30/Long Body Sportvan] Wheelbase: 125 in. Length: 202.2 in. Width: 79.5 in. Height: 82.3 in. GVW: 9,200 lb. Payload: 4,101 lb. Tires: P215/75R15 black sidewall.

CHASSIS: [G30/Extended Body Chevy van] Wheelbase: 146 in. Length: 223.1 in. Width: 79.5 in. Height: 82.3 in. GVW: 9,200 lb. Payload: 3,951 lb. Tires: P215/75R15 black sidewall.

CHASSIS: [G30/Extended Body 12-Passenger Sportvan] Wheelbase: 146 in. Length: 223.1 in. Width: 79.5 in. Height: 82.3 in. GVW: 9,200 lb. Payload: 4,101 lb. Tires: P215/75R15 black sidewall.

CHASSIS: [K10 Blazer 4x4] Wheelbase: 111.5 in. Length: 188 in. Width: 77.1 in. Height: 75 in. GVW: 6,250 lb. Payload: 1,517 lb. Tires: LT245/75R16C black sidewall.

CHASSIS: [Suburban C1500] Wheelbase: 131.5 in. Length: 219.5 in. Width: 77 in. Height: 73.6 in. GVW: 6,800 lb. Payload: 2,117 lb. Tires: P235/75R-15XLS black sidewall.

CHASSIS: [Suburban K1500] Wheelbase: 131.5 in. Length: 219.5 in. Width: 77 in. Height: 74.9 in. GVW: 7,200 lb. Payload: 2,052 lb. Tires: P235/75R-15XLS black sidewall.

CHASSIS: [Suburban C2500] Wheelbase: 131.5 in. Length: 219.5 in. Width: 77 in. Height: 73.6 in. GVW: 8,600 lb. Payload: 3,370 lb. Tires: P235/75R-15XLS black sidewall.

CHASSIS: [Suburban K2500] Wheelbase: 131.5 in. Length: 219.5 in. Width: 77 in. Height: 74.9 in. GVW: 8,600 lb. Payload: 2,944 lb. Tires: P235/75R-15XLS black sidewall.

1992 Chevrolet 1/2-Ton C1500 4x2 Extended-Cab Silverado Fleetside Pickup (Jean A. Allan photo)

CHASSIS: [C1500 Sportside Regular-Cab Short Box Pickup] Regular-Cab. Short Box. Wheelbase: 117.5 in. Length: 194.1 in. Width: 77.1 in. Height: 70.4 in. GVW: 5,600 lb. Payload: 2,231 lb. Tires: P225/75R15 black sidewall AS SBR tires.

CHASSIS: [C1500 Fleetside Regular-Cab Short Box Pickup] Wheelbase: 117.5 in. Length: 194.1 in. Width: 76.8 in. Height: 70.4 in. GVW: 5,600 lb. Payload: 2,231 lb. Tires: P225/75R15 black sidewall AS SBR tires.

CHASSIS: [C1500 Fleetside Regular-Cab Short Box "Work Truck" Pickup] Wheelbase: 117.5 in. Length: 194.1 in. Width: 76.8 in. Height: 70.4 in. GVW: 5,600 lb. Payload: 2,231 lb. Tires: P225/75R15 black sidewall AS SBR tires.

CHASSIS: [C1500 Fleetside Regular-Cab Long Box Pickup] Wheelbase: 131.5 in. Length: 212.6 in. Width: 76.8 in. Height: 70.4 in. GVW: 6,100 lb. Payload: 2,231 lb. Tires: P225/75R15 black sidewall AS SBR tires.

CHASSIS: [C1500 Fleetside Regular-Cab Long Box "Work Truck" Pickup] Wheelbase: 131.5 in. Length: 212.6 in. Width: 76.8 in. Height: 70.4 in. GVW: 6,100 lb. Payload: 2,231 lb. Tires: P225/75R15 black sidewall AS SBR tires.

CHASSIS: [C1500 Sportside Extended-Cab Short Box Pickup] Wheelbase: 141.5 in. Length: 218.0 in. Width: 77.1 in. Height: 70.6 in. GVW: 6,600 lb. Payload: 2,200 lb. Tires: P225/75R15 black sidewall AS SBR tires.

CHASSIS: [C1500 Fleetside Extended-Cab Short Box Pickup] Wheelbase: 141.5 in. Length: 218.0 in. Width: 76.8 in. Height: 70.6 in. GVW: 6,600 lb. Payload: 2,200 lb. Tires: P225/75R15 black sidewall AS SBR tires.

CHASSIS: [C1500 Fleetside Extended-Cab Long Box Pickup] Wheelbase: 155.5 in. Length: 237.0 in. Width: 76.8 in. Height: 70.6 in. GVW: 6,600 lb. Payload: 2,200 lb. Tires: P225/75R15 black sidewall AS SBR tires.

CHASSIS: [K1500 Sportside Regular-Cab Short Box Pickup] Wheelbase: 117.5 in. Length: 194.1 in. Width: 77.1 in. Height: 73.8 in. GVW: 6,100 lb. Payload: 1,980 lb. Tires: P225/75R15 black sidewall AS SBR tires.

CHASSIS: [K1500 Fleetside Regular-Cab Short Box Pickup] Wheelbase: 117.5 in. Length: 194.1 in. Width: 77.1 in. Height: 73.8 in. GVW: 6,100 lb. Payload: 1,980 lb. Tires: P225/75R15 black sidewall AS SBR tires.

CHASSIS: [K1500 Fleetside Regular-Cab Short Box "Work Truck" Pickup] Wheelbase: 117.5 in. Length: 194.1 in. Width: 77.1 in. Height: 73.8 in. GVW: 6,100 lb. Payload: 1,980 lb. Tires: P225/75R15 black sidewall AS SBR tires.

CHASSIS: [K1500 Fleetside Regular-Cab Long Box Pickup] Wheelbase: 131.5 in. Length: 212.6 in. Width: 76.8 in. Height: 73.8 in. GVW: 6,100 lb. Payload: 1,980 lb. Tires: P225/75R15 black sidewall AS SBR tires.

CHASSIS: [K1500 Fleetside Regular-Cab Long Box "Work Truck" Pickup] Wheelbase: 131.5 in. Length: 212.6 in. Width: 76.8 in. Height: 73.8 in. GVW: 6,100 lb. Payload: 1,980 lb. Tires: P225/75R15 black sidewall AS SBR tires.

CHASSIS: [K1500 Sportside Extended-Cab Short Box Pickup] Wheelbase: 141.5 in. Length: 218.0 in. Width: 77.1 in. Height: 73.8 in. GVW: 6,600 lb. Payload: 2,105 lb. Tires: P225/75R15 black sidewall AS SBR tires.

CHASSIS: [K1500 Fleetside Extended-Cab Short Box Pickup] Wheelbase: 141.5 in. Length: 218.0 in. Width: 76.8 in. Height: 73.8 in. GVW: 6,600 lb. Payload: 2,105 Lb. Tires: P225/75R15 black sidewall AS SBR tires.

CHASSIS: [K1500 Fleetside Extended-Cab Long Box Pickup] Wheelbase: 155.5 in. Length: 237.0 in. Width: 76.8 in. Height: 73.8 in. GVW: 6,600 lb. Payload: 2,105 lb. Tires: P225/75R15 black sidewall AS SBR tires.

CHASSIS: [C2500 Fleetside Regular-Cab Long Box Pickup] Wheelbase: 131.5 in. Length: 212.6 in. Width: 76.8 in. Height: 73 in. GVW: 7,200 lb. Payload: 2,231 lb. Tires: P225/75R15 black sidewall AS SBR tires.

CHASSIS: [C2500 Heavy-duty Fleetside Regular-Cab Long Box Pickup] Wheelbase: 131.5 in. Length: 212.6 in. Width: 76.8 in. Height: 73 in. GVW: 7,200 lb. Payload: 2,231 lb. Tires: P225/75R15 black sidewall AS SBR tires.

CHASSIS: [C2500 Fleetside Extended-Cab Short Box Pickup] Wheelbase: 141.5 in. Length: 218.0 in. Width: 76.8 in. Height: 74 in. GVW: 8,600 lb. Payload: 2,366 lb. Tires: P225/75R15 black sidewall AS SBR tires.

CHASSIS: [C2500 Fleetside Extended-Cab Long Box Pickup] Wheelbase: 155.5 in. Length: 237.0 in. Width: 76.8 in. Height: 74 in. GVW: 8,600 lb. Payload: 2,366 lb. Tires: P225/75R15 black sidewall AS SBR tires.
CHASSIS: [K2500 Fleetside Regular-Cab Long Box Pickup] Wheelbase: 131.5 in. Length: 212.6 in. Width: 76.8 in. Height: 73.8 in. GVW: 7,200 lb. Payload: 1,980 lb. Tires: P225/75R15 black sidewall AS SBR tires.
CHASSIS: [K2500 Heavy-duty Fleetside Regular-Cab Long Box Pickup] Wheelbase: 131.5 in. Length: 212.6 in. Width: 76.8 in. Height: 73.8 in. GVW: 7,200 lb. Payload: 1,980 lb. Tires: P225/75R15 black sidewall AS SBR tires.
CHASSIS: [K2500 Fleetside Extended-Cab Short Box Pickup] Wheelbase: 141.5 in. Length: 218.0 in. Width: 76.8 in. Height: 73.8 in. GVW: 8,600 lb. Payload: 2,105 lb. Tires: P225/75R15 black sidewall AS SBR tires.
CHASSIS: [K2500 Fleetside Extended-Cab Long Box Pickup] Wheelbase: 155.5 in. Length: 237.0 in. Width: 76.8 in. Height: 73.8 in. GVW: 8,600 lb. Payload: 2,105 lb. Tires: P225/75R15 black sidewall AS SBR tires.
CHASSIS: [C3500 Fleetside Regular-Cab Long Box Pickup] Wheelbase: 131.5 in. Length: 212.6 in. Width: 76.8 in. Height: 70.4 in. GVW: 10,000 lb. Payload: 1,980 lb. Tires: P225/75R15 black sidewall AS SBR tires.
CHASSIS: [K3500 Fleetside Regular-Cab Long Box Pickup] Wheelbase: 131.5 in. Length: 212.6 in. Width: 76.8 in. Height: 73.8 in. GVW: 10,000 lb. Payload: 1,980 lb. Tires: P225/75R15 black sidewall AS SBR tires.
CHASSIS: [C3500 Fleetside Extended-Cab Long Box Pickup] Wheelbase: 155.5 in. Length: 237.0 in. Width: 76.8 in. Height: 70.4 in. GVW: 10,000 lb. Payload: 2,200 lb. Tires: P225/75R15 black sidewall AS SBR tires.
CHASSIS: [K3500 Fleetside Extended-Cab Long Box Pickup] Wheelbase: 155.5 in. Length: 237.0 in. Width: 76.8 in. Height: 73.8 in. GVW: 10,000 lb. Payload: 2,105 lb. Tires: P225/75R15 black sidewall AS SBR tires.
CHASSIS: [C/K 3500 Pickup] Motor home chassis. Wheelbase: 183.5 in. Tires: P225/75R15 black sidewall AS SBR tires.

1992 Chevrolet 1/2-Ton S10 Blazer 2-door Sport Utility 4x4 (CMD)

SELECTED OPTIONS
GEO TRACKER OPTIONS: PEG 2 package ($302). Air conditioning ($745). Convertible rear seat ($445). Power steering ($275). Tilt steering wheel ($115). Trailering Special equipment ($109). Alloy wheels ($335). Three-speed automatic transmission ($595).
S/T SERIES PICKUP OPTIONS: AAA6/1SB Tahoe PEG package ($1,202-$2,189). Air conditioning ($755). Air dam with fog lamps ($115). Optional axle ratio ($44). Locking rear differential ($525). Heavy-duty battery ($56). Bumper equipment ($229). Cold climate package ($109-$233). Heavy-duty radiator ($56). Heavy-duty radiator and engine oil cooler ($118). Driver convenience package RPO ZM7 with Comfortilt steering wheel and intermittent wiper system ($204). California emissions package (no charge). 2.8-liter EFI V-6 ($620). 4.3-liter EFI V-6 ($620). Five-lead wiring harness ($41). Electronic instrumentation ($195). ZQ2 operating convenience package ($367). Special two-tone paint ($41-$296). Wheel opening moldings ($13-$43). UT5 radio ($201). UM7 AM/FM stereo ($131-$336). UM6 stereo ($253-$454). UX1 stereo ($150-$537). Rear jump seat ($240). Reclining high-back bucket seats with custom cloth trim ($223). Reclining high-back bucket seats with leather trim ($475). Heavy-duty shock absorbers ($40). Four-speed automatic overdrive transmission ($890). N40 power steering for S10 only, standard on T10. Cast aluminum wheels ($284-$340). Argent aluminum wheels ($248). Sliding rear window ($113).
S/T-SERIES BLAZER OPTIONS: Air conditioning ($780). Air dam with fog lamps ($115). Optional axle ratio ($44). Locking rear differential ($252). Heavy-duty battery ($56). Spare tire and wheel carrier ($159). Cold climate package ($56). Front center console ($135). Heavy-duty radiator ($56). Heavy-duty radiator and engine oil cooler ($118). Driver convenience package RPO ZM7 including Comfortilt steering wheel and intermittent wiper system ($204). Driver convenience package RPO ZM8 including rear window defroster and tailgate release ($197). California emissions package ($100). Color-keyed front floor mats for two-door only ($20). Rear color-keyed floor mats ($18). Deep tinted glass RPO AJ1 ($118). Deep tinted glass with light tinted rear window RPO AA3 ($225). Electronic instrumentation ($195). Black luggage carrier ($169). Exterior electric remote mirrors ($83). Visor mirrors, left and right side ($75). Black wheel opening molding ($13-$43). Operating convenience package including power door locks and power windows ($367-$542). Special two-tone paint ($218). Deluxe two-tone paint ($177). Electronically tuned AM/FM stereo radio with seek-and-scan, and digital clock ($131). Electronically tuned AM/FM stereo radio with seek-and-scan and stereo cassette tape player ($122-$253). Electronically tuned AM/FM stereo radio with seek-and-scan, stereo cassette tape player with search-and-repeat, graphic equalizer and digital clock ($150-$403). Delete radio ($95 credit). Special custom cloth reclining high-back bucket seats ($74). Deluxe cloth reclining high-back bucket seats ($26). Folding rear bench seat ($409). Leather reclining high-back bucket seats in two-door ($25-$750). Transfer case and front differential skid plates and steering linkage shield ($75). Front and rear heavy-duty shock absorbers ($40). Electronic speed control ($238) CAA1/1SA Tahoe PEG 1 ($4,829-$4,901). CAA2/1SB Tahoe PEG 2 ($3,403-$3,775). CAA3/1SC Tahoe PEG 3 ($4,070). Trailering Special equipment ($109-$211). Four-speed automatic overdrive transmission ($890). Rally wheels ($82). Argent Silver aluminum wheels ($248). Cast aluminum wheels ($284-$340). Sliding rear quarter window ($257). Rear window wiper/washer ($125).

ASTRO OPTIONS: Air conditioning ($523-$845). Optional rear axle ratio ($44). Locking rear differential. ($252) Deluxe front and rear chromed bumpers ($128). Black luggage carrier ($126). Cold climate package ($46). Roof-mounted console ($83). Engine oil cooler. Heavy-duty radiator ($58). Heavy-duty radiator and engine oil cooler ($118). Power door locks ($223). Driver convenience package includes Comfortilt steering wheel and speed control ($434). Operating convenience package includes power door locks and power windows ($383). YC6 decor trim package ($633-$1,092). YC7 decor trim package Astro LT ($2,848). California emissions ($100). 4.3-liter CPI V-6. Complete tinted glass ($157). Deep-tinted glass ($161). Rear heater ($205). Electronic instrumentation ($195). Deluxe below-eye-line mirrors ($52). Electric mirror ($150). Custom two-tone paint and bumper equipment ($329). UM7 radio ($151). UM6 stereo ($273). UX1 stereo system ($423). Seven-passenger seating ($852-$1,043). Eight passenger seating ($395-$877). Seat back recliner and dual armrests ($245). Six-way power seat ($240). Stowage compartment ($30). Astro Sport suspension ($248-$340). Front and rear heavy-duty shock absorbers. Heavy-duty Trailering Special equipment ($564). Light-duty Trailering Special equipment ($109). Aluminum wheels ($340). Argent Silver Rally wheels ($92).
LUMINA OPTIONS: PEG 1 ($1,070-$1,085. PEG 2 ($2,118-$2,133). UM6 radio ($140). U1C radio ($396) Custom two-tone exterior paint ($148). 3.8-liter SFI V-6 ($619). Air conditioning ($830). Front and rear air conditioning ($1,280). California emissions ($100). Deep-tinted glass ($245). Power door locks and tailgate ($300). Twin remote fold-away mirrors ($78). AG9 power seat ($270). AB3 six-passenger seating with twin front bucket seats ($510). ZP7 seven-passenger seating with twin front bucket seats ($425-$660). Load leveling suspension ($170). Electric speed control with resume feature ($225). Comfortilt steering wheel ($145). P205/70R15 black sidewall touring radial tires ($35 extra). V92 trailering package ($150). Four-speed automatic transmission ($200). Cast aluminum 15-in. wheels with locks ($275). Power windows with "express down" on driver's window ($275).
G-SERIES VAN OPTIONS: Preferred Equipment Group V1A2 ($1,116). Air conditioning ($975). ZQ2 convenience group ($434). Heavy-duty cooling system ($56). 5.0-liter EFI V-8 ($575). 5.7-liter EFI V-8 ($845). 7.4-liter EFI V-8 ($470). 6.2-liter diesel V-8 ($2,400). 6.2-liter heavy-duty diesel V-8 ($1,555). Front area carpeting and wheelhouse rubber mats ($147). Deep-tinted glass ($306).Swing-out glass package ($226). Heater ($205) TR9 auxiliary lighting package ($156). Deluxe two-tone paint ($269). UM6 stereo equipment ($263). UX1 stereo equipment ($413). Trailering equipment package ($132). Heavy-duty Trailering Special package ($508). Rally wheels ($121). Cast aluminum wheels ($331). Wheelcovers for G30 ($42).
K10 BLAZER OPTIONS: K5A2 Silverado package ($2,676). K5A3 Silverado package ($3,833).Sport Blazer package ($3,326). Air conditioning ($845). Deep-tinted glass ($215). B71 molding package ($180). Conventional two-tone ($180). Special two-tone ($265). Deluxe two-tone ($290). Locking differential ($252). Roof mounted luggage carrier ($126). Off-road chassis equipment ($270). ZQ2 convenience package ($367). ZQ3 convenience package ($383). UM7 AM/FM stereo ($170). UM6 ETR AM/FM stereo cassette ($122-$292). UX1 stereo system ($150-$442). All-tinted glass ($215). Conventional two-tone paint ($180). Deluxe two-tone paint ($290). Custom cloth reclining high-back bucket seats ($435). Skid plate package w/o Z71 ($175).Tape striping ($69). Tachometer ($59). Trailering Special equipment package ($408). Four-speed automatic overdrive transmission ($890). Rally wheel trim ($60). Cast aluminum wheels ($250-$310).
SUBURBAN OPTIONS: N1A2/1SB Silverado package ($3,507). N1A3/1SC Silverado package ($4,778-$4,839). N2A2/1SC Silverado package ($4,528-$4,589). Air conditioning ($845). Locking differential ($252). Roof carrier ($126). ZQ2 convenience group ($542-$606). California emissions ($100). 7.4-liter EFI V-8 ($470). UX1 stereo system ($150-$442). Deep-tinted glass ($305). B71 molding package ($180). Conventional two-tone paint ($180). Deluxe two-tone paint ($265).L6 custom cloth interior with front bucket seats ($560). L6 custom cloth interior with front bucket seats, center seat and rear seat ($612). Skid plate package ($175). Trailering equipment package ($273-$408). Rally wheel trim ($18-$60). Cast aluminum wheels ($268-$310).

1992 Chevrolet 1/2-Ton C1500 Sportside Short Box Pickup 4x2 (CMD)

C/K PICKUP OPTIONS: Air conditioning RPO C60 ($705). Optional axle ratios ($44). Locking differential RPO G80 ($252). Auxiliary heavy-duty battery, not avail. with B3J, RPO TP2 ($134). Painted rear step bumper, requires E63 body (RPO V43): $130. Front deluxe chromed bumper with rub strip, K10703 only RPO VG3 ($26). Chromed rear step bumper with rub strip RPO VB3 ($229). Front black bumper guards RPO V27 ($32). Heavy-duty chassis equipment, K1500 only, RPO F44 ($38). Off-road package, available for K1500 only, includes skid plate and Bilstein shock absorbers RPO Z71 ($270). Cold climate package, not avail. with B3J, includes engine block heater RPO V10 ($33). Convenience group includes power door locks and windows RPO ZQ2 ($367). Convenience group includes tilt wheel and speed control RPO ZQ3 ($383). Engine oil cooling system RPO KC4 ($135). Heavy-duty radiator RPO VO1 ($56). Heavy-duty radiator and transmission oil cooler RPO VO2 ($63). Rear window defogger RPO C49 ($154). 5.0 liter V-8 RPO LO3 ($575). 5.7 liter V-8 RPO LO5 ($840). 6.2 liter diesel V-8 RPO LH6 ($1,825-$2,400). Locking fuel filler cap RPO NO5 ($18). Cargo area lamp RPO UF2 ($36). Dome and reading lamp RPO C95 ($33). Roof marker lamps, not available with California emissions (RPO U01) ($52). Auxiliary lighting includes dome and reading lamps and ash tray, glove box and under hood lamps RPO TR9 ($94). Below eye-line type stainless steel mirrors RPO D45 ($45). Camper-type stainless steel mirrors RPO DF2 ($53). Black exterior moldings RPO B84 ($90). Exterior bright moldings RPO B85 ($17). Conventional two-tone exterior paint RPO ZY2 ($132). Special two-tone exterior paint RPO ZY3 ($215). Deluxe two-tone exterior paint RPO ZY4 ($243). Electronically tuned AM/FM stereo radio with seek-and-scan and digital clock RPO UM7 ($210). Electronically-tuned AM/FM stereo radio with seek-and-scan, stereo cassette, tape and digital clock RPO UM6 ($332). Electronically-tuned AM/FM stereo radio with seek-and-scan, stereo cassette player with search-and-repeat, graphic equalizer and digital clock RPO UX1 ($482). Radio delete option RPO UL5 (save $77). Scottsdale trim package RPO Z62 for pickups ($573-$604). Heavy-duty front and rear shock absorbers RPO F51 ($40). Silverado trim package RPO YE9 for Regular-Cab pickup ($981-$1012). Off-road skid plate RPO NZZ ($95). Heavy-duty front springs K1500 only, requires F44 heavy-duty chassis [not available with B3J or RPO Z71 off-road chassis] RPO F60 ($63). Body striping RPO D85 ($69). Tow hooks, standard on K1500, RPO V76 ($38). Heavy-duty Trailering Special equipment RPO Z82 ($408 with RPO Z71 or XQ8, $448 without RPO Z71 or ZQ8. Four-speed manual transmission RPO MM4 ($98). Four-speed automatic transmission with overdrive RPO MXO ($860). Three-speed automatic transmission RPO MX1 ($625). Wheelcovers RPO PO1 ($42). Aluminum wheels, K1500 only, RPO PF4 ($295). Sliding rear window RPO A28 ($113). Camper Special chassis equipment, K2500 and K3500 only, RPO Z81 ($280 without B2J, $148 with B3J). Deep-tinted glass, RPO AJ1 ($150). Sport equipment package for Sport Truck includes V43 black bumpers, black wheel flares, deluxe front appearance, black mirrors, GL-LT265/75R16 black sidewall tires, PF4 aluminum wheels with special hubcaps and 4x4 Sport decal, RPO BPY ($1,140.20). Sport steering wheel RPO NK3 ($7). Rear-mounted fuel tank, available for K2500/K3500 chassis & cab models, approximate capacity of 31-gallons RPO NK7 ($63). Special chassis camper equipment, includes TP2 auxiliary battery without B3J equipment, camper wiring harness and DF2 mirrors, RPO Z81 ($280 for K-series Pickups, $143 with B3J, $81 for V3500). Dual rear wheels, available for C/K3500 models only, includes plastic rear fender extensions with side marker lamps on front and rear sides and dual rear chassis provisions, RPO RO5 ($1,038 , $1101 with MX1 transmission). RPO RO5 plus VO2 heavy-duty radiator and transmission oil cooler ($785 for V35008).

NOTE 15: Options and prices shown are representative. The actual cost of an option or option package often varies according to other packages that the options are combined with on specific vehicles. Preferred Equipment Group (PEG) options offer specific optional equipment at discount prices. Some "options" may be standard equipment on certain models, such as V-8s in C/K3500 pickups. Descriptions of options are edited. Full option contents can be determined by consulting sales literature.

HISTORICAL: Chevrolet trucks were built in 12 factories in 1993. Geo Trackers were made at the CAMI plant in Ingersoll, Ontario, Canada. S-Series pickups were assembled in Pontiac, Michigan and Shreveport, Louisiana. S-Series Blazers built at Pontiac, Michigan and Moraine, Ohio. Astros were made in Baltimore, Maryland. Chevy Van models were sourced from factories in Scarborough, Ontario, Canada and Flint, Michigan. Full-size Blazers and Suburbans were made in the Chevrolet factory in Janesville, Wisconsin. C/K pickups were built in Fort Wayne, Indiana; Oshawa, Canada; Pontiac, Michigan; and Janesville, Wisconsin. Lumina APVs were assembled at Tarrytown, N.Y. Jim Perkins continued as general manager of Chevrolet Motor Division. J.N. Janowiak was national manager of truck merchandising and R.M. Wisner was manager of truck advertising. Chevrolet new-truck sales (and market penetration) were: 35,683 Astro Vans (3.07 percent), 80,132 Astro Wagons (6.89 percent), 43,174 Lumina passenger vans (3.71 percent), 607 Lumina cargo vans (0.05 percent), 20,614 Blazers (1.77 percent), 147,742 S-Series Blazers (12.70 percent), 450,650 C/K pickups (38.74 percent), 191,982 S10/T10 pickups (16.50 percent), 7,313 Sportvans (0.63 percent), 56,839 Suburbans (4.89 percent), 32,666 Canadian-built Geo Trackers (2.81 percent), 83,971 Chevy Vans (7.22 percent), and 973 W4 Tiltmaster imports (0.08 percent). This gave the company total light-duty truck sales of 1,163,368 units and 24.76 percent of the overall light-duty truck market.

1993

1993 Geo Tracker Convertible 4x4 (CMD)

1/4-TON — GEO TRACKER — L4: Chevrolet dealers sold the Suzuki-designed Geo Tracker as a small Sport Utility Vehicle. It was actually built at the CAMI Automotive, Inc. factory in Ingersoll, Ontario, Canada. Trackers had a small pickup box, and were considered trucks. They were offered as a two-door Convertible with front-wheel-drive only. The Convertible also came in 4x4 format, with or without optional LSi trim. The hardtop model came only as a 4x4, in the base or LSi trim levels. There were no major changes in the Tracker for 1994. Standard equipment included a 1.6-liter SOHC inline four-cylinder engine, power front disc/rear drum brakes, five-speed manual transmission, and (4x2 model) P195/75R-15 tires or (4x4 models) P205/75R-15 tires.

1993 Chevrolet 1/2-Ton S10 Tahoe Long Box Pickup 4x4 (CMD)

1/2-TON — S (4x2)/T (4x4) SERIES PICKUP — L4/V-6: The S10/T10 Pickup, and Extended-Cab models shared many innovations and improvements with the 1993 S-Blazer. These included the addition of an internal balance shaft to the 4.3-liter V-6, and the use of Solar-Ray tinted glass in all windows. A single, more reliable controller was used for the engine, transmission and anti-lock brakes. An improved O-ring seal on the intake manifold thermostat reduced coolant leaks. The V-6 engine also had revised spark plugs, which improved engine idle quality. In factory nomenclature, S10 indicated 4x2, and T10 indicated 4x4, even though both said S10 on the fenders. The S10/T10 also had new color-keyed door trim, air conditioning, and radio bezels. A dual note horn was standard, and the convenience tray now had a soft liner. Two new exterior colors-Dove Gray, and Khaki replaced Aquamarine Green, and Sky Blue. A revised High Solids Enamel painting process was used for 1993. It involved the use of corrosion-resistant steel, eight-stage zinc-phosphate coating, use of an E-coat (ELPO), a primer surface with anti-chip protection on body side panels, and on the leading edges of the hood, front fenders, A-pillars and roof. The paint used was an acrylic enamel. A new beige color joined charcoal, blue, and gray as interior colors choices for 1993. A paint treatment featuring a middle break line with a blended stripe was available for the first time in 1993. The Pickup, and Extended-Cab models with the Tahoe trim level had a redesigned chrome and gray grille. The taillight bezels were now black. The left and right side split-visors had lighted vanity mirrors, and extenders. Door-activated reading lamps with a delay-off feature were installed. The Extended-Cab had a parcel restraint net in the storage area behind the seat. The RPO D55 floor console was raised to match the height of the door arm rest. The console used in conjunction with the manual transmission included a coin tray that, with the automatic, included a dual cup holder. The floor shifter console was revised with a deeper right-hand side shifter tray. A 12-volt outlet was also installed. A new RPO D48 electric dual remote mirror option was introduced for 1993. A new electronic 4L60-E Hydramatic four-speed automatic overdrive transmission was available for the S10. A new heavy-duty cooling system option (RPO V08) for trucks with the automatic transmission was introduced. It included an engine oil cooler as well as a transmission oil cooler. An anti-theft sleeve was added to the Comfortilt steering wheel/intermittent windshield wiper option (RPO ZM7). All-new deluxe cloth reclining seats were available. They were fitted with manual two-position lumbar adjustment. This option also included a floor console. The new deluxe cloth 60/40 split-bench front seat option included an easy-entry passenger seat feature on the Extended-Cab model. This feature was listed in the "interim availability" category. A new RPO 5P2 fifteen-inch aluminum five-spoke wheel option was also introduced for 1993. Options introduced late in the 1992 model-year for the entry level EL model, and continued for 1993, included automatic transmission, power steering, a heavy-duty battery, rear painted bumper, Cold climate package, two-tone paint, AM/FM stereo radio with cassette tape player and clock, shield package, heavy-duty shock absorbers, upper body stripe, and P205/75R15 white-lettered tires. S/T-series Pickups were built in factories in Pontiac, Michigan, and Shreveport, Louisiana. Standard equipment in 4x2 models included a 2.5-liter EFI inline four-cylinder engine, power front disc brakes, five-speed manual transmission with overdrive, and P195/75R14 all-season black sidewall tires. The 4x4 models had a base 4.3-liter Vortec V-6 in place of the inline four-cylinder engine.

1993 Chevrolet 1/2-Ton S10 Blazer Tahoe LT 2-door Sport Utility 4x2 (CMD)

1/2-TON — S (4x2)/T (4x4) BLAZER — V-6: For 1993, an enhanced power train package including a 4.3 liter CPI V-6 was optional in S-Blazers. This Enhanced Vortec CPI V-6 had 35 more horsepower than the base engine, although the standard 4.3 liter EFI Vortec V-6 did have a five-horsepower increase for 1993. Compared to the 1992 version it featured less noise and vibration, and smoother performance. A five-speed manual overdrive transmission was standard with the base VortecV-6. The Enhanced Vortec V-6 was linked to a standard Hydramatic 4L60-E electronic four-speed automatic transmission. This power train had been introduced interim 1992. An internal balance shaft was added to the V-6 engine for smoother performance. It reduced vibration in the higher rpm ranges. Theftdeterring improvements were made to the S-Blazer's tilt steering column. They increased the time required to bypass the steering column ignition key. Four-wheel antilock brakes continued as standard equipment. A new aluminum wheel was optional. New interior convenience features included an illuminated entry light under the inside rear view mirror, keyless entry, and convenience net (with Tahoe and Tahoe LT trim packages), a floor console with a 12-volt power outlet (limited model availability), and an overhead console with lights and storage areas. Cup holders were included with the automatic transmission, and a stowage tray was fitted to vehicles with manual transmission. Solar-Ray tinted glass, optional sun visors, and a redesigned luggage rack were also new for 1993. Coat hooks were now installed at both sides of the cargo compartment (in addition to coat hooks behind the front doors). The convenience tray now had a soft liner. A dual note horn was now used. Seating changes included manual lumbar adjusters, and the former deluxe cloth interior now came in four colors. Both features were standard equipment. Identification of the 1993 base two-door S-Blazer was aided by its new black grille, and body color front and rear bumpers. The grille of the S-Blazer two-door Tahoe and four-door Tahoe (base) was now chrome and gray. The black body side moldings for these models were wider, and had revised bright inserts. The black rub strips and bright inserts on the Tahoe chrome front and rear bumpers were also revised. A power driver's seat and recliner were new for the Tahoe LT package. Beige was a new interior color. New exterior colors for the S-Blazer were Dove Gray and Khaki. They replaced Aquamarine Green and Sky Blue. The paint process included primer surface with anti-chip protection extended to the entire vehicle. The Tahoe trim package on two-door models had new optional two-tone paint and striping. The color-keyed front and rear floor mats for the Tahoe trim level S-series Blazers were carpeted. All tailgates had a Chevrolet nameplate which was bright and black. This was identical to that previously used on models with an outside spare tire carrier. Also found on the 1993 models were black taillight bezels, color-keyed door trim, an air conditioner, and radio bezels. Three trim options were offered for the two-door S-Blazer: Standard, Tahoe and Tahoe LT. The four-door model had two trim levels: Tahoe (standard) and Tahoe LT. New or revised options included a new padded cover with Blazer lettering (without red underlines) for the outside spare tire carrier (RPO P16). The floor console (RPO D55), which was standard for the two-door S-Blazer Tahoe, was raised to match the height of the door arm rest. The transfer case floor shifter console had a revised design. On the standard 4x4 version, the shifter tray was deeper on the right-hand side. On models with an electronic shift transfer case, the console was similar, but had a larger tray. A new overhead console option (RPO DK6) was offered. A new heavy-duty cooling system option (RPO VO8) included an engine oil cooler. Color-keyed, carpeted removable front (RPO B32) and rear (RPO B33) floor mats were now optional for the two-door base S-Blazer. They were included with the Tahoe package and standard for four-door models. Standard as an interim 1993 option was a new deluxe cloth 60/40 front split-bench seat. Other standard S-Blazer features were power front disc/rear drum AWAL brakes, and P205/75R15 all-season steel-belted radial black sidewall tires.

1/2-TON — ASTRO VAN SERIES M (RWD)/L (AWD) — V-6: The content and optional equipment of the Astro was fine-tuned for 1993. The optional (RPO PF3) aluminum wheels had a new brushed appearance. All cloth interiors had Scotchguard protection on their seats, door and quarter trim panels. A new instrument panel cluster with analog gauges for improved appearance and readability was used for 1993. The speedometer graphics were revised from 85 mph to 100 mph. The instrument cluster also had an improved printed circuit design, increased telltale capacity, and a new "flag in window" shift indicator system. The optional heavy-duty cooling package (RPO VO8) now included a heavy-duty radiator, engine oil cooler and transmission oil cooler. A new steel sleeve steering column with the Comfortilt steering wheel was designed for enhanced security. Improvements included three steel shields, a revised lock cylinder, and a new lock bolt spring. A new transmission/brake shift interlock required the driver to depress the brake pedal before shifting out of "park." The standard Hydramatic 4L60-E four-speed automatic overdrive transmission (RPO MX0) was now electronically-controlled. All-wheel antilock brakes (AWAL) were standard for all models in 1993, including the Cargo Van and the Extended-Body Cargo Van. The new-for-1993 AWAL system included three sensors and was less complex than in previous years. An improved brake hose material was used. The Astro Sport package was canceled for 1993. Three new colors were offered: Light Quasar Blue Metallic, Indigo Blue Metallic, and Medium Quasar Blue Metallic. They replaced the colors Smoke Blue Metallic, Catalina Blue Metallic, and Slate Metallic. A color that had been previously limited to the 1992 LT model, Teal Blue, was now available for all Astros. The standard 4.3-liter EFI V-6 had improved electronic spark control and new spark plugs. The standard custom vinyl interior and the optional custom cloth interior were offered in beige, blue, garnet or gray. The LT trim was available in beige or gray. Cargo Vans equipped with a driver's seat only were available in either blue or beige. Also standard were power front disc/rear drum AWAL brakes and P205/75R15 all-season steel-belted radial black sidewall tires.

1993 Chevrolet 1/2-Ton L10 Astro Extended-Body Passenger Minivan 4x4 (CMD)

1/2-TON — LUMINA WAGON SERIES U05 (FWD) — V-6: The versatile front-wheel-drive Lumina minivan had a new optional power sliding door for 1993. The standard five-passenger version had plenty of room. An option was easily removable modular seating including a seven-passenger layout. Luxury level LS seat trim was available. The LS package included such exterior enhancements as moldings and aero skirting. Two-tone paint schemes were available as well. Standard equipment included a driver's side air bag, and four-wheel antilock brake system with front discs and rear drums. The Lumina offered 112.6 cu.-ft. of cargo capacity. Its GVWR was 5,126 lb. Standard equipment included a 3.1-liter MFI V-6, power front disc/rear drum AWAL brakes, three-speed automatic transmission, and P205/70R15 steel-belted radial all-season black sidewall tires.

1993 Chevrolet 1-Ton G30 Beauville Sportvan 4x2 (CMD)

1/2-TON, 3/4-TON, 1-TON VAN — G SERIES 10, 20, 30 (RWD) — V-6/V-8: The G10 1/2-ton series offered 110- and 125-in. wheelbase Chevy Vans. A new-for-1993 4.3-liter Vortec V-6 increased the standard engine to 155 hp at 4000 rpm, a gain of five horsepower. G20 models had 260 cu.-ft. of cargo capacity. In the Sportvan model, eight-passenger bench seating was standard and five-passenger bucket seating was optional. The G20 Sportvan had a GVWR of 6,600 to 6,875 lb. The G30 1-ton series included 125-in. wheelbase Chevy Van and Sportvan models, plus 146-in. extended wheelbase versions of both. The standard-body G30 Sportvan also had 260 cu.-ft. of cargo capacity and came with standard 12-passenger bench seating or optional eight-passenger bucket seating. Its GVWR was 7,400 to 9,200 lb. The Extended-Body model had a 306 cu.-ft. cargo capacity. Twelve-passenger seating was standard and 15-passenger seating was optional. The longer Sportvan had a GVWR of 8,600 to 9,200 lb. A cutaway version of the G Series van chassis was also available for builders of motor homes, airport buses and other special-bodied trucks. Standard equipment for small Chevy Vans included the 4.3-liter EFI Vortec V-6, heavy-duty front disc/rear drum four-wheel anti-lock brakes, four-speed manual transmission with overdrive and P205/75R15 black sidewall tires. The G20 Sportvan had the same standard features as the G10 model, but a 5.7-liter EFI V-8 was standard in G30 models. The 1-ton G30 model was also available in Hi-Cube Van form with 10-ft. and 12-ft. body options. This was the last year for the Hi-Cube models.

1-TON — P30 STEP-VAN — V-8: Also making its last appearance in 1993 was the long-running Chevrolet Step-Van multi-stop delivery truck. As in the past, it looked like a big box and represented the perfect cargo carrier for stop-and-go delivery service. The only model offered was a 1-ton version with a 10-1/2-foot long body.

1993 Chevrolet 1/2-Ton K1500 Blazer 2-door Sport Utility 4x4

1/2-TON — K1500 BLAZER 4x4 — V-8: After adopting the styling, chassis and power train of the full-size K Pickup in 1992, the Blazer entered 1993 in the envious position of having its production facilities unable to keep pace with demand. New for 1993 was the optional electronic four-speed Hydramatic automatic transmission. This transmission was the first General Motors rear-wheel electronic transmission to interface with cruise control. The 4L60-E weighed seven pounds less than its non-electric predecessor (the 4L60). This new transmission monitored such items as the fuel-injection rate, ignition timing, internal transmission temperature, idle speed and exhaust gas recirculation several times a second. It then determined the proper shift points, and shift smoothness. The transmission also had a built-in learning feature that allowed the system to adapt to its environment, and make subtle adjustments in clutch pressure to match it. The 4L60 also had fail-safe controls that defaulted to operable gear ratios should a problem develop, allowing the driver to maintain vehicle control and reach a safe location. A second safety feature permitted second-gear starts when increased wheel traction was desired. A new single-rail shift control improved both reliability, and durability. The 5.7-liter EFI V-8 and five-speed manual transmission remained the standard power train. The fan was not engaged upon engine start to reduce noise. Other standard features included four-wheel antilock brakes (AWAL), and the shift-on the fly Insta-Trac system. The tilt steering column had a new steel sleeve for 1993 to reduce theft. Specific details included three steel shields, revised lock cylinder and a new lock bolt spring. An electronic fuel shut-off automatically limited maximum vehicle speed to less than the tire speed rating. A deluxe front appearance option (RPO V22) was now available with the Cheyenne decor. Indigo Blue Metallic was a new exterior color for 1993. It replaced Brilliant Blue Metallic. The other exterior colors for 1993 were Black, Olympic White, Ultra Silver Metallic, Dark Gray Metallic, Victory Red, Dark Garnet Red Metallic, Light French Blue Metallic, Medium Dark Teal Metallic, and Beige Metallic. Both a Sport appearance package and new coordinated striping colors were also available. The special two-tone paint feature (RPO ZY3) was not offered for 1993. It had been phased-out during the 1992 model run. An anti-chip paint coating was more widely used for 1993. It was installed on the leading edges of the hood, roof, and the A-pillars. Four interior colors were available for 1993: Beige, blue, garnet and gray. Blazers with the standard Cheyenne trim had vinyl seating. The upper level Silverado had custom cloth trim. The passenger side of the optional Silverado 40/60 split bench seats and the standard Cheyenne low-back bucket seats reclined for 1993. Other changes included Scotchguard protection for seats and door fabric, and the use of Solar-Ray glass for a cooler interior. Also new for 1993 was a dual-stud air cleaner, a more durable oil filter, improved cruise control, and user-friendly radio controls. The cruise control improvement included increased reliability of the circuit board component, and a "soft pedal off" feature to eliminate the pedal slapping the sole of the driver's foot when the cruise was turned off at the column switch. Installed, interim 1993, was an improved brake hose material that provided reduced moisture ingression, improved heat resistance, sealability, ozone resistance, hot/cold fatigue resistance, and flex fatigue resistance.

1993 Chevrolet 1/2-Ton C1500 Suburban 4-door wagon 4x2 (CMD)

1/2-TON, 3/4-TON — C (4x2) /K (4x4) SUBURBAN — V-8: Power train changes were the major developments for 1993. Like the Blazer, the Suburban used the all-new Hydramatic 4L60-E four-speed optional transmission. This large, four-door wagon came with rear-wheel-drive or four-wheel-drive. It could be had in 1/2-ton-rated C1500/K1500 models or 3/4-ton-rated C2500/K2500 models. All shared a giant 149.5 cu.-ft. cargo capacity. The Suburbans could handle payloads between 1,688 lb. and 3,430 lb. The GVWR was 6,800 lb. to 8,600 lb. Three-passenger seating was standard. Five-, six-, eight- and nine-passenger options were available. Standard equipment included a 5.7-liter EFI V-8, front disc/rear drum four-wheel anti-lock brakes, a four-speed automatic transmission with overdrive, and P235/75R-15XLS all-season black sidewall steel-belted radial tires. The only new color offered for Suburban models was Indigo Blue Metallic.

1993 Chevrolet 1/2-Ton C1500 Sportside Short Box "Sport" Pickup 4x2 (CMD)

1/2-TON, 3/4-TON, 1-TON — C (4x2)/K (4x4) PICKUP — V-6/V-8: Power train changes were also the major developments for 1993 Pickups. The 6.5-liter turbo diesel was now offered for Crew-Cab models and Extended-Cab Pickups with GVWRs over 8,500 lb. The 4.3-liter Vortec V-6 was upgraded with a new balance shaft intended to dampen vibrations in high rpm ranges. Other developments involved revised cylinder heads with improved flow characteristics, a revised Throttle-Body-Injection unit for a smoother idle, a new quiet fan drive that reduced engine noise (especially during cold starts), a new thermostat, a revised oil filter, and a new dual-stud air cleaner. Both the 5.0- and 5.7-liter V-8 engines were improved in these areas. The 5.0-liter V-8 also had new low-tension piston pins for 1993. Beginning in 1993, a modified version of the 5.7-liter V-8 was available for conversion to compressed natural gas, propane or to dual fuel capability with gasoline. As with the other V-8 engines, the 7.4-liter V-8 had a modified Throttle-Body-Injection unit, and a larger radiator (midyear release). Other improvements included a one-piece dipstick, new spark plug shields, revised intake manifold, a machined water pump outlet, and a quiet fan drive. A new electronic four-speed automatic Hydramatic 4L60-E transmission was available for trucks under-8,500 lb. GVWR. A new Sportside Sport Pickup for the 1500 series Regular-Cab included Silverado trim, Sport decals, a body-color Dura-Grille, a Sportside box, cast aluminum wheels, painted exterior mirrors, and color-keyed front and rear bumpers. The Sportside Sport Pickup was offered in Summit White, Onyx or Victory Red. All models had a new "Leading Edge" anti-chip coating applied to the leading edges of the hood, roof and A-pillars. Solar-Ray tinted glass was standard in all windows. Scotchguard fabric protector was applied to all cloth seat and door trim panels. The Extended-Cab was now available with two-passenger seating, giving customers a choice of two-, three-, five-, or six-passenger seating. A 40/60-split-bench seat in cloth or vinyl, and low-back bucket seats in cloth or vinyl were available with the Cheyenne option. It previously required the Scottsdale trim. A seat-back recliner was added to the passenger side on the 40/60 split-bench seat and low-back bucket seats. Dual cup holders were now mounted on the instrument panel (this feature was not available with bucket seats). A steel sleeve steering column was used with the Comfortilt steering wheel for improved security. The sun visors were now cloth-covered. The radio controls were revised with a new control panel and improved button operation. A full-cloth headliner was now optional for Regular-Cab Pickups. A cloth headliner continued as standard for the Silverado decor on Pickups, and Extended-Cab models. A new electronic fuel shut-off automatically limited maximum engine speed to less than tire speed rating. A deluxe front appearance (RPO V22) was available as an option with Cheyenne models. The Cheyenne K3500 Chassis-Cab with Crew-Cab was available with a new auxiliary lighting option. Four new 1993 exterior colors were introduced: Light Quasar Blue Metallic, Teal Green Metallic, Indigo Blue Metallic, and Dark Garnet Red Metallic. They replaced Brilliant Blue Metallic, Smoke Blue Metallic, Catalina Blue Metallic, and Crimson Red Metallic. The only new color offered for the Crew-Cab and chassis-and-cab models was Indigo Blue Metallic. The Scottsdale decor was canceled for 1993. Phased out during 1992, and not offered for 1993, was the special two-tone paint option. Standard features included the 4.3-liter EFI V-6, power rear antilock brakes, five-speed manual overdrive transmission, and P225/75R15 steel-belted black sidewall tires. A high-performance 454SS package (PEG PSS1) was available. It included YE9 Silverado trim, a black grille with red bow tie, sliding rear window, 15-in. chrome-plated wheels, the Sport package, air conditioning, a locking differential, an oil cooler, auxiliary lighting, a cargo area lamp, an AM/FM ETR stereo system (with Seek-and-Scan, Search-and-Repeat cassette, graphic equalizer and digital clock), heavy-duty cooling system, Sport steering wheel, speed control, Sport Handling chassis package, analog gauges with tachometer, and E63 body code.

I. D. DATA: The VIN plate was mounted on the lower left side windshield corner. The VIN consisted of 17 symbols. The first three symbols identify the country, the manufacturer and the type of vehicle. The fourth symbol designates the GVW range. The fifth, sixth and seventh symbols identify the line and chassis type, series and body type. The eighth symbol identifies the engine: [Chevrolet engines] C=6.2-liter/130 hp diesel V-8, H=5.0-liter V-8, J=6.2-liter/148 hp diesel V-8, K=5.7-liter V-8, N=7.4-liter V-8, R=2.8-liter V-6, Z=4.3-liter V-6. [GM engines] A= 5.7-liter V-8 or 2.5-liter L4, D=3.1-liter V-6, F=6.5-liter diesel V-8, L=3.8-liter V-6, W=4.3-liter V-6. The ninth symbol is the check digit. The tenth symbol indicates model year. The eleventh symbol identifies the assembly plant. The last six symbols are the sequential production number.

Model	Body Type	Price	Weight	Prod. Total
CE/CJ Geo Tracker — 1/2-Ton — 86.6 in. w.b. — 1.6-liter MFI L4				
CE10367	4x2 Convertible	10,330	2,189	Note 13
CJ10316	4x4 Hardtop	11,750	2,387	Note 13
CJ10367	4x4 Convertible	11,585	2,365	Note 13
CJ10316/B2Z	4x4 LSi Hardtop	12,328	2,397	Note 13
CJ10367/B2Z	4x4 LSi Convertible	12,076	2,375	Note 13
NOTE 1: A $300 dealer destination charge applied to Geo Trackers effective Aug. 14, 1992.				
S10 Fleetside Pickup — 1/2-Ton — 108.3/117.9/122.9 in. w.b. — 2.5-liter EFI L4				
S10603	Reg. Cab EL X81	8745	2635	Note 13
S10603	Reg. Cab Short Box	10,130	2913	Note 13
S10803	Reg. Cab Long Box	10,430	3000	Note 13
S10653	Ext. Cab Short Box	11,630	3024	Note 13
T10 4x4 Fleetside Pickup — 1/2-Ton — 108.3/117.9/122.9 in. w.b. — 4.3-liter EFI V-6				
T10603	Reg. Cab EL X81	12,545	-	Note 13
T10603	Reg. Cab SWB	13,696	-	Note 13
T10803	Reg. Cab LS LWB	13,996	-	Note 13
T10653	Ext. Cab LS Short Box	15,196	-	Note 13
NOTE 2: A $470 dealer destination charge applied to S-Series Pickups effective Jan. 22, 1993.				
S10 Blazer 4x2 Sport Utility Wagon — 1/2-Ton — 100.5/107 in. w.b. — 4.3-liter EFI V-6				
CS10516	2-dr Tailgate	14,823	3198	Note 13
CS10506	4-dr Tailgate	15,783	3365	Note 13
T10 Blazer 4x4 Sport Utility Wagon — 1/2-Ton — 100.5/107 in. w.b. — 4.3-liter EFI V-6				
CT10516	2-dr Tailgate	16,583	3512	Note 13
CT10506	4-dr Tailgate	17,953	3748	Note 13
NOTE 3: A $475 dealer destination charge applied to S-Blazers effective Jan. 22, 1993.				
M10 Astro Minivan (rear-wheel-drive) — 1/2-Ton — 111 in. w.b. — 4.3-liter MFI V-6				
CM10906	Standard Cargo Van	14,695	3653	Note 13
CM11006	Extended Cargo Van	15,365	3741	Note 13
CM10906/ZW9	Standard CS Van	15,605	3998	Note 13
CM11006/ZW9	Extended CS Van	16,295	4064	Note 13
L10 Astro Minivan (all-wheel-drive) — 1/2-Ton — 111 in. w.b. — 4.3-liter CPI V-6				
CL10906/ZW9	Standard CS Van	16,222	-	Note 13
CL11006/ZW9	Extended CS Van	16,530	-	Note 13
NOTE 4: A $545 dealer destination charge applied to Astros effective Nov. 18, 1992.				
U05 Lumina Minivan — 1/2-Ton — 109.8 in. w.b. — 3.1-liter EFI V-6				
1UM05	Cargo Van	14,695	3370	Note 13
1UM06	Wagon	15,895	3492	Note 13
1UM06	Wagon LS	17,995	-	Note 13
NOTE 5: A $530 dealer destination charge applied to Lumina minivans effective Aug. 14, 1992.				
G10 Van — 1/2-Ton — 110 in./125 in. w.b. — 4.3-liter EFI V-6				
CG11005/ZW9	SWB Chevy Van	14,600	3647	Note 13
CG11006/ZW9	SWB Sportvan	16,360	4248	Note 13
G20 Van — 3/4-Ton — 110/125 in. w.b. — 4.3-liter EFI V-6				
CG21005/ZW9	SWB Chevy Van	14,720	3905	Note 13
CG21305/ZW9	LWB Chevy Van	16,110	4550	Note 13
G30 Van — 1-Ton — 125/146 in. w.b. — 5.7-liter heavy-duty EFI V-8				
CG31305/ZW9	LWB Chevy Van	15,040	4380	Note 13
CG31306/ZW9	LWB Sportvan 12P	19,000	5266	Note 13
CG31605/ZW9	EWB Chevy Van	17,530	4881	Note 13
CG31606/ZW9	EWB Sportvan 12P	20,485	5642	Note 13
CG31305/ZW9	LWB Cutaway Van	15,952	4032	Note 13
G30 Hi-Cube Van — 1-Ton — 125/146 in. w.b. — 5.7-liter heavy-duty EFI V-8				
CG31	10-ft. Van	19,952	4788	N/A
CG31	12-ft. Van	21,416	5547	N/A
NOTE 6: A $580 dealer destination charge applied to full-size vans effective Dec. 18, 1992.				
P30 — 1-Ton Step-Van — 125/178 in. w.b. — 5.7-liter heavy-duty EFI V-8				
P32	10.5-ft. Step-Van	18,439	6068	N/A
K1500 Blazer — 1/2-Ton — 111.5 in. w.b. — 5.7-liter Light-duty EFI V-8				
CK10516	Utility Hardtop	20,005	4608	Note 13
NOTE 7: A $595 dealer destination charge applied to full-size Blazers effective Feb. 15, 1993.				
C/K 1500 Suburban — 1/2-Ton — 131.5 in. w.b. — 5.7-liter Light-duty EFI V-8				
CC10906/ZW9	Panel Door (4x2)	19,170	4657	Note 13
CK10906/ZW9	Panel Door (4x4)	21,370	-	Note 13
C/K 2500 Suburban — 3/4-Ton — 131.5 in. w.b. — 5.7-liter Light-duty EFI V-8				
CC20906/ZW9	Panel Door (4x2)	20,375	5002	Note 13
CK20906/ZW9	Panel Door (4x4)	22,575	-	Note 13
NOTE 8: A $580 dealer destination charge applied to Suburbans effective Dec. 18, 1992.				
C1500 Pickup — 1/2-Ton Short Box — 117.5 in. w.b. — 4.3-liter EFI V-6				
CC10703	Regular-Cab Sportside	13,985	3743	Note 13
CC10703	Regular-Cab Fleetside	13,585	3717	Note 13

1993 Geo 1/2-Ton Tracker 4x2 Convertible Sport Utility (CMD)

1993 Chevrolet 1/2-Ton S10 4x2 Extended-Cab Short Box Pickup (CMD)

1993 Chevrolet 1/2-Ton S10 EL 4x2 Regular-Cab Long Box Pickup (CMD)

1993 Chevrolet 1/2-Ton T10 Blazer 4x4 two-door Sport Utility Vehicle (CMD)

1993 Chevrolet 1/2-Ton S10 Tahoe 4x2 Regular-Cab Short Box Pickup (CMD

1993 Chevrolet 1/2-Ton S10 Blazer 4x2 four-door Sport Utility Vehicle (CMD)

1993 Chevrolet 1/2-Ton Astro LT All-Wheel-Drive Extended-Body Minivan (CMD)

1993 Chevrolet 1-ton C3500 4x2 Fleetside Crew-Cab Long Box Pickup (CMD)

1993 Chevrolet 1/2-Ton Astro CL Rear-Wheel-Drive Extended-Body Minivan (CMD)

1993 Chevrolet 3/4-Ton K2500 4x4 Extended-Cab Fleetside Long Box Pickup (CMD)

1993 Chevrolet 3/4-Ton K2500 4x4 Suburban Sport Utility Wagon (CMD

1993 Chevrolet 1-Ton K3500 4x4 Extended-Cab Fleetside Long Box "Dooley" Pickup (CMD)

Standard Catalog of Chevrolet Trucks

Model	Body Type	Price	Weight	Prod. Total
C1500 Pickup — 1/2-Ton Long Box — 131.5 in. w.b. — 4.3-liter EFI V-6				
CC10903	Regular-Cab Fleetside	13,885	3860	Note 13
CC10903	Regular-Cab Work Truck	11,225	3740	Note 13
C1500 Pickup — 1/2-Ton Short Box — 141.5 in. w.b. — 4.3-liter EFI V-6				
CC10753	Extended-Cab Sportside	15,530	4128	Note 13
CC10753	Extended-Cab Fleetside	15,130	4032	Note 13
C1500 Pickup — 1/2-Ton Long Box — 155.5 in. w.b. — 4.3-liter EFI V-6				
CC10903	Extended-Cab Fleetside	15,390	4127	Note 13

NOTE 9: Add approximately $2,250 for CK1500 Pickups with 4x4.

Model	Body Type	Price	Weight	Prod. Total
C2500 Pickup — 3/4-Ton Long Box — 131.5 in. w.b. — 4.3-liter EFI V-6				
CC20924	Chassis & Cab	15,569	4002	Note 13
CC20903	Regular-Cab Fleetside	14,425	4021	Note 13
C2500 Pickup — 3/4-Ton Short Box — 141.5 in. w.b. — 4.3-liter EFI V-6				
CC20954	Chassis & Extended-Cab	17,244	-	Note 13
CC20953	Extended-Cab Fleetside	16,240	4160	Note 13
C2500 Pickup — 3/4-Ton Long Box — 155.5 in. w.b. — 4.3-liter EFI V-6				
CC20903	Extended-Cab Fleetside	16,520	4261	Note 13

NOTE 10: Add approximately $1,875 for CK2500 Pickups with 4x4.

Model	Body Type	Price	Weight	Prod. Total
C3500 Pickup — 1-Ton Long Box — 131.5 in. w.b. — 5.7-liter EFI V-8				
CC30924	Chassis & Cab	15,704	4263	Note 13
CC30903	Regular-Cab Fleetside	16,164	4638	Note 13
C3500 Pickup — 1-Ton Long Box — 155.5 in. w.b. — 5.7-liter V-8				
CC30903	Extended-Cab Fleetside	17,824	4874	Note 13
C3500 Pickup — 1-Ton Long Box — 168.5 in. w.b. — 5.7-liter V-8				
CC30933	Crew-Cab Fleetside	18,144	5176	Note 13
CC30933	Crew-Cab & Chassis	17,694	4904	Note 13
CC30934	H-D Crew-Cab & Chassis	18,989	5270	Note 13

NOTE 11: Add approximately $2,240 for CK3500 Pickups with 4x4.

NOTE 12: A $595 dealer destination charge applied to C/K Pickups effective Feb. 15, 1993.

NOTE 13: Model-year production: [S10 Pickup] 180,342, [C/K1500] 376,592, [C/K2500] 66,847, [C/K3500] 37,904, [Geo Tracker (Canadian-made)] 35,327, [S-Blazer] 139,555, [K1500 Blazer] 20,205, [Suburban] 84,163, [Lumina APV Wagon] 52,561, [Lumina APV Cargo Van] 417, [Astro Wagon] 90,392, [Astro Cargo Van] 35,462, [Sportvan] 6,653, [Chevy Van] 102,586.

NOTE 14: The percentage of above trucks with four-wheel-drive was: [S10 Pickup] 13.6 percent, [C/K1500] 33.6 percent, [C/K2500] 57.5 percent, [C/K3500] 8.1 percent, [Geo Tracker/Canadian-made] 57.2 percent, [S-Blazer] 76.5 percent, [K1500 Blazer] 100 percent, [Suburban] 53.4 percent, [Lumina APV Wagon] none, [Lumina APV Cargo Van] none, [Astro Wagon] 15.4 percent, [Astro Cargo Van] 6.5 percent, [Sportvan] none, [Chevy Van] none.

1993 Chevrolet 1-Ton C3500 Crew-Cab "Big Dooley" Pickup 4x2 (CMD)

GASOLINE ENGINES (DISPLACEMENT ORDER)

ENGINE: Inline. Four-cylinder. Bore & stroke: 2.95 x 3.54 in. Displacement: 1.6-liter (97 cid). BHP: 80 at 5400 rpm. Torque: unknown. Multiport-fuel-injection. Suzuki-built. [Standard in Geo Tracker]

ENGINE: Inline. Four-cylinder. Bore & stroke: 4.00 x 3.00 in. Displacement: 2.5-liter (151 cid). BHP: 105 at 4800 rpm. Torque: 135 lb.-ft. at 3200 rpm. Compression ratio: 8.3:1. EFI/Throttle-body-injection. VIN Code A. GM-built. [Standard in S10]

ENGINE: V-block. Six-cylinder. Bore & stroke: 3.52 x 2.99 in. Displacement: 2.8-liter (173 cid). BHP: 125 at 4800 rpm. Torque: 150 lb.-ft. at 2400 rpm. EFI/Throttle-body-injection. VIN Code R. Chevrolet-built. [Optional in S10]

ENGINE: V-block. Six-cylinder. Bore & stroke: 3.5 x 3.331 in. Displacement: 3.1-liter (191 cid). BHP: 120 at 4200 rpm. Torque: 175 lb.-ft. at 2200 rpm. Compression ratio: 8.5:1. Multiport-fuel-injection. VIN Code D. GM-built. [Standard in Lumina]

ENGINE: V-block. Six-cylinder. Bore & stroke: 3.8 x 3.4 in. Displacement: 3.8-liter (231 cid). BHP: 165-170 hp at 4800 rpm. Torque: 220-225 lb.-ft. at 3200 rpm. Sequential-port-fuel-injection (SFI). VIN Code L. GM-built. [Optional in Lumina APV]

ENGINE: V-block. Six-cylinder. Bore & stroke: 4.0 x 3.48 in. Displacement: 4.3-liter (262 cid). BHP: 165 at 4000 rpm. Torque: 235 lb.-ft. at 2400 rpm. Compression ratio: 9.1:1. EFI/Throttle-body-injection. VIN Code Z. Chevrolet-built. [Standard in regular Astro, C/K1500, C/K2500, T10, S-Blazer, G10, and G20, optional in S10]

ENGINE: V-block. Enhanced six-cylinder. Bore & stroke: 4.0 x 3.48 in. Displacement: 4.3-liter (262 cid). BHP: 200 at 4400 rpm. Torque: 260 lb.-ft. at 3600 rpm. Compression ratio 9.1:1. Single-point-injected. VIN Code W. GM-built. [Standard in Astro Extended-Body, optional in regular Astro]

ENGINE: V-block. Eight-cylinder. Bore & stroke: 3.74 x 3.48 in. Displacement: 5.0-liter (305 cid). BHP: 170 at 4000 rpm. Torque: 255 lb.-ft. at 2400 rpm. EFI/Throttle-body-injection. VIN Code H. Chevrolet-built. [Optional in C/K1500, C/K2500, G10, G20]

ENGINE: V-block. Eight-cylinder. Bore & stroke: 4.0 x 3.48 in. Displacement: 5.7-liter (350 cid). BHP: 195 at 4000 rpm. Torque: 300 lb.-ft. at 2400 rpm. Compression ratio: 9.1:1. EFI/Throttle-body-injection. VIN Code A. GM-built. [Standard in G30]

ENGINE: V-block. Eight-cylinder. Bore & stroke: 4.0 x 3.48 in. Displacement: 5.7-liter (350 cid). BHP: 210 at 4000 rpm. Compression ratio: 9.1:1. Torque: 300 lb.-ft. at 2800 rpm. EFI/Throttle-body-injection. VIN Code K. Chevrolet-built [Standard in C/K Blazer, C/K3500, and Suburban]

ENGINE: V-block. Eight-cylinder. Bore & stroke: 4.25 x 4.00 in. Displacement: 7.4-liter (454 cid). BHP: 230 at 3600 rpm. Torque: 385 lb.-ft. at 1600 rpm. Throttle-body- fuel-injection. VIN Code N. [Optional in C/K1500, C/K2500, C/K3500, Suburban, and G30]

DIESEL ENGINES (DISPLACEMENT ORDER)

ENGINE: V-block. Heavy-duty. Diesel. Eight-cylinder. Bore & stroke: 3.98 x 3.82 in. Displacement: 6.2-liter (379 cid). BHP: 130 at 3600 rpm. Torque: 240 lb.-ft. at 2000 rpm. VIN Code C. Chevrolet-built. [Optional in C/K2500 Pickup, optional in G30 Pickup]

ENGINE: V-block. Light-duty. Diesel. Eight-cylinder. Bore & stroke: 3.98 x 3.82 in. Displacement: 6.2-liter (379 cid). BHP: 148 at 3600 rpm. Torque: 248 lb.-ft. at 2000 rpm. VIN Code J. Chevrolet-built. [Optional in G30 vans]

ENGINE: V-block. Eight-cylinder. Turbocharged. Bore & stroke: 4.06 x 3.82 in. Displacement: 6.5-liter (400 cid). BHP: 190 at 3400 rpm. Torque: 240 lb.-ft. at 2000 rpm. VIN Code F. GM-built. [Optional in all C/K2500 Pickups and C/K3500 Crew-Cabs]

CHASSIS: [Geo Tracker (All)] Wheelbase: 86.6 in. Length: 142.5 in. Width: 64.2 in. Height: 65.6 in. Tires: (4x2) P195/75R-15, (4x4) P205/75R15 black sidewall.

CHASSIS: [S10] Regular-Cab. Short Box. Wheelbase: 108.3 in. Length: 178.2 in. Width: 64.7 in. Height: 61.3 in. GVW: 4,200 lb. Payload: 1,565 lb. Tires: P195/75R14 black sidewall.

CHASSIS: [T10] Regular-Cab. Short Box. Wheelbase: 108.5 in. Length: 178.2 in. Width: 64.7 in. Height: 63.4 in. GVW: 4,650 lb. Payload: 1,415 lb. Tires: P205/75R15 black sidewall.

CHASSIS: [S10] Regular-Cab. Long Box. Wheelbase: 117.9 in. Length: 194.2 in. Width: 64.7 in. Height: 61.3 in. GVW: 4,200 lb. Payload: 1,565 lb. Tires: P195/75R14 black sidewall.

CHASSIS: [T10] Regular-Cab. Long Box. Wheelbase: 117.9 in. Length: 194.2 in. Width: 64.7 in. Height: 63.4 in. GVW: 4,650 lb. Payload: 1,415 lb. Tires: P205/75R15 black sidewall

CHASSIS: [S10] Extended-Cab. Short Box. Wheelbase: 122.9 in. Length: 192.8 in. Width: 64.7 in. Height: 61.3 in. GVW: 4,200 lb. Payload: 1,366 lb. Tires: P195/75R14 black sidewall.

CHASSIS: [T10] Extended-Cab. Short Box. Wheelbase: 122.9 in. Length: 192.8 in. Width: 64.7 in. Height: 63.4 in. GVW: 4,650 lb. Payload: 1,283 lb. Tires: P205/75R15 black sidewall.

CHASSIS: [S-Blazer 4x2] Two-door. Wheelbase: 100.5 in. Length: 170.3 in. Width: 65.4 in. Height: 64.1 in. GVW: 4,350 lb. Payload: 1,152 lb. Tires: P205/75R15 black sidewall.

CHASSIS: [S-Blazer 4x4] Two-door. Wheelbase: 100.5 in. Length: 170.3 in. Width: 65.4 in. Height: 64.3 in. GVW: 4,700 lb. Payload: 1,188 lb. Tires: P205/75R15 black sidewall.

CHASSIS: [S-Blazer 4x2] Four-door. Wheelbase: 107 in. Length: 176.8 in. Width: 65.4 in. Height: 64.1 in. GVW: 4,850 lb. Payload: 1,485 lb. Tires: P205/75R15 black sidewall.

CHASSIS: [S-Blazer 4x4] Four-door. Wheelbase: 107 in. Length: 176.8 in. Width: 65.4 in. Height: 64.3 in. GVW: 5,100 lb. Payload: 1,352 lb. Tires: P205/75R15 black sidewall.

CHASSIS: [Astro Cargo regular-body] Wheelbase: 111 in. Length: 176.8 in. Width: 77.5 in. Height: 76.2 in. GVW: 5,950 lb. Payload: 1,757 lb. Tires: P205/75R15 black sidewall.

CHASSIS: [Astro Cargo regular-body AWD] Wheelbase: 111 in. Length: 176.8 in. Width: 77.5 in. Height: 76.2 in. GVW: 5,950 lb. Payload: 1,748 lb. Tires: P205/75R15 black sidewall.

CHASSIS: [Astro Cargo Extended-Body] Wheelbase: 111 in. Length: 186.8 in. Width: 77.5 in. Height: 76.2 in. GVW: 6,100 lb. Payload: 1,891 lb. Tires: P205/75R15 black sidewall.

CHASSIS: [Astro Cargo Extended-Body AWD] Wheelbase: 111 in. Length:. 186.8 in. Width: 77.5 in. Height: 76.2 in. GVW: 6,100 lb. Payload: 1,841 lb. Tires: P205/75R15 black sidewall.

CHASSIS: [Astro Passenger regular-body] Wheelbase: 111 in. Length: 176.8 in. Width: 77.5 in. Height: 76.2 in. GVW: 5,950 lb. Payload: 1,757 lb. Tires: P205/75R15 black sidewall.

CHASSIS: [Astro Passenger regular-body AWD] Wheelbase: 111 in. Length: 176.8 in. Width: 77.5 in. Height: 76.2 in. GVW: 5,950 lb. Payload: 1,748 lb. Tires: P205/75R15 black sidewall.

CHASSIS: [Astro Passenger Extended-Body] Wheelbase: 111 in. Length: 186.8 in. Width: 77.5 in. Height: 76.2 in. GVW: 6,100 lb. Payload: 1,891 lb. Tires: P205/75R15 black sidewall.

CHASSIS: [Astro Passenger Extended-Body AWD] Wheelbase: 186.8 in. Width: 77.5 in. Height: 76.2 in. GVW: 6,100 lb. Payload: 1,841 lb. Tires: P205/75R15 black sidewall.

CHASSIS: [Lumina] Wheelbase: 109.8 in. Length: 194.2 in. Width: 73.9 in. Height: 65.7 in. GVW: 4,935 lb. Payload: 1,357 lb. Tires: P205/70R15 black sidewall.

CHASSIS: [G10/Short Body] Chevy Van. Wheelbase: 110 in. Length: 178.1 in. Width: 79.5 in. Height: 79.4 in. GVW: 6,000 lb. Payload: 1,754 lb. Tires: P215/75R15 black sidewall.

CHASSIS: [G10/Long Body] Chevy Van/Sportvan. Wheelbase: 125 in. Length: 202.1 in. Width: 79.5 in. Height: 79.5 in. GVW: 6,000 lb. Payload: 1,428 lb. Tires: P215/75R15 black sidewall.

CHASSIS: [G20/Short Body] Chevy Van. Wheelbase: 110 in. Length: 178.1 in. Width: 79.5 in. Height: 79.4 in. GVW: 6,000 lb. Payload: 1,754 lb. Tires: P215/75R15 black sidewall.

CHASSIS: [G20/Long Body] Chevy Van/Sportvan. Wheelbase: 125 in. Length: 202.1 in. Width: 79.5 in. Height: 79.5 in. GVW: 6,875 lb. Payload: 2,142 lb. Tires: P215/75R15 black sidewall.

CHASSIS: [G30/Long Body Chevy Van] Wheelbase: 125 in. Length: 202.1 in. Width: 79.5 in. Height: 79.5 in. GVW: 9,200 lb. Payload: 3,951 lb. Tires: P215/75R15 black sidewall.

CHASSIS: [G30/Long Body Sportvan] Wheelbase: 125 in. Length: 202.1 in. Width: 79.5 in. Height: 79.5 in. GVW: 9,200 lb. Payload: 4,101 lb. Tires: P215/75R15 black sidewall.

1993 Chevrolet 1/2-Ton S10 Blazer Tahoe LT 4-door Sport Utility 4x4 (CMD)

CHASSIS: [G30/Extended Body Chevy Van] Wheelbase: 146 in. Length: 223.1 in. Width: 79.5 in. Height: 82.3 in. GVW: 9,200 lb. Payload: 3,951 lb. Tires: P215/75R15 black sidewall
CHASSIS: [G30/Extended Body 12-Passenger Sportvan] Wheelbase: 146 in. Length: 223.1 in. Width: 79.5 in. Height: 82.3 in. GVW: 9,200 lb. Payload: 4,101 lb. lb. Tires: P215/75R15 black sidewall
CHASSIS: [K10 Blazer 4x4] Wheelbase: 111.5 in. Length: 188 in. Width: 77.1 in. Height: 75 in. GVW: 6,250 lb. Payload: 1,517 lb. Tires: LT245/75R16C black sidewall.
CHASSIS: [Suburban C1500] Wheelbase: 131.5 in. Length: 219.5 in. Width: 77 in. Height: 74.9 in. GVW: 6,800 lb. Payload: 2,117 lb. Tires: P235/75R-15XLS black sidewall.
CHASSIS: [Suburban K1500] Wheelbase: 131.5 in. Length: 219.5 in. Width: 77 in. Height: 73.6 in. GVW: 7,200 lb. Payload: 2,052 lb. Tires: P235/75R-15XLS black sidewall.
CHASSIS: [Suburban C2500] Wheelbase: 131.5 in. Length: 219.5 in. Width: 77 in. Height: 74.9 in. GVW: 8,600 lb. Payload: 3,370 lb. Tires: P235/75R-15XLS black sidewall.
CHASSIS: [Suburban K2500] Wheelbase: 131.5 in. Length: 219.5 in. Width: 77 in. Height: 73.6 in. GVW: 8,600 lb. Payload: 2,944 lb. Tires: P235/75R-15XLS black sidewall.
CHASSIS: [C1500 Sportside Regular-Cab Short Box Pickup] Regular-Cab. Short Box. Wheelbase: 117.5 in. Length: 194.1 in. Width: 77.1 in. Height: 70.4 in. GVW: 5,600 lb. Payload: 2,231 lb. Tires: P225/75R15 black sidewall ALSBR tires.
CHASSIS: [C1500 Fleetside Regular-Cab Short Box Pickup] Wheelbase: 117.5 in. Length: 194.1 in. Width: 76.8 in. Height: 70.4 in. GVW: 5,600 lb. Payload: 2,231 lb. Tires: P225/75R15 black sidewall ALSBR tires.
CHASSIS: [C1500 Fleetside Regular-Cab Short Box "Work Truck" Pickup] Wheelbase: 117.5 in. Length: 194.1 in. Width: 76.8 in. Height: 70.4 in. GVW: 5,600 lb. Payload: 2,231 lb. Tires: P225/75R15 black sidewall ALSBR tires.
CHASSIS: [C1500 Fleetside Regular-Cab Long Box Pickup] Wheelbase: 131.5 in. Length: 212.6 in. Width: 76.8 in. Height: 70.4 in. GVW: 6,100 lb. Payload: 2,231 lb. Tires: P225/75R15 black sidewall ALSBR tires.
CHASSIS: [C1500 Fleetside Regular-Cab Long Box "Work Truck" Pickup] Wheelbase: 131.5 in. Length: 212.6 in. Width: 76.8 in. Height: 70.4 in. GVW: 6,100 lb. Payload: 2,231 lb. Tires: P225/75R15 black sidewall ALSBR tires.
CHASSIS: [C1500 Sportside Extended-Cab Short Box Pickup] Wheelbase: 141.5 in. Length: 218.0 in. Width: 77.1 in. Height: 70.6 in. GVW: 6,600 lb. Payload: 2,200 lb. Tires: P225/75R15 black sidewall ALSBR tires.
CHASSIS: [C1500 Fleetside Extended-Cab Short Box Pickup] Wheelbase: 141.5 in. Length: 218.0 in. Width: 76.8 in. Height: 70.6 in. GVW: 6,600 lb. Payload: 2,200 lb. Tires: P225/75R15 black sidewall ALSBR tires.
CHASSIS: [C1500 Fleetside Extended-Cab Long Box Pickup] Wheelbase: 155.5 in. Length: 237.0 in. Width: 76.8 in. Height: 70.6 in. GVW: 6,600 lb. Payload: 2,200 lb. Tires: P225/75R15 black sidewall ALSBR tires.
CHASSIS: [K1500 Sportside Regular-Cab Short Box Pickup] Wheelbase: 117.5 in. Length: 194.1 in. Width: 77.1 in. Height: 73.8 GVW: 6,100 lb. Payload: 1,980 lb. Tires: P225/75R15 black sidewall ALSBR tires.
CHASSIS: [K1500 Fleetside Regular-Cab Short Box Pickup] Wheelbase: 117.5 in. Length: 194.1 in. Width: 77.1 in. Height: 73.8 in. GVW: 6,100 lb. Payload: 1,980 lb. Tires: P225/75R15 black sidewall ALSBR tires.
CHASSIS: [K1500 Fleetside Regular-Cab Short Box "Work Truck" Pickup] Wheelbase: 117.5 in. Length: 194.1 in. Width: 77.1 in. Height: 73.8 in. GVW: 6,100 lb. Payload: 1,980 lb. Tires: P225/75R15 black sidewall ALSBR tires.
CHASSIS: [K1500 Fleetside Regular-Cab Long Box Pickup] Wheelbase: 131.5 in. Length: 212.6 in. Width: 76.8 in. Height: 73.8 in. GVW: 6,100 lb. Payload: 1,980 lb. Tires: P225/75R15 black sidewall ALSBR tires.
CHASSIS: [K1500 Fleetside Regular-Cab Long Box "Work Truck" Pickup] Wheelbase: 131.5 in. Length: 212.6 in. Width: 76.8 in. Height: 73.8 in. GVW: 6,100 lb. Payload: 1,980 lb. Tires: P225/75R15 black sidewall ALSBR tires.
CHASSIS: [K1500 Sportside Extended-Cab Short Box Pickup] Wheelbase: 141.5 in. Length: 218.0 in. Width: 77.1 in. Height: 73.8 in. GVW: 6,600 lb. Payload: 2,105 lb. Tires: P225/75R15 black sidewall ALSBR tires.
CHASSIS: [K1500 Fleetside Extended-Cab Short Box Pickup] Wheelbase: 141.5 in. Length: 218.0 in. Width: 76.8 in. Height: 73.8 in. GVW: 6,600 lb. Payload: 2,105 lb. Tires: P225/75R15 black sidewall ALSBR tires.
CHASSIS: [K1500 Fleetside Extended-Cab Long Box Pickup] Wheelbase: 155.5 in. Length: 237.0 in. Width: 76.8 in. Height: 73.8 in. GVW: 6,600 lb. Payload: 2,105 lb. Tires: P225/75R15 black sidewall ALSBR tires.
CHASSIS: [C2500 Fleetside Regular-Cab Long Box Pickup] Wheelbase: 131.5 in. Length: 212.6 in. Width: 76.8 in. Height: 73 in. GVW: 7,200 lb. Payload: 2,231 lb. Tires: P225/75R15 black sidewall ALSBR tires.
CHASSIS: [C2500 Heavy-duty Fleetside Regular-Cab Long Box Pickup] Wheelbase: 131.5 in. Length: 212.6 in. Width: 76.8 in. Height: 73 in. GVW: 7,200 lb. Payload: 2,231 lb. Tires: P225/75R15 black sidewall ALSBR tires.
CHASSIS: [C2500 Fleetside Extended-Cab Short Box Pickup] Wheelbase: 141.5 in. Length: 218.0 in. Width: 76.8 in. Height: 74 in. GVW: 8,600 lb. Payload: 2,366 lb. Tires: P225/75R15 black sidewall ALSBR tires.
CHASSIS: [C2500 Fleetside Extended-Cab Long Box Pickup] Wheelbase: 155.5 in. Length: 237.0 in. Width: 76.8 in. Height: 74 in. GVW: 8,600 lb. Payload: 2,366 lb. Tires: P225/75R15 black sidewall ALSBR tires.
CHASSIS: [K2500 Fleetside Regular-Cab Long Box Pickup] Wheelbase: 131.5 in. Length: 212.6 in. Width: 76.8 in. Height: 73.8 in. GVW: 7,200 lb. Payload: 1,980 lb. Tires: P225/75R15 black sidewall ALSBR tires.
CHASSIS: [K2500 Heavy-duty Fleetside Regular-Cab Long Box Pickup] Wheelbase: 131.5 in. Length: 212.6 in. Width: 76.8 in. Height: 73.8 in. GVW: 7,200 lb. Payload: 1,980 lb. Tires: P225/75R15 black sidewall ALSBR tires.
CHASSIS: [K2500 Fleetside Extended-Cab Short Box Pickup] Wheelbase: 141.5 in. Length: 218.0 in. Width: 76.8 in. Height: 73.8 in. GVW: 8,600 lb. Payload: 2,105 lb. Tires: P225/75R15 black sidewall ALSBR tires.
CHASSIS: [K2500 Fleetside Extended-Cab Long Box Pickup] Wheelbase: 155.5 in. Length: 237.0 in. Width: 76.8 in. Height: 73.8 in. GVW: 8,600 lb. Payload: 2,105 lb. Tires: P225/75R15 black sidewall ALSBR tires.
CHASSIS: [C3500 Fleetside Regular-Cab Long Box Pickup] Wheelbase: 131.5 in. Length: 212.6 in. Width: 76.8 in. Height: 70.4 in. GVW: 10,000 lb. Payload: 1,980 lb. Tires: P225/75R15 black sidewall ALSBR tires.
CHASSIS: [K3500 Fleetside Regular-Cab Long Box Pickup] Wheelbase: 131.5 in. Length: 212.6 in. Width: 76.8 in. Height: 73.8 in. GVW: 10,000 lb. Payload: 1,980 lb. Tires: P225/75R15 black sidewall ALSBR tires.
CHASSIS: [C3500 Fleetside Extended-Cab Long Box Pickup] Wheelbase: 155.5 in. Length: 237.0 in. Width: 76.8 in. Height: 70.4 in. GVW: 10,000 lb. Payload: 2,200 lb. Tires: P225/75R15 black sidewall ALSBR tires.
CHASSIS: [K3500 Fleetside Extended-Cab Long Box Pickup] Wheelbase: 155.5 in. Length: 237.0 in. Width: 76.8 in. Height: 73.8 in. GVW: 10,000 lb. Payload: 2,105 lb. Tires: P225/75R15 black sidewall ALSBR tires.
CHASSIS: [C/K 3500 Pickup] Motor home chassis. Wheelbase: 183.5 in. Tires: P225/75R15 black sidewall ALSBR tires.
SELECTED OPTIONS (*)
GEO TRACKER OPTIONS: Base equipment group with UL1 radio ($301). Base equipment group with UL0 radio ($496). Air conditioning ($745). Rear folding bench seat, front-wheel-drive Convertible only ($445). Three-speed automatic transmission ($595). Tilt steering ($115). 15-in. alloy wheels with steel spare wheel ($335).

S/T-SERIES PICKUP OPTIONS: Four-speed automatic transmission with overdrive ($890). 2.8-liter EFI V-6 ($390). 4.3-liter EFI V-6, requires power steering ($620). Driver convenience package intermittent wipers and Comfortilt steering ($204). ETR AM radio with clock ($201). AM/FM ETR stereo with cassette, Seek-and-Scan, and digital clock ($332). All-weather air conditioning ($755). Air dam with fog lamps for 4x2s only ($115). Front console ($145).4x4 off-road suspension package ($182). Deluxe cloth interior, Regular-Cab ($194). 4x4 underbody shield package ($126). Trailer Special package ($408). EL option package for XL81 ($233). Wheel opening and back exterior moldings ($43). Operating convenience package ($367). Special two-tone paint ($241). Custom two-tone paint ($275). Speed control ($238). 15 x 7 Argent Silver aluminum wheel rims ($248). 15 x 7 cast aluminum wheels ($280).
S-BLAZER OPTIONS: CAA2 Tahoe package ($1,097). CAA3 Tahoe package ($2,900). LTB1 Tahoe LT package ($4,304). AAA2 Tahoe package ($640). AAA3 Tahoe package ($2,619). LTA1 Tahoe LT package, 4x2 ($3,979), 4x4 ($3,777). Air conditioning ($780). Air dam and fog lamps for 4x2 only ($115). Spare wheel and tire carrier ($159). Cold climate package ($109-$179). D55 front seat separator ($145) DK6 console ($83). H-D cooling system ($135). Driver convenience package, two-door ($367), four-door ($542). Enhanced power train with 4.3-liter CPI V-6 and four-speed automatic transmission ($1,160). Tinted glass packages ($144-$225). Full-instrumentation package ($195). Keyless entry system ($135). Special two-tone paint with body striping ($218). Custom two-tone paint with graduated body striping ($275). UM7 AM/FM stereo ($131). UM6 AM/FM stereo cassette ($253). UX1 premium sound system ($403). U1C AM/FM stereo ($537). Special custom cloth bench seats ($405). Deluxe cloth reclining high-back bucket seats with manually-adjusted lumbar support (($102). Power driver seat ($392). Folding rear bench seat with arm rests ($409). Off-road suspension ($122-$182). P205/75R15 white-letter tires ($121). P235/75R15 white outline letter tires ($296). PA3 cast aluminum wheels ($248-$340). 5P2 special aluminum wheels for 4x4s ($280-$340). Sliding rear quarter window ($257). Rear window wiper system ($125).
ASTRO OPTIONS: ASA3 plus convenience group with eight-passenger seating ($1,352). ASA4 plus convenience group ($2,032). ASA5 includes ASA4 features plus luggage carrier, roof console, six-way power seat and more ($3,133). Air conditioning, front ($845), front and rear ($1,368). Deluxe front and rear chrome bumpers ($128). Dutch doors with rear wiper and electric release ($364). Black luggage carrier ($126). DK6 console ($83). Locking differential ($252). ZQ3 convenience group with tilt wheel and speed control ($383). ZQ2 convenience group with power windows and door locks ($434). Heavy-duty cooling system ($198). YC6 Custom Luxury CL decor package ($1,092). YC7 Luxury Touring LT decor package ($2,848). Electric rear window defogger ($154). Power door lock system ($223). TR9 auxiliary lighting package ($133). Electronic instrumentation ($195). Electric remote-control mirrors ($150). ZY2 custom two-tone paint ($104-$329). ZY3 special two-tone paint ($172). ZY4 deluxe two-tone paint ($251-$476). 4.3-liter CPI V-6 with oil and transmission coolers and heavy-duty cooling in CM models ($500). UM7 AM/FM stereo ($151). UM6 AM/FM stereo cassette ($273). UX1 premium sound system ($423). U1C AM/FM stereo ($557). ZP7 seven-passenger seating ($1,043). Arm rests ($245). Six-way power driver's seat ($240). Trailering Special equipment ($507). PF3 cast-aluminum wheels ($248-$340). Argent Silver Rally wheels ($92).

1993 Chevrolet 1/2-Ton U05 Lumina APV "LS" Passenger Minivan 4x2 (CMD

LUMINA OPTIONS: Base Preferred Equipment Group with UM6 radio ($140). Base Preferred Equipment Group with U1C radio ($396). WPA1 Preferred Equipment Group ($482). WPA1 Preferred Equipment Group with UM6 radio (add $140). WPA1 Preferred Equipment Group with U1C radio (add $396). WPA2 Equipment Group ($1,130). WPA2 Equipment Group with U1C radio ($1,145). WVA1 Preferred Equipment Group ($698). 3.8-liter SFI engine ($619). Air conditioning ($830). Front and rear air conditioning teamed with WVA1, WPA1 or WPA2 ($450). Roof carrier ($145). Electric rear window defogger ($170). Deep-tinted glass ($245). Power door and tailgate locks ($300). Power driver's seat ($270). Bucket seats and five-passenger modular rear seat ($660). Electric speed control with resume ($225). Load leveling suspension ($170). Self-sealing tires ($150 extra). Trailering package ($150). Comfortilt steering wheel ($145). Four-speed automatic transmission ($200). Cast aluminum 15-in. wheels with locks ($275). Power windows with "express" down ($275).
G-SERIES SPORTVAN OPTIONS: Front air conditioning ($975). Front and rear air conditioning ($599-1,574). Locking differential ($252). ZQ2 convenience group: $434. ZQ3 convenience group ($383). 5.0-liter EFI V-8 ($575). 5.7-liter EFI V-8 ($845). 7.4-liter EFI V-8 ($605). 6.2-liter diesel V-8 ($2,400). 6.2-liter heavy-duty diesel V-8 ($1,555). Deep-tinted glass ($306). G20 GVWR package with 5.7-liter V-8 ($263). Rear heater ($205). Auxiliary lighting package ($133). Sportvan Beauville decor package ($818). UM7 stereo ($141). UM6 stereo ($263). UX1 stereo ($413). ZP3 interior with one adult rear seat for 15-passenger seating ($371). Custom cloth seat trim with reclining bucket seats ($402). Trailering equipment ($508). Aluminum wheels ($210-$331). Rally wheels ($121).
G-SERIES CARGO VAN OPTIONS: Preferred Equipment Group G1A2 ($1,363). Air conditioning ($975). ZQ2 convenience group ($434). Heavy-duty cooling system ($63). 5.0-liter EFI V-8 ($575). 5.7-liter EFI V-8 ($845). 7.4-liter EFI V-8 ($605). 6.2-liter diesel V-8 ($2,400). 6.2-liter heavy-duty diesel V-8 ($1,555). Front area carpeting and wheelhouse rubber mats ($147). Swing-out glass package ($226). Heater ($205) TR9 auxiliary lighting package ($156). UM6 stereo equipment ($218). U1C stereo equipment ($492). Trailering equipment package ($132). Heavy-duty Trailering Special package ($508). Rally wheels ($121). Cast aluminum wheels ($331). Wheelcovers for G30 ($42).

K10 BLAZER OPTIONS: K5A2 Silverado package ($2,287). K5A3 Silverado package ($2,704). K5A4 Silverado Sport package ($3,299). Air conditioning ($845). V22 appearance package ($191). Locking differential ($252). Roof mounted luggage carrier ($126). Off-road chassis equipment ($400).ZQ2 convenience package ($367). ZQ3 convenience package ($383). B71 molding package with PEG K5A3 ($180). UM7 AM/FM stereo ($170). UM6 ETR AM/FM stereo cassette ($122-$292). UX1 stereo system ($150-$442). All-tinted glass ($215). Conventional two-tone paint ($180). Deluxe two-tone paint ($290).Custom cloth reclining high-back bucket seats ($341). Skid plate package w/o Z71 ($225). Trailering Special equipment package ($460). Four-speed automatic overdrive transmission ($890). Rally wheel trim ($60). Cast aluminum wheels ($250-$310).

SUBURBAN OPTIONS: N1A2/1SB Silverado package ($3,968-$4,052). N1A3/1SC Silverado package ($4,495-4,556). N2A2/1SC Silverado package ($4,227-$4,288). Air conditioning ($845). V22 appearance package ($191). Locking differential ($252). Roof carrier ($126).Tailgate body ($198). ZQ2 convenience group ($383). California emissions ($100). 7.4-liter EFI V-8 ($605). UX1 stereo system ($150-$235). Deep-tinted glass ($305). Conventional two-tone paint ($180). Deluxe two-tone paint ($290). Skid plate package ($225). Trailering Equipment package ($273-$408).Rally wheel trim ($18). Cast aluminum wheels ($268-$310).

1993 Chevrolet 3/4-Ton C2500 Fleetside Long Box Pickup 4x2 (CMD)

C/K PICKUP OPTIONS: P1A2 Cheyenne PEG($475). P1A3 Silverado PEG ($1,258). P1A4 Silverado PEG ($1,380-$1,880). PSP1 Sport PEG ($1,938-$2,460). R9A Work truck packages for C/K2500 models ($479-$684). R9C convenience package ($372-$452). Air conditioning ($805). Appearance package ($191) Heavy-duty battery ($134). Painted rear step bumper ($130). Chrome rear step bumper ($229). Off-road package ($270). ZQ8 Sport handling package ($664-$865). 5.0-liter EFI V-8 ($575-$845). 7.4-liter EFI V-8 ($470-$1,315). 6.2-liter naturally aspirated diesel V-8 ($1,555-$2,400). 6.2-liter heavy-duty diesel V-8 ($2,225-$3,100). Conventional two-tone paint ($132). Deluxe two-tone paint ($243). Body moldings ($107). UP4 radio equipment ($162). UM7 stereo equipment ($170-$332). UM6 radio package ($122-$454). UX1 stereo equipment ($150-$442). Custom vinyl low-back reclining bucket seats ($289). Custom vinyl split bench seat $174). Trailering Special package ($210-$$448). Five-speed manual transmission with deep low and overdrive ($98). Four-speed automatic transmission with overdrive ($890). Bright metal wheelcovers ($42). Cast aluminum wheels ($250-310). C/K3500 dual rear wheels ($955).

NOTE 15: Options and prices shown are representative. The actual cost of an option or option package often varies according to other packages that the options are combined with on specific vehicles. Preferred Equipment Group (PEG) options offer specific optional equipment at discount prices. Some "options" may be standard equipment on certain models, such as V-8s in C/K3500 Pickups. Descriptions of options are edited. Full option contents can be determined by consulting sales literature.

HISTORICAL: Chevrolet trucks were built in 12 factories in 1993. Geo Trackers were made at the CAMI plant in Ingersoll, Ontario, Canada. S-Series Pickups were assembled in Pontiac, Michigan and Shreveport, Louisiana. S-Blazers built at Pontiac, Michigan and Moraine, Ohio. Astros were made in Baltimore, Maryland. Chevy Van models were sourced from factories in Scarborough, Ontario, Canada and Flint, Michigan. Full-size Blazers and Suburbans were made in the Chevrolet factory at Janesville, Wisconsin. C/K Pickups were built in Fort Wayne, Indiana; Oshawa, Ontario, Canada; Pontiac, Michigan; and Janesville, Wisconsin. Lumina APVs were assembled at Tarrytown, N.Y. Jim Perkins continued as general manager of Chevrolet Motor Division. J.N. Janowiak was national manager of truck merchandising and R.M. Wisner was manager of truck advertising. Chevrolet new-truck sales (and market penetration) were: 38,996 Astro Vans (2.95 percent), 86,571 Astro Wagons (6.55 percent), 41,035 Lumina passenger vans (3.11 percent), 409 Lumina Cargo Vans (0.03 percent), 22,852 Blazers (1.73 percent), 167,421 S-Blazers (12.67 percent), 513,147 C/K Pickups (38.83 percent), 25,225 P-Series Step-Vans (1.91 percent), 183,700 S10/T10 Pickups (13.90 percent), 6,329 Sportvans (0.48 percent), 82,615 Suburbans (6.25 percent), 42,312 Canadian-built Geo Trackers (3.20 percent), 98,146 Chevy Vans (7.43 percent), and 1,121 W4 Tiltmaster imports (0.08 percent). This gave the company total light-duty truck sales of 1,309,879 units and 24.36 percent of the overall light-duty truck market.

1994

1/4-TON — GEO TRACKER — L4: Chevrolet dealers continued selling the Suzuki-designed Geo Tracker as a small Sport Utility Vehicle. They had a small pickup box. Tracker models started with a two-door convertible with front-wheel-drive only. The convertible also came in 4x4 format, with or without optional LSi trim. The hardtop model came only as a 4x4, in the base or LSi trim levels. There were no major changes in the Tracker for 1994. Standard equipment for the front-wheel-drive convertible included a wide-stance tuned suspension, a "truck tough" frame, a heavy-duty heater and defroster, side window defoggers, full carpeting, Scotchguard fabric protection, black bumpers with rub strips, a center high-mounted stop lamp, composite halogen headlamps, zinc-galvanized body panels, front and rear tow hooks, an outside locking spare tire and wheel, a spare tire cover with blue or green lettering, a center console with storage tray, a day/night inside rear view mirror, door storage bins, full carpeting, a locking glove box, warning tones, a trip odometer, integral head restraints, reclining high-back "easy enter" bucket seats, and stainless steel styled wheels. The 4x4 models added black rocker panel moldings, rear swing-out window glass, a rear defogger, a tachometer, a fold-and-stow rear bench seat, manual locking hubs, and larger tires. The 4x4 Lsi models also had body-color bumpers with integral rub strips, black body side moldings with gray stripes, a rear window wiper/washer, a spare tire cover with gray lettering, floor mats, power steering, tinted glass, custom cloth upholstery, adjustable head restraints, flip, fold-and-stow rear bucket seats, automatic locking hubs, and Lsi styled wheels. Colors for all Trackers included Tropical Green Metallic, White, Black Licorice, and Mystic Magento Metallic. Sky Blue Metallic and Bright Red colors were used for base models only. Exclusive finishes for Lsi models included Medium Quasar Blue Metallic, Shadow Gray Metallic, and Brilliant Red Metallic. The standard Geo Tracker power team consisted of a 1.6-liter SOHC inline four-cylinder engine with multiport fuel-injection, and a five-speed manual transmission with overdrive. Power front disc/rear drum rear wheel antilock brakes were regular equipment. Also standard were (4x2 model) P195/75R-15 tires or (4x4 models) P205/75R-15 tires. Tracker buyers had a choice of linear cloth bucket seats, expressive cloth bucket seats or custom cloth bucket seats at the same price.

1/2-TON — S (4x2)/T (4x4) SERIES PICKUP — L4/V-6: Revised S-Series Pickups were introduced in 1994. They were all-new from the inside out, with more power, more room, more precision, and more safety enhancements than ever before offered in this compact model. The windshield was moved forward and there was a 20 percent increase in glass area. This new generation of personal pickups offered five exceptional models in two lines. The S10 was the 4x2 series and the T10 was the 4x4 series (Both had S10 badges on the fenders). The S/T-series models were all roomier, more comfortable, more powerful, and safer than Chevrolet's previous compact pickups. They had more contemporary styling with a smooth, down-turned aerodynamic nose. The wraparound grille had wedge-shaped parking lamps at each corner, deep-set rectangular headlights, and a twin-air-slot opening with a big gold Chevrolet bow tie emblem in the middle of the center bar. The S/T interior was also redesigned. Standard equipment included a 2.2-liter multiport-fuel-injected (MFI) inline four-cylinder engine, power front disc/rear drum rear-wheel antilock brakes, five-speed manual transmission with overdrive, power steering, halogen headlamps, Solar-Ray tinted glass, Dark Argent grille, color-keyed rear close-out panel (instead of rear bumper), and P205/75R15 black sidewall tires. Compact pickups with V-6 power also had all-wheel antilock brakes, and LS models had a rear bumper. The base series offered Short and Long Box Regular-Cab models, plus an Extended-Cab Short Box model. LS features also consisted of color-keyed molded plastic door panels with cloth inserts, color-keyed carpeting, left- and right-hand mirrors, a lighted visor mirror, swing-out rear quarter windows (with Extended-Cab), a chrome grille (except Super Sport), and a 60/40 split bench seat with deluxe cloth upholstery. The Short Box models had a 6.1-foot box, regardless of cab configuration. The Long Box model had a 7.4-foot box. GVW ranges were 4,200 to 5,150 lb. A three-passenger bench seat was standard in all S-Series Pickups. Twin bucket seats were optional. The Extended-Cab model could also be ordered with four-passenger seating. New model-options included a Super Sport (SS) version of the 4x2 truck, and a ZR2 version of the 4x4 truck. The Super Sport equipment included fog lamps, color-keyed bumpers and grille, a color-keyed rear filler panel (in place of rear bumper), 15-in. cast aluminum wheels with bright center caps, special badging on doors, tailgate, and grille. Leather-wrapped steering wheel (LS trim required), 195-hp Enhanced Vortec V-6, automatic transmission, 3.42:1 ratio rear axle, P215/65R-15 tires, Sport suspension, heavy-duty shock absorbers, front stabilizer bar, and locking differential. The ZR2 equipment included a 3.9-in. wider track front and rear, 31 x 10.5-in. special tires, 15-in. cast aluminum wheels, Spectre Gray bumpers and wheel flares, air dam with built-in tow hooks, and a larger rear axle. Standard S/T series colors were Midnight Black (#19), Brilliant Blue Metallic (#22), Teal Green Metallic (#38), Khaki (#52), Purple Metallic (#21), Quicksilver Metallic (#96), Raspberry Red Metallic (#85), Apple Red (#72), and Dark Cherry Red Metallic (#94). Super Sports came only in Midnight Black, Apple Red, or Frost White. ZR2s came only in Midnight Black, Brilliant Blue, Quicksilver, Apple Red or Frost White. Interior options offered were custom vinyl, deluxe cloth, and custom cloth.

1994 Chevrolet 1/2-Ton S10 Blazer "LT" 2-door Sport Utility 4x4 (CMD)

1/2-TON — S (4x2)/T (4x4) SERIES BLAZER — V-6: For 1994 Chevrolet presented the latest refinement of the compact Sport Utility Vehicle in its new S-Blazer. The S-Blazer came in 4x2 and 4x4 models with two-door and four-door body configurations. The two-door model, with 67.3 cu.-ft. of cargo capacity, had a 6.5-in. shorter wheelbase than the four-door. Two-passenger seating was standard and four-passenger seating was optional in the two-door. The four-door came with standard three-passenger seating in 4x2 format, with options to seat two, five or six persons. The 4x4 four-door had standard six-passenger seating, with five-passenger bucket seating optional. The LT (Luxury Touring) version of the four-door had standard bucket seating for five. The four-door had a larger 74.3 cu.-ft. cargo capacity. Respective GVW ranges for the two body types were 4,350 to 4,700 lb. and 4,850 to 5,100 lb. The S-Blazer had a squarer look than the S-

Series Pickup up front. The grille was rectangular in shape with vertical slit-type parking lamps on either side. Single rectangular headlamps sat outside the radiator air opening. A horizontal bar across the center of the opening held a gold Chevrolet bow tie in its center. Three vertical members divided the radiator opening into eight narrow rectangular segments. Standard equipment included a 4.3-liter EFI V-6, power front disc/rear drum brakes, four-wheel ABS brake system, five-speed manual gear box with overdrive, and P205/75R15 black sidewall tires.

1994 Chevrolet 1/2-Ton M10 Astro "CL" Extended-body Minivan 4x2 (CMD)

1/2-TON — ASTRO VAN SERIES M (RWD)/L (AWD) — V-6: Chevrolet's popular Astro M10 rear-wheel-drive (RWD) minivan was the perfect American family vehicle. It came in Standard-Body and Extended-Body models in two series. The models in the L10 series had all-wheel-drive (AWD) for improved year-round traction. A driver's facial air bag was a new item of standard equipment. Other standard features were a 4.3-liter EFI V-6 (4.3-liter CPI V-6 in AWD models), front disc/rear drum four-wheel ABS brakes, a four-speed automatic transmission with overdrive, and P205/75R15 black sidewall tires. The Standard-Body model had a 151.8 cu.-ft. cargo capacity and a 5,700 to 5,950-lb. GVW range. The Extended-Body model had 170.4 cu.-ft. of cargo capacity and a 5,950 to 6,100-lb. GVWR. Astros came in CS, CL, and LT trim levels. Standard equipment on the CS included a driver's airbag, padded arm rests, color-keyed door panels, tinted windows, a headliner, a jack and wheel wrench, door pockets, a prismatic rear view mirror, right-hand passenger assist handles, Scotchguard fabric protection, custom vinyl high-back bucket seats, a center three-passenger bench seat, storage boxes, an ash tray, a cigar lighter, analog gauges, a heater and defroster, an AM radio with digital clock, bumpers color-keyed to the lower body, a black grille, halogen headlamps, and a two-speed intermittent wiper/washer system. CL models added color-keyed floor mats, swing-out glass in the sliding door, a right-hand lighted visor mirror, a front air dam, and a black grille with Argent headlamps. Also included on LTs were special velour bucket seats, a leather-wrapped steering wheel, and more. Astro paint colors included Dark Autumnwood Metallic (#56), Light Autumnwood Metallic (#55), Onyx Black (#41), Light Quasar Blue Metallic (#20), Medium Quasar Blue Metallic (#80), Teal Blue Metallic (#86), Fieldstone Gray Metallic (#16), Burnt Red Metallic (#76), Deep Red Metallic (#75), Sterling Silver Metallic (#15), Light Teal Metallic (#34), and Ivory White (#10). Interior options included custom vinyl, custom cloth, and velour cloth.

1994 Chevrolet 1/2-Ton U05 Lumina APV "LS" Passenger Minivan 4x2 (CMD)

1/2-TON — LUMINA APV WAGON SERIES U05 (FWD) — V-6: The versatile front-wheel-drive (FWD) Lumina minivan could willingly wear as many hats as its owner. The standard five-passenger version had plenty of room for kids and cargo. An option was easily removable modular seating. With an optional seven-passenger layout, the Lumina Wagon could be used to haul the troops off to school. No all-wheel-drive version of the Lumina was offered. Luxury level LS seat trim was available. The LS package included such exterior enhancements as moldings and aero skirting. Two-tone paint schemes were available as well. Standard equipment included a driver's side air bag, a console, cloth upper/carpeted lower interior door panels, full floor carpeting, color-keyed front and rear floor mats, tinted glass, a wheel jack and wrench, a lighting package, a 10-in. prismatic rear view mirror, four-wheel antilock brakes, a rear power outlet, Scotchguard fabric protection, a cigar lighter, an ash tray, analog gauges, a lighted glove box, a heater and defroster, a four-way manual seat adjuster, AM/FM stereo sound, a headlights-on buzzer, a roof antenna, gray or black bumper fascias and rocker panel moldings, halogen headlamps, a tailgate liftglass, a stainless steel exhaust system, power steering, and a four-wheel antilock brake system with front discs and rear drums. The standard power team linked a 3.1-liter EFI V-6 to a

three-speed automatic transmission. Standard were size P205/70R15 black sidewall tires. New for 1994 was a three inch shorter frontal design that made the Lumina Wagon easier to park. The Lumina offered 112.6 cu.-ft. of cargo capacity. Its GVW range was 5,126 lb. Lumina color choices were Bright Aqua Metallic (#43), Black (#41), Light Adriatic Blue Metallic (#36), Medium Adriatic Blue Metallic (#30), Light Gray Metallic (#14), Malachite Metallic (#44), Medium Garnet Red Metallic (#72), and Bright White (#16). Interior options were cloth or custom cloth upholstery.

1/2-TON, 3/4-TON, 1-TON VAN — G SERIES 10, 20, 30 (RWD)-- V-6/V-8: Chevrolet advertised that it takes a big van to satisfy big plans and big dreams. Chevrolet's big vans were the tried-and-true, rear-wheel-drive G Series full-size models. The G10 1/2-ton series offered 110- and 125-in. wheelbase Chevy Vans with a standard EFI V-6 engine. The G20 3/4-ton series offered the same models, plus a passenger-carrying Sportvan with the same base engine. Both G20 models had 260 cu.-ft. of cargo capacity. In the Sportvan model, eight-passenger bench seating was standard and five-passenger bucket seating was optional. The G20 Sportvan had a GVW range of 6,600 to 6,875 lb. The G30 1-ton series included 125-in. wheelbase Chevy Van and Sportvan models, plus 146-in. extended wheelbase versions of both. A 5.7-liter EFI heavy-duty V-8 was standard in G30s. The Standard-Body G30 Sportvan also had 260 cu.-ft. of cargo capacity and came with standard 12-passenger bench seating or optional eight-passenger bucket seating. Its GVW range was 7,400 to 9,200 lb. The Extended-Body model had a 306 cu.-ft. cargo capacity. Twelve-passenger seating was standard and 15-passenger seating was optional. The longer Sportvan had a GVW range of 8,600 to 9,200 lb. A cutaway version of the G Series van chassis was also available for builders of motor homes, airport buses and other special-bodied trucks. Standard equipment for small Chevy Vans also included heavy-duty front disc/rear drum four-wheel anti-lock brakes, four-speed manual transmission with overdrive and P215/75R15 black sidewall tires. Paint colors offered for the big vans were Sand Beige Metallic (#57), Onyx Black (#41), Brilliant Blue Metallic (#22), Indigo Blue Metallic (#39), Emerald Green Metallic (#43), Gunmetal (#14), Quicksilver Metallic (#96), Mahogany Red Metallic (#83), Victory Red (#74), and Summit White (#50). Interiors were offered in custom vinyl and custom cloth.

1/2-TON — K1500 BLAZER (4x4) — V-8: The full-size, four-wheel-drive Chevrolet Blazer returned in 1994. This V-8-powered Sport Utility Vehicle had all the rugged off-road capabilities and on-road comfort that define a great 4x4. Only a single four-door wagon model was offered. It had 99.4 cu.-ft. of cargo capacity and a GVW range of 6,250 to 6,450 lb. Five-passenger bucket seating was standard. Six-passenger bench seating was optional. Other options included a luxury-level Silverado exterior treatment and Silverado custom cloth interior trim. On the Blazer's standard equipment list was a 5.7-liter EFI V-8, power front disc/rear drum all-wheel anti-lock braking, a five-speed manual transmission and LT245/75R16C black sidewall tires.

1994 Chevrolet 1/2-Ton C1500 Suburban panel door wagon 4x2 (CMD)

1/2-TON, 3/4-TON — C (4x2) /K (4x4) SUBURBAN — V-8: "You simply won't find a more unique combination of your favorite driving attributes and pure Chevy value than in the brilliant new Suburban for 1994," said the Chevrolet sales catalog. This large, four-door wagon came with rear-wheel-drive or four-wheel-drive. It could be had in 1/2-ton-rated C1500/K1500 models or 3/4-ton-rated C2500/K2500 models. All shared a giant 149.5 cu.-ft. cargo capacity. The Suburbans could handle payloads between 1,688 lb. and 3,430 lb. The GVW range was 6,800 lb. to 8,600 lb. Three-passenger seating was standard. Five-, six-, eight- and nine-passenger options were available. Standard equipment included a 5.7-liter EFI V-8, front disc/rear drum four-wheel anti-lock brakes, a four-speed automatic transmission with overdrive and P235/75R-15XLS black sidewall tires.

1/2-TON, 3/4-TON, 1-TON — C (4x2)/K (4x4) PICKUP — V-6/V-8: Chevrolet's full-size, rear-wheel-drive C Series pickups came in C1500 (1/2-ton), C2500 (3/4-ton), and C3500 (1-ton) lines. The four-wheel-drive K Series Pickups came in K1500 (1/2-ton), K2500 (3/4-ton), and K3500 (1-ton) lines. Buyers could choose from Regular-, Extended-, and Crew-Cabs. There was also a choice between the 6.5-foot short box and the 8-ft. long box. Fleetside and Sportside rear fender designs were offered. The standard wheelbase for pickups was 117.5 in. Five different wheelbases were offered: 117.5 in. for Regular-Cab Short Box models, 131.5 in. for Regular-Cab Long Box models, 141.5 in. for Extended-Cab Short Box models, 155.5 in. for Extended-Cab Long Box models, and 168.5 in. for Crew-Cab Long Box models. Three-passenger bench seating was standard in all full-sized Chevrolet Pickups, except Crew-Cab models, which came with twin three-passenger bench seats. Front bucket seats were optional for all models. Extended-Cab Pickups could be optioned with a rear bench seat. Standard equipment included a 4.3-liter EFI V-6, front disc/rear drum brakes with ABS, five-speed manual transmission with overdrive, and P225/75R15 black sidewall ALSBR tires. Of interest to enthusiasts was a Sportside Sport model option with "step-side" short-box design and the following standard features: Oynx Black, Teal Green Metallic or Victory Red finish, matching bumpers and mirrors, new-design grille, and aluminum wheel finish. Buyers could add a Sport Handling package with chrome wheels, special springs, and Bilstein gas shocks on 4x2 models or Z71 off-road package on 4x4 versions. Colors that 1994 C/K Pickups came in were Dark Autumnwood Metallic (#56), Teal Green Metallic (#38), Onyx Black (#41), Light Autumnwood Metallic (#55), Quicksilver Metallic (#96), Burnt Red Metallic (#76), Atlantic Blue Metallic (#30), Dark Garnet Red Metallic (#84), Indigo Blue Metallic (#39), Victory Red (#754), Light Quasar Blue Metallic (#20), Summit White (#50), and Teal Blue Metallic (#36). Interiors came in vinyl, custom cloth and cloth.

I. D. DATA: The VIN plate was mounted on the lower left side windshield corner. The VIN consisted of 17 symbols. The first three symbols identify the country, the manufacturer and the type of vehicle. The fourth symbol designated the GVW range. The fifth, sixth and seventh symbols identify the line and chassis type, series and body type. The eighth symbol identifies the engine: [Chevrolet engines] H=5.0-liter V-8, K=5.7-liter V-8, N=7.4-liter V-8, Z=4.3-liter V-6. [GM engines] A= 5.7-liter V-8, D=3.1-liter V-6, F=6.5-liter diesel V-8 (190 hp), L=3.8-liter V-6, M=7.0-liter V-8, P=6.5-liter diesel (155 hp), S=6.5-liter diesel V-8 (180 hp), W=4.3-liter V-6, 4=2.2-liter L4. The ninth symbol is the check digit. The tenth symbol indicates model year. The eleventh symbol identifies the assembly plant. The last six symbols were the sequential production number.

1994 Geo Tracker Convertible 4x2 (CMD)

Model	Body Type	Price	Weight	Prod. Total
CE/CJ Geo Tracker — 1/2-Ton — 86.6 in. w.b. — 1.6-liter MFI L4				
CE10367	4x2 Convertible	10,486	2,189	-
CJ10316	4x4 Hardtop	11,848	2,387	-
CJ10367	4x4 Convertible	11,695	2,365	-
CJ10316/B2Z	4x4 LSi Hardtop	13,247	2,397	-
CJ10367/B2Z	4x4 LSi Convertible	12,995	2,375	-

NOTE 1: A $300 dealer destination charge applied to Geo Trackers effective Feb. 1, 1994.

S10 Fleetside Pickup — 1/2-Ton — 108.3/117.9/122.9 in. w.b. — 2.2-liter MFI L4				
S10603	Reg. Cab Short Box	9655	2905	-
S10803	Reg. Cab Long Box	9955	3000	-
S10603	Reg. Cab LS Short Box	10,790	-	-
S10803	Reg. Cab LS Long Box	11,366	-	-
S10653	Ext. Cab LS Short Box	11,790	3157	-
T10 4x4 Fleetside Pickup — 1/2-Ton — 108.3/122.9 in. w.b. — 4.3-liter EFI V-6				
T10603	Reg. Cab SWB	14,155	-	-
T10803	Reg. Cab LWB	14,455	-	-
T10603	Reg. Cab LS SWB	15,290	-	-
T10803	Reg. Cab LS LWB	15,866	-	-
T10653	Ext. Cab LS Short Box	16,310	-	-

NOTE 2: A $470 dealer destination charge applied to S-Series Pickups effective Feb. 1, 1994.

S10 Blazer 4x2 Sport Utility Wagon — 1/2-Ton — 100.5/107 in. w.b. — 4.3-liter EFI V-6				
CS10516	2-dr Tailgate	15,641	3205	-
CS10506	4-dr Tailgate	16,931	3446	-
T10 Blazer 4x4 Sport Utility Wagon — 1/2-Ton — 100.5/107 in. w.b. — 4.3-liter CPI V-6				
CT10516	2-dr Tailgate	17,437	3506	-
CT10506	4-dr Tailgate	19,165	3811	-

NOTE 3: A $475 dealer destination charge applied to S-Series Blazers effective Jan. 10, 1994.

M10 Astro Minivan (rear-wheel-drive) — 1/2-Ton — 111 in. w.b. — 4.3-liter EFI V-6				
CM10906	Standard Cargo Van	15,344	3653	-
CM11006	Extended Cargo Van	15,817	3741	-
CM10906/ZW9	Standard CS Van	16,278	3998	-
CM11006/ZW9	Extended CS Van	16,580	4064	-
L10 Astro Minivan (all-wheel-drive) — 1/2-Ton — 111 in. w.b. — 4.3-liter CPI V-6				
CL10906/ZW9	Standard CS Van	17,437	-	-
CL11006/ZW9	Extended CS Van	19,165	-	-

NOTE 4: A $545 dealer destination charge applied to Astros effective Jan. 10, 1994.

U05 Lumina APV Minivan — 1/2-Ton — 109.8 in. w.b. — 3.1-liter EFI V-6				
1UM05	Cargo Van	15,485	3344	-
1UM06	Wagon	16,815	3554	-

NOTE 5: A $530 dealer destination charge applied to Lumina minivans effective Jan. 10, 1994.

G10 Van — 1/2-Ton — 110/125 in. w.b. — 4.3-liter EFI V-6				
CG11005/ZW9	SWB Chevy Van	15,936	3867	-
CG11006/ZW9	LWB Chevy Van	16,120	4500	-
G20 Van — 3/4-Ton — 110/125 in. w.b. — 4.3-liter EFI V-6				
CG21005/ZW9	SWB Chevy Van	15,905	3905	-
CG21305/ZW9	LWB Chevy Van	16,110	4550	-
CG21305/ZW9	LWB Sportvan 8P	18,875	4625	-
G30 Van — 1-Ton — 125/146 in. w.b. — 5.7-liter Heavy-duty EFI V-8				
CG31305/ZW9	LWB Chevy Van	16,237	4380	-
CG31306/ZW9	LWB Sportvan 12P	20,227	5266	-
CG31605/ZW9	EWB Chevy Van	18,357	4881	-
CG31606/ZW9	EWB Sportvan 12P	21,383	5642	-
CG31305/ZW9	LWB Cutaway Van	16,738	4032	-

NOTE 6: A $580 dealer destination charge applied to full-size vans effective Jan. 10, 1994.

K1500 Blazer 4x4 — 1/2-Ton — 111.5 in. w.b. — 5.7-liter EFI V-8				
CK10516	Utility Hardtop	21,330	4757	-

NOTE 7: A $600 dealer destination charge applied to full-size Blazers effective Feb. 1, 1994.

C/K 1500 Suburban — 1/2-Ton — 131.5 in. w.b. — 5.7-liter EFI V-8				
CC10906/ZW9	Panel Door (4x2)	20,406	4672	-
CK10906/ZW9	Panel Door (4x4)	22,657	-	-

Model	Body Type	Price	Weight	Prod. Total
C/K 2500 Suburban — 3/4-Ton — 131.5 in. w.b. — 5.7-liter EFI V-8				
CC20906/ZW9	Panel Door (4x2)	21,639	5227	-
CK20906/ZW9	Panel Door (4x4)	23,858	-	-

NOTE 8: A $640 dealer destination charge applied to Suburbans effective Feb. 1, 1994.

C1500 Pickup — 1/2-Ton Short Box — 117.5 in. w.b. — 4.3-liter EFI V-6				
CC10703	Regular-Cab Sportside	14,690	3748	-
CC10703	Regular-Cab Fleetside	14,027	3725	-
C1500 Pickup — 1/2-Ton Long Box — 131.5 in. w.b. — 4.3-liter EFI V-6				
CC10903	Regular-Cab Fleetside	14,307	3865	-
C1500 Pickup — 1/2-Ton Short Box — 141.5 in. w.b. — 4.3-liter EFI V-6				
CC10753	Extended-Cab Sportside	16,266	4133	-
CC10753	Extended-Cab Fleetside	15,854	4110	-
C1500 Pickup — 1/2-Ton Long Box — 155.5 in. w.b. — 4.3-liter EFI V-6				
CC10903	Extended-Cab Fleetside	16,697	4247	-

NOTE 9: Add approximately $2,350 for CK1500 Pickups with 4x4.

C2500 Pickup — 3/4-Ton Long Box — 131.5 in. w.b. — 4.3-liter EFI V-6				
CC20924	Chassis & Cab	16,233	4007	-
CC20903	Regular-Cab Fleetside	15,114	4006	-
C2500 Pickup — 3/4-Ton Short Box — 141.5 in. w.b. — 4.3-liter EFI V-6				
CC20953	Extended-Cab Fleetside	17,642	4270	-
C2500 Pickup — 3/4-Ton Long Box — 155.5 in. w.b. — 4.3-liter EFI V-6				
CC10903	Extended-Cab Fleetside	18,529	4337	-

NOTE 10: Add approximately $2,025 for CK2500 Pickups with 4x4.

C3500 Pickup — 1-Ton Long Box — 131.5 in. w.b. — 5.7-liter EFI V-8				
CC30924	Chassis & Cab	17,029	4273	-
CC30903	Regular-Cab Fleetside	16,847	4649	-
C3500 Pickup — 1-Ton Long Box — 155.5 in. w.b. — 5.7-liter V-8				
CC30903	Extended-Cab Fleetside	20,092	5325	-
C3500 Crew-Cab Pickup — 1-Ton Long Box — 168.5 in. w.b. — 5.7-liter V-8				
CC30933	Fleetside	19,356	5290	-
CC30933	Chassis	18,579	4915	-
CC30934	H-D Cab & Chassis	20,025	5281	-

NOTE 11: Add approximately $3,300 for CK3500 Pickups with 4x4.
NOTE 12: A $600 dealer destination charge applied to Suburbans effective Feb. 1, 1994.

1994 Chevrolet 1/2-Ton S10 Blazer 4-door Sport Utility 4x4 (CMD)

GASOLINE ENGINES (DISPLACEMENT ORDER)
ENGINE: Inline. Four-cylinder. Bore & stroke: 2.95 x 3.54 in. Displacement: 1.6-liter (97 cid). BHP: 80 at 5400 rpm. Torque: unknown. Multiport-fuel-injection. Suzuki-built. [Standard in Geo Tracker]
ENGINE: Inline. Four-cylinder. Bore & stroke: 3.5 x 3.46 in. Displacement: 2.2-liter (133 cid). BHP: 118 at 5200 rpm. Torque: 130 lb.-ft. at 2800 rpm. EFI/Throttle-body-injection. VIN Code 4. GM-built. [Standard in S10]
ENGINE: V-block. Six-cylinder. Bore & stroke: 3.5 x 3.331 in. Displacement: 3.1-liter (191 cid). BHP: 120 at 4200 rpm. Torque: 175 lb.-ft. at 2200 rpm. Multiport-fuel-injection. VIN Code D. GM-built. [Standard in Lumina APV]
ENGINE: V-block. Six-cylinder. Bore & stroke: 3.8 x 3.4 in. Displacement: 3.8-liter (231 cid). BHP: 165-170 hp at 4800 rpm. Torque: 220-225 lb.-ft. at 3200 rpm. Sequential-port-fuel-injection (SFI). VIN Code L. GM-built. [Optional in Lumina APV]
ENGINE: V-block. Vortec six-cylinder. Bore & stroke: 4.0 x 3.48 in. Displacement: 4.3-liter (262 cid). BHP: 155-165 at 4000 rpm. Torque: 230-235 lb.-ft. at 2400 rpm. EFI/Throttle-body-injection. VIN Code Z. Chevrolet-built. [Standard in regular Astro, C/K1500, C/K2500, T10/S10 Extended-Cab, S-Blazer, G10, and G20]
ENGINE: V-block. Enhanced Vortec six-cylinder. Bore & stroke: 4.0 x 3.48 in. Displacement: 4.3-liter (262 cid). BHP: 200 at 4400 rpm. Torque: 260 lb.-ft. at 3600 rpm. Central-point-injected. VIN Code W. GM-built. [Standard in Astro extended-body, optional in regular Astro]
ENGINE: V-block. Eight-cylinder. Bore & stroke: 3.74 x 3.48 in. Displacement: 5.0-liter (305 cid). BHP: 170-175 at 4200 rpm. Torque: 255-265 lb.-ft. at 2800 rpm. EFI/Throttle-body-injection. VIN Code H. GM-built. [Optional in C/K Pickups with GVWR less than 8,600 lb., optional in G10/G20 vans]
ENGINE: V-block. Heavy-duty. Eight-cylinder. Bore & stroke: 4.0 x 3.48 in. Displacement: 5.7-liter (350 cid). BHP: 190-195 at 4000 rpm. Torque: 300 lb.-ft. at 2400 rpm. EFI/Throttle-body-injection. VIN Code A. GM-built. [Standard in G30]
ENGINE: V-block. Light-Duty. Eight-cylinder. Bore & stroke: 4.0 x 3.48 in. Displacement: 5.7-liter (350 cid). BHP: 200-210 at 4000 rpm. Torque: 300 lb.-ft. at 2800 rpm. EFI/Throttle-body-injection. VIN Code K. Chevrolet-built [Standard in C/K Blazer, C/K3500, and Suburban, optional in G10/G20]
ENGINE: V-block. Eight-cylinder. Bore & stroke: 4.25 x 4.00 in. Displacement: 7.4-liter (454 cid). BHP: 230 at 3600 rpm. Torque: 385 lb.-ft. at 1600 rpm. Throttle-body-fuel-injection. VIN Code N. Chevrolet-built. [Optional in C/K3500, optional in G30]

DIESEL ENGINES (DISPLACEMENT ORDER)
ENGINE: V-block. Light-duty. Eight-cylinder. Bore & stroke: 4.06 x 3.82 in. Displacement: 6.5-liter (400 cid). BHP: 155 at 3600 rpm. Torque: 275 lb.-ft. at 1700 rpm. VIN Code P. GM-built. [Optional in G20/G30, optional in C/K1500/2500]
ENGINE: V-block. Heavy-duty. Eight-cylinder. Bore & stroke: 4.06 x 3.82 in. Displacement: 6.5-liter (400 cid). BHP: 180 at 3400 rpm. Torque: 360 lb.-ft. at 1700 rpm. VIN Code S. GM-built. [Optional in C/K3500 Crew-Cab]

1994 Geo 1/2-Ton Tracker LSi 4x4 Sport Utility Hardtop(CMD)

1994 Chevrolet 1/2-Ton Astro Rear-Wheel-Drive Standard-Body Cargo Van (CMD)

1994 Chevrolet 1/2-Ton S10 EL 4x2 Regular-Cab SS Short Box Pickup (CMD)

1994 Chevrolet 1/2-Ton K1500 Blazer 4x4 Sport Utility Wagon (CMD)

1994 Chevrolet 1/2-Ton S10 Blazer 4x2 two-door Sport Utility Vehicle (CMD)

1994 Chevrolet 1/2-Ton K1500 4x4 Regular-Cab Fleetside Long Box Pickup (CMD)

1994 Chevrolet 1/2-Ton Astro LT All-Wheel-Drive Extended-Body Minivan (CMD)

1994 Chevrolet 3/4-Ton K2500 4x4 Suburban Sport Utility Wagon (CMD)

ENGINE: V-block. Eight-cylinder. Turbocharged. Bore & stroke: 4.06 x 3.82 in. Displacement: 6.5-liter (400 cid). BHP: 190 at 3400 rpm. Torque: 240 lb.-ft. at 2000 rpm. VIN Code F. GM-built. [Optional in all C/K Pickups with GVWRs (automatic) 11,000 to 14,500 lb., (manual) 9,000 to 12,000 lb., optional in Suburbans]

CHASSIS: [Geo Tracker (All)] Wheelbase: 86.6 in. Length: 142.5 in. Width: 64.2 in. Height: 65.6 in. Tires: P205/75R15 black sidewall.

1994 Chevrolet 1/2-Ton S10 Pickup with ZR2 option 4x4 (CMD)

CHASSIS: [S10] Regular-Cab. Short Box. Wheelbase: 108.3 in. Length: 178.2 in. Width: 64.7 in. Height: 61.3 in. GVW: 4,200-4,600 lb. Payload: 1,078-1,703 lb. Tires: P205/75R15 black sidewall.
CHASSIS: [T10] Regular-Cab. Short Box. Wheelbase: 108.3 in. Length: 178.2 in. Width: 64.7 in. Height: 63.4 in. GVW: 4,650-5,150 lb. Payload: 1,010-1,701 lb. Tires: P205/75R15 black sidewall.
CHASSIS: [S10] Regular-Cab. Long Box. Wheelbase: 117.9 in. Length: 204.1. Width: 64.7 in. Height: 61.3 in. GVW: 4,600-4,900 lb. Payload: 983-1,743 lb. Tires: P205/75R15 black sidewall.
CHASSIS: [T10] Regular-Cab. Long Box. Wheelbase: 117.9 in. Length: 194.2 in. Width: 64.7 in. Height: 63.4 in. GVW: 4,650-5,150 lb. Payload: 1,113-1,596 lb. Tires: P205/75R15 black sidewall.
CHASSIS: [S10] Extended-Cab. Short Box. Wheelbase: 122.9 in. Length: 192.8 in. Width: 64.7 in. Height: 61.3 in. GVW: 4,600 lb. Payload: 1,369-1,519 lb. Tires: P205/75R15 black sidewall.
CHASSIS: [T10] Extended-Cab. Short Box. Wheelbase: 122.9 in. Length: 192.8 in. Width: 64.7 in. Height: 63.4 in. GVW: 4,650-5,150 lb. Payload: 1,011-1,482 lb. Tires: P205/75R15 black sidewall.
CHASSIS: [S-Blazer 4x2] Two-door. Wheelbase: 100.5 in. Length: 170.3 in. Width: 65.4 in. Height: 64.1 in. GVW: 4,350 lb. Payload: 975 lb. Tires: P205/75R15 black sidewall.
CHASSIS: [S-Blazer 4x4] Two-door. Wheelbase: 100.5 in. Length: 170.3 in. Width: 65.4 in. Height: 64.3 in. GVW: 4,700 lb. Payload: 1,164 lb. Tires: P205/75R15 black sidewall.
CHASSIS: [S-Blazer 4x2] Four-door. Wheelbase: 107 in. Length: 176.8 in. Width: 65.4 in. Height: 64.1 in. GVW: 4,850 lb. Payload: 1,069 lb. Tires: P205/75R15 black sidewall.
CHASSIS: [S-Blazer 4x4] Four-door. Wheelbase: 107 in. Length: 176.8 in. Width: 65.4 in. Height: 64.3 in. GVW: 5,100 lb. Payload: 1,453 lb. Tires: P205/75R15 black sidewall.
CHASSIS: [Astro Cargo regular-body] Wheelbase: 111 in. Length: 176.8 in. Width: 77.5 in. Height: 76.2 in. GVW: 5,700 lb. Payload: 1,740 lb. Tires: P205/75R15 black sidewall.
CHASSIS: [Astro Cargo regular-body AWD] Wheelbase: 111 in. Length: 176.8 in. Width: 77.5 in. Height: 76.2 in. GVW: 5,950 lb. Payload: 1,697 lb. Tires: P205/75R15 black sidewall.
CHASSIS: [Astro Cargo extended-body] Wheelbase: 111 in. Length: 186.8 in. Width: 77.5 in. Height: 76.2 in. GVW: 5,950 lb. Payload: 1,911 lb. Tires: P205/75R15 black sidewall.
CHASSIS: [Astro Cargo extended-body AWD] Wheelbase: 111 in. Length: 186.8 in. Width: 77.5 in. Height: 76.2 in. GVW: 6,100 lb. Payload: 1,783 lb. Tires: P205/75R15 black sidewall.
CHASSIS: [Astro Passenger regular-body] Wheelbase: 111 in. Length: 176.8 in. Width: 77.5 in. Height: 76.2 in. GVW: 5,700 lb. Payload: 1,340 lb. Tires: P205/75R15 black sidewall.
CHASSIS: [Astro Passenger regular-body AWD] Wheelbase: 111 in. Length: 176.8 in. Width: 77.5 in. Height: 76.2 in. GVW: 5,950 lb. Payload: 1,670 lb. Tires: P205/75R15 black sidewall.
CHASSIS: [Astro Passenger extended-body] Wheelbase: 111 in. Length: 186.8 in. Width: 77.5 in. Height: 76.2 in. GVW: 5,950 lb. Payload: 1,914 lb. Tires: P205/75R15 black sidewall.
CHASSIS: [Astro Passenger extended-body AWD] Wheelbase: 111 in. Length: 186.8 in. Width: 77.5 in. Height: 76.2 in. GVW: 6,100 lb. Payload: 1,783 lb. Tires: P205/75R15 black sidewall.
CHASSIS: [Lumina] Wheelbase: 109.8 in.. Length: 194.2 in. Width: 73.9 in. Height: 65.7 in. GVW: 5,126 lb. Payload: 1.357 lb. Tires: P205/70R15 black sidewall.
CHASSIS: [G10/Short Body] Chevy Van. Wheelbase: 110 in.. Length: 178.1 in. Width: 79.5 in. Height: 79.4 in. GVW: 6,000 lb. Payload: 1,754 lb. Tires: P215/75R15 black sidewall.
CHASSIS: [G10/Long Body] Chevy Van/Sportvan. Wheelbase: 125 in.. Length: 202.1 in. Width: 79.5 in. Height: 79.5 in. GVW: 6,000 lb. Payload: 1,428 lb. Tires: P215/75R15 black sidewall.
CHASSIS: [G20/Short Body] Chevy Van. Wheelbase: 110 in.. Length: 178.1 in. Width: 79.5 in. Height: 79.4 in. GVW: 6,600 lb. Payload: 1,452 lb. Tires: P215/75R15 black sidewall.
CHASSIS: [G20/Long Body] Chevy Van/Sportvan. Wheelbase: 125 in.. Length: 202.1 in. Width: 79.5 in. Height: 79.5 in. GVW: 6,875 lb. Payload: 2,142 lb. Tires: P215/75R15 black sidewall.
CHASSIS: [G30/Long Body Chevy Van] Wheelbase: 125 in.. Length: 202.1 in. Width: 79.5 in. Height: 79.5 in. GVW: 7,400 lb. Payload: 2,152 lb. Tires: P215/75R15 black sidewall.
CHASSIS: [G30/Long Body Sportvan] Wheelbase: 125 in.. Length: 202.1 in. Width: 79.5 in. Height: 79.5 in. GVW: 8,600 lb. Payload: 2,426 lb. Tires: P215/75R15 black sidewall.

CHASSIS: [G30/Extended Body Chevy Van] Wheelbase: 146 in. Length: 223.1 in. Width: 79.5 in. Height: 82.3 in. GVW: 9,200 lb. Payload: 3,476 lb. Tires: P215/75R15 black sidewall.
CHASSIS: [G30/Extended Body 12-Passenger Sportvan] Wheelbase: 146 in. Length: 223.1 in. Width: 79.5 in. Height: 82.3 in. GVW: 9,200 lb. Payload: 4,101 lb. lb. Tires: P215/75R15 black sidewall.
CHASSIS: [K10 Blazer 4x4] Wheelbase: 111.5 in. Length: 188 in. Width: 77.1 in. Height: 75 in. GVW: 6,250-6,450 lb. Payload: 1,333-1,540 lb. Tires: LT245/75R16C black sidewall.
CHASSIS: [Suburban C1500] Wheelbase: 131.5 in. Length: 219.5 in. Width: 77 in. Height: 74.9 in. GVW: 6,800 lb. Payload: 2,117 lb. Tires: P235/75R-15XLS black sidewall.
CHASSIS: [Suburban K1500] Wheelbase: 131.5 in. Length: 219.5 in. Width: 77 in. Height: 73.6 in. GVW: 7,200 lb. Payload: 2,052 lb. Tires: P235/75R-15XLS black sidewall.
CHASSIS: [Suburban C2500] Wheelbase: 131.5 in. Length: 219.5 in. Width: 77 in. Height: 74.9 in. GVW: 8,600 lb. Payload: 3,370 lb. Tires: P235/75R-15XLS black sidewall.
CHASSIS: [Suburban K2500] Wheelbase: 131.5 in. Length: 219.5 in. Width: 77 in. Height: 73.6 in. GVW: 8,600 lb. Payload: 2,944 lb. Tires: P235/75R-15XLS black sidewall.
CHASSIS: [C1500 Sportside Regular-Cab Short Box Pickup] Regular-Cab. Short Box. Wheelbase: 117.5 in. Length: 194.1 in. Width: 77.1 in. Height: 70.4 in. GVW: 5,600 lb. Payload: 1,570 lb. Tires: P225/75R15 black sidewall ALSBR tires.

1994 Chevrolet 1/2-Ton C1500 Fleetside Short Box Pickup 4x2 (CMD)

CHASSIS: [C1500 Fleetside Regular-Cab Short Box Pickup] Wheelbase: 117.5 in. Length: 194.1 in. Width: 76.8 in. Height: 70.4 in. GVW: 5,600 lb. Payload: 1,581 lb. Tires: P225/75R15 black sidewall ALSBR tires.
CHASSIS: [C1500 Fleetside Regular-Cab Short Box "Work Truck" Pickup] Wheelbase: 117.5 in. Length: 194.1 in. Width: 76.8 in. Height: 70.4 in. GVW: 5,600 lb. Payload: 1,882 lb. Tires: P225/75R15 black sidewall ALSBR tires.
CHASSIS: [C1500 Fleetside Regular-Cab Long Box Pickup] Wheelbase: 131.5 in. Length: 212.6 in. Width: 76.8 in. Height: 70.4 in. GVW: 5,600 lb. Payload: 1,486-2,298 lb. Tires: P225/75R15 black sidewall ALSBR tires.
CHASSIS: [C1500 Fleetside Regular-Cab Long Box "Work Truck" Pickup] Wheelbase: 131.5 in. Length: 212.6 in. Width: 76.8 in. Height: 70.4 in. GVW: 6,100 lb. Payload: 1,486-2,298 lb. Tires: P225/75R15 black sidewall ALSBR tires.
CHASSIS: [C1500 Sportside Extended-Cab Short Box Pickup] Wheelbase: 141.5 in. Length: 218.0 in. Width: 77.1 in. Height: 70.6 in. GVW: 6,200 lb. Payload: 1,506-2,100 lb. Tires: P225/75R15 black sidewall ALSBR tires.
CHASSIS: [C1500 Fleetside Extended-Cab Short Box Pickup] Wheelbase: 141.5 in. Length: 218.0 in. Width: 76.8 in. Height: 70.6 in. GVW: 6,200 lb. Payload: 1,506-2,210 lb. Tires: P225/75R15 black sidewall ALSBR tires.
CHASSIS: [C1500 Fleetside Extended-Cab Long Box Pickup] Wheelbase: 155.5 in. Length: 237.0 in. Width: 76.8 in. Height: 70.6 in. GVW: 6,200 lb. Payload: 1,345-2,084 lb. Tires: P225/75R15 black sidewall ALSBR tires.
CHASSIS: [K1500 Sportside Regular-Cab Short Box Pickup] Wheelbase: 117.5 in. Length: 194.1 in. Width: 77.1 in. Height: 73.8 in. GVW: 6,100 lb. Payload: 1,660-1,991 lb. Tires: P225/75R15 black sidewall ALSBR tires.
CHASSIS: [K1500 Fleetside Regular-Cab Short Box Pickup] Wheelbase: 117.5 in. Length: 194.1 in. Width: 76.8 in. Height: 73.8 in. GVW: 6,100 lb. Payload: 1,627-1,991 lb. Tires: P225/75R15 black sidewall ALSBR tires.
CHASSIS: [K1500 Fleetside Regular-Cab Short Box "Work Truck" Pickup] Wheelbase: 117.5 in. Length: 194.1 in. Width: 77.1 in. Height: 73.8 in. GVW: 6,100 lb. Payload: 1,486-2,298 lb. Tires: P225/75R15 black sidewall ALSBR tires.

1994 Chevrolet 1/2-Ton K1500 Extended-Cab Fleetside Short Box Pickup 4x4 (CMD)

CHASSIS: [K1500 Fleetside Regular-Cab Long Box Pickup] Wheelbase: 131.5 in. Length: 212.6 in. Width: 76.8 in. Height: 73.8 in. GVW: 6,100 lb. Payload: 1,203-1,861 lb. Tires: P225/75R15 black sidewall ALSBR tires.
CHASSIS: [K1500 Fleetside Regular-Cab Long Box "Work Truck" Pickup] Wheelbase: 131.5 in. Length: 212.6 in. Width: 76.8 in. Height: 73.8 in. GVW: 6,100 lb. Payload: 1,980 lb. Tires: P225/75R15 black sidewall ALSBR tires.
CHASSIS: [K1500 Sportside Extended-Cab Short Box Pickup] Wheelbase: 141.5 in. Length: 218.0 in. Width: 77.1 in. Height: 73.8 in. GVW: 6,200-6,800 lb. Payload: 1,307-2,064 lb. Tires: P225/75R15 black sidewall ALSBR tires.
CHASSIS: [K1500 Fleetside Extended-Cab Short Box Pickup] Wheelbase: 141.5 in. Length: 218.0 in. Width: 76.8 in. Height: 73.8 in. GVW: 6,200-6,800 lb. Payload: 1,390-2,046 lb. Tires: P225/75R15 black sidewall ALSBR tires.
CHASSIS: [K1500 Fleetside Extended-Cab Long Box Pickup] Wheelbase: 155.5 in. Length: 237.0 in. Width: 76.8 in. Height: 73.8 in. GVW: 6,200-6,800 lb. Payload: 1,187-1,863 lb. Tires: P225/75R15 black sidewall ALSBR tires.

1994 Chevrolet 1/2-Ton K1500 Sportside Short Box Pickup 4x4 (CMD)

CHASSIS: [C2500 Fleetside Regular-Cab Long Box Pickup] Wheelbase: 131.5 in. Length: 212.6 in. Width: 76.8 in. Height: 73 in. GVW: 7,200 lb. Payload: 2,519 lb. Tires: P225/75R15 black sidewall ALSBR tires.
CHASSIS: [C2500 Heavy-duty Fleetside Regular-Cab Long Box Pickup] Wheelbase: 131.5 in. Length: 212.6 in. Width: 76.8 in. Height: 73 in. GVW: 8,600 lb. Payload: 4,207 lb. Tires: P225/75R15 black sidewall ALSBR tires.
CHASSIS: [C2500 Fleetside Extended-Cab Short Box Pickup] Wheelbase: 141.5 in. Length: 218.0 in. Width: 76.8 in. Height: 74 in. GVW: 7,200 lb. Payload: 2,339-2,916 lb. Tires: P225/75R15 black sidewall ALSBR tires.
CHASSIS: [C2500 Fleetside Extended-Cab Long Box Pickup] Wheelbase: 155.5 in. Length: 237.0 in. Width: 76.8 in. Height: 74 in. GVW: 8,600 lb. Payload: 3,316-3,853 lb. Tires: P225/75R15 black sidewall ALSBR tires.
CHASSIS: [K2500 Fleetside Regular-Cab Long Box Pickup] Wheelbase: 131.5 in. Length: 212.6 in. Width: 76.8 in. Height: 73.8 in. GVW: 7,200-8,600 lb. Payload: 2,240-3,842 lb. Tires: P225/75R15 black sidewall ALSBR tires.
CHASSIS: [K2500 Heavy-duty Fleetside Regular-Cab Long Box Pickup] Wheelbase: 131.5 in. Length: 212.6 in. Width: 76.8 in. Height: 73.8 in. GVW: 8,600 lb. Payload: 2,240-3,842 lb. Tires: P225/75R15 black sidewall ALSBR tires.
CHASSIS: [K2500 Fleetside Extended-Cab Short Box Pickup] Wheelbase: 141.5 in. Length: 218.0 in. Width: 76.8 in. Height: 73.8 in. GVW: 7,200 lb. Payload: 1,956-2,573 lb. Tires: P225/75R15 black sidewall ALSBR tires.
CHASSIS: [K2500 Fleetside Extended-Cab Long Box Pickup] Wheelbase: 155.5 in. Length: 237.0 in. Width: 76.8 in. Height: 73.8 in. GVW: 8,600 lb. Payload: 2,790-3,444 lb. Tires: P225/75R15 black sidewall ALSBR tires.
CHASSIS: [C3500 Fleetside Regular-Cab Long Box Pickup] Wheelbase: 131.5 in. Length: 212.6 in. Width: 76.8 in. Height: 70.4 in. GVW: 9,000-10,000 lb. Payload: 3,485-5,024 lb. Tires: P225/75R15 black sidewall ALSBR tires.
CHASSIS: [K3500 Fleetside Regular-Cab Long Box Pickup] Wheelbase: 131.5 in. Length: 212.6 in. Width: 76.8 in. Height: 73.8 in. GVW: 9,200-10,000 lb. Payload: 3,771-4,649 lb. Tires: P225/75R15 black sidewall ALSBR tires.
CHASSIS: [C3500 Fleetside Extended-Cab Long Box Pickup] Wheelbase: 155.5 in. Length: 237.0 in. Width: 76.8 in. Height: 70.4 in. GVW: 10,000 lb. Payload: 4,324-4,758 lb. Tires: P225/75R15 black sidewall ALSBR tires.
CHASSIS: [K3500 Fleetside Extended-Cab Long Box Pickup] Wheelbase: 155.5 in. Length: 237.0 in. Width: 76.8 in. Height: 73.8 in. GVW: 10,000 lb. Payload: 3,934-4,270 lb. Tires: P225/75R15 black sidewall ALSBR tires.
CHASSIS: [C3500 Fleetside Crew-Cab Long Box Pickup] Wheelbase: 168.5 in. Length: 248 in. Width: 76.8 in. Height: 70.4 in. GVW: 9,000-10,000 lb. Payload: 3,194-4,393 lb. Tires: P235/75R15 black sidewall ALSBR tires.
CHASSIS: [K3500 Fleetside Crew-Cab Long Box Pickup] Wheelbase: 168.5 in. Length: 248 in. Width: 76.8 in. Height: 70.4 in. GVW: 9,200-10,000 lb. Payload: 3,003-3,980 lb. Tires: P235/75R15 black sidewall ALSBR tires.
CHASSIS: [C/K 3500 Pickup] Motor home chassis. Wheelbase: 183.5 in. Tires: P225/75R15 black sidewall ALSBR tires.

SELECTED OPTIONS

GEO TRACKER OPTIONS: Base equipment group with UL1 radio ($306). Base equipment group with UL0 radio ($501). Base equipment group with UP0 radio ($897). Expression color appearance package ($425-$499). Air conditioning ($745). Rear folding bench seat, front-wheel-drive convertible only ($445). Three-speed automatic transmission: $595. Tilt steering ($118). 15-in. alloy wheels with steel spare wheel ($298).

S/T SERIES PICKUP OPTIONS: LS cab trim ($225-235). Four-speed ETC automatic transmission with overdrive ($927). 4.3-liter EFI V-6 ($850). 4.3-liter CPI V-6 includes H-D cooling, tachometer and ABS brakes ($559 for 4x4 or $1400 for 4x2). Convenience package with power door locks, power windows, and electric remote mirrors ($475). Tilt steering and speed control ($383). ETR AM radio with clock ($95). AM/FM ETR stereo with cassette, seek & scan, and digital clock ($348). All-Weather air conditioning ($805). Air dam with fog lamps for 4x2s only ($115). ZR2 4x4 off-road package ($328 to $481). Wide-Stance sport performance package ($1,645). Deluxe cloth interior, Regular-Cab ($135), Extended-Cab ($156). 4x4 underbody shield package ($126). SS package including LS decor, locking differential, ANL air dam with fog lamps, body-color wheels and grille, SS badging, leather-wrapped steering wheel, rear bumper and more ($629). Trailering Special package ($408).

1994 Chevrolet 1/2-Ton S10 Extended-Cab Pickup 4x4 (CMD)

S-SERIES BLAZER OPTIONS: CAA2 Tahoe package ($1,378). CAA3 Tahoe package ($2,968). LTB1 Tahoe LT package ($4,270). AAA2 Tahoe package ($651) 4x4 molding package ($190). AAA3 Tahoe package ($2,390). LTA1 Tahoe LT package, 4x2 ($3,801), 4x4 ($3,635). Air conditioning ($805). Air dam and fog lamps for 4x2 only ($115). Spare wheel and tire carrier ($159). Cold climate package ($109-$179). D55 front seat separator ($145) DK6 console ($83). H-D cooling system ($135). Operating convenience package, two-door ($367), four-door ($542). Tilt steering wheel ($383). Enhanced power train with 4.3-liter CPI V-6 ($1,160). Tinted glass packages ($144-$225). Full-instrumentation package ($195). Keyless entry system ($135). Luggage carrier ($126). Special two-tone paint with body striping ($227). Custom two-tone paint with graduated body striping ($275). UM7 AM/FM stereo ($131). UM6 AM/FM stereo cassette ($253). UX1 premium sound system ($403). UC1 AM/FM stereo ($537). Deluxe custom cloth high-back bucket seats ($211-$221). Deluxe custom cloth high-back power bucket seats (($501). Folding rear bench seat with arm rests ($409-$435). Off-road suspension ($122-$182). P205/75R15 white-letter tires ($121). P235/75R15 white outline letter tires ($286). PA3 cast aluminum wheels ($248-$340). 5P2 special aluminum wheels for 4x4s ($280). Sliding rear quarter window ($257). Rear window wiper system ($125).

ASTRO OPTIONS: ASA3 plus convenience group with eight-passenger seating ($1,493). ASA4 plus convenience group ($2,700). ASA5 includes ASA4 features plus luggage carrier, roof console, six-way power seat and more ($3,479). Air conditioning, front ($845), front and rear ($1,368). Deluxe front and rear chrome bumpers ($128). Dutch doors with rear wiper and electric release ($364). Locking differential ($252). Luggage carrier ($126). ZQ3 convenience group with tilt wheel and speed control ($383). ZQ2 convenience group with power windows and door locks ($434). H-D cooling system ($198). YC6 Custom Luxury CL decor package ($1,086). YC7 Luxury Touring LT decor package ($1,804). ZL7 Custom Sport CS value package ($465). Electric rear window defogger ($154). Power door lock system ($223). TR9 auxiliary lighting package ($127). Electronic instrumentation ($195). Electric remote-control mirrors ($150). ZY2 custom two-tone paint ($104-$329). ZY3 special two-tone paint ($172). ZY4 deluxe two-tone paint ($476). 4.3-liter CPI V-6 with oil and transmission coolers and H-D cooling ($500). UM7 AM/FM stereo ($151). UM6 AM/FM stereo cassette ($273). UX1 premium sound system ($423). U1C AM/FM stereo ($557). ZP7 seven-passenger seating ($1,043). Arm rests ($245). Six-way power driver's seat ($240). Trailering Special equipment ($507). PF3 cast-aluminum wheels.

LUMINA OPTIONS: Base Preferred Equipment group with UM6 radio ($140). Base Preferred Equipment Group with U1C radio ($396). WPA1 Preferred Equipment Group with UM6 radio (add $918). WPA1 Preferred Equipment Group with U1C radio ($396). WPA2 Equipment Group ($2,323). WPA2 Equipment Group with U1C radio ($2,579). WPA3 Preferred Equipment Group ($2,843) WPA3 Preferred Equipment Group with U1C radio ($3,099). 3.8-liter SFI engine ($619). Air conditioning ($830). Front and rear air conditioning teamed with WPA2 or WPA3 ($450). Electric rear window defogger ($170). Power sliding door ($295). Remote keyless entry system ($125). Deep-tinted glass ($245). Power door and tailgate locks ($300). U1C radio ($256). Power driver's seat ($270). Dual integral child seats ($885). Single integral child's seat ($785). Bucket seats and five-passenger modular rear seat ($660). Electric speed control with resume ($225). Manual, non-removable sun roof ($300). Load leveling suspension ($170). Self-sealing tires ($150 extra). Traction Control ($350). Trailering package ($320). Four-speed automatic transmission ($200). Cast aluminum 15-in. wheels with locks ($275). Power windows with "express" down ($275).

1994 Chevrolet 3/4-Ton G20 Extended-body Sportvan Passenger Wagon 4x2 (CMD)

G-SERIES VAN OPTIONS: Front air conditioning ($975). Front and rear air conditioning ($599-1,574). Locking differential ($252). ZQ2 convenience group: $434. ZQ3 convenience group ($383). California emissions ($100). 5.0-liter EFI V-8 ($575). 7.4-liter EFI V-8 ($605). 7.4-liter diesel V-8 ($2,870). 6.5-liter heavy-duty diesel V-8 ($1,655). Alternative fuel system ($125). Deep-tinted glass ($380). C6Q GVWR package ($319). Rear heater ($205). Auxiliary lighting package ($156). Remote keyless entry system ($175). Beauville decor package ($137-$269). UM7 stereo ($141). UM6 stereo ($253). UX1 stereo ($413). ZP3 interior with one adult rear seat for 15-passenger seating ($317). Custom cloth seat trim with reclining bucket seats ($402). Trailering equipment ($310). Aluminum wheels ($189-$310). Rally wheels ($121).

[G-Series Cargo Vans] Preferred Equipment Group GVA2 ($1,118). Air conditioning ($975). ZQ2 convenience group ($434). Heavy-duty cooling system ($198). 5.0-liter EFI V-8 ($575). 5.7-liter EFI V-8 ($865). 7.4-liter EFI V-8 ($605). 6.5-liter diesel V-8 ($2,870). 6.5-liter heavy-duty diesel V-8 ($1,655). Front area carpeting and wheel house rubber mats ($157). Deep-tinted glass ($240). Heater ($205) TR9 lighting package ($156). UM6 stereo equipment ($218). U1C stereo equipment ($517). Trailering equipment package ($310).

K10 BLAZER OPTIONS: K5A2 Silverado package ($1,855). K5A3 Silverado package ($2,407). K5A4 Silverado Sport package ($3,056). Air conditioning ($845). V22 appearance package ($191). Locking differential ($252). Roof mounted luggage carrier ($126). Off-road chassis equipment ($400). ZQ3 convenience package ($383). 6.5-liter turbo diesel engine ($2,825). UX1 stereo system ($150-$272). All-tinted glass ($215). Conventional two-tone paint ($180). Deluxe two-tone paint ($290). 6-way power seat adjuster ($240). Custom cloth reclining high-back bucket seats ($341). Skid plate package ($225). Trailering equipment package ($210-$345). Four-speed automatic overdrive transmission ($930). Cast aluminum wheels ($250-$310). Rear window washer/wiper ($125). Rear window washer/wiper/defogger ($279).

1994 Chevrolet 1/2-Ton K1500 Blazer 2-door Sport Utility 4x4 (CMD)

SUBURBAN OPTIONS: N1A2/1SB Silverado package ($3812-$3,876). N1A3/1SC Silverado package ($5,517-$5,581. N2A2/1SB Silverado package ($3,812-$3,876). N2A3/1SC Silverado package ($5,267-$5,331). Suburban "Upfitter" package ($4,163-$4,303). Air conditioning ($845). V22 appearance package ($191). Locking differential ($252). 7.4-liter EFI V-8 ($605). 6.5-liter Turbo Diesel V-8 ($2,825). UX1 stereo system ($150-$235). All-tinted glass ($215). Conventional two-tone paint ($180). Deluxe two-tone paint ($290). Skid plate package ($225). Trailering Equipment package ($210). Cast aluminum wheels ($250-$310). Rear window washer/wiper/defogger ($279). Custom cloth trim with reclining split bench seat ($174). Custom cloth interior with reclining bucket seats ($540). Custom leather trim on reclining high-back bucket seats ($1,555-$1,920). Cast aluminum wheels for C1500 Suburban ($250-310). Cast aluminum wheels for K1500 Suburban ($250-310).

C/K PICKUP OPTIONS: PSP1/1SA Preferred Equipment package ($2,048-$2,603). Cheyenne package ($575). P1A3/1SC Silverado package ($1,262). P1A4/1SD Silverado package ($2,084). Work Truck packages for C/K2500 models ($1,308-$3,056). Air conditioning ($805). Appearance package ($191) Heavy-duty battery ($134). Painted rear step bumper ($130). Chrome rear step bumper ($229). Off-road package ($270). Camper Special equipment $233). Sport handling package ($974). Electric rear window defogger ($154). 5.0-liter EFI V-8 ($575-$865). 7.4-liter EFI V-8 ($470-$605). 6.5-liter naturally aspirated diesel V-8 ($2,295). 6.5-liter Turbo Diesel V-8 ($3,095-$3,670). Deep-tinted glass ($107-$115). Body moldings ($107). UP4 radio equipment ($162). UM7 stereo equipment ($170-$332). UM6 radio package ($292-$454). Five-speed manual transmission with deep low and overdrive ($98). Four-speed automatic transmission with overdrive ($930). Trailering Special package ($210-$250. Bright metal wheelcovers ($42). Cast aluminum wheels ($250-310). C/K3500 dual rear wheels ($955). Crew-Cab dual rear wheels ($857). Sliding rear window ($113).

NOTE 13: Options and prices shown are representative. The actual cost of an option or option package often varies according to other packages that the options are combined with on specific vehicles. Preferred Equipment Group (PEG) options offer specific optional equipment at discount prices. Some "options" may be standard equipment on certain models, such as V-8s in C/K3500 Pickups. Descriptions of options are edited. Full option contents can be determined by consulting sales literature.

HISTORICAL: Chevrolet trucks were built in 13 factories in 1994. Geo Trackers were made at the CAMI plant in Ingersoll, Ontario, Canada. They had no major changes. S-Series Pickups were assembled in Pontiac, Michigan and Shreveport, Louisiana. They featured an all-new, aerodynamic exterior, a restyled interior, and a new 4x2 Super Sport model. Also new was a ZR2 4x4 package. An all-new S-Series Blazer was due out in mid-1994, as a 1995 model. However, its launch was delayed until August 1994. The carryover S-Blazers were built at Pontiac, Michigan and Moraine, Ohio. Astros were made in Baltimore, Maryland. New for 1994 Astros was a standard driver's airbag and new side door beams. Sportvan and Chevy Van models were sourced from factories in Scarborough, Ontario, Canada and Flint, Michigan. A new 6.5-liter 155-hp naturally aspirated diesel engine was available in these trucks. Full-size Blazers and Suburbans were made in the Chevrolet factory at Janesville, Wisconsin. A new 6.5-liter Turbo Diesel engine was available. C/K Pickups were built in Fort Wayne, Indiana, Oshawa, Canada, Pontiac, Michigan and Janesville, Wisconsin. They could be had with a new 6.5-liter naturally-aspirated diesel or the 6.5-liter Turbo Diesel V-8. Jim C. Perkins remained general manager of Chevrolet Motor Division.

1995 CHEVROLET

1/4-TON — GEO TRACKER — L4: Chevrolet dealers continued selling the Suzuki-designed Geo Tracker as a small Sport Utility Vehicle. Tracker models started with a two-door Convertible. In the base model it came with front-wheel-drive or all-wheel-drive. The convertible also came in 4x4 format with LSi trim. The hardtop model came only as a 4x4, in the base or LSi trim levels. Standard equipment for the front-wheel -drive Convertible included a wide-stance tuned suspension, a "truck tough" frame, a heavy-duty heater and defroster, side window defoggers, full carpeting, Scotchguard fabric protection, black bumpers with rub strips, a center high-mounted stop lamp, composite halogen headlamps, zinc-galvanized body panels, front and rear tow hooks, an outside locking spare tire and wheel, a spare tire cover with blue or green lettering, a center console with storage tray, a day/night inside rear view mirror, door storage bins, full carpeting, a locking glove box, warning tones, a trip odometer, integral head restraints, reclining high-back "easy enter" bucket seats, and stainless steel styled wheels. The 4x4 models added black rocker panel moldings, rear swing-out window glass, a rear defogger, a tachometer, a fold-and-stow rear bench seat, manual locking hubs, and larger tires. The 4x4 Lsi models also had body-color bumpers with integral rub strips. The standard Geo Tracker power team consisted of a 1.6-liter SOHC inline four-cylinder engine with multiport-fuel-injection, and a five-speed manual transmission with overdrive. Power front disc/rear drum rear wheel antilock brakes were regular equipment. Also standard were (4x2 model) P195/75R-15 tires or (4x4 models) P205/75R-15 tires. Tracker buyers had a choice of linear cloth bucket seats, expressive cloth bucket seats or custom cloth bucket seats at the same price. Convertibles could be had with an "Expressions" color appearance package that came in blue, green or tan.

1/2-TON — S (4x2)/T (4x4) SERIES PICKUP — L4/V-6: After being revised in 1994, the S10 Pickups were modestly updated for 1995. The S10 was the 4x2 series and the T10 was the 4x4 series (Both had S10 badges on the fenders). The roomier, more comfortable, more powerful, and safer S10 had been very quickly accepted. It again had contemporary styling with a smooth, down-turned aerodynamic nose. The wraparound grille had wedge-shaped parking lamps at each corner, deep-set rectangular headlights, and a twin-air-slot opening with a big, gold Chevrolet bow tie emblem in the middle of the center bar. Standard equipment included a 2.2-liter multiport-fuel-injected (MFI) inline four-cylinder engine, power front disc/rear drum rear-wheel antilock brakes, five-speed manual transmission with overdrive, power steering, halogen headlamps, Solar-Ray tinted glass, Dark Argent grille, color-keyed rear close-out panel (instead of rear bumper), and P205/75R15 black sidewall tires. Compact pickups with V-6 power also had all-wheel antilock brakes, and LS models had a rear bumper. The base series offered short (6-ft.) and long (7-ft. 4-in.) boxes for Regular-Cab models. The LS series included both, plus an Extended-Cab Short Box model. LS features also consisted of color-keyed molded plastic door panels with cloth inserts, color-keyed carpeting, left- and right-hand mirrors, a lighted visor mirror, swing-out rear quarter windows (with Extended-Cab), a chrome grille (except Super Sport), and a 60/40 split bench seat with deluxe cloth upholstery. All models were available as 4x2 or 4x4 trucks. GVWR ranges were 4,200 to 5,150 lb. A three-passenger bench seat was standard in all S-Series pickups. Twin bucket seats were optional. The Extended-Cab model could also be ordered with four-passenger seating. Model-options included a Super Sport (SS) version of the 4x2 truck, and a ZR2 version of the 4x4 truck. The RPO ZM5 Super Sport equipment included LS trim, a locking differential, N60 cast aluminum wheels with special bright hubcaps, a body color grille, rear step bumper delete (includes close-out panel), special SS badging on doors and tailgate and grille, red bow tie on grille and hubcaps, NP5 leather-wrapped steering wheel, L35 enhanced Vortec V-6, automatic transmission, 3.42:1 ratio rear axle, ZQ8 Sport suspension, and ZY1 solid paint. The ZR2 Wide-Stance equipment included a 4,650-lb. GVWR package, unique revised frame for wider tread, strengthened front differential gears and drive axles, unique rear axle with 8.5-in. ring gear, heavy rear suspension. front stabilizer bar, 45-mm Bilstein gas shocks, unique front fenders and pickup box outer panels, modified jack and spare tire stowage, a three-inch higher body, LS trim, a 3.73 axle ratio, 31 x 10.5-in. special tires, ZY1 solid paint, and either the LB4 or the L35 4.3-liter V-6 engines. Bucket seats were required with the ZR2 option.

1995 Chevrolet 1/2-Ton S-Series Extended-Cab "LS" Pickup 4x4 (CMD)

1/2-TON — BLAZER (4x2/4x4) — V-6: Chevrolet introduced the all-new 1995 Blazer at the 1994 Chicago Auto Show on February 4, 1994. The new vehicle hit Chevrolet dealerships by the summer of 1994. The "S" designation was dropped from advertising and promotions. The Blazer name then became synonymous with the compact Sport Utility Vehicle, and plans were made to rename Chevrolet's full-size SUV the Tahoe. The new aero-styled Blazer came in 4x2 and 4x4 models with two-door and four-door body configurations. The two-door model, with 67.3 cu.-ft. of cargo capacity, had a 6.5-in. shorter wheelbase than the four-door. Two-passenger seating was standard and four-passenger seating was optional in the two-door. The four-door came with standard three-passenger seating in 4x2 format, with options to seat two, five or six persons. The 4x4 four-door had standard six-passenger seating, with five-passenger bucket seating optional. The LT (Luxury Touring) version of the four-door had standard bucket seating for five. Standard equipment included a 4.3-liter EFI V-6, power front disc/rear drum brakes with four-wheel ABS, driver's air bag, power steering, air conditioning, front and rear stabilizers, solar-controlled tinted glass, coolant and temperature and oil pressure gauges, a voltmeter, AM/FM radio, digital clock, dual outside mirrors, trip odometer, front bucket seats with manual lumbar adjustment and console (three-door), 60/40 reclining cloth front bench seat with storage arm rest (five-door), cup holders, door map pockets, floor mats, cargo area tie-down hooks, intermittent wipers, gay/night rear view mirror, color-keyed bumpers, five-lead trailer wiring harness, full-size spare, four-speed ECT automatic transmission, and P205/75R15 black sidewall All-Season steel-belted radial tires. The four-wheel-drive model added a manual transfer case, a folding rear bench seat (five-door), tow hooks, and dark gray bumpers.

1/2-TON — ASTRO VAN SERIES M (RWD)/L (AWD) — V-6: Chevrolet's popular Astro M10 rear-wheel-drive (RWD) minivan was the perfect American family vehicle. It came in Standard-Body and Extended-Body models in two series. The models in the L10 series had all-wheel-drive (AWD) for improved year-round traction. Standard CS equipment included a driver's facial air bag, front air conditioning, dual door arm rests, passenger side assist handles, coat hooks, vinyl door panels with carpet inserts, full-body Solar-Ray tinted glass, full-length cloth headliner, jack and tools, auxiliary lighting, front and middle and rear dome lights, Custom vinyl upholstery with front bucket seats and Scotchguard protection, five-passenger seating with center three-passenger adjustable bench, molded storage compartments, dual sun shades with mirror and map band, lighted ash tray, gauges, glove box, heater/defogger, four-spoke black steering wheel, key-in-ignition and headlamps on warning tones, ETR AM/FM stereo, molded gray front bumper/painted gray rear bumper, rear Dutch doors, molded gray grille, halogen headlamps, dual black below-eye-line mirrors, under-floor spare carrier, two-speed intermittent wiper/washer system, front disc/rear drum all-wheel antilock brakes, brake/transmission shift interlock, power steering, P215/75R-15 black sidewall All-Season steel-belted radial tires, compact spare, and 4.3-liter (262-cid) CPI V-6 engine with four-speed electronically controlled automatic transmission. The CL added color-keyed floor mats, a swing-out left-hand front quarter window, eight-passenger seating, illuminated sun shade mirror, tilt steering, color-keyed bumpers, a deluxe grille with bright accents, and composite halogen headlamps. In addition to all CS/CL features, top-of-the-line Astro LTs had deep-tinted side and rear windows, power windows, remote keyless door locks, special wide velour or high-back front bucket seats with reclining seat backs, adjustable head restraints and integral arm rests, a storage compartment with zippered pouch, and a leather-wrapped four-spoke steering wheel. The Standard-Body model had 151.8 cu.-ft. of cargo capacity and a 5,700 to 5,950-lb. GVWR range. The Extended-Body model had 170.4 cu.-ft. of cargo capacity and a 5,950 to 6,100-lb. GVWR. Astro paint colors included Dark Autumnwood Metallic (No. 56), Light Autumnwood Metallic (No. 55), Onyx Black (No. 41), Medium Quasar Blue Metallic (No. 80), Teal Blue Metallic (No. 36), Fieldstone Gray Metallic (No. 16), Burnt Red Metallic (No. 76), Deep Red Metallic (No. 75), Victory Red Metallic (No. 75), Sterling Silver Metallic (No. 15), Light Teal Metallic (No. 34), and Ivory White (No. 10). Interior options included Custom vinyl, Custom cloth, and velour cloth.

1995 Chevrolet 1/2-Ton U05 Lumina Passenger Minivan 4x2 (CMD)

1/2-TON — LUMINA APV WAGON SERIES U05 (FWD) — V-6: The 1995 Lumina Minivan stood worlds apart with its sleek, aerodynamic styling, uncommon versatility, and impressive list of features. It represented a spacious "shuttle" carrying a crew of up to seven with available modular seating. Removal of the rear seating created an impressively large 112.6 cu.-ft. cargo area. The Lumina could also tow up to 3,000 lb. with its 170-hp "3800" V-6 and proper trailering options. Its seven-passenger seating option, with five modular seats, was tops over all competitors. The composite exterior body panels of the Lumina resisted dings, and could never rust. They were bonded to a steel space frame, creating an inherently rigid, quiet and long-lasting body structure. The suspension was calibrated for precise driver control, and tuned for a car-like ride. Standard features included a driver's air bag, center console, cloth upper/carpeted lower door panels, floor carpeting, front and rear color-keyed floor mats, tinted glass with Solar-Ray windshield, jack and wrench, auxiliary lighting, footwell lights, sliding rear door light, rear lift-gate light, front and rear reading lights, 10-in. prismatic rear view mirror, five-passenger cloth seating with four-way manual front seat adjuster and Scotchguard protection, cigarette lighter and ash tray with light, gauges, heater and defogger, headlights-on warning buzzer, intermittent windshield wiper control system, ETR AM/FM stereo, roof-integrated antenna, gray or black bumper fascias and rocker panel moldings and rear step pad, sliding side door, composite halogen headlamps, one-piece rear lift-gate with handle, black-painted fold-away mirrors (left-hand remote-controlled), rear window wiper and washer, front disc/rear drum all-wheel antilock braking, stainless steel exhaust system, front-wheel-drive running gear, 20-gallon fuel tank, rack-and-pinion steering with integral power assist, P205/70R-15 black sidewall radial tires, under-body spare carrier, and 3.1-liter EFI V-6 with three-speed automatic transmission. A 3.8-liter "3800" V-6 with SFI and four-speed ECT automatic overdrive transmission was optional. Lumina color choices were Bright Aqua Metallic (No. 43), Light Adriatic Blue Metallic (No. 36), Medium Adriatic Blue Metallic (No. 30), Light Gray Metallic (No. 14), Malachite Metallic (No. 44), Medium Garnet Red Metallic (No. 72), Dark Teal Metallic (No. 35), and Bright White (No. 16). Interior options were cloth or LS Custom cloth upholstery in medium blue, medium gray or ruby red, depending upon body colors.

1/2-TON, 3/4-TON, 1-TON VAN — G SERIES 10, 20, 30 (RWD) — V-6/V-8: Chevrolet's big vans were again the tried-and-true, rear-wheel-drive G series full-size models. The G10 1/2-ton series offered 110- and 125-in. wheelbase Chevy Vans with a standard 4.3-liter EFI V-6 engine. The G20 3/4-ton series offered the same models, plus an eight-passenger Sportvan with the same base engine. Both G20 models had 260 cu.-ft. of cargo capacity. In the Sportvan model, eight-passenger bench seating was standard and five-passenger bucket seating was optional. The G20 Sportvan had a GVWR range of 6,600-lb. to 6,875 lb. The G30 1-ton series included 125-in. wheelbase Chevy Van and Sportvan models, plus 146-in. Extended-Body versions of both. The 5.7-liter V-8 was standard in G30s. The Standard-Body G30 Sportvan also had 260 cu.-ft. of cargo capacity and came with standard 12-passenger bench seating or optional eight-passenger bucket seating. Its GVWR range was 7,400 to 9,200 lb. The Extended-Body model had a 306 cu.-ft. cargo capacity. Twelve-passenger seating was standard, and 15-passenger seating was optional. The longer Sportvan had a GVWR range of 8,600 lb. to 9,200 lb. A cutaway version of the G Series van chassis was also available for builders of motor homes, airport buses and other special-bodied trucks. Standard equipment for small Chevy Vans also included heavy-duty front disc/rear drum four-wheel anti-lock brakes, four-speed manual transmission with overdrive and P215/75R15 black sidewall tires. Paint colors offered for the big vans were Sand Beige Metallic (No. 57), Onyx Black (No. 41), Brilliant Blue Metallic (No. 22), Indigo Blue Metallic (No. 39), Emerald Green Metallic (No. 43), Gunmetal (No. 14), Quicksilver Metallic (No. 96), Mahogany Red Metallic (No. 83), Victory Red (No. 74), and Summit White (No. 50). Interiors were offered in Custom vinyl and Custom cloth.

1/2-TON — TAHOE (4x4) — V-8: Chevrolet's totally redesigned full-size Sport Utility Vehicle relinquished the Blazer name to its smaller sibbling. Formerly known as the K-Blazer, it was now called the Tahoe. A three-door wagon version was made available first, with a five-door wagon model following in midyear. The front of the "big" SUV looked like the front of a Chevrolet full-size C/K Pickup, since it was based on that model. Rear-wheel-drive, and all-wheel-drive versions were marketed. All models had a driver-side air bag, in addition to the passenger side air bag of last year. Tahoes came standard with a 5.7-liter V-8 with 200 hp. A 180-hp 6.5-liter turbo-diesel was optional. Gas-engine Tahoes featured a standard five-speed manual gear box. An ECT four-speed automatic was optional with gas engines, and standard with the diesel. For 1995, the automatic transmission gained an inter-lock feature to prevent shifting when the brake was not applied. Also included was a new type of 100,000-mile automatic transmission fluid. The five-door Tahoe fit between the three-door Tahoe, and the Suburban in size and utility. It had a six-inch longer wheelbase than the three-door model, and was 10 in. longer overall. The five-door's spare was mounted under the truck to provide more interior cargo space. General Motor's Insta-Trac system was standard on all Tahoes. It was a part-time, on-demand system with shift-on-the-fly capability. The Tahoe came with an LS decor package featuring air conditioning, ATC stereo cassette, rear defogger and wiper/washer, and luggage carrier. Also available was an LT decor package including all base and LS features, plus a power seat, and remote keyless entry system. Standard features also included front disc/rear drum all-wheel antilock braking and LT245/75R16C black sidewall tires.

C (4x2) /K (4x4) SUBURBAN — V-8: "One-of-a-kind handsome. One-of-a-kind comfortable. One-of-a-kind capable" is how Chevrolet described its Suburban for 1995. This large, four-door Station Wagon came with rear-wheel-drive or four-wheel-drive. It could be had in 1/2-ton-rated C1500/K1500 models or 3/4-ton-rated C2500/K2500 models. All shared a giant 149.5 cu.-ft. cargo capacity. The Suburbans could handle payloads between 1,688-lb. and 3,430-lb.. The GVWR range was 6,800-lb. to 8,600-lb.. Three-passenger seating was standard. Five-, six-, eight- and nine-passenger options were available. Standard equipment included a driver's air bag, entry assist handle, embossed black vinyl floor covering, Solar-Ray tinted glass, full-length cloth headliner, head restraints, jack and tools, automatic dome lights, auxiliary lighting, Custom vinyl bench seats with Scotchguard protection, full-size spare, dual sun shades with right-hand visor mirror, four cargo tie-downs, black fiber rear door/tailgate trim panels, color-keyed vinyl door trim panels with arm rests and reflectors, cigarette lighter in ash tray with light, pop-out cup holders, gauges, bin-type glove box, heater/defroster with side window defoggers, auxiliary 12-volt power ports, a four-spoke graphite color steering wheel, headlamp and ignition buzzers, ETR AM/FM stereo and cassette and four speakers, black air dam (C/K1500), chrome bumpers (including guards with diesel), dual rear panel doors (or tailgate), Argent molded Dura-grille, halogen headlamps, dual below-eye-line mirrors, black body side moldings with bright trim, bright wheel opening moldings, front disc/rear drum power-assisted four-wheel antilock braking, P235/75R-15XL tires (C/K1500), 5.7-liter (350-cid) 200-hp EFI V-8, and four-speed automatic overdrive transmission. The LS Suburban added a rear cargo net, front air conditioning, floor carpeting, color-keyed front and rear floor mats, deep-tinted glass, power door locks, power windows, a rear defogger (with panel doors only), a rear wiper/washer, Custom cloth 60/40 front bench seat with lumbar support, sun shades with lighted mirrors, cloth insert door panels with lower carpeting, map pockets and lighted reflectors, rear door/tailgate cloth trim panels, a leather-wrapped steering wheel, premium eight-speaker sound system, bright grille accents, dual composite halogen headlights, electric OSRV mirrors, and underhood service lamp. The top-of-the-line LT Suburban also had leather-surfaced reclining front bucket seats with power lumbar adjustment., a center floor console, an overhead console, a 60/40 center bench seat, and a three-passenger rear bench seat. Colors that 1995 Suburbans came in were Teal Blue Metallic (No. 36), Onyx Black (No. 41), Light Autumnwood Metallic (No. 55), Quicksilver Metallic (No. 96), Burnt Red Metallic (No. 76), Indigo Blue Metallic (No. 39), Victory Red (No. 74), Atlantic Blue Metallic (No. 30), Summit White (No. 50), and Emerald Green Metallic (No. 43). Interiors came in beige, blue, gray or red. Vinyl, Custom cloth, and Custom leather trims are offered.

1995 Chevrolet 1/2-Ton K1500 Extended-Cab Sportside Short Bed "Z71" Pickup 4x4 (CMD)

1995 Chevrolet 3/4-Ton K2500 Fleetside Long Bed Pickup 4x4 (CMD)

1/2-TON, 3/4-TON, 1-TON — C (4x2)/K (4x4) PICKUP — V-6/V-8: Chevrolet's full-size, rear-wheel-drive C Series pickups came in C1500 (1/2-ton), C2500 (3/4-ton), and C3500 (1-ton) lines. The four-wheel-drive K Series pickups came in K1500 (1/2-ton), K2500 (3/4-ton), and K3500 (1-ton) lines. Buyers could choose from Regular-Cab, Extended-Cab, and Crew-Cab models. There was also a choice between the 6.5-foot "Short Box" and the 8-foot "Long Box." Fleetside and Sportside rear fender designs were offered. Fancier interiors were featured for 1995 and promoted as "the newest, most luxuriously comfortable interiors we've ever featured in a full-size pickup." The standard wheelbase for pickups was 117.5 in. Five different wheelbases were offered: 117.5 in. for Regular-Cab Short Box models, 131.5 in. for Regular-Cab Long Box models, 141.5 in. for Extended-Cab Short Box models, 155.5 in. for Extended-Cab Long Box models, and 168.5 in. for Crew-Cab Long Box models. Three-passenger bench seating was standard in all full-sized Chevrolet Pickups, except Crew-Cab models, which came with twin three-passenger bench seats. Front bucket seats were optional for all models. Extended-Cab Pickups could be optioned with a rear bench seat. Standard equipment included a 4.3-liter EFI V-6, front disc/rear drum brakes with ABS, five-speed manual transmission with overdrive, and P225/75R15 black sidewall All-Season SBR tires. Of interest to enthusiasts was a Sportside Sport model option with a "Step-Side" Short-Box design and the following standard features: Oynx Black, Victory Red or Summit White finish, body-color bumpers and mirrors, black air dam with fog lights (C10) or tow hooks (K10), new-design body-color grille, aluminum wheels, and Chevrolet tailgate decal. Buyers could add a Sport Handling package with chrome wheels, special springs, and Bilstein gas shocks on 4x2 models or Z71 off-road package on 4x4 versions. Colors that 1995 C/K pickups came in were Teal Green Metallic (No. 38), Onyx Black (No. 41), Light Autumnwood Metallic (No. 55), Quicksilver Metallic (No. 96), Dark Garnet Red Metallic (No. 84), Indigo Blue Metallic (No. 39), Victory Red (No. 74), Light Quasar Blue Metallic (No. 20), Summit White (No. 50), and Emerald Green Metallic (No. 43). Interiors came in beige, blue, gray or red. Vinyl, cloth, Custom cloth, and Custom leather trims are offered.

1995 Chevrolet 1/2-Ton T-Series ZR2 Pickup 4x4(CMD)

I. D. DATA: The VIN plate was mounted on the lower left side windshield corner. The VIN consisted of 17 symbols. The first three symbols identify the country, the manufacturer and the type of vehicle. The fourth symbol designates the GVWR range. The fifth, sixth and seventh symbols identify the line and chassis type, series and body type. The eighth symbol identifies the engine: [Chevrolet engines] H=5.0-liter V-8, K=5.7-liter V-8, N=7.4-liter V-8, Z=4.3-liter V-6. [GM engines] A= 5.7-liter V-8, D=3.1-liter V-6, F=6.5-liter diesel V-8 (190 hp), L=3.8-liter V-6, M=7.0-liter V-8, P=6.5-liter diesel (155 hp), S=6.5-liter diesel V-8 (180 hp), W=4.3-liter V-6, 4=2.2-liter L4. The ninth symbol is the check digit. The tenth symbol indicates model-year. The 11th symbol identifies the assembly plant. The last six symbols are the sequential production number.

Model	Body Type	Price	Weight	Prod. Total
CE/CJ Geo Tracker — 1/2-Ton — 86.6 in. w.b. — 1.6-liter MFI L4 (16-valve in 4x4s)				
CE10367	4x2 Convertible	11,670	2,189	-
CJ10316	4x4 Hardtop	13,015	2,387	-
CJ10367	4x4 Convertible	12,935	2,365	-
CJ10316/B2Z	4x4 LSi Hardtop	14,485	2,397	-
CJ10367/B2Z	4x4 LSi Convertible	14,305	2,375	-

NOTE 1: A $300 dealer destination charge applied to Geo Trackers effective Feb. 1, 1994.

Model	Body Type	Price	Weight	Prod. Total
S10 Fleetside Pickup — 1/2-Ton — 108.3/117.9/122.9 in. w.b. — 2.2-liter MFI L4				
S10603	**Reg.-Cab** Short Box	9823	2905	-
S10803	**Reg.-Cab** Long Box	10,116	3000	-
S10603	**Reg.-Cab** LS Short Box	11,410	-	-
S10803	**Reg.-Cab** LS Long Box	11,705	-	-
S10653	**Ext.-Cab** LS Short Box	12,510	3157	-
T10 4x4 Fleetside Pickup — 1/2-Ton — 108.3/122.9 in. w.b. — 4.3-liter EFI V-6				
T10603	**Reg.-Cab** SWB	14,765	-	-
T10803	**Reg.-Cab** LWB	15,340	-	-
T10603	**Reg.-Cab** LS SWB	15,770	-	-
T10803	**Reg.-Cab** LS LWB	16,335	-	-
T10653	**Ext.-Cab** LS Short Box	16,870	-	-

NOTE 2: A $480 dealer destination charge applied to S-Series pickups effective Aug. 1, 1994.

Model	Body Type	Price	Weight	Prod. Total
Blazer 4x2 Sport Utility Wagon — 1/2-Ton — 100.5/107 in. w.b. — 4.3-liter EFI V-6				
CS10516	2-dr Tailgate	16,145	3205	-
CS10506	4-dr Tailgate	19,851	3446	-
Blazer 4x4 Sport Utility Wagon — 1/2-Ton — 100.5/107 in. w.b. — 4.3-liter CPI V-6				
CT10516	2-dr Tailgate	19,905	3506	-
CT10506	4-dr Tailgate	21,953	3811	-

NOTE 3: A $485 dealer destination charge applied to S-Series Blazers effective Aug. 1, 1994.

Model	Body Type	Price	Weight	Prod. Total
M10 Astro Minivan (rear-wheel-drive) — 1/2-Ton — 111 in. w.b. — 4.3-liter EFI V-6				
CM10906	Standard Cargo Van	17,492	3653	-
CM11006	Extended Cargo Van	17,785	3741	-
CM10906ZW9	Standard CS Van	18,288	3998	-
L10 Astro Minivan (all-wheel-drive) — 1/2-Ton — 111 in. w.b. — 4.3-liter CPI V-6				
CL10906/ZW9	Standard CS Van	20,488	-	-

NOTE 4: A $555 dealer destination charge applied to Astros effective Aug. 1, 1994.

Model	Body Type	Price	Weight	Prod. Total
U05 Lumina APV Minivan — 1/2-Ton — 109.8 in. w.b. --3.1-liter EFI V-6				
1UM05	Cargo Van	16,235	3344	-
1UM06	Wagon	17,595	3554	-

NOTE 5: A $540 dealer destination charge applied to Lumina minivans effective June 30, 1994.

Model	Body Type	Price	Weight	Prod. Total
G10 Van — 1/2-Ton — 110/125 in. w.b. — 4.3-liter EFI V-6				
CG11005/ZW9	SWB Chevy Van	16,839	3867	-
CG11006/ZW9	LWB Chevy Van	17,023	4500	-
G20 Van — 3/4-Ton — 110/125 in. w.b. — 4.3-liter EFI V-6				
CG21005/ZW9	SWB Chevy Van	16,808	3905	-
CG21305/ZW9	LWB Chevy Van	17,013	4550	-
CG21306/ZW9	LWB Sportvan 8P	19,636	4625	-
G30 Van — 1-Ton — 125/146 in. w.b. — 5.7-liter Heavy-duty EFI V-8				
CG31305/ZW9	LWB Chevy Van	17,167	4380	-
CG31306/ZW9	LWB Sportvan 12P	21,030	5266	-
CG31605/ZW9	EWB Chevy Van	20,262	4881	-
CG31606/ZW9	EWB Sportvan 12P	22,186	5642	-
CG31305/ZW9	LWB Cutaway Van	-	-	-

NOTE 6: A $590 dealer destination charge applied to full-size vans effective Aug. 1, 1994.

Model	Body Type	Price	Weight	Prod. Total
Tahoe 4x4 — 1/2-Ton — 111.5 in. w.b. — 5.7-liter EFI V-8				
CK10516	Utility Hardtop	21,830	4757	-

NOTE 7: A $610 dealer destination charge applied to full-size Blazers effective Aug. 1, 1994.

Model	Body Type	Price	Weight	Prod. Total
C/K 1500 Suburban — 1/2-Ton — 131.5 in. w.b. — 5.7-liter EFI V-8				
CC10906/ZW9	Panel Door (4x2)	21,587	4672	-
CK10906/ZW9	Panel Door (4x4)	22,820	-	-
C/K 2500 Suburban — 3/4-Ton — 131.5 in. w.b. — 5.7-liter EFI V-8				
CC20906/ZW9	Panel Door (4x2)	23,893	5227	-
CK20906/ZW9	Panel Door (4x4)	25,039	-	-

NOTE 8: A $650 dealer destination charge applied to Suburbans effective Aug. 1, 1994.

Model	Body Type	Price	Weight	Prod. Total
C1500 Regular-Cab Pickup — 1/2-Ton Short Box — 117.5 in. w.b. --4.3-liter EFI V-6				
CC10703/E62	Sportside	15,610	3748	-
CC10703/E63	Fleetside Work Truck	13,387	-	-
CC10703/E63	Fleetside	14,797	3725	-
C1500 Pickup — 1/2-Ton Long Box — 131.5 in. w.b. --4.3-liter EFI V-6				
CC10903	Regular-cab Fleetside	15,077	3865	-
C1500 Extended-Cab Pickup — 1/2-Ton Short Box — 141.5 in. w.b. --4.3-liter EFI V-6				
CC10753	Sportside	17,269	4133	-
CC10753	Fleetside	16,757	4110	-
C1500 Extended-Cab Pickup — 1/2-Ton Long Box — 155.5 in. w.b. --4.3-liter EFI V-6				
CC10903	Fleetside	17,700	4247	-

NOTE 9: Add approximately $2,350 for CK1500 Pickups with 4x4.

Model	Body Type	Price	Weight	Prod. Total
C2500 Pickup — 3/4-Ton Long Box — 131.5 in. w.b. — 4.3-liter EFI V-6				
CC20924	Chassis & Cab	-	4007	-
CC20903	Regular-cab Fleetside	15,759	4006	-
C2500 Extended-Cab Pickup — 3/4-Ton Short Box — 141.5 in. w.b. — 4.3-liter EFI V-6				
CC20953		18,770	4270	-
C2500 Extended-Cab Pickup — 3/4-Ton Long Box — 155.5 in. w.b. — 4.3-liter EFI V-6				
CC10903	Fleetside	18,827	4337	-

NOTE 10: Add approximately $2,025 for CK2500 Pickups with 4x4.

Model	Body Type	Price	Weight	Prod. Total
C3500 Pickup — 1-Ton Long Box — 131.5 in. w.b. --5.7-liter EFI V-8				
CC30924	Chassis & Cab	-	4273	-
CC30903	Regular-cab Fleetside	17,458	4649	-
C3500 Extended-Cab Pickup — 1-Ton Long Box — 155.5 in. w.b. — 5.7-liter V-8				
CC30903	Fleetside	20,784	5325	-
C3500 Crew-Cab Pickup — 1-Ton Long Box — 168.5 in. w.b. — 5.7-liter V-8				
CC30933	Fleetside	20,044	5290	-
CC30933	Cab & chassis	-	4915	-
CC30934	H-D Cab & chassis	-	5281	-

NOTE 11: Add approximately $3,300 for CK3500 Pickups with 4x4.

NOTE 12: A $610 dealer destination charge applied to C/K Models effective Aug. 1, 1994.

GASOLINE ENGINES (DISPLACEMENT ORDER)

ENGINE: Inline. Four-cylinder. Bore & stroke: 2.95 x 3.54 in. Displacement: 1.6-liter (97 cid). BHP: 80 at 5400 rpm. Torque: unknown. Multiport-fuel-injection. Suzuki-built. [Standard in Geo Tracker 4x2]

ENGINE: Inline. Four-cylinder. Bore & stroke: 2.95 x 3.54 in. Displacement: 1.6-liter (97 cid). 16-valve. BHP: 95 at 5400 rpm. Torque: unknown. Multiport-fuel-injection. Suzuki-built. [Standard in Geo Tracker 4x4]

ENGINE: Inline. Four-cylinder. Bore & stroke: 3.5 x 3.46 in. Displacement: 2.2-liter (133 cid). BHP: 118 at 5200 rpm. Torque: 130 lb.-ft. at 2300 rpm. EFI/Throttle-body-injection. VIN Code 4. GM-built. [Standard in S10]

ENGINE: V-block. Six-cylinder. Bore & stroke: 3.5 x 3.331 in. Displacement: 3.1-liter (191 cid). BHP: 120 at 4200 rpm. Torque: 175 lb.-ft. at 2200 rpm. Multiport-fuel-injection. VIN Code D. GM-built. [Standard in Lumina APV]

ENGINE: V-block. Six-cylinder. Bore & stroke: 3.8 x 3.4 in. Displacement: 3.8-liter (231 cid). BHP: 165-170 hp at 4800 rpm. Torque: 220-225 lb.-ft. at 3200 rpm. Sequential-port-fuel-injection (SFI). VIN Code L. GM-built. [Optional in Lumina APV]

ENGINE: V-block. Vortec six-cylinder. Bore & stroke: 4.0 x 3.48 in. Displacement: 4.3-liter (262 cid). BHP: 155-165 at 4000 rpm. Torque: 230-235 lb.-ft. at 2400 rpm. EFI/Throttle-body-injection. VIN Code Z. Chevrolet-built. [Standard in C/K1500, C/K2500, T10, S10 Extended-Cab, Blazer, G10, and G20]

1995 Chevrolet 1/2-Ton K1500 4x4 Extended-Cab Sportside Z71 Short Box Pickup (CMD)

1995 Chevrolet 1/2-Ton S-Series LS 4x2 Regular-Cab Short Box Pickup (CMD)

1995 Chevrolet 1/2-Ton C1500 4x2 Regular-Cab Fleetside Long Box Pickup (CMD)

1995 Chevrolet 1/2-Ton S-Series LS 4x2 Extended-Cab Short Box Pickup (CMD)

1995 Chevrolet C/K Pickup and C/K Suburban Interior (CMD)

1995 Chevrolet 1/2-Ton S-Series ZR2 4x4 Regular-Cab Short Box Pickup (CMD)

ENGINE: V-block. Enhanced Vortec six-cylinder. Bore & stroke: 4.0 x 3.48 in. Displacement: 4.3-liter (262 cid). BHP: 200 at 4400 rpm. Torque: 260 lb.-ft. at 3600 rpm. Central-point-injected. VIN Code W. GM-built. [Standard in all Astros, Optional in S10]
ENGINE: V-block. Eight-cylinder. Bore & stroke: 3.74 x 3.48 in. Displacement: 5.0-liter (305 cid). BHP: 170-175 at 4200 rpm. Torque: 255-265 lb.-ft. at 2800 rpm. EFI/Throttle-body-injection. VIN Code H. GM-built. [Optional in C/K pickups with GVWR less than 8,600-lb., optional in G10/G20 vans]]
ENGINE: V-block. Heavy-duty. Eight-cylinder. Bore & stroke: 4.0 x 3.48 in. Displacement: 5.7-liter (350 cid). BHP: 190-195 at 4000 rpm. Torque: 300 lb.-ft. at 2400 rpm. EFI/Throttle-body-injection. VIN Code A. GM-built. [Standard in G30, optional in G10 and G20]
ENGINE: V-block. Light-Duty. Eight-cylinder. Bore & stroke: 4.0 x 3.48 in. Displacement: 5.7-liter (350 cid). BHP: 200-210 at 4000 rpm. Torque: 300 lb.-ft. at 2800 rpm. EFI/Throttle-body-injection. VIN Code K. Chevrolet-built [Standard in Tahoe, C/K3500, and Suburban]
ENGINE: V-block. Eight-cylinder. Bore & stroke: 4.25 x 4.00 in. Displacement: 7.4-liter (454 cid). BHP: 230 at 3600 rpm. Torque: 385 lb.-ft. at 1600 rpm. Throttle-body-fuel-injection. VIN Code N. Chevrolet-built. [Optional in C/K3500, optional in G30]

DIESEL ENGINES (DISPLACEMENT ORDER)
ENGINE: V-block. Light-duty. Eight-cylinder. Bore & stroke: 4.06 x 3.82 in. Displacement: 6.5-liter (400 cid). BHP: 155 at 3600 rpm. Torque: 275 lb.-ft. at 1700 rpm. VIN Code P. GM-built. [Optional in G20/G30, optional in C/K1500/2500]
ENGINE: V-block. Heavy-duty. Eight-cylinder. Bore & stroke: 4.06 x 3.82 in. Displacement: 6.5-liter (400 cid). BHP: 180 at 3400 rpm. Torque: 360 lb.-ft. at 1700 rpm. VIN Code S. GM-built. [Optional in C/K3500 Crew-cab]
ENGINE: V-block. Eight-cylinder. Turbocharged. Bore & stroke: 4.06 x 3.82 in. Displacement: 6.5-liter (400 cid). BHP: 190 at 3400 rpm. Torque: 240 lb.-ft. at 2000 rpm. VIN Code F. GM-built. [Optional in all C/K pickups with GVWRs (automatic) 11,000 to 14,500-lb., (manual) 9,000 to 12,000-lb., optional in Suburbans]

1995 Chevrolet 1/2-Ton S-Series "SS" Pickup 4x2 (CMD)

CHASSIS: [Geo Tracker (All)] Wheelbase: 86.6 in. Length: 142.5 in. Width: 64.2 in. Height: 65.6 in. Tires: P205/75R15 black sidewall.
CHASSIS: [S10] Regular-Cab. Short Box. Wheelbase: 108.3 in. Length: 178.2 in. Width: 64.7 in. Height: 61.3 in. GVWR: 4,200-4,600 lb. Payload: 1,078-1,703 lb. Tires: P205/75R15 black sidewall.
CHASSIS: [T10] Regular-Cab. Short Box. Wheelbase: 108.3 in. Length: 178.2 in. Width: 64.7 in. Height: 63.4 in. GVWR: 4,650-5,150 lb. Payload: 1,010-1,701 lb. Tires: P205/75R15 black sidewall.
CHASSIS: [S10] Regular-Cab. Long Box. Wheelbase: 117.9 in. Length: 204.1. Width: 64.7 in. Height: 61.3 in. GVWR: 4,600-4,900 lb. Payload: 983-1,743 lb. Tires: P205/75R15 black sidewall.
CHASSIS: [T10] Regular-Cab. Long Box. Wheelbase: 117.9 in. Length: 194.2 in. Width: 64.7 in. Height: 63.4 in. GVWR: 4,650-5,150 lb. Payload: 1,113-1,596 lb. Tires: P205/75R15 black sidewall
CHASSIS: [S10] Extended-Cab. Short Box. Wheelbase: 122.9 in. Length: 192.8 in. Width: 64.7 in. Height: 61.3 in. GVWR: 4,600 lb. Payload: 1,369-1,519 lb. Tires: P205/75R15 black sidewall.
CHASSIS: [T10] Extended-Cab. Short Box. Wheelbase: 122.9 in. Length: 192.8 in. Width: 64.7 in. Height: 63.4 in. GVWR: 4,650-5,150 lb. Payload: 1,011-1,482 lb. Tires: P205/75R15 black sidewall.
CHASSIS: [Blazer 4x2] Two-door. Wheelbase: 100.5 in. Length: 174.7 in. Width: 67.8 in. Height: 66 in. GVWR: 4,350 lb. Payload: 975 lb. Tires: P205/75R15 black sidewall.
CHASSIS: [Blazer 4x4] Two-door. Wheelbase: 100.5 in. Length: 174.7 in. Width: 67.8 in. Height: 66.9 in. GVWR: 4,700 lb. Payload: 1,164 lb. Tires: P235/75R15 black sidewall.
CHASSIS: [Blazer 4x2] Four-door. Wheelbase: 107.0 in. Length: 181.2 in. Width: 67.8 in. Height: 65.9 in. GVWR: 4,850 lb. Payload: 1,069 lb. Tires: P205/75R15 black sidewall.
CHASSIS: [Blazer 4x4] Four-door. Wheelbase: 107.0 in. Length: 181.2 in. Width: 67.8 in. Height: 67.0 in. GVWR: 5,100 lb. Payload: 1,453 lb. Tires: P235/75R15 black sidewall.
CHASSIS: [Astro Cargo Regular-Body] Wheelbase: 111 in. Length: 176.8 in. Width: 77.5 in. Height: 76.2 in. GVWR: 5,700 lb. Payload: 1,740 lb. Tires: P205/75R15 black sidewall.
CHASSIS: [Astro Cargo Regular-Body AWD] Wheelbase: 111 in. Length: 176.8 in. Width: 77.5 in. Height: 76.2 in. GVWR: 5,950 lb. Payload: 1,697 lb. Tires: P205/75R15 black sidewall.
CHASSIS: [Astro Cargo Extended-Body] Wheelbase: 111 in. Length: 186.8 in. Width: 77.5 in. Height: 76.2 in. GVWR: 5,950 lb. Payload: 1,911 lb. Tires: P205/75R15 black sidewall.
CHASSIS: [Astro Cargo Extended-Body AWD] Wheelbase: 111 in. Length: 186.8 in. Width: 77.5 in. Height: 76.2 in. GVWR: 6,100 lb. Payload: 1,783 lb. Tires: P205/75R15 black sidewall.
CHASSIS: [Astro Passenger Regular-Body] Wheelbase: 111 in. Length: 176.8 in. Width: 77.5 in. Height: 76.2 in. GVWR: 5,700 lb. Payload: 1,340 lb. Tires: P205/75R15 black sidewall.
CHASSIS: [Astro Passenger Regular-Body AWD] Wheelbase: 111 in. Length: 176.8 in. Width: 77.5 in. Height: 76.2 in. GVWR: 5,950 lb. Payload: 1,670 lb. Tires: P205/75R15 black sidewall.
CHASSIS: [Astro Passenger Extended-Body] Wheelbase: 111 in. Length: 186.8 in. Width: 77.5 in. Height: 76.2 in. GVWR: 5,950 lb. Payload: 1,914 lb. Tires: P205/75R15 black sidewall.

CHASSIS: [Astro Passenger Extended-Body AWD] Wheelbase: 111 in. Length: 186.8 in. Width: 77.5 in. Height: 76.2 in. GVWR: 6,100 lb. Payload: 1,783 lb. Tires: P205/75R15 black sidewall.
CHASSIS: [Lumina] Wheelbase: 109.8 in. Length: 194.2 in. Width: 73.9 in. Height: 65.7 in. GVWR: 5,126 lb. Payload: 1.357 lb. Tires: P205/70R15 black sidewall.
CHASSIS: [G10/Short Body] Chevy Van. Wheelbase: 110 in. Length: 178.1 in. Width: 79.4 in. Height: 79.5 in. GVWR: 6,000 lb. Payload: 1,754 lb. Tires: P215/75R15 black sidewall.
CHASSIS: [G10/Long Body] Chevy Van/Sportvan. Wheelbase: 125 in. Length: 202.1 in. Width: 79.5 in. Height: 79.5 in. GVWR: 6,000 lb. Payload: 1,428 lb. Tires: P215/75R15 black sidewall.
CHASSIS: [G20/Short Body] Chevy Van. Wheelbase: 110 in. Length: 178.1 in. Width: 79.4 in. Height: 79.4 in. GVWR: 6,600 lb. Payload: 1,452 lb. Tires: P215/75R15 black sidewall
CHASSIS: [G20/Long Body] Chevy Van/Sportvan. Wheelbase: 125 in. Length: 202.1 in. Width: 79.5 in. Height: 79.5 in. GVWR: 6,875 lb. Payload: 2,142 lb. Tires: P215/75R15 black sidewall.
CHASSIS: [G30/Long Body Chevy Van] Wheelbase: 125 in. Length: 202.1 in. Width: 79.5 in. Height: 79.5 in. GVWR: 7,400 lb. Payload: 2,152 lb. Tires: P215/75R15 black sidewall.
CHASSIS: [G30/Long Body Sportvan] Wheelbase: 125 in. Length: 202.1 in. Width: 79.5 in. Height: 79.5 in. GVWR: 8,600 lb. Payload: 2,426 lb. Tires: P215/75R15 black sidewall.
CHASSIS: [G30/Extended Body Chevy Van] Wheelbase: 146 in. Length: 223.1 in. Width: 79.5 in. Height: 82.3 in. GVWR: 9,200 lb. Payload: 3,476 lb. Tires: P215/75R15 black sidewall.
CHASSIS: [G30/Extended Body 12-Passenger Sportvan] Wheelbase: 146 in. Length: 223.1 in. Width: 79.5 in. Height: 82.3 in. GVWR: 9,200 lb. Payload: 4,101 lb. Tires: P215/75R15 black sidewall.
CHASSIS: [Tahoe three-door] Wheelbase: 111.5 in. Length: 188.5 in. Width: 77.1 in. Height: 75 in. GVWR: 6,250-6,450 lb. Payload: 1,333-1,540 lb. Tires: LT245/75R16C black sidewall.
CHASSIS: [Tahoe five-door] Wheelbase: 117.5 in. Length: 198.5 in. Width: 77.1 in. Height: 75 in. GVWR: 6,250-6,450 lb. Payload: 1,333-1,540 lb. Tires: LT245/75R16C black sidewall.
CHASSIS: [Suburban C1500] Wheelbase: 131.5 in. Length: 219.5 in. Width: 77 in. Height: 74.9 in. GVWR: 6,800 lb. Payload: 2,117 lb. Tires: P235/75R-15XLS black sidewall.
CHASSIS: [Suburban K1500] Wheelbase: 131.5 in. Length: 219.5 in. Width: 77 in. Height: 73.6 in. GVWR: 7,200 lb. Payload: 2,052 lb. Tires: P235/75R-15XLS black sidewall.
CHASSIS: [Suburban C2500] Wheelbase: 131.5 in. Length: 219.5 in. Width: 77 in. Height: 74.9 in. GVWR: 8,600 lb. Payload: 3,370 lb. Tires: P235/75R-15XLS black sidewall.
CHASSIS: [Suburban K2500] Wheelbase: 131.5 in. Length: 219.5 in. Width: 77 in. Height: 73.6 in. GVWR: 8,600 lb. Payload: 2,944 lb. Tires: P235/75R-15XLS black sidewall.
CHASSIS: [C1500 Sportside Regular-Cab Short Box Pickup] Regular-cab. Short Box. Wheelbase: 117.5 in. Length: 194.1 in. Width: 77.1 in. Height: 70.4 in. GVWR: 5,600 lb. Payload: 1,570 lb. Tires: P225/75R15 black sidewall ALSBR tires.
CHASSIS: [C1500 Fleetside Regular-Cab Short Box Pickup] Wheelbase: 117.5 in. Length: 194.1 in. Width: 76.8 in. Height: 70.4 in. GVWR: 5,600 lb. Payload: 1,581 lb. Tires: P225/75R15 black sidewall ALSBR tires.
CHASSIS: [C1500 Fleetside Regular-Cab Short Box "Work Truck" Pickup] Wheelbase: 117.5 in. Length: 194.1 in. Width: 76.8 in. Height: 70.4 in. GVWR: 5,600 lb. Payload: 1,882 lb. Tires: P225/75R15 black sidewall ALSBR tires.
CHASSIS: [C1500 Fleetside Regular-Cab Long Box Pickup] Wheelbase: 131.5 in. Length: 212.6 in. Width: 76.8 in. Height: 70.4 in. GVWR: 5,600 lb. Payload: 1,486-2,298 lb. Tires: P225/75R15 black sidewall.
CHASSIS: [C1500 Fleetside Regular-Cab Long Box "Work Truck" Pickup] Wheelbase: 131.5 in. Length: 212.6 in. Width: 76.8 in. Height: 70.4 in. GVWR: 6,100 lb. Payload: 1,486-2,298 lb. Tires: P225/75R15 black sidewall ALSBR tires.

1995 Chevrolet 1/2-Ton C1500 Extended-Cab Sportside Short Bed Pickup 4x2 (CMD)

CHASSIS: [C1500 Sportside Extended-Cab Short Box Pickup] Wheelbase: 141.5 in. Length: 218.0 in. Width: 77.1 in. Height: 70.6 in. GVWR: 6,200 lb. Payload: 1,506-2,100 lb. Tires: P225/75R15 black sidewall ALSBR tires.
CHASSIS: [C1500 Fleetside Extended-Cab Short Box Pickup] Wheelbase: 141.5 in. Length: 218.0 in. Width: 76.8 in. Height: 70.6 in. GVWR: 6,200 lb. Payload: 1,506-2,210 lb. Tires: P225/75R15 black sidewall ALSBR tires.
CHASSIS: [C1500 Fleetside Extended-Cab Long Box Pickup] Wheelbase: 155.5 in. Length: 237.0 in. Width: 76.8 in. Height: 70.6 in. GVWR: 6,200 lb. Payload: 1,345-2,084 lb. Tires: P225/75R15 black sidewall ALSBR tires.
CHASSIS: [K1500 Sportside Regular-Cab Short Box Pickup] Wheelbase: 117.5 in. Length: 194.1 in. Width: 77.1 in. Height: 73.8 GVWR: 6,100 lb. Payload: 1,660-1,991 lb. Tires: P225/75R15 black sidewall ALSBR tires.
CHASSIS: [K1500 Fleetside Regular-Cab Short Box Pickup] Wheelbase: 117.5 in. Length: 194.1 in. Width: 77.1 in. Height: 73.8 in. GVWR: 6,100 lb. Payload: 1,627-1,991 lb. Tires: P225/75R15 black sidewall ALSBR tires.
CHASSIS: [K1500 Fleetside Regular-Cab Short Box "Work Truck" Pickup] Wheelbase: 117.5 in. Length: 194.1 in. Width: 77.1 in. Height: 73.8 in. GVWR: 6,100 lb. Payload: 1,486-2,298 lb. Tires: P225/75R15 black sidewall ALSBR tires.

CHASSIS: [K1500 Fleetside Regular-Cab Long Box Pickup] Wheelbase: 131.5 in. Length: 212.6 in. Width: 76.8 in. Height: 73.8 in. GVWR: 6,100 lb. Payload: 1,203-1,861 lb. Tires: P225/75R15 black sidewall ALSBR tires.
CHASSIS: [K1500 Fleetside Regular-Cab Long Box "Work Truck" Pickup] Wheelbase: 131.5 in. Length: 212.6 in. Width: 76.8 in. Height: 73.8 in. GVWR: 6,100 lb. Payload: 1,980 lb. Tires: P225/75R15 black sidewall ALSBR tires.
CHASSIS: [K1500 Sportside Extended-Cab Short Box Pickup] Wheelbase: 141.5 in. Length: 218.0 in. Width: 77.1 in. Height: 73.8 in. GVWR: 6,200-6,800 lb. Payload: 1,307-2,064 lb. Tires: P225/75R15 black sidewall ALSBR tires.
CHASSIS: [K1500 Fleetside Extended-Cab Short Box Pickup] Wheelbase: 141.5 in. Length: 218.0 in. Width: 76.8 in. Height: 73.8 in. GVWR: 6,200-6,800 lb. Payload: 1,390-2,046 lb. Tires: P225/75R15 black sidewall ALSBR tires.
CHASSIS: [K1500 Fleetside Extended-Cab Long Box Pickup] Wheelbase: 155.5 in. Length: 237.0 in. Width: 76.8 in. Height: 73.8 in. GVWR: 6,200-6,800 lb. Payload: 1,187-1,863 lb. Tires: P225/75R15 black sidewall ALSBR tires.
CHASSIS: [C2500 Fleetside Regular-Cab Long Box Pickup] Wheelbase: 131.5 in. Length: 212.6 in. Width: 76.8 in. Height: 73 in. GVWR: 7,200 lb. Payload: 2,519 lb. Tires: P225/75R15 black sidewall ALSBR tires.
CHASSIS: [C2500 Heavy-duty Fleetside Regular-cab Long Box Pickup] Wheelbase: 131.5 in. Length: 212.6 in. Width: 76.8 in. Height: 73 in. GVWR: 8,600 lb. Payload: 4,207 lb. Tires: P225/75R15 black sidewall ALSBR tires.
CHASSIS: [C2500 Fleetside Extended-Cab Short Box Pickup] Wheelbase: 141.5 in. Length: 218.0 in. Width: 76.8 in. Height: 74 in. GVWR: 7,200 lb. Payload: 2,339-2,916 lb. Tires: P225/75R15 black sidewall ALSBR tires.
CHASSIS: [C2500 Fleetside Extended-Cab Long Box Pickup] Wheelbase: 155.5 in. Length: 237.0 in. Width: 76.8 in. Height: 74 in. GVWR: 8,600 lb. Payload: 3,316-3,853 lb. Tires: P225/75R15 black sidewall ALSBR tires.
CHASSIS: [K2500 Fleetside Regular-Cab Long Box Pickup] Wheelbase: 131.5 in. Length: 212.6 in. Width: 76.8 in. Height: 73.8 in. GVWR: 7,200-8,600 lb. Payload: 2,240-3,842 lb. Tires: P225/75R15 black sidewall ALSBR tires.
CHASSIS: [K2500 Heavy-duty Fleetside Regular-Cab Long Box Pickup] Wheelbase: 131.5 in. Length: 212.6 in. Width: 76.8 in. Height: 73.8 in. GVWR: 8,600 lb. Payload: 2,240-3,842 lb. Tires: P225/75R15 black sidewall ALSBR tires.
CHASSIS: [K2500 Fleetside Extended-Cab Short Box Pickup] Wheelbase: 141.5 in. Length: 218.0 in. Width: 76.8 in. Height: 73.8 in. GVWR: 7,200 lb. Payload: 1,956-2,573 lb. Tires: P225/75R15 black sidewall ALSBR tires.
CHASSIS: [K2500 Fleetside Extended-Cab Long Box Pickup] Wheelbase: 155.5 in. Length: 237.0 in. Width: 76.8 in. Height: 73.8 in. GVWR: 8,600 lb. Payload: 2,790-3,444 lb. Tires: P225/75R15 black sidewall ALSBR tires.
CHASSIS: [C3500 Fleetside Regular-Cab Long Box Pickup] Wheelbase: 131.5 in. Length: 212.6 in. Width: 76.8 in. Height: 70.4 in. GVWR: 9,000-10,000 lb. Payload: 3,485-5,024 lb. Tires: P225/75R15 black sidewall ALSBR tires.
CHASSIS: [K3500 Fleetside Regular-Cab Long Box Pickup] Wheelbase: 131.5 in. Length: 212.6 in. Width: 76.8 in. Height: 73.8 in. GVWR: 9,200-10,000 lb. Payload: 3,771-4,649 lb. Tires: P225/75R15 black sidewall ALSBR tires.
CHASSIS: [C3500 Fleetside Extended-Cab Long Box Pickup] Wheelbase: 155.5 in. Length: 237.0 in. Width: 76.8 in. Height: 70.4 in. GVWR: 10,000 lb. Payload: 4,324-4,758 lb. Tires: P225/75R15 black sidewall ALSBR tires.
CHASSIS: [K3500 Fleetside Extended-Cab Long Box Pickup] Wheelbase: 155.5 in. Length: 237.0 in. Width: 76.8 in. Height: 73.8 in. GVWR: 10,000 lb. Payload: 3,934-4,270 lb. Tires: P225/75R15 black sidewall ALSBR tires.
CHASSIS: [C3500 Fleetside Crew-Cab Long Box Pickup] Wheelbase: 168.5 in. Length: 248 in. Width: 76.8 in. Height: 70.4 in. GVWR: 9,000-10,000 lb. Payload: 3,194-4,393 lb. Tires: P235/75R15 black sidewall ALSBR tires.
CHASSIS: [K3500 Fleetside Crew-Cab Long Box Pickup] Wheelbase: 168.5 in. Length: 248 in. Width: 76.8 in. Height: 70.4 in. GVWR: 9,200-10,000 lb. Payload: 3,003-3,980 lb. Tires: P235/75R15 black sidewall ALSBR tires.
CHASSIS: [C/K 3500 Pickup] Motor home chassis. Wheelbase: 183.5 in. Tires: P225/75R15 black sidewall ALSBR tires.

1995 Chevrolet 1-Ton K3500 Crew-cab "Big Dooley" Pickup 4x4 (CMD)

SELECTED OPTIONS
GEO TRACKER OPTIONS: Base equipment group with UL1 radio ($306). Base equipment group with ULO radio ($526). Base equipment group with UPO radio ($726). Expression color appearance package ($425-$499). Air conditioning ($745). Body side moldings ($59-$85). Rear folding bench seat, front-wheel-drive convertible only ($445). Three-speed automatic transmission: $595. Tilt steering ($118). 15-in. alloy wheels with steel spare wheel ($335).
S/T SERIES PICKUP OPTIONS: PEG 2 ($524-$556). Air conditioning ($805). Air dam with fog lamps ($115). Locking differential ($252). Heavy-duty battery ($56). Rear step bumper ($55). Remote mirrors ($475). Tilt steering and speed control ($383). 4.3-liter EFI V-6 ($900). 4.3-liter CPI V-6 ($1409). Floor mats ($20). Keyless remote entry ($135). Special two-tone paint ($227). Sport two-tone paint ($172). RPO UM7 AM/FM ETR stereo with cassette, Seek-and-Scan, and digital clock ($226). RPO UM6 AM/FM ETR stereo with cassette, Seek-and-Scan, and digital clock ($348). ZR2 Wide-Stance 4x4 off-road package ($1,725). Deluxe cloth interior, Regular-Cab ($191), Extended-Cab ($166). 4x4 underbody shield package ($126). SS package including LS decor, locking differential, ANL air dam with fog lamps, body-color wheels and grille, SS badging, leather-wrapped steering wheel, rear bumper and more ($629). Leather-wrapped steering wheel ($54). ZQ8 Sport suspension ($316). ZM6 Off-Road suspension ($596). Four-speed automatic overdrive transmission ($990). Aluminum wheels ($240-$340). Sliding rear window ($113). Trailering Special package ($408).
BLAZER OPTIONS: PEG 1SBX ($1,670-$2,145). Blazer LT PEG 1SCX ($2,838-$3,313). Blazer LS PEG 1SDX ($3,546-$4,021). Blazer LT PEG 1SFX ($5,222-$5,689). Air dam with fog lamps ($115). Locking differential ($252). Outside spare and carrier ($159). YC5 LS with exterior appearance package ($348). ZQ6 Driver convenience package ($475-$550). Tilt steering and speed control ($383). Rear window convenience package ($322). Massachusetts or California emissions ($100). Remote keyless entry system ($135). Luggage carrier ($126). Sport two-tone paint ($172). RPO UX1 AFM ETR stereo with cassette, Seek-and-Scan, digital clock, tape search, graphic equalizer, and six speakers ($205-$327). RPO U1C ETR stereo with CD player, Seek-and-Scan, digital clock, tape search, graphic equalizer, and six speakers with PEGs ($124-$284).RPO UM6 AM/FM ETR stereo with cassette, Seek-and-Scan, and digital clock ($348). Reclining high-back bucket seats ($161). Split folding rear seat ($475). Six-way power driver's seat ($240). Rear compartment shade ($69). 4x4 shield package ($126). Touring suspension ($197). Off-Road suspension ($166-$555). Premium Ride suspension ($197). P205/75R-15 white-lettered tires ($121-$192). On/off Road steel-belted radial tires P235/75R15 ($143-$335). Tachometer ($59). Heavy-duty trailering special equipment ($123). Argent Silver aluminum wheels ($248-$280).

1995 Chevrolet 1/2-Ton S-Series Extended-Cab "ZR2" Pickup 4x2 (CMD)

ASTRO OPTIONS: Air conditioning, front ($523). Dutch doors with rear wiper and electric release ($305-$364). Locking differential ($252). Luggage carrier ($126). Cold climate package ($46). Electric rear window defogger ($154). Power door lock system ($223). Floor mats ($47-$69). Deep-tinted glass ($290). Rear heater ($205). Electronic instrumentation ($195). Below-eye-line mirrors ($98). Body side moldings ($121). Special two-tone paint ($196-$251). $1,086). YC7 Luxury Touring LT decor package ($1,804). ZL7 Custom Sport CS value package ($465). Electric rear window defogger ($154). Power door lock system ($223). TR9 auxiliary lighting package ($127). Electronic instrumentation ($195). Electric remote-control mirrors ($150). ZY2 custom two-tone paint ($104-$329). RPO UX1 AFM ETR stereo with cassette, Seek-and-Scan, digital clock, tape search, graphic equalizer, and six speakers ($272). RPO U1C ETR stereo with CD player, Seek-and-Scan, digital clock, tape search, graphic equalizer, and six speakers ($406). RPO UM6 AM/FM ETR stereo with cassette, Seek-and-Scan, and digital clock ($122). Seven-passenger seating with PEG 1SCX ($1,043). Seven-passenger seating with PEG 1SDX ($403). Eight-passenger seating with PEGs 1SAHX or 1SKX ($240). Leather-wrapped steering wheel ($54). White stripe tires ($60 extra). White-lettered tires ($88 extra). Trailering Special equipment ($340). Rally wheel rims ($92). PEG 2 RPO 1SBX ($628). PEG 3 RPO 1SCX ($2,062). PEG 4 RPO 1SDX ($1,759). PEG 5 RPO 1SFX ($2,505). PEG 6 RPO 1SGX ($2,809). PEG 7 RPO 1SHX ($3,612). PEG 8 RPO 1SXJ ($4,586). PEG 9 RPO 1SKX ($5.032).
LUMINA OPTIONS: PEG 1 RPO 1SBX ($1,578). PEG 2 RPO 1SCX ($3,223). PEG 3 RPO 1SDX ($3,843). Air conditioning ($830). Roof carrier ($145). Electric rear window defogger ($170). Power sliding door ($350). 3.8-liter SFI V-6 ($619). Custom two-tone paint ($148). Deep-tinted glass ($245). Engine block heater ($20). Power door and tailgate locks ($300). Luggage area cargo net ($30). Twin remote fold-away mirrors ($78). Six-way electric driver's seat ($270). Seven-passenger seating with dual integral child seats ($225-$885). Seven-passenger seating with one integral child's seat ($125-$785). Seven-passenger seating ($660). Electric speed control with resume ($225). Sun roof ($300). Load leveling suspension ($170). Tilt steering ($145). P205/70R15 Touring tires ($35 extra). Self-sealing tires option, requires radial Touring tires ($150). Traction control ($350). Trailering package ($220). Four-speed automatic transmission ($200). 15-inch cast aluminum wheels ($275). Power windows with express-down driver's window ($275).
G-SERIES VAN OPTIONS: PEG2 RPO 1SBX ($1,097). Beauville PEG2 RPO 1SCX ($3,006). Beauville PEG 4 RPO 1SDX ($4,429-$4,506). Front air conditioning ($975). Front and rear air conditioning ($599-1,574). Locking differential ($252). Cold Climate package ($48). Heavy-duty cooling without trailering package ($198). Rear window defogger ($95). Power door lock system without Beauville trim ($223). California emissions for vans with under-8,600 GVWR ($100). 5.0-liter EFI V-8 ($575). 5.7-liter V-8 in G20s ($865). 7.4-liter EFI V-8 ($605). 7.4-liter diesel V-8 ($2,870). 6.5-liter heavy-duty diesel V-8 ($1,655). Alternative fuel system ($125). Deep-tinted glass ($380). C6Q GVWR package ($319). Rear heater ($205). Auxiliary lighting package ($156). Remote keyless entry system ($135). UM6 stereo ($122). U1C stereo ($274). ZP3 interior with one adult rear seat for 15-passenger seating ($371). Custom cloth seat trim with reclining bucket seats ($402). Trailering equipment ($310). Aluminum wheels ($189-$310). Rally wheels ($121).
G-SERIES CARGO VAN OPTIONS: Preferred Equipment Group GVA2 ($1,118). Air conditioning ($975). ZQ2 convenience group ($434). Heavy-duty cooling system ($198). 5.0-liter EFI V-8 ($575). 5.7-liter EFI V-8 ($865). 7.4-liter EFI V-8 ($605). 6.5-liter diesel V-8 ($2,870). 6.5-liter heavy-duty diesel V-8 ($1,655). Front area carpeting and wheel house rubber mats ($157). Deep-tinted glass ($240). Heater ($205) TR9 lighting package ($156). UM6 stereo equipment ($218). U1C stereo equipment ($517). Trailering equipment package ($310).
TAHOE OPTIONS: Tahoe LS PEG 1SBX ($3,928-$3,969). Tahoe LT PEG 1SCX ($5,580-$5,641). Air conditioning ($845). Locking differential ($252). Off road chassis equipment ($383-$400). Heavy-duty cooling ($135). Electric rear window defogger ($154). California emissions ($100). Diesel engine ($2,860). Deep-tinted glass ($215). Remote keyless entry ($135). Power door locks ($156-$220). Camper type stainless steel mirrors ($53). Electric remote-control pained mirror (no charge). Wheel opening flares ($180). Conventional two-tone paint ($180). UM6 radio ($147). ULO radio ($202). UNO radio ($100-$302). UPO radio ($200-$402). Rear window wiper/washer and defogger ($240). Power seat ($240). Reclining high-back bucket seats ($277) Sport package ($302)Heavy-duty front springs ($63). Trailering Special equipment ($164-$395). Four-speed electronic-controlled transmission ($930). Cast aluminum wheels ($310).

SUBURBAN OPTIONS: Suburban LS PEG 1SAX ($6,546-$6,796). Suburban LT PEG 1SCX ($8,851-$9,162). Upfitter ($5,952). Suburban "Upfitter" package ($5,891-$5,952). LT PEG 1SCX ($8,851-$8,912). Air conditioning ($845). Front and rear air conditioning ($1,295). 4.10 ratio axle with base engine ($135). Locking differential ($252). Convenience group ($383). Heavy-duty cooling ($135). Heavy-duty transmission ($96). California emissions ($100). 7.4-liter EFI V-8 ($605). 6.5-liter Turbo V-8 ($2,860). Alternative fuel system for CK1500 ($125). Deep-tinted glass with PEG 1SAX ($305). Auxiliary rear passenger heater ($205). Remote keyless entry ($135). Roof marker lamps for C/K2500 ($52). Power door locks ($223-$287). Stainless steel camper type mirrors ($53). Wheel flare moldings for C/K1500 ($180). Conventional two-tone paint ($180). Deluxe two-tone paint ($290). UM6 ETR AM/FM stereo with Seek-and-Scan, cassette tape, and digital clock ($147). UNO ETR AM/FM stereo with Seek-and-Scan, automatic tone control, CD player, digital clock, theft lock and speed compensated volume ($100-$302). UPO ETR AM/FM stereo with Seek-and-Scan, automatic tone control, CD player, digital clock, cassette tape, theft lock, and speed compensated volume ($200-$402). Electric rear window defogger ($154). Wiper washer with defogger ($279). Power driver's seat ($240). AT5 seating with center folding seat ($632). AS3 seating with center folding seat and rear seat ($1,182). AE7 reclining split bench seat ($148). A95 reclining high-back bucket seat ($224-$430). Skid plate package ($225). Heavy-duty front springs ($63). All-season tubeless tires ($171-$460). On/off road steel-belted radial tires ($57-$182). Rally wheel trim ($60). Cast aluminum wheels ($250-$310).

C/K PICKUP OPTIONS: Cheyenne PEG 1SAX (No charge or credit of $200-$1200). Silverado PEG 1SBX (Credit of $750-$1500). R9A convenience package ($1,335). Bright appearance package ($582-$613). R9D leather package including remote keyless entry, leather bucket seats, power seats, overhead console, electromatic mirrors, and compass ($2,302). BYP Sport package includes aluminum or chrome wheels, for 4x2 ($208) or 4x4 ($456). R9A convenience package ($1,335). R9B bright appearance package for C/K2500 ($582-$613). R9D leather package, including bed liner, A95 seats, keyless remote entry and power seats ($1,827). APR W/T "Work Truck" package ($1,218-$2,022). Upfitter package ($2,864). California emissions system ($100). 5.0-liter EFI V-8 in C/K1500 ($575). 5.7-liter EFI V-8 in C/K1500 ($865). 5.7-liter EFI V-8 in C/K2500 ($290). 7.4-liter EFI V-8 in C/K2500 ($605). 7.4-liter EFI V-8 in C/K3500 and Crew-Cab ($470). 6.5-liter diesel V-8 in C/K1500 ($2,295-$2,870). 6.5-liter diesel V-8 in C/K2500 ($2,295-$2,870). 6.5-liter diesel V-8 in C/K2500 ($2,295-$2,870). 6.5-liter Turbo V-8 in C/K1500 and C/K2500 ($3,130-$3,705). 6.5-liter turbo diesel V-8 in C/K2500 and C/K3500 Crew-Cab ($2,860). Alternative fuel system ($125). Deep-tinted glass ($72-$107). Deep-tinted glass in Crew-Cab ($180). Remote keyless entry system ($125). Roof marker lamps ($52). Power door locks ($156). Power door locks in Crew-Cab ($223). Electric remote-control painted mirrors with Crew-Cab ($98) Bright body side moldings ($76-$107). Conventional two-tone paint ($132). Deluxe two-tone paint ($243). UM6 ETR AM/FM stereo with Seek-and-Scan, cassette tape, and digital clock ($147). UNO ETR AM/FM stereo with Seek-and-Scan, automatic tone control, CD player, digital clock, theft lock and speed compensated volume ($100-$302). UPO ETR AM/FM stereo with Seek-and-Scan, automatic tone control, CD player, digital clock, cassette tape, theft lock, and speed compensated volume ($200-$402). Electric rear window defogger ($154). Wiper washer with defogger ($279). Power driver's seat ($240). Painted rear step bumper ($130). Chrome rear step bumper ($229). Off-road package ($270). Camper Special equipment $233). Sport handling package ($974). Electric rear window defogger ($154). Five-speed manual transmission with deep low and overdrive ($98). Four-speed automatic transmission with overdrive ($930). Trailering Special package ($210-$250). Bright metal wheelcovers ($42). Cast aluminum wheels ($250-$310). C/K3500 dual rear wheels ($955). Crew-Cab dual rear wheels ($857). Sliding rear window ($113).

1995 Chevrolet 1/2-Ton C1500 "Work Truck" Fleetside Long Bed Pickup 4x2 (CMD)

NOTE 13: Options and prices shown are representative. The actual cost of an option or option package often varies according to other packages that the options are combined with on specific vehicles. Preferred Equipment Group (PEG) options offer specific optional equipment at discount prices. Some "options" may be standard equipment on certain models, such as V-8s in C/K3500 pickups. The prices shown are those charged when the item or equipment was not part of a PEG or package and are presented as a measure of comparative value. Descriptions of options are edited. Full option contents can be determined by consulting sales literature.

HISTORICAL: The new Tahoe, and especially the midyear four-door version, made Chevrolet news at the start of model-year 1995. In December 1994, Chevrolet settled the C/K Pickup controversy with the U.S. Government dropping its efforts to force a recall of older C/Ks in exchange for a multi-million dollar commitment to future auto safety efforts from GM.

Chevrolet Truck Milestones

Even in 1926, Chevrolet put its trucks through some rigorous testing at the GM Proving Grounds. (GM)

1918	Chevrolet truck production started with four-cylinder, valve-in-head engine.
1926	First enclosed cab used on a Chevrolet truck.
	Balloon tires used on Chevrolet trucks for first time.

The Suburban Carryall, an all-steel station wagon on a panel truck chassis, first bowed in 1935. (CMD)

1928	Sedan Delivery model added to Chevrolet truck line up.
1929	Commercial vehicle production reached a peak of 334,963 units.
	Chevrolet Trucks adopt use of new overhead valve six-cylinder engine.

1931	Chevrolet dedicates its first commercial body plant in Indianapolis, Ind.
1937	First Chevrolet all-steel truck cab produced.
1942	Chevrolet halts production of trucks for civilian market.
1944	Civilian truck output resumes on a small scale.

Chevrolet's 1946 model was a continuation of the prewar series first brought out in 1941. (CMD)

1947	Complete restyling: Indianapolis commercial body plant celebrates a 50 percent expansion.
	Forward-Control truck added to Chevrolet line up.
1950	Production of Chevrolet trucks achieves an all-time record.

Advance-Design Chevy trucks entered production on May 1, 1947 and changed little until 1955. (CMD)

1951	Ventipane style truck cab windows introduced.
	Chevrolet builds approximately one-third of all U.S.-built trucks.
1952	Chevrolet Truck Div. offers a new 212-in. school bus chassis.
1953	(Nov. 28) One piece curved windshield adopted for 1954 Chevrolet trucks.
	(Nov. 28) GM Hydra-Matic Drive introduced on light-duty 1954 Chevrolet trucks.
1954	Advance-Design trucks get new cross-bar grille and open drive line.

Ventipanes were added to Advance-Design models in 1951; push-button door handles in 1952. (CMD)

1955	All-new "Task-Force" light-duty trucks introduced.
	First V-8 offered as optional equipment in Chevrolet light-duty trucks.
	Cameo Carrier Pickup with slab-sided fiberglass pickup box outer panels introduced.

Innovative exterior styling and a luxury flavor characterized the new-for-1955 Cameo Carrier. (CMD)

1957	Chevrolet adds 283 cid 160-hp Taskmaster V-8 to trucks.
	First Chevrolet factory-built four-wheel-drive trucks released.
1958	(Oct. 31) Chevy truck line up with 128 models and five engines introduced.
	Chevrolet assumes body production for three forward-control "Step-Van" models.
	All trucks with GVW ratings up to 9,600 lb. are called Apaches.
	All medium-duty trucks with GVW ratings up to 21,000 lb. are called Vikings.

Standard Catalog of Chevrolet Trucks

Chevy sold this 1958 Apache Step-Side railroad track inspection truck. (Fairmont Railway Motors photo) 7

Fleetside trucks with flush outer pickup box/fender panels made of steel were first seen in 1958. (CMD)

1958	Heavy-Duty trucks with GVW ratings up to 25,000 lb. are called Spartans (Feb.) Three all-steel Apache "Fleetside" pickups with styling like Cameo Carrier introduced. Cameo Carrier is discontinued after release of Apache Fleetside models. Two four-wheel-drive Fleetside pickups added to line and midyear.

All-new in 1959 was the El Camino sedan-pickup with passenger car styling and a load box. (CMD)

Standard Catalog of Chevrolet Trucks

An "Amblewagon" ambulance conversion was offered for the Corvair 95 van. (Dr. George Johnson)

1959	El Camino Sedan-Pickup introduced.
	Chevrolet features new "Color-Break" two-tone paint
	Hot-selling six gets economy camshaft that gives 10 percent better fuel economy.
	3,482,242 Chevrolet trucks in operation as of July 1, 1958.

Hoods, glass and roofs were revised in 1962, but most 1960-1966 Chevy trucks had this look. (CMD)

1960	Busiest year since 1955; production increases 20 percent.
	All-new Apache styling for cab model trucks and unit-body Suburban and Panel.
1961	Corvair 95 Series of commercial trucks introduced.
	Innovative Corvair 95 Rampside pickup is part of new line.
	Corvair Greenbrier Sports Wagon was also offered as a commercial unit.

1962	Kansas City truck production moved to St. Louis factory.
	Van Nuys truck production moved to Oakland factory.
	Biggest year for Chevrolet truck making and marketing since 1950.
1963	First Chevrolet four-cylinder engine since 1928 available in new Chevy Van.
	New coil suspension system and ladder frames for Chevy trucks.
	Model count reduced from 203 in 1962 to 178 in 1963.

In 1964, the El Camino moved to the Chevelle chassis and this is the 1968 El Camino SS-396. (CMD)

1964	El Camino revived as midsize model on Chevelle platform.
	April production of 55,324 Chevy trucks is all-time record.
	Six-cylinder Chevrolet trucks outsell V-8s by 2-to-1 margin.
1965	Chevrolet truck line up includes 327 models with 126 of 131 new ones being diesels.
	Corvair 95 truck-line discontinued.
	Chevy Van gets "Big Six" engine option.
	New factory-installed air conditioning unit designed exclusively for Chevy trucks.

Front ends of light-duty trucks were restyled in 1969 and three new 350-cid V-8s were released. (CMD)

1966	New 3-speed Turbo-Hydramatic transmission optional in 3/4- and 1-ton trucks.
	Six new engines introduced for 3666-model Chevrolet truck line up.
	Experimental Turbo Titan III "Truck of Tommorow" seen at Chevrolet auto show exhibits.
1967	Longer, lower cab models with increased glass area designed for camper conversions.
	Optional Custom Sport Truck (CST) package with bucket seats introduced.

1967	El Camino extensively restyled and SS-396 model gains the spotlight.
	G-Series vans marketed with two wheelbases and optional V-8s for the first time.
	Fifteen safety features added to all Chevrolet light-duty trucks including dual master brake cylinder, brake warning lights, four-way hazard flashers, energy-absorbing steering column, padded instrument panel, padded sun visors, folding front seat back latch, and thicker laminated windshield glass.
1968	New 307 cid/200 hp and 396 cid/310 hp V-8s for Chevy light-duty trucks.
	New 3/4- and 1-ton Step-Vans equipped with IFS, coil springs, power steering, and V-8.
	V-8-powered Chevy trucks outsell six-cylinder models for the first time.

The Blazer Sport Utility Vehicle bowed in mid-1969. This is the 1970 four-wheel-drive model. (CMD)

1969	Four-wheel-drive K-5 Blazer Sport Utility Vehicle introduced as a mid-1969 model.
	Front end of light-duty trucks restyled.
	Three new 350-cid V-8s released in light-duty models.
	Plans to quarter production of G-Series vans in new Lordstown, Ohio factory announced.
	Chevrolet announced intentions to move into the heavy-duty truck market in 1970.

A boom in travel and camping sold many Chevy C10 pickups with camper shells in the 1970s. (CMD)

1970	For first time since 1961, nine Fisher Body plants begin Chevy/GMC truck production.
	New Chevy Van/Sportvan/Beauville G-Series vans assembled in Lordstown.
	Light-duty trucks get optional air shocks for models with coil springs.
	Two-wheel-drive Blazer added to new truck-line.
	Midyear strike halts truck production and lowers output by 28 percent.

New in 1971 was a Vega Panel Express with 68.7 cu. ft. of room and a 650 lb. payload capacity. (CMD)

1971	Top-of-the-line Cheyenne with chrome bumpers and carpeting introduced.
	Light-duty trucks feature standard front disc brakes for first time.
	All Chevrolet truck engine modified to operate on low lead fuels.
	Fuel evaporative system from California made standard in 1/2-ton trucks.
	Highest Chevrolet truck production in history.
	Vega panel delivery truck introduced.
1972	Chevrolet's first-ever half-million-units 1/2-ton truck model sales year.
	Stellite-faced exhaust valves added to 350- and 400-cid V-8s in 3/4- and 1-ton trucks.
	Acrylic enamel paint used on light-duty truck cabs.
	Exhaust valve rotators added to 307-, 350- and 400-cid V-8s
	Four-barrel version of 350-cid V-8 for G-Series vans.
	Six-cylinder Suburban no longer available.
	New sliding load door for Chevy Van and Sportvan.
1973	Light Utility Vehicle (mini-pickup) built by Isuzu of Japan marketed as Chevrolet LUV.
	All-new light-duty trucks promoted as most extensively changed in company's history.
	Retail delivery of 1,055,273 Chevrolet truck eclipses 1972 Ford sales record.
	"Big Dooley" name adopted for dual-rear-wheel extended-cab 1-ton pickups.

Collectors are already gathering up 1979 El Caminos with the "Black Knight" option package. (CMD)

1974	Second-best sales year in Chevrolet truck history.
	New El Camino Classic model bows.
	AM/FM radio made optional in G-Series vans.
1975	Last year for Vega Panel Express.
	Totally restyled El Camino gets new Estate and Conquista trim packages.
	C10 pickup with standard bed marketed as "Fleetwood" model for 1975.
	Fuel tank relocated outside cab on frame rails in a later-to-become-controversial change.
	Safety enhanced via new energy-absorbing steering column.
	Four-Wheel-Drive Suburban returns.

The 1978 Suburban K10 was a 4X4 with a $6,348 price tag.

1976	New body design for the Blazer features integral roll bar.
	"Vantastic" option package introduced for G-vans.
	All-time high output of Blazers, Suburbans and G-vans.
1977	Power door locks introduced for Chevrolet trucks.
	New rear window defroster.
	New "Nomad" added to G-van line up as cargo-and-passenger model.
	"Caravan" model added to Sportvan line as a custom van.
1978	New down-sized El Camino bows.
	Cab and unit-body trucks get new grille and rectangular headlamps.
	C/K pickups get new 5.7-liter diesel V-8.
	New all-time sales record of 1,317,466 trucks is set.
1979	Catalytic converter added to Class 2 trucks with GVW ratings up to 8,500 lb.
	Four-Wheel-Drive version of Isuzu-built LUV "captive import" mini-pickup introduced.

Trucks like this 1982 Chevy 4x4 Step-Box "Shorties" saw revived popularity with outdoor fans. (CMD)

Standard Catalog of Chevrolet Trucks

1980	El Camino "Black Knight" option introduced.
	Old Cars Weekly/Krause Publications replaces its tried-and-true 1972 go-to-car-shows Suburban with a new 3/4-ton 1979 Suburban. This second "Old Cars" truck would ultimately rack up over 350,000 miles traveling to old car shows and auctions nationwide.
	General Motors announces plans to build Chevrolet LUV pickup in U.S.
	Fuel crisis sends truck sales plummeting to one-half 1979 levels; dealer deliveries drop 46%.
1981	Current Chevrolet general manager Jim Perkins takes helm of truck division after 1980 sales dive.
	C/K pickups and Blazer get new aerodynamic front end restyling and lose weight.
	Computerized engine control system introduced to boost operating economy of Chevy trucks.
	SE ("Special Economy") full-size pickup model introduced in November 1981.
	LUV mini-pickup is completely restyled.
1982	Chevrolet is number 1 in truck sales for first time since 1976.
	Michael H. Erdman becomes Chevrolet's Sales Manager Truck
	Production of compact S10 pickup starts in summer of 1981 at Moraine, Ohio.

Chevy's new-size 1985 Astro Van with rear-wheel-drive had real truck-like towing capacity. (CMD)

1983	Compact S-10 pickup introduced in fall of 1982 as a 1983 model.
	Extended-Cab, four-wheel-drive, and diesel S10 models added.
	Chevy sells 15,000 last copies of discontinued LUV pickup.
	El Camino available with diesel engine for first time.
1984	Chevrolet cars and trucks named official vehicles of XIV Olympic games.
	U.S. Army purchases 30,000 K-series 4x4 trucks and 23,000 Blazer 4x4s.
	S-10 pickup gets "Durango" trim package.

This 4x4 S-Blazer was one of the many Chevy trucks celebrating a 75th anniversary in 1986. (CMD)

1985	S-10 Blazer 4x4 introduced.
	All-new Astro minivan introduced.
	El Camino gets 4.3-liter V-6 as its base engine.
	"Choo-Choo Customs" El Camino conversion available from approved aftermarket supplier.
	Chevrolet trucks marketed with $10,000 "seat belt insurance" policy.
	Sales go sharply upwards to 1,300,000 trucks.
	Ralph J. Kramer named Chevrolet Public Relations Manager.
1986	Throttle-Body-Injection system introduced on Chevy trucks.
	Chevrolet provides "Official Trucks" for 1986 Indianapolis 500 Mile Race.
	75th anniversary of Chevrolet cars and trucks celebrated.
	Texas Monthly picks Chevy Suburban as "National Car of Texas."
1987	New GMT400 "1988" Chevrolet 1500 R/V pickup bows in mid-1987 in smaller lines.
	"Old-fashioned" C/K trucks still merchandised in heavier-duty lines.
	Suburban also continues to use the C/K sheet metal.
	Sales run six percent under projections.
	El Caminos built exclusively in Mexico for U.S. sale; last year for El Camino

Chevy's new 10 Series pickup bowed as the 1988 R/V, but larger pickups still had C/K styling. (CMD)

1988	All-new R/V cab models replace C/Ks in lighter-duty lines.
	Sportside and Extended-Cab models of R/V pickups introduced.
	S-10s get powerful 4.3-liter V-6 at midyear.
	El Caminos no longer marketed.
	Chrome Yellow S-Blazer concept vehicle with 4-wheel steering seen at Iola Old Car Show.

Roaring into the market in 1990 was the 454 SS. This 1991 edition had performance upgrades. (CMD)

Standard Catalog of Chevrolet Trucks

1989	GMT 400 trucks now promoted as C/K models; heavy-duty versions added.
	Suzuki-built Geo Tracker Sport Utility Vehicle introduced at Chevy dealerships.
	Production of the Lumina APV front-wheel-drive minivan starts in Tarrytown, N.Y.
1990	Lumina APV introduced.
	Geo Tracker enters North American production at CAMI Automotive, Inc. in Canada.
	Full-size SS454 high-performance pickup released.
	Four-door S-Blazer introduced in spring as 1991 model.

Chevy's famous "Texas Cadillac," the Suburban, was totally restyled and modernized for 1992. (CMD)

1991	New rear-wheel-drive Geo Tracker convertible introduced.
	New midyear V-6 for Astro vans.
	SS454 gets new 7.4-liter V-8 and ETC 4-speed automatic transmission as standard equipment.

Chevrolet Truck Movers & Shakers

1950
Manager of Commercial & Truck Dept.	J.W. Burke
Assistant Manager Commercial & Truck Dept.	E.P. Feely

1951
Manager of Commercial & Truck Dept.	J.W. Burke
Assistant Manager Commercial & Truck Dept.	E.P. Feely

1952
Manager of Commercial & Truck Dept.	J.W. Burke
Assistant Manager Commercial & Truck Dept.	H.F. Blackenship
Assistant Manager Commercial & Truck Dept.	T.T. Brown
Assistant Manager Commercial & Truck Dept.	H.C. King
Assistant Manager Commercial & Truck Dept.	M.D. Madora
Assistant Manager Commercial & Truck Dept.	S.L. Reed

1953
Manager of Commercial & Truck Dept.	J.W. Burke
Assistant Manager Commercial & Truck Dept.	H.F. Blackenship
Assistant Manager Commercial & Truck Dept.	T.T. Brown
Assistant Manager Commercial & Truck Dept.	H.C. King
Assistant Manager Commercial & Truck Dept.	M.D. Madora
Assistant Manager Commercial & Truck Dept.	S.L. Reed

1954
Manager of Commercial & Truck Dept.	J.W. Burke
Assistant Manager Commercial & Truck Dept.	H.F. Blackenship
Assistant Manager Commercial & Truck Dept.	T.T. Brown
Assistant Manager Commercial & Truck Dept.	H.C. King
Assistant Manager Commercial & Truck Dept.	M.D. Madora
Assistant Manager Commercial & Truck Dept.	S.L. Reed

1955
Manager of Commercial & Truck Dept.	J.W. Burke
Assistant Manager Commercial & Truck Dept.	H.F. Blackenship
Assistant Manager Commercial & Truck Dept.	T.T. Brown
Assistant Manager Commercial & Truck Dept.	H.C. King
Assistant Manager Commercial & Truck Dept.	M.D. Madora
Assistant Manager Commercial & Truck Dept.	S.L. Reed
Advertising Agency	Campbell-Ewald Co.

1956
Manager of Commercial & Truck Dept.	H.P. Sattler
Assistant Manager Commercial & Truck Dept.	H.F. Blackenship
Assistant Manager Commercial & Truck Dept.	T.T. Brown
Assistant Manager Commercial & Truck Dept.	H.C. King
Assistant Manager Commercial & Truck Dept.	M.D. Madora
Assistant Manager Commercial & Truck Dept.	S.L. Reed
Assistant Manager Commercial & Truck Dept.	J.E. Conlan
Advertising Agency	Campbell-Ewald Co.

1957
Assistant General Sales Manager in Charge of Commercial & Truck Dept.	H.P. Sattler
Manager Commercial & Truck Dept.	J.E. Conlan
Assistant Manager Commercial & Truck Dept.	H.F. Blackenship
Assistant Manager Commercial & Truck Dept.	T.T. Brown
Assistant Manager Commercial & Truck Dept.	H.C. King
Assistant Manager Commercial & Truck Dept.	M.D. Madora
Assistant Manager Commercial & Truck Dept.	S.L. Reed
Advertising Agency	Campbell-Ewald Co.

The Chevrolet Astro Van entered production in 1984 as a 1985 model (CMD)

One of Chevrolet's all-new full-size trucks on the production line at Ft. Wayne, Ind. (CMD)

1964

Assistant General Sales Manager	
Truck & Fleet Sales	R.A. Koether
Manager New & Used Truck Merchandising	Harold Andersen
Assistant Manager	P.J. Bauer
Assistant Manager	N.F. Ficke
Assistant Manager	O.H. Henry
Assistant Manager	M.D. Madora
Assistant Manager	R.R. Sheehan
Assistant Manager	R.M. Sigler
Assistant Manager	D.L. Westcott
Assistant Manager	B.N. White
Advertising Agency	Campbell-Ewald Co.

1965

Assistant General Sales Manager Truck & Fleet Sales	R.A. Koether
Manager New & Used Truck Merchandising	Harold Andersen
Assistant Manager	P.J. Bauer
Assistant Manager	N.F. Ficke
Assistant Manager	O.H. Henry
Assistant Manager	M.D. Madora
Assistant Manager	R.R. Sheehan
Assistant Manager	R.M. Sigler
Assistant Manager	D.L. Westcott
Assistant Manager	B.N. White
Advertising Agency	Campbell-Ewald Co.

1966

Assistant General Sales Manager Truck & Fleet Sales	R.M. O'Connor
Manager New & Used Truck Merchandising	Harold Andersen
Assistant Manager	P.J. Bauer
Assistant Manager	N.F. Ficke
Assistant Manager	O.H. Henry
Assistant Manager	R.R. Sheehan
Assistant Manager	D.L. Westcott
Assistant Manager	B.N. White
Assistant Manager	R.E. Downing
Assistant Manager	C.A. Matson
Advertising Agency	Campbell-Ewald Co.

1967

Assistant General Sales Manager Truck & Fleet Sales	R.M. O'Connor
Manager New & Used Truck Merchandising	E.J. O'Rourke
Assistant Manager	P.J. Bauer
Assistant Manager	N.F. Ficke
Assistant Manager	O.H. Henry

Assistant Manager	R.M. Sigler
Assistant Manager	D.L. Westcott
Assistant Manager	B.M White
Assistant Manager	R.E. Downing
Assistant Manager	C.A. Matson
Assistant Manager	D.M. Livingston
Assistant Manager	C.R. Worthington
Advertising Agency	Campbell-Ewald Co.

1968

Assistant General Sales Manager Truck & Fleet Sales	T.L. Pritchett
Manager New & Used Truck Merchandising	O.H. Henry
Assistant Manager	P.J. Bauer
Assistant Manager	N.F. Ficke
Assistant Manager	M.G. Heathman
Assistant Manager	C.A. Matson
Assistant Manager	D.M. Livingston
Assistant Manager	C.R. Worthington
Advertising Agency	Campbell-Ewald Co.

1969

Assistant General Sales Manager	
Truck & Fleet Sales	T.L. Pritchett
Manager New & Used Truck Merchandising	O.H. Henry
Assistant Manager	P.J. Bauer
Assistant Manager	N.F. Ficke
Assistant Manager	M.G. Heathman
Assistant Manager	C.A. Matson
Assistant Manager	D.M. Livingston
Assistant Manager	C.R. Worthington
Assistant Manager	J.T. Riley
Advertising Agency	Campbell-Ewald Co.

1970

Assistant General Sales Manager Truck Sales	A.T. Olson
Manager Truck Merchandising Dept.	O.H. Henry
Manager Heavy-Duty Truck Sales	C.R. Worthington
Assistant Manager	P.J. Bauer
Assistant Manager	N.F. Ficke
Assistant Manager	J.D. Sharry
Assistant Manager	S.R. Blum
Assistant Manager	L.C. Horn
Assistant Manager	D.M. Fogg
Assistant Manager	D.M. Livingston
Assistant Manager	J.T. Riley
Assistant Manager	L.D. Hollenstine
Assistant Manager	R.D. Henry
Assistant Manager	L.P. Schinzing

Assistant Manager	S.E. McGraw
Assistant Manager	R.L. Albinson
Advertising Agency	Campbell-Ewald Co.

1971

Assistant General Sales Manager Truck Sales	A.T. Olson
Manager Light/Medium Truck Merchandising	J.T. Riley
Manager Heavy-Duty Truck Sales	C.R. Worthington
Assistant Manager	R.L. Albinson
Assistant Manager	P.J. Bauer
Assistant Manager	S.R. Blum
Assistant Manager	L.E. Bowling
Assistant Manager	R.J. Daneke
Assistant Manager	N.F. Ficke
Assistant Manager	R.R. McKenna
Assistant Manager	L.P. Schinzing
Assistant Manager	D.M. Fogg
Assistant Manager	R.D. Henry
Assistant Manager	L.D. Hollenstine
Assistant Manager	S.E. McGraw
Assistant Manager	J.D. Sharry
Advertising Agency	Campbell-Ewald Co.

1972

Assistant General Sales Manager Truck Sales	A.T. Olson
Manager Light/Medium Truck Merchandising	J.T. Riley
Manager Heavy-Duty Truck Sales	T.A. Nisbet, Jr.
Recreational Vehicles Manager	O.H. Henry
Special Projects Manager	W.P. Stewart
Assistant Manager	R.L. Albinson
Assistant Manager	P.J. Bauer
Assistant Manager	S.R. Blum
Assistant Manager	R.J. Daneke
Assistant Manager	N.F. Ficke
Assistant Manager	R.R. McKenna
Assistant Manager	L.P. Schinzing
Assistant Manager	D.M. Fogg
Assistant Manager	R.D. Henry
Assistant Manager	S.E. McGraw
Assistant Manager	J.D. Sharry
Assistant Manager	K.L. Milliken
Assistant Manager	W.R. Bishop, Jr.
Assistant Manager	L.C. Horn
Advertising Agency	Campbell-Ewald Co.

1973

Assistant General Sales Manager Truck Sales	A.T. Olson
Manager Light/Medium Truck Merchandising	J.T. Riley
Manager Heavy-Duty Truck Sales	T.A. Nisbet, Jr.
Recreational Vehicles Manager	L.P. Schinzing
Special Projects Manager	W.P. Stewart
Assistant Manager	R.L. Albinson
Assistant Manager	S.R. Blum
Assistant Manager	R.J. Daneke
Assistant Manager	N.F. Ficke
Assistant Manager	R.R. McKenna
Assistant Manager	D.M. Fogg
Assistant Manager	R.D. Henry
Assistant Manager	S.E. McGraw
Assistant Manager	J.D. Sharry
Assistant Manager	K.L. Milliken
Assistant Manager	W.R. Bishop, Jr.
Assistant Manager	L.C. Horn
Assistant Manager	R.L. Higginbotham
Assistant Manager	P. Dupont
Assistant Manager	C.E. McDowell
Advertising Agency	Campbell-Ewald Co.

1974

Assistant General Sales Manager Truck Sales	A.T. Olson
Manager Light/Medium Truck Merchandising	D.M. Livingston
Manager Heavy-Duty Truck Sales	T.A. Nisbet, Jr.
Recreational Vehicles Manager	L.P. Schinzing
Special Projects Manager	W.P. Stewart
Assistant Manager	S.R. Blum
Assistant Manager	R.J. Daneke
Assistant Manager	N.F. Ficke
Assistant Manager	R.R. McKenna
Assistant Manager	D.M. Fogg
Assistant Manager	R.D. Henry
Assistant Manager	S.E. McGraw
Assistant Manager	J.D. Sharry
Assistant Manager	W.R. Bishop, Jr.
Assistant Manager	L.C. Horn
Assistant Manager	R.L. Higginbotham
Assistant Manager	P. Dupont
Assistant Manager	C.E. McDowell
Assistant Manager	G.A. Armstrong
Assistant Manager	A.R. Babin
Assistant Manager	J.F. Sillick
Advertising Agency	Campbell-Ewald Co.

1975

Assistant General Sales Manager Truck Sales	J.T. Riley
Manager Light/Medium Truck Merchandising	L.P. Schinzing
Manager Heavy-Duty Truck Sales	T.A. Nisbet, Jr.
Manager of Recreational Vehicles Manager	J.F. Sillick
Manager Import Vehicles	W.P. Stewart
Assistant Manager	S.R. Blum
Assistant Manager	R.J. Daneke
Assistant Manager	D.M. Fogg
Assistant Manager	R.D. Henry
Assistant Manager	S.E. McGraw
Assistant Manager	J.D. Sharry
Assistant Manager	W.R. Bishop, Jr.
Assistant Manager	L.C. Horn
Assistant Manager	P. Dupont
Assistant Manager	C.E. McDowell
Assistant Manager	G.A. Armstrong
Assistant Manager	D.A. Evans
Assistant Manager	R.J. Gray
Assistant Manager	P.L. Maxey
Assistant Manager	L.E. Bowling
Assistant Manager	C.E. Murphy, Jr.
Assistant Manager	T.W. Shaver
Assistant Manager	R.F. Stevens, Jr.
Assistant Manager	J.A. Thornton, Jr.
Assistant Manager	D.W. Watzlawick
Assistant Manager	J.R. Williams
Assistant Manager	L.D. Hollenstine
Advertising Agency	Campbell-Ewald Co.

1976

Sales Manager Trucks	J.T. Riley
Manager Light/Medium Truck Merchandising	L.P. Schinzing
Manager Heavy-Duty Truck Sales	T.A. Nisbet, Jr.
Manager of Recreational Vehicles Manager	J.F. Sillick
Manager Import Vehicles	W.P. Stewart
Assistant Manager	R.J. Daneke
Assistant Manager	D.M. Fogg
Assistant Manager	R.D. Henry
Assistant Manager	J.D. Sharry
Assistant Manager	W.R. Bishop, Jr.
Assistant Manager	L.C. Horn
Assistant Manager	P. Dupont
Assistant Manager	C.E. McDowell
Assistant Manager	G.A. Armstrong
Assistant Manager	D.A. Evans
Assistant Manager	R.J. Gray
Assistant Manager	L.E. Bowling
Assistant Manager	C.E. Murphy, Jr.
Assistant Manager	T.W. Shaver
Assistant Manager	R.F. Stevens, Jr.
Assistant Manager	J.A. Thornton, Jr.
Assistant Manager	D.W. Watzlawick
Assistant Manager	J.R. Williams

Assistant Manager	L.D. Hollenstine
Assistant Manager	J.S. McClellan
Advertising Agency	Campbell-Ewald Co.

1977

Sales Manager Trucks	J.T. Riley
Manager Light/Medium Truck Merchandising	L.P. Schinzing
Manager Heavy-Duty Truck Sales	T.A. Nisbet, Jr.
Manager of Recreational Vehicles Manager	J.F. Sillick
Manager Import Vehicles	W.P. Stewart
Director of Public Relations	J.L. Tolley
Assistant Manager	R.J. Daneke
Assistant Manager	R.D. Henry
Assistant Manager	J.D. Sharry
Assistant Manager	W.R. Bishop, Jr.
Assistant Manager	L.C. Horn
Assistant Manager	C.E. McDowell
Assistant Manager	G.A. Armstrong
Assistant Manager	D.A. Evans
Assistant Manager	L.E. Bowling
Assistant Manager	C.E. Murphy, Jr.
Assistant Manager	T.W. Shaver
Assistant Manager	R.F. Stevens, Jr.
Assistant Manager	J.A. Thornton, Jr.
Assistant Manager	J.R. Williams
Assistant Manager	L.D. Hollenstine
Assistant Manager	J.S. McClellan
Assistant Manager	R.L. Neal
Assistant Manager	T.P. Cutler
Assistant Manager	T.D. Hoxie
Assistant Manager	C.L. Lavender
Assistant Manager	M.S. Timmington
Advertising Agency	Campbell-Ewald Co.

1978

Sales Manager Trucks	D.A. Bouchard
Manager Light/Medium Truck Merchandising	R.L. Higginbotham
Manager Heavy-Duty Truck Sales	T.A. Nisbet, Jr.
Manager of Recreational Vehicles Manager	J.F. Sillick

Manager Import Vehicles	W.P. Stewart
Director of Public Relations	J.L. Tolley
Assistant Manager	R.J. Daneke
Assistant Manager	R.D. Henry
Assistant Manager	J.D. Sharry
Assistant Manager	W.R. Bishop, Jr.
Assistant Manager	L.C. Horn
Assistant Manager	D.A. Evans
Assistant Manager	L.E. Bowling
Assistant Manager	C.E. Murphy, Jr.
Assistant Manager	R.F. Stevens, Jr.
Assistant Manager	J.A. Thornton, Jr.
Assistant Manager	J.R. Williams
Assistant Manager	L.D. Hollenstine
Assistant Manager	J.S. McClellan
Assistant Manager	T.P. Cutler
Assistant Manager	C.L. Lavender
Assistant Manager	M.S. Timmington
Assistant Manager	F.F. Raine, Jr.
Assistant Manager	D.A. Patterson
Assistant Manager	D.W. Reardon
Advertising Agency	Campbell-Ewald Co.

1979

Sales Manager Trucks	D.A. Bouchard
Manager Light/Medium Truck Merchandising	R.L. Higginbotham
Manager Heavy-Duty Truck Sales	T.A. Nisbet, Jr.
Manager of Recreational Vehicles Manager	J.F. Sillick
Manager Import Vehicles	W.P. Stewart
Director of Public Relations	J.J. Williams
Assistant Manager	R.J. Daneke
Assistant Manager	R.D. Henry
Assistant Manager	J.D. Sharry
Assistant Manager	W.R. Bishop, Jr.
Assistant Manager	L.C. Horn
Assistant Manager	D.A. Evans
Assistant Manager	L.E. Bowling
Assistant Manager	C.E. Murphy, Jr.

The GMT400 pickup was first produced as the 1988 Chevy R/V series, but later renamed C/K. (CMD)

Chevy-badged Isuzu W7 Tiltmasters show up in light truck production totals starting in 1990. (CMD)

Assistant Manager	R.F. Stevens, Jr.
Assistant Manager	J.A. Thornton, Jr.
Assistant Manager	J.R. Williams
Assistant Manager	L.D. Hollenstine
Assistant Manager	J.S. McClellan
Assistant Manager	T.P. Cutler
Assistant Manager	C.L. Lavender
Assistant Manager	M.S. Timmington
Assistant Manager	F.F. Raine, Jr.
Assistant Manager	D.A. Patterson
Assistant Manager	D.W. Reardon
Advertising Agency	Campbell-Ewald Co.

1980

Sales Manager Trucks	Donald A. Bouchard
Manager Light/Medium Truck Merchandising	Richard L. Higginbotham
Manager of Recreational Vehicles Manager	John F. Sillick
Director of Public Relations	James J. Williams
Advertising Agency	Campbell-Ewald Co.

1981

Sales Manager Trucks	Jimmie C. Perkins
Truck Merchandising Manager	Jack L. Sherman
Manager of Special Vehicles	John F. Sillick
Director of Public Relations	James J. Williams
Truck Advertising Manager	Harry J. Cordess
Advertising Agency	Campbell-Ewald Co.

1982

Sales Manager Trucks	Michael H. Erdman
Truck Merchandising Manager	Jack L. Sherman
Manager of Special Vehicles	John F. Sillick
Director of Public Relations	James J. Williams
Truck Advertising Manager	Harry J. Cordess
Advertising Agency	Campbell-Ewald Co.

1983

Sales Manager Trucks	Michael H. Erdman
Truck Merchandising Manager	Jeffrey P. Hurlbert
Manager of Special Vehicles	John F. Sillick
Director of Public Relations	James J. Williams
Truck & Station Wagon Advertising Manager	Harry J. "Pete" Cordess
Advertising Agency	Campbell-Ewald Co.

1984

Sales Manager Trucks	Michael H. Erdman
Truck Merchandising Manager	Jeffrey P. Hurlbert
Manager of Special Vehicles	John F. Sillick
Director of Public Relations	James J. Williams
Truck & Station Wagon Advertising Manager	Harry J. "Pete" Cordess
Advertising Agency	Campbell-Ewald Co.

1985

Sales Manager Trucks	John M. Kelly
Truck Merchandising Manager	Frank F. Raine, Jr.
Truck & Station Wagon Advertising Manager	H.J. (Pete) Cordes
Director of Public Relations	Ralph J. Kramer
Advertising Agency	Campbell-Ewald Co.

1986

GM vice president & Chevrolet general manager	Robert D. Burger
Marketing Manager Trucks	John M. Kelley
Manager Truck & Station Wagon Advertising	H.J. (Pete) Cordes
Truck Merchandising Manager	Frank F. Raine, Jr.
Director of Public Relations	Ralph J. Kramer
Advertising Agency	Campbell-Ewald Co.

1987

GM vice president & Chevrolet general manager	Robert D. Burger
Marketing Manager Trucks	John M. Kelley
Manager Truck & Station Wagon Advertising	G.N. Perkins
Truck Merchandising Manager	Tom P. Cutler
Director of Public Relations	Ralph J. Kramer
Advertising Agency	Campbell-Ewald Co.

1988

GM vice president & Chevrolet general manager	Robert D. Burger
Marketing Manager Trucks	John M. Kelley
Manager Truck Advertising	Thomas P. Cutler
Truck Merchandising Manager	Kenneth P. Wechselberger
Director of Public Relations	Ralph J. Kramer
Advertising Agency	Campbell-Ewald Co.

1989

GM vice president & Chevrolet general manager	Robert D. Burger

Marketing Manager Trucks   F.F. Raine, Jr.
Truck Merchandising Manager   W.L. Ames
Manager Truck Advertising   Candace M. Robbins
Director of Public Relations   Ralph J. Kramer
Advertising Agency   Campbell-Ewald Co.
1990
GM vice president & Chevrolet general manager Jim C. Perkins
Marketing Manager Trucks   Frank F. Raine, Jr.
Manager Truck &
Station Wagon Advertising   Candice M. Robbins
Truck Merchandising Manager   W.L. Ames
Director of Public Relations   Ralph J. Kramer
Advertising Agency   Lintas: Campbell-Ewald Co.
1991
GM vice president & Chevrolet
general manager   Jim C. Perkins
Marketing Manager Trucks   F.F. Raine, Jr.
Manager Truck Advertising   Mac Whisner
National Manager Truck Merchandising   J.N. Janowiak
Truck Merchandising Manager   W.L. Ames
Director of Public Relations   Ralph J. Kramer
Advertising Agency   Lintas: Campbell-Ewald Co.
1992
GM vice president & Chevrolet general manager Jim C. Perkins
Marketing Manager Trucks   F.F. Raine, Jr.
Manager Truck Advertising   Mac Whisner
National Manager Truck Merchandising   J.N. Janowiak
Director of Public Relations   Ralph J. Kramer
Advertising Agency   Lintas: Campbell-Ewald Co.
1993
GM vice president & Chevrolet general manager Jim C. Perkins
Marketing Manager Trucks   F.F. Raine, Jr.
Manager Truck Advertising   Mac Whisner
National Manager Truck Merchandising   J.N. Janowiak
Director of Public Relations   Ralph J. Kramer
Advertising Agency   Lintas: Campbell-Ewald Co.
1994
GM vice president & Chevrolet general manager Jim C. Perkins
Marketing Manager Trucks   F.F. Raine, Jr.
Manager Truck Advertising   Mac Whisner
National Manager Truck Merchandising   J.N. Janowiak
Director of Public Relations   Ralph J. Kramer
Advertising Agency   Lintas: Campbell-Ewald Co.

Chevrolet Truck Calendar-Year Registrations or Production

Year	Calendar-Year Registrations	Percent of Total
1930	118,253	28.79 %
1931	99,600	31.73 %
1932	60,784	33.69 %
1933	99,880	40.62 %
1934	157,507	39.00 %
1935	167,129	32.73 %

Note: Only registration figures are available for 1930-1935. Registration totals typically run lower than production totals. For example, Chevrolet truck registrations were 204,344 in 1936; 183,674 in 1937; 119,479 in 1938; 169,457 in 1939; 185,636 in 1940; and 212,797 in 1941.

Year	Calendar-Year Production	Percent of U.S. Industry Total
1936	255,467	32.56 %
1937	261,964	29.47 %
1938	164,186	32.58 %
1939	246,187	34.19 %
1940	247,689	31.53 %
1941	321,804	29.41 %
1942	119,077	13.68 %
1945	94,634	13.50 %
1946	270,140	28.67 %
1947	335,343	27.12 %
1948	389,690	28.46 %
1949	383,543	33.88 %
1950	494,573	36.79 %
1951	426,115	30.17 %
1952	332,115	27.27 %
1953	361,833	30.06 %
1954	325,515	31.83 %
1955	393,312	31.55 %
1956	353,509	32.01 %
1957	351,739	32.39 %
1958	278,615	31.98 %
1959	326,093	28.61 %
1960	394,014	32.88 %
1961	342,658	30.39 %
1962	396,918	31.65 %
1963	483,119	33.01 %
1964	523,790	33.56 %
1965	619,691	34.71 %
1966	621,417	35.22 %
1967	549,663	34.67 %
1968	680,499	34.88 %
1969	683,694	34.83 %
1970	490,884	28.59 %
1971	739,480	35.69 %
1972	770,773	31.10 %
1973	1,013,784	33.77 %
1974	838,959	29.44 %
1975	758,428	33.56 %
1976	1,048,135	35.02 %
1977	1,122,769	32.19 %
1978	1,216,050	32.67 %
1979	1,015,092	33.25 %
1980	515,038	31.43 %
1981	548,383	32.45 %
1982	672,634	35.18 %
1983	865,144	35.40 %
1984	1,008,231	31.85 %
1985	1,181,941	34.08 %
1986	1,152,263	31.44 %
1987	1,152,400	30.12 %
1988	1,259,648	30.72 %
1989	1,219,249	30.10 %
1990	1,068,596	28.86 %
1991	868,533	27.34 %
1992	948,381	24.90 %
1993	1,142,575	24.80 %

[Source: Chevrolet Motor Division]

Chevrolet Truck Production/Shipments by GVW Rating

Weight Class	0-lb. 5,000 lb.	5,001 lb. 10,000 lb.	10,001 lb. 14,000 lb.	14,001 lb. 16,000 lb.
1949	201,537	97,678	27,469	56,859
1950	265,515	102,669	27,848	98,541
1951	215,175	79,659	26,701	104,580
1952	171,114	67,263	17,675	76,098
1953	203,242	71,517	17,815	69,259
1954	170,824	64,599	13,590	76,502
1955	219,805	64,589	15,130	93,788
1956	194,015	59,182	14,201	77,620
1957	198,538	55,575	16,575	75,279
1958	157,911	46,310	9,924	59,628
1959	196,307	49,566	9,456	64,895

Weight Class	0-lb. 6,000 lb.	6,001 lb. 10,000 lb.	10,001 lb. 14,000 lb.	14,001 lb. 16,000 lb.
1960	253,882	58,170	6,065	7,481
1961	221,400	54,013	6,364	6,954
1962	253,499	66,898	3,715	8,413
1963	317,100	85,400	50	9,400
1964	358,000	90,600	0	7,900
1965	427,100	111,600	0	8,600
1966	418,100	115,600	0	8,800
1967	364,500	110,000	0	6,900
1968	464,000	136,000	0	7,600
1969	458,100	143,700	0	6,100
1970	318,200	114,400	0	4,100
1971	500,700	176,200	0	4,200
1972	517,828	185,448	0	0
1973	658,939	278,405	0	0
1974	556,581	239,245	0	0
1975	398,356	322,436	0	0
1976	571,786	425,399	0	0
1977	586,813	481,738	0	0
1978	616,229	543,079	0	0
1979	531,207	435,840	0	0

Year				
1980	298,050	194,141	0	0
1981	299,018	221,778	0	0
1982	415,648	234,337	0	0
1983	548,749	295,725	0	0
1984	601,533	385,519	0	0
1985	756,634	397,961	0	0
1986	801,431	339,541	0	0
1987	871,846	542,811	154	0
1988	875,849	576,371	0	0
1989	809,273	631,297	0	0
1990	810,416	522,588	0	496
1991	708,672	151,800	0	2,436
1992	732,578	207,255	0	2,540
1993	799,440	326,343	0	4,946

Note: This charts shows production or shipments of Chevrolet trucks of the four lowest GVW rating classes in the calendar-year. This is not total Chevrolet calendar-year production. Production totals are exact. Some shipment totals are rounded-off to the nearest 100. *[Source: American Automobile Manufacturers Association]*

Factory Option Installation Rates For Chevy Light Trucks 1971-1979
(In percent)

Optional equipment installation rates were recorded by Chevrolet's advertising agency in the 1970s and show extensive documentation. They very detailed and difficult to understand without an intricate knowledge of vehicles codes. For same years, the statistics are expressed as a percentage figure that relates the number of trucks built with the option to the total number of trucks for which that option was available. Therefore, the figures are not relative to total model-year production. For example, not all Step-Vans were offered with V-8 engines, so the installation rate would tell what percentage of trucks that offered this option had it installed. Another quirk is that the figures were originally combined totals for Chevrolet and GMC models built in the same factories.

Of course, these figures are useful to history buffs and collectors, because they show what options were available and they reflect optional equipment trends. For instance, they show that the popularity of V-8 engines, air conditioning, and AM/FM radios took a jump between 1971 and 1972. In fact, the usage of all the selected options for these years increased in 1972. Also note that even though the figures in the "Total Trucks with Option Available" fluctuate somewhat, they all fall within a range that shows far fewer trucks made in 1971 than in 1972. This was due to a strike during 1971, which is an important factor to old truck hobbyists.

As optional equipment came to play a larger role in truck manufacturing, Chevrolet Motor Division and its advertising agency began to record more data. In some reports, these statistics were related directly to total model-year production, rather than the total number of trucks with the option available. You will find such information in the charts for later-model trucks. Note that there may be some statistical rounding off in some of the figures.

Option	Total Trucks w/Option Avail.	Percent w/Option
1971		
Standard V-8	590,117	29
Optional	581,193	46
Automatic Transmission	585.953	49
Power Steering	580,345	38
Power Brakes	578,188	52
Air Conditioning	568,422	18
Tinted Glass	576,833	30
AM Radio	585,102	49
AM/FM Radio	576,889	0.9

* Statistics for this year are for combined Chevrolet and GMC trucks made in the same factories.

1972		
Standard V-8	775,675	20
Optional	782,709	65
Automatic Transmission	792,725	59
Power Steering	781,621	56
Power Brakes	782,782	72
Air Conditioning	776,781	26

Option	Total Trucks w/Option Avail.	Percent w/Option
Tinted Glass	791,581	37
AM Radio	779,704	57
AM/FM Radio	800,565	2.3

* Statistics for this year are for combined Chevrolet and GMC trucks made in the same factories.

Percent of Trucks w/Option

1973

Option	C10	C20	C30	Chevy Van	El. Camino	Blazer	Sport Van	Step Van
Automatic Transmission	65.8	68.9	30.4	72.3	93.2	76.5	89.4	53.9
Power Brakes	50.1	100	100	69.4	93.3	100	100	94.5
Disc Brakes	100	100	100	100	100	100	100	100
Power Steering	63.5	79.2	60.5	48.6	96.1	90.5	83.9	21.3
AM Radio	65.2	68.5	46.8	40.4	78	74.9	77.1	76.9
AM/FM Radio	5.3	5.6	4.3	N/A	16.6	13	N/A	N/A
Small V-8	79.8	76.3	67.3	78.7	93.5	97.7	95.4	45
Big V-8	6.7	18.9	22.3	N/A	6.5	N/A	N/A	21.7
Air Conditioning	36.1	35.2	21	7.4	67.8	44.1	35.6	8
Posi Axle	11.7	11.8	8.8	9.4	17.9	37.9	17	1.3
Wheel Covers	35.8	0.5	3.4	N/A	61.5	32.4	N/A	N/A
Deluxe Interior	49.2	49.2	24.4	22.9	57.4	54.8	17	N/A

1973 Chevrolet light-duty trucks model-year Production: [C10] 482,630; [C20] 195,714; [C30] 42,210; [Chevy Van] 67,881; [El Camino] 64,967; [Blazer] 48,183; [Sportvan] 21,528; [Step-Van] 29,341; [Total] 952,454.

1974

Option	C10	C20	C30	Chevy Van	El. Camino	Blazer	Sport Van	Suburban Carryall	Step Van
Automatic Trans.	63.4	66.9	28.9	73.5	95.8	81.5	91.5	89.3	56.2
Power Disc Brakes	41.5	100	100	76.7	100	100	100	100	90.8
Power Steering	63.3	85.5	68.9	41.8	97.3	95	89.1	71.5	42
AM Radio	71.6	74.5	49.4	43.4	77.5	77.4	69	67.7	N/A
AM/FM Radio	3.6	3.7	3.9	2.4	16.4	11.8	10.3	12.5	N/A
Small V-8	74.4	78.6	64.4	77	66.4	96	94.2	62.7	57.6
Big V-8	5.9	15.8	23.8	N/A	33.1	N/A	N/A	33.7	7.0
Air Conditioning	33.3	30.7	20	11.6	72.4	47.4	64	76	2.1
Posi Axle	3.3	14.3	10.1	3.6	9.9	8.6	5.1	8.6	1.0
Wheel Covers	29.3	0.3	1.8	N/A	70.3	34.2	N/A	24.1	1.7
Deluxe Interior	47.3	47.3	22.6	21.6	44.5	59.5	17	72.5	N/A
Exterior Trim Pkg.	47.3	47.3	22.6	21.6	44.5	59.5	17	72.5	N/A
Four-Wheel-Drive	9.8	21.6	N/A	21.1	N/A	94.6	N/A	N/A	N/A

1974 Chevrolet light-duty trucks model-year production: [C10] 445,699; [C20] 178,829; [C30] 39,964; [Step-Van] 19,759; [El Camino] 51,223; [Blazer] 56,798; [Suburban] 41,882; [Chevy Van] 70,763; [Sportvan] 20,779; [Total] 925,696.

1975

Option	C10	C20	C30	Step Van	El. Camino	Suburban Carryall	Blazer	Sport Van	Chevy Van
Automatic Trans.	66.7	64.6	23.3	69.2	97.8	87.5	82.9	91	74.6
Power Disc Brakes	64.7	100	100	100	94.6	100	100	100	72.3
Power Steering	72.3	85.6	68.9	44.2	98.6	90.9	95.8	95.4	64.2
AM Radio	71.0	72.9	48.8	N/A	71	57.7	72.4	62	42.7
Six-cylinder	19.1	11.7	24.1	17.5	19.5	26.7	5.4	3.1	0.6
Small V-8	74.2	77.3	51.2	61.6	76.2	72.6	92.8	88.8	73.4
Big V-8	6.6	11	24.1	17.5	19.5	26.7	5.4	3.1	0.6
Air Conditioning	35	29.4	20.4	1.2	74.7	56.7	47.5	50.2	14.7
Posi Axle	6.9	15.6	7.0	1.4	9.7	20.7	20.7	7.6	4.4
Wheel Covers	26.5	0.3	6.1	7.8	57	19.5	24.3	7.5	4
Interior Trim Pkg.	47.8	44.7	21.7	N/A	92	64.1	57.2	73.5	24
Exterior Trim Pkg.	47.8	44.7	21.7	N/A	92	64.1	57.2	73.5	24
Four-Wheel-Drive	17.4	34.1	N/A	N/A	N/A	22.8	92.7	N/A	N/A

1975 Chevrolet light-duty trucks model-year production: [C10] 318,234; [C20] 144,632; [C30] 44,929; [Step-Van] 16,877; [El Camino] 33,620; [Suburban] 30,032; [Blazer] 50,548; [Sportvan] 21,326; [Chevy Van] 87,290; [Total] 747,488.

1976

Option	C10	C20	C30	Step Van	El. Camino	Suburban Carryall	Blazer	Sport Van	Chevy Van
Automatic Trans.	68.7	68.5	55	61.2	77.4	67.4	74.6	80.6	71.4
Four-speed Trans	7.6	28.2	70.6	20.9	N/A	7.1	13.4	N/A	N/A

Option	C10	C20	C30	Step Van	El Camino	Suburban	Blazer	Sport Van	Chevy Van
Power Disc Brakes	72.3	100	100	100	100	100	100	100	77.2
Power Steering	77.3	92.4	82.9	75.1	99	93.6	96.2	94.1	69.1
AM Radio	62.5	67.6	49.7	N/A	56.3	48.8	57	49.3	32.7
AM/FM	8.5	6.5	6.8	N/A	17	21.6	19	23.2	5.6
Stereo System	N/A	N/A	N/A	N/A	13	N/A	N/A	N/A	N/A
Six-cylinder	22.6	6.0	15.7	16.8	5.1	1.8	3.7	9.8	24.8
Small V-8	69.4	74.8	55	61.2	77.4	67.4	74.6	80.6	71.4
Big V-8	8.0	19.2	29.3	22	17.5	30.8	21.7	9.6	3.8
Air Conditioning	39.6	34.8	31	3.5	80.1	65.3	54.7	58.1	21.8
Posi Axle	8.1	15.8	6.2	0.7	9.3	20.8	22.5	8.8	4.9
Cruise Control	6.8	8.0	7.9	N/A	22.4	35.4	18.5	31.7	9.8
Wheel Covers	37.5	6.6	11.7	1.4	40.9	25.5	17.9	25.6	12.8
Styled Wheels	15.4	N/A	N/A	N/A	51.3	14.1	33.2	15.7	6.6
Int./Ext. Trim Pkg.	52.8	49.4	32	N/A	83.7	75.8	61.9	71	11.5
Ext. Trim Pkg. only	N/A	N/A	N/A	N/A	1.8	11.7	4.4	67.2	15.8
Bumper Guards	7.6	4.4	5.4	N/A	46.6	14.5	16.8	7.9	1.1
Towing Special Pkg.	0.6	1.2	0.2	N/A	N/A	12.9	4.9	N/A	N/A
Bucket Seats	1.0	0.9	3.0	100	9.7	N/A	100	100	100
Tilt Steering	18.3	18	14	N/A	47.9	34.8	35.7	79.2	47.1
Four-Wheel-Drive	20.4	32.4	N/A	N/A	N/A	23.5	90.2	N/A	N/A

1976 Chevrolet light-duty trucks model-year production: [C10] 458,424; {C20] 172,419; [C30] 45,299; [Step-Van] 20,043; [El Camino] 44,800; [Suburban] 44,977; [Blazer] 74,389; [Sportvan] 26,860; [Chevy Van] 125,695; [Total] 1,012,996.

1977

Option	C10	C20	C30	Step Van	El Camino	Suburban Carryall	Blazer	Sport Van	Chevy Van
Automatic Trans.	74	70	32	78	98.9	88.4	84.2	86	94.5
Four-speed Trans	8.0	28	68	21	N/A	9.8	14.3	N/A	N/A
Power Disc Brakes	78	100	100	100	100	100	100	100	84.3
Power Steering	85	95	90	81	99.5	96.6	97.8	94.9	81.4
AM Radio	53.6	59.4	45.3	N/A	44.5	38.1	42.8	38.5	26.1
AM/FM	11.5	8.1	6.9	N/A	20.1	25.9	23.1	30.2	7.4
Stereo System	N/A	N/A	N/A	N/A	16.9	N/A	N/A	N/A	N/A
Six-cylinder	18.0	5.0	11	17	3.2	1.3	1.8	19.6	7.9
Small V-8	74	75	60	61	96.8	67.5	71	72.7	80.2
Big V-8	8.0	20	29	22	N/A	31.2	27.1	7.7	11.9
Air Conditioning	43.9	37.8	33.1	3.9	85.2	71.5	58.9	29.6	62.7
Posi Axle	10	18	9.0	1.0	9.1	22.1	27.2	8.6	5.2
Cruise Control	11.4	12.1	9.4	N/A	39.4	44.3	27.7	40	17.6
Optional Wheel Covers	22.1	3.0	9.0	0.5	25.5	21.9	16.8	24	9.9
Styled Wheels	22	N/A	N/A	N/A	67.5	20	40.8	24	9.9
Int./Ext. Trim Pkg.	56	52.1	35.3	N/A	N/A	79.7	66.6	70.6	3.3
Ext. Trim Pkg. only	4.0	2.4	1.9	N/A	1.1	10.9	10.1	67.5	13.9
Front Bumper Guards	9.0	5.1	6.9	N/A	52.1	17.6	17.0	9.9	2.0
Towing Special Pkg.	1.0	1.6	0.5	N/A	N/A	17.7	5.9	N/A	N/A
Bucket Seats	1.3	1.0	2.9	100	8.8	N/A	100	100	100
Tilt Steering	23.3	21.5	16.8	N/A	65.2	42.7	41.7	39.1	26.3
Four-Wheel-Drive	21	31	8.0	N/A	N/A	20.9	87.8	N/A	N/A
Radial Tires	6.0	N/A	N/A	N/A	99.7	29.5	12.1	35.8	10.4

1977 Chevrolet light-duty trucks model-year production: [C10] 525,791; [C20] 189,150; [C30] 60,779; [Step-Van] 30,886; [El Camino] 54,321; [Suburban] 60,273; [Blazer] 86,838; [Sportvan] 43,386; [Chevy Van] 147,377; [Total] 1,198,801.

1978

Option	C10	C20	C30	Step Van	El Camino	Suburban Carryall	Blazer	Sport Van	Chevy Van
Automatic Trans.	75.6	69.5	31.5	78.4	94.9	84.5	86.5	95.9	89.3
Four-speed Trans	8.5	29	68.5	20.3	3.3	12.5	12	N/A	N/A
Power Disc Brakes	81.2	100	100	100	99.9	100	100	100	89.1
Power Steering	87.2	95.9	93.4	80	99.4	96.2	99.4	97	87.5
AM Radio	49.5	55.4	43.5	N/A	39.6	33.2	36.6	30.8	23
AM/FM	13.4	8.8	6.6	N/A	21.5	26.1	25.2	18.9	3.7
Stereo System	N/A	N/A	N/A	N/A	21.3	N/A	N/A	22.8	4.8
Tape Player	N/A	N/A	N/A	N/A	8.4	N/A	N/A	7.9	2.2
CB Radio	N/A	N/A	N/A	N/A	N/A	N/A	N/A	0.3	0.1
Six-cylinder	19.1	6.4	7.9	20.3	12.2	1.4	2.4	18.1	8.1

Option	C10	C20	C30	Step Van	El. Camino	Suburban Carryall	Blazer	Sport Van	Chevy Van
Small V-8	14.9	N/A	N/A	N/A	47.6	9.9	15.3	3.4	12.9
Big V-8	61.8	93.6	92.1	79.7	40.2	88.7	82.3	88.5	69
Air Conditioning	45.3	35.3	35.7	1.4	83.7	73.4	62.5	70.1	32.5
Posi Axle	11.3	19.4	9.8	1.0	9.0	25	32.5	8.4	4.8
Cruise Control	13	12.1	9.8	N/A	41.3	47.1	34.2	46.7	24.1
Optional Wheel Covers	18.1	3.8	4.7	0.2	9.3	18.9	8.8	12.5	8.4
Styled Wheels	26.6	N/A	N/A	N/A	73.9	25.9	57.7	31.8	11.5
Dual Rear Wheels	N/A	N/A	71.2	79.3	N/A	N/A	N/A	N/A	12.3
Int./Ext. Trim Pkg.	56.2	49.4	35.9	N/A	N/A	78.2	70	72.8	4.4
Ext. Trim Pkg. only	3.1	1.6	2.2	N/A	39.9	12.5	70.3	68.1	11.3
Tape Stripes	4.3	1.6	2.2	N/A	22.2	8.8	7.1	N/A	0.4
Two-tone Finish	38.1	35.7	22.7	N/A	62.1	56.6	33.9	64.6	7.9
Front Bumper Guards	8.8	4.9	8.8	N/A	46.1	20	18.1	11.4	1.7
Towing Special Pkg.	0.6	1.6	0.6	N/A	N/A	17.1	5.9	N/A	N/A
Bucket Seats	1.5	0.9	2.4	41.5	9.6	2.9	100	100	100
Power Door Locks	4.5	2.3	4.8	N/A	15	N/A	16.8	N/A	N/A
Power Windows	4.9	2.5	4.8	N/A	17.5	N/A	16.2	N/A	N/A
Tilt Steering	25.5	20.8	19.9	32.5	66.5	46.3	46.5	46.9	35.2
Four-Wheel-Drive	24.5	37.1	11.3	N/A	N/A	24.5	88.4	N/A	N/A
Radial Tires	7.2	0.5	N/A	N/A	100	29	11.8	33	9.5
Regular Bumper	11	2.9	9.1	N/A	100	100	100	93.3	84.1
Step Bumper	47.6	52.3	16.2	39.6	N/A	N/A	N/A	4.7	5.0

1978 Chevrolet light-duty trucks model-year production: [C10] 540,968; [C20] 176,735; [C30] 68,010; [Step-Van] 28,127; [El Camino] 54,286; [Suburban] 57,788; [Blazer] 88,858; [Sportvan] 44,058; [Chevy Van] 203,007; [Total] 1,261,837.

1979

Option	C10	C20	C30	Step Van	El. Camino	Suburban Carryall	Blazer	Sport Van	Chevy Van
Automatic Trans.	75.8	67.9	35.7	93.4	87.3	86.6	79.3	97.3	90.1
Four-speed Trans	9.7	31.3	64.3	19.7	3.1	11.8	12.7	N/A	N/A
Power Disc Brakes	80.3	100	100	100	100	100	100	100	90.2
Power Steering	89.5	96.4	95.4	82.6	99.3	98.1	99.4	96.4	89.5
AM Radio	46.9	52.5	42.2	N/A	42.1	29.2	29.9	28.6	24.3
AM/FM	14.8	9.8	7.8	N/A	18.6	28.4	27.7	17.3	3.4
Stereo System	N/A	N/A	N/A	N/A	11.3	N/A	N/A	16.4	2.1
Tape Player	N/A	N/A	N/A	N/A	7.6	N/A	N/A	8.5	2.2
CB Radio	N/A	N/A	N/A	N/A	0.9	N/A	N/A	1.6	0.3
Six-cylinder	25.5	3.1	6.7	14	16	1.0	3.2	7.2	18.7
Small V-8	20	N/A	N/A	N/A	80.4	5.5	14.2	3.2	12.3
Big V-8	4.1	12.9	30.7	27.4	N/A	30.3	14.6	10.3	7.3
Air Conditioning	47.3	38.1	38.1	2.0	83	77.5	67.7	74	40
Cruise Control	14.5	12.9	10.9	N/A	41.1	51.3	40.7	49.5	28.5
Optional Wheel Covers	15.5	5.2	6.8	N/A	16	18.7	7.9	12.6	6.2
Styled Steel Wheels	31.1	N/A	N/A	N/A	84	32.1	64.1	37.3	14.4
Styled Alum. Wheels	0.2	N/A	N/A	N/A	N/A	N/A	N/A	N/A	N/A
Dual Rear Wheels	N/A	N/A	68.0	83.5	N/A	N/A	N/A	N/A	10
Int./Ext. Trim Pkg.	56.3	48.4	37.8	N/A	N/A	81.4	73.6	69	2.8
Ext. Trim Pkg. only	2.4	1.2	1.3	N/A	44.9	13.3	6.2	67.6	8.8
Towing Special Pkg.	0.5	1.6	1.0	N/A	N/A	17.7	3.3	N/A	N/A
Bucket Seats	1.6	1.0	2.3	44.9	13.3	6.2	100	100	100
Power Door Locks	6.2	3.3	5.0	N/A	13.2	N/A	23.5	14.4	6.8
Power Windows	6.7	3.3	5.0	N/A	15.5	N/A	23.5	9.7	5.3
Tilt Steering	29.7	22.3	20.8	32.3	61.9	52.9	52.8	49.6	37.2
Four-Wheel-Drive	24.8	39.4	11.8	N/A	N/A	30	89.8	N/A	N/A
Radial Tires	64.4	1.9	N/A	N/A	100	35.7	13.8	43.9	14.6
Regular Bumper	9.6	2.6	5.7	N/A	100	100	100	96.5	86.6
Step Bumper	47.4	51	17.8	42.6	N/A	N/A	N/A	3.5	4.9

1979 Chevrolet light-duty trucks model-year production: [C10] 535,056; [C20] 148,782; [C30] 80,500; [Step-Van] 28,536; [El Camino] 58,008; [Suburban] 54,987; [Blazer] 90,987; [Sportvan] 40,560; [Chevy Van] 212,513, [Total] 1,249,929.

[Source: Standard Catalog of American Light-Duty Trucks 1896-1986]

Price Guide Section

How To Use Chevrolet Truck Pricing Guide

On the following pages is a **LIGHT-DUTY TRUCK PRICING GUIDE.** The value of a truck is a "ballpark" estimate at best. The estimates contained here are based upon national and regional data compiled by the editors of *Old Cars Weekly* and *Old Cars Price Guide*. These data include actual bids and prices at collector car auctions and sales, classified and display advertising of such vehicles, verified reports of private sales and input from experts.

Value estimates are listed for trucks in six different states of condition. These conditions (1-6) are illustrated and explained in the **VEHICLE CONDITION SCALE** on the page next following. Modified-truck values are not included, but can be estimated by figuring the cost of restoring to original condition and adjusting the figures shown here.

Appearing below is a section of chart taken from the **LIGHT-DUTY TRUCK PRICING GUIDE** to illustrate the following elements:

A. **MAKE** The make of truck, or marque name, appears in large, boldface type at the beginning of each value section.

B. **DESCRIPTION** The extreme left-hand column indicates truck year, model name, body type, engine configuration and, in some cases, wheelbase.

C. **CONDITION CODE** The six columns to the right are headed by the numbers one through six (1-6) which correspond to the conditions described in the **VEHICLE CONDITION SCALE** on the following page.

D. **VALUE** The value estimates, in dollars, appear below their respective condition code headings and across from the truck descriptions.

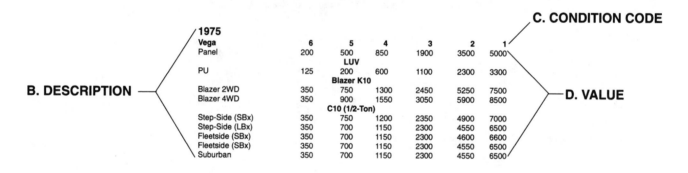

A. MAKE ——————— **CHEVROLET**

C. CONDITION CODE

B. DESCRIPTION

1975 Vega	6	5	4	3	2	1
Panel	200	500	850	1900	3500	5000
LUV						
PU	125	200	600	1100	2300	3300
Blazer K10						
Blazer 2WD	350	750	1300	2450	5250	7500
Blazer 4WD	350	900	1550	3050	5900	8500
C10 (1/2-Ton)						
Step-Side (SBx)	350	750	1200	2350	4900	7000
Step-Side (LBx)	350	700	1150	2300	4550	6500
Fleetside (SBx)	350	700	1150	2300	4600	6600
Fleetside (SBx)	350	700	1150	2300	4550	6500
Suburban	350	700	1150	2300	4550	6500

D. VALUE

VEHICLE CONDITION SCALE

EXCELLENT CONDITION

FINE CONDITION

VERY GOOD CONDITION

GOOD CONDITION

RESTORABLE CONDITION

PARTS TRUCK   (Sample truck is a Dodge)

1) EXCELLENT: Restored to current maxiumum professional standards of quality in every area, or perfect original with components operating and appearing as new. A 95-plus point show vehicle that is not driven.

2) FINE: Well-restored, or a combination of superior restoration and excellent original. Also, an *extremely* well-maintained original showing very minimal wear.

3) VERY GOOD: Completely operable original or "older restoration" showing wear. Also, a good amateur restoration, all presentable and serviceable inside and out. Plus, combinations of well-done restoration and good operable components or a partially restored vehicle with all parts necessary to complete and/or valuable NOS parts.

4) GOOD: A driveable vehicle needing no or only minor work to be functional. Also, a deteriorated restoration or a very poor amateur restoration. All components may need restoration to be "excellent," but the vehicle is mostly useable "as is."

5) RESTORABLE: Needs *complete* restoration of body, chassis and interior. May or may not be running, but isn't weathered, wrecked or stripped to the point of being useful only for parts.

6) PARTS VEHICLE: May or may not be running, but is weathered, wrecked and/or stripped to the point of being useful primarily for parts.

CHEVROLET TRUCKS

	6	5	4	3	2	1
1918						
Series "490"						
1/2-Ton Light Dly	400	1250	2100	4200	7400	10,500
Series "T"						
1-Ton Flare Exp	400	1200	2000	4000	7100	10,100
1-Ton Covered Flare	400	1200	2050	4100	7100	10,200
1919						
Series "490"						
1/2-Ton Light Dly	400	1250	2100	4200	7400	10,500
Series "T"						
1-Ton Flare Exp	400	1200	2000	4000	7100	10,100
1-Ton Covered Flare	400	1200	2050	4100	7100	10,200
1920						
Series "490"						
Light Dly Wag 1-Seat	400	1300	2200	4400	7700	11,000
Light Dly Wag 2-Seat	400	1350	2200	4400	7800	11,100
Model T						
Flareboard Exp	400	1200	2000	4000	7100	10,100
Covered Flare	400	1200	2050	4100	7100	10,200
1921						
Series "490"						
Open Exp	400	1300	2200	4400	7700	11,000
Canopy Exp 3 Seat	400	1350	2250	4500	7800	11,200
Series G						
Open Exp	400	1250	2100	4200	7400	10,500
Canopy Exp	400	1250	2100	4200	7400	10,600
Series T						
Open Exp	400	1300	2200	4400	7700	11,000
Canopy Exp	400	1350	2250	4500	7800	11,200
1922						
Series "490"						
Dly Wag	450	1400	2300	4600	8100	11,500
Panel Dly	450	1450	2400	4800	8400	12,000
Sta Wag	500	1550	2600	5200	9100	13,000
Series G						
Exp	400	1200	2000	4000	7000	10,000
Canopy Exp	400	1200	2050	4100	7100	10,200
Series T						
Open Exp	400	1200	2000	4000	7100	10,100
Canopy Exp	400	1250	2050	4100	7200	10,300
Canopy Exp w/curtains	400	1250	2100	4200	7400	10,500
1923						
Series B Superior						
Canopy Exp	400	1300	2200	4400	7700	11,000
Panel Dly	400	1350	2200	4400	7800	11,100
Sta Wag	500	1550	2600	5200	9100	13,000
Series D Superior						
Utl Dly (Exp)	400	1200	2000	4000	7000	10,000
Cattle Body (Stake)	400	1200	2050	4100	7100	10,200
Dly Wag	400	1200	2000	4000	7100	10,100
Panel Body	400	1300	2200	4400	7700	11,000
Gravity Dump	400	1250	2100	4200	7400	10,500
Petroleum Tanker	400	1300	2200	4400	7700	11,000
1924						
Series F						
Open Exp	400	1250	2100	4200	7400	10,500
Canopy Exp	400	1300	2150	4300	7500	10,700
Panel Dly	400	1300	2200	4400	7700	11,000
Sta Wag	450	1500	2500	5000	8800	12,500
Series H						
Open Cab Grain/Stock Body	400	1200	2000	4000	7000	10,000
Closed Cab Grain/Stock Body	450	1140	1900	3800	6650	9500
Flareboard Exp	450	1080	1800	3600	6300	9000
Panel Body	450	1140	1900	3800	6650	9500
Dump/Coal Body	400	1200	2000	4000	7000	10,000
Tanker (3 compartment)	400	1250	2100	4200	7400	10,600
1925						
Series M - (1924-25) - (1-Ton)						
Flareboard Exp	450	1140	1900	3800	6650	9500
Panel Body	400	1200	2000	4000	7000	10,000
Series K - (1/2-Ton)						
Flareboard Exp	450	1130	1900	3800	6600	9400
Panel Body	400	1200	2000	4000	7000	10,000
Sta Wag	450	1450	2400	4800	8400	12,000
Series R - (1-Ton)						
Flareboard Exp	450	1160	1950	3900	6800	9700
Panel Body	400	1200	2050	4100	7100	10,200
Grain Body	400	1200	2000	4000	7100	10,100
Stake-Platform	400	1200	2000	4000	7100	10,100
Tanker (3 compartment)	400	1250	2100	4200	7400	10,500
Dump Body	400	1200	2050	4100	7100	10,200
Wrecker	400	1200	2000	4000	7100	10,100
1926						
Series V						
Rds PU (Factory)	450	1450	2450	4900	8500	12,200
Commercial Rds (Factory)	450	1450	2400	4800	8400	12,000
Hercules Panel Dly	400	1250	2100	4200	7400	10,500
Springfield Ctry Clb Suburban	450	1500	2500	5000	8800	12,500
Springfield Panel Dly	450	1400	2300	4600	8100	11,500
Series X - (1926-27)						
Flareboard Exp (Factory)	400	1200	2000	4000	7000	10,000
Canopy Exp (Factory)	400	1200	2050	4100	7100	10,200
Screenside Exp (Factory)	400	1250	2100	4200	7400	10,500
Peddler's Wag (Factory)	400	1300	2150	4300	7600	10,800

	6	5	4	3	2	1
Mifflinburg Depot Hack	450	1400	2300	4600	8100	11,500
Springfield 12P Suburban	450	1400	2300	4600	8100	11,600
Proctor-Keefe Dump	400	1250	2100	4200	7600	10,500
Mifflinburg Jitney/Exp	450	1140	1900	3800	6650	9500
Platform Stake	400	1200	2000	4000	7000	10,000
Rack Body w/Coach Front	400	1250	2100	4200	7400	10,500
1927						
Capitol AA Series						
Rds PU	450	1500	2500	5000	8700	12,400
Commercial Rds	450	1450	2400	4800	8500	12,100
Open Exp	400	1250	2100	4200	7400	10,500
Sta Wag	450	1450	2400	4800	8400	12,000
Panel Dly	450	1400	2300	4600	8100	11,500
Series LM						
Open Exp	400	1250	2100	4200	7400	10,600
Panel Dly	450	1400	2300	4600	8100	11,600
Dump	400	1250	2100	4200	7400	10,500
Suburban (Sta Wag)	450	1500	2500	5000	8800	12,500
School Bus	400	1300	2200	4400	7700	11,000
Peddler's Wagon	400	1250	2100	4200	7400	10,500
Cattle Body/Stake	400	1200	2000	4000	7000	10,000
Canopy Exp	400	1300	2200	4400	7700	11,000
Screenside Exp	400	1350	2250	4500	7800	11,200
1928						
Series National AB						
Rds w/Slip-in PU Box	450	1450	2400	4800	8400	12,000
Rds w/Panel Carrier	450	1450	2400	4800	8500	12,100
PU Exp	450	1400	2350	4700	8300	11,800
Canopy Dly	450	1400	2300	4600	8100	11,600
Screenside Dly	450	1400	2350	4700	8200	11,700
Panel Dly	400	1300	2200	4400	7700	11,000
Sed Dly	450	1400	2350	4700	8300	11,800
Henney Hearse	400	1300	2150	4300	7600	10,800
Henney Ambulance	400	1250	2100	4200	7400	10,600
Series LO/LP						
Open Exp Dly	450	1400	2350	4700	8300	11,800
Canopy Exp	450	1450	2400	4800	8400	12,000
Screenside Exp	450	1450	2450	4900	8500	12,200
Panel Dly	450	1400	2350	4700	8200	11,700
Platform Stake	400	1250	2100	4200	7400	10,500
Dump Body	400	1300	2150	4300	7600	10,800
Peddler's Wag	400	1250	2100	4200	7400	10,500
Tow Truck	400	1300	2200	4400	7700	11,000
Tank Truck	450	1400	2300	4600	8100	11,500
1929						
International Series AC						
Rds w/Slip-in Cargo Box	500	1550	2600	5200	9100	13,000
Rds w/Panel Carrier	500	1550	2600	5200	9200	13,100
Open Exp	400	1300	2200	4400	7700	11,000
Canopy Exp	450	1450	2400	4800	8400	12,000
Sed Dly	450	1500	2500	5000	8800	12,500
Screenside Exp	450	1450	2400	4800	8400	12,000
Panel Dly	450	1450	2400	4800	8400	12,000
Ambassador Panel Dly	550	1700	2800	5600	9800	14,000
1930						
Rds PU	500	1600	2700	5400	9500	13,500
PU Exp	450	1450	2400	4800	8400	12,000
Panel Dly	450	1450	2400	4800	8400	12,000
DeL Panel Dly	550	1700	2800	5600	9800	14,000
Sed Dly	550	1750	2900	5800	10,200	14,500
DeL Sed Dly	550	1800	3000	6000	10,500	15,000
Canopy Exp	500	1550	2600	5200	9100	13,000
Screenside Exp	500	1550	2600	5200	9100	13,000
1931						
Open Cab PU	550	1700	2800	5600	9800	14,000
Closed Cab PU	450	1450	2400	4800	8400	12,000
Panel Dly	500	1550	2600	5200	9100	13,000
Canopy Dly (curtains)	550	1700	2800	5600	9800	14,000
Canopy Dly (screens)	550	1700	2800	5600	9800	14,000
Sed Dly	600	1850	3100	6200	10,900	15,500
DeL Sta Wag	550	1800	3000	6000	10,500	15,000

NOTE: Add 5 percent for Deluxe 1/2-Ton models.

	6	5	4	3	2	1
1932						
Open Cab PU	550	1800	3000	6000	10,500	15,000
Closed Cab PU	500	1550	2600	5200	9100	13,000
Canopy Exp	550	1750	2900	5800	10,200	14,500
Screenside Exp	550	1750	2900	5800	10,200	14,500
Panel Dly	500	1600	2700	5400	9500	13,500
Spl Panel Dly	550	1750	2900	5800	10,200	14,500
Sed Dly	600	1900	3200	6400	11,200	16,000
Spl Sed Dly	650	2050	3400	6800	11,900	17,000

NOTE: Add 5 percent for Special Equipment on models other than those noted as "Specials" above. Add 2 percent for Canopy Tops on both pickups.

	6	5	4	3	2	1
1933						
Sed Dly	450	1450	2400	4800	8400	12,000
Spl Sed Dly	500	1600	2700	5400	9500	13,500
Closed Cab PU	400	1200	2000	4000	7000	10,000
Panel Dly	400	1200	2000	4000	7000	10,000
Spl Panel Dly	400	1300	2200	4400	7700	11,000
Canopy Exp	400	1250	2100	4200	7400	10,500
Spl Canopy Exp	400	1300	2200	4400	7700	11,000
Screenside Exp	400	1300	2200	4400	7700	11,000

NOTE: Add 2 percent for canopied pickups.

	6	5	4	3	2	1
1934						
Closed Cab PU	400	1200	2000	4000	7000	10,000
Canopy PU	400	1250	2100	4200	7400	10,500

1928 Chevrolet Screenside Delivery Truck (OCW)

	6	5	4	3	2	1
Canopy Exp (curtains)	400	1200	2000	4000	7000	10,000
Canopy Exp (screens)	400	1200	2000	4000	7000	10,000
Panel Dly	400	1200	2000	4000	7000	10,000
Sed Dly	400	1300	2200	4400	7700	11,000

NOTE: Add 5 percent for "Special" models.

1935
Series EB

	6	5	4	3	2	1
Closed Cab PU	400	1300	2200	4400	7700	11,000
Spl PU	400	1250	2100	4200	7400	10,500
Canopy Top PU	400	1250	2100	4200	7400	10,500
Panel Dly	400	1200	2000	4000	7000	10,000
Spl Panel Dly	400	1250	2100	4200	7400	10,500
Canopy (curtains)	400	1300	2200	4400	7700	11,000
Canopy (screens)	400	1300	2200	4400	7700	11,000

Series EC

	6	5	4	3	2	1
Sed Dly	450	1450	2400	4800	8400	12,000
Suburban	400	1300	2200	4400	7700	11,000

1936
Series FC

	6	5	4	3	2	1
Sed Dly	450	1500	2500	5000	8800	12,500

Series FB (1/2-Ton)

	6	5	4	3	2	1
PU	400	1300	2200	4400	7700	11,000
Panel Dly	400	1300	2200	4400	7700	11,000
Suburban	450	1400	2300	4600	8100	11,500

1937
Series GB

	6	5	4	3	2	1
Sed Dly	450	1400	2300	4600	8100	11,500

Series GC

	6	5	4	3	2	1
PU	400	1300	2200	4400	7700	11,000
Panel	400	1250	2100	4200	7400	10,500
Canopy Exp	400	1300	2200	4400	7700	11,000
Carryall Suburban	400	1350	2250	4500	7800	11,200

Series GD

	6	5	4	3	2	1
PU	400	1200	2000	4000	7000	10,000
Stake	450	1080	1800	3600	6300	9000

Series GE

	6	5	4	3	2	1
PU	450	1160	1950	3900	6800	9700
Stake	450	1050	1800	3600	6200	8900

1938
Series HB

	6	5	4	3	2	1
Cpe PU	400	1250	2050	4100	7200	10,300
Sed Dly	450	1400	2300	4600	8100	11,500

Series HC

	6	5	4	3	2	1
PU	400	1300	2200	4400	7700	11,000
Panel	400	1250	2100	4200	7400	10,500
Canopy Exp	400	1300	2200	4400	7700	11,000
Suburban	400	1350	2250	4500	7800	11,200

Series HD

	6	5	4	3	2	1
PU	400	1200	2000	4000	7000	10,000
Panel	400	1250	2100	4200	7400	10,500
Stake	450	1080	1800	3600	6300	9000

Series HE

	6	5	4	3	2	1
PU	450	1160	1950	3900	6800	9700
Panel	400	1200	2000	4000	7000	10,000
Stake	350	1020	1700	3400	5950	8500

1939
Series JB

	6	5	4	3	2	1
Cpe PU	400	1250	2100	4200	7400	10,500
Sed Dly	450	1450	2400	4800	8400	12,000

Series JC

	6	5	4	3	2	1
PU	400	1350	2250	4500	7800	11,200
Panel	400	1250	2100	4200	7400	10,600
Canopy Exp	400	1350	2250	4500	7800	11,200
Suburban	450	1350	2300	4600	8000	11,400

Series JD

	6	5	4	3	2	1
PU	400	1200	2000	4000	7000	10,000
Panel	400	1250	2100	4200	7400	10,500
Stake	450	1080	1800	3600	6300	9000

Series VA

	6	5	4	3	2	1
Panel	400	1200	2000	4000	7000	10,000

1940
Series KB

	6	5	4	3	2	1
Cpe PU	450	1400	2300	4600	8100	11,500
Sed Dly	450	1500	2500	5000	8800	12,500

Series KH

	6	5	4	3	2	1
Cpe PU	450	1450	2400	4800	8400	12,000
Sed Dly	500	1550	2600	5200	9100	13,000

Series KC

	6	5	4	3	2	1
PU	450	1400	2300	4600	8100	11,500
Panel	400	1300	2150	4300	7600	10,800
Canopy Exp	450	1350	2300	4600	8000	11,400
Suburban	450	1400	2300	4600	8100	11,600

Series KP

	6	5	4	3	2	1
Panel	400	1300	2150	4300	7500	10,700

Series KD

	6	5	4	3	2	1
PU	400	1200	2000	4000	7100	10,100
Panel	400	1250	2100	4200	7400	10,600
Platform	450	1080	1800	3600	6300	9000
Stake	450	1090	1800	3650	6400	9100

Series KF

	6	5	4	3	2	1
Panel	400	1250	2050	4100	7200	10,300
Platform	450	1050	1800	3600	6200	8900
Stake	450	1080	1800	3600	6300	9000

Series WA

	6	5	4	3	2	1
Open Exp	950	1100	1850	3700	6450	9200
Panel	400	1200	2000	4000	7000	10,000
Canopy	400	1250	2100	4200	7300	10,400

1941
Series AG

	6	5	4	3	2	1
Cpe PU	450	1400	2350	4700	8200	11,700
Sed Dly	450	1500	2500	5000	8800	12,500

Series AJ

	6	5	4	3	2	1
Panel Dly	400	1300	2150	4300	7600	10,800

Series AK

	6	5	4	3	2	1
PU	450	1400	2300	4600	8100	11,500
Panel Dly	400	1300	2150	4300	7600	10,800
Canopy	450	1350	2300	4600	8000	11,400
Suburban	450	1400	2300	4600	8100	11,600

Series AL

	6	5	4	3	2	1
PU	400	1300	2200	4400	7700	11,000
Panel Dly	400	1250	2050	4100	7200	10,300

	6	5	4	3	2	1
Platform	450	1080	1800	3600	6300	9000
Stake	450	1090	1800	3650	6400	9100
Series AN						
Exp	950	1100	1850	3700	6450	9200
Panel Dly	400	1200	2000	4000	7000	10,000
Platform	450	1050	1800	3600	6200	8900
Stake	450	1080	1800	3600	6300	9000
Series YR						
Canopy	400	1300	2150	4300	7600	10,800
1942						
Series BG						
Cpe PU	400	1250	2100	4200	7400	10,500
Sed Dly	400	1300	2200	4400	7700	11,000
Series BJ						
Double-Duty Pkg Dly	450	1080	1800	3600	6300	9000
Series BK						
PU	400	1300	2200	4400	7700	11,000
Canopy	400	1200	2050	4100	7100	10,200
Suburban	400	1250	2100	4200	7400	10,500
Series BL						
PU	400	1250	2100	4200	7400	10,500
Panel Dly	400	1200	2000	4000	7000	10,000
Platform	450	1050	1800	3600	6200	8900
Stake	450	1080	1800	3600	6300	9000
Series BN						
Panel Dly	450	1080	1800	3600	6300	9000
1944-1946						
Series DJ						
Sed Dly	400	1300	2200	4400	7700	11,000
Series BK/CK						
PU	400	1200	2000	4000	7000	10,000
Panel	450	1170	1975	3900	6850	9800
Suburban	400	1200	2000	4000	7000	10,000
Canopy	400	1140	1900	3800	6650	9500

NOTE: The Coupe Express was listed in the DJ Series, but none are believed to have been built. Therefore, no prices are given for this model.

	6	5	4	3	2	1
1946						
Series DJ						
Sed Dly	450	1400	2300	4600	8100	11,500
Series DP						
PU	400	1200	2000	4000	7000	10,000
Panel	450	1150	1900	3850	6700	9600
Canopy	450	1170	1975	3900	6850	9800
Suburban	400	1200	2000	4000	7000	10,000
Series DR						
PU	450	1140	1900	3800	6650	9500
Panel	450	1050	1800	3600	6200	8900
Platform	350	950	1550	3150	5450	7800
Stake	350	975	1600	3200	5500	7900
Series DS						
Exp	350	1000	1650	3350	5800	8300
Panel	350	975	1600	3200	5600	8000
Canopy Exp	350	1000	1650	3300	5750	8200
1947						
Series 1500						
Sed Dly	450	1450	2400	4800	8400	12,000
Series 3100						
PU	400	1250	2100	4200	7400	10,500
Panel	350	1020	1700	3400	5950	8500
Canopy Exp	450	1080	1800	3600	6300	9000
Suburban	950	1100	1850	3700	6450	9200
Series 3600						
PU	350	975	1600	3200	5600	8000
Platform	350	840	1400	2800	4900	7000
Stake	350	860	1450	2900	5050	7200
Series 3800						
PU	350	900	1500	3000	5250	7500
Panel	350	820	1400	2700	4760	6800
Canopy Exp	350	840	1400	2800	4900	7000
Platform	350	820	1400	2700	4760	6800
Stake	350	840	1400	2800	4900	7000
1948						
Series 1500						
Sed Dly	450	1450	2400	4800	8400	12,000
Series 3100						
PU	450	1500	2500	5000	8800	12,500
Panel	450	1080	1800	3600	6300	9000
Canopy Exp	450	1140	1900	3800	6650	9500
Suburban	450	1160	1950	3900	6800	9700
Series 3600						
PU	400	1300	2200	4400	7700	11,000
Platform	350	975	1600	3200	5600	8000
Stake	350	975	1600	3250	5700	8100
Series 3800						
PU	400	1250	2100	4200	7400	10,500
Panel	450	1050	1750	3550	6150	8800
Canopy Exp	450	1080	1800	3600	6300	9000
Platform	350	950	1550	3150	5450	7800
Stake	350	975	1600	3200	5600	8000
1949						
Series 1500						
Sed Dly	450	1450	2400	4800	8400	12,000
Series 3100						
PU	450	1500	2500	5000	8800	12,500
Panel Dly	450	1080	1800	3600	6300	9000
Canopy Exp	450	1140	1900	3800	6650	9500
Suburban Carryall	450	1160	1950	3900	6800	9700
Cantrell Sta Wag	550	1800	3000	6000	10,500	15,000
Olsen Kurbside Van	350	900	1500	3000	5250	7500
Series 3600/3700						
PU	400	1300	2200	4400	7700	11,000
Platform	350	975	1600	3200	5600	8000
Stake Bed	350	975	1600	3250	5700	8100
Series 3800/3900						
PU	400	1250	2100	4200	7400	10,500
Panel Dly	450	1050	1750	3550	6150	8800
Canopy Exp	450	1080	1800	3600	6300	9000
Platform	350	950	1550	3150	5450	7800
Stake Bed	350	975	1600	3200	5600	8000
1950						
Series 1500						
Sed Dly	450	1500	2500	5000	8800	12,600
Series 3100						
PU	450	1500	2500	5000	8800	12,500
Panel Dly	450	1080	1800	3600	6300	9000
Canopy Exp	450	1140	1900	3800	6650	9500
Suburban Carryall	450	1160	1950	3900	6800	9700

	6	5	4	3	2	1
Series 3600/3700						
PU	400	1250	2100	4200	7400	10,500
Platform	350	975	1600	3200	5600	8000
Stake Bed	350	975	1600	3250	5700	8100
Series 3800/3900						
PU	400	1250	2100	4200	7400	10,500
Panel Dly	450	1050	1750	3550	6150	8800
Platform	350	950	1550	3150	5450	7800
Stake Bed	350	975	1600	3200	5600	8000
1951						
Series 1500						
Sed Dly	450	1500	2500	5000	8800	12,600
Series 3100						
PU	450	1500	2500	5000	8800	12,500
Panel Dly	450	1080	1800	3600	6300	9000
Canopy Exp	450	1140	1900	3800	6650	9500
Suburban Carryall	450	1160	1950	3900	6800	9700
Series 3600/3700						
PU	400	1250	2100	4200	7400	10,500
Platform	350	975	1600	3200	5600	8000
Stake Bed	350	975	1600	3250	5700	8100
Series 3800/3900						
PU	400	1250	2100	4200	7400	10,500
Panel Dly	450	1050	1750	3550	6150	8800
Platform	350	950	1550	3150	5450	7800
Stake Bed	350	975	1600	3200	5600	8000
1952						
Series 1500						
Sed Dly	500	1500	2550	5100	8900	12,700
Series 3100						
PU	450	1500	2500	5000	8800	12,500
Panel Dly	350	1040	1700	3450	6000	8600
Canopy Exp	450	1140	1900	3800	6650	9500
Suburban Carryall	450	1160	1950	3900	6800	9700
Series 3600/3700						
PU	400	1250	2100	4200	7400	10,500
Platform	350	975	1600	3200	5600	8000
Stake Bed	350	975	1600	3250	5700	8100
Series 3800/3900						
PU	400	1250	2100	4200	7400	10,500
Panel Dly	450	1050	1750	3550	6150	8800
Platform	350	950	1550	3150	5450	7800
Stake Bed	350	975	1600	3200	5600	8000
1953						
Series 1500						
Sed Dly	500	1550	2600	5200	9100	13,000
Series 3100						
PU	450	1500	2500	5000	8800	12,500
Panel Dly	350	1040	1700	3450	6000	8600
Canopy Exp	450	1140	1900	3800	6650	9500
Suburban Carryall	450	1160	1950	3900	6800	9700
Series 3600/3700						
PU	400	1250	2100	4200	7400	10,500
Platform	350	975	1600	3200	5600	8000
Stake Bed	350	975	1600	3250	5700	8100
Series 3800/3900						
PU	400	1250	2100	4200	7400	10,500
Panel Dly	450	1050	1750	3550	6150	8800
Platform	350	950	1550	3150	5450	7800
Stake Bed	350	975	1600	3200	5600	8000
1954						
Series 1500						
Sed Dly	500	1550	2600	5200	9100	13,000
Series 3100						
PU	500	1550	2600	5200	9100	13,000
Panel	400	1200	2000	4000	7000	10,000
Canopy	450	1140	1900	3800	6650	9500
Suburban	400	1250	2100	4200	7400	10,500
Series 3600						
PU	400	1300	2200	4400	7700	11,000
Platform	350	975	1600	3250	5700	8100
Stake	350	1000	1650	3350	5800	8300
Series 3800						
PU	400	1300	2200	4400	7700	11,000
Panel	450	1080	1800	3600	6300	9000
Canopy	450	1080	1800	3600	6300	9000
Platform	350	975	1600	3200	5600	8000
Stake	350	975	1600	3250	5700	8100
1955						
First Series						
Series 3100						
PU	500	1550	2600	5200	9100	13,000
Panel	400	1200	2000	4000	7000	10,000
Canopy	450	1140	1900	3800	6650	9500
Suburban	400	1250	2100	4200	7400	10,500
Series 3600						
PU	400	1300	2200	4400	7700	11,000
Platform	350	975	1600	3250	5700	8100
Stake	350	1000	1650	3350	5800	8300
Series 3800						
PU	450	1080	1800	3600	6300	11,000
Panel	350	975	1600	3250	5700	9000
Canopy	450	1080	1800	3600	6300	9000
Platform	350	975	1600	3200	5600	8000
Stake	350	975	1600	3250	5700	8100
Second Series						
Series 1500						
Sed Dly	550	1700	2800	5600	9800	14,000
Series 3100						
PU	500	1550	2600	5200	9100	13,000
Cus Cab PU	500	1600	2700	5400	9500	13,500
Panel Dly	400	1200	2000	4000	7000	10,000
Suburban	400	1200	2050	4100	7100	10,200
Cameo Carrier	650	2050	3400	6800	11,900	17,000
Cantrell Sta Wag	550	1700	2800	5600	9800	14,000
Series 3400/3500/3700						
Walk-In Dly Van	350	840	1400	2800	4900	7000
School Bus	200	720	1200	2400	4200	6000
Series 3200						
PU (LBx)	350	1020	1700	3400	5900	8400
Series 3600						
PU	350	975	1600	3200	5600	8000
Cus Cab PU	350	1020	1700	3400	5950	8500
Platform	350	840	1400	2800	4900	7000
Platform & Stake	350	900	1500	3000	5250	7500
Cantrell Sta Wag	550	1700	2800	5600	9800	14,000

Standard Catalog of Chevrolet Trucks

Series 3800	6	5	4	3	2	1
PU	350	950	1550	3100	5400	7700
Panel Dly	350	1020	1700	3400	5950	8500
Platform	350	770	1300	2550	4480	6400
Platform & Stake	350	800	1350	2700	4700	6700

NOTE: 1955-up prices based on top of the line models.
   Deduct 10 percent for 6-cyl.

1956

Series 1500	6	5	4	3	2	1
Sed Dly	500	1550	2600	5200	9100	13,000
Series 3100						
PU	450	1450	2400	4800	8400	12,000
Cus Cab PU	450	1500	2500	5000	8800	12,500
Panel Dly	450	1080	1800	3600	6300	9000
Suburban	400	1200	2000	4000	7000	10,000
Cameo Carrier	650	2050	3400	6800	11,900	17,000
Cantrell Sta Wag	550	1700	2800	5600	9800	14,000
Series 3400/3500/3700						
Walk-In Dly Van	350	840	1400	2800	4900	7000
School Bus	200	720	1200	2400	4200	6000
Series 3200						
PU (LBx)	350	1020	1700	3400	5900	8400
Series 3600						
PU	350	975	1600	3200	5600	8000
Cus Cab PU	350	1020	1700	3400	5950	8500
Platform	350	840	1400	2800	4900	7000
Platform & Stake	350	880	1500	2950	5180	7400
Cantrell Sta Wag	550	1700	2800	5600	9800	14,000
Series 3800						
PU	350	950	1550	3100	5400	7700
Panel Dly	350	1020	1700	3400	5950	8500
Platform	350	770	1300	2550	4480	6400
Platform & Stake	350	800	1350	2700	4700	6700

NOTE: 1955-up prices based on top of the line models.
   Deduct 10 percent for 6-cyl.

1957

Series 1500	6	5	4	3	2	1
Sed Dly	550	1750	2900	5800	10,200	14,500
Series 3100						
PU	500	1550	2600	5200	9100	13,000
Cus Cab PU	500	1600	2700	5400	9500	13,500
Panel Dly	450	1080	1800	3600	6300	9000
Suburban	400	1300	2200	4400	7700	11,000
Cameo Carrier	650	2050	3400	6800	11,900	17,000
Cantrell Sta Wag	550	1750	2900	5800	10,200	14,500
Series 3400/3500/3700						
Walk-In Dly Van	350	840	1400	2800	4900	7000
School Bus	200	720	1200	2400	4200	6000
Series 3200						
PU (LBx)	350	1020	1700	3400	5900	8400

Series 3600	6	5	4	3	2	1
PU	350	975	1600	3200	5600	8000
Cus Cab PU	350	1020	1700	3400	5950	8500
Platform	350	840	1400	2800	4900	7000
Platform & Stake	350	880	1500	2950	5180	7400
Cantrell Sta Wag	550	1700	2800	5600	9800	14,000
Series 3800						
PU	350	975	1600	3200	5600	8000
Panel Dly	350	1020	1700	3400	5950	8500
Platform	350	770	1300	2550	4480	6400
Platform & Stake	350	800	1350	2700	4700	6700

NOTE: 1955-up prices based on top of the line models.
   Deduct 10 percent for 6-cyl.

1958

Series 1100	6	5	4	3	2	1
Sed Dly	450	1400	2300	4600	8100	11,500
Series 3100						
Stepside PU	450	1080	1800	3600	6300	9000
Fleetside PU	450	1140	1900	3800	6650	9500
Cameo PU	550	1800	3000	6000	10,500	15,000
Panel	350	1020	1700	3400	5900	8400
Suburban	350	1040	1750	3500	6100	8700
Series 3200						
Stepside (LBx)	350	1020	1700	3400	5900	8400
Fleetside (LBx)	350	1040	1700	3450	6000	8600
Series 3400/3500						
Step Van (104" wb)	350	975	1600	3200	5600	8000
Step Van (125" wb)	350	1000	1650	3300	5750	8200
Series 3600						
Stepside PU	350	975	1600	3200	5600	8000
Fleetside PU	350	1000	1650	3350	5800	8300
Stake	350	840	1400	2800	4900	7000
Series 3700						
Step Van (137" wb)	350	950	1500	3050	5300	7600
Series 3800						
PU	350	880	1500	2950	5180	7400
Panel	350	860	1450	2900	5050	7200
Stake	350	840	1400	2800	4900	7000

NOTE: 1955-up prices based on top of the line models.
   Deduct 10 percent for 6-cyl.

1959

Series 1100	6	5	4	3	2	1
Sed Dly	400	1250	2100	4200	7400	10,500
El Camino	450	1400	2300	4600	8100	11,500
Series 3100						
Stepside PU	450	1080	1800	3600	6300	9000
Fleetside PU	450	1140	1900	3800	6650	9500
Cameo PU	550	1700	2800	5600	9800	14,000
Panel	350	1020	1700	3400	5900	8400
Suburban	350	1040	1700	3450	6000	8600

1937 Chevrolet 1/2 Ton Pickup Truck (WP&L)

	6	5	4	3	2	1
Series 3200						
Stepside PU	350	1020	1700	3400	5900	8400
Fleetside PU	350	1040	1700	3450	6000	8600
Series 3400/3500						
Panel (104" wb)	350	975	1600	3200	5500	7900
Panel (125" wb)	350	975	1600	3200	5600	8000
Series 3600						
Stepside PU	350	975	1600	3200	5500	7900
Fleetside PU	350	975	1600	3250	5700	8100
Series 3700						
Panel (137" wb)	350	950	1500	3050	5300	7600
Series 3800						
PU	350	880	1500	2950	5180	7400
Panel	350	840	1400	2800	4900	7000
Stake	350	830	1400	2950	4830	6900

NOTE: 1955-up prices based on top of the line models.
Deduct 10 percent for 6-cyl.

1960

	6	5	4	3	2	1
Series 1100						
Sed Dly	400	1300	2200	4400	7700	11,000
El Camino	450	1400	2300	4600	8100	11,500
Series C14 - (1/2-Ton)						
Stepside PU	450	1080	1800	3600	6300	9000
Fleetside PU	450	1140	1900	3800	6650	9500
Panel	350	1020	1700	3400	5900	8400
Suburban	350	1040	1750	3500	6100	8700
Series C15 "Long Box" - (1/2-Ton)						
Stepside PU	350	1020	1700	3400	5900	8400
Fleetside PU	350	1040	1700	3450	6000	8600
Series C25 - (3/4-Ton)						
Stepside PU	350	1020	1700	3400	5900	8400
Fleetside PU	350	1040	1700	3450	6000	8600
8-ft. Stake	350	830	1400	2950	4830	6900
Series C36 - (1-Ton)						
Stepside	350	880	1500	2950	5180	7400
Panel	350	840	1400	2800	4900	7000
9-ft. Stake	350	830	1400	2950	4830	6900
Step Vans						
Walk-In Dly (104" wb)	350	975	1600	3200	5500	7900
Walk-In Dly (125" wb)	350	975	1600	3200	5600	8000
Walk-In Dly (137" wb)	350	950	1500	3050	5300	7600

NOTE: 1955-up prices based on top of the line models.
Deduct 10 percent for 6-cyl.

1961

	6	5	4	3	2	1
Corvair Series 95						
Loadside	200	670	1200	2300	4060	5800
Rampside	200	730	1250	2450	4270	6100
Corvan Series						
Corvan Panel	200	720	1200	2400	4200	6000
Greenbriar Spt Van	350	780	1300	2600	4550	6500
Fleetside Pickups						
C10 PU (SBx)	400	1200	2000	4000	7000	10,000
C10 PU (LBx)	450	1160	1950	3900	6800	9700
K10 PU (SBx)	450	1150	1900	3850	6700	9600
K10 PU (LBx)	450	1140	1900	3800	6650	9500
C20 PU (LBx)	350	1020	1700	3400	5900	8400
K20 PU (LBx)	350	975	1600	3250	5700	8100
Stepside Pickups						
C10 PU (SBx)	450	1160	1950	3900	6800	9700
C10 PU (LBx)	450	1150	1900	3850	6700	9600
K10 PU (SBx)	450	1140	1900	3800	6650	9500
K10 PU (LBx)	450	1130	1900	3800	6600	9400
C20 PU (LBx)	350	1000	1650	3350	5800	8300
K20 PU (LBx)	350	975	1600	3200	5600	8000
C30 PU (8-1/2 ft. bed)	350	975	1600	3200	5500	7900
Step Vans						
P10 Walk-In	200	670	1200	2300	4060	5800
P20 Walk-In	200	700	1200	2350	4130	5900
P30 Walk-In	200	720	1200	2400	4200	6000
Panel/Suburban/Stake-Bed						
C10 Panel	200	685	1150	2300	3990	5700
C10 Suburban	350	830	1400	2950	4830	6900
C20 Panel	200	650	1100	2150	3780	5400
C20 Suburban	350	800	1350	2700	4700	6700
C20 Stake	200	650	1100	2150	3780	5400
C30 Panel (10-1/2 ft. bed)	200	660	1100	2200	3850	5500
C30 Stake	200	660	1100	2200	3850	5500

NOTE: 1955-up prices based on top of the line models. C is conventional drive model. K is 4-wheel drive (4WD) model. 10 is the 1/2-Ton series. 30 is the 1-Ton series. Short box has 6-1/2 ft. bed. Long box has 8-ft. bed.

1962

	6	5	4	3	2	1
Corvair Series 95						
Loadside	200	670	1200	2300	4060	5800
Rampside	200	730	1250	2450	4270	6100
Corvan Series						
Corvan Panel Van	200	685	1150	2300	3990	5700
Greenbriar Spt Van	350	780	1300	2600	4550	6500
Fleetside Pickups						
C10 PU (SBx)	450	1170	1975	3900	6850	9800
C10 PU (LBx)	450	1160	1950	3900	6800	9700
K10 PU (SBx)	450	1150	1900	3850	6700	9600
K10 PU (LBx)	450	1140	1900	3800	6650	9500
C20 PU (LBx)	350	1020	1700	3400	5900	8400
K20 PU (LBx)	350	975	1600	3250	5700	8100
Stepside Pickups						
C10 PU (SBx)	450	1160	1950	3900	6800	9700
C10 PU (LBx)	450	1150	1900	3850	6700	9600
K10 PU (SBx)	450	1140	1900	3800	6650	9500
K10 PU (LBx)	450	1130	1900	3800	6600	9400
C20 PU (LBx)	350	1000	1650	3350	5800	8300
K20 PU (LBx)	350	975	1600	3200	5600	8000
C30 PU (8-1/2 ft. bed)	350	975	1600	3200	5500	7900
Step Vans						
P10 Walk-In	200	670	1200	2300	4060	5800
P20 Walk-In	200	700	1200	2350	4130	5900
P30 Walk-In	200	720	1200	2400	4200	6000
Panel/Suburban/Stake-Bed						
C10 Panel	200	685	1150	2300	3990	5700
C10 Suburban	350	830	1400	2950	4830	6900
K10 Panel	200	650	1100	2150	3780	5400
K10 Suburban	350	800	1350	2700	4700	6700
C20 Stake	200	650	1100	2150	3780	5400
C30 Panel (10-1/2 ft. bed)	200	660	1100	2200	3850	5500
C30 Stake	200	660	1100	2200	3850	5500

NOTE: 1955-up prices based on top of the line models. C is conventional drive model. K is 4-wheel drive (4WD) model. 10 is 1/2-Ton series. 20 is 3/4-Ton series. 30 is 1-Ton series. Short box has 6-1/2 ft. bed. Long box has 8-ft. bed.

1963

	6	5	4	3	2	1
Corvair Series 95						
Loadside	200	670	1200	2300	4060	5800
Rampside	200	730	1250	2450	4270	6100
Corvan Series						
Corvan Panel Van	200	685	1150	2300	3990	5700
Greenbriar Spt Van	350	790	1350	2650	4620	6600
Fleetside Pickups						
C10 PU (SBx)	450	1170	1975	3900	6850	9800
C10 PU (LBx)	450	1160	1950	3900	6800	9700
K10 PU (SBx)	450	1150	1900	3850	6700	9600
K10 PU (LBx)	450	1140	1900	3800	6650	9500
C20 PU (LBx)	350	1020	1700	3400	5900	8400
K20 PU (LBx)	350	975	1600	3250	5700	8100
Stepside Pickups						
C10 PU (SBx)	450	1160	1950	3900	6800	9700
C10 PU (LBx)	450	1150	1900	3850	6700	9600
K10 PU (SBx)	450	1140	1900	3800	6650	9500
K10 PU (LBx)	450	1130	1900	3800	6600	9400
C20 PU (LBx)	350	1000	1650	3350	5800	8300
K20 PU (LBx)	350	975	1600	3200	5600	8000
C30 PU (8-1/2 ft. bed)	350	975	1600	3200	5500	7900
Step Vans						
P10 Walk-In	200	670	1200	2300	4060	5800
P20 Walk-In	200	700	1200	2350	4130	5900
P30 Walk-In	200	720	1200	2400	4200	6000
Panel/Suburban/Stake-Bed						
C10 Panel	200	685	1150	2300	3990	5700
C10 Suburban	350	830	1400	2950	4830	6900
K10 Panel	200	650	1100	2150	3780	5400
K10 Suburban	350	800	1350	2700	4700	6700
C20 Stake	200	650	1100	2150	3780	5400
C30 Panel (10-1/2 ft. bed)	200	660	1100	2200	3850	5500
C30 Stake	200	660	1100	2200	3850	5500

NOTE: 1955-up prices based on top of the line models. C is conventional drive model. K is 4-wheel drive (4WD) model. 10 is 1/2-Ton series. 20 is 3/4-Ton series. 30 is the 1-Ton series. Short box has 6-1/2 ft. bed. Long box has 8-ft. bed.

1964

	6	5	4	3	2	1
El Camino						
Spt PU	400	1200	2000	4000	7000	10,000
Cus Spt PU	400	1250	2100	4200	7400	10,500
Corvair Series 95						
Loadside	200	670	1200	2300	4060	5800
Rampside	200	730	1250	2450	4270	6100
Corvan Series						
Panel Van	200	685	1150	2300	3990	5700
Greenbriar Spt Van	350	800	1350	2700	4700	6700
Fleetside Pickups						
C10 PU (SBx)	450	1170	1975	3900	6850	9800
C10 PU (LBx)	450	1160	1950	3900	6800	9700
K10 PU (SBx)	450	1150	1900	3850	6700	9600
K10 PU (LBx)	450	1140	1900	3800	6650	9500
C20 PU (LBx)	350	1020	1700	3400	5900	8400
K20 PU (LBx)	350	975	1600	3250	5700	8100
Stepside Pickups						
C10 PU (SBx)	450	1160	1950	3900	6800	9700
C10 PU (LBx)	450	1150	1900	3850	6700	9600
K10 PU (SBx)	450	1140	1900	3800	6650	9500
K10 PU (LBx)	450	1130	1900	3800	6600	9400
C20 PU (LBx)	350	1000	1650	3350	5800	8300
C30 PU (8-1/2 ft. bed)	350	975	1600	3200	5500	7900
G10 Chevy Van Series						
Panel Van	200	730	1250	2450	4270	6100
Step Van Series						
P10 Walk-In	200	670	1200	2300	4060	5800
P20 Walk-In	200	700	1200	2350	4130	5900
P30 Walk-In	200	720	1200	2400	4200	6000
Panel/Suburban/Stake-Bed						
C10 Panel	200	685	1150	2300	3990	5700
C10 Suburban	350	830	1400	2950	4830	6900
K10 Panel	200	650	1100	2150	3780	5400
K10 Suburban	350	800	1350	2700	4700	6700
C20 Stake	200	650	1100	2150	3780	5400
C30 Panel (10-1/2 ft. bed)	200	660	1100	2200	3850	5500
C30 Stake	200	660	1100	2200	3850	5500

NOTE: 1955-up prices based on top of the line models. C is conventional drive model. K is 4-wheel drive (4WD) model. 10 is 1/2-Ton series. 20 is 3/4-Ton series. 30 is 1-Ton series. Short box has 6-1/2 ft. bed. Long box has 8-ft. bed.

1965

	6	5	4	3	2	1
El Camino						
Spt PU	400	1200	2000	4000	7000	10,000
Cus Spt PU	400	1250	2100	4200	7400	10,500
Corvair Series 95						
Greenbriar Spt Van	350	820	1400	2700	4760	6800
Fleetside Pickups						
C10 PU (SBx)	450	1170	1975	3900	6850	9800
C10 PU (LBx)	450	1160	1950	3900	6800	9700
K10 PU (SBx)	450	1150	1900	3850	6700	9600
K10 PU (LBx)	450	1140	1900	3800	6650	9500
C20 PU (LBx)	350	1020	1700	3400	5900	8400
K20 PU (LBx)	350	975	1600	3250	5700	8100
Stepside Pickups						
C10 PU (SBx)	450	1160	1950	3900	6800	9700
C10 PU (LBx)	450	1150	1900	3850	6700	9600
K10 PU (SBx)	450	1140	1900	3800	6650	9500
K10 PU (LBx)	450	1130	1900	3800	6600	9400
C20 PU (LBx)	350	1000	1650	3350	5800	8300
C30 PU (8-1/2 ft. bed)	350	975	1600	3200	5500	7900
G12 Chevy Van Series						
Panel Van	200	700	1200	2350	4130	5900
Spt Van	200	720	1200	2400	4200	6000
Cus Spt Van	200	730	1250	2450	4270	6100
DeL Spt Van	200	745	1250	2500	4340	6200
Step Van Series						
P10 Panel	200	670	1200	2300	4060	5800
P20 Panel	200	700	1200	2350	4130	5900
P30 Panel	200	720	1200	2400	4200	6000
Panel/Suburban/Stake-Bed						
C10 Panel	200	685	1150	2300	3990	5700
C10 Suburban	350	830	1400	2950	4830	6900
K10 Panel	200	650	1100	2150	3780	5400
K10 Suburban	350	800	1350	2700	4700	6700
C20 Stake	200	650	1100	2150	3780	5400
C30 Panel	200	660	1100	2200	3850	5500
C30 Stake	200	660	1100	2200	3850	5500

NOTE: Greenbriar remained available in 1965. 1955-up prices based on top of the line models. C is conventional drive model. K is 4-wheel drive (4WD) model. 10 is 1/2-Ton series. 20 is 3/4-Ton series. 30 is 1-Ton series. Short box has 6-1/2 ft. bed. Long box has 8-ft. bed.

1949 Chevrolet 3/4 Ton Stake Truck (CMD)

	6	5	4	3	2	1
1966						
El Camino						
Spt PU	400	1200	2000	4000	7000	10,000
Cus Spt PU	400	1250	2100	4200	7400	10,500
Fleetside Pickup Series C10/C20						
C14 PU (SBx)	450	1170	1975	3900	6850	9800
C15 PU (LBx)	450	1160	1950	3900	6800	9700
K14 PU (SBx)	450	1150	1900	3850	6700	9600
K15 PU (LBx)	450	1140	1900	3800	6650	9500
C25 PU (LBx)	350	1020	1700	3400	5900	8400
K25 PU (LBx)	350	975	1600	3250	5700	8100
Stepside Pickup Series C10/C20/C30						
C14 PU (SBx)	450	1160	1950	3900	6800	9700
C15 PU (LBx)	450	1150	1900	3850	6700	9600
K14 PU (SBx)	450	1140	1900	3800	6650	9500
K15 PU (LBx)	450	1130	1900	3800	6600	9400
C25 PU (LBx)	350	1000	1650	3350	5800	8300
K25 PU (LBx)	350	975	1600	3200	5600	8000
1-Ton PU (8-1/2 ft. bed)	350	975	1600	3200	5500	7900
Chevy Van Series						
G12 Panel Van	200	700	1200	2350	4130	5900
G12 Spt Van	200	720	1200	2400	4200	6000
G12 Cus Spt Van	200	730	1250	2450	4270	6100
G12 DeL Spt Van	200	745	1250	2500	4340	6200
Step Van Series						
P10 Panel	150	500	800	1550	2700	3900
P20 Panel	150	500	800	1600	2800	4000
P30 Panel	150	550	850	1650	2900	4100
Panel/Suburban/Stake-Bed						
C14 Panel	150	475	775	1500	2650	3800
C14 Suburban	200	675	1000	2000	3500	5000
K14 Panel	125	450	700	1400	2450	3500
K14 Suburban	150	650	975	1950	3350	4800
C25 Stake	125	450	700	1400	2450	3500
C36 Panel	125	450	750	1450	2500	3600
C36 Stake	125	450	750	1450	2500	3600

NOTE: C is conventional drive model. K is 4-wheel drive (4WD) model. 14 is 1/2-Ton Short box (6-1/2 ft. bed). 15 is 1/2-Ton Long box (8-ft. bed). 25 is 3/4-Ton. 36 is 1-Ton.

	6	5	4	3	2	1
1967						
El Camino Series						
Spt PU	400	1200	2000	4000	7000	10,000
Cus Spt PU	450	1450	2400	4800	8400	10,500
Fleetside Pickups						
C10 PU (SBx)	450	1450	2400	4800	8400	12,000
C10 PU (LBx)	400	1300	2200	4400	7700	11,000
K10 PU (SBx)	400	1300	2150	4300	7500	10,700
K10 PU (LBx)	400	1250	2100	4200	7400	10,500
C20 PU (LBx)	450	1170	1975	3900	6850	9800
C20 PU (8-1/2 ft. bed)	450	1160	1950	3900	6800	9700
K20 PU (LBx)	450	1160	1950	3900	6800	9700
K20 PU (8-1/2 ft. bed)	450	1150	1900	3850	6700	9600
C30 PU (8-1/2 ft. bed)	450	1050	1750	3550	6150	8800
Stepside Pickups						
C10 PU (SBx)	400	1300	2200	4400	7700	11,000
C10 PU (LBx)	400	1250	2100	4200	7400	10,600

	6	5	4	3	2	1
C20 PU (LBx)	450	1160	1950	3900	6800	9700
K20 PU (LBx)	450	1150	1900	3850	6700	9600
C30 PU (8-1/2 ft. bed)	450	1050	1750	3550	6150	8800
Chevy Van Series						
G10 Panel Van	350	820	1400	2700	4760	6800
G10 Spt Van	350	840	1400	2800	4900	7000
G10 Cus Spt Van	350	870	1450	2900	5100	7300
G10 DeL Spt Van	350	950	1500	3050	5300	7600
G20 Panel Van	350	790	1350	2650	4620	6600
G20 Spt Van	350	820	1400	2700	4760	6800
G20 Cus Spt Van	350	840	1400	2800	4900	7000
G20 DeL Spt Van	350	870	1450	2900	5100	7300
Step Van Series (Code "P")						
P10 Steel Panel	350	820	1400	2700	4760	6800
P20 Steel Panel	350	800	1350	2700	4700	6700
P30 Steel Panel	350	790	1350	2650	4620	6600
Panel/Suburbans/Stakes						
C10 Panel	350	840	1400	2800	4900	7000
C10 Suburban	350	1000	1650	3350	5800	8300
C20 Stake	350	860	1450	2900	5050	7200
C20 Panel	350	820	1400	2700	4760	6800
C20 Suburban	350	950	1550	3150	5450	7800
C30 Stake	350	870	1450	2900	5100	7300

NOTE: 1955-up prices based on top of the line models. Add 5 percent for 4WD. C is conventional drive model. K is 4-wheel drive (4WD) model. 10 is 1/2-Ton series. 20 is 3/4-Ton series. 30 is 1-Ton series. Short box has 6-1/2 ft. bed. Long box has 8-ft. bed.

	6	5	4	3	2	1
1968						
El Camino Series						
Spt PU	400	1200	2000	4000	7000	10,000
Cus Spt PU	400	1250	2100	4200	7400	10,500
NOTE: Add 15 percent for SS-396 option.						
Fleetside PU						
C10 PU (SBx)	450	1450	2400	4800	8400	12,000
C10 PU (LBx)	400	1300	2200	4400	7700	11,000
K10 PU (SBx)	400	1300	2150	4300	7500	10,700
K10 PU (LBx)	400	1250	2100	4200	7400	10,500
C20 PU (LBx)	450	1170	1975	3900	6850	9800
C20 PU (8-1/2 ft. bed)	450	1160	1950	3900	6800	9700
K20 PU (LBx)	450	1160	1950	3900	6800	9700
K20 PU (8-1/2 ft. bed)	450	1150	1900	3850	6700	9600
Stepside Pickups						
C10 PU (SBx)	4200	13,450	22,400	44,800	78,400	11,000
C10 PU (LBx)	400	1250	2100	4200	7400	10,600
K10 PU (SBx)	400	1250	2100	4200	7400	10,500
K10 PU (LBx)	400	1250	2100	4200	7300	10,400
C20 PU (LBx)	450	1160	1950	3900	6800	9700
K20 PU (LBx)	450	1150	1900	3850	6700	9600
C30 PU (8-1/2 ft. bed)	450	1050	1750	3550	6150	8800
Chevy Van Series						
G10 Panel Van	350	820	1400	2700	4760	6800
G10 Spt Van	350	840	1400	2800	4900	7000
G10 Cus Spt Van	350	870	1450	2900	5100	7300
G10 DeL Spt Van	350	950	1500	3050	5300	7600
G20 Panel Van	350	790	1350	2650	4620	6600
G20 Spt Van	350	820	1400	2700	4760	6800

	6	5	4	3	2	1
G20 Cus Spt Van	350	840	1400	2800	4900	7000
G20 DeL Spt Van	350	870	1450	2900	5100	7300
Step Van Series						
P10 Panel	350	820	1400	2700	4760	6800
P20 Panel	350	800	1350	2700	4700	6700
P30 Panel	350	790	1350	2650	4620	6600
Panel/Suburban/Stake-Bed						
C10 Panel	350	840	1400	2800	4900	7000
C10 Suburban	350	1000	1650	3350	5800	8300
C20 Stake	350	820	1400	2700	4760	6800

NOTE: 1955-up prices based on top of the line models. C is conventional drive model. K is 4-wheel drive (4WD) model. 10 is 1/2-Ton series. 20 is 3/4-Ton series. 30 is 1-Ton series. Short box has 6-1/2 ft. bed. Long box has 8-ft. bed.

1969

	6	5	4	3	2	1
El Camino Series						
Spt PU	400	1300	2200	4400	7700	11,000
Cus Spt PU	450	1400	2300	4600	8100	11,500

NOTE: Add 15 percent for SS-396 option.

	6	5	4	3	2	1
Blazer Series - (4WD)						
Blazer	450	1450	2400	4800	8400	12,000
Fleetside Series						
C10 PU (SBx)	500	1550	2600	5200	9100	13,000
C10 PU (LBx)	450	1500	2500	5000	8800	12,500
K10 PU (SBx)	400	1300	2200	4400	7700	11,000
K10 PU (LBx)	400	1300	2150	4300	7600	10,800
C20 PU (LBx)	450	1170	1975	3900	6850	9800
C20 PU (long horn)	450	1150	1900	3850	6700	9600
K20 PU (LBx)	400	1250	2100	4200	7400	10,600
K20 PU (long horn)	400	1300	2150	4300	7500	10,700
C30 PU (long horn)	450	1050	1750	3550	6150	8800
Stepside Series						
C10 PU (SBx)	400	1300	2200	4400	7700	11,000
C10 PU (LBx)	400	1250	2100	4200	7400	10,500
K10 PU (SBx)	400	1300	2200	4400	7700	11,000
K10 PU (LBx)	400	1300	2150	4300	7500	10,700
C20 PU (LBx)	400	1300	2150	4300	7600	10,800
C20 PU (long horn)	400	1300	2150	4300	7500	10,700
K20 PU (LBx)	400	1300	2150	4300	7500	10,700
K20 PU (long horn)	400	1250	2100	4200	7400	10,600
C30 PU (long horn)	450	1050	1750	3550	6150	8800
Chevy Van Series G10 - (1/2-Ton) - (90" wb)						
Panel Van	350	840	1400	2800	4900	7000
Spt Van	350	950	1500	3050	5300	7600
Cus Spt Van	350	900	1500	3000	5250	7500
DeL Spt Van	350	950	1550	3100	5400	7700
Chevy Van Series G20 - (3/4-Ton) - (108" wb)						
Panel Van	350	820	1400	2700	4760	6800
Spt Van	350	880	1500	2950	5180	7400
Cus Spt Van	350	870	1450	2900	5100	7300
DeL Spt Van	350	900	1500	3000	5250	7500
Step Vans						
P10 - (1/2-Ton) - (102"wb)	350	820	1400	2700	4760	6800
P20 - (3/4-Ton) - (125"wb)	200	700	1050	2050	3600	5100
P30 - (1-Ton) - (125"wb)	200	700	1050	2100	3650	5200
Panel/Suburban Series C10/K10 - (115" wb)						
C10 Panel	450	1050	1750	3550	6150	8800
C10 Suburban	400	1250	2050	4100	7200	10,300
K10 Panel	350	1040	1700	3450	6000	8600
K10 Suburban	400	1200	2000	4000	7100	10,100
Panel/Suburban Series C20/K20 - (127" wb)						
C20 Panel	350	1040	1700	3450	6000	8600
C20 Suburban	450	1120	1875	3750	6500	9300
K20 Panel	350	1020	1700	3400	5900	8400
K20 Suburban	450	1090	1800	3650	6400	9100

NOTE: 1955-up prices based on top of the line models. C is conventional drive model. K is 4-wheel drive (4WD) model. 10 is 1/2-Ton series. 20 is 3/4-Ton series. 30 is 1-Ton series. Short box pickup has 6-1/2 ft. bed and 115" wb. Long box pickup has 8-ft. bed and 127" wb. Long horn pickup has 8-1/2 to 9-ft. bed and 133" wb.

1970

	6	5	4	3	2	1
El Camino Series						
Spt PU	450	1400	2300	4600	8100	11,500
Cus Spt PU	450	1400	2300	4600	8100	11,500

NOTE: Add 15 percent for SS-396 option.

	6	5	4	3	2	1
Blazer Series K10 - (4WD)						
Blazer	400	1300	2200	4400	7700	11,000
Fleetside Pickups						
C10 PU (SBx)	500	1550	2600	5200	9100	13,000
C10 PU (LBx)	450	1500	2500	5000	8800	12,500
K10 PU (SBx)	400	1300	2200	4400	7700	11,000
K10 PU (LBx)	400	1300	2150	4300	7600	10,800
C20 PU (LBx)	450	1170	1975	3900	6850	9800
C20 PU (long horn)	450	1150	1900	3850	6700	9600
K20 PU (LBx)	400	1250	2100	4200	7400	10,600
K20 PU (long horn)	400	1300	2150	4300	7500	10,700
C30 PU (long horn)	450	1050	1750	3550	6150	8800
Stepside Pickups						
C10 PU (SBx)	450	1400	2300	4600	8100	11,500
C10 PU (LBx)	400	1300	2200	4400	7700	11,000
K10 PU (SBx)	400	1300	2200	4400	7600	10,900
K10 PU (LBx)	400	1300	2150	4300	7500	10,700
C20 PU (LBx)	400	1300	2150	4300	7600	10,800
K20 PU (LBx)	400	1300	2150	4300	7500	10,700
C30 PU (long horn)	450	1050	1750	3550	6150	8800
Chevy Van Series G10 - (1/2-Ton) - (90" wb)						
Panel Van	350	840	1400	2800	4900	7000
Spt Van	350	950	1500	3050	5300	7600
Cus Spt Van	350	900	1500	3000	5250	7500
DeL Spt Van	350	950	1550	3100	5400	7700
Chevy Van Series G20 - (3/4-Ton) - (108" wb)						
Panel Van	350	820	1400	2700	4760	6800
Spt Van	350	880	1500	2950	5180	7400
Cus Spt Van	350	870	1450	2900	5100	7300
DeL Spt Van	350	870	1450	2900	5100	7300
Step Vans						
P10 - (102" wb)	350	820	1400	2700	4760	6800
P20 - (125" wb)	200	700	1050	2050	3600	5100
P30 - (125" wb)	200	700	1050	2100	3650	5200
Panel/Suburban Series C10/K10 - (115" wb)						
C10 Panel	350	840	1400	2800	4900	7000
C10 Suburban	350	1020	1700	3400	5950	8500
K10 Panel	350	820	1400	2700	4760	6800
K10 Suburban	350	1000	1650	3350	5800	8300
Panel/Suburban Series C20/K20 - (127" wb)						
C20 Panel	350	820	1400	2700	4760	6800
C20 Suburban	350	900	1500	3000	5250	7500
K20 Panel	350	790	1350	2650	4620	6600
K20 Suburban	350	870	1450	2900	5100	7300

	6	5	4	3	2	1
Series C30 - (133" wb)						
1-Ton Stake (9-ft. bed)	200	720	1200	2400	4200	6000

NOTE: C is conventional drive model. K is 4-wheel drive (4WD) model. 10 is 1/2-Ton series. 20 is 3/4-Ton series. 30 is 1-Ton series. Short box pickup has 6-1/2 ft. bed and 115" wb. Long box pickup has 8-ft. bed and 127" wb. Long horn pickup has 8-1/2 to 9-ft. bed and 133" wb.

1971

	6	5	4	3	2	1
Vega Panel Series						
Panel Exp	200	675	1000	2000	3500	5000
El Camino (V-8)						
Spt PU	400	1300	2200	4400	7700	11,000
Cus Spt PU	450	1400	2300	4600	8100	11,500
Blazer Series K10 - (4WD)						
Blazer	450	1400	2300	4600	8100	11,500
Fleetside Pickups						
C10 PU (SBx)	500	1600	2700	5400	9500	13,500
C10 PU (LBx)	500	1550	2600	5200	9100	13,000
K10 PU (SBx)	450	1400	2300	4600	8100	11,500
K10 PU (LBx)	400	1350	2250	4500	7900	11,300
C20 PU (LBx)	400	1300	2150	4300	7600	10,800
C20 PU (long horn)	400	1250	2100	4200	7400	10,500
K20 PU (LBx)	400	1250	2100	4200	7400	10,600
K20 PU (long horn)	400	1300	2150	4300	7500	10,700
C30 PU (long horn)	450	1050	1750	3550	6150	8800
Stepside Pickups						
C10 PU (SBx)	450	1400	2300	4600	8100	11,500
C10 PU (LBx)	400	1300	2200	4400	7700	11,000
K10 PU (SBx)	400	1250	2100	4200	7400	10,600
K10 PU (LBx)	400	1250	2050	4100	7200	10,300
C20 PU (LBx)	400	1250	2050	4100	7200	10,300
K20 PU (LBx)	400	1200	2050	4100	7100	10,200
C30 PU (long horn)	400	1200	2000	4000	7100	10,100
Chevy Van Series G10 - (1/2-Ton) - (110" wb)						
Panel Van	350	975	1600	3200	5600	8000
Spt Van	350	1000	1650	3350	5800	8300
Beauville	450	1050	1750	3550	6150	8800
Chevy Van Series G20 - (3/4-Ton) - (110" wb)						
Panel Van	350	900	1500	3000	5250	7500
Spt Van	350	975	1600	3250	5700	8100
Beauville	350	1000	1650	3350	5800	8300
Chevy Van Series G30 - (1-Ton) - (110" wb)						
Panel Van	350	870	1450	2900	5100	7300
Spt Van	350	900	1500	3000	5250	7500
Beauville	350	950	1550	3150	5450	7800
Step Vans						
P10 Step Van	350	840	1400	2800	4900	7000
P20 Step Van	350	850	1450	2850	4970	7100
P30 Step Van	350	860	1450	2900	5050	7200
Panels/Suburbans/Stakes						
C10 Suburban	400	1300	2200	4400	7700	11,000
K10 Suburban	450	1140	1900	3800	6650	9500
C20 Suburban	450	1140	1900	3800	6650	9500
K20 Suburban	450	1050	1750	3550	6150	8800
C20 Stake	350	950	1550	3150	5450	7800
C30 Stake	350	950	1550	3150	5450	7800

NOTE: 1955-up prices based on top of the line models.
See previous notes for 1969-1970 explaining "model" information.

1972

	6	5	4	3	2	1
Vega (1/2-Ton)						
Panel Exp	200	675	1000	2000	3500	5000
LUV Pickup (1/2-Ton)						
PU	150	650	950	1900	3300	4700
El Camino (V-8)						
Spt PU	450	1400	2300	4600	8100	11,500
Cus Spt PU	450	1450	2400	4800	8400	12,000
Blazer (4WD)						
C10 Blazer	400	1200	2000	4000	7000	10,000
K10 Blazer	450	1450	2400	4800	8400	12,000
Fleetside Pickups						
C10 PU (SBx)	500	1600	2700	5400	9500	13,500
C10 PU (LBx)	500	1550	2600	5200	9100	13,000
K10 PU (SBx)	450	1400	2350	4700	8300	11,800
K10 PU (LBx)	450	1400	2300	4600	8100	11,500
C20 PU (SBx)	400	1300	2150	4300	7600	10,800
C20 PU (LBx)	400	1300	2200	4400	7700	11,000
K20 PU (SBx)	400	1250	2100	4200	7400	10,600
K20 PU (LBx)	400	1300	2150	4300	7500	10,700
C30 PU (long horn)	450	1050	1750	3550	6150	8800
Stepside Pickups						
C10 PU (SBx)	450	1450	2400	4800	8400	12,000
C10 PU (LBx)	450	1400	2300	4600	8100	11,500
K10 PU (SBx)	400	1300	2150	4300	7600	10,800
K10 PU (LBx)	400	1250	2100	4200	7400	10,500
K10 PU (LBx)	400	1300	2150	4300	7600	10,800
K20 PU (LBx)	400	1250	2050	4100	7200	10,300
C30 PU (long horn)	400	1200	2000	4000	7100	10,100
Chevy Van						
G10 Panel Van	350	975	1600	3200	5600	8000
G10 Spt Van	350	1000	1650	3350	5800	8300
G10 Beauville	450	1050	1750	3550	6150	8800
G20 Panel Van	350	950	1550	3150	5450	7800
G20 Spt Van	350	975	1600	3200	5600	8000
G20 Beauville	350	1000	1650	3350	5800	8300
Step Vans						
P10	350	820	1400	2700	4760	6800
P20	350	790	1350	2650	4620	6600
P30	350	770	1300	2550	4480	6400
Suburban						
C10 Suburban	400	1300	2200	4400	7700	11,000
K10 Suburban	450	1140	1900	3800	6650	9500
C20 Suburban	450	1140	1900	3800	6650	9500
K20 Suburban	450	1050	1750	3550	6150	8800
Stake Bed						
C20 Stake	350	950	1550	3150	5450	7800
C30 Stake	350	950	1550	3150	5450	7800

NOTE: 1955-up prices based on top of the line models.

1973

	6	5	4	3	2	1
Vega						
Panel	200	675	1000	2000	3500	5000
LUV						
PU	125	400	675	1350	2300	4300
El Camino						
PU	350	900	1500	3000	5250	7500
Cus PU	350	975	1600	3200	5600	8000
Blazer K10						
Blazer 2WD	350	1020	1700	3400	5950	8500
Blazer 4WD	450	1140	1900	3800	6650	9500

	6	5	4	3	2	1
C10 (1/2-Ton)						
Stepside (SBx)	450	1140	1900	3800	6650	9500
Stepside (LBx)	450	1080	1800	3600	6300	9000
Fleetside (SBx)	400	1200	2000	4000	7000	10,000
Fleetside (LBx)	450	1140	1900	3800	6650	9500
Suburban	450	1140	1900	3800	6650	9500
K10 - 4WD - (1/2-Ton)						
Stepside (SBx)	350	800	1350	2700	4700	6700
Stepside (LBx)	350	820	1400	2700	4760	6800
Fleetside (SBx)	350	830	1400	2950	4830	6900
Fleetside (LBx)	350	840	1400	2800	4900	7000
Suburban	450	1170	1975	3900	6850	9800
C20 - (3/4-Ton)						
Stepside (LBx)	350	780	1300	2600	4550	6500
Fleetside (LBx)	350	800	1350	2700	4700	6700
6P (LBx)	200	750	1275	2500	4400	6300
Suburban	350	840	1400	2800	4900	7000
K20 - 4WD - (3/4-Ton)						
Stepside (LBx)	350	820	1400	2700	4760	6800
Fleetside (LBx)	350	830	1400	2950	4830	6900
6P (LBx)	350	780	1300	2600	4700	6500
Suburban	350	840	1400	2800	4900	7000
C30 - (1-Ton)						
Stepside (LBx)	200	750	1275	2500	4400	6300
Fleetside (LBx)	350	780	1300	2600	4550	6500
6P (LBx)	200	745	1250	2500	4340	6200
Series CG Panels/Vans (1/2-Ton)						
Panel	200	660	1100	2200	3850	5500
Spt Van	350	780	1300	2600	4550	6500
Beauville	350	800	1350	2700	4700	6700
Series CG Panels/Vans (3/4-Ton)						
Panel	200	700	1075	2150	3700	5300
Spt Van	200	750	1275	2500	4400	6300
Beauville	350	780	1300	2600	4550	6500
Series CG Panels						
Vans (1-Ton)						
Panel	200	700	1050	2050	3600	5100
Spt Van	200	730	1250	2450	4270	6100
Beauville	200	750	1275	2500	4400	6300
Step Vans						
P10 Panel	200	700	1050	2050	3600	5100
P20 Panel	200	675	1000	2000	3500	5000
P30 Panel	200	675	1000	1950	3400	4900

NOTE: 1955-up prices based on top of the line models.

1974
	6	5	4	3	2	1
Vega						
Panel	200	720	1200	2400	4200	6000
LUV						
PU	150	575	875	1700	3000	4300

	6	5	4	3	2	1
El Camino						
PU	350	780	1300	2600	4550	6500
Cus PU	350	840	1400	2800	4900	7000
Blazer K10						
Blazer 2WD	350	1020	1700	3400	5950	8500
Blazer 4WD	450	1140	1900	3800	6650	9500
C10 - (1/2-Ton)						
Stepside (SBx)	350	975	1600	3200	5600	8000
Stepside (LBx)	350	900	1500	3000	5250	7500
Fleetside (SBx)	350	1020	1700	3400	5950	8500
Fleetside (LBx)	350	1000	1650	3300	5750	8200
Suburban	350	1020	1700	3400	5950	8500
K10 - 4WD - (1/2-Ton)						
Stepside (SBx)	350	800	1350	2700	4700	6700
Stepside (LBx)	350	820	1400	2700	4760	6800
Fleetside (SBx)	350	830	1400	2950	4830	6900
Fleetside (LBx)	350	840	1400	2800	4900	7000
Suburban	450	1080	1800	3600	6300	9000
C20 - (3/4-Ton)						
Stepside (LBx)	350	780	1300	2600	4550	6500
Fleetside (LBx)	350	800	1350	2700	4700	6700
6P (LBx)	200	750	1275	2500	4400	6300
Suburban	350	840	1400	2800	4900	7000
K20 - 4WD - (3/4-Ton)						
Stepside (LBx)	350	820	1400	2700	4760	6800
Fleetside (LBx)	350	830	1400	2950	4830	6900
6P (LBx)	350	800	1350	2700	4700	6700
Suburban	350	860	1450	2900	5050	7200
C30 - (1-Ton)						
Stepside (LBx)	200	750	1275	2500	4400	6300
Fleetside (LBx)	350	780	1300	2600	4550	6500
6P (LBx)	200	745	1250	2500	4340	6200
Series CG Panels/Vans (1/2-Ton)						
Panel	200	660	1100	2200	3850	5500
Spt Van	350	780	1300	2600	4550	6500
Beauville	350	800	1350	2700	4700	6700
Series CG Panels/Vans (3/4-Ton)						
Panel	200	700	1075	2150	3700	5300
Spt Van	200	750	1275	2500	4400	6300
Beauville	350	780	1300	2600	4550	6500
Series CG Panels/Vans (1-Ton)						
Panel	200	700	1050	2050	3600	5100
Spt Van	200	730	1250	2450	4270	6100
Beauville	200	750	1275	2500	4400	6300
Step Vans						
P10 Panel	200	700	1050	2050	3600	5100
P20 Panel	200	675	1000	2000	3500	5000
P30 Panel	200	675	1000	1950	3400	4900

NOTE: 1955-up prices based on top of the line models.

1960 Chevrolet El Camino Pickup (CMD)

1975

	6	5	4	3	2	1
Vega						
Panel	200	720	1200	2400	4200	6000
LUV						
PU	150	475	775	1500	2650	3800
El Camino						
PU	350	780	1300	2600	4550	6500
Cus PU	350	840	1400	2800	4900	7000
Blazer K10						
Blazer 2WD	350	975	1600	3200	5600	8000
Blazer 4WD	450	1080	1800	3600	6300	9000
C10 (1/2-Ton)						
Stepside (SBx)	350	900	1500	3000	5250	7500
Stepside (LBx)	350	840	1400	2800	4900	7000
Fleetside (SBx)	350	850	1450	2850	4970	7100
Fleetside (LBx)	350	840	1400	2800	4900	7000
Suburban	350	860	1450	2900	5050	7200
K10 - 4WD - (1/2-Ton)						
Stepside (SBx)	350	800	1350	2700	4700	6700
Stepside (LBx)	350	820	1400	2700	4760	6800
Fleetside (SBx)	350	830	1400	2950	4830	6900
Fleetside (LBx)	350	780	1300	2600	4550	6500
Suburban	350	870	1450	2900	5100	7300
C20 - (3/4-Ton)						
Stepside (LBx)	350	780	1300	2600	4550	6500
Fleetside (LBx)	350	800	1350	2700	4700	6700
6P (LBx)	200	750	1275	2500	4400	6300
Suburban	350	840	1400	2800	4900	7000
K20 - 4WD - (3/4-Ton)						
Stepside (LBx)	200	750	1275	2500	4400	6300
Fleetside (LBx)	350	770	1300	2550	4480	6400
6P (LBx)	200	720	1200	2400	4200	6000
Suburban	350	860	1450	2900	5050	7200
C30 (1-Ton)						
Stepside (LBx)	200	750	1275	2500	4400	6300
Fleetside (LBx)	350	780	1300	2600	4550	6500
6P (LBx)	200	745	1250	2500	4340	6200
Panels/Vans (1/2-Ton)						
Panel	200	660	1100	2200	3850	5500
Spt Van	350	780	1300	2600	4550	6500
Beauville	350	800	1350	2700	4700	6700
Panels/Vans (3/4-Ton)						
Panel	200	700	1075	2150	3700	5300
Spt Van	200	750	1275	2500	4400	6300
Beauville	350	780	1300	2600	4550	6500
Panels/Vans (1-Ton)						
Panel	200	700	1050	2050	3600	5100
Spt Van	200	730	1250	2450	4270	6100
Beauville	200	750	1275	2500	4400	6300
Step Vans						
P10 Panel	200	700	1050	2050	3600	5100
P20 Panel	200	675	1000	2000	3500	5000
P30 Panel	200	675	1000	1950	3400	4900

NOTE: 1955-up prices based on top of the line models.

1976

	6	5	4	3	2	1
LUV						
PU	150	500	800	1600	2800	4000
El Camino						
PU	350	780	1300	2600	4550	6500
Cus PU	350	840	1400	2800	4900	7000
Blazer K10						
Blazer 2WD	350	840	1400	2800	4900	7000
Blazer 4WD	350	975	1600	3200	5600	8000
C10 (1/2-Ton)						
Stepside (SBx)	350	830	1400	2950	4830	6900
Stepside (LBx)	350	840	1400	2800	4900	7000
Fleetside (SBx)	350	850	1450	2850	4970	7100
Fleetside (LBx)	350	860	1450	2900	5050	7200
Suburban	350	840	1400	2800	4900	7000
K10 - 4WD - (1/2-Ton)						
Stepside (SBx)	350	800	1350	2700	4700	6700
Stepside (LBx)	350	820	1400	2700	4760	6800
Fleetside (SBx)	350	830	1400	2950	4830	6900
Fleetside (LBx)	350	840	1400	2800	4900	7000
Suburban	350	820	1400	2700	4760	6800
C20 (3/4-Ton)						
Stepside (LBx)	350	780	1300	2600	4550	6500
Fleetside (LBx)	350	800	1350	2700	4700	6700
6P (LBx)	200	750	1275	2500	4400	6300
Suburban	350	790	1350	2650	4620	6600
K20 - 4WD - (3/4-Ton)						
Stepside (LBx)	350	820	1400	2700	4760	6800
Fleetside (LBx)	350	830	1400	2950	4830	6900
6P (LBx)	350	780	1300	2600	4550	6500
Suburban	350	820	1400	2700	4760	6800
C30 (1-Ton)						
Stepside (LBx)	200	750	1275	2500	4400	6300
Fleetside (LBx)	350	780	1300	2600	4550	6500
6P (LBx)	200	745	1250	2500	4340	6200
Panels/Vans (1/2-Ton)						
Panel	200	660	1100	2200	3850	5500
Spt Van	350	780	1300	2600	4550	6500
Beauville	350	800	1350	2700	4700	6700
Panels/Vans (3/4-Ton)						
Panel	200	700	1075	2150	3700	5300
Spt Van	200	750	1275	2500	4400	6300
Beauville	350	780	1300	2600	4550	6500
Panels/Vans (1-Ton)						
Panel	200	700	1050	2050	3600	5100
Spt Van	200	730	1250	2450	4270	6100
Beauville	200	750	1275	2500	4400	6300
Step Vans						
P10 Steel Panel	200	675	1000	2000	3500	5000
P20 Steel Panel	200	675	1000	1950	3400	4900
P30 Steel Panel	150	650	975	1950	3350	4800

NOTE: 1955-up prices based on top of the line models.

1977

	6	5	4	3	2	1
LUV						
PU	150	500	800	1600	2800	4000
El Camino						
PU	200	745	1250	2500	4340	6200
Cus PU	350	800	1350	2700	4700	6700
SS PU	350	975	1600	3200	5500	7900
Blazer K10						
Blazer 4WD	350	950	1550	3100	5400	7700
Chevy Van 10						
Panel	200	700	1050	2100	3650	5200
Spt Van	200	745	1250	2500	4340	6200
Beauville Spt Van	350	780	1300	2600	4550	6500
Chevy Van 20						
Panel	200	675	1000	2000	3500	5000
Spt Van	200	720	1200	2400	4200	6000
Beauville Spt Van	200	745	1250	2500	4340	6200
Chevy Van 30						
Panel	200	675	1000	2000	3500	5000
Spt Van	200	700	1200	2350	4130	5900
Beauville Spt Van	200	730	1250	2450	4270	6100
Cube Van	150	650	975	1950	3350	4800
Step Vans						
P10	150	650	950	1900	3300	4700
P20	150	600	950	1850	3200	4600
P30	150	600	900	1800	3150	4500
C10 (1 2-Ton)						
Stepside (SBx)	350	780	1300	2600	4550	6500
Stepside (LBx)	350	790	1350	2650	4620	6600
Fleetside (SBx)	350	790	1350	2650	4620	6600
Fleetside (LBx)	350	800	1350	2700	4700	6700
Suburban	350	820	1400	2700	4760	6800
C20 (3 4-Ton)						
Stepside PU	200	745	1250	2500	4340	6200
Fleetside PU	350	770	1300	2550	4480	6400
Bonus Cab PU	200	750	1275	2500	4400	6300
Crew Cab PU	200	745	1250	2500	4340	6200
Suburban	350	770	1300	2550	4480	6400
C30 (1-Ton)						
Stepside PU	200	720	1200	2400	4200	6000
Fleetside PU	200	745	1250	2500	4340	6200
Bonus Cab PU	200	730	1250	2450	4270	6100
Crew Cab PU	200	720	1200	2400	4200	6000

NOTE: 1955-up prices based on top of the line models.
Add 5 percent for 4WD Pickups & Suburbans.

1978

	6	5	4	3	2	1
LUV						
PU	150	500	800	1600	2800	4000
LBx	150	550	850	1650	2900	4100
El Camino - (V-8)						
PU	200	745	1250	2500	4340	6200
SS PU	350	800	1350	2700	4700	6700
Blazer - K10 - (V-8)						
Blazer 4WD	350	860	1450	2900	5050	7200
Chevy Van 10						
Panel	200	700	1050	2100	3650	5200
Spt Van	200	745	1250	2500	4340	6200
Beauville Spt Van	350	780	1300	2600	4550	6500
Chevy Van 20						
Panel	200	675	1000	2000	3500	5000
Spt Van	200	720	1200	2400	4200	6000
Beauville Spt Van	200	745	1250	2500	4340	6200
Chevy Van 30						
Panel	200	675	1000	2000	3500	5000
Spt Van	200	700	1050	2100	3650	5200
Beauville Spt Van	200	660	1100	2200	3850	5500
Hi-Cube	150	650	975	1950	3350	4800
Step Vans						
P10	150	600	950	1850	3200	4600
P20	150	600	900	1800	3150	4500
P30	150	550	850	1675	2950	4200
C10 (1/2-Ton)						
Stepside (SBx)	350	780	1300	2600	4550	6500
Stepside (LBx)	350	790	1350	2650	4620	6600
Fleetside (SBx)	350	790	1350	2650	4620	6600
Fleetside (LBx)	350	800	1350	2700	4700	6700
Suburban	350	820	1400	2700	4760	6800
C20 (3/4-Ton)						
Stepside PU	200	745	1250	2500	4340	6200
Fleetside PU	350	770	1300	2550	4480	6400
Bonus Cab PU	200	750	1275	2500	4400	6300
Crew Cab PU	200	745	1250	2500	4340	6200
Suburban	350	770	1300	2550	4480	6400
C30 (1-Ton)						
Stepside PU	200	720	1200	2400	4200	6000
Fleetside PU	200	745	1250	2500	4340	6200
Bonus Cab PU	200	730	1250	2450	4270	6100
Crew Cab PU	200	720	1200	2400	4200	6000
"Big Dooley"	350	800	1350	2700	4700	6700

NOTE: 1955-up prices based on top of the line models.
Add 5 percent for 4WD models.

1979

	6	5	4	3	2	1
LUV						
PU	150	500	800	1600	2800	4000
LBx	150	550	850	1650	2900	4100
El Camino - (V-8)						
PU	200	745	1250	2500	4340	6200
Cus PU	350	800	1350	2700	4700	6700
SS PU	350	820	1400	2700	4760	6800
Blazer - K10 - (V-8)						
Blazer 4WD	350	950	1550	3100	5400	7700
Chevy Van 10						
Panel	200	700	1050	2100	3650	5200
Spt Van	200	745	1250	2500	4340	6200
Beauville Spt Van	350	780	1300	2600	4550	6500
Chevy Van 20						
Panel	200	675	1000	2000	3500	5000
Spt Van	200	720	1200	2400	4200	6000
Beauville Spt Van	200	745	1250	2500	4340	6200
Caravan	350	800	1350	2700	4700	6700
Chevy Van 30						
Panel	200	675	1000	2000	3500	5000
Spt Van	200	700	1050	2100	3650	5200
Beauville Spt Van	350	780	1300	2600	4550	6500
Hi-Cube Van	150	650	975	1950	3350	4800
Step Vans						
P10	150	600	950	1850	3200	4600
P20	150	600	900	1800	3150	4500
P30	150	550	850	1675	2950	4200
C10 - (V-8)						
Stepside (SBx)	350	780	1300	2600	4550	6500
Stepside (LBx)	350	790	1350	2650	4620	6600
Fleetside (SBx)	350	790	1350	2650	4620	6600
Fleetside (LBx)	350	800	1350	2700	4700	6700
Suburban	350	820	1400	2700	4760	6800
C20 - (V-8)						
Stepside PU	200	745	1250	2500	4340	6200

1967 Chevrolet C10 Fleetside Long Box Pickup Truck (CMD)

	6	5	4	3	2	1
Fleetside PU	350	770	1300	2550	4480	6400
Bonus Cab PU	200	750	1275	2500	4400	6300
Crew Cab PU	200	745	1250	2500	4340	6200
Suburban	350	770	1300	2550	4480	6400
C30 - (V-8)						
Stepside PU	200	720	1200	2400	4200	6000
Fleetside PU	200	745	1250	2500	4340	6200
Bonus Cab PU	200	730	1250	2450	4270	6100
Crew Cab PU	200	720	1200	2400	4200	6000
"Big Dooley"	350	820	1400	2700	4760	6800

NOTE: 1955-up prices based on top of the line models.
Add 5 percent for 4WD models.

1980
LUV
	6	5	4	3	2	1
PU	150	500	800	1600	2800	4000
LBx PU	150	550	850	1650	2900	4100
El Camino - (1/2-Ton) - (117" wb)						
PU	200	750	1275	2500	4400	6300
Cus PU	350	820	1400	2700	4760	6800
SS PU	350	830	1400	2950	4830	6900
Blazer - K10						
Blazer 4WD	350	950	1550	3150	5450	7800
G10 Chevy Van - (1/2-Ton) - (110" or 125" wb)						
Panel	200	700	1050	2100	3650	5200
Spt Van	200	745	1250	2500	4340	6200
Beauville Spt Van	350	780	1300	2600	4550	6500
G20 Chevy Van - (3/4-Ton) - (110" or 125" wb)						
Panel	200	675	1000	2000	3500	5000
Spt Van	200	720	1200	2400	4200	6000
Beauville Spt Van	200	745	1250	2500	4340	6200
Nomad	350	780	1300	2600	4550	6500
G30 Chevy Van - (1/2-Ton) - (125" or 146" wb)						
Panel	200	675	1000	2000	3500	5000
Spt Van	200	720	1200	2400	4200	6000
Beauville Spt Van	350	770	1300	2550	4480	6400
Hi-Cube Van	150	650	975	1950	3350	4800
C10 - (1/2-Ton) - (117" or 131" wb)						
Stepside SBx PU	350	790	1350	2650	4620	6600
Stepside LBx PU	350	800	1350	2700	4700	6700
Fleetside SBx PU	350	800	1350	2700	4700	6700
Fleetside LBx PU	350	820	1400	2700	4760	6800
Suburban	350	830	1400	2950	4830	6900

	6	5	4	3	2	1
C20 - (3/4-Ton) - (131" or 164" wb)						
Stepside PU	200	750	1275	2500	4400	6300
Fleetside PU	350	780	1300	2600	4550	6500
Bonus Cab PU	350	770	1300	2550	4480	6400
Crew Cab PU	200	750	1275	2500	4400	6300
Suburban	350	780	1300	2600	4550	6500
C30 - (1-Ton) - (131" or 164" wb)						
Stepside PU	200	720	1200	2400	4200	6000
Fleetside PU	200	745	1250	2500	4340	6200
Bonus Cab PU	200	750	1275	2500	4400	6300
Crew Cab PU	200	720	1200	2400	4200	6000
"Big Dooley"	350	780	1300	2600	4550	6500
Step- Vans (V-8)						
Step-Van (1/2-Ton)	150	600	950	1850	3200	4600
Step-Van (3/4-Ton)	150	600	900	1800	3150	4500
Step-Van (1-Ton)	150	550	850	1675	2950	4200

1981
Luv - (1/2-Ton) - (104.3" or 117.9" wb)
	6	5	4	3	2	1
PU SBx	150	550	850	1650	2900	4100
PU LBx	150	550	850	1675	2950	4200
El Camino - (1/2-Ton) - (117" wb)						
PU	350	820	1400	2700	4760	6800
SS PU	350	830	1400	2950	4830	6900
Blazer K10 - (1/2-Ton) - (106.5" wb)						
Blazer 4WD	350	975	1600	3200	5600	8000
G10 Chevy Van - (1/2-Ton) - (110" or 125" wb)						
Chevy Van	200	700	1075	2150	3700	5300
Spt Van	200	745	1250	2500	4340	6200
Bonaventure	350	770	1300	2550	4480	6400
Beauville	350	790	1350	2650	4620	6600
G20 Chevy Van - (1/2-Ton) - (110" or 125" wb)						
Chevy Van	200	700	1050	2100	3650	5200
Spt Van	200	730	1250	2450	4270	6100
Bonaventure	200	750	1275	2500	4400	6300
Beauville	350	780	1300	2600	4550	6500
Nomad	350	780	1300	2600	4550	6500
Step Van	200	675	1000	2000	3500	5000
G30 Chevy Van - (1-Ton) - (125" or 146" wb)						
Chevy Van	200	700	1050	2050	3600	5100
Spt Van	200	720	1200	2400	4200	6000
Bonaventure	200	745	1250	2500	4340	6200
Beauville	350	770	1300	2550	4480	6400
Hi Cube 10	200	720	1200	2400	4200	6000
Hi Cube 12	200	720	1200	2400	4200	6000

	6	5	4	3	2	1
Step Van	200	660	1100	2200	3850	5500
C10 - (1/2-Ton) - (117" or 131" wb)						
Stepside PU SBx	350	820	1400	2700	4760	6800
Stepside PU LBx	350	800	1350	2700	4700	6700
Fleetside PU SBx	350	830	1400	2950	4830	6900
Fleetside PU LBx	350	840	1400	2800	4900	7000
Suburban	350	860	1450	2900	5050	7200
C20 - (3/4-Ton) - (131" or 164" wb)						
Stepside PU LBx	350	800	1350	2700	4700	6700
Fleetside PU LBx	350	820	1400	2700	4760	6800
Fleetside PU Bonus Cab LBx	350	840	1400	2800	4900	7000
Fleetside PU Crew Cab LBx	350	830	1400	2950	4830	6900
Suburban	350	860	1450	2900	5050	7200
C30 - (1-Ton) - (131" or 164" wb)						
Stepside PU LBx	350	790	1350	2650	4620	6600
Fleetside PU LBx	350	800	1350	2700	4700	6700
Fleetside PU Bonus Cab LBx	350	820	1400	2700	4760	6800
Fleetside PU Crew Cab LBx	350	800	1350	2700	4700	6700

NOTE: Add 15 percent for 4WD.

1982

	6	5	4	3	2	1
Luv - (1/2-Ton) - (104.3" or 117.9" wb)						
PU SBx	150	550	850	1650	2900	4100
PU LBx	150	550	850	1675	2950	4200
El Camino - (1/2-Ton) - (117" wb)						
PU	200	670	1200	2300	4060	5800
SS PU	200	700	1200	2350	4130	5900
Blazer K10 - (1/2-Ton) - (106.5" wb)						
HdTp 4WD	350	840	1400	2800	4900	7000
G10 Chevy Van - (1/2-Ton) - (110" or 125" wb)						
Chevy Van	150	575	875	1700	3000	4300
Spt Van	200	700	1050	2100	3650	5200
Bonaventure	200	650	1100	2150	3780	5400
Beauville	200	670	1150	2250	3920	5600
G20 Chevy Van - (3/4-Ton) - (110" or 125" wb)						
Chevy Van	150	600	900	1800	3150	4500
Spt Van	150	650	950	1900	3300	4700
Bonaventure	200	700	1075	2150	3700	5300
Beauville	200	660	1100	2200	3850	5500
Step-Van	150	575	900	1750	3100	4400
G30 Step Van - (1-Ton) - (125" or 146" wb)						
Chevy Van	150	575	900	1750	3100	4400
Spt Van	200	675	1000	2000	3500	5000
Bonaventure	200	700	1050	2100	3650	5200
Beauville	200	660	1100	2200	3850	5500
Hi Cube 10	150	575	900	1750	3100	4400
Hi Cube 12	150	575	900	1750	3100	4400
Step-Van	150	550	850	1675	2950	4200
S10 - (1/2-Ton) - (108" or 118" wb)						
Fleetside PU SBx	150	575	875	1700	3000	4300
Fleetside PU LBx	150	575	900	1750	3100	4400
C10 - (1/2-Ton) - (117" or 131" wb)						
Stepside PU SBx	200	670	1200	2300	4060	5800
Fleetside PU SBx	200	700	1200	2350	4130	5900
Fleetside PU LBx	200	670	1150	2250	3920	5600
Suburban	200	750	1275	2500	4400	6300
C20 - (3/4-Ton) - (131" or 164" wb)						
Stepside PU LBx	200	685	1150	2300	3990	5700
Fleetside PU LBx	200	670	1200	2300	4060	5800
Fleetside PU Bonus Cab LBx	200	730	1250	2450	4270	6100
Fleetside PU Crew Cab LBx	200	685	1150	2300	3990	5700
Suburban	200	750	1275	2500	4400	6300
C30 - (1-Ton) - (131" or 164" wb)						
Stepside PU LBx	200	660	1100	2200	3850	5500
Fleetside PU LBx	200	670	1150	2250	3920	5600
Fleetside PU Bonus Cab LBx	200	700	1200	2350	4130	5900
Fleetside PU Crew Cab LBx	200	685	1150	2300	3990	5700

NOTE: Add 15 percent for 4WD.

1983

	6	5	4	3	2	1
El Camino - (1/2-Ton) - (117" wb)						
PU	200	670	1200	2300	4060	5800
SS PU	200	700	1200	2350	4130	5900
S10 - (1/2-Ton) - (100.5" wb)						
Blazer 2WD	150	600	900	1800	3150	4500
Blazer 4WD	200	675	1000	2000	3500	5000
Blazer K10 - (1/2-Ton) - (106.5" wb)						
Blazer 4WD	350	840	1400	2800	4900	7000
G10 Chevy Van - (1/2-Ton) - (110" or 125" wb)						
Chevy Van	150	575	875	1700	3000	4300
Spt Van	150	550	850	1675	2950	4200
Bonaventure	150	575	900	1750	3100	4400
Beauville	200	670	1150	2250	3920	5600
G20 Chevy Van - (3/4-Ton) - (110" or 125" wb)						
Chevy Van	150	550	850	1675	2950	4200
Spt Van	200	700	1050	2050	3600	5100
Bonaventure	200	660	1100	2200	3850	5500
Beauville	200	685	1150	2300	3990	5700
Step Van	150	500	800	1600	2800	4000
G30 Chevy Van - (1-Ton) - (125" or 146" wb)						
Chevy Van	150	550	850	1650	2900	4100
Spt Van	200	675	1000	2000	3500	5000
Bonaventure	200	700	1050	2100	3650	5200
Beauville	200	660	1100	2200	3850	5500
Hi Cube 10	150	550	850	1675	2950	4200
Hi Cube 12	150	575	875	1700	3000	4300
Step Van	150	550	850	1650	2900	4100
S10 - (1/2-Ton) - (108" or 122" wb)						
Fleetside PU SBx	150	475	750	1475	2600	3700
Fleetside PU LBx	150	475	775	1500	2650	3800
Fleetside PU Ext Cab	150	500	800	1600	2800	4000
C10 - (1/2-Ton) - (117" or 131" wb)						
Stepside PU SBx	200	670	1200	2300	4060	5800
Fleetside PU SBx	200	700	1200	2350	4130	5900
Fleetside PU LBx	200	670	1150	2250	3920	5600
Suburban	200	750	1275	2500	4400	6300
C20 - (3/4-Ton) - (131" or 164" wb)						
Stepside PU LBx	200	685	1150	2300	3990	5700
Fleetside PU LBx	200	670	1200	2300	4060	5800
Fleetside PU Bonus Cab LBx	200	730	1250	2450	4270	6100
Fleetside PU Crew Cab LBx	200	670	1150	2250	3920	5600
Suburban	200	750	1275	2500	4400	6300
C30 - (1-Ton) - (131" or 164" wb)						
Stepside PU LBx	200	660	1100	2200	3850	5500
Fleetside PU LBx	200	670	1150	2250	3920	5600
Fleetside PU Bonus Cab LBx	200	670	1200	2300	4060	5800
Fleetside PU Crew Cab LBx	200	685	1150	2300	3990	5700

NOTE: Add 15 percent for 4WD.

1984

	6	5	4	3	2	1
El Camino - (1/2-Ton) - (117" wb)						
PU	200	650	1100	2150	3780	5400
SS PU	200	670	1150	2250	3920	5600
S10 - (1/2-Ton) - (100.5" wb)						
Blazer 2WD	150	500	800	1600	2800	4000
Blazer 4WD	200	675	1000	2000	3500	5000
K10 Blazer - (1/2-Ton) - (106.5" wb)						
Blazer 4WD	350	900	1500	3000	5250	7500
G10 Chevy Van - (1/2-Ton) - (110" or 125" wb)						
Chevy Van	200	700	1050	2100	3650	5200
Spt Van	200	685	1150	2300	3990	5700
Bonaventure	200	700	1200	2350	4130	5900
Beauville	200	730	1250	2450	4270	6100
G20 Chevy Van - (3/4-Ton) - (110" or 125" wb)						
Chevy Van	200	700	1050	2050	3600	5100
Spt Van	200	670	1150	2250	3920	5600
Bonaventure	200	670	1200	2300	4060	5800
Beauville	200	720	1200	2400	4200	6000
Step-Van	200	675	1000	2000	3500	5000
G30 Chevy Van - (1/2-Ton) - (125" or 146" wb)						
Chevy Van	150	650	950	1900	3300	4700
Spt Van	200	660	1100	2200	3850	5500
Bonaventure	200	685	1150	2300	3990	5700
Beauville	200	700	1200	2350	4130	5900
Hi Cube 10	150	650	950	1900	3300	4700
Hi Cube 12	150	650	975	1950	3350	4800
Step-Van	150	550	850	1675	2950	4200
S10 - (1/2-Ton) - (108" or 118" wb)						
Fleetside PU SBx	150	550	850	1675	2950	4200
Fleetside PU LBx	150	575	875	1700	3000	4300
Fleetside PU Ext Cab	150	600	900	1800	3150	4500
C10 - (1/2-Ton) - (117" or 131" wb)						
Stepside PU SBx	350	770	1300	2550	4480	6400
Stepside PU LBx	350	780	1300	2600	4550	6500
Fleetside PU LBx	200	750	1275	2500	4400	6300
Suburban	350	840	1400	2800	4900	7000
C20 - (3/4-Ton) - (131" or 164" wb)						
Stepside PU LBx	200	750	1275	2500	4400	6300
Fleetside PU LBx	350	770	1300	2550	4480	6400
Fleetside PU Bonus Cab LBx	350	800	1350	2700	4700	6700
Fleetside PU Crew Cab LBx	350	790	1350	2650	4620	6600
Suburban	350	860	1450	2900	5050	7200
C30 - (1-Ton) - (131" or 164" wb)						
Stepside PU LBX	200	730	1250	2450	4270	6100
FLeetside PU LBx	200	745	1250	2500	4340	6200
FLeetside PU Bonus Cab LBx	200	750	1275	2500	4400	6300
Fleetside PU Crew Cab LBx	200	745	1250	2500	4340	6200

NOTE: Add 15 percent for 4WD.

1985

	6	5	4	3	2	1
El Camino - (1/2-Ton) - (117" wb)						
PU	350	790	1350	2650	4620	6600
SS PU	350	820	1400	2700	4760	6800
S10 Blazer - (1/2-Ton) - (100.5" wb)						
Blazer 2WD	200	720	1200	2400	4200	6000
Blazer 4WD	350	830	1400	2950	4830	6900
K10 Blazer - (1/2-Ton) - (106.5" wb)						
Blazer 4WD	350	975	1600	3200	5600	8000
Astro - (1/2-Ton) - (111" wb)						
Cargo Van	200	675	1000	2000	3500	5000
Van	200	670	1150	2250	3920	5600
CS Van	200	670	1200	2300	4060	5800
CL Van	200	720	1200	2400	4200	6000
G10 Chevy Van - (1/2-Ton) - (110" or 125" wb)						
Chevy Van	200	660	1100	2200	3850	5500
Spt Van	200	720	1200	2400	4200	6000
Bonaventure	200	730	1250	2450	4270	6100
Beauville	350	780	1300	2600	4550	6500
G20 Chevy Van - (3/4-Ton) - (110" or 125" wb)						
Chevy Van	200	700	1050	2050	3600	5100
Spt Van	200	670	1200	2300	4060	5800
Bonaventure	200	720	1200	2400	4200	6000
Beauville	200	745	1250	2500	4340	6200
Nomad	200	720	1200	2400	4200	6000
Step-Van	150	575	900	1750	3100	4400
G30 Chevy Van - (1-Ton) - (125" or 146" wb)						
Chevy Van	150	650	975	1950	3350	4800
Spt Van	200	700	1050	2100	3650	5200
Bonaventure	200	650	1100	2150	3780	5400
Beauville	200	730	1250	2450	4270	6100
Hi Cube 10	150	650	975	1950	3350	4800
Hi Cube 12	200	675	1000	1950	3400	4900
Step-Van	150	600	900	1800	3150	4500
S10 - (1/2-Ton) - (108.3" or 123" wb)						
Fleetside PU SBx	150	600	900	1800	3150	4500
Fleetside PU LBx	150	575	900	1750	3100	4400
Fleetside PU Ext Cab	150	600	950	1850	3200	4600
C10 - (1/2-Ton) - (117" or 131" wb)						
Stepside PU SBx	200	730	1250	2450	4270	6100
Fleetside PU SBx	200	745	1250	2500	4340	6200
Fleetside PU LBx	200	720	1200	2400	4200	6000
Suburban	350	870	1450	2900	5100	7300
C20 - (3/4-Ton) - (131" or 164" wb)						
Stepside PU LBx	200	730	1250	2450	4270	6100
Fleetside PU LBx	200	745	1250	2500	4340	6200
Fleetside PU Bonus Cab LBx	350	800	1350	2700	4700	6700
Fleetside PU Crew Cab LBx	350	830	1400	2950	4830	6900
Suburban	350	880	1500	2950	5180	7400
C30 - (1-Ton) - (131" or 164" wb)						
Stepside PU LBx	200	720	1200	2400	4200	6000
Fleetside PU LBx	200	730	1250	2450	4270	6100
Fleetside PU Bonus Cab LBx	200	730	1250	2450	4270	6100
Fleetside PU Crew Cab LBx	350	820	1400	2700	4760	6800

NOTE: Add 15 percent for 4WD.

1986

	6	5	4	3	2	1
El Camino - (1/2-Ton) - (117" wb)						
PU	350	770	1300	2550	4480	6400
SS PU	350	820	1400	2700	4760	6800
S10 Blazer - (1/2-Ton) - (100.5" wb)						
Blazer 2WD	350	780	1300	2600	4550	6500
Blazer 4WD	350	900	1500	3000	5250	7500
K10 Blazer - (1/2-Ton) - (106.5" wb)						
Blazer 4WD	450	1080	1800	3600	6300	9000
Astro - (1/2-Ton) - (111" wb)						
Cargo Van	200	700	1075	2150	3700	5300
Van	350	790	1350	2650	4620	6600
CS Van	350	820	1400	2700	4760	6800
CL Van	350	840	1400	2800	4900	7000

	6	5	4	3	2	1
G10 Van - (1/2-Ton) - (110" or 125" wb)						
Chevy Van	200	720	1200	2400	4200	6000
Short Van	350	780	1300	2600	4550	6500
Bonaventure	350	790	1350	2650	4620	6600
Beauville	350	820	1400	2700	4760	6800
G20 Van - (3/4-Ton) - (110" or 125" wb)						
Chevy Van	350	770	1300	2550	4480	6400
Spt Van	350	820	1400	2700	4760	6800
Bonaventure	350	840	1400	2800	4900	7000
Beauville	350	860	1450	2900	5050	7200
Step-Van	200	720	1200	2400	4200	6000
G30 Van - (1-Ton) - (125" wb)						
Chevy Van	200	670	1200	2300	4060	5800
Spt Van	350	800	1350	2700	4700	6700
Bonaventure	350	830	1400	2950	4830	6900
Beauville	350	900	1500	3000	5250	7500
Hi Cube 10	350	780	1300	2600	4550	6500
Hi Cube 12	350	780	1300	2600	4550	6500
Step-Van	200	745	1250	2500	4340	6200
S10 - (1/2-Ton) - (108" or 123" wb)						
Fleetside PU SBx	200	660	1100	2200	3850	5500
Fleetside PU LBx	200	670	1150	2250	3920	5600
Fleetside PU Ext Cab	200	700	1200	2350	4130	5900
C10 - (1/2-Ton) - (117.5" or 131.5" wb)						
Stepside PU SBx	350	800	1350	2700	4700	6700
Fleetside PU SBx	350	820	1400	2700	4760	6800
Fleetside PU LBx	350	790	1350	2650	4620	6600
Suburban	350	900	1500	3000	5250	7500
C20 - (3/4-Ton) - (131.5" or 164.5" wb)						
Stepside PU LBx	350	820	1400	2700	4760	6800
Fleetside PU LBx	350	830	1400	2950	4830	6900
Fleetside PU Bonus Cab LBx	350	860	1450	2900	5050	7200
Fleetside PU Crew Cab LBx	350	880	1500	2950	5180	7400
Suburban	350	950	1550	3150	5450	7800
C30 - (1-Ton) - (131.5" or 164.5" wb)						
Stepside PU LBx	350	800	1350	2700	4700	6700
Fleetside PU LBx	350	820	1400	2700	4760	6800
Fleetside PU Bonus Cab LBx	350	850	1450	2850	4970	7100
Fleetside PU Crew Cab LBx	350	870	1450	2900	5100	7300

NOTE: Add 15 percent for 4WD.

1987

	6	5	4	3	2	1
El Camino - (1/2-Ton) - (117.1" wb)						
PU	350	900	1500	3000	5250	7500
SS PU	350	975	1600	3200	5600	8000
K10 Blazer - (106.5" wb)						
Blazer 4WD	400	1250	2100	4200	7400	10,500
S10 Blazer - 100.5" wb						
2WD	350	780	1300	2600	4550	6500
4WD	350	1020	1700	3400	5950	8500
Astro - (111" wb)						
Cargo Van	350	780	1300	2600	4550	6500
Van	350	840	1400	2800	4900	7000
CS Van	350	1020	1700	3400	5950	8500
CL Van	450	1080	1800	3600	6300	9000
LT Van	450	1140	1900	3800	6650	9500
G10 Van - (1/2-Ton) - (110" or 125" wb)						
Chevy Van	350	840	1400	2800	4900	7000
Spt Van	350	900	1500	3000	5250	7500
Bonaventure	450	1080	1800	3600	6300	9000
Beauville	400	1200	2000	4000	7000	10,000
G20 Van - (3/4-Ton) - (110" or 125" wb)						
Chevy Van	350	900	1500	3000	5250	7500
Spt Van	350	1020	1700	3400	5950	8500
Bonaventure	450	1140	1900	3800	6650	9500
Beauville	400	1250	2100	4200	7400	10,500
Step-Van	450	1140	1900	3800	6650	9500
G30 Van - (1-Ton) - (125" or 146" wb)						
Chevy Van	350	975	1600	3200	5600	8000
Spt Van	450	1140	1900	3800	6650	9500
Bonaventure	400	1200	2000	4000	7000	10,000
Beauville	400	1250	2100	4200	7400	10,500
Hi Cube 10	450	1140	1900	3800	6650	9500
Hi Cube 12	450	1140	1900	3800	6650	9500
Step-Van	950	1100	1850	3700	6450	9200
S10 - (108.3" or 122.9" wb)						
Fleetside PU SBx	150	650	950	1900	3300	4700
Fleetside PU LBx	200	675	1000	2000	3500	5000
R10 - (1/2-Ton) - (117.5" or 131.5" wb)						
Stepside PU SBx	350	780	1300	2600	4550	6500
Fleetside PU SBx	350	780	1300	2600	4550	6500
Fleetside PU LBx	350	800	1350	2700	4700	6700
Suburban	400	1200	2000	4000	7000	10,000
R20- (3/4-Ton) - (129.5" or 164.5" wb)						
Stepside PU LBx	350	900	1500	3000	5250	7500
Fleetside PU LBx	350	900	1500	3000	5250	7500
Bonus Cab PU LBx	350	975	1600	3200	5600	8000
Crew Cab PU LBx	350	1000	1650	3350	5800	8300
Suburban	400	1300	2200	4400	7700	11,000
R30 - (1-Ton) - (131.5" or 164.5" wb)						
Stepside PU LBx	350	975	1600	3200	5600	8000
Fleetside PU LBx	350	975	1600	3200	5600	8000
Bonus Cab PU LBx	450	1080	1800	3600	6300	9000
Crew Cab PU LBx	450	1120	1875	3750	6500	9300

1988

	6	5	4	3	2	1
Blazer - (106.5" wb)						
V10 4WD	400	1200	2000	4000	7000	10,000
S10 2WD	200	720	1200	2400	4200	6000
S10 4WD	350	975	1600	3200	5600	8000
Astro - (111" wb)						
Cargo Van	200	720	1200	2400	4200	6000
CS Van	350	975	1600	3200	5600	8000
CL Van	350	1020	1700	3400	5950	8500
LT Van	450	1080	1800	3600	6300	9000

1985 Chevrolet S-10 Pickup Truck (CMD)

1991 Chevrolet C1500 Regular-Cab 454SS Fleetside Pickup Truck (CMD)

	6	5	4	3	2	1
G10 Van - (1/2-Ton) - (110" or 125" wb)						
Chevy Van	350	780	1300	2600	4550	6500
Spt Van	350	975	1600	3200	5600	8000
Bonaventure	350	1020	1700	3400	5950	8500
Beauville	450	1080	1800	3600	6300	9000
G20 Van - (3/4-Ton) - (110" or 125" wb)						
Chevy Van	350	840	1400	2800	4900	7000
Spt Van	350	1020	1700	3400	5950	8500
Bonaventure	450	1140	1900	3800	6650	9500
Beauville	400	1200	2000	4000	7000	10,000
Step-Van	450	1140	1900	3800	6650	9500
G30 Van - (1-Ton) - (125" or 146" wb)						
Chevy Van	450	1080	1800	3600	6300	9000
Spt Van	450	1140	1900	3800	6650	9500
Bonaventure	400	1200	2000	4000	7000	10,000
Beauville	400	1300	2200	4400	7700	11,000
Hi Cube 10	450	1140	1900	3800	6650	9500
Hi Cube 12	400	1200	2000	4000	7000	10,000
Step-Van	450	1160	1950	3900	6800	9700
S10 Pickup - (108.3" or 122.9" wb)						
Fleetside SBx	200	675	1000	2000	3500	5000
Fleetside LBx	200	700	1050	2100	3650	5200
Fleetside Ext Cab	200	660	1100	2200	3850	5500
C1500 - (1/2-Ton) - (117.5" or 131.5" wb)						
Sportside PU SBx	350	840	1400	2800	4900	7000
Fleetside PU SBx	350	840	1400	2800	4900	7000
Fleetside PU LBx	350	900	1500	3000	5250	7500
Fleetside PU Ext Cab LBx	350	1020	1700	3400	5950	8500
Suburban	400	1300	2200	4400	7700	11,000
C2500 - (3/4-Ton) - (129.5" or 164.5" wb)						
Stepside PU LBx	450	1080	1800	3600	6300	9000
Fleetside PU LBx	450	1080	1800	3600	6300	9000
Bonus Cab PU LBx	350	1020	1700	3400	5950	8500
Crew Cab PU LBx	450	1050	1750	3550	6150	8800
Suburban	450	1450	2400	4800	8400	12,000
C3500 - (1-Ton) - (131.5" or 164.5" wb)						
Stepside PU LBx	350	1020	1700	3400	5950	8500
Fleetside PU LBx	350	1020	1700	3400	5950	8500
Bonus Cab PU LBx	450	1140	1900	3800	6650	9500
Crew Cab PU LBx	450	1170	1975	3900	6850	9800

1989
Blazer - (106.5" wb)

	6	5	4	3	2	1
V1500 4WD	450	1400	2300	4600	8100	11,500

	6	5	4	3	2	1
S10 2WD	350	900	1500	3000	5250	7500
S10 4WD	450	1140	1900	3800	6650	9500
Astro - (111" wb)						
Cargo Van	350	900	1500	3000	5250	7500
CS Van	450	1140	1900	3800	6650	9500
CL Van	450	1140	1900	3800	6650	9500
LT Van	400	1250	2100	4200	7400	10,500
G10 Van - (1/2-Ton) - (110" or 125" wb)						
Chevy Van	350	975	1600	3200	5600	8000
Spt Van	450	1080	1800	3600	6300	9000
Beauville	450	1140	1900	3800	6650	9500
G-20 Van - (3/4-Ton) - (110" or 125" wb)						
Chevy Van	450	1080	1800	3600	6300	9000
Spt Van	450	1140	1900	3800	6650	9500
Beauville	400	1250	2100	4200	7400	10,500
Step-Van	400	1200	2000	4000	7000	10,000
G30 Van - (1-Ton) - (125" or 146" wb)						
Chevy Van	450	1140	1900	3800	6650	9500
Spt Van	400	1200	2000	4000	7000	10,000
Beauville	400	1300	2200	4400	7700	11,000
Hi Cube 10	400	1200	2000	4000	7000	10,000
Hi Cube 12	400	1300	2200	4400	7700	11,000
Step-Van	400	1200	2000	4000	7000	10,000
S10 Pickup - (108.3" or 122.9" wb)						
Fleetside SBx	200	660	1100	2200	3850	5500
Fleetside LBx	200	670	1200	2300	4060	5800
Fleetside Ext Cab SBx	200	700	1200	2350	4130	5900
C1500 - (1/2-Ton) - (117.5" or 131.5" wb)						
Stepside PU SBx	350	1020	1700	3400	5950	8500
Fleetside PU SBx	350	1020	1700	3400	5950	8500
Fleetside PU LBx	450	1080	1800	3600	6300	9000
Fleetside PU Ext Cab LBx	450	1140	1900	3800	6650	9500
Suburban	500	1600	2700	5400	9500	13,500
C2500 - (3/4-Ton) - (129.5" or 164.5" wb)						
Stepside PU LBx	450	1140	1900	3800	6650	9500
Fleetside PU LBx	450	1140	1900	3800	6650	9500
Bonus Cab PU LBx	400	1200	2000	4000	7000	10,000
Crew Cab PU LBx	400	1250	2050	4100	7200	10,300
Suburban	500	1550	2600	5200	9100	13,000
C3500 - (1-Ton) - (131.5" or 164.5" wb)						
Stepside PU LBx	400	1200	2000	4000	7000	10,000
Fleetside PU LBx	400	1200	2000	4000	7000	10,000
Bonus Cab PU LBx	400	1300	2200	4400	7700	11,000
Crew Cab PU LBx	400	1350	2250	4500	7900	11,300

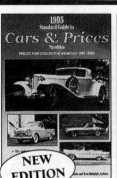

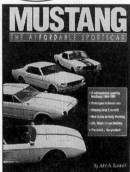
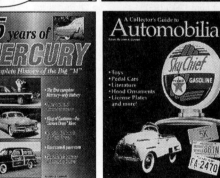